FUNDAMENTAL PRINCIPLES OF BACTERIOLOGY

Fundamental Principles of
BACTERIOLOGY

A. J. SALLE, B.S., M.S., Ph.D.

Professor of Bacteriology
University of California
Los Angeles

FIFTH EDITION

McGRAW-HILL BOOK COMPANY, INC.

New York   Toronto   London

1961

FUNDAMENTAL PRINCIPLES OF BACTERIOLOGY

To the memory of
Cecelia Daverso Salle
this book is affectionately dedicated

Preface

What one man has failed to achieve, another has accomplished, and that what was unknown to one age has been cleared up by the following age, and that the sciences and arts are not cast in a mould, but are formed and shaped by degrees through repeated handling and polishing . . . and in manipulating and kneading this new matter over and over again, stirring and warming it, I open up for him who comes after me some facility for profiting by it more at his ease, and I make it more pliable and manageable for him . . . as much will the second do for the third.

MICHEL DE MONTAIGNE

This book has been thoroughly revised and completely rewritten to bring the contents up to date. Every chapter has been included in the revision. To name the significant changes that have been made would mean the inclusion of almost the entire book.

The author has attempted to include only sound fundamental material to give the beginner a solid foundation for more advanced work on the subject. Explanations of all phenomena are included insofar as it was possible to do so.

Much of the material appears for the first time and may require proper evaluation by others before it can be accepted as fact. The student should be warned against uncritical acceptance of views that may not be solidly established. It is believed that the training afforded by contemporary science and education should prove adequate to develop critical, inquiring students.

Emphasis is placed on the use of chemisty for a clearer understanding of the composition of bacteria and the reactions they produce. A student may conceivably pursue bacteriology without much of the chemistry contained in the book, and the instructor may wish to eliminate most of it in a beginning course. For some phases of bacteriology, emphasis on chemistry is perhaps not necessary. However, it is included for those inquiring students who may desire it for a clearer understanding of the subject and especially for proper development of certain phases of bacteriology where it is highly necessary.

Many new illustrations have been added. Also, some of the old illustrations have been replaced with new and better ones. The original materials used for the illustrations were prepared with great care and photographed with all the technical skill at our command.

The chapter on the Bacteriology of the Sea, prepared by Dr. C. E. ZoBell for the fourth edition, has been revised by the same author and brought up to date. A new chapter on Bacterial Genetics has been written by Dr. W. R. Romig and incorporated in the text.

The outline classification of bacteria and the names of the organisms used throughout the text are based on the seventh edition of "Bergey's Manual of Determinative Bacteriology," which is generally accepted as standard throughout the world. The author is greatly indebted to the editor-in-chief, the late Dr. Robert S. Breed, for permission to quote from that book.

The author is indebted to Mrs. Mary Edgert, Charles R. Manclark, and Smith Shadomy for their aid in reading and checking the proofs, and to all who have offered valuable suggestions and criticisms during the preparation of the manuscript.

The author has attempted to acknowledge the sources of the text materials and the illustrations. Any errors or omissions are entirely unintentional. He alone accepts full responsibility for any defects that may be inherent in the plan and scope of the book and for any errors which may have escaped detection.

A. J. Salle

Contents

CHAPTER 1

Introduction

Biology is that branch of knowledge which treats of living organisms. The two major divisions of biology are botany, the science of plant life, and zoology, the science of animal life. Bacteriology deals with the study of organisms known as bacteria (singular, bacterium). The term includes a large group of typically unicellular microscopic organisms widely distributed in air, water, soil, the bodies of living plants and animals, and dead organic matter. Microbiology in its broadest meaning is the science which deals with the study of all kinds of microorganisms, both plant and animal, such as bacteria, yeasts, molds, algae, and protozoa. The modern tendency is to confine the term to the study of organisms classified with the lowest groups of botanical or plant life, i.e., bacteria, yeasts, and molds. The term *microbe* is taken from the French and means a microscopic organism or microorganism, being usually applied to the pathogenic forms. The term *germ,* in popular usage, refers to any microorganism but especially to any of the pathogenic or disease-producing bacteria. The terms microbe and germ are probably synonymous with bacterium. Although this book will include a discussion of the lowest groups of plant life, the major portion of the material will be devoted to the study of organisms classified with the bacteria.

Man, who is forever classifying things, has placed living organisms into either the plant or the animal kingdom. Most living organisms possess the characteristics of one kingdom or the other and may be sharply differentiated. However, bacteria are intermediate or borderline forms and display the characteristics of both plants and animals. For this reason it is not possible to classify them with either the plants or the animals. After all, it makes little difference whether bacteria are plants or animals so long as their fundamental characteristics are known and understood.

CLASSIFICATION OF BACTERIA AND RELATED ORGANISMS

For the sake of convenience bacteria are classified with the plants. However, this does not mean necessarily that they are more closely related to plants than to animals.

In the outline given below, the bacteria are placed in that division of the plant kingdom known as the *Protophyta*. This division contains 3 classes and 12 orders as follows:

Division I. *Protophyta,* primitive plants.
 Class I. *Schizophyceae,* the blue-green algae. Organisms which possess the photosynthetic pigment phycocyanin in addition to chlorophyll.
 Class II. *Schizomycetes,* the bacteria. Organisms which usually do not contain photosynthetic pigments. None contains phycocyanin. Reproduce normally by fission (page 404).
  Order I. *Pseudomonadales.* Cells coccoid, straight or curved rods, or spiral in form. Sometimes occur as chains of cells. Cells may contain photosynthetic purple or green pigments. Not in trichomes. Usually motile by means of polar flagella. Occasionally nonmotile (page 405).
  Order II. *Chlamydobacteriales.* Cells in trichomes that are frequently in a sheath. Occasionally motile (swarm spores) or nonmotile conidia are developed. The sheaths may contain a deposit of ferric hydroxide, and the trichomes may be attached to a substrate (page 412).
  Order III. *Hyphomicrobiales.* Cells reproduce by a process of budding rather than by ordinary cell division (fission). May be attached to a substrate by a stalk. One genus, *Rhodomicrobium,* contains species with photosynthetic pigments (page 413).
  Order IV. *Eubacteriales.* Cells spherical or rod-shaped; no trichomes though chains of cells may occur. Motile by means of peritrichous flagella or nonmotile. Not acid-fast (page 414).
  Order V. *Actinomycetales.* Cells rigid and may grow out into a branching mycelium-like structure which may even develop chains of aerial conidia giving colonies a superficial resemblance to mold colonies. In two genera spores develop within sporangia (sporangiospores), and in one of these genera the spores are motile. Where cells occur singly or in simple branched forms, they are frequently acid-fast (page 422).
  Order VI. *Caryophanales.* Cells in trichomes (page 423).
  Order VII. *Beggiatoales.* Cells rigid, usually large, and may occur as coccoid cells or trichomes. Sulfur granules may occur on the surface or within the cells. Move by a gliding, oscillating, or rolling, jerky motion like that of some blue-green algae. No flagella present (page 423).
  Order VIII. *Myxobacterales.* Cells flexuous, creeping on a substrate. Frequently pointed at both ends. Fruiting bodies are usually developed from a thin spreading colony (pseudoplasmodium). Slime bacteria (page 425).
  Order IX. *Spirochaetales.* Cells in the form of longer or shorter spirals. Swim freely by flexion of cells (page 426).
  Order X. *Mycoplasmatales.* Nonmotile, highly pleomorphic organisms of a very delicate character. Possess filterable stages (page 426).
 Class III. *Microtatobiotes.* Organisms do not contain photosynthetic pigments or phycocyanin. Cells so minute that the exact form of reproduction not clearly understood as yet. All possess filterable stages (page 427).
  Order I. *Rickettsiales.* Individual organisms are not ultramicroscopic except perhaps in rare filterable phases and are usually more than 0.1 μ in diameter. Parasites of members of the animal kingdom (page 427).
  Order II. *Virales.* Individual organisms are usually ultramicroscopic and filterable. Except for a few pox viruses of animals and a few plant viruses, the virus particles are less than 0.1 μ in diameter. Parasites of both the plant and animal kingdoms (page 429).
Division II. *Thallophyta,* thallus plants, includes the (1) green, brown, and red algae; (2) fungi (yeasts and molds); and (3) lichens. The simpler forms are unicellular; in the higher forms, the plant body is a thallus, being commonly undifferentiated into roots, stems, and leaves. The *Thallophyta* may be schematically represented as shown in Fig. 1.

Subdivision I. *Algae,* autotrophic thallophytes containing chlorophyll. The group
comprises practically all seaweeds such as rockweed, sea moss, sea lettuce, etc.,
and allied fresh-water or nonaquatic forms, such as pond scums, stonewarts,
and fallen stars. They often have leaf-like and stem-like parts but not a true
vascular system (leaves and stems). Algae range in size from the microscopic cells
which color snow red to the giant kelp with broad fronds sometimes extending
more than 600 ft. from their holdfast on the bottom.

Subdivision II. *Fungi,* the yeasts and molds.

    Class I. *Myxomycetes,* the slime molds. These occur on damp earth and decay-
ing vegetable matter and consist of naked masses of protoplasm which creep
very slowly over the surface and ingest solid food. Ultimately these masses
(plasmodia) come to rest and organize spores which give rise to peculiar
bodies known as myxamoebae, which again form plasmodia. They are often of
considerable size and contain no chlorophyll.

    Class II. *Phycomycetes,* the algal fungi, includes a large class of parasitic or
saprophytic organisms. The plant body ranges from an undifferentiated mass
of protoplasm to a much-branched and well-developed mycelium. The vegetative mycelium is usually nonseptate. Multiplication is mainly asexual, by the
formation of conidia or sporangia, but the group shows every form of transi-

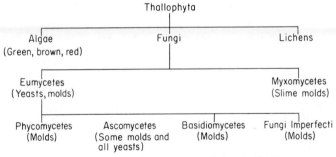

Fig. 1. A schematic representation of the Thallophyta.

tion from asexual spore formation through simple conjugation to perfect sexual
multiplication by the union of egg and sperm in the higher forms of Phycomycetes.

    Class III. *Ascomycetes,* the sac fungi. This is a large class of higher fungi dis-
tinguished by the presence of septate hyphae and by having their spores
produced in sacs, or asci. It comprises many groups of molds. A group of unicellular fungi, the yeasts, is generally included under the Ascomycetes. They
reproduce by budding, by fission, by asexual spore formation, and by copulation.

    Class IV. *Basidiomycetes,* the basidia fungi. This includes a large group of
fungi characterized by having a septate mycelium and bearing the spores on a
basidium. Chlamydospores are also formed. The lower Basidiomycetes includes
many fungi parasitic on plants.

    Class V. *Fungi Imperfecti.* The fungi in this class are separated from the others
in not having well-defined fruiting bodies. They produce neither asci nor
basidia, but only conidia. The fungi that cannot be classified with the
Phycomycetes, Ascomycetes, and Basidiomycetes are placed in this group.

Subdivision III. *Lichens,* composite plants.

    Class VI. *Lichenes,* the lichens. A lichen is a composite organism consisting of a
mold living symbiotically with an alga. The mold obtains food materials from
the alga, while the alga is in turn protected from external injury or exposure.
The fructifications of the lichens are produced by the molds, not by the algae,
which are always vegetative. The vegetable indicator litmus is derived from
a lichen.

Division III. *Bryophyta,* a division of the plant kingdom including the liverworts and the mosses. They are characterized by the presence of archegonia of complex structure and by a certain amount of differentiation into stem and leaf. The group shows certain similarities in structure, linking it with the Pteridophyta on the one hand and with the Thallophyta on the other.

Class I. *Hepaticae,* the liverworts. This includes the true liverworts and scale mosses which are small, often moss-like plants. The gametophyte consists of a simple thallus or a thalloid shoot. The liverworts inhabit moist places, old logs, tree trunks, etc., and have a corresponding hygromorphic structure. Only a few true aquatic forms have been found. Some delicate forms grow among the mosses. The antheridia and archegonia are variously developed on the thallus.

Class II. *Musci,* the mosses. The mosses include a large number of forms found in all parts of the world. They are characterized as small, leafy, often tufted stems bearing sex organs, which give rise to the development of oöspores. The oöspores develop into naked, stalked capsules containing asexual spores. The asexual spores germinate and give rise to a structure known as a *protonema* on which the gametophyte, or moss plant proper, originates by budding. The mosses are formed on dry soil, on rocks, on tree trunks, in swamps, in tropical forests, and in water.

Division IV. *Pteridophyta,* a division of the plant kingdom including the ferns, water ferns, horsetails, and club mosses. They represent the highest type of flower-less plants, having well-developed vascular and tegumentary systems, and displaying complete differentiation into roots, stems, and leaves. The sporophyte is the conspicuous generation, the gametophyte being reduced to a small thalloid body, the prothallium, bearing archegonia and antheridia. With the exception of a few tree ferns, practically all the Pteridophyta are herbaceous.

Class I. *Psilophytineae.* These are considered the most primitive of the Pteridophyta. They are leafless or have small leaves. The sporangia are terminal, not on leaves. They are isosporous.

Class II. *Lycopodineae,* the club mosses. The leaves are small. Sporangia are solitary on the upper surface of the sporophyll. They may be isosporous or heterosporous. Spermatozoids are biciliate.

Class III. *Psilotineae.* Leaves are small. Roots are absent. Sporangia are pluri-locular on the upper surface of the sporophyll. They are isosporous. The spermatozoids are multiciliate.

Class IV. *Equisetineae,* the horsetails. The leaves are small and in whorls. The sporangia are borne in numbers on the lower side of the sporophyll. They may be isosporous or heterosporous. The spermatozoids are multiciliate.

Class V. *Isoetineae.* The leaves are large in proportion to the stem. The sporangia are solitary on the upper surface of the sporophyll. They are heterosporous. The spermatozoids are multiciliate.

Class VI. *Filicineae,* the ferns. The leaves are large. The sporangia are numerous on the lower side of the leaves. They may be isosporous or heterosporous. The spermatozoids are multiciliate.

Class VII. *Pteridospermae,* the seed ferns. The leaves are large. They are heterosporous. The microsporangia are numerous on the lower side of the sporophyll. The macrosporangium contains only one macrospore.

Division V. *Spermatophyta,* the seed plants. This is the most numerous group of plants. The group is characterized by the marked development of the sporo-phyte, with great differentiation of its parts into roots, stems, leaves, flowers, etc., by the extreme reduction of the gametophyte and by the development of seeds. All the members are heterosporous. Fertilization of the egg cell occurs either through a pollen tube emitted by the microspore or by spermatozoids.

Subdivision I. *Gymnospermae,* the cone-bearing plants: pines, hemlocks, etc. This group includes plants having seeds naked or not enclosed in an ovary. In some plants fertilization is accomplished by spermatozoids.

Subdivision II. *Angiospermae,* the flowering plants. The plants have the seeds in a closed ovary. The group contains the vast majority of the seed plants.

Class I. *Dicotyledoneae,* having two cotyledons. Includes most flowering plants. Leaves net-veined. Vascular bundles form a cylinder in stem. Flower parts usually in fives, fours, or twos.

Class II. *Monocotyledoneae,* having one cotyledon. Includes the grasses, lilies, orchids, palms, etc. Leaves parallel-veined, bundles scattered in the stem. Flower parts in sixes or threes.

DISTRIBUTION OF BACTERIA

Bacteria are widely distributed in nature, being found almost everywhere. They are present in still ponds and ditches, in running streams and rivers, in sea water, in soil, in air, in foods, in petroleum oil from deeply seated regions, in rubbish and manure heaps, in decaying organic matter of all kinds, on the body surface, in body cavities, and in the intestinal tracts of man and animals. The kinds and numbers vary from one locality to another, depending upon the environmental conditions.

Some bacteria are always present in certain places. The common occurrence of one or more species in a particular environment is spoken of as the natural flora of that environment. For example, the normal souring of milk is caused by *Streptococcus lactis.* This organism is a normal inhabitant of the soil and is present on grains and hay. Since these are consumed by cows, the organism appears in manure and on the coat of the animals, from where it gains entrance to milk at the time of collection. Practically every sample of raw or pasteurized milk contains the organism.

Bacteria in Soil. The numbers and kinds of organisms present in soil depend upon the type of soil, quantity of plant and animal debris (humus), acidity or alkalinity, depth, degree of aeration, moisture content, and treatment. The great majority of soil organisms are found in the surface layer. The numbers decrease with depth, owing to lack of oxygen and food materials. The bacterial population of rich garden soil is considerably greater than that of a poor, uncultivated soil.

Bacteria in Air. Bacteria are found in air, being carried there principally by wind currents. Organisms do not grow and multiply in air because conditions are not favorable for this to occur. There is no such thing as a normal atmospheric flora. The numbers and kinds depend upon location, amount of moisture, dust particles, wind currents, and the presence of toxic gases. The air over the oceans, far removed from shore, also shows the presence of microorganisms. In general, marine air contains fewer microorganisms than terrestrial air. The air over high mountains is usually free from organisms. The air of the city and country differ as to kinds of species and numbers present. Dusty rooms usually show considerably more organisms than do rooms kept free from dust. Bacteria are found usually adhering to particles of dust, which means that the more particles suspended in air, the greater will be the extent of microbial contamination. Viable spores of bacteria, yeasts, and molds are commonly found in air because these bodies are more resistant to the ultraviolet rays of the sun than are the vegetative cells producing them. These bodies are a frequent cause of air contamination in bacteriological laboratories and, because of their great resistance to heat, require high temperatures for their destruction.

Bacteria in Water. Most waters contain large numbers of bacteria. The numbers may vary considerably depending upon the source of the water, e.g., deep or shallow wells, springs, rivers, lakes, ponds, or streams. Water polluted with sewage may contain thousands or even millions of organisms per milliliter. Under some conditions disease organisms may also be present. Practically all bacterial species found in soil may at times be present in water. Some species are always present and constitute the natural flora of that water. Usually fewer bacteria occur in sea water than in soil. This is probably due to its poorer qualities as a culture medium.

Bacteria in Food. Foods are rarely free from living organisms. Some organisms are of benefit in producing desirable fermentations such as occur in the oxidation of alcohol to vinegar, the lactic fermentation of cabbage to sauerkraut, etc. Frequently, the undesirable organisms may gain access to foods and produce abnormal changes. Some diseases or intoxications may be produced by the consumption of foods contaminated with certain organisms or their growth products.

Bacteria in Milk. Normal udders of cows are probably never free from bacteria, which means that freshly drawn milk is not sterile. The first milk drawn always contains more organisms than milk collected at the close of the operation, because most of the bacteria are washed away from the udders early in the process. However, most of the bacteria present in milk are not those which are present in the udders but forms which gain entrance after the milk has been collected. Unless the milk is properly stored immediately after collection, the organisms present may be capable of producing undesirable changes, making the milk unfit for human consumption.

Bacteria of the Body. The outer surface of the skin of the body always contains bacteria. The same applies to the respiratory passages and the alimentary and intestinal tracts. These environments contain normal floras which are for the most part harmless. Occasionally a species may invade the body by penetrating the broken skin or mucous membrane. Unless the body is invaded by massive numbers, the organisms are usually destroyed by the defense mechanisms of the host. Sometimes the body cannot destroy the invaders. Under these conditions a disease process may be established.

It has been said that as much as one-third of the dry weight of the intestinal contents of man is composed of bacterial cells.

Escherichia coli is found in the large intestine of man. Other organisms are present, but in an adult on a mixed diet this organism predominates. *E. coli*, then, is largely responsible for the natural flora of the large intestine. Changes in the environment produce changes in the bacterial flora. If the diet of an adult is changed from a high-protein to a high-carbohydrate diet, the *E. coli* organisms will gradually disappear, only to be replaced by a much larger rod-shaped organism known as *Lactobacillus acidophilus*. If this particular diet is maintained, *L. acidophilus* will now become the predominating organism of the large intestine.

FUNCTIONS OF BACTERIA

Those who are not familiar with the elementary rudiments of bacteriology have an erroneous conception of the role of bacteria in nature. Since the early development of bacteriology was concerned with a study of disease-producing organisms, the impression is generally held that the sole purpose of bacteria on this earth is to cause human ills. This statement is entirely erroneous. Only a few bacterial species are harmful to man. The great majority are not only harmless but absolutely necessary for the existence of living things. Life could not exist in the complete absence of bacteria.

Plants and animals owe their existence to the fertility of the soil, and this, in turn, depends upon the activity of the soil population. Plants absorb their nutrients from the soil in the form of minerals. They cannot utilize organic compounds such as fats, carbohydrates, and proteins. The soil organisms attack human and animal carcasses and mineralize the organic constituents, making them available to plants. The same is true for the remains of plant crops such as plant stubble and leaves. In the absence of soil organisms plants could not live or grow, and in the absence of plants there would be no animal life on this earth. Man, of course, is dependent upon both plants and animals for food.

A few species of soil bacteria are capable of invading the roots of certain plants where they take free nitrogen from the air and convert it into organic compounds which are utilized by the plants. The bacteria, in turn, derive their nutrients from the sap of the plants. This may be cited as an excellent example of a symbiotic relationship occurring in nature between two different species. In the absence of fertilizers such as animal manures, nitrates, and ammonium salts, there would be no available nitrogen in the soil were it not for the activities of these organisms. Sulfur and phosphorus, two elements necessary for plant growth, are converted into soluble inorganic salts by bacteria and absorbed by plant roots.

Fertile soils may always be distinguished from poor soils in containing greater numbers of viable organisms. If the soil is rich in plant remains, is well-aerated, contains sufficient moisture, shows the right temperature and hydrogen-ion concentration (reaction), many organisms will be present to attack the plant and animal residues, converting the insoluble and indiffusible constituents into soluble, inorganic compounds utilizable by plants.

Bacteria are necessary for the disposal of sewage. They convert the insoluble proteins, fats, and carbohydrates (cellulose) into soluble, odorless compounds which may be disposed of in an inoffensive manner.

The souring of milk is the result of bacterial action. This is the first step in the preparation of butter. The separation of butterfat is more easily accomplished and the yield improved if the milk or cream is first permitted to sour. Also, bacteria are selected which improve the aroma and flavor of the butter.

Various types of industrial fermentations are produced by the action of bacteria, yeasts, and molds on carbohydrates. Butyric acid, acetone, butyl alcohol, lactic acid, and propionic acid are produced by bacterial action. Ethyl alcohol is formed by yeasts. Gluconic acid and citric acid are the result of the activities of molds.

These are only a few examples of the activities of organisms in nature. Many other useful purposes will be discussed in the various chapters of this book.

REFERENCES

Alexander, G.: "General Biology," New York, Thomas Y. Crowell Company, 1956.
Breed, R. S., E. G. D. Murray, and N. R. Smith: "Bergey's Manual of Determinative Bacteriology," Baltimore, The Williams & Wilkins Company, 1957.
Brian, P. W.: Microbiology, *J. Roy. Soc. Arts,* **101:**194, 1953.
Gabriel, M. L., and S. Fogel: "Great Experiments in Biology," Englewood Cliffs, N.J., Prentice-Hall, Inc., 1955.
Hall, T. H., and F. Moog: "Life Science," New York, John Wiley & Sons, Inc., 1955.
Hardin, G.: "Biology," San Francisco, W. H. Freeman and Company, 1954.
Johnson, W. H., R. A. Laubengayer, and L. E. de Lanney: "General Biology," New York, Henry Holt and Company, Inc., 1956.
Pauli, W. F.: "The World of Life," Boston, Houghton Mifflin Company, 1949.
Weisz, P. B.: "Biology," New York, McGraw-Hill Book Company, Inc., 1954.
Wells, H., and P. H. Wells: "General Biology," New York, McGraw-Hill Book Company, Inc., 1956.
Whaley, W. G., O. P. Breland, C. Heimsch, A. Phelps, and G. S. Rabideau: "Principles of Biology," New York, Harper & Brothers, 1954.

CHAPTER 2

The Microscope

Bacteria are so small that they cannot be seen with the naked eye. They must be greatly magnified before they can be clearly seen and studied. The use of a microscope is, therefore, absolutely indispensable to the bacteriologist and to the biologist in general.

A microscope may be defined as an optical instrument, consisting of a lens or a combination of lenses, for making enlarged or magnified images of minute objects. The term is compounded from the two Greek words μῖκρός, micro, small, and σκοπεῖν, scope, to view.

A simple microscope, or a single microscope, consists merely of a single lens or magnifying glass held in a frame, usually adjustable, and often provided with a stand for conveniently holding the object to be viewed and a mirror for reflecting the light. A compound microscope differs from a simple one in that it consists of two sets of lenses, one known as an objective and the other as an eyepiece, commonly mounted in a holder known as a body tube (Fig. 2). The one nearest the specimen, called the objective, magnifies the specimen a definite amount. The second lens system, the eyepiece, further magnifies the image formed by the objective, so that the image seen by the eye has a magnification equal to the product of the magnifications of the two systems. The individual or initial magnification of the objectives and eyepieces is engraved on each such part. Accurate focusing is attained by a special screw appliance known as a fine adjustment. Compound microscopes give much greater magnifications than simple microscopes and are necessary for viewing and examining such minute objects as bacteria.

Every user of the microscope should first understand the principles involved in order that the instrument may be employed to the greatest advantage. As Sir A. E. Wright stated:

Every one who has to use the microscope must decide for himself the question as to whether he will do so in accordance with a system of rule of thumb, or whether he will seek to supersede this by a system of reasoned action based upon a study of his instrument and a consideration of the scientific principle of microscopical technique.

9

GENERAL PRINCIPLES OF OPTICS

The path of light through a compound microscope is illustrated in Fig. 3. The light, in passing through the condenser, object in plane I,

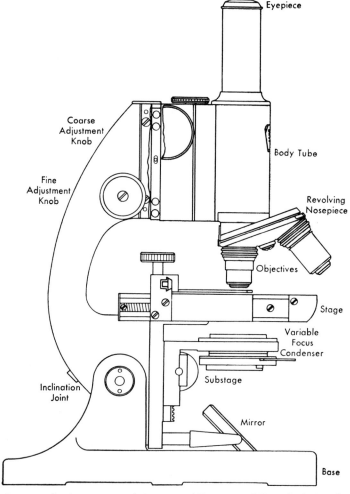

FIG. 2. Compound microscope and its parts. (*Courtesy of Bausch & Lomb Optical Company.*)

and objective lens, would form a real and inverted image in plane II if the ocular or eyepiece were removed. In the presence of the ocular F, the rays are intercepted, forming the image in plane III. The real image is

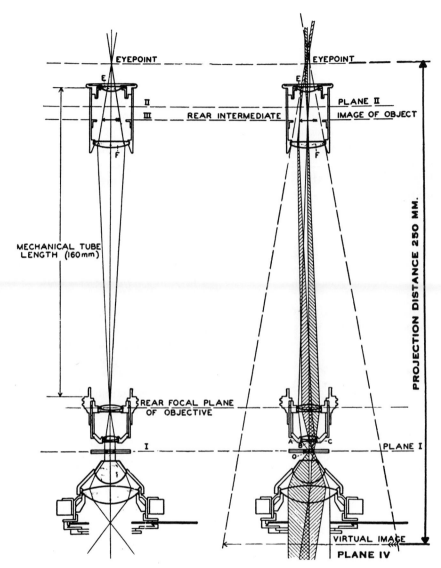

FIG. 3. Path of light through a microscope. (*From Photomicrography, courtesy of Eastman Kodak Company.*)

then examined, with the eye lens E of the ocular acting as a single magnifier and forming a virtual image in plane IV. The distance between the virtual image (plane IV) and the eyepoint is known as the projection distance. The object is magnified first by the objective lens and second by the ocular, or eyepiece. With a tube length of 160 mm. (most microscope manufacturers have adopted 160 mm. as the standard tube length), the total magnification of the microscope is equal to the magnifying power of the objective lens multiplied by the magnifying power of the ocular.

The above magnifications are obtained on a ground glass placed 10 in. from the ocular of the microscope. After the microscope has been set at the proper tube length, the total magnification may be computed by multiplying the magnifying power of the objective by that of the eyepiece and by one-tenth of the distance from the eyepiece to the ground glass measured in inches. For example, if the ground glass is placed 10 in. from the eyepiece of the microscope, the total magnification will be as given on the ocular and objective. If the ground glass is placed 20 in. from the eyepiece, the magnification will be twice as great. If placed 5 in. from the eyepiece, the magnification will be one-half as great. To take a specific example:

Magnification of objective..............	97×
Magnification of ocular.................	10×
Distance of ground glass from ocular....	7 in.
Total magnification..................	97 × 10 × 0.7(0.1 × 7) = 679×

It may be seen that almost any degree of magnification could be obtained by using oculars of different magnifying powers or by varying the length of the draw tube. Even though the magnifying powers of the microscope could be greatly increased in this manner, the amount of detail that can be seen is not improved since this is strictly limited by the structure of light.

Structure of Light. According to the undulatory, or wave, theory, light is transmitted from luminous bodies to the eye and other objects by an undulatory or vibrational movement. The velocity of this transmission is about 186,300 miles per second, and the vibrations of the ether are transverse to the direction of propagation of the wave motion. The waves vary in length from 3850 to 7600 angstrom

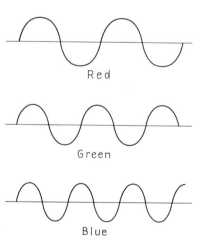

Red

Green

Blue

Fig. 4. Wave lengths of light of different colors.

units (A.) approximately. The color evoked when the energy impinges on the retina varies in a complex way with the wave length, the amplitude of vibration, and various other factors and conditions. Waves of a similar character whose lengths fall above or below the limits mentioned are not perceptible to the average eye under normal conditions. Those between 1000 and 3850 A. constitute ultraviolet light and are manifested by their photographic or other chemical action. Those exceeding 7600 A. are the infrared waves and are detected by their thermal effects.

When a beam of white light is passed through a prism, a spectrum is obtained in which several colors form a series from deep red through orange, yellow, green, blue, and indigo to deepest violet. The wave lengths of the various colors are different; red shows the longest and violet the shortest waves of the visible spectrum.

The length of a light wave is the distance from the crest of one wave to the crest of the next (Fig. 4). The unit of measurement is the angstrom unit (A.), which is equal to 1/10,000,000 mm., or to approximately 1/250,-000,000 in. The visible spectrum, together with the corresponding wave lengths of the light rays in angstrom units, may be represented as shown

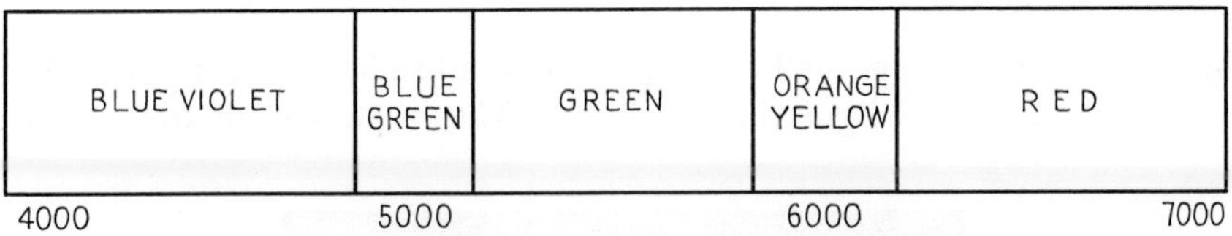

BLUE VIOLET	BLUE GREEN	GREEN	ORANGE YELLOW	R E D
4000	5000		6000	7000

FIG. 5. Light rays of the visible spectrum and their corresponding wave lengths in angstrom units.

in Fig. 5. Visible light waves, ranging in length from 4000 to 7000 A., may be roughly divided into three portions: blue-violet, from 4000 to 5000 A.; green, from 5000 to 6000 A.; red, from 6000 to 7000 A.

OBJECTIVES

The objective is the most important lens on a microscope because its properties may make or mar the final image. An objective capable of utilizing a large angular cone of light coming from the specimen will have better resolving power than an objective limited to a smaller cone of light. The chief functions of the objective lens are (1) to gather the light rays coming from any point of the object, (2) to unite the light in a point of the image, and (3) to magnify the image.

There are three major types of objectives, namely, achromatic, fluorite, and apochromatic. The achromats are the simplest in construction and the least expensive. They are adequate for most purposes. Correction for both color and spherical aberration is quite good in the lower-power objectives, but the control of aberrations becomes more difficult as the power is increased. Aberrations are largely eliminated by the use of fluorite (semiapochromatic) objectives and, especially, the apochromats. The latter are more highly corrected with respect to aberrations than any other type of objective and are preferred for the most critical work.

Numerical Aperture. The resolving power of an objective may be defined as its ability to separate distinctly two small elements in the structure of an object that are a short distance apart. The measure for the resolving power of an objective is the numerical aperture (N.A.). The larger the numerical aperture, the greater the resolving power of the objective and the finer the detail it can reveal.

Since the limit of detail or resolving power of an objective is fixed by the structure of light, objects smaller than the smallest wave length of visible light cannot be seen. In order to see such minute objects, it would be necessary to use rays of shorter wave length. Invisible rays, such as ultraviolet light, are shorter than visible rays but, since they cannot be used for visual observation (photography only), their usefulness is limited.

The image of an object formed by the passage of light through a microscope will not be a point but, in consequence of the diffraction of the light at the diaphragm, will take the form of a bright disk surrounded by concentric dark and light rings (Fig. 6). The brightness of the central

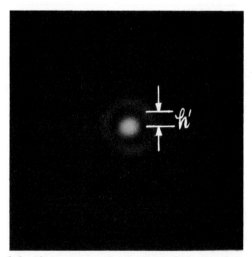

FIG. 6. The Airy disk. Photomicrograph of a pinhole in an aluminum mirror taken with a high-power dry objective. *h'*, the radius of the first dark ring, is a measure of the resolving power. (*Courtesy of Bausch & Lomb Optical Company.*)

disk will be greatest in the center, diminishing rapidly toward the edge. The image cone of light composed of a bright disk surrounded by concentric dark and light rings is spoken of as the antipoint. If two independent points in the object are equidistant from the microscope lens, each will produce a disk image with its surrounding series of concentric dark and light rings. The disks will be clearly visible if completely separated, but if the images overlap they will merge into a single bright area, the central portion of which appears quite uniform. The two disks will not, therefore, be seen as separate images. It is not known how close the centers of the images can be and still be seen as separate antipoints.

The minimum distance between the images of two distinct object points decreases as the angle of light *AOC* (Fig. 3), coming from the object *O*, increases. The angle formed by the extreme rays is known as the aperture of the objective. The ability of the objective lens system to form distinct images of two separate object points is proportional to the trigonometric sine of the angle. The latter, then, is a measure of the resolving power of the objective. Actually, however, the sine of angle *AOB* is used, which is just one-half of angle *AOC*. This is usually referred to as sin μ. Since the sine of an angle may be defined as the ratio of the side opposite the angle in a right-angled triangle to the hypotenuse, then

$$\sin \mu = \frac{AB}{AO}$$

The light in passing through the objective is influenced by the refractive index *n* of the space directly in front of the lens. This is another factor that affects the resolving power of an objective. The two factors, refractive index *n* and sin μ, may be combined into a single expression, the numerical aperture, which may be expressed as follows:

$$\text{N.A.} = n \sin \mu$$

Importance of N.A. If a very narrow pencil of light is used for illumination, the finest detail that can be revealed by a microscope with sufficient magnification is equal to

$$\frac{\text{w.l.}}{\text{N.A.}}$$

where w.l. is the wave length of the light used for illumination and N.A. is the numerical aperture of the objective. The resolving power of the objective is proportional to the width of the pencil of light used for illumination. This means that the wider the pencil of light, the greater the resolving power. The maximum is reached when the whole aperture of the objective is filled with light. In this instance, the resolving power is twice as great. The finest detail that the objective can reveal is now equal to

$$\frac{\text{w.l.}}{2 \text{ N.A.}}$$

For example, the brightest part of the spectrum shows a wave length of 5300 A. An objective having a numerical aperture equal to 1.00 will resolve two lines separated by a distance of 5300 A./1.00 = 5300 A. (48,-000 lines to the inch) if a very narrow pencil of light is used, and 5300 A./(2 × 1.00) = 2650 A. (95,000 lines to the inch) if the whole aperture of the objective is filled with light.

From the above, it is evident that the maximum efficiency of an objective is not reached unless the back lens is filled with light. This may be ascertained by removing the eyepiece from the microscope and viewing the back lens of the objective with the naked eye. If the back lens is completely filled with light, the efficiency will then be according to the numbers engraved on the objective.

Resolving Power. The relation between wave length and resolving power is illustrated in Fig. 7. The shorter the wave length of light, the

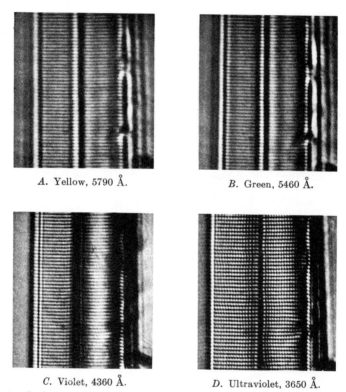

A. Yellow, 5790 Å. B. Green, 5460 Å.

C. Violet, 4360 Å. D. Ultraviolet, 3650 Å.

Fig. 7. *Amphipleura pellucida*, a diatom. Effect of light of different wave lengths on the resolving power of the objective. (*From Photomicrography, courtesy of Eastman Kodak Company.*)

finer the detail revealed by the objective. With an objective having an N.A. of 1.00 and a yellow filter (light transmission of 5790 to 5770 A.), it is possible to see about 88,000 lines to an inch; with a green filter (light transmission of 5460 A.), about 95,000 lines to an inch; with a violet filter (light transmission of 4360 A.), about 115,000 lines to an inch; and with ultraviolet light (light transmission of 3650 A.), about 140,000 lines to an inch.

Immersion Objectives. When a dry objective is used, an air space is present on both sides of the microscope slide and cover slip. The largest cone of light coming from O (Fig. 8) that could possibly be used is 180° in air, which is equal to an angle of about 82° in the glass. This corresponds to a numerical aperture of 1.0. In actual practice, however, these figures become 143 and 77°, respectively, owing to the fact that the air space must be wide enough to correspond to a practical working distance of the objective. Rays of greater angular aperture than 82° in glass, which originate at the object point O by diffraction, will be completely reflected at the upper surface of the cover slip t.

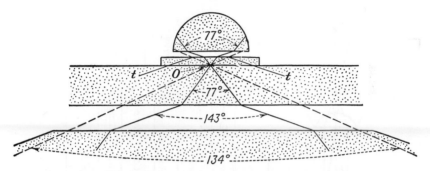

Fig. 8. Passage of light through an object on a glass slide using dry and immersion objectives. See text for details. (*Redrawn from Photomicrography, courtesy of Eastman Kodak Company.*)

The refractive index n of the air is equal to 1.0. If the air space between the cover slip and the objective is filled with a fluid having a higher refractive index, such as water ($n = 1.33$), or, what is still better, a liquid having a refractive index approaching that of glass, such as cedarwood oil ($n = 1.51$), angles greater than 82° are obtained. Numerical apertures greater than 1.0 are realized by this method. Cedarwood oil causes the light ray to pass right through the homogeneous medium, with the result that a cone of light of about 134° is obtained, which corresponds to a numerical aperture of 1.4. Finer detail can, therefore, be resolved by this procedure. With an oil-immersion objective and a numerical aperture of 1.4, two lines as close together as 1/100,000 in. (0.2 μ) can be separated. This means, then, that the greater the numerical aperture of the

TABLE 1

Medium	Refractive index at 25°C.
Water	1.33
Mineral (paraffin) oil	1.47
Cedarwood oil	1.51
Sandalwood oil	1.51
Shillaber's immersion oil	1.52
Balsam	1.53
Crown oil	1.55

objective, the greater will be its resolving power or ability to record fine detail.

The refractive indexes of a number of media that have been employed for immersion objectives are given in Table 1.

Depth of Focus. The depth of focus is known also as the depth of sharpness or penetration. The depth of focus of an objective depends upon the N.A. and the magnification, and is inversely proportional to both. This means that the higher the N.A., and the magnification, the lower the depth of focus. Therefore, high-power objectives must be more carefully

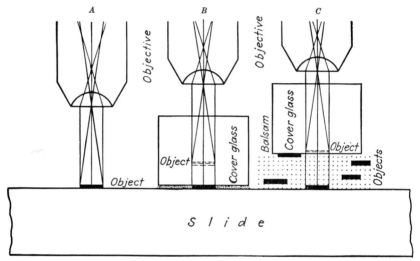

Fig. 9. Working distance of an objective. *A*, object not covered with a cover slip. *B*, *C*, object covered with a cover slip. (*Redrawn from Gage, "The Microscope," Comstock Publishing Associates, Inc.*)

focused than low-power objectives. These conditions cannot be changed by the optician.

Equivalent Focus. Objectives are sometimes designated by their equivalent focal lengths measured in either inches or millimeters. An objective designated by an equivalent focus of $\frac{1}{12}$ in., or 2 mm., means that the lens system produces a real image of the object of the same size as is produced by a simple biconvex or converging lens having a focal distance of $\frac{1}{12}$ in., or 2 mm.

Working Distance of Uncovered Objects. If the object on a glass slide is not covered with a cover slip, the working distance may be defined as the distance between the front lens of the objective and the object on the slide when in sharp focus. The working distance is always less than the equivalent focus of the objective. This is shown in Fig. 9A.

The working distance may be determined easily by noting the number of complete turns of the micrometer screw (fine adjustment) required to raise the objective from the surface of the slide, where the object is located, to a point where the microscope is in sharp focus.

To take a specific example:

> Each turn of the micrometer screw = 0.1 mm.
> Number of turns required to bring object in sharp focus = 6
> Working distance = 6 × 0.1 = 0.6 mm.

Working Distance of Covered Objects. If the object is covered with a cover slip, the free distance from the upper surface of the cover slip to the front of the objective will be less than in the case of an uncovered object. It is obvious from this that if the cover glass is thicker than the working distance of the objective, it will be impossible to get the object in focus. On the other hand, if the glass is thin it will be possible to get the object in focus, but the focus of the microscope on a covered object will be different from that on an uncovered object. It follows from this that an object covered with a glass cover slip or other highly refractive body will appear as if raised, and the amount of elevation will depend upon the refractive index of the glass or other medium covering the object. Also, the greater the refraction of the covering body, the more will be the apparent elevation. This is shown in Fig. 9B,C. The apparent depth of the object below the surface of the covering medium may be calculated by taking the reciprocal of its index of refraction. For example, if a glass cover slip is used, it will have an index of refraction of 1.52. The reciprocal of this figure is $1/1.52 = \frac{2}{3}$, approximately. This means that the apparent depth of the object is only two-thirds its actual depth.

The working distance of covered objects may be determined by noting the number of complete turns of the micrometer screw (fine adjustment) required to raise the objective from the surface of the cover slip to a point where the objective is in sharp focus.

To take a specific example:

> Each turn of micrometer screw = 0.1 mm.
> Number of turns required to bring object in sharp focus = 3.5
> Working distance = 3.5 × 0.1 = 0.35 mm.

Aberrations in Objectives. Perfect lens systems have not yet been designed. All lens systems have aberrations to a greater or lesser degree, depending upon the skill of the designer and the magnitude of the design problem. Lens systems are made up of lenses having spherical surfaces, and such surfaces do not form perfect images. This defect may be largely counteracted by combining lens shapes and different glasses.

The principal defects in the image are the result of chromatic aberration, spherical aberration, distortion, curvature of field, astigmatism, coma, and lateral color.

Chromatic Aberration. White light in passing through a prism is broken up into its constituent colors, the wave lengths of which are different (page 13). A simple or compound lens, composed of only one material, will exhibit different focal lengths for the various constituents of white light. This is due to the dispersive power of the lens. Every wave length is differently refracted, the shortest waves most and the longest waves least. The blue-violet rays cross the lens axis first and the red rays last. There will be a series of colored foci of the various constituents of white light extending along the axis (Fig. 10). As a result, the lens will not pro-

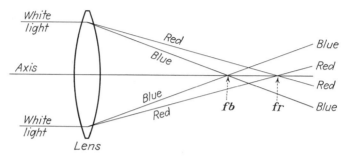

Fig. 10. Chromatic aberration with white light. White light, in passing through a lens, is dispersed into its constituent colors. The red or long waves are refracted less than the blue or short waves. The blue rays (*fb*) cross the optical axis of the lens before the red rays (*fr*). The blue light will focus nearer the lens than the red light.

duce a sharp image with white light. Instead, the image will be surrounded by colored zones or halos which interfere with the visual observation of its true color. This is spoken of a chromatic aberration. It may be lessened by reducing the aperture of the lens or, better still, by using a lens composed of more than one material (compound lens). Two or more different glasses or minerals are necessary for correcting the chromatic aberration of an objective, and the amount of correction depends upon the dispersive powers of the components of the objective.

If two optical glasses are carefully selected to image light of two different wave lengths at the same focal point, the lens is said to be achromatic, and an objective containing such a lens system is spoken of as an achromatic objective. The remaining rays of the white light will be imaged at approximately the same point. An achromatic objective will yield images free from pronounced color halos. If the focus is shifted slightly, faint green and pink halos may be observed. The slight residual color will not prove objectionable for the usual microscopic work. Achromats are the universal objectives for visual work and are very satisfactory in photomicrography when used in monochromatic light (obtained by the use of filters).

Lens systems corrected for light of three different wave lengths are called apochromatic objectives. These objectives are composed of fluorite in combination with lenses of optical glass. The images produced by objectives in this group exhibit only a faint blue or yellow residual color.

Since these objectives are corrected for three colors instead of for two, they are superior to the achromats. Their finer color correction makes possible a greater usable numerical aperture. The violet rays are brought to the same focus as visual rays. This fact makes these objectives excellent for photographic use for both white and monochromatic light.

Another group of objectives exhibit qualities intermediate between the achromats and the apochromats. They are called *semiapochromats*. If the mineral fluorite is used in their construction, they are termed fluorite objectives. These objectives also yield excellent results when used for photomicrography.

Spherical Aberration. This refers to the greater power in the outer portion of a spherical surface than in the inner portion. This is overcome by judicious combinations of convergent and divergent lens elements, properly shaped to minimize the variation of focal power with aperture. Spherical aberration causes some of the light which should be in the cen-

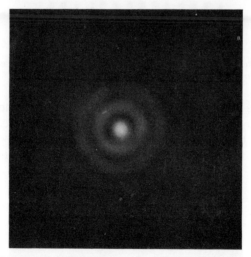

FIG. 11. Spherical aberration. This causes some of the light which should be in the central spot to diffuse out into the ring structure, resulting in a loss in contrast in the normal microscope preparation. (*Courtesy of Bausch & Lomb Optical Company.*)

tral spot to diffuse out into the ring structure (Fig. 11). This causes a loss in contrast in the normal microscope preparation.

Distortion. This type of aberration renders a square object as an image with curved sides. If the rulings near the edge appear curved inward, it is known as cushion distortion. If the opposite effect occurs, where the rulings appear curved outward, it is known as barrel distortion. Distortion is caused by the lens surface having different magnifications at the marginal and central portions of the image.

Curvature of Field. This aberration is caused by a spherical lens surface

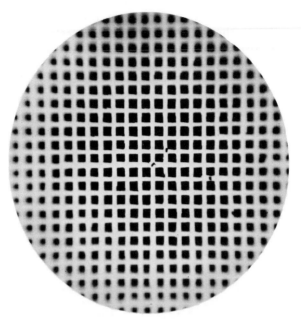

Fig. 12. Curvature of field. The center is sharply focused, the periphery is out of focus. (*Courtesy of Bausch & Lomb Optical Company.*)

which produces a curved image of a flat object due to the marginal portions of the image coming to a focus at a different distance than the central portions of the image (Fig. 12).

Astigmatism. If a marginal point object is drawn out into two separate-

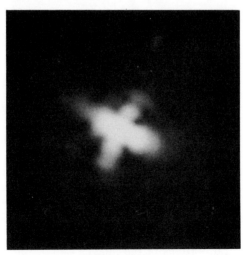

Fig. 13. The appearance of a point object due to the presence of astigmatism. (*Courtesy of Bausch & Lomb Optical Company.*)

line images lying at different distances from the lens surface, it is called astigmatism (Fig. 13). It results in a general deterioration of the off-axis image. An astigmatic image can never be focused sharply except for detail parallel or perpendicular to a radius of the field.

Coma. This name is given to the defect in which different circular concentric zones of the lens surface give different magnifications to an off-axis image. This results in a point object being imaged as a comet-shaped image (Fig. 14). Coma in the center of the field is an indication of damage to the objective.

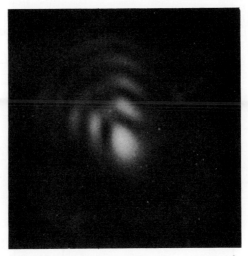

Fig. 14. The appearance of a point object due to the presence of coma. (*Courtesy of Bausch & Lomb Optical Company.*)

Lateral Color. The presence of this defect results in light of one color being imaged at a greater magnification than light of another color. This causes an off-axis image of a point object to be spread out into a tiny spectrum or spread of color.

OCULARS

The chief functions of the ocular, or eyepiece, are the following:

1. It magnifies the real image of the object as formed by the objective.
2. It corrects some of the defects of the objective.
3. It images cross hairs, scales, or other objects located in the eyepiece.

Several types of eyepiece are employed, depending upon the kind of objective located on the microscope. Those most commonly used are known as Huygenian, hyperplane, and compensating oculars.

Huygenian Eyepiece. In this type of eyepiece, two simple plano-convex lenses are employed, one of which is below the image plane (Fig. 15). The convex surfaces of both lenses face downward. Oculars in this group are sometimes spoken of as negative eyepieces. This type of ocular is made with a large field lens, which bends the pencils of light coming from

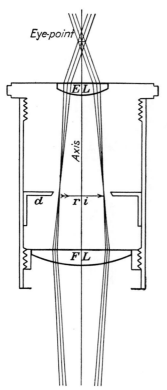

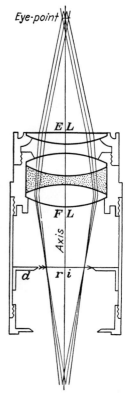

Fig. 15. Huygenian eyepiece. *EL,* eye lens; *FL,* field lens; *ri,* real image formed between the ocular lenses and the diaphragm *d.* (*Redrawn from Gage, "The Microscope," Comstock Publishing Associates, Inc.*)

Fig. 16. Compensating eyepiece. *EL,* eye lens; *FL,* field lens composed of three components; *ri,* real image formed below the lenses at the diaphragm *d.* (*Redrawn from Gage, "The Microscope," Comstock Publishing Associates, Inc.*)

the objective toward the axis without altering to any great extent the convergence or divergence of the rays in the individual pencils. Above the field lens, and at some distance from it, is a smaller lens known as the eye lens, the function of which is to convert each pencil of light into a parallel or only slightly diverging ray system capable of being focused by the eye. The rays, after emerging through this lens, then pass through a small circular area known as the Ramsden disk, or eyepoint. It may be seen that the real image of the object is formed between the two eyepiece lenses. In an eyepiece of this type, the distance separating the two lenses is always a little greater than the focal length of the eye lens. The reason for this is to prevent any dirt on the field lens from being seen sharply focused by the eye. An image should be viewed with the eye placed at the Ramsden disk in order to obtain the largest field of view and also to obtain the maximum brightness over the field.

The Huygenian eyepiece works well with the low-power achromats but gives undercorrected curvature of field and lateral color with the intermediate and higher power objectives. The degree of compensation required increases with the objective power, making it highly desirable to have a graded series of eyepieces. Therefore, the Huygenian eyepiece should be used to cover the low powers; the hyperplane eyepiece, the intermediate powers; and the compensating eyepiece, the high powers.

Hyperplane Eyepiece. Apochromatic objectives, when used with compensating eyepieces, give fields that are not flat. Flat-field eyepieces have been designed to correct this defect. They give much flatter fields than do the other two types but they are less perfectly corrected chromatically. Oculars of this type are referred to as hyperplane, planoscopic, periplane, etc. They may be employed with the higher power achromatic, fluorite, and apochromatic objectives without introducing chromatic aberrations in the image. Their color compensation falls about midway between the Huygenian and the compensating eyepieces.

Compensating Eyepiece. Oculars of this type consist of an achromatic triplet combination of lenses (Fig. 16). These eyepieces are more perfectly corrected than are those of the Huygenian and hyperplane types. A compensating eyepiece is corrected to neutralize the chromatic difference of magnification of the apochromatic objectives. Such eyepieces are intended, therefore, to be used primarily with apochromatic objectives, although they may be employed with the higher power achromatic and fluorite objectives with good results.

CONDENSERS

Several methods are employed for illuminating the object under examination. In bacteriology, the two methods commonly used are (1) illumination by transmitted light and (2) dark-field illumination.

Illumination by Transmitted Light. A condenser may be defined as a series of lenses for illuminating, with transmitted light, an object to be studied on the stage of the microscope. It is located under the stage of the microscope between the mirror and the object, whereas the objective and ocular lenses are located above the stage. It is sometimes referred to as a substage condenser. The most popular substage optical system is known as the Abbe condenser (Fig. 17A).

A condenser is necessary for the examination of an object with an oil-immersion objective to obtain adequate illumination. A condenser is also preferable when working with high-power dry objectives. Probably the most commonly employed condenser has a 1.25 N.A.

A good condenser sends light through the object under an angle sufficiently large to fill the aperture of the back lens of the objective. When this is accomplished, the objective will show its highest numerical aperture. This may be determined by first focusing the oil-immersion objective on the object. The eyepiece is then removed from the ocular tube. The back lens of the objective is observed by looking down the microscope tube, care being taken not to disturb the focus. The back lens of the ob-

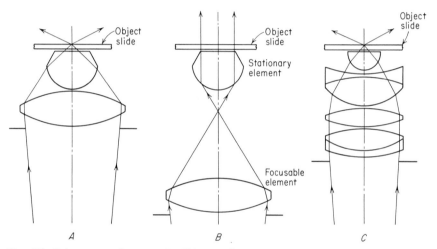

Fig. 17. Substage condensers. A, Abbe condenser; B, variable-focus condenser; C, achromatic condenser. (*Courtesy of Bausch & Lomb Optical Company.*)

jective should be evenly illuminated. If it is not, the mirror should be properly centered. If the condenser has a smaller numerical aperture than the objective, the peripheral portion of the back lens of the objective will not be illuminated, even though the condenser iris diaphragm is wide open. If the condenser has a greater numerical aperture than that of the objective, the back lens of the objective may receive too much light, resulting in a decrease in contrast. The smaller the aperture, the greater the depth of focus and the greater the contrast of the components of the image. The lowest permissible aperture is reached when diffraction bands become evident about the border of the object imaged. This difficulty may be largely overcome by closing the iris diaphragm of the condenser until the leaves of the iris appear around the edges of the back lens of the objective. The diaphragm is then said to be properly set. The setting of the iris diaphragm will vary with different objectives.

The Abbe condenser is a 1.25-N.A. condenser utilizing only two lenses. Because of its simplicity and good light-gathering ability, it has become extensively used for general microscopy. It is, of course, not corrected for spherical or chromatic aberration, but for general visual observation it serves very well.

The variable-focus condenser (Fig. 17B) is a two-lens condenser, 1.25 N.A. maximum, in which the upper lens element is fixed and the lower one focusable. By this means it is possible to fill the field of low-power objectives without the necessity of removing the top element. This condenser is basically similar to the 1.25-N.A. Abbe when the lower lens is raised to its top position. When the focusable lens is lowered, the focus of the light is brought in between the elements, and when this focus is at the point indicated in the diagram, the light emerges as a large-diameter parallel bundle.

The achromatic condenser (Fig. 17C) is a 1.40-N.A. condenser that is corrected for both chromatic and spherical aberrations. Because of its high degree of correction, it is recommended for research microscopy and color photomicrography where the highest degree of perfection in the image is desired.

Dark-field Illumination. The microscope is most commonly employed by allowing the light to pass through the object. This is called microscopy in transmitted light or bright-field microscopy. An object cannot be seen in bright-field microscopy unless it absorbs or refracts the light passing through it. Contrast is thus set up between the object and the surrounding medium. Objects that display feeble contrast with the background are difficult to see in bright-field illumination.

If the aperture of the condenser is opened completely and a dark-field stop inserted below the condenser, the light rays reaching the object form a hollow cone. If a stop of suitable size is selected, all the direct rays from the condenser can be made to pass outside the objective. Any object within this beam of light will reflect some light into the objective and be visible. This method of illuminating an object, where the object appears self-luminous against a dark field, is known as dark-field illumination.

Three types of condensers are employed for dark-field illumination: (1) the Abbe, (2) the paraboloid, and (3) the cardioid.

The Abbe condenser is probably more commonly employed than the other two because it is especially suitable for objects that do not require the highest magnifications to make them visible. It may be employed either by inserting a dark-field stop below the condenser (Fig. 18) or by unscrewing the top part of the condenser and substituting for it a dark-field element (Fig. 18A).

The paraboloid condenser is designed to be used with high-power oil-immersion objectives and an intense source of light (Fig. 19). In using this condenser, it is necessary to place cedar oil or glycerin between the

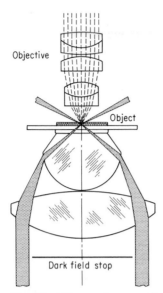

Fig. 18. Abbe condenser with dark-field stop inserted below the condenser. (*From Dark Field Optical Systems, courtesy of Bausch & Lomb Optical Company.*)

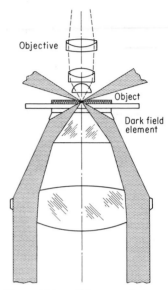

Fig. 18A. Abbe condenser. (*From Dark Field Optical Systems, courtesy of Bausch & Lomb Optical Company.*)

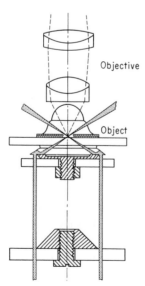

Fig. 19. Paraboloid condenser. (*From Dark Field Optical Systems, courtesy of Bausch & Lomb Optical Company.*)

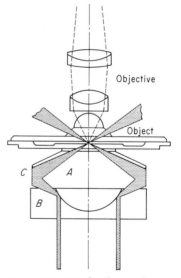

Fig. 20. Cardioid condenser. (*From Dark Field Optical Systems, courtesy of Bausch & Lomb Optical Company.*)

condenser and the slide. Also, the specimen must be mounted in a liquid or cement and protected with a cover slip. The numerical aperture of the objective must not be greater than that of the condenser.

The cardioid condenser is the most refined type of dark-field illuminator (Fig. 20). It is especially designed to be used for the examination of colloidal solutions or suspensions, i.e., particles measuring less than 0.25 μ in diameter.

The cardioid condenser is best employed with a strong arc lamp. Since the concentration of light is so great, ordinary glass slides and cover slips

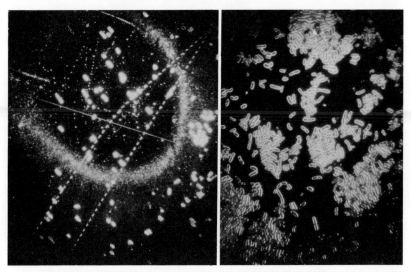

FIG. 21. Slides for dark-field microscopy. Left, sunlight dark-field photomicrograph of *Caryophanon* on glass slide with good cover slip. Note scratches and dirt. Right, same on mica slide with good cover slip. Note clear background and excellent dark-field effect. (*After Pijper.*)

should not be used. Visible defects and the difficulty of removing foreign objects from the glass ruin the visibility of ultramicroscopic particles. It is better to employ fused-quartz object slides and fused-quartz cover slips. They are free from bubbles and other imperfections and can be heated in a flame to drive off all dirt, after being chemically cleaned. Pijper (1951) recommended the use of thin microscope slides to which were cemented pieces of mica of similar shape by means of Canada balsam. When the balsam had hardened, a thin layer of mica was split off with a sharp knife, which left an untouched, scratch-free, and dust-free surface, perfectly suited for dark-field microscopy (Fig. 21).

For more information on the microscope see Allen (1940), American Optical Company (1945), Gage (1941), Muñoz and Charipper (1943), and Wredden (1948).

PHASE MICROSCOPY

The principle of the phase microscope is not new, having been discovered as early as 1892, but it has only recently been developed to practical use. It complements rather than replaces existing methods of microscopy.

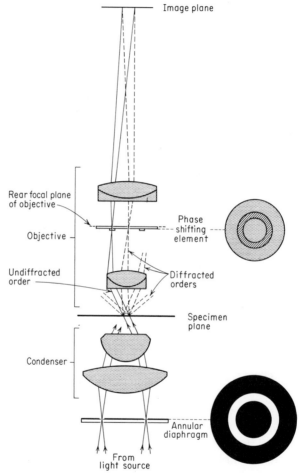

Fig. 22. Schematic diagram of the general optical arrangement of a phase microscope. (*Courtesy of Bausch & Lomb Optical Company.*)

Phase microscopy is a method for controlling the contrast in the image and making visible unstained living microorganisms and cytological details within them. Phase microscopy also greatly enhances visibility of stained material of low contrast.

The method employed for fixing and staining bacteria may make a difference in their size. The bacterial cell usually shrinks considerably dur-

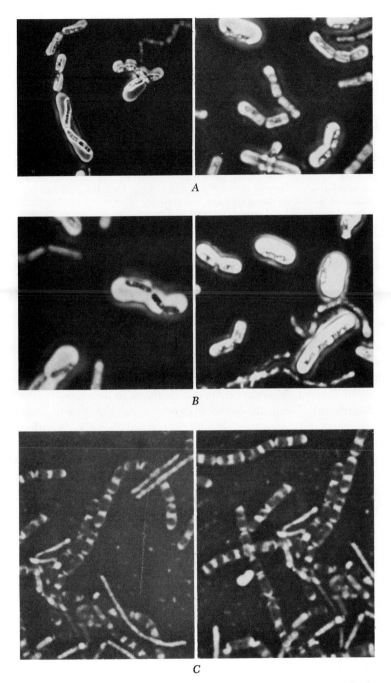

Fig. 23. Phase micrographs of *Azotobacter agile* after light nigrosine background staining. *A*, *B*, large young rods with internal differentiation; *C* may represent concentrations of material at poles and along lines of division rather than "chromatinic bodies." (*After Eisenstark, McMahon, and Eisenstark.*)

ing drying and fixing. Since microorganisms show sharp edges under the phase microscope in unstained preparations, accurate measurement of living cells is now possible.

A schematic diagram of the general optical arrangement of a phase microscope is shown in Fig. 22. An annular aperture in the diaphragm, placed in the focal plane of the substage condenser, controls the illumination on the object. The aperture is imaged by the condenser and objective at the rear focal plane, or exit pupil, of the objective. In this plane a phase shifting element, or phase plate, is placed.

Light, shown by the solid lines and undeviated by the object structure, in passing through the phase altering pattern, acquires a one-quarter wave length of green light advance over that diffracted by the object structure (broken lines) and passing through that region of the phase plate not covered by the altering pattern. The resultant interference effects of the two portions of light form the final image. Altered phase relations in the illuminating rays, induced by otherwise invisible elements in the specimen, are translated into brightness differences by the phase altering plate.[1]

Photomicrographs of preparations of *Azotobacter agile*, taken by phase microscopy after light nigrosin background staining, are shown in Fig. 23.

For more information see Bennett et al. (1951), Brice (1947), Eisenstark and McMahon (1949), and Richards (1952).

FLUORESCENCE MICROSCOPY

Fluorescence is a property of some substances to excite emission of visible light by the absorption of invisible ultraviolet radiations. The exact mechanism of this phenomenon is not clearly understood. Some materials are autofluorescent, whereas others can be made to fluoresce by treatment with fluorescent chemicals called fluorochromes. Equipment includes a source of ultraviolet rays, suitable filters for isolating the radiations, and a standard microscope.

Some applications of fluorescence microscopy include examination of acid-fast bacteria (*M. tuberculosis*, etc.), differentiation of living and dead microorganisms, examination of hair for mold spores, and location of chemotherapeutic agents in tissues.

For more information see Richards (1950).

ELECTRON MICROSCOPE

Within the past fifteen years a new type of instrument has been developed having a higher resolving power than the usual microscope. This instrument is known as the electron microscope (Figs. 24 and 25).

The electron microscope uses as its radiation a beam of high-speed electrons having an equivalent wave length of X-ray dimensions (about 0.05 angstrom unit or one-fifth of a billionth of an inch). It is this extremely short wave length which gives the electron microscope its fundamental

[1] Taken from "The Theory of the Microscope," Bausch & Lomb Optical Company, 1951.

superiority over the light microscope. A close analogy exists between the action of a magnetic or electric field of rotational symmetry on an electron beam and the action of a glass lens on a light beam (Fig. 26).

These electrons obtain their high velocity and low wave length as a

FIG. 24. RCA electron microscope, type EMU-3. (*Courtesy of Radio Corporation of America.*)

result of their acceleration through about 50,000 volts. After reaching this high velocity (about 70,000 miles per second, or about two-fifths the velocity of light), the electrons penetrate a specially prepared specimen and are then focused by means of magnetic fields so as to form an enlarged image on either a fluorescent screen or a photographic plate.

An optical-lens microscope magnifies about 2000 diameters. If ultraviolet light is used, this magnification can be increased to about 3000

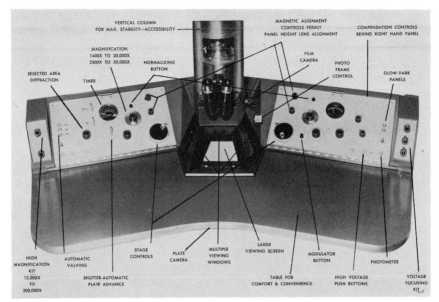

Fig. 25. Details of electron microscope, type EMU-3 control panels. (*Courtesy of Radio Corporation of America.*)

diameters. With the electron microscope, the maximum magnification available is about 30,000 diameters. However, under the best conditions this 30,000× image will contain much more detail than the unaided eye can see. By exposing a suitable photoplate to this image and through later

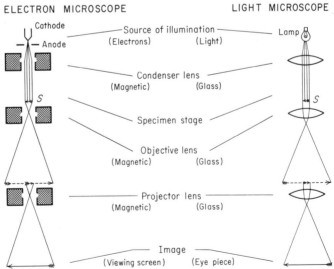

Fig. 26. Similarity of light and electron microscopes. (*Courtesy of Radio Corporation of America.*)

optical enlargement of this image by 10 diameters, a final magnification of 300,000 diameters can be obtained. The resolving power is so much greater than that of the ordinary optical microscope that it is now possible to obtain images of protein molecules, virus crystals, bacteriophages, unstained flagella, internal structures of bacteria, etc.

For more information on the electron microscope see Burton and Kohl (1946); Gabor (1948); Hall (1953); Hillier (1946, 1949, 1950); Hillier and Baker (1946); Hillier, Knaysi, and Baker (1948); Williams (1947); Wyckoff (1949); and Zworykin et al. (1945).

DAMAGING EFFECTS OF MOLD GROWTH ON LENSES

Surfaces of optical glass are susceptible to mold growth, especially when the temperature and relative humidity are high for appreciable periods. The etching of the glass, according to Richards (1949), is due chiefly to (1) the moisture associated with the mold leaching the surface, and (2) the organic acids produced as end products of mold metabolism.

A number of molds have been isolated from optical surfaces, including species of *Alternaria, Aspergillus, Basisporium, Cladosporium, Monilia, Penicillium,* and *Pullularia.* Cleanliness, lowered humidity, and fungicidal agents have been found useful in protecting lens surfaces from fouling by molds.

REFERENCES

Allen, R. M.: "The Microscope," London, Chapman & Hall, Ltd., 1940.
———: "Photomicrography," Princeton, N.J., D. Van Nostrand Company, Inc., 1958.
American Optical Company: "Three American Microscope Builders," Buffalo, N.Y., 1945.
Bausch & Lomb Optical Company: Dark-field optical systems, Catalogue D-22, Rochester, N.Y.
Bennett, A. H., H. Jupnik, H. Osterberg, and O. W. Richards: "Phase Microscopy," New York, John Wiley & Sons, Inc., 1951.
Brice, A. T.: "The Phase Principle in Microscopy," London, British Intelligence Objectives Subcommittee, 1947.
Burton, E. F., and W. H. Kohl: "The Electron Microscope," New York, Reinhold Publishing Corporation, 1946.
Eastman Kodak Co.: Photography through your microscope, Rochester, N.Y., 1952.
Eisenstark, A., and K. J. McMahon: Some phase-microscope observations of *Azotobacter agile, Soil Sci.,* 68:329, 1949.
———, ———, and R. Eisenstark: A cytological study of a pleomorphic strain of *Azotobacter* with the electron and phase microscopes and the Robinow nuclear-staining technique, *J. Bact.,* 59:75, 1950.
Gabor, D.: "The Electron Microscope," New York, Chemical Publishing Company, Inc., 1948.
Gage, S. H.: "The Microscope," Ithaca, N.Y., Comstock Publishing Company, Inc., 1941.
Hall, C. E.: "Introduction to Electron Microscopy," New York, McGraw-Hill Book Company, Inc., 1953.
Hillier, J.: Electron microscopy, *Am. Ceramic Soc. Bull.,* 25:438, 1946.

————: Some remarks on the image contrast in electron microscopy and the two-component objective, *J. Bact.*, **57**:313, 1949.

————: Electron microscopy, *Ann. Rev. Microbiol.*, **4**:1, 1950.

————, and R. F. Baker: The mounting of bacteria for electron microscope examination, *J. Bact.*, **52**:411, 1946.

————, G. Knaysi, and R. F. Baker: New preparation techniques for the electron microscopy of bacteria, *ibid.*, **56**:569, 1948.

Muñoz, F. D., and H. A. Charipper: "The Microscope and Its Use," New York, Clay-Adams Co, Inc., 1943.

Pijper, A.: Slides and cover-glasses for dark-ground microscopy, *J. Roy. Microscop. Soc.*, **71**:176, 1951.

Reisner, J. H.: Electron diffraction on the electron microscope, *Scient. Instr.*, RCA, **3**:1, 1958.

Richards, O. W.: Microscopy-fluorescence, *Medical Physics*, **2**:530, 1950.

————: Phase microscopy, *Wallerstein Lab. Commun.*, **15**:155, 1952.

Rooseboom, M.: "Microscopium," Leiden, Holland, National Museum for the History of Science, 1956.

Shillaber, C. P.: "Photomicrography," New York, John Wiley & Sons, Inc., 1944.

Sjostrand, F. S., and J. Rhodin: "Electron Microscopy," New York, Academic Press, Inc., 1957.

Williams, R. C.: The electron microscope in biology, *Growth Symposium*, **11**:205, 1947.

Wredden, J. H.: "The Microscope," New York, Grune & Stratton, Inc., 1948.

Wyckoff, R. W. G.: "Electron Microscopy," New York, Interscience Publishers, Inc., 1949.

————: "The World of the Electron Microscope," New Haven, Conn., Yale University Press, 1958.

Zworykin, V. K., G. A. Morton, E. G. Ramberg, J. Hillier, and A. W. Vance: "Electron Optics and the Electron Microscope," New York, John Wiley & Sons, Inc., 1945.

CHAPTER 3

Dyes and Staining Solutions

Bacteria are semitransparent and difficult to see in the unstained state. Staining is necessary to make the cells visible and to reveal the presence of various internal and external structures. The presence of certain structures in bacteria aids in their identification and classification.

Natural dyes predominated during the early years of bacteriology, but at present only a few of them are being used. They have been gradually discarded in favor of the artificial or synthetic dyes. Since the first artificial dyes were produced from aniline, they are generally referred to as aniline dyes. However, a large number of them are not derived from aniline and bear no relation to the compound. Since all of them are derived from one or more substances found in coal tar, they are more correctly referred to as coal-tar dyes.

The coal-tar dyes may be considered as derivatives of the cyclic compound benzene or benzole:

$$
\begin{array}{c}
\text{H} \\
| \\
\text{C} \\
\diagup\ \ \diagdown\!\!= \\
\text{HC}\quad\quad\text{CH} \\
\|\quad\quad\ | \\
\text{HC}\quad\quad\text{CH} \\
\diagdown\ \ \diagup\!= \\
\text{C} \\
| \\
\text{H}
\end{array}
$$

The empirical formula is C_6H_6. It is customary to write the structural formula by omitting the double bonds and the hydrogen atoms, abbreviating it to a hexagon, each corner of which represents an atom of carbon and one of hydrogen:

This hexagon is known as the benzene ring.

One or more hydrogen atoms may be replaced by some element or radical. For example, if one hydrogen atom is replaced by a hydroxyl (OH) group, the compound phenol, or carbolic acid, is produced:

If another hydrogen atom is replaced by a methyl group (CH_3), the compound known as cresol is produced. Three different cresols are possible, depending upon which hydrogen atoms are substituted:

The substituted radicals are in the 1-2 or ortho, 1-3 or meta, and 1-4 or para positions. The compounds are named orthocresol, metacresol, and paracresol, respectively. The prefixes are usually abbreviated to the letters *o*-, *m*-, and *p*-.

The quinones are compounds produced by the elimination of two hydroxyl-hydrogen atoms from aromatic dihydroxy derivatives. The simplest quinone is benzoquinone. It is also called *quinone,* the formula for which is

The benzene ring of the quinones contains two double bonds instead of three as in cresol. The formula of benzoquinone shows that it is not a true benzene derivative but the diketone of a *p*-hydrobenzene. Substances containing the quinone ring are called *quinonoid compounds.* The double bonds in the quinonoid compounds are supposed to be fixed, not mobile as in benzene. A large number of dyes contain the quinone ring.

DYES

Definition of a Dye. A dye may be defined as an organic compound containing both chromophore and auxochrome groups linked to benzene rings. A chromophore group imparts to the compound the property of color. Compounds of benzene containing chromophore radicals have been called *chromogens.* Such a compound, even though colored, is not a dye. It possesses no affinity for, nor ability to unite with, fibers and tissues.

The color may be easily removed by mechanical methods. To be a dye it must contain not only a chromophore group but also another group that imparts to the compound the property of electrolytic dissociation. Such groups are known as auxochromes. In some instances they may alter the shade of the dye but are not the cause of the color. The function of auxochrome groups is to furnish salt-forming properties to the compound.

This may be illustrated by the following example: The nitro group (NO_2) may be considered a chromophore. When three hydrogen atoms in the benzene molecule are replaced by three nitro groups, the compound trinitrobenzene is formed:

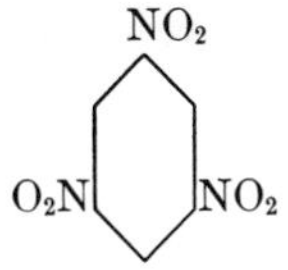

$$NO_2 \qquad O_2N \qquad NO_2$$

This yellow-colored compound is a chromogen but not a dye. It does not dissociate electrolytically and is unable, therefore, to form salts with either acids or bases. If, however, another hydrogen atom is replaced by an auxochrome group, such as (OH), the compound known as picric acid is formed:

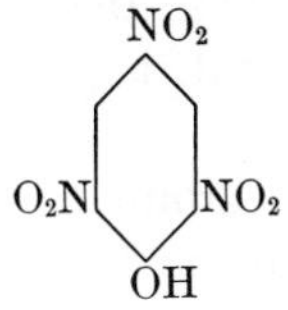

$$NO_2 \qquad O_2N \qquad NO_2 \qquad OH$$

This compound is also yellow in color and is capable of dissociating as follows:

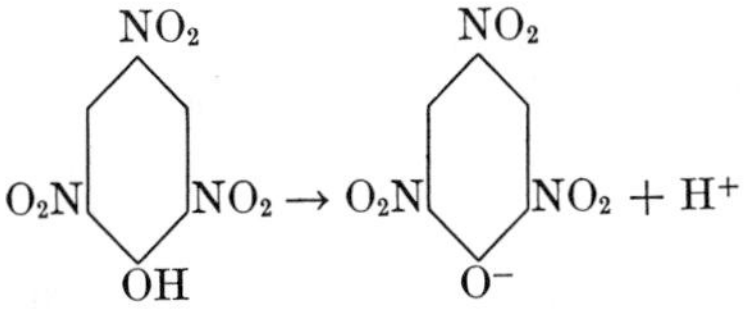

$$NO_2 \qquad O_2N \qquad NO_2 \quad \rightarrow \quad O_2N \qquad NO_2 + H^+ \qquad OH \qquad O^-$$

The dye portion of the molecule has a negative electrical charge. Therefore, it is an acid dye, being capable of forming salts with bases. The color of picric acid is due to the chromophoric nitro groups (NO_2), and its dyeing properties are due to the auxochromic hydroxyl group (OH), which imparts to the compound the property of electrolytic dissociation.

Acidic and Basic Dyes. The dyes of commerce are not acids or bases in the true sense. The terms do not refer to the hydrogen-ion concentrations of their solutions. The distinction depends on whether the dye portion of the molecule has a positive or negative electrical charge. Acidic dyes ionize to give the dye portion of the molecule a negative electrical charge. They are salts of color acids, usually the sodium salts, sometimes the potassium, calcium, or ammonium salts. Basic dyes ionize to give the dye portion of the molecule a positive electrical charge. They are salts of color bases, usually the chloride, sometimes the sulfate or acetate.

Some auxochromic groups are acidic (e.g., OH), whereas others are basic (e.g., NH_2). The amino group is basic by virtue of the ability of its nitrogen atom to become pentavalent on the addition of water or acid:

With water:

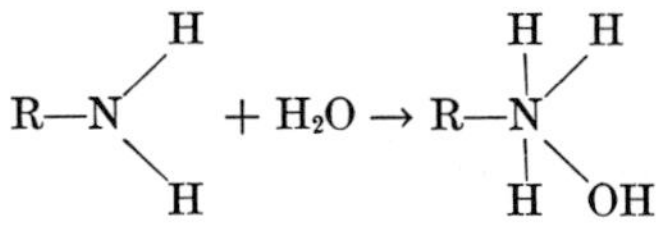

$$R-N\begin{array}{c}H\\\\H\end{array} + H_2O \rightarrow R-N\begin{array}{c}H \quad H\\H\\H \quad OH\end{array}$$

Amine   Organic ammonium base

With an acid:

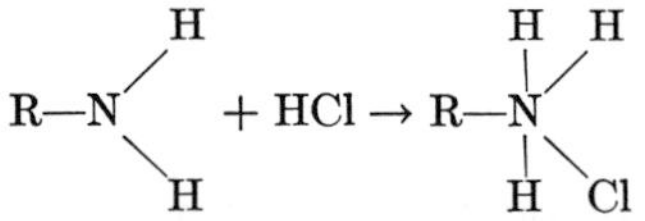

$$R-N\begin{array}{c}H\\\\H\end{array} + HCl \rightarrow R-N\begin{array}{c}H \quad H\\H\\H \quad Cl\end{array}$$

Amine   Amine hydrochloride

The hydroxyl group is weakly acid by virtue of its power to furnish hydrogen ions by dissociation. The more of either one of these two groups (i.e., OH or NH_2) in a compound, the stronger acid or base it becomes. The amino group is a stronger base than the hydroxyl group is an acid. If one of each of these two radicals is present, the basic character of the amino radical predominates.

Some dyes have the sulfonic group (SO_2OH) attached to a benzene ring. It is a strongly acid group, possessing salt-forming properties. The radical is only weakly auxochromic. It serves two very important purposes in the dye molecule: (1) It renders a dye soluble in water, and (2) it changes a basic dye to one acid in character by the introduction of the sulfonic group into the benzene ring. Since the radical is only weakly auxochromic, a compound containing a chromophore and a sulfonic acid group is not a dye unless a true auxochrome radical is also present.

Both acidic and basic dyes are used in bacteriology. The acidic dyes are used chiefly to stain cytoplasm. The basic dyes stain acid constituents (nuclei, metachromatic granules) more intensely than cytoplasmic material.

Chromophores. In order that a compound be a dye, it must contain at least one group that imparts to the substance the property of color. This is known as a chromophore group. Some chromophores are basic in reaction; others are acidic.

Basic Chromophores. The basic chromophores include (1) the azo group, (2) the azine group, and (3) the indamine group.

1. The azo group

$$-N=N-$$

is found in all azo dyes. In these compounds a benzene ring is attached to each nitrogen atom. The dyes in this group may be considered as derivatives of azobenzene:

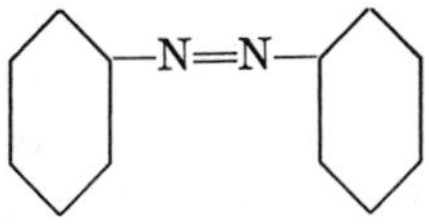

$$\bigcirc\!\!-\!\!N\!\!=\!\!N\!\!-\!\!\bigcirc$$

Examples of dyes containing this chromophore are Bismarck brown, methyl red, and methyl orange.

2. The azine group

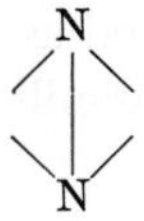

$$\underset{N}{\overset{N}{\bigwedge}}$$

is found in the phenazines. Neutral red and the safranines are examples of azine dyes.

3. The indamine group

$$-N=$$

is found in the indamines, the thiazines, and other dyes. Many of the dyes have two benzene rings attached to a nitrogen atom. One of the rings shows the quinonoid structure:

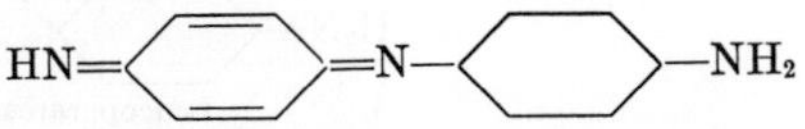

$$HN\!\!=\!\!\bigcirc\!\!=\!\!N\!\!-\!\!\bigcirc\!\!-\!\!NH_2$$

The thiazines have the two benzene rings further joined together by an atom of sulfur. The simplest thiazine nucleus has the following structure:

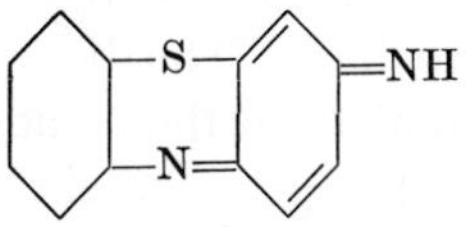

$$\bigcirc\!\!\overset{S}{\underset{N}{\bigcirc}}\!\!=\!\!NH$$

The best-known dye having the thiazine base is methylene blue.

Acid Chromophores. The acid chromophores include (1) the nitro group and (2) the quinonoid ring.

1. The nitro group (NO_2) is found in many compounds, an example of which is picric acid.

2. The quinonoid ring

occurs in many dyes such as the indamines, the xanthenes, and the di- and triphenyl methanes. Some of the well-known dyes in this group are rosolic acid, fuchsin, the methyl violets, methyl green, crystal violet, and pararosaniline.

LEUCO COMPOUNDS

The chromophores all have unsatisfied affinities and are easily reduced by combining with hydrogen at the double bonds. The nitro group may be reduced to an amino radical; the bond between the nitrogen atoms of the azine group may break and be replaced by two atoms of hydrogen; the double bonds of the quinonoid ring may break and one atom of hydrogen be taken up by each valence set free. A reduction of the chromophore group results in a loss of color. These decolorized dyes are known as leuco compounds. Dyes can often be used as indicators of oxidation and reduction. The decolorization of pararosaniline may be represented by the following equation:

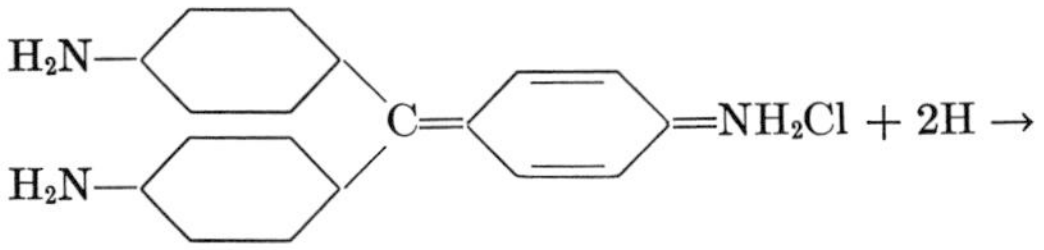

Pararosaniline

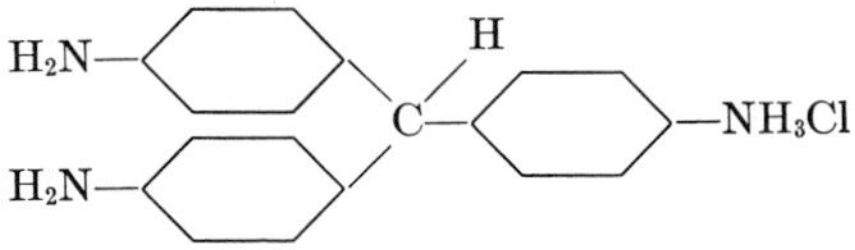

Leucopararosaniline

CLASSIFICATION OF BIOLOGICAL DYES

The important dyes used in bacteriology are given below. Some of them are acidic; others are basic. The basic dyes, for reasons already given, are the most important from the standpoint of the bacteriologist. The dyes are classified according to the chromophore groups they contain.

I. The nitro dyes. The chromophore is —NO_2. The dyes are all acid:

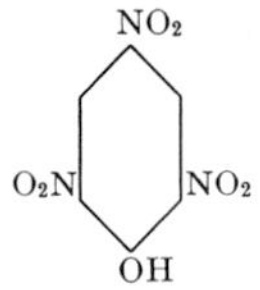

Picric acid

Group includes: *aurantia, Martius yellow, picric acid.*

II. The azo group. The azo group may be subdivided into the (1) monoazo dyes and (2) disazo and polyazo dyes.

1. Monoazo dyes. The chromophore —N=N— joins together benzene or naphthalene rings. In the monoazo dyes the group occurs only once:

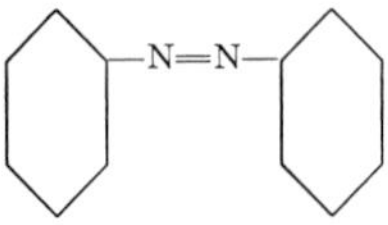

A hydroxyl or amino group on a benzene ring is usually in the para position in relation to the azo group. The azo chromophore is distinctly acid. The addition of OH groups makes the dyes acid; the addition of NH_2 groups makes the dyes basic.

Group includes: *Bordeaux red, brilliant yellow S, chrysoidin Y, fast yellow, Janus green B, methyl orange, methyl red, orange G, orange II, Sudan R.*

2. Disazo and polyazo dyes. Sometimes the chromophore occurs more than once in a molecule:

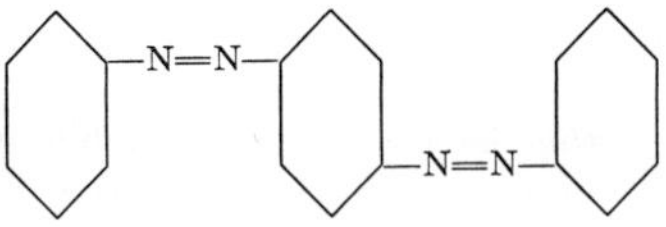

−N=N−   −N=N−

Group includes: *azo blue, Biebrich scarlet* (water soluble), *Bismarck brown Y, Congo red, Evans blue, Sudan black B, Sudan IV, trypan blue, vital red.*

III. The anthraquinone group. The anthraquinone dyes include derivatives of anthracene through its oxidation product anthraquinone:

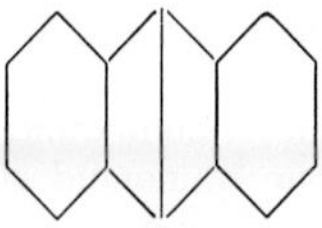

Anthracene 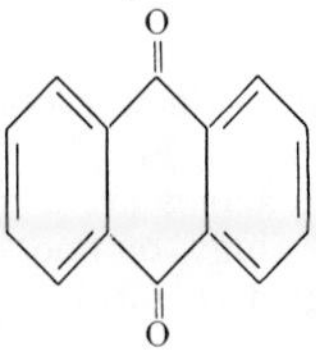   Anthraquinone

The quinonoid ring is the chromophore and anthraquinone the chromogen.

Group includes: *alizarin, alizarin red S, purpurin.*

IV. The thiazole dyes. The dyes in this group contain the thiazole ring

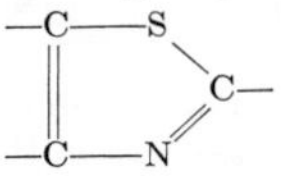

−C−S
     \
      C−
     /
−C−N

in which the indamine group is the chromophore.

Group includes: *geranine G, primuline, titan yellow G, thioflavine S.*

V. The quinonimine dyes. The dyes of this group contain two chromophores, the indamine group —N= and the quinonoid ring:

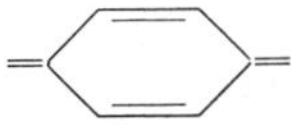

They are derivatives of the theoretical compound para-quinone-di-imine:

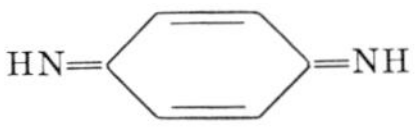

HN=   =NH

In a typical formula, one of the imine hydrogen atoms is replaced by a phenyl group:

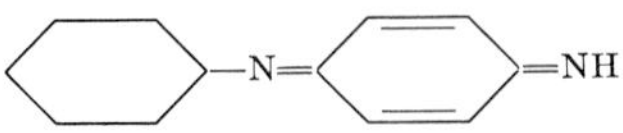

−N=   =NH

1. The indamines. The indamine dyes consist of methylated amino derivatives of indamine.

There are no members of any biological importance.

2. The indophenols. The indophenols are closely related to the indamines. The simplest member of this group is indophenol:

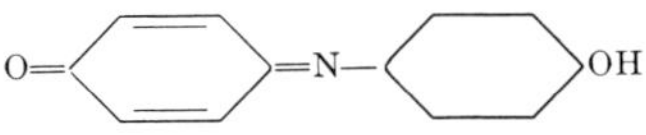

O=   =N−   OH

Group includes: *indophenol blue.*

3. The thiazines. The thiazines have a phenyl and a quinonoid ring joined together by an atom of sulfur and one of nitrogen to form a third closed ring:

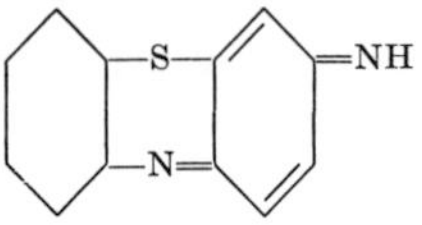

This group contains some of the most important biological dyes.

Group includes: *azure A, azure B, methylene azure, methylene blue, methylene green, methylene violet, thionine, toluidine blue O.*

4. The oxazines. In the oxazines, the sulfur of the thiazines is replaced by an atom of oxygen:

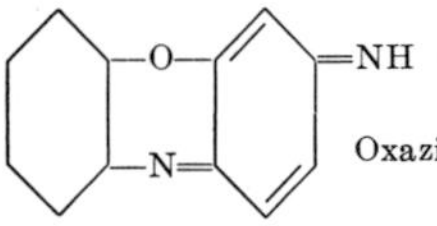

Group includes: *brilliant cresyl blue, cresyl violet, new blue R, Nile blue sulfate, resazurin.*

5. The azines. The azines are derivatives of phenazine, a compound consisting of two benzene rings, or one benzene ring and one quinonoid ring, joined together through two nitrogen atoms to form a third ring:

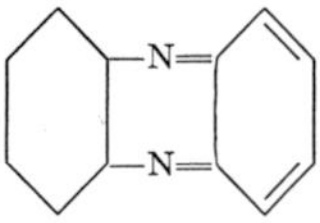

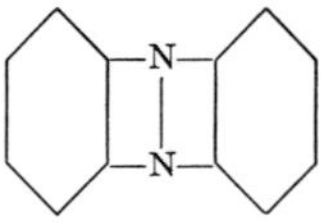

In the first formula the quinonoid ring is the chromophore; in the second formula the azine group $=N—N=$ is the chromophore.

    a. The aminoazines. The aminoazines are produced by the introduction of one or more amino groups into the phenazine molecule. They are useful chiefly as indicators.

       Group includes: *neutral red, neutral violet.*

    b. The safranines. In the safranines one of the nitrogen atoms of the azine group is pentavalent and another benzene ring is attached to it.

       Group includes: *amethyst violet, azocarmine G, safranine O.*

    c. The indulines. The indulines are highly phenylated amino derivatives of the safranines.

       Group includes: *induline* (alcohol soluble), *induline* (water soluble), *nigrosine* (water soluble).

VI. The phenylmethane dyes. This group comprises the most important dyes used in bacteriology. The compounds are substituted methanes. One or more hydrogen atoms of methane may be replaced by methyl, ethyl, or phenyl groups. If three hydrogen atoms are replaced by ethyl groups, the compound triethylmethane is formed:

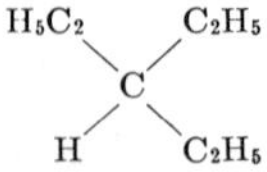

If two hydrogens of methane are replaced by phenyl groups, diphenylmethane is formed:

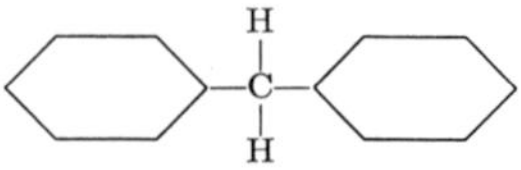

If three hydrogens are replaced, triphenylmethane is produced:

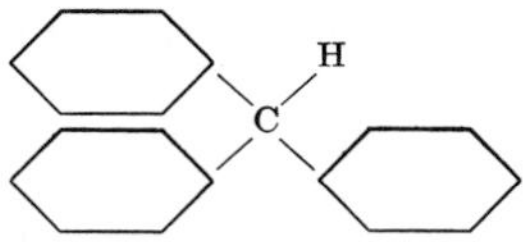

The introduction of amino and other groups, and substituted amino groups, accounts for the large number of compounds possible.

1. The diamino triphenylmethane dyes. With the exception of the sulfonated derivatives, these are strongly basic dyes. They are derivatives of diamino triphenylmethane:

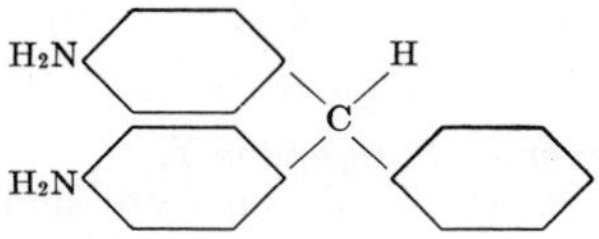

Group includes: *brilliant green, fast green FCF, light green SF (yellowish), malachite green.*

2. The triamino triphenylmethane dyes. These are also strongly basic dyes, except the sulfonated derivatives which are acid. They are derivatives of triamino triphenylmethane:

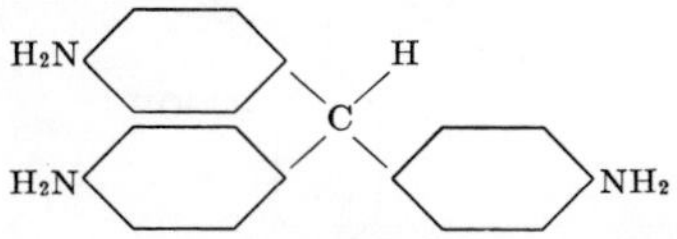

Group includes: *acid fuchsin, basic fuchsin, crystal violet, ethyl green, ethyl violet, Hofmann's violet, methyl blue, methyl green, methyl violet, new fuchsin, pararosaniline, rosaniline, spirit blue, Victoria blue 4R.*

3. The hydroxy triphenylmethane dyes. These are triphenylmethane derivatives in which the amino groups of the rosanilines are replaced with hydroxyl groups giving the dyes acidic rather than basic properties:

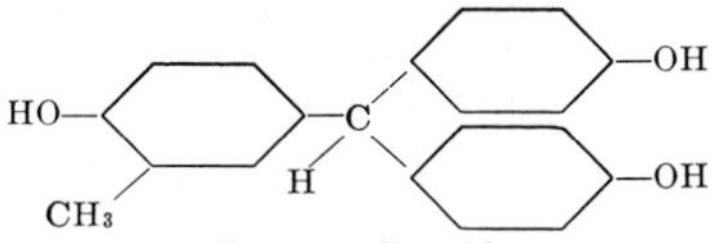

Leucorosolic acid

The members of this group are used chiefly as indicators.
Group includes: *rosolic acid.*

4. Diphenyl-naphthyl methane dyes. These are naphthyl derivatives of the diphenylmethane dyes.
Group includes: *Victoria blue B, Victoria blue R, night blue, wool green S.*

VII. The xanthene dyes. The xanthenes are derivatives of the compound xanthene:

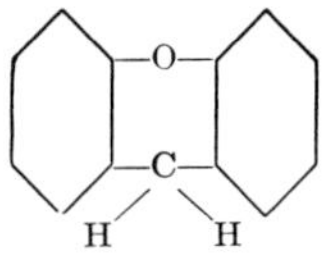

Some of the dyes are basic; others are acidic. The most useful indicators used in bacteriology fall in this group.

1. The pyronine dyes. The pyronines are methylated diamino derivatives of xanthene. They are closely related to the diphenylmethane dyes. Their formula is similar to the oxazines except that the nitrogen atom of the central ring is replaced by a —CH= radical. Three formulas are possible:

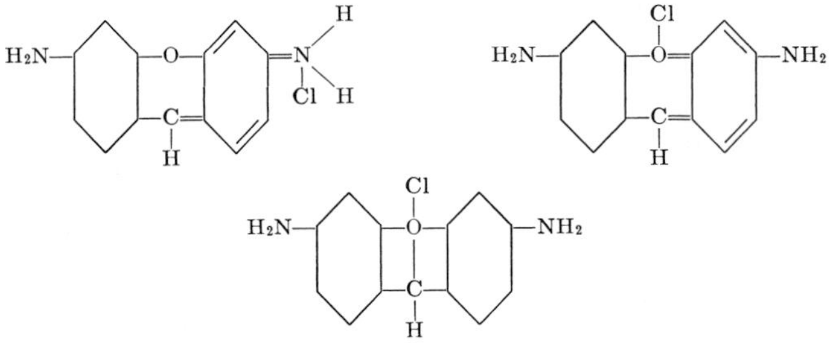

Group includes: *pyronine B, pyronine Y.*

2. The rhodamine dyes. The rhodamines are similar to the pyronines except that they have another benzene ring to which is attached a carboxyl group in the ortho position:

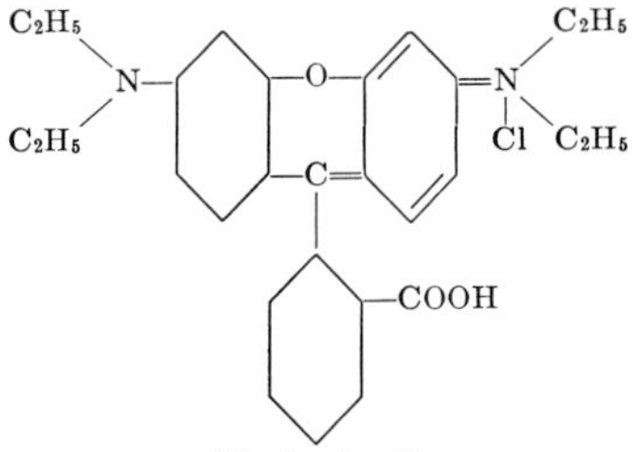

Rhodamine *B*

Since the dyes contain two amino groups to one carboxyl, they are basic in character.

Group includes: *fast acid blue R, rhodamine B.*

3. The fluorane dyes. The fluoranes are derivatives of the nondye compound fluorane:

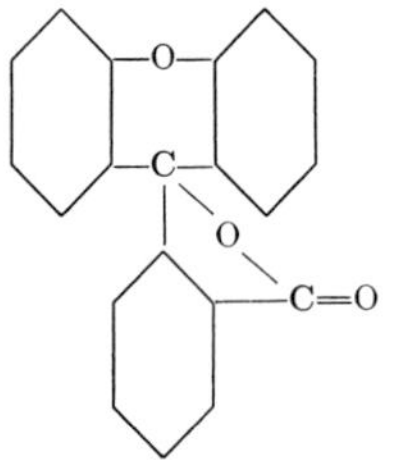

They are sometimes considered as derivatives of fluorescein, a salt of dihydroxyfluorane:

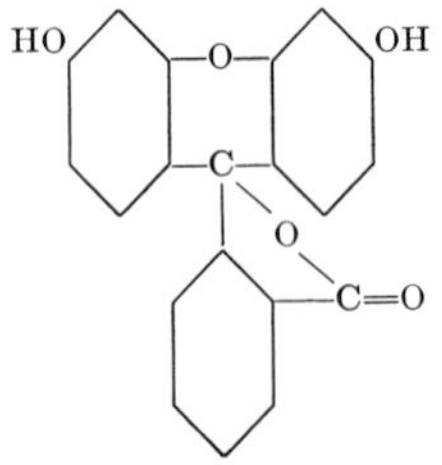

Group includes: *eosin B, eosine Y (yellowish), ethyl eosin, erythrosin (bluish), erythrosin (yellowish), fluorescein, Mercurochrome 220, phloxine B, rose bengale.*

4. The phenolphthalein and the sulfonephthalein dyes. A phthalein is a compound of phthalic anhydride

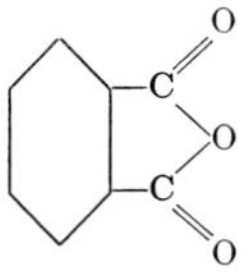

with phenol or a phenol derivative. A phenolphthalein is a compound of phthalic acid with two molecules of phenol:

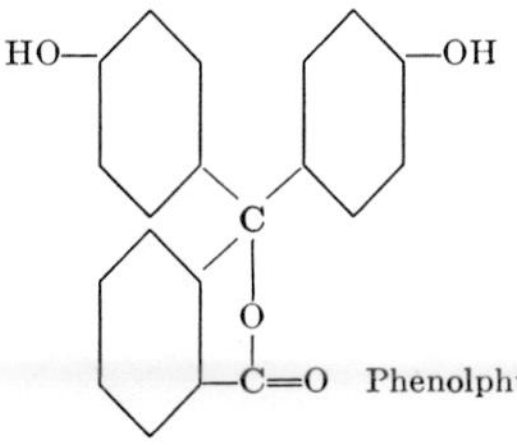

Phenolphthalein

A sulfonephthalein is a compound of orthosulfobenzoic acid

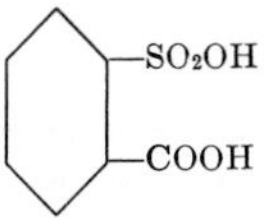

with phenol or a phenol derivative:

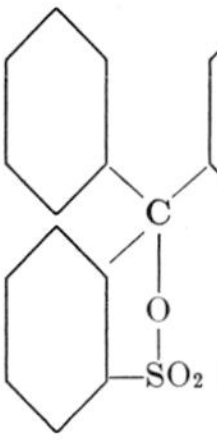

Sulfonephthalein

Group includes: *bromochlorophenol blue, bromocresol green, bromocresol purple, bromophenol blue, bromophenol red, bromothymol blue, chlorocresol green, chlorophenol red, cresolphthalein, cresol red, metacresol purple, phenolphthalein, phenol red, thymol blue.*

5. The acridine dyes. The acridines are derivatives of acridine

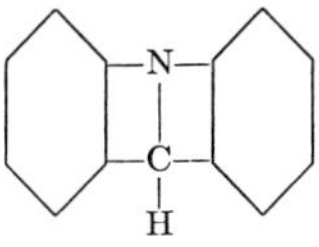

a compound closely related to xanthene. The dyes of this group are used chiefly as disinfectants against bacteria and protozoa rather than as stains. Group includes: *acridine orange NO, acridine yellow, acriflavine, atabrine, neutral acriflavine, phosphine, rivanol.*

VIII. The natural dyes. Natural dyes predominated during the early years of biology, but they have been largely replaced by the synthetic dyes. The group of natural dyes still found useful includes those which have not yet been synthesized. Only a few are of any importance in bacteriology.

1. Indigo. Several species of plants of the genus *Indigofera* contain a glucoside, indican, which on fermentation yields the dye indigo:

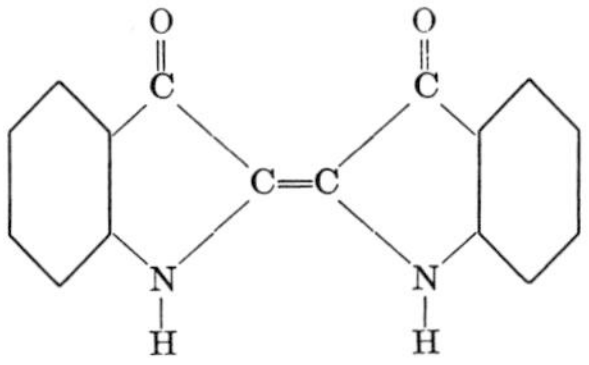

2. Indigo carmine. This dye is the sodium salt of indigo disulfonic acid. It is a blue-colored dye having acidic properties:

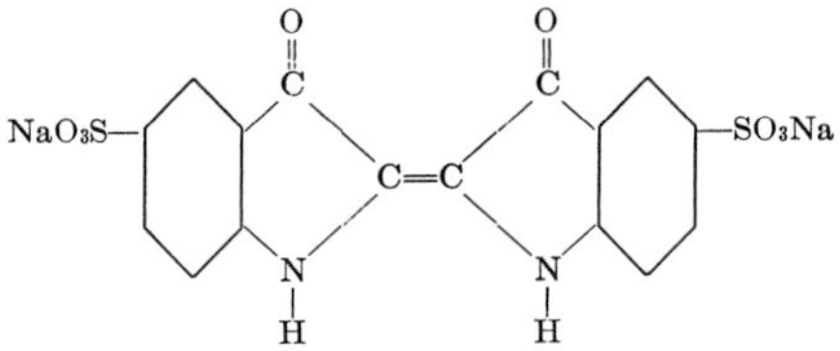

3. Cochineal. This principle is obtained by grinding the dried bodies of the female insect *Coccus cacti* and extracting with water. Cochineal possesses no affinity for tissues and is of limited value when used alone. However, it becomes a useful dye when converted into carmine.

4. Carmine. This dye is prepared by treating cochineal with alum or other metal salts. Cochineal is not a dye but when converted into carmine becomes a valuable nuclear stain. The exact formula of carmine is not known.

5. Orcein. Orcein is obtained from the lichens *Lecanora tinctoria* and *Roccella tinctoria*. The plants contain certain colorless, crystalline, phenolic compounds. One of these compounds is orcinol

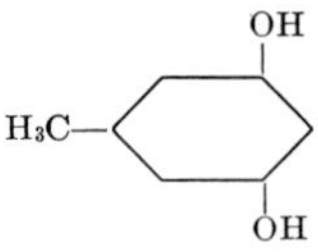

which changes to orcein, a violet-colored compound, on the addition of ammonia and oxygen (air). It is a weakly acidic dye. The exact formula is not known.

6. Litmus. Litmus is obtained from the same lichens as orcein by treating them first with lime and soda, followed by ammonia and air. Litmus is believed to contain more than one colored compound, but the primary colored principle is known as azolitmin. The exact formula is not known.

7. Brazilin. Brazilin is obtained by extracting the bark from brazilwood. It is colorless when freshly extracted but becomes oxidized to the red dye brazilein on exposure to air:

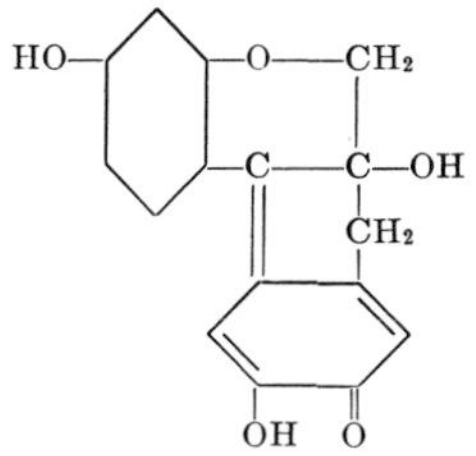

In combination with alum or iron, it is employed as a nuclear stain.

8. Hematoxylin. Hematoxylin is obtained from logwood, a legume growing in South America and other tropical areas. It is prepared by extracting the wood with water, evaporating the extract to dryness, extracting the residue with ether, evaporating the ether extract to dryness, dissolving the residue in water, filtering, and setting aside for crystals to separate from the aqueous extract.

Like brazilin, hematoxylin is not a dye, but on standing in air it is oxidized to the dye hematein, which is homologous with brazilein and is believed to have the following formula:

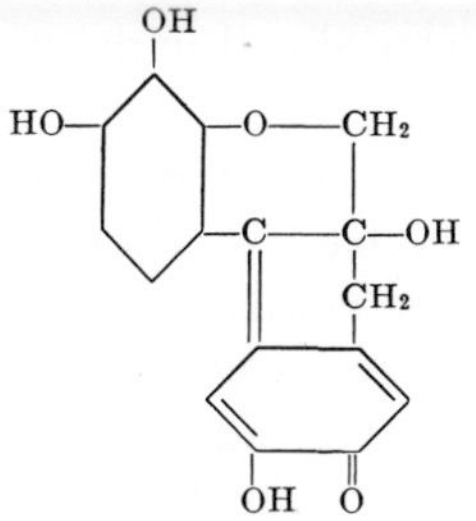

THEORIES OF STAINING

Many theories have been advanced to explain the phenomenon of staining. All of them attempt to explain the process on a purely physical or chemical basis.

Physical. In a chemical reaction, a new compound is formed having properties different from the original reacting substances. Furthermore, it is impossible to recover the original reactants by means of simple solvents.

A physical process may be defined as a reaction between two substances in which a new compound is not formed. When bacteria are stained, there is no evidence that the dye has been changed chemically to form a new compound. It is usually possible to extract all or nearly all of the dye from the bacterial cells by sufficiently long immersion in water, alcohol, or other solvent. The bacterial protoplasm never completely removes all of the dye from solution. This is contrary to a chemical reaction, which tends to continue until one of the components of the reaction is exhausted.

The proponents of the physical theory claim that all staining reactions can be explained on the basis of capillarity, osmosis, adsorption, and absorption. There does not appear to be any general agreement on the amount of weight that should be given to each force, although all agree that they occur in the process of staining.

Chemical. It is well established that some parts of a cell are acidic in reaction whereas others are basic. This fact led chemists to explain the phenomenon of staining on a purely chemical basis. The coal-tar dyes are either anionic (acid) or cationic (basic); i.e., the dye portion of the molecule is either the negative or the positive ion. The proponents of the theory state that the acid constituents of the cell (nuclei, chromatin) react with basic dyes, and the basic constituents (cytoplasm) react with acid dyes. The process is not so simple as this, however, and probably does not explain all of the facts.

It is well known that bacteria normally possess a negative electrical charge. McCalla (1940a, b) showed that bacteria attract positively charged ions, according to the equation

$$(n \text{ bases}^+) + (B^{n-}) \rightleftharpoons (n \text{ bases}^+)(B^{n-})$$

where B represents the bacterial cell with an unknown number of negative ionic valences, n.

McCalla (1941) found that when a negatively charged bacterial cell is treated with magnesium, the base is adsorbed to the cell until a neutral system is produced. In other words, the positively charged magnesium ions are attracted to the negative valences of the bacterial cell. If a basic stain, such as methylene blue, is added to the bacteria saturated with magnesium, the metal is displaced by the stain, according to the equation,

$$(\tfrac{1}{2}n\text{Mg}^{++})(B^{n-}) + n\text{S}^+\text{Cl}^- \rightleftharpoons (n\text{S}^+B^{n-}) + \tfrac{1}{2}n\text{MgCl}_2$$

where S represents the stain (methylene blue ion). The magnesium is displaced by the methylene blue in stoichiometrical proportions.

In a later communication McCalla and Clark (1941) showed that basic dyes are adsorbed at pH values higher than the isoelectric point, and acid dyes at pH values lower than the isoelectric point. Under normal conditions bacteria possess negative charges and therefore attract positively charged particles. On the other hand, bacteria placed in a solution having a pH lower than the isolectric point become positively charged (see Fig. 27, page 55). Under these conditions, they are capable of attracting negatively charged dyes, such as acid fuchsin.

McCalla concluded that the reaction of stains with bacteria is an adsorption exchange process reaching stoichiometrical proportions. On the basic side of the isoelectric point, basic stains act as cations, replacing similarly charged ions from the bacterial system; on the acid side of the isoelectric point, acid stains act as anions, replacing similarly charged ions from the bacterial system. Stains appear to react with the bacterial cell at the same positions as do inorganic cations and anions.

Summarizing, it may be stated that available evidence seems to point to the fact that staining is neither entirely physical nor entirely chemical but a combination of both.

For more information see Harris (1951), Finkelstein and Bartholomew (1953).

STAINING SOLUTIONS

Preparations employed for staining bacteria are largely aqueous solutions. In most cases concentrated solutions of the dyes are prepared by dissolving in alcohol, then diluting the alcoholic solutions with water. Since alcohol removes dyes from stained cells, pure alcoholic solutions of dyes should not be employed.

Staining solutions generally contain low concentrations of dyes. Rarely do the concentrations amount to more than 1 per cent. A very dilute staining solution acting for a relatively long period of time will, in general, produce much better results than a more concentrated solution acting over a shorter interval. This is the method followed where it is desired to reveal internal structures in bacteria. In actual practice, however, the more concentrated staining solutions are used because of the greater saving in time. Where time is not a factor, more dilute preparations should be employed.

Mordant. A mordant may be defined as any substance which is capable of forming insoluble compounds with stains and which causes their fixation to bacteria.

Mordants are generally applied first to the bacterial smear, followed by the addition of the staining solution. Under some conditions a mordant is added to a staining solution, and the preparation applied to the bacteria in one application.

Some compounds which have been used as mordants include ammonium oxalate, phenol, tannic acid, and salts of aluminum, iron, tin, zinc, copper, and chromium.

Examples of staining procedures employing mordants are the Gram stain, the acid-fast stain, and various flagella stains.

Simple Stains. Many different kinds of staining solution are employed in the various bacteriological procedures. Some are for general use; others are designed for special purposes. A simple staining solution is one that contains only a single dye dissolved in a solvent. It is applied to the bacteria in one application. The bacteria are given the characteristic color of the dye solution. The purpose of a simple stain is to distinguish bacteria from nonliving material and to reveal their shapes and sizes. The simple staining solutions that are employed probably more than any of the others for routine purposes are carbolfuchsin, crystal violet, and methylene blue.

Carbolfuchsin Stain. This stain is prepared by dissolving about 0.3 per cent of basic fuchsin, a triamino triphenylmethane or rosaniline dye, in a 5 per cent solution of phenol. The phenol is added as a mordant. For use as a simple stain, it is usually advisable to dilute the solution about ten times with distilled water.

For information on the composition of the various fuchsins of commerce, see pages 60 and 61.

Crystal Violet Stain. Crystal violet is also a member of the triamino triphenylmethane dyes. Chemically it is hexamethyl pararosaniline (see page 54).

The dye is also known as methyl violet 10B, gentian violet, hexamethyl violet, and violet C, G, or 7B. It produces the deepest shade of the pararosanilines and is considered the most satisfactory of all the violet compounds as a simple bacterial stain.

Methylene Blue Stain. Methylene blue chloride is preferred for biological work. It is tetramethylene thionine chloride, a basic dye, having the following formula:

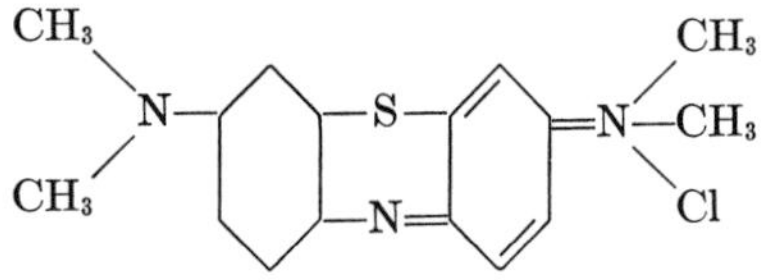

Methylene blue is used perhaps more than any other dye in biological work. Because of its strongly basic nature, it stains nuclei and nucleic acid granules very intensely. It is very useful in making a rapid survey of the bacterial population of milk (see page 575). The dye is usually preferred in staining smears for the diagnosis of diphtheria. It is used in combination with eosin for staining blood films. Methylene blue is incorporated with eosin in a lactose agar base for distinguishing typical *Escherichia coli* from typical *Aerobacter aerogenes* (page 553). These are only a few of its many uses in bacteriology.

Differential Stains. Differential stains are composed of more than one dye. In some staining techniques the dyes are applied separately; in others they are mixed and applied in one solution. The two most important differential stains used in bacteriology are the Gram stain and the acid-fast stain.

Gram Stain. This important differential stain was discovered by Christian Gram (1884).

In this method of staining, the bacterial film is covered with a solution of one of the methyl violet dyes and allowed to act for a definite period of time. The stain is washed off and a dilute solution of iodine added. This is allowed to remain for the same period of time. Next the slide is treated with alcohol or a mixture of alcohol and acetone until almost all of the dye is removed from the film. Finally a counterstain such as safranine, dilute carbolfuchsin, Bismarck brown, or pyronine B is added.

Some organisms retain the violet stain, even after treatment with the decolorizing agent, and the color is not modified by the application of the counterstain. Other organisms readily lose the primary stain and take the counterstain. Those retaining the first stain are called Gram-positive organisms; those failing to retain the primary stain but taking the counterstain are called Gram-negative organisms. Organisms may be placed into either of the two groups on the basis of the Gram stain.

The pararosaniline dyes give the best results in the Gram stain. The two most important members are methyl violet and crystal violet.

Strictly speaking, methyl violet is the name given to the tetramethyl pararosaniline compound. Commercially, the name is usually applied to various mixtures of the tetra-, penta-, and hexamethyl pararosanilines.

Their structural formulas are given below.

The shade of color of pararosaniline is deepened by increasing the number of methyl groups in the molecule. Hence, hexamethyl pararosaniline is deepest in shade and tetramethyl pararosaniline lightest of the three compounds. The names methyl violet 3R, 2R, R, B, 2B, 3B, etc., refer to the number of methyl groups present. The letter R denotes the red shades and B the blue shades. Hexamethyl pararosaniline (crystal violet) contains six methyl groups and is considered the most satisfactory primary stain in the Gram technique.

The ability of cells to retain the Gram stain is not a property applicable to all living matter in general but is confined almost entirely to the yeasts and bacteria. The cells of higher plants and animals do not retain the primary stain. Molds stain somewhat irregularly. Granules present in the mycelia tend to retain the stain. The Gram reaction is not a hard and fast one. It may vary with the age of the culture, with the pH of the medium, with the choice of stains, and perhaps in other ways. Bartholomew and Mittwer (1952a) found that ultraviolet light of 2537 A. caused Gram-positive organisms to stain Gram-negative. Since dead Gram-positive organisms are said to stain Gram-negatively, it is most likely that the ultraviolet rays produced a destructive action on the cells.

Tetramethyl pararosaniline
(methyl violet)

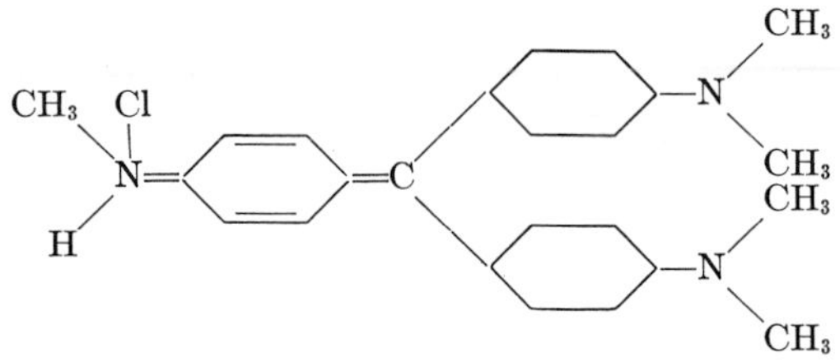

Pentamethyl pararosaniline

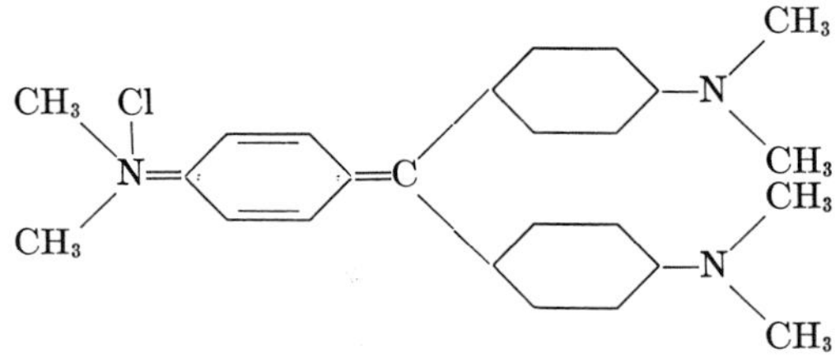

Hexamethyl pararosaniline
(crystal violet)

The common assumption seems to be that Gram-positive organisms give the most vigorous reaction when they are very young, with a tendency to become negative as they grow older. This assumption appears to be correct in examining the results on spherical bacteria but not necessarily on the rod-shaped organisms. Hucker (1923, 1927) examined a large number of rod-shaped bacteria from the soil and found that a greater number of positive reactions was obtained on the fourth and seventh days. The results showed such great variation that no definite time could be determined at which any organism gains or loses its power to retain the violet stain.

Gianni (1952) found that the Gram-positive organisms *Bacillus subtilis* and *B. anthracis* stained Gram-negatively when cultures were 2 to 3 hr. old. Then the Gram-positive substance developed under the cell wall to reverse the reaction.

A number of theories have been advanced to explain the mechanism of the Gram stain. Stearn and Stearn (1923, 1924a, b) based their theory on a chemical combination between dye and bacterial protein. Proteins and amino acids are amphoteric compounds, i.e., have the power to react with both acids and bases by virtue of their amino (NH_2) and carboxyl (COOH) groups. In acid solutions they react with acids; in alkaline solutions they react with bases.

Isoelectric Point. According to the classical theory, the isoelectric point may be defined as that pH where an amphoteric compound shows the least amount of dissociation, or, stated differently, it is that pH where the maximum amount of the compound is present in the un-ionized or molecular state.

Opposed to this theory is the newer concept known as the "zwitterion" hypothesis, which states that the isoelectric point is that pH where the acidic and basic groups of the amphoteric compound are completely ionized (see page 214). On the acid side of the isoelectric point, the compound behaves as a base; on the basic side, it behaves as an acid.

Basic and acid dyes also combine with proteins. The basic dyes react on the basic side of the isoelectric points and the acid dyes on the acid side of the isoelectric points. The amount of combination in either case is proportional to the degree of acidity or alkalinity of the solutions. At the isoelectric points, proteins do not combine with either acid or basic dyes. Using the protein casein as an example, the action of acid and basic dyes may be represented as shown in Fig. 27.

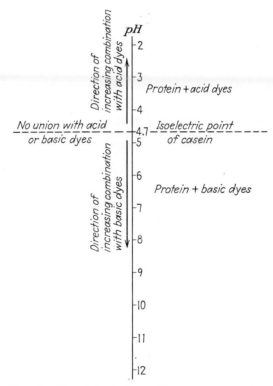

Fig. 27. Combination of acid and basic dyes with casein, an amphoteric compound.

Stearn and Stearn found that the staining reactions of bacteria are due largely to their protein content. Bacteria behave as amphoteric compounds, combining with acid dyes in acid solution and basic dyes in basic solution. Combination with either acid or basic dyes does not occur at the isoelectric point. Since organisms contain more than one protein, the isoelectric point does not have a fairly definite value but rather a series of points extending over two or three pH units. An isoelectric range or zone rather than a point is found. Stearn and Stearn found that Gram-positive organisms have an isoelectric zone at a lower pH range than Gram-negative bacteria.

On the basis of their experimental data Stearn and Stearn concluded:

1. Gram-positive organisms can be rendered Gram-negative by increasing acidity.
2. Gram-negative organisms can be rendered Gram-positive by increasing alkalinity.
3. Acid dye-positive organisms can be rendered Gram-negative by increasing alkalinity.
4. Basic dye-positive organisms can be rendered Gram-negative by increasing acidity.
5. At the isoelectric range, there is little tendency for any stain to be retained. This range is characteristic of each species.
6. There appears to be good evidence that the proteins of bacteria are not simple proteins but a loose combination of proteins with lipoidal or fatty substances. An example of such a fatty substance is lecithin, and a combination of lecithin and protein is known as lecithoprotein.
7. The lipoidal material extracted from Gram-positive organisms differs from that extracted from Gram-negative organisms in that the former contains a much larger proportion of unsaturated acids that have a great affinity for oxidizing agents. All mordants (such as iodine) used in the Gram stain are oxidizing agents. Their effect is in general to render the substance oxidized more acid in character. This increases the affinity of an organism for basic dyes.
8. The change of Gram character with age is especially true of those organisms which are only weakly Gram-positive and are cultivated in media containing fermentable substances that become acid in reaction as growth proceeds.

For more information see Harden and Harris (1953), Kennedy and Woodhour (1956).

Another approach to the explanation of the Gram reaction depends upon evidence suggesting the existence of an outer layer surrounding a Gram-negative core.

Henry and Stacey (1943) treated heat-killed Gram-positive organisms with a 2 per cent bile solution and were able to dissolve away an outer surface layer. The Gram-positive organisms so treated became Gram-negative. The extracted material was composed of polysaccharides, protein, and the magnesium salt of ribonucleic acid. The extracted material could be "replated" back on the Gram-negative "skeleton" forms, restoring their Gram reaction, provided the skeleton was maintained in a suitable state of reduction by the presence of formalin. Neither the skeleton nor the extracted material was Gram-positive except in combination, and recombination of these materials was not possible unless the skeleton was reduced by the presence of formalin.

Bartholomew and Umbreit (1944) used a 2 per cent solution of sodium choleate or of bile salts instead of whole bile and obtained similar results. They also observed that a solution of pure crystalline ribonuclease (see page 286) was capable of destroying the Gram-positive character of heat-killed cells.

On the basis of their results, Bartholomew and Umbreit concluded:

When ribonucleic acid is removed by bile salts, it will no longer unite with the cell protein if the latter has been oxidized with air. Sulfhydryl groups are autoxidizable with air when exposed on the protein surface.

The recombination is possible, however, even on exposure to air, if the "skeletons" are treated with formaldehyde. The latter unites in low concentration with sulfhydryl groups and prevents their autoxidation.

Iodine is essential to the Gram reaction, and it is the only known material which reacts with sulfhydryl groups of proteins even when these are located deep within the protein molecule. Furthermore, while the relations (if any) between hydroquinone, stannous chloride, or pyrogallol and sulfhydryl groups are not known, mercuric chloride, which can partially replace iodine, does react with sulfhydryl (Fildes, 1940).

In considering the data as a whole one can scarcely fail to conclude that the Gram-positive character of a cell resides in an outer layer of material surrounding a Gram-negative core. The important material in this outer layer is magnesium ribonucleate. The ribonucleate in combination with the cell protein is responsible for the Gram-positive characteristics, and crystal violet and iodine react chemically with this combination.

Baker and Bloom (1948) found that Gram-positiveness could be imposed upon normal Gram-negative *Escherichia coli* by the addition of a highly viscous desoxyribonucleic acid. The Gram-positiveness could be removed by washing the treated cells with distilled water but not with 0.85 per cent sodium chloride solution. Desoxyribonucleic acid is soluble in distilled water but not in saline.

From available evidence it may be stated that both ribonucleic and desoxyribonucleic acids are capable of imposing Gram-positiveness on Gram-negative bacteria and that both types may be present in the outer shell of Gram-positive bacteria (see page 667). Neither type of acid has been shown to be present in the outer shell of Gram-negative bacteria.

Libenson and McIlroy (1955) and Gerhardt, Vennes, and Britt (1956) reported that if the Gram-positive reaction is dependent upon the formation of a complex combination between the components of the Gram stain and the cell-wall proteins, it should be expected that bacteria disintegrated by physical means would still retain the Gram stain since such treatment could not change the chemical nature of the cell-wall constituents. On the contrary, disintegrated Gram-positive organisms lost the ability to retain the primary dye and stained Gram-negatively.

The cell wall of both Gram-positive and Gram-negative bacteria is permeable to crystal violet. However, the cell wall of the former is not permeable to the dye-iodine complex formed within the cell. The experimental results with a protein-free diffusion cell and the low solubility of the crystal violet-iodine complex in alcohol and acetone would support the view that the positive Gram reaction consists essentially in the formation of a substantial amount of dye-iodine complex within the cell not readily removed by the solvent. The cell wall of the Gram-negative bacteria, unlike that of the Gram-positive, would be practically impermeable to crystal violet. The organisms will appear colored after treatment with crystal violet because of the adsorption of the dye on the outer surface of the cell wall, and the complex formed after treatment with iodine will be easily removed by the solvent.

Neither sulfhydryl groups nor basic proteins played any specific role in the mechanism of the Gram stain.

Libenson and McIlroy supported the view that the permeability of the cell wall to crystal violet, the low solubility of the dye-iodine complex in alcohol and acetone, and the free access of the solvent to the complex constituted the main factors involved in the mechanism of the Gram stain.

Barbaro and Kennedy (1954) indicated that bacterial species could be arranged in a continuous series with reference to their behavior in the quantitative Gram stain. The crystal violet nitrogen per milligram of bacterial nitrogen retained by Gram-positive organisms was 0.29 and 0.18 mg.; by Gram-variable organisms, 0.08 and 0.07 mg. Gram-negative bacteria failed to retain significant amounts of crystal violet.

The amount of crystal violet adsorbed by Gram-positive, Gram-variable, and Gram-negative bacteria was related directly to the concentration of the dye. The amount of crystal violet remaining in the cells after decolorization was related directly to the concentration of the primary stain.

In a later report Barbaro, Kennedy, and Collins (1956) found that the degree of Gram positivity could be altered by chemical treatment of the cells before staining. The Gram-negative species *Escherichia coli* increased in Gram positivity after treatment with crystal violet, sodium bisulfite, or sodium hydroxide. The Gram-positive organism *Staphylococcus aureus* decreased in Gram positivity after treatment with picric acid. The omission of Gram's iodine from the staining procedure in converted *E. coli* resulted in complete removal of crystal violet by decolorization. Microscopically, crystal violet was still retained when iodine was omitted from the procedure. The counterstain safranine was capable of replacing or masking the residual crystal violet.

The cell walls of microorganisms have little affinity for dyes. However, the walls of Gram-positive species can be stained with certain dyes. Basic fuchsin and the methyl violets are the most suitable for this purpose. On the other hand, the cell walls of Gram-negative bacteria are not stained by the above dyes.

Lamanna and Mallette (1954) reported that the specificity of the triphenylmethanes as primary dyes in the Gram stain rested on the ability of solutions of these dyes to stain the cell walls of Gram-positive organisms. The cell walls of Gram-negative bacteria were unable to sorb the primary basic dye employed in the Gram stain (Fig. 28).

Some characteristics of Gram-positive and Gram-negative bacteria are given in Table 2.

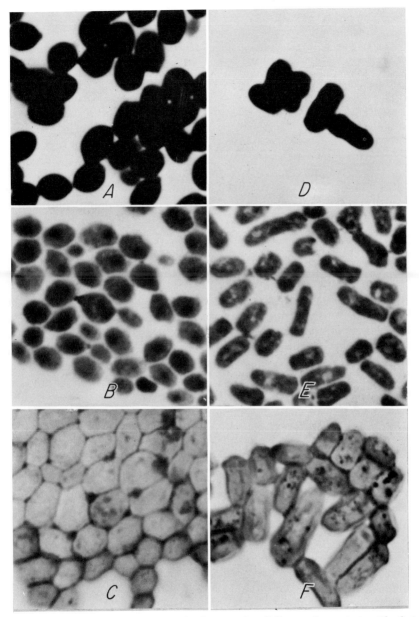

FIG. 28. *Saccharomyces cerevisiae:* *A,* Gram stain. Cells are in contact with their neighbors, indicating the cell walls have taken the crystal violet stain. *B,* safranine stain. Cell walls have not taken the stain as spaces around the cells indicate. *C,* cell wall stain. Cell walls have taken the stain.

Schizosaccharomyces pombe: *D,* Gram stain. Cells are in contact with their neighbors, indicating the cell walls have taken the crystal violet stain. *E,* safranine stain. Cell walls have not taken the stain as spaces around the cells indicate. *F,* cell wall stain. Cell walls have taken the stain. (*All after Lamanna and Mallette.*)

TABLE 2

Gram-positive bacteria	Gram-negative bacteria
Contain magnesium ribonucleate	Do not contain magnesium ribonucleate
Very sensitive to triphenylmethane dyes	Less sensitive to triphenylmethane dyes
Sensitive to penicillin	Sensitive to streptomycin
Resistant to alkalies; not dissolved by 1% KOH	Sensitive to alkalies; dissolved by 1% KOH
Isoelectric range pH 2.5–4	Isoelectric range pH 4.5–5.5
Usually cocci or spore-forming rods (exceptions, *Lactobacillus, Corynebacterium*)	Usually non-spore-forming rods (exception, *Neisseria*, which are cocci)
May be acid-fast	Probably never acid-fast

For more information see Bartholomew and Finkelstein (1958), Bartholomew and Mittwer (1951, 1952b), Finkelstein and Bartholomew (1953), Fischer and Larose (1952), Gianni et al. (1954), Hoffman (1951), Kennedy and Woodhour (1956), Larose (1957), MacLeod and Roe (1956), Welsch (1948), Wensinck and Boevé (1957).

Acid-fast Stain. The great majority of bacteria are easily stained by the usual simple procedures. However, there are some exceptions. Some bacteria are surrounded by a covering composed of fatty or waxy materials. These organisms are not readily stained but when once stained retain the color even after treatment with drastic decolorizing agents. They are called acid-fast because the stained bacteria are resistant to decolorization with acid alcohol. The two best-known members of the acid-fast group are the organisms causing tuberculosis (*Mycobacterium tuberculosis*) and leprosy (*M. leprae*).

The acid-fast method of staining the organism of tuberculosis was first announced by Ehrlich (1882). He prepared a saturated solution of aniline oil in water, then added a known volume of an alcoholic solution of methyl violet. Smears were covered with this staining solution and allowed to stand for the dye to penetrate the waxy covering of the tubercle bacilli. Ehrlich found that the organisms were not decolorized when treated with strong hydrochloric acid solutions but that tissue and other bacteria lost their color. He used Bismarck brown Y as the counterstain for the aniline oil methyl violet. By this method the acid-fast organisms appeared purple; everything else on the slide stained brown. Later Ziehl (1882) substituted phenol for the aniline oil to improve the keeping qualities of the stain. Neelsen (1883) substituted carbolfuchsin for the aniline oil methyl violet and decolorized the smears with sulfuric acid instead of hydrochloric acid. This modification, with slight changes, is known as the Ziehl-Neelsen method, but is essentially the same as the procedure recommended by Ehrlich.

The basic fuchsin of commerce is a mixture of pararosaniline, rosaniline, and magenta II. Another dye, new fuchsin, may be purchased in pure form and is frequently employed in the acid-fast staining method.

The formulas are as follows:

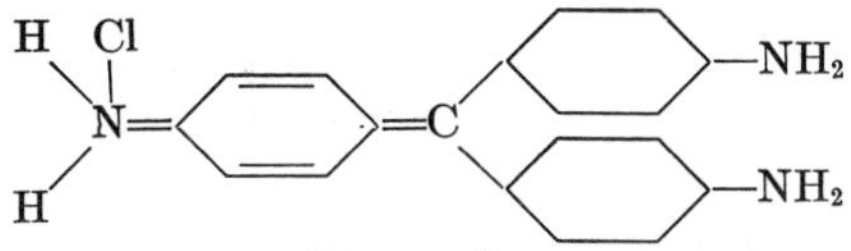

$$H\diagdown N=\langle\ \rangle=C\big\langle\ \big\rangle-NH_2,\ \big\langle\ \big\rangle-NH_2$$

Pararosaniline

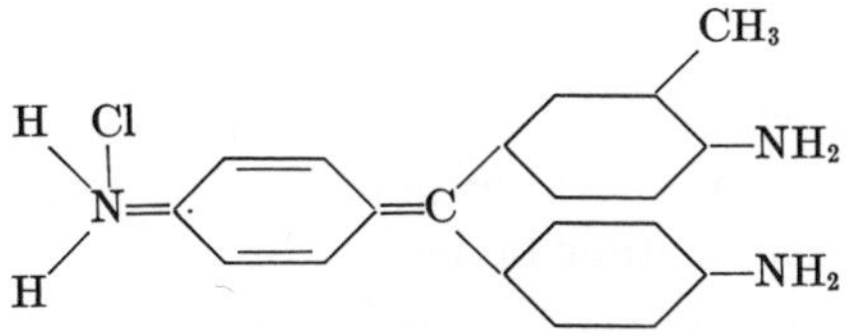

Rosaniline

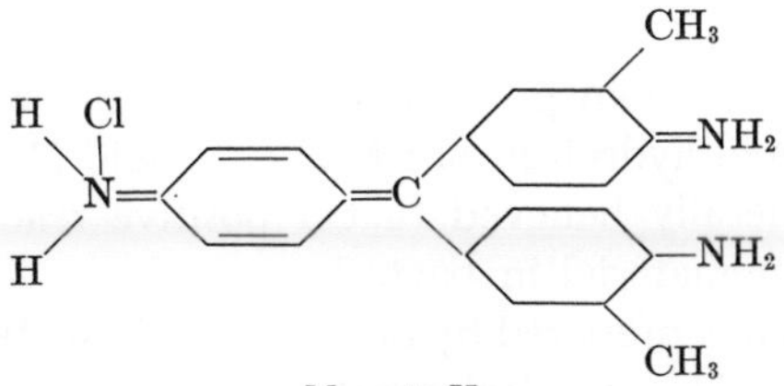

Magenta II

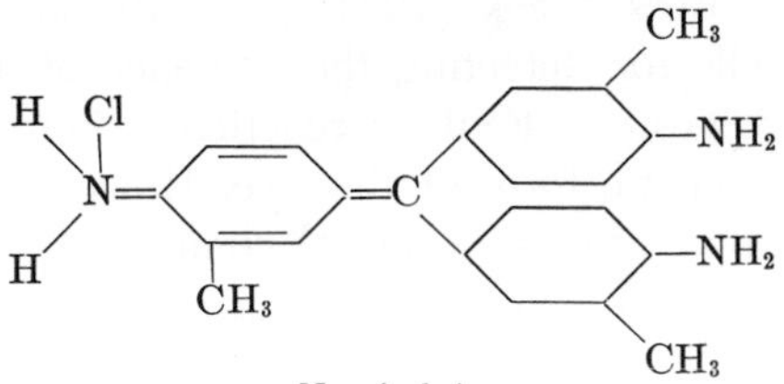

New fuchsin

The more methyl groups present in the molecule, the deeper will be the shade of red. New fuchsin with three methyl groups is the deepest in shade and pararosaniline with no methyl groups is the least so of the above compounds. Generally speaking, the deeper the shade of dye used in the acid-fast stain, the better will be the degree of differentiation.

Tubercle bacilli can be made to stain solid or beaded by varying the staining procedure. The presence of beads depends to a large extent on the conditions under which the staining reaction is carried out. Addition of small amounts of electrolytes to the dye solution increases the number of beads with all dyes. Washing the stained smears with alcohol, after decolorization with acid alcohol, removes practically all beads and leaves most cells evenly stained with a pink tinge.

The composition of the phenylmethane dye also affects the appearance of the stained tubercle bacilli. Smears stained with rosaniline or pararosaniline acetate show 50 to 100 per cent beaded organisms. On the other hand, smears stained with rosaniline or pararosaniline chloride show solidly stained rods. For best results the chloride salts should be used in the Ziehl-Neelsen technique.

Woodhour (1956) reported that virulent *M. tuberculosis* were more strongly acid-fast than nonvirulent forms. The data indicated the existence of quantitative degrees of acid-fastness among mycobacteria whether stained with carbolfuchsin or crystal violet. The virulent strains could be distinguished from the nonvirulent by the amount of dye taken up by the cells.

Feulgen Stain. Basic fuchsin is a powerful nuclear dye and has long been used in its chromatic form in numerous bacteriological procedures.

Chromosomes or chromatinic bodies are composed of desoxyribonucleo-protein, a compound of desoxyribonucleic acid (DNA) and a basic protein. The Feulgen reaction is almost a specific test for DNA. It employs acid hydrolysis of the DNA with the liberation of aldehyde groups. The aldehyde groups from DNA give a deep color reaction with the Feulgen reagent, whereas acid hydrolysis of ribonucleic acid (RNA) gives a negative test. It is generally believed that a positive reaction indicates the presence of nuclear material in bacteria.

The Feulgen stain is prepared by decolorizing basic fuchsin with sulfurous acid or sulfite. The decolorized stain is then known as Schiff's reagent. Feulgen and Rossenbeck (1924) were the first to apply Schiff's reagent to tissue cells for detecting the presence of aldehyde-like substances in nuclei. A positive Feulgen reaction is indicated by the reappearance of the chromatic form of the dye. However, the restored dye is different chemically from the original compound, being violet rather than red in color. The Feulgen technique brings out certain structures in the nuclei of some cells which are not revealed by the usual methods of staining.

The Feulgen reaction requires acid hydrolysis of the nuclear material in order to give a positive test. This hydrolysis is believed to release an aldehyde radical in the DNA (see page 556). Baker (1942) and Stowell (1945, 1946) considered a positive Schiff or Feulgen reaction to be due to the formation of an addition compound between aldehyde and the decolorized dye-sulfite complex, resulting in the restoration of the chromatic form of the basic fuchsin. De Lamater (1948) postulated the following linkage between Feulgen's reagent and DNA:

$$HN = \langle \text{ring} \rangle = C \begin{cases} \langle \text{ring} \rangle NH \cdot SO_2 \cdot C \overset{H}{\underset{R}{\overset{\diagup}{-}}} OH \\ \langle \text{ring} \rangle NH \cdot SO_2 \cdot C \overset{H}{\underset{R}{\overset{\diagup}{-}}} OH \end{cases}$$

where R represents the nucleic acid component.

A number of modifications of the original Feulgen technique have been recommended, one being as follows:

1. Prepare a smear and fix cells in an appropriate fixative such as Schaudinn's solution (mercuric chloride dissolved in a solution of alcohol in distilled water).
2. Hydrolyze cells in normal hydrochloric acid for 5 min. at room temperature, for 5 min. at 60°C., and for 5 min. more at room temperature.
3. Wash cells in distilled water.
4. Mordant cells in 2 per cent solution of formalin for 4 min.
5. Wash cells in distilled water.
6. Apply 0.5 per cent basic fuchsin decolorized with 0.5 gm. of sodium sulfite plus 10 ml. of normal hydrochloric acid.
7. Wash in distilled water and examine.
Nuclear material stains a deep red color.

STAINING OF BACTERIA

Preparation of Smears. A bacterial smear is prepared by removing a loopful of a liquid culture from a tube, by means of a sterile wire loop, and spreading the liquid on a glass slide over an area of about ½ sq. in. If a solid culture is used, a minute amount of the growth is first emulsified in a drop of distilled water, previously placed in the center of a glass slide, then spread out over an area of about ½ sq. in. The smear is carefully dried by holding the slide high over a low gas flame to avoid steaming. The dried smear is fixed by quickly passing the slide five or six times through the upper portion of the Bunsen flame. This prevents the film from being washed off during the staining process. The dried and fixed smear is then covered with the staining solution and allowed to stand for a definite period of time. This will vary, depending upon the staining solution used. Finally the slide is washed in water, dried by blotting, and examined under the microscope.

Viability of Fixed and Stained Organisms. It is generally stated that bacteria in dried, fixed, and stained smears are no longer viable and that danger from infections is not possible if pathogenic organisms are so treated. Thurn (1914) reported that heat-fixed but unstained smears of *Staphylococcus aureus*, *Salmonella typhosa*, *Escherichia coli*, *Bacillus anthracis*, *Vibrio comma*, *Corynebacterium diphtheriae*, and *Saccharomyces cerevisiae* still contained viable organisms. Eighteen preparations of pathogenic and nonpathogenic organisms failed to show viable organisms after being stained by the Gram method. On the other hand, *B. anthracis* survived 1 min. and *B. mesentericus* 3 min. of treatment with carbolfuchsin, and both organisms survived 5 min. of treatment with methylene blue. Morton (1939) showed that certain organisms were capable of surviving treatment with basic fuchsin, Hucker's crystal violet, aqueous safranine, and methylene blue stains.

Care should be observed in the handling of stained preparations in the laboratory, especially if pathogenic organisms are being examined, since the process of staining is no indication that the organisms are necessarily killed.

For more information see Committee on Bacteriological Technic (1957), Conn (1933, 1953), Conn and Darrow (1948).

REFERENCES

Baker, H., and W. L. Bloom: Further studies on the Gram stain, *J. Bact.*, **56**:387, 1948.

Baker, J. R.: Some aspects of cytological technique. From "Cytology and Cell Physiology," by G. Bourne, New York, Oxford University Press, 1942.

Barbaro, J. F., and E. R. Kennedy: A quantitative Gram reaction, *J. Bact.*, **67**:603, 1954.

——, ——, and R. M. Collins: Quantitative studies of differential staining reactions. II. The effect of the fixative and of chemical treatment of fixed bacteria on the adsorption and retention of dye, *J. Bact.*, **72**:451, 1956.

Bartholomew, J. W., and H. Finkelstein: Relationship of cell wall staining to Gram differentiation, *J. Bact.*, **75**:77, 1958.

—— and T. Mittwer: Cell structure in relation to the Gram reaction as shown during lysis of *Bacillus subtilis*, *J. Gen. Microbiol.*, **5**:39, 1951.

—— and ——: Effect of ultraviolet irradiation on Gram positiveness, *J. Bact.*, **63**:779, 1952a.

—— and ——: The Gram stain, *Bact. Rev.*, **16**:1, 1952b.

—— and W. W. Umbreit: Ribonucleic acid and the Gram stain, *J. Bact.*, **48**:567, 1944.

Committee on Bacteriological Technic: "Manual of Microbiological Methods," New York, McGraw-Hill Book Company, Inc., 1957.

Conn, H. J.: "The History of Staining," Geneva, N.Y., Commission on Standardization of Biological Stains, 1933.

——: "Biological Stains," Geneva, N.Y., Commission on Standardization of Biological Stains, 1953.

—— and M. A. Darrow: "Staining Procedures," Geneva, N.Y., Biotech. Publications, 1948.

DeLamater, E. D.: Basic fuchsin as a nuclear stain, *Stain Technol.*, **23**:161, 1948.

Ehrlich. P.: Note without title, *Deut. Med. Wochschr.*, **8**:269, 1882.

Feulgen, R., and H. Rossenbeck: Mikroskopisch-chemischer Nachweis einer Nucleinsaure vom Typus der Thymonucleinsaure und die darauf beruhende elektive Farbung von Zellkernen in mikroskopischen Praparaten, *Z. phys. Chem.*, **135**:203, 1924.

Fildes, P.: The mechanism of the antibacterial action of mercury, *Brit. J. Exp. Path.*, **21**:67, 1940.

Finkelstein, H., and J. W. Bartholomew: Quantitative determination of dye uptake by bacterial cells, *Stain Tech.*, **28**:177, 1953.

Fischer, R., and P. Larose: Mechanism of Gram stain reversal, *J. Bact.*, **64**:435, 1952.

Gerhardt, P., J. W. Vennes, and E. M. Britt: Gram reaction of isolated protoplasts and surface membranes of *Bacillus megaterium*, *J. Bact.*, **72**:721, 1956.

Gianni, A.: Sulle fasi di sviluppo della gram-positività nei germi, *Bollettino Ist. Sieroterapico Milanese*, **31**:427, 1952.

——, A. Zamboni, B. Della Torre, and C. C. Novati: Il polipeptide dell'acido glutamico estraibile dal *B. subtilis* e suo rapporto con la gram-positività, *ibid.*, **33**:129, 1954.

Gram, C.: Über die isolirte Färbung der Schizomyceten in Schnitt- und Trokenpräparaten, *Fortschr. Med.*, **2**:185, 1884.

Harden, V. P., and J. O. Harris: The isoelectric point of bacterial cells, *J. Bact.*, **65**:198, 1953.

Harris, J. O.: A study of the relationship between the surface charge and the adsorption of acid dyes by bacterial cells, *J. Bact.*, **61**:649, 1951.

Henry, H., and M. Stacey: Histochemistry of the Gram-staining reaction for microorganisms, *Nature*, **151**:671, 1943.

Hoffman, H.: Localization of bacterial nucleic acids, and mechanism of the Gram reaction, *Nature*, **168**:464, 1951.

Hucker, G. J.: Methods of Gram staining, *N.Y. Agr. Exp. Sta. Tech. Bull.*, 93, 1923.

————: Further studies on the methods of Gram staining, *ibid.*, 128, 1927.

Kennedy, E. R., and A. F. Woodhour: Quantitative studies of differential staining reactions. I. The effect of pH on the quantity of dye retained by bacteria and the apparent isoelectric point, *J. Bact.*, **72**:447, 1956.

Lamanna, C.: The nature of the acid-fast stain, *J. Bact.*, **52**:99, 1946.

———— and M. F. Mallette: The cytological basis for the role of the primary dye in the Gram stain, *J. Bact.*, **68**:509, 1954.

Larose, P.: Quantitative nature of the Gram stain, *ibid.*, **74**:267, 1957.

Libenson, L., and A. P. McIlroy: On the mechanism of the Gram stain, *J. Infectious Diseases*, **97**:22, 1955.

MacLeod, C. M., and A. S. Roe: Effect of silicate on Gram staining and viability of pneumococci and other bacteria, *J. Exp. Med.*, **103**:453, 1956.

McCalla, T. M.: Cation adsorption by bacteria, *J. Bact.*, 40:23, 1940a.

————: Physico-chemical behavior of soil bacteria in relation to the soil colloid, *ibid.*, **40**:33, 1940b.

————: The reaction of certain stains with bacteria, *Stain Technol.*, **16**:27, 1941.

———— and F. E. Clark: Dye adsorption by bacteria at varying H-ion concentrations, *ibid.*, **16**:95, 1941.

Morton, H. E.: The survival of microorganisms in fixed and stained preparations, *Am. J. Clin. Path.*, **9**:68, 1939.

Neelsen, F.: Ein casuistischer Beitrag zur Lehre von der Tuberkulose, *Centr. Med. Wiss.*, **21**:497, 1883.

Stearn, E. W., and A. E. Stearn: The mechanical behavior of dyes, especially gentian violet, in bacteriological media, *J. Bact.*, **8**:567, 1923.

———— and ————: The chemical mechanism of bacterial behavior. I. Behavior toward dyes—factors controlling the Gram reaction, *ibid.*, **9**:463, 1924a; II. A new theory of the Gram reaction, *ibid.*, **9**:479, 1924b.

Stowell, R. E.: Feulgen reaction for thymonucleic acid, *Stain Technol.*, **20**:45, 1945.

————: The specificity of the Feulgen reaction for thymonucleic acid, *ibid.*, **21**:137, 1946.

Thurn, O.: Über die Lebensfähigkeit an Objektträgern angetrockneter ungefarbter und gefarbter Bakterien, *Centr. Bakt.*, Abt. I. Orig., **74**:81, 1914.

Welsch, M.: La réaction de Gram, son mécanisme, sa signification, *Rev. Méd. de Liége*, **3**:257, 1948.

Wensinck, F., and J. J. Boevé: Quantitative analysis of the Gram reaction, *J. Gen. Microbiol.*, **17**:401, 1957.

Woodhour, A. F.: III. A quantitative acid-fast stain, *J. Wash. Acad. Sci.*, **46**:344, 1956.

Ziehl, F.: Zur Färbung des Tuberkelbacillus, *Deut. med. Wochschr.*, **8**:451, 1882.

CHAPTER 4

Morphology of Bacteria

Bacteria belong to the class of organisms known as the *Schizomycetes* (*schizo,* fission, and *mycetes,* fungi). The organisms are single-celled and reproduce normally by transverse or binary fission (see page 2).

The class Schizomycetes is divided into ten orders. The largest order is the *Eubacteriales;* it includes most of the common bacterial species.

Bacteria are typically unicellular plants, the cells being usually small, sometimes ultramicroscopic. They are frequently motile. By means of modern techniques, a true nucleus has been demonstrated in bacterial cells. Individual cells may be spherical or straight, curved or spiral rods. Cells may occur in regular or irregular masses, or even in cysts. Where they remain attached to each other after cell division, they may form chains or even definite trichomes. The latter may show some differentiation into holdfast cells and into motile or nonmotile reproductive cells. Some grow as branching mycelial threads whose diameter is not greater than that of ordinary bacterial cells, i.e., about 1 μ. Some species produce pigments. The true purple and green bacteria possess photosynthetic pigments much like or related to the true chlorophylls of higher plants. The phycocyanin found in blue-green algae does not occur in the Schizomycetes. Multiplication is typically by cell division. Endospores are formed by some species of Eubacteriales. Sporocysts are found in Myxobacteriales. Bacteria are free-living, saprophytic, parasitic, or even pathogenic. The latter types cause diseases of either plants or animals.

Filament Formation. Cells that reproduce and divide in a normal manner may be induced to grow in filaments by changing the conditions of the medium. According to Webb (1953),

. . . the division of the bacterial cell follows a complex sequence, which in many respects, resembles that occurring in the cellular reproduction of higher forms. It is now known, for example, that bacterial cell division entails division of the nuclear element, division of the cytoplasm, secretion of new cell wall material, and the separation of the daughter cells.

Some or all of the events of this sequence are readily thrown out of balance, or even completely inhibited. Thus bacteria, particularly the rod-shaped organisms, may be induced to elongate into filaments by various treatments which apparently inhibit cell division but which do not inhibit growth. Such an effect is produced by various chemical substances, by sub-bacteriostatic concentration of certain antibacterial agents, as, for example, methyl violet, sulfonamides, *m*-cresol, penicillin, irradiation, and higher temperatures of incubation.

These changes in morphology induced by chemical substances are usually temporary, since reversion to normal form occurs promptly when the filamentous bacteria are subcultured in the absence of the inhibitory agents. Irradiation, on the other hand, may give rise to a temporary or permanent induction of filamentous cells.

From observations such as these the concept has arisen that bacterial growth, in the sense of an irreversible increase in cell substance or volume, and cell division may be considered to some extent as separate and independent processes; at least, in so far as growth may occur either with or without the operation of the cell division mechanism.

Variation in the magnesium (Mg) content of the medium may exert a marked effect on cell division of some bacteria. In a Mg-deficient medium, Gram-positive rods grow in the form of long filaments. Such filaments revert to normal forms when transferred to the same medium supplemented with suitable concentrations of Mg. Filament formation is enhanced by the addition of zinc and cobalt. Inhibition of cell division occurs also in media supplemented with an excess of Mg.

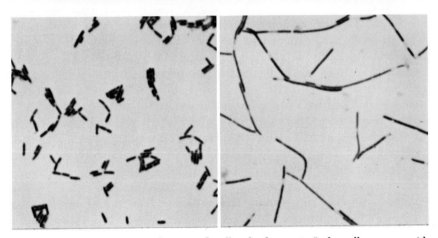

FIG. 29. Filament formation by *Lactobacillus leichmannii*. Left, cells grown with vitamin B_{12}; right, vitamin B_{12} replaced with a deficient amount of thymidine. Smears prepared from 24-hr. cultures and stained with crystal violet. (*Courtesy of Deibel, Downing, Niven, Jr., and Schweigert.*)

Deibel et al. (1956) produced filamentous *Lactobacillus leichmannii* in the absence of vitamin B_{12} (Fig. 29). Reversion to the normal cell form occurred on the addition of either vitamin B_{12} to a medium lacking the growth factor or of an excess of the desoxyriboside thymidine.

For more information see Hughes (1956), Nickerson and Sherman (1952).

Shape of Bacteria. Bacteria exhibit three fundamental shapes: (1) spherical, (2) rod, and (3) spiral or curved rod. All bacteria exhibit pleomorphism in more or less degree under normal or other conditions, but a bacterial species is still generally associated with a definite cell form when grown on a standard medium under controlled conditions.

The spherical bacteria (singular, coccus; plural, cocci) divide in one, two, or three planes, producing pairs or chains, clusters, or packets of cells. Some are apparently perfect spheres; others are slightly elongated or ellipsoidal in shape.

The streptococci divide in only one plane. They grow normally in pairs or chains. Depending upon the species, the distal ends of each pair may be lancet-shaped, or flattened at the adjacent sides to resemble a coffee bean.

The staphylococci divide in two planes, producing pairs, tetrads, or clusters of bacteria, the latter resembling bunches of grapes.

The sarcinae divide in three planes, producing regular packets. These are cubicle masses with one layer of bacteria atop another.

The rod forms also show considerable variation. A rod is usually considered to be a cylinder with the ends more or less rounded. Some rod forms are definitely ellipsoidal in shape. The ends of rods also show considerable variation. Some species are markedly rounded; others exhibit flat ends perpendicular to the sides. Gradations between these two forms may be seen.

Rods may show marked variation in their length/width ratio. Some rods are very long in comparison to their width; others are so short they may be confused with the spherical forms.

The shape of an organism may also vary depending upon certain environmental factors, such as temperature of incubation, age of the culture, concentration of the substrate, and composition of the medium. Bacteria usually exhibit their characteristic morphology in young cultures and on media possessing favorable conditions for growth.

Young cells are, in general, larger than old organisms of the same species. As a culture ages, the cells become progressively larger until a maximum is reached, after which the reverse effect occurs. Bacterial variations resulting from changes in age are only temporary; the original forms reappear when the organisms are transferred to fresh medium.

Bacterial variation is discussed in greater detail in Chap. 16.

For more information see Chapman (1960).

Size of Bacteria. Bacteria vary greatly in size according to the species. Some are so small they approach the limit of visibility when viewed with the light microscope. Others are so large they are almost visible with the normal eye. However, the sizes of the majority of bacteria occupy a range intermediate between these two extremes. Regardless of size, none can be clearly seen without the aid of a microscope.

A spherical form is measured by its diameter; a rod or spiral form by its length and width. Calculation of the length of a spiral organism by this method gives only the apparent length, not the true length. The true length may be computed by actually measuring the length of each turn of the spiral. Mathematical expressions have been formulated for making such computations.

The method employed for fixing and staining bacteria may make a difference in their size. The bacterial cell shrinks considerably during drying and fixing. This will vary somewhat depending upon the type of medium employed for their cultivation. Shrinkage generally averages about one-third of the length of the cell as compared to an unstained

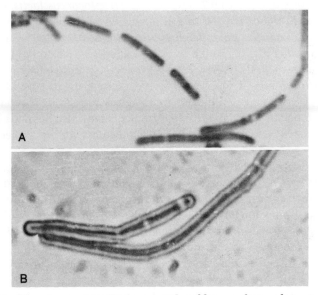

Fig. 30. *Bacillus cereus.* A, cells from a 6-hr.-old agar slant culture incubated at 33°C. and stained with methylene blue; B, cells from the same culture but stained by a different technique to reveal the cell wall. (*Courtesy of Dr. Knaysi.*)

hanging-drop preparation. Young cells of *Bacillus megaterium* may shrink from 15 to 25 per cent when transferred from nutrient broth to the same medium containing sodium chloride in 2 M concentration.

Measurements show some variation depending upon the staining solution used and the method of application. In dried and fixed smears, the cell wall and slime layer do not stain with weakly staining dyes such as methylene blue but do stain with the intensely staining pararosaniline, new fuchsin, crystal violet, and methyl violet (Fig. 30). The great majority of bacteria have been measured in fixed and stained preparations. In some instances dried, negatively stained smears have been used. Therefore, the method employed should be specified when measurements of bacteria are reported; otherwise the results will be of doubtful value.

The unit for measuring bacteria is the micron. It is expressed by the symbol μ. It is 0.001 mm. or 0.0001 cm. A millimicron is 0.001 μ or 0.000001 mm. It is expressed by the symbol mμ.

Some bacteria measure as large as 80 μ in length; others as small as 0.2 μ. However, the majority of the commonly encountered bacteria, including the disease producers, measure about 0.5 μ in diameter for the spherical cells and 0.5 by 2 to 3 μ for the rod forms. Bacteria producing spores are generally larger than the non-spore-producing species. The sizes of some common species in dried and stained smears are as follows: *Escherichia coli,* 0.5 by 1 to 3 μ; *Proteus vulgaris,* 0.5 to 1 by 1 to 3 μ; *Salmonella typhosa,* 0.6 to 0.7 by 2 to 3 μ; *Streptococcus lactis,* 0.5 to 1 μ in diameter; *S. pyogenes,* 0.6 to 1 μ in diameter; *Staphylococcus aureus,* 0.8 to 1 μ in diameter; *Lactobacillus acidophilus,* 0.6 to 0.9 by 1.5 to 6 μ; *Bacillus subtilis* rods, 0.7 to 0.8 by 2 to 3 μ, spores, 0.6 to 0.9 by 1 to 1.5 μ; *B. megaterium* rods, 0.9 to 2.2 by 1 to 5 μ, spores, 1 to 1.2 by 1.5 to 2 μ; *B. anthracis* rods, 1 to 1.3 by 3 to 10 μ, spores, 0.8 to 1 by 1.3 to 1.5 μ.

The most commonly employed method for measuring bacteria is by means of an ocular micrometer. Measurements may also be made by using a camera-lucida attachment and drawing oculars, or by projecting the real image on a screen and measuring the bacteria.

The same factors that cause variations in the shape of bacteria also affect their size. With few exceptions, young cells are much larger than old or mature forms. Cells of *B. subtilis* from a 4-hr. culture measure five to seven times longer than cells from a 24-hr. culture. Variations in width are less pronounced. The organism *Corynebacterium diphtheriae* is a notable exception to the rule of decreasing cell size with age.

Variations in cell size with age are due to a variety of factors. The major causes appear to be changes in the environment with the accumulation of waste products. An increase in the osmotic pressure of the medium will also cause a decrease in cell size and may very well be the most important factor.

THE BACTERIAL CELL

Bacteria do not show the same morphological picture. Differences in structure exist between species. It is generally agreed that a bacterial cell consists of a compound membrane enclosing cytoplasm and nuclear material and often containing various granules, fat globules, and one or more vacuoles. In addition, some species contain resistant bodies known as spores, and some have one or more organs of locomotion called flagella.

The term protoplasm is used to indicate the thick viscous semifluid or almost jelly-like colorless, transparent material which makes up the essential substance of both the cell body and the nucleus, including the cytoplasmic membrane but not the cell wall. It contains a high percentage of water and holds fine granules in suspension.

Cytoplasmic Membrane. This membrane appears in young cells as an interfacial fluid film, becoming thicker and denser as surface-active material accumulates. It is finally converted into a firm structure (Fig. 31). The membrane is believed to be composed mainly of lipide and protein. Polysaccharide has not been demonstrated as a component.

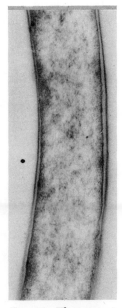

The membrane is acid in reaction because of its content of ribonucleic acid. It stains deeply with basic and neutral dyes over a wide range of pH. The membrane stains Gram-positive in Gram-positive bacteria and acid-fast in acid-fast organisms. It is a semipermeable membrane and is principally responsible for the Gram and acid-fast reactions. When a cell is plasmolyzed by immersion in a hypertonic solution, this membrane is drawn in with the cytoplasmic constituents. The thickness of the membrane varies even in a single cell. Measurements on a strain of *Bacillus cereus* at various stages of development ranged from 5 to 10 mμ in thickness.

For more information see Chapman and Kroll (1957) and Murray (1957).

Cell Wall. The cell wall is a more rigid structure and is responsible for the form of the bacterial body. It behaves as a selectively permeable membrane and apparently plays a fundamental role in the life activities of the cell.

Fig. 31. Electron micrograph of an ultrathin section of *Spirillum serpens*, showing cell wall and inner cytoplasmic membrane. (*Courtesy of Chapman and Kroll.*)

The cell wall has a low affinity for dyes, which means that it is probably not stained in some of the usual staining procedures. It is lightly stained by certain basic dyes such as basic fuchsin and the methyl violets. Where deep staining of the wall is desired, the use of a mordant, such as tannic acid, is necessary. The mordant not only increases the affinity of the cell for dye, but it may increase the thickness of the wall (Fig. 32).

The cell wall accounts for an average of about 20 per cent of the dry weight of bacteria and represents the major structural component. In thickness, it ranges from 10 to 23 mμ, depending upon the species.

According to Salton (1952, 1953), chemical analyses of cell walls have revealed differences in Gram-positive and Gram-negative bacteria. Cell walls of Gram-positive bacteria are lacking in aromatic and certain sulfur-containing amino acids, arginine, and proline. On the other hand, cell walls of Gram-negative bacteria show the presence of aromatic and sulfur-containing amino acids, arginine, and proline.

Gram-negative cell walls are generally richer in lipides than Gram-positive bacteria.

Cell walls of a number of Gram-positive and negative bacteria contain the amino acid diaminopimelic acid.

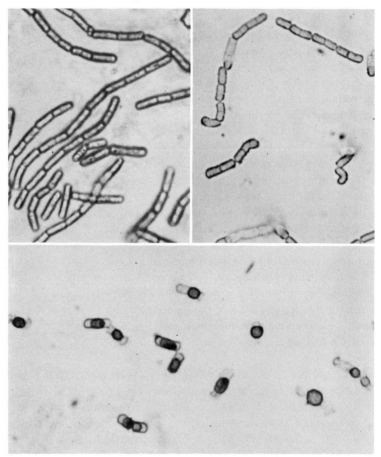

Fig. 32. Cell-wall stain of *Bacillus* M. Upper left, stained with tannic acid violet; upper right, stained with alcian blue; lower, treated with egg albumin and stained with Hale's cell-wall stain. (*Courtesy of Tomcsik and Grace.*)

Polysaccharides have been detected in both Gram-positive and Gram-negative bacteria. The polysaccharide is determined as reducing substances after acid hydrolysis. Some polysaccharides yielded only one reducing sugar; others yielded two or more sugars.

Gram-positive organisms gave rhamnose, galactose, and glucose; glucose only; rhamnose only; arabinose, galactose, and mannose. Gram-nega-

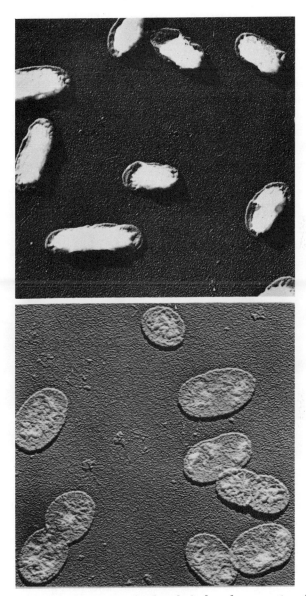

FIG. 33. *Rickettsia typhi.* Upper, air-dried and shadowed preparation showing cell walls surrounding the central, shrunken protoplasm; lower, purified preparation of cell walls. Sample taken 4 hr. after addition of 1 per cent sodium desoxycholate. (*Courtesy of Schaechter, Tousimis, Cohn, Rosen, Campbell, and Hahn.*)

tive bacteria yielded galactose and glucose; galactose, glucose, mannose, and rhamnose.

In addition, all organisms studied contained an amino sugar or hexosamine. Generally, the walls of Gram-positive bacteria are richer in hexosamine than the Gram-negative forms.

Work (1957) pointed to the existence in Gram-positive bacteria of a common basal structure containing the following constituents: a hexosamine component comprising glucosamine and muramic acid and sometimes also galactosamine; a peptide component made up of alanine, glutamic acid, and either diaminopimelic acid or lysine with sometimes also glycine, aspartic acid, or serine; and usually a polysaccharide containing not more than four different sugar residues. Other substances may also be attached to the walls, as for example the protein antigens.

Smithies, Gibbons, and Bayley (1955) reported a relatively high nitrogen content in the walls of several halophilic bacteria which indicated

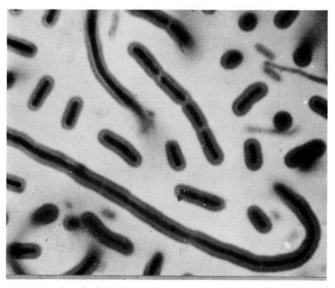

FIG. 34. Capsules of *Klebsiella pneumoniae*. (*After Klieneberger-Nobel.*)

that the cell material was predominantly protein. They contained only small amounts of lipides. The cell walls were lipoprotein.

Barkulis and Jones (1957) found that approximately one-third of streptococcal cell walls was made up of rhamnose and hexosamine. The remaining two-thirds was protein in nature.

Electron micrographs of the cell walls and protoplasm of *Rickettsia typhi* are shown in Fig. 33.

For more information see Cummins and Harris (1956), Graziosi and Tecce (1957), Hayashi and Barkulis (1959), Kakutani (1957), Salton (1956), Strange (1959), Tanaka (1957), Tomcsik and Grace (1955), Trucco and Pardee (1958), Yoshida et al. (1956).

Capsules. Extracellular material of a slimy or gelatinous nature is formed by many bacteria, especially those producing mucoid growths. This material may remain firmly adherent as a discrete covering layer on each cell, or it may part freely from the cells. In the former case it is known as a capsule; in the latter, as free slime or gum.

Capsules and slime are believed to be distinct from the morphological and biochemical point of view. The capsule is a part of the cell, the slime a secretion. According to Klieneberger-Nobel (1948), capsules are of definite shape, of more or less definite density throughout, and of definite outline (Fig. 34), whereas slime envelopes are amorphous and can be drawn out into manifold structures, are most concentrated in the vicinity of the bacterial cells, and decrease in density with increasing distance from the cell.

Broth cultures of capsule-producing organisms are usually stringy in texture, and agar colonies exhibit a very moist, glistening surface which is described as mucoid. Capsule formation is dependent upon the com-

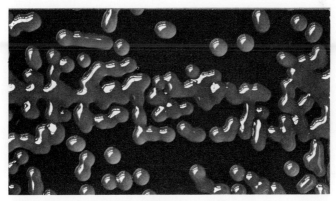

Fig. 35. *Leuconostoc mesenteroides.* Three-day culture on 10 per cent raw sugar agar incubated at room temperature. (*After McCleskey, Faville, and Barnett.*)

position of the medium but especially the variant phase of the organism. Some disease-producing organisms form large capsules in culture media rich in animal fluids. Others produce prominent capsules when cultures are incubated at low temperatures (4 to 20°C.).

Chemical analyses of capsular material from a number of bacteria show wide differences in composition. For this reason it is impossible to make statements which apply to all bacteria. In some organisms the capsular material appears to be a glycoprotein; in others, a protein-polysaccharide complex; in still others, a polysaccharide framework with the spaces filled in by a larger amount of glutamyl polypeptide.

Capsular material is difficult to distinguish from those gums which flow away from the cells as they are formed. Organisms producing gums do so when grown in sugar solutions. Some organisms produce gums only in the presence of a specific sugar; others produce gums in the presence of any one of several sugars. In the absence of sugar, usually very little, if any, gum is formed. Organisms producing gums of this type are the cause of considerable losses in the sugar industry. The increased viscosity produced by the gum interferes with the filtration of the sugar solution.

The species commonly encountered in sugar-cane juice is *Leuconostoc mesenteroides* (Fig. 35). The cells are surrounded by a thick, gelatinous, colorless polysaccharide consisting of dextran (glucose polymer).

The formation of gums is of common occurrence by soil bacteria. From 5 to 16 per cent of such forms have been shown to be capable of synthesizing gums from sugars.

For more information see Bailey and Oxford (1959), Labaw and Mosley (1954), Thorne (1956), Tomcsik (1956), and Wilkinson (1958).

Bacterial Protoplasts. When the cell wall is damaged, the protoplasm usually disintegrates. However, methods are available for removing the

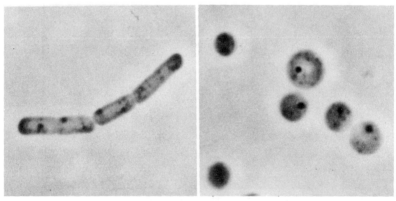

Fig. 36. Photomicrographs of *Bacillus megaterium*. Left, cells before lysis with lysozyme; right, cells after lysis with lysozyme in 0.02 *M* sucrose and 0.03 *M* phosphate. (*Courtesy of Weibull.*)

cell membranes without destroying the vital nature of protoplasm. The term protoplast is used to indicate living protoplasm exclusive of the cell membranes.

Action of Lysozyme. Some bacteria are rapidly lysed or dissolved by the action of lysozyme. Weibull (1953) reported that lysozyme possessed a specific depolymerizing action on the cell wall and that this appeared to be the only portion of the cell that was affected by such treatment. As a result of the destruction of the wall, the protoplasts were liberated.

Protoplasmic structures are not very stable. Consequently, if protective agents were not employed, destruction of the walls was accompanied by a rapid lysis of the protoplasts, followed by the liberation of most of the cell protein and nucleic acid in soluble form. This could be prevented by employment of the enzyme in a 0.2 *M* solution of sucrose or cane sugar. After digestion of the cell walls, the living protoplasts rounded up into spheres (Fig. 36).

Spiegelman, Aronson, and Fitz-James (1958) found that digestion of protoplasts of *Bacillus megaterium* led to the liberation of nuclear bodies of the protoplasts. Such bodies were collected by centrifugation for 5 min. at $10,000 \times g$.

Properties of Protoplasts. The difficulty in handling and studying protoplasts is their extreme fragility and sensitivity to osmotic shock, shaking, centrifugation, and aeration. Removal of the cell wall does not change the structure and capabilities of the protoplasm. Permeability, respiration, and spore formation appear to be the same for protoplasts and intact cells. Also both can support the development of bacteriophages. Under special conditions the protoplasts grow and probably divide like intact cells. However, there is no evidence that protoplasts form colonies. The metabolism of protoplasts and intact cells appear to be very similar but probably not identical.

Filterability of Protoplasts. Sinkovics (1958) reported the spontaneous occurrence of units in aged cultures of *Escherichia coli* which conformed to the description of artificially induced bacterial protoplasts. The disintegration of cells from aged cultures was preceded by swelling of the cell and rupture of the rigid cell wall. Centrifugation of the culture gave a supernate which, after filtration, contained units capable of regeneration when placed in fresh medium. The smallest units capable of regeneration measured about 350 mμ in diameter. The units underwent fusion before cell-wall formation occurred.

The results supported the assumption that aged *E. coli* cultures could survive in the form of units having no cell walls and which, under adequate conditions, regenerated into vegetative forms.

For more information see Britt and Gerhardt (1958), Fitz-James (1958), McQuillen (1956), Millman (1958), Weibull (1955, 1956), and Zinder and Arndt (1956).

Polysaccharide Structures. Polysaccharides occur (1) in cell walls, (2) extracellularly in capsules and gums, and (3) inside of bacterial cells. The first two have already been discussed.

Pennington (1949) revealed the presence of polysaccharides by treating bacteria with sodium metaperiodate followed by staining with sulfite-decolorized basic fuchsin (Fig. 37). In *Bacillus cereus* the polysaccharide was concentrated in the cytoplasmic membrane as well as in the cell wall.

Selective staining of polysaccharide in the cell is said to depend upon the oxidizing action of periodate on such chemical configurations as α, β glycols and α-hydroxyketones. Polyaldehydes generated by this selective oxidation react with sulfite-decolorized fuchsin. Polysaccharide areas in the cell are colored red by the stain.

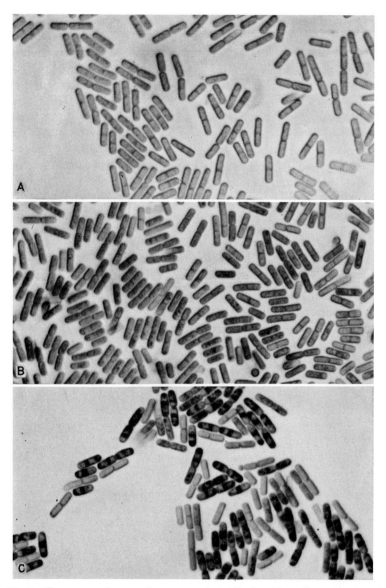

Fig. 37. *Bacillus cereus* (grown from spores) oxidized with sodium metaperiodate and stained with sulfite-decolorized basic fuchsin. Upper, 2-hr.-old cells; center, 6-hr.-old cells; lower, 10-hr.-old cells. (*After Pennington.*)

For more information see Järvi and Levanto (1950); Lankford, Hoyo, and Lutteringer (1951); and Wilkinson (1958).

Nucleus. The question of the presence of a well-defined nucleus in bacteria has been the subject of investigations by bacteriologists almost from the beginning of bacteriology.

Some of the earlier cytologists maintained that bacteria were very primitive organisms devoid of nuclei and consisting simply of cytoplasm, granules, and vacuoles. This view was based on their failure to observe a nucleus in a bacterial cell. Others held the view that the nuclear material was present in a diffuse form throughout the cytoplasm. Still others believed that the whole cell should be regarded as a "naked nucleus," corresponding to the nucleus of higher organisms. The naked nucleus is regarded as a primitive form of living matter. Since bacteria

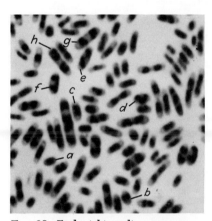

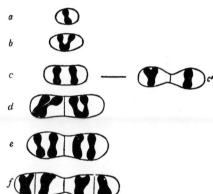

FIG. 38. *Escherichia coli,* grown on an agar slant for 45 to 90 min. at 37°C. *a–h,* successive stages in the development of a coccoid element with a central pair of closely contiguous chromatinic bodies into a typical rod-shaped bacterium with four chromatinic structures. Note the V-shaped division stage at *d.* The dumbbell body forming the left limb of the V is much broader than the right one, and it seems plausible to assume that it is preparing for the next division. (*After Robinow.*)

FIG. 39. *Escherichia coli.* Diagram of successive division stages of the chromatinic bodies from the beginning of the lag phase, after transfer to a fresh nutrient medium, to the first division of the growing organism. *c–c′* and *c–f* are alternative modes of development, *c–f* being that most commonly followed. (*After Robinow.*)

have the structural and physiological attributes of true cells, this concept cannot apply to these organisms.

Much of the confusion was caused by the inadequacy of the staining procedures. By means of the HCl-Giemsa staining technique of Piekarski, many observations have been reported demonstrating the presence of chromatinic structures in bacteria.

Robinow (1944) prepared wet smears of *Escherichia coli.* Slides were fixed in osmic acid vapor, dried, and immersed in normal HCl for about 9 min. at 53 to 55°C., then washed and stained in 1:20 Giemsa solution for 10 to 60 min., depending on the staining properties of the specimen.

The chromatinic structures in *E. coli* from old cultures were too small

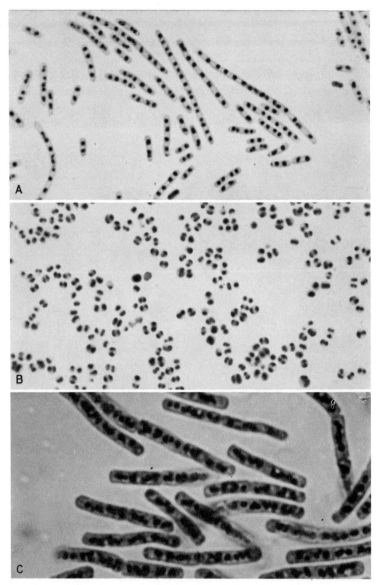

FIG. 40. Chromatinic structures in bacteria. A, *Escherichia coli,* ×2400; B, Staphylococcus aureus, ×2400; C, *Bacillus megaterium,* ×3300. (*After Smith.*)

to be resolved accurately. After transfer to fresh medium the chromatinic structures increased in size and gave rise to short, often dumbbell-shaped rods or chromosomes, which multiplied by splitting lengthwise in a plane more or less parallel to the short axis of the cell (Figs. 38 and 39). A single cell of *E. coli* contained one chromatinic body or one or two pairs of these representing primary and secondary division products.

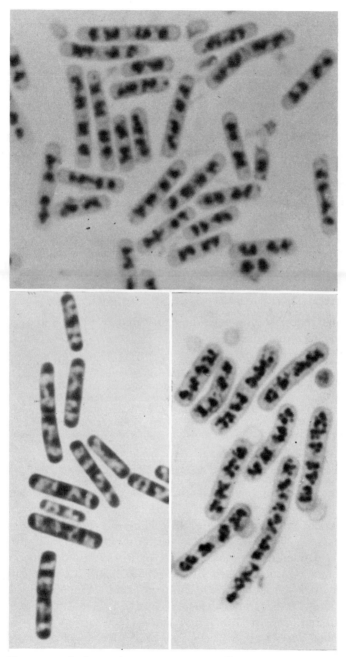

Fig. 41. Chromatinic bodies in bacteria. Upper, *Bacillus cereus,* successive stages of growth and direct division of the chromatin bodies in bacteria of increasing length; lower left, *B. cereus,* chromatin bodies stand out, unstained, from the basophile cytoplasm; lower right, *B. megaterium,* successive stages of the third division of the chromatin bodies in a group of cells growing out of recently germinated spores. (*Courtesy of Robinow.*)

The Smith (1950) technique consisted of fixing the smear in osmium tetroxide vapor, immersion in HCl, mordanting in dilute formaldehyde, and staining with aqueous basic fuchsin. The method was said to possess certain advantages over the procedure of Robinow (Fig. 40).

Another cause of confusion in the recognition of nuclear structures in bacteria was the lack of appreciation for the ages of the cultures. At certain times nuclear structures cannot be seen. In general, most of the early observations of tidy, intelligible "nuclei" were made on preparations from very young cultures, whereas haphazardly scattered, unintelligible granules of chromatin were persistently observed in preparations made from cultures of the same bacteria beyond the logarithmic growth phase.

Recognition of the fact that the configuration of nuclear material in bacteria might change with age removed one of the chief causes of confusion. As Dobell said (1911),

My own belief is that the nucleus in bacteria may display not one but many forms during the whole life cycle. Many of the nuclear structures which have been shown to exist in these organisms should, I think, be regarded as temporary states rather than as permanent conditions. The different results which have been reached by different workers when working, apparently, upon the same species, may to some extent find an explanation in this circumstance.

The chromatin bodies, according to Robinow (1956), appear to have the following properties:

They are simple structures of relatively low density, not markedly basophilic but reacting positively in the Feulgen test. Normally they lie separately in the cytoplasm, and all those in one bacterium are homologous. Changes in the balance of ions in the cytoplasm may cause the aggregation of several chromatin bodies into a single continuous structure. This effect is reversible. Growth and division of chromatin bodies are attended by changes of form only, not by visible changes of texture (Fig. 41). In the simplest type of body, that which in profile looks like a bar or dumbbell, division begins at one end and causes the successive appearance of V-, U-, and H-shaped phases. The chromatin structures of certain bacteria are netlike or spongelike, and their mode of division is not easily imagined.

Direct division of the chromatin bodies of E. coli has been demonstrated by Mason and Powelson (1956) in a series of remarkable phase-contrast photomicrographs (Fig. 42). These observations were made on living bacteria. The nuclear areas in the dividing cells appeared to be as clearly defined as the areas in fixed, hydrolyzed, and stained cells.

For more information see Bisset (1955, 1956); Chance (1957); De Lamater (1956); Elliot (1956); Hoffman (1951); Hunter-Szybalska, Szybalski, and DeLamater (1956); Knaysi (1955); Robinow (1956b); Whitfield and Murray (1956); and Yuasa (1956).

Vacuoles. Vacuoles have been identified in young bacteria. They are cavities in the protoplasm and contain a fluid known as cell sap. As the cells approach maturity, some of the water-soluble reserve food materials manufactured by the cell dissolve in the vacuoles. Insoluble constituents precipitate out as cytoplasmic inclusion bodies.

Metachromatic Granules. The best-known inclusion bodies in bacterial cells are known as volutin or metachromatic granules (Fig. 43). The granules are small in young cells and become larger with the age of the culture. They are believed to originate in the cytoplasm of young cells and to localize in the vacuoles of mature forms. The granules show a

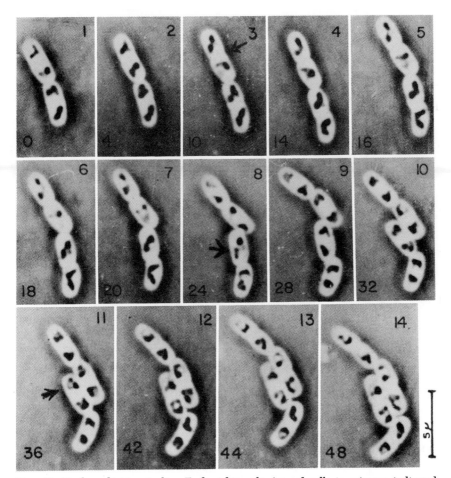

Fig. 42. Nuclear division in live *Escherichia coli*. Age of cells in minutes indicated in lower left-hand corner of each photograph. (*Courtesy of Mason and Powelson.*)

strong affinity for basic dyes, indicating that they are acid in character. They are usually considered to be a reserve source of food.

Grula and Hartsell (1954) found the granules to be composed of metaphosphate or another form of inorganic phosphate, some fat, and possibly small amounts of protein. Their presence and size in cells were related to the phosphate concentration of the growth medium in the presence of

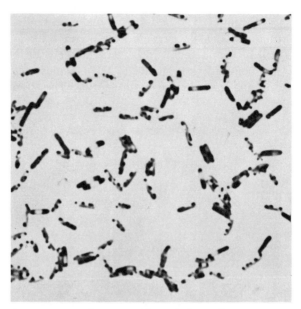

FIG. 43. Metachromatic granules in *Bacillus subtilis*. Culture 18 hr. old and stained with a 1:5000 solution of crystal violet.

an energy source and specific divalent ions (Mn and Zn). Older cells possessed larger granules. Their basophilic nature did not depend on either ribonucleic acid (RNA) or desoxyribonucleic acid.

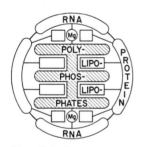

FIG. 43A. Composite representation of a metachromatic granule. (*After Widra.*)

On the other hand, Widra (1959) found metachromatic granules to contain protein-bound lipide, RNA, and polyphosphates (Fig. 43A).

For more information see Bisset (1954), Knaysi (1959), and Smith, Wilkinson, and Duguid (1954).

Fat Globules. Bacteria are capable of storing fat in the form of globules. Fat globules may be demonstrated in 24-hr. cultures and usually reach a maximum in about 48 hr. (Fig. 44).

Some cells may contain only one large globule; others may show the presence of a number of small, scattered globules.

It is generally believed that fat is stored as reserve food material. Globules usually cannot be demonstrated in young, vigorously growing cells. As cells age and slow down in activity, fat globules appear in the cytoplasm and may be recognized by appropriate staining.

For more information see Burdon (1946).

Motility. Bacterial motion is generally associated with the presence of organs of locomotion known as flagella (singular, flagellum). They were first observed in stained preparations by Cohn (1875). The presence of flagella does not mean necessarily that the organisms are always motile, but it indicates a potential power to move.

Independent bacterial motion is a true movement of translation and must be distinguished from the quivering or back-and-forth motion exhibited by very small particles suspended in a liquid. This latter type of motion is called Brownian movement (after Brown, 1828) and is caused by the bombardment of the bacteria by the molecules of the suspending fluid.

Properties of Flagella. Flagella are very delicate organs and easily detached from the cell. In the stained condition they are long, slender, undulating organs. They are directed backward to the direction of mo-

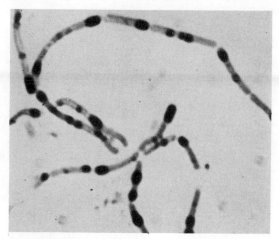

Fig. 44. *Bacillus cereus,* showing fat globules. From a 48-hr. glycerin agar culture stained with Sudan black B and safranine. Fat globules appear bluish black; cytoplasm stains pink. (*Courtesy of Burdon, Stokes, and Kimbrough.*)

tion at an angle of about 45°. Reversal of direction occurs by swinging the flagella through an angle of about 90°. Turning movements take place by swinging the flagella forward on one side only. They propel the organism by a spiral or corkscrew motion.

The thickness of flagella varies from species to species. In *Proteus vulgaris* they measure about 12 mμ. This figure is considerably below the shortest wave length of visible light and explains why flagella cannot be seen in hanging-drop preparations or in smears stained by the usual simple procedures. When special staining methods are employed, sufficient dye becomes deposited on the flagella to make their diameters greater than the wave length of visible light. They may then be seen under a light microscope.

Chemistry of Flagella. Flagella and bacterial bodies differ in composition. Flagella break up on boiling or when exposed to pH values below

4 or above 11. Their composition is largely protein, having a molecular weight of about 41,000. Weibull (1949) found the flagella of *P. vulgaris* to be composed of 98 per cent protein, traces of carbohydrate and fat, and no phosphorus. The protein contained only 14 known amino acids. It is an incomplete protein, lacking in some of the essential amino acids.

Fig. 45. Electron micrograph of the flagella of *Spirillum serpens*, ×30,000. Note the passage of the flagella through the cell wall and into the cytoplasm. (*Courtesy of van Iterson, Delft, Holland.*)

It is well established that the *H* antigens of bacteria are associated with the flagella and the *O* antigens with the bodies (see page 683). Purified flagella are agglutinated by *H* antiserum but not by *O* antiserum; *O* antigens are not agglutinated by *H* antiserum. This is another indication that flagella and bacterial bodies differ in composition.

For more information see Gard, Heller, and Weibull (1955), Kobayashi, Rinker, and Koffler (1959).

Origin of Flagella. Some believe flagella originate from the cell wall; others believe they traverse the cell wall into the protoplasm.

Flagella differ chemically both from the cell wall and the protoplasm.

Two observations have been made relative to the site of origin of flagella.

Electron micrographs by van Iterson (see Boltjes, 1948) and others show the flagella penetrating the faint outer zones and extending into the cytoplasm (Fig. 45). If the outer zone is the cell wall, then the flagella have their origin in the cytoplasm.

Weibull (1953) showed that removal of the cell wall of some bacteria by means of lysozyme produces a spherical protoplast which still retains the flagella of the treated cell. The obvious conclusion is that flagella have their origin in some cell structure deeper than the cell wall.

Number and Arrangement of Flagella. The number and arrangement of flagella vary with different bacteria, but they are generally constant for each species. Some have only one flagellum; others have two or more flagella.

In rod-shaped cells the flagella arise either at one or both poles, or are distributed laterally with the poles being generally bare. In some species flagella are located both laterally and at the poles. A species may show considerable variation in the number and arrangement of flagella. Single *Alcaligenes* cultures may contain forms with a polar flagellum only; some with several lateral flagella; and some with both lateral and polar flagella. Sometimes a species may show cells which are flagellated in one environment and nonflagellated in another.

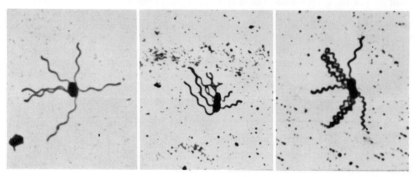

FIG. 46. Flagella of *Proteus* species. Left, *P. mirabilis* showing normal flagella; center, *P. morganii* with 6 normal and 2 curly flagella; right, *P. mirabilis* with 1 normal and several curly flagella. (*Courtesy of Leifson, Carhart, and Fulton.*)

Leifson, Carhart, and Fulton (1955) reported the presence of four definite types of curvature in the flagella of *Proteus vulgaris* (Fig. 46). Individual organisms may have more than one type of flagella, and individual flagella may have one or two types of curves.

Environmental factors, particularly pH, may change the curvature of the flagella on some strains, but not on all strains. In acid media the curly curvature tends to predominate; in alkaline media the normal predominates.

Organisms have been classified on the basis of the number and arrangement of flagella as follows:

Monotrichous—a single flagellum at one end of the cell.
Lophotrichous—two or more flagella at one end or both ends of the cell.
Amphitrichous—one flagellum at each end.
Peritrichous—flagella surrounding the cell.

Staining of Flagella. The staining of flagella is a difficult technique, especially in the hands of the beginner. For this reason many methods have been proposed. Regardless of the method employed, the film must first be treated with a mordant to make the flagella take the stain heavily. Mordants consist usually of a mixture of tannic acid and some metallic salt. In some methods the mordant and stain are applied separately; in others they are combined in one solution.

Boltjes (1948) came to the following conclusions on the staining of bacterial flagella:

Four factors at least influence the results of staining—the skill of the investigator, the organism studied, the culture medium on which the organism was grown, and the staining method. Of these the first is perhaps the most and the last the least important. The importance of skill is shown by the repeated failure of students to stain flagella although their teacher has no difficulty in demonstrating flagella at the same time and with the same suspension. Further, one usually has success with a new formula only after a number of trials; first attempts to stain an unknown bacterium are often a failure. Another point is that as a rule flagella can be clearly seen only in a rather small part of the preparation. The different colours of the stained bacteria show clearly that during the staining process conditions are not everywhere alike, and since many flagella are torn off during drying, we need not wonder that in most cases only a few bacteria are successfully stained. Notwithstanding all this, it is certain that when one has had some experience with the staining technique, the results are so consistent that there will never be any confusion between bacteria with true polar flagella, such, for example, as *Pseudomonas fluorescens* or *Vibrio comma,* and peritrichous bacteria like *Proteus mirabilis* and *Salmonella typhosa.* I therefore consider flagella staining to be a reliable procedure.

Photomicrographs of the arrangement of flagella on bacteria, according to Leifson (1951), are shown in Fig. 47.

For more information see Astbury, Beighton, and Weibull (1955); De Robertis and Franchi (1951); Graudal and Birch-Andersen (1958); Houwink and van Iterson (1950); Leifson and Hugh (1953); Rinker and Koffler (1951); Stocker (1956); and Tawara (1957).

The Pijper Theory of Motility. In a series of investigations Pijper et al. (1957) questioned the belief that flagella are responsible for motility. He added methyl cellulose to a culture of a motile organism to increase the viscosity of the medium. This treatment decreased the motility of the cells. Under these conditions the cells exhibited a gyratory undulating movement like other aquatic creatures. He concluded that flagella were not organs of locomotion but only artifacts—useless appendages, polysaccharide twirls—the result, not the cause, of bacterial motility. To quote,

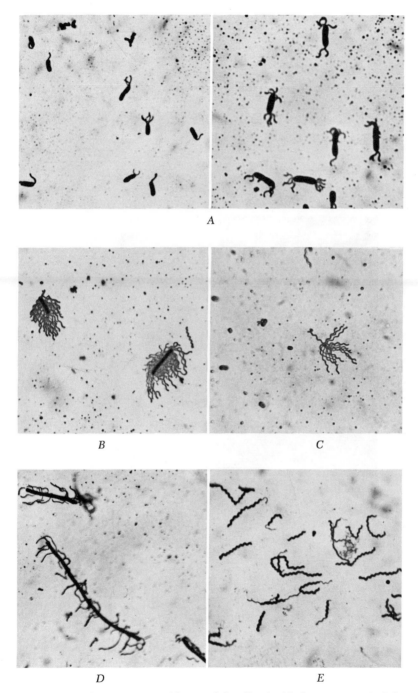

FIG. 47. Shape and arrangement of bacterial flagella. A, *Alcaligenes* spp.; B, *Salmonella typhosa*; C, *Proteus vulgaris*; D, mutant of a nitrogen-fixing organism; E, *Treponema pallidum*. (*After Leifson.*)

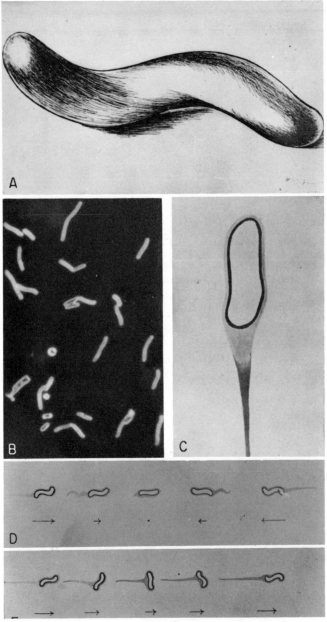

Fig. 48. Shape and motility of bacteria. *A*, perspective drawing of model of motile bacterium showing spiral shape; *B*, dividing typhoid bacilli lying still. Spiral shapes well adapted to "slipping"; *C*, diagram of motile bacterium with tail: transition of slime layer into tail, explaining dark spot between body and tail; *D*, diagram of sudden reversal in motile bacterium, showing transition of tail into slime layer and back again at other end; *E*, diagram of motile bacterium turning half-somersault: tail remains in place. (*After Pijper.*)

That motile bacteria always exhibit a gyratory undulating movement was confirmed by making a slow motion cinemicrographic film of fast-swimming bacteria in broth, and also by examining the same bacteria at lower temperatures, which reduced their speed [Fig. 48].

This spirillar motion of bacteria is sufficient to propel them, and there is no need to invoke special motor organs like flagella. There is no evidence to show that the flagella-like appendages of bacteria act as motile organs—in fact all the evidence when critically examined points the other way.

Analysis of the structure of bacteria excludes the possibility that tails, "flagella," or the thin wavy threads are live organs, or that they are in direct communication with the living parts of the cell. There is no evidence from either electron pictures or stained preparations that it is otherwise.

Not only does the visible gyratory undulating movement of motile bacteria satisfy all requirements for locomotion, but it is possible for bacteria grown under special conditions to swim in this fashion without showing tails or other supposed motor organs.

Notwithstanding the findings and conclusions of Pijper, evidence at present appears to be overwhelmingly in favor of flagella as organs of locomotion.

As has already been stated, Weibull (1948, 1949) reported the flagella of *P. vulgaris* to be composed of 98 per cent protein. This contradicts Pijper's statement that flagella are formed from the carbohydrate slime layer that is peeled off into a number of thin, wavy threads.

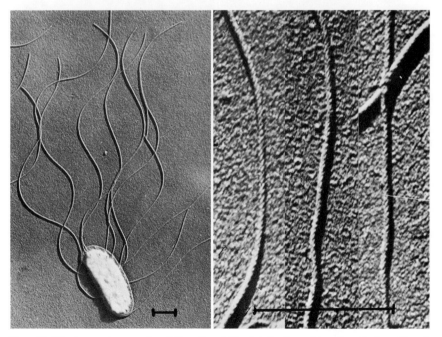

Fig. 49. Electron micrographs of flagella of *Bordetella bronchiseptica*. Left, cell and attached flagella, ×13,000; right, three sections of flagella showing a helical structure, ×77,000. Palladium shadowed. (*Courtesy of Labaw and Mosley.*)

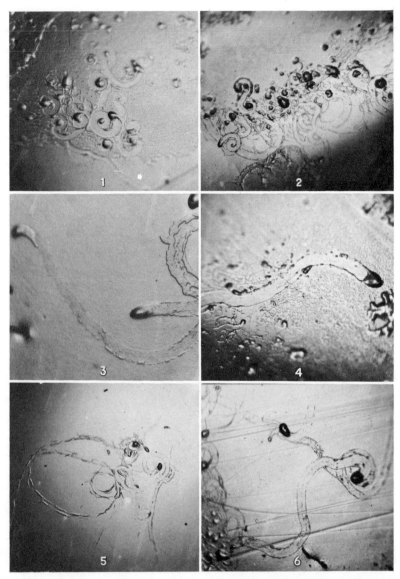

Fig. 50. Rotating and migrating colonies of *Clostridium oedematiens*. 1, Type B, 24 hr., showing numerous wandering cell groups sweeping clean curved tracks through swarm film. 2, Type B, 24 hr., showing numerous wandering daughter colonies and fairly short tracks. 3, Type A, 24 hr., showing tracks and moving colonies. 4, Type B, 24 hr., showing a large wandering cell group pushing through the swarm film. 5, Type B, 24 hr. The discarded bacilli along the tracks have multiplied considerably. 6, Type B, 72 hr., showing large daughter colonies and well-defined tracks. (*Courtesy of Turner and Eales.*)

Several investigators, among them Labaw and Mosley (1955), by means of electron microscopy, demonstrated the presence on *Brucella bronchiseptica* of uniform flagella having an external contour of a counterclockwise or left-handed triple helix (Fig. 49). The average periodicity along the length of the flagella was 19 mμ, with an average diameter of 13.9 mμ.

For more information see Houwink (1956), Kvittingen (1955), Smith (1954), Winkler and Tscheuschner (1958).

Motion of Colonies. Several organisms have been described which exhibit colonial motility when grown on a solid medium.

Shinn (1938) prepared lapse-time motion pictures of individual colonies of *Bacillus alvei* grown on agar plates and measured their velocities. The linear motions of colonies measuring 0.2 to 0.5 mm. in diameter averaged about 14 mm. per hr. Comparing this figure with the speed of individual cells of other species of motile bacteria gave the following results:

Salmonella typhosa	65 mm. per hr.
Bacillus megaterium	27 mm. per hr.
B. alvei (colonies)	14 mm. per hr.

The colonies exhibited not only linear motion but also a slow rotary movement. The direction of rotation of 200 to 300 colonies observed was counterclockwise, with the exception of two colonies in which it was clockwise.

Turner and Eales (1941a, b) reported that the rotation of an aerobe occurred very early during growth (Fig. 50). The cells segregated in small groups and aligned themselves concentrically around a common center to form disk-like plaques one or a few cells thick. The rate of rotation was greater in smaller groups. As multiplication continued, successive layers were gradually built up in terrace fashion and the colony grew in height. The colonies then began to migrate. When a colony mi-

Fig. 51. Sketch of convoluted track of a wandering colony, showing two series of clockwise spirals followed by a final counterclockwise spiral. The colony had increased considerably in size after coming to rest and showed curved radial markings indicating rotation. The total length of the track was about 2 cm. (*After Turner and Eales.*)

grated, it left a peculiar "track" on the surface of the agar. A small number of cells were left behind, mostly at the edges of the track, which formed two parallel lines separated by the width of the moving colony.

Typical migrating colonies pursued curved or spiral paths which were often very elaborate and of relatively great length, even 2 or 3 cm. (Fig. 51). The direction of rotation was either clockwise or counterclockwise. After wandering for a variable distance, a colony approached the center of its spiral path with rapidly shortening radius, ceased to migrate, began to rotate around its center, lost its elongated shape, and increased in size to several times the width of the track at the end of which it was formed.

For more information see Murray and Elder (1949).

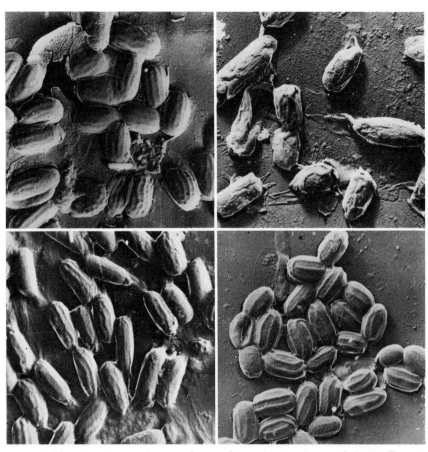

FIG. 52. Electron micrographs of carbon replicas of spores. Upper left, *Bacillus circulans;* upper right, *B. subtilis;* lower left, *B. alvei;* lower right, *Clostridium perfringens.* (*Courtesy of Bradley and Franklin.*)

Endospores. Endospores are bodies produced within the cells of a considerable number of bacterial species. They are more resistant to unfavorable environmental conditions, such as heat, cold, desiccation, osmosis, and chemicals, than the vegetative cells producing them. However, it is debatable if such extreme conditions actually occur in nature. For instance, the resistance of spores to high temperatures is a laboratory phenomenon and probably never occurs in a natural environment.

The bulk of evidence indicates the existence of a close relationship between spore formation and the exhaustion of nutrients essential for continued vegetative growth. Sporulation is a defense mechanism to protect the cell when the occasion arises.

Spore formation is limited almost entirely to two genera of rod-shaped bacteria: *Bacillus* (aerobic or facultatively anaerobic), and *Clostridium* (anaerobic or aerotolerant). With one possible exception, the common spherical bacteria do not sporulate. Some spore-bearing species can be made to lose their ability to produce spores. When the ability to produce spores is once lost, it is seldom regained. Sporulation is not a process to increase bacterial numbers because a cell rarely produces more than one spore.

For more information see Foster (1956).

Morphology of Spores. Spores may be spherical, ellipsoidal, or cylindrical in shape. The position of the spore in a cell may be central, subterminal, or terminal. A fully grown spore may have a diameter greater than that of the vegetative cell. This causes a bulging of the cell. The resulting forms are known as clostridium if central, and plectridium if terminal. As a rule, each species has its own characteristic size, shape, and position of the spore, but this is subject to variation under different environmental conditions.

Franklin and Bradley (1957), by means of electron microscopy of carbon replicas, reported that the spores of a majority of species of *Bacillus* and *Clostridium* are readily distinguished by surface patterns. The surfaces may be smooth or ribbed, with the ribs usually longitudinal (Fig. 52).

Drawings of the surface sculpturing of spores of *B. polymyxa* are shown in Fig. 53. The sculpturing consists of a single endless ridge in the form

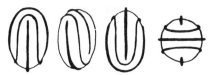

Fig. 53. Surface structure of a spore of *Bacillus polymyxa*. From left to right: side view; same rotated a quarter turn from right to left; same rotated a further quarter turn; view of a pole. (*From Franklin and Bradley.*)

of two loops, similar to the marking on a tennis ball, together with two other separate ridges terminating within the loops. An electron micrograph of ultrathin sections of such spores, by van den Hooff and Aninga (1956), is shown in Fig. 54. The spore coat consists of an outer and an inner layer separated by a space. The outer layer is sometimes called the exine and the inner layer the intine. The intine faintly follows the surface relief. The central core is separated from the intine by a regular nonosmophilic space. A peripheral spot may be observed in the core which probably represents nuclear material.

For more information see Bradley and Franklin (1958), Dondero and Holbert (1957), Hashimoto and Naylor (1958), Mayall and Robinow (1957).

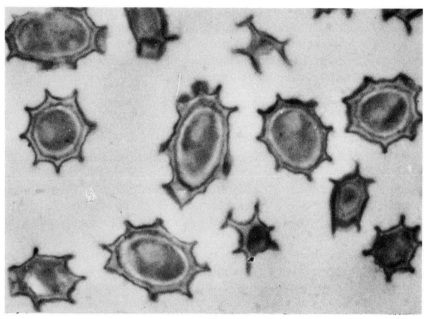

Fig. 54. Electron micrograph of ultrathin sections of spores of *Bacillus polymyxa*. See text for details. (*Courtesy of van den Hooff and Aninga.*)

Parasporal Bodies. When sporulation of *Bacillus laterosporus* is complete, the spores are cradled in canoe-shaped bodies (Fig. 55). According to Hannay (1957):

On sporulation the slender vegetative rods swell and form larger spindle-shaped cells in which the spores are formed. When the spores mature they lie in a lateral position cradled in canoe-shaped parasporal bodies which are highly basophilic and can be differentiated from the surrounding vegetative cell cytoplasm with dilute basic dyes. On completion of sporulation the vegetative cell protoplasm and the cell wall lyse, leaving the spore cradled in its parasporal body. This attachment continues indefinitely on the usual culture medium and even persists after the spores have germinated. In thin sections of sporing cells the bodies are differentiated from the cell protoplasm by differences in structure. Whereas the protoplasm has a granular appearance, in both longitudinal and cross-sections the parasporal body comprises electron-dense lamellae running parallel with the membranes of the spore coat and less electron-dense material in the interstices of the lamellae. The inner surface of the body is contiguous with that of the spore coat as if it were part of the spore, rather than a separate body attached to the spore. The staining reactions of the parasporal body are not consistent with those of any substance described in bacteria.

For more information see Fitz-James and Young (1958).

Composition of Spores. Ross and Billing (1957), by means of refractive index measurements on spores and vegetative cells of *B. cereus, B. cereus* var. *mycoides,* and *B. megaterium,* found the values to be very high and comparable with that of dehydrated protein. This suggested that they contained much less water than the vegetative cells.

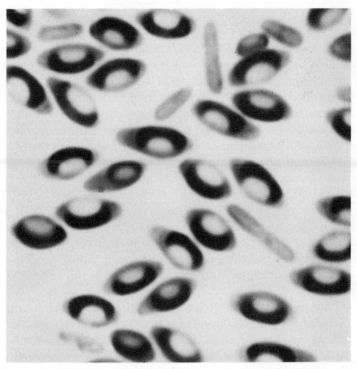

Fig. 55. Parasporal bodies of *Bacillus laterosporus.* See text for description. (*Courtesy of Hannay.*)

Strange and Dark (1956) demonstrated the presence of a hexosamine-containing peptide in the spore coats of *B. megaterium* and *B. subtilis.* The breakdown of an insoluble peptide complex might well be one of the first steps of the germination process. It was believed that the release of the hexosamine-amino acid complex was the result of the action of lysozyme present in the spores.

For more information see Foster (1960).

Enzymes of Spores. The presence of enzyme systems in *Bacillus* spores has been reported. Some of these are an inorganic pyrophosphatase that requires manganese for activation, adenine ribosidase that hydrolyzes adenosine, an enzyme that functions possibly to lyse the sporangium and free the spore during germination, highly active alanine racemase that catalyzes the conversion of L-alanine to D-alanine, several glucose dehydrogenases, and an aldolase.

For more information see Doi, Halvorson, and Church (1959); Lawrence (1955); Levinson, Sloan, and Hyatt (1958); Stewart and Halvorson (1953); Strange and Dark (1957).

Sporulation Process. Conditions necessary for sporulation in one species do not necessarily apply to another. The subject appears to be in such a state of confusion that it is impossible to discuss sporulation in terms of generalities.

The conditions which have been reported as favoring sporulation include addition of salts of metals such as manganese, chromium, nickel, etc., to the medium; shaking a culture of vegetative cells of sporing aerobes with distilled water at 37°C.; addition of tomato juice to a medium; incubating the cultures at an appropriate temperature; addition of calcium carbonate to a carbohydrate medium to prevent excessive accumulation of acid, and to maintain the pH at 5.5 or above; the necessity of oxygen; addition to the medium of certain amino acids; etc.

For more information see Amaha, Ordal, and Touba (1956); Bowen and Smith (1955); Grelet (1957); Powell and Hunter (1953); Roth, Lively, and Hodge (1955); Roth, Lively, and Metcalfe (1958); Weinberg (1955); Zoha and Sadoff (1958).

Germination of Spores. With the exception of some constituents such as high concentrations of calcium, dipicolinic acid, and in *Bacillus sphaericus*, α, ε-diaminopimelic acid, spores are similar to the vegetative cells in composition.

When a spore prepares itself for germination, it loses its refractility, which coincides with an imbibition of water. This stage is associated with a loss in heat resistance, stainability, and dry weight. Later the spore coat breaks, followed by the emergence from the spore case of a new germ cell which eventually matures into a vegetative cell.

Spore germination has been defined in various ways. According to Campbell (1957), "Spore germination may be regarded as the change from a heat resistant spore to a heat labile entity which may not necessarily be a true vegetative cell." Later development, leading eventually to the formation of a mature vegetative cell, is called outgrowth.

Some conditions which stimulate germination are as follows: (1) Treatment at 90 to 100°C. for 1 to 2 min. stimulates germination. (2) Spores which fail to germinate overcome this dormancy when activated by heat. (3) The use of certain agents such as alanine, glucose, and adenosine stimulates spore germination in most sporing species. In some species other amino acids may be substituted for the alanine. The same applies to glucose. (4) Yeast extract and mixtures of vitamin-free amino acids have also been shown to stimulate germination.

Spores germinate in a variety of ways. There is a considerable degree

of constancy in the method of spore germination for each species. Lamanna (1940) classified the modes of germination as follows:

I. Spore germination by shedding of spore coat. Characteristics of this method are
  A. Spore does not expand greatly in volume previous to the germ cell breaking
    through the spore coat. The limit of volume increase of the spore may be
    considered to be twice its original volume.
  B. Spore coat does not lose all its refractive property previous to germination.
  C. After the second division of the germ cell, giving a chain of three organisms,
    the original spore coat, remaining attached to the cells, is visible for a long
    time after germination.
    1. Equatorial germination (Fig. 56).
    2. Polar germination (Fig. 56).
    3. Comma-shaped expansion (Fig. 56).

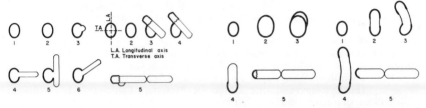

FIG. 56. Methods of spore germination. From left to right: equatorial germination
without splitting along transverse axis; equatorial germination with splitting along
transverse axis; polar germination; spore germination by comma-shaped expansion.
(*After Lamanna.*)

II. Spore germination by absorption of the spore coat. Characteristics of this method
  are
  A. The spore expands greatly during germination. A tripling or greater increase
    of the original volume occurs (Fig. 57).
  B. The spore loses its characteristic refractiveness during germination, so that it
    is difficult to say when the spore has disappeared and the germ cell appeared.
  C. After the second division of the germ cell, even if a thin capsule originally
    remains, all traces of the spore coat are gone.

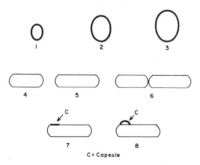

FIG. 57. Spore germination by absorption. (*After Lamanna.*)

Some strains germinating by absorption regularly show a thin capsule remaining
about one end of the growing cell. This would appear as a polar germination
(Fig. 57). In other cases, equatorial capsules are seen (Fig. 57). Yet, in all
instances, the spore is considered to germinate by absorption inasmuch as the
three characteristics of the method are still adhered to.

For more information see Bisset (1955); Halvorson and Church (1957); Hitzman, Halvorson, and Ukita (1957); Knaysi (1951); Lawrence (1955); Levinson and Hyatt (1955); Levinson and Sevag (1954); Mol (1957); Mudd, Payne, and Sall (1958); Powell (1957); Riemann (1957); Roth and Lively (1956); Stedman (1956); Stedman et al. (1956); Treadwell, Jann, and Salle (1958); Wolf and Mahmoud (1957).

REFERENCES

Amaha, M., Z. J. Ordal, and A. Touba: Sporulation requirements of *Bacillus coagulans* var. *thermoacidurans* in complex media, *J. Bact.*, 72:34, 1956.

Astbury, W. T., E. Beighton, and C. Weibull: The structure of bacterial flagella, *Symposium Soc. Exp. Biol.*, 9:282, 1955.

Bailey, R. W., and A. E. Oxford: The nature of the capsular polysaccharides of the dextran-producing organisms *Leuconostoc mesenteroides*, *L. dextranicum* and *Streptococcus bovis*, *J. Gen. Microbiol.*, 20:258, 1959.

Barkulis, S. S., and M. F. Jones: Studies of streptococcal cell walls. I. Isolation, chemical composition, and preparation of M protein, *J. Bact.*, 74:207, 1957.

Bisset, K. A.: The production of stainable granules in bacteria by the adsorption of DNA upon the cell envelopes, *Exp. Cell. Res.*, 7:232, 1954.

———: "The Cytology and Life History of Bacteria," Baltimore, The Williams & Wilkins Company, 1955.

———: Cellular organization in bacteria. From "Bacterial Anatomy," edited by E. T. C. Spooner and B. A. D. Stocker, London, Cambridge University Press, 1956.

Boltjes, T. Y. K.: Function and arrangement of bacterial flagella, *J. Path. Bact.*, 60:275, 1948.

Bowen, J. F., and E. S. Smith: Sporulation in *Clostridium pasteurianum*, *Food Research*, 20:655, 1955.

Bradley, D. E., and J. G., Franklin: Electron microscope survey of the surface configuration of spores of the genus *Bacillus*, *J. Bact.*, 76:618, 1958.

Britt, E. M., and P. Gerhardt: Bacterial permeability. Lysine pooling by intact cells and protoplasts of *Micrococcus lysodeikticus*, *J. Bact.*, 76:281, 1958.

Brown, R.: A brief account of microscopical observations made in the months of June, July, and August, 1827, on the particles contained in pollen of plants; and on the general existence of active molecules in organic and inorganic bodies, *Phil. Mag. and Ann. of Philosophy*, N.S., 4:161, 1828.

Burdon, K. L.: Fatty material in bacteria and fungi revealed by staining dried, fixed slide preparations, *J. Bact.*, 52:665, 1946.

Campbell, L. L., Jr.: Bacterial spore germination-definitions and methods of study. Taken from H. Halvorson and B. Church, Biochemistry of spores of aerobic bacilli with special reference to germination, *Bact. Rev.*, 21:112, 1957.

Chance, H. L.: Nuclear division in *Escherichia coli* as revealed by acid fuchsin, *J. Bact.*, 74:67, 1957.

Chapman, G. B.: Electron microscopy of cellular division in *Sarcina lutea*, *J. Bact.*, 79:132, 1960.

——— and A. J. Kroll: Electron microscopy of ultrathin sections of *Spirillum serpens*, *J. Bact.*, 73:63, 1957.

Cohn, F.: Untersuchungen über Bakterien, II. *Beitr. Biol. Pflanzen*, Bd. I, Heft 3:141, 1875.

Cummins, C. S., and H. Harris: The chemical composition of the cell wall in some Gram-positive bacteria and its possible value as a taxonomic character, *J. Gen. Microbiol.*, 14:583, 1956.

Deibel, R. H., M. Downing, C. F. Niven, Jr., and B. S. Schweigert: Filament formation by *Lactobacillus leichmannii* when desoxyribosides replace vitamin B_{12} in the growth medium, *J. Bact.*, 71:255, 1956.

DeLamater, E. D.: Bacterial chromosomes and their mechanism of division. From "Bacterial Anatomy," edited by E. T. C. Spooner and B. A. D. Stocker, London, Cambridge University Press, 1956.

De Robertis, E., and C. M. Franchi: Electron microscope observation on the fine structure of bacterial flagella, *Exp. Cell. Res.*, 2:295, 1951.

Dobell, C.: Contributions to the cytology of the bacteria, *Quart. J. Micros. Sci.*, 56:395, 1911.

Doi, R., H. Halvorson, and B. Church: III. The mechanism of glucose and hexosephosphate oxidation in extracts of *Bacillus cereus* spores, *J. Bact.*, 77:43, 1959.

Dondero, N. C., and P. E. Holbert: The endospore of *Bacillus polymyxa*, *J. Bact.*, 74:43, 1957.

Elliott, C. G.: Chromosomes in micro-organisms. From "Bacterial Anatomy," edited by E. T. C. Spooner and B. A. D. Stocker, London, Cambridge University Press, 1956.

Fitz-James, P. C.: Studies on the morphology and nucleic acid content of protoplasts of *Bacillus megaterium*, *J. Bact.*, 75:369, 1958.

———— and I. E. Young: Morphological and chemical studies of the spores and parasporal bodies of *Bacillus laterosporus*, *J. Biophys. Biochem. Cytol.*, 4:639, 1958.

Foster, J. W.: Morphogenesis in bacteria: some aspects of spore formation, *Quart. Rev. Biol.*, 31:102, 1956.

————: Dipicolinic acid and bacterial spores. Lecture delivered at the University of Maryland during the academic year 1959–1960.

Franklin, J. G., and D. E. Bradley: A further study of the spores of species of the genus *Bacillus* in the electron microscope using carbon replicas, and some preliminary observations on *Clostridium welchii*, *J. Appl. Bact.*, 20:467, 1957.

Gard, S., L. Heller, and C. Weibull: Immunological studies on purified flagella from *Proteus X₁₉*, *Acta Path. Microbiol. Scand.*, 36:30, 1955.

Graudal, H., and A. Birch-Andersen: Studies on the motility and flagellation of a motile *Streptococcus*, *Acta Path. Microbiol. Scand.*, 43:185, 1958.

Graziosi, F., and G. Tecce: Contributo alla conoscenza della struttura e della composizione chimica della parete cellulare in *Bacillus megatherium*, *Giorn. Microbiol.*, 3:143, 1957.

Grelet, N.: Growth limitation and sporulation, *J. Appl. Bact.*, 20:315, 1957.

Grula, E. A., and S. E. Hartsell: Intracellular structures in *Caulobacter vibrioides*, *J. Bact.*, 68:498, 1954.

Halvorson, H., and B. Church: Biochemistry of spores of aerobic bacilli with special reference to germination, *Bact. Rev.*, 21:112, 1957.

Hannay, C. L.: The parasporal body of *Bacillus laterosporus* Laubach, *J. Biophys. Biochem. Cytol.*, 3:1001, 1957.

Hashimoto, T., and H. B. Naylor: II. Electron microscopic studies on sporulation of *Clostridium sporogenes*, *J. Bact.*, 75:647, 1958.

Hayashi, J. A., and S. S. Barkulis: III. The amino acids of the trypsin-treated cell wall, *J. Bact.*, 77:177, 1959.

Hitzman, D. O., H. O. Halvorson, and T. Ukita: Requirements for production and germination of spores of anaerobic bacteria, *J. Bact.*, 74:1, 1957.

Hoffman, H.: The cytochemistry of bacterial nuclear structures, *J. Bact.*, 62:561, 1951.

Houwink, A. L.: Flagella, gas vacuoles and cell-wall structure in *Halobacterium halobium*; an electron microscope study, *J. Gen. Microbiol.*, 15:146, 1956.

———— and W. van Iterson: Electron microscopical observations on bacterial cytology. II. A study on flagellation, *Biochim. Biophys. Acta*, 5:10, 1950.

Hughes, W. H.: The structure and development of the induced long forms of bacteria. From "Bacterial Anatomy," edited by E. T. C. Spooner and B. A. D. Stocker, London, Cambridge University Press, 1956.

Hunter-Szybalska, M. E., W. Szybalski, and E. D. DeLamater: Temperature synchronization of nuclear and cellular division in *Bacillus megaterium*, *J. Bact.*, 71:17, 1956.

Järvi, O., and A. Levanto: On the structure of bacterial cells, as seen by the use of histochemical polysaccharide tests, *Acta Path.*, **27**:473, 1950.

Kakutani, I.: Electron microscopical observation of bacterial cell wall, *Shikoku Acta Medica*, **10**:224, 1957.

Klieneberger-Nobel, E.: Capsules and mucoid envelopes of bacteria, *J. Hyg.*, **46**:345, 1948.

Knaysi, G.: "Elements of Bacterial Cytology," Ithaca, N.Y., Comstock Publishing Company, Inc., 1951.

———: The structure, composition, and behavior of the nucleus in *Bacillus cereus*, *J. Bact.*, **69**:117, 1955.

———: Chemical composition of the granules of *Mycobacterium thamnopheos*, with special reference to their biological identity and the chemical nature of volutin, *ibid.*, **77**:532, 1959.

Kobayashi, T., J. N. Rinker, and H. Koffler: Purification and chemical properties of flagellin, *Arch. Biochem. Biophys.*, **84**:342, 1959.

Kvittingen, J.: Some observations on the nature and significance of bacterial flagella, *Acta Path. Microbiol. Scand.*, **37**:89, 1955.

Labaw, L. W., and V. M. Mosley: Demonstration of striated fibers in the capsule of the Lisbonne strain of lysogenic *Escherichia coli*, *J. Bact.*, **67**:576, 1954.

——— and ———: Periodic structure in the flagella of *Brucella bronchiseptica*. *Biochim. Biophys. Acta*, **17**:322, 1955.

Lamanna, C.: The taxonomy of the genus *Bacillus*. I. Modes of spore germination, *J. Bact.*, **40**:347, 1940.

Lankford, C. E., H. Hoyo, and J. F. Lutteringer: Intracellular polysaccharide of *Enterobacteriaceae*, *J. Bact.*, **62**:621, 1951.

Lawrence, N. L.: The cleavage of adenosine by spores of *Bacillus cereus*, *J. Bact.*, **70**:577, 1955.

Leifson, E.: Staining, shape, and arrangement of bacterial flagella, *J. Bact.*, **62**:377, 1951.

———, S. R. Carhart, and Mac D. Fulton: Morphological characteristics of flagella of *Proteus* and related bacteria, *J. Bact.*, **69**:73, 1955.

——— and R. Hugh: Variation in shape and arrangement of bacterial flagella, *J. Bact.*, **65**:263, 1953.

Levinson, H. S., and M. T. Hyatt: The stimulation of germination and respiration of *Bacillus megaterium* spores by manganese, L-alanine and heat, *J. Bact.*, **70**:358, 1955.

——— and M. G. Sevag: Manganese and the proteolytic activity of spore extracts of *Bacillus megaterium* in relation to germination, *J. Bact.*, **67**:615, 1954.

———, J. D. Sloan, Jr., and M. T. Hyatt: Pyrophosphatase activity of *Bacillus megaterium* spore and vegetative cell extracts, *J. Bact.*, **75**:291, 1958.

Mason, D. J., and D. M. Powelson: Nuclear division as observed in live bacteria by a new technique, *J. Bact.*, **71**:474, 1956.

Mayall, B. H., and C. F. Robinow: Observations with the electron microscope on the organization of the cortex of resting and germinating spores of *B. megaterium*, *J. Appl. Bact.*, **20**:333, 1957.

McQuillen, K.: Capabilities of bacterial protoplasts. From "Bacterial Anatomy," edited by E. T. C. Spooner and B. A. D. Stocker, London, Cambridge University Press, 1956.

Millman, I.: Formation of protoplasts from mycobacteria by mycobacteriophage, *Proc. Soc. Exp. Biol. Med.*, **99**:216, 1958.

Mol, J. H. H.: The temperature characteristics of spore germination and growth of *Bacillus cereus*, *J. Appl. Bact.*, **20**:454, 1957.

Mudd, S., J. I. Payne, and T. Sall: Spore germination and sporogenesis in *Bacillus megaterium*, *J. Bact.*, **75**:118, 1958.

Murray, R. G. E.: Direct evidence for a cytoplasmic membrane in sectioned bacteria, *Can. J. Microbiol.*, **3**:531, 1957.

——— and R. H. Elder: The predominance of counterclockwise rotation during swarming of *Bacillus* species, *J. Bact.*, **58**:351, 1949.

Nickerson, W. J., and F. G. Sherman: II. Respiration of normal and filamentous cells of *Bacillus cereus*, *J. Bact.*, **64**:667, 1952.

Pennington, D.: The use of periodate in microbiological staining, *J. Bact.*, **57**:163, 1949.

Pijper, A.: Bacterial flagella and motility, *Ergeb. Mikrobiol. Immunitätsforsch. Exp. Ther.*, **30**:37, 1957.

Powell, J. F.: Biochemical changes occurring during spore germination in *Bacillus* species, *J. Appl. Bact.*, **20**:349, 1957.

———— and J. R. Hunter: Sporulation in distilled water, *J. Gen. Physiol.*, **36**:601, 1953.

Riemann, H.: Some observations on the germination of *Clostridium* spores and the subsequent delay before the commencement of vegetative growth, *J. Appl. Bact.*, **20**:404, 1957.

Rinker, J. N., and H. Koffler: Preliminary evidence that bacterial flagella are not "polysaccharide twirls," *J. Bact.*, **61**:421, 1951.

Robinow, C. F.: Cytological observations on *Bact. coli, Proteus vulgaris,* and various aerobic spore-forming bacteria with special reference to the nuclear structures, *J. Hyg.*, **43**:413, 1944.

————: The chromatin bodies of bacteria, *Bact. Rev.*, **20**:207, 1956*a*.

————: The chromatin bodies of bacteria. From "Bacterial Anatomy," edited by E. T. C. Spooner and B. A. D. Stocker, London, Cambridge University Press, 1956*b*.

Ross, K. F. A., and E. Billing: The water and solid content of living bacterial spores and vegetative cells as indicated by refractive index measurements, *J. Gen. Microbiol.*, **16**:418, 1957.

Roth, N. G., and D. H. Lively: Germination of spores of certain aerobic bacilli under anaerobic conditions, *J. Bact.*, **71**: 162, 1956.

————, ————, and H. M. Hodge: Influence of oxygen uptake and age of culture on sporulation of *Bacillus anthracis* and *Bacillus globigii*, *J. Bact.*, **69**:455, 1955.

————, ————, and S. N. Metcalfe, Jr.: Correlation of environmental and biological changes occurring in a complex medium during growth and sporulation of *Bacillus* species, *J. Bact.*, **75**:436, 1958.

Salton, M. R. J.: The nature of the cell walls of some Gram-positive and Gram-negative bacteria, *Biochim. Biophys. Acta*, **9**:334, 1952.

————: IV. The composition of the cell walls of some Gram-positive and Gram-negative bacteria, *Biochim. Biophys. Acta*, **10**:512, 1953.

————: Bacterial cell walls. From "Bacterial Anatomy," edited by E. T. C. Spooner and B. A. D. Stocker, London, Cambridge University Press, 1956.

Schaechter, M., A. J. Tousimis, Z. A. Cohn, H. Rosen, J. Campbell, and F. E. Hahn: Morphological, chemical and serological studies of the cell walls of *Rickettsia mooseri*, *J. Bact.*, **74**:822, 1957.

Shinn, L. E.: A cinematographic analysis of the motion of colonies of *B. alvei*, *J. Bact.*, **36**:419, 1938.

Sinkovics, J.: Occurrence and filterability of protoplast-like elements in aged bacterial cultures, *Nature*, **181**:566, 1958.

Smith, A. G.: Electron and light microscopic studies of bacterial nuclei, *J. Bact.*, **59**:575, 1950.

Smith, I. W.: Flagellation and motility in *Aerobacter cloacae* and *Escherichia coli*, *Biochim. Biophys. Acta*, **15**:20, 1954.

————, J. F. Wilkinson, and J. P. Duguid: Volutin production in *Aerobacter aerogenes* due to nutrient imbalance, *J. Bact.*, **68**:450, 1954.

Smithies, W. R., N. E. Gibbons, and S. T. Bayley: The chemical composition of the cell and cell wall of some halophilic bacteria, *Can. J. Microbiol.*, **1**:605, 1955.

Spiegelman, S., A. I. Aronson, and P. C. Fitz-James: Isolation and characterization of nuclear bodies from protoplasts of *Bacillus megaterium*, *J. Bact.*, **75**:102, 1958.

Stedman, R. L.: Biochemical aspects of bacterial endospore formation and germination, *Am. J. Pharm.*, **128**:84, 114, 1956.

————, E. Kravitz, M. Anmuth, and J. Harding: Autoinhibition of bacterial endospore germination, *Science*, **124**:403, 1956.

Stewart, B. T., and H. O. Halvorson: Studies on the spores of aerobic bacteria. I. The occurrence of alanine racemase, *J. Bact.*, **65**:160, 1953.

Stocker, B. A. D.: Bacterial flagella: morphology, constitution and inheritance. From "Bacterial Anatomy," edited by E. T. C. Spooner and B. A. D. Stocker, London, Cambridge University Press, 1956.

Strange, R. E.: Cell-wall lysis and the release of peptides in *Bacillus* species, *Bact. Rev.*, **23**:1, 1959.

———— and F. A. Dark: The composition of the spore coats of *Bacillus megatherium, B. subtilis* and *B. cereus*, *Biochem. J.*, **62**:459, 1956.

———— and ————: A cell wall lytic enzyme associated with spores of *Bacillus* species, *J. Gen. Microbiol.*, **16**:236, 1957.

Tanaka, S.: II. Technique for separation of bacterial cell wall and introduction of a new bacterial disintegrator, *Shikoku Acta Medica*, **10**:28, 1957.

Tawara, J.: Electron-microscopic study on the flagella of *Vibrio comma*, *J. Bact.*, **73**:89, 1957.

Thorne, C. B.: Capsule formation and glutamyl polypeptide synthesis by *Bacillus anthracis* and *Bacillus subtilis*. From "Bacterial Anatomy," edited by E. T. C. Spooner and B. A. D. Stocker, London, Cambridge University Press, 1956.

Tomcsik, J.: Bacterial capsules and their relation to the cell wall. From "Bacterial Anatomy," edited by E. T. C. Spooner and B. A. D. Stocker, London, Cambridge University Press, 1956.

———— and J. B. Grace: Bacterial cell walls as revealed by the specific cell-wall reaction and by direct staining with alcian blue, *J. Gen. Microbiol.*, **13**:105, 1955.

Treadwell, P. E., G. J. Jann, and A. J. Salle: Studies on factors affecting the rapid germination of spores of *Clostridium botulinum*, *J. Bact.*, **76**:549, 1958.

Trucco, R. E., and A. B. Pardee: Synthesis of *Escherichia coli* cell walls in the presence of penicillin, *J. Biol. Chem.*, **230**:435, 1958.

Turner, A. W., and C. E. Eales: An aerobic, sporulating bacillus that forms rotating and migrating colonies, *Australian J. Exp. Biol. Med. Sci.*, **19**:161, 1941*a*.

———— and ————: Motile daughter colonies in the *Cl. oedematiens* group and some other clostridia (*Cl. botulinum* C, *Cl. tetani*, *Cl. septicum*), *ibid.*, **19**:167, 1941*b*.

van den Hooff, A., and S. Aninga: An electron microscope study on the shape of the spores of *Bacillus polymyxa*, *Antonie van Leeuwenhoek*, **22**:327, 1956.

Webb, M.: Effects of magnesium on cellular division in bacteria, *Science*, **118**:607, 1953.

Weibull, C.: Some chemical and physicochemical properties of the flagella of *Proteus vulgaris*, *Biochim. Biophys. Acta*, **2**:351, 1948.

————: Chemical and physicochemical properties of the flagella of *Proteus vulgaris* and *Bacillus subtilis*, a comparison, *ibid.*, **3**:378, 1949.

————: The isolation of protoplasts from *Bacillus megaterium* by controlled treatment with lysozyme, *J. Bact.*, **66**:688, 1953.

————: Osmotic properties of protoplasts of *Bacillus megaterium*, *Exp. Cell. Res.*, **9**:294, 1955.

————: Bacterial protoplasts; their formation and characteristics. From "Bacterial Anatomy," edited by E. T. C. Spooner and B. A. D. Stocker, London, Cambridge University Press, 1956.

Weinberg, E. D.: The effect of Mn^{++} and antimicrobial drugs on sporulation of *Bacillus subtilis* in nutrient broth, *J. Bact.*, **70**:289, 1955.

Whitfield, J. F., and R. G. E. Murray: The effects of the ionic environment on the chromatin structures of bacteria, *Can. J. Microbiol.*, **2**:245, 1956.

Widra, A.: Metachromatic granules of microorganisms, *J. Bact.*, **78**:664, 1959.

Wilkinson, J. F.: The extracellular polysaccharides of bacteria, *Bact. Rev.*, **22**:46, 1958.

Winkler, A., and I. Tscheuschner: Zur Struktur der Oberfläche und Geiss der Sprillen, *Zentr. Bakt.* I Orig., **172**:397, 1958.

Wolf, J., and S. A. Z. Mahmoud: The germination and enzymic activities of *Bacillus* spores at low temperatures, *J. Appl. Bact.*, **20**:124, 1957.

Work, E.: Biochemistry of the bacterial cell wall, *Nature*, **179**:841, 1957.

Yoshida, N., et al.: XIII. Studies on the chemical composition of bacterial cell wall and spore membranes, *Tokushima J. Exp. Med.*, **3**:8, 1956.

Yuasa, A.: Nucleus and spindle of *Bacillus megatherium* in fission and sporulation, *Nature*, **177**:386, 1956.

Zinder, N. D., and W. F. Arndt: Production of protoplasts of *Escherichia coli* by lysozyme treatment, *Proc. Nat. Acad. Sci.*, **42**:586, 1956.

Zoha, S. M. S., and H. L. Sadoff: Production of spores by a putrefactive anaerobe, *J. Bact.*, **76**:203, 1958.

CHAPTER 5

Yeasts

The yeasts are spherical, ovoid, or rod-shaped ascomycetous fungi in which the usual and dominant growth is unicellular (Fig. 58). They are widely distributed in nature, being found in soil, in dust, and on fruits and leaves of many plants. The organisms are particularly numerous in the soils of orchards and vineyards. Yeasts appear as a surface froth or as a thick sediment in fruit juices, malt worts, and other saccharine liquids.

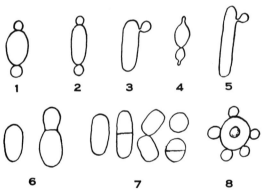

Fig. 58. Various types of yeast cells. 1, *Saccharomyces cerevisiae;* 2, *S. ellipsoideus;* 3, *S. pastorianus;* 4, *S. apicule;* 5, *Mycoderma;* 6, *Saccharomycodes;* 7, *Schizosaccharomyces;* 8, *Torula.* (*From Guilliermond's Clef dichotomique pour la détermination des levures, courtesy of Librairie le François, Paris.*)

It has been known for some time that numerous species of yeasts and yeast-like fungi will, under certain conditions, grow in the form of filaments or mycelia, whereas under other conditions they will grow in yeast phases. It is common to find occasional short chains of yeast phase cells in young, actively growing yeast cultures, but the designation of "filamentous" should not be made unless such growth becomes the usual morphology and is accompanied by cell elongation. There are thus two basic morphological types to be considered: the ellipsoidal or ovoid yeast-like cell and the elongated cell, the latter being elongated beyond that which

106

is the usual morphology. In this respect the yeasts differ from the molds, which are typically filamentous. On the other hand, some molds may grow temporarily as single cells and take on the appearance of yeasts. Some of the mucors grow as single cells capable of budding under reduced oxygen tensions. The organisms causing sporotrichosis, coccidioidal granuloma, and blastomycosis may appear as single cells in the tissues of the host, whereas mycelia develop on artificial culture media. Members of the genus *Monilia* grow as single cells on the surface of culture media exposed to air but develop mycelia under partial anaerobic conditions.

Filament formation in yeasts may be enhanced by controlling a number of environmental factors such as temperature, presence of certain nutritional substances, effect of carcinogenic chemicals, age of the culture, and irradiation.

The fact that molds display dimorphism has led some investigators to believe that the yeasts were at one time mold-like but have permanently lost the ability to produce mycelia. For example, the mold *Aspergillus oryzae*, when grown under a reduced oxygen environment, has been shown to give rise to yeast-like cells from the conidia that were submerged in the medium. The cells failed to revert to the mycelial stage but grew permanently as yeasts, even under aerobic conditions.

For more information see Hill and Gebhardt (1956), Scherr and Weaver (1953).

THE CYTOLOGY OF YEASTS

The structure of the yeast cell, according to Lindegren (1952), is shown in Fig. 59.

Cell Membranes. Special staining methods reveal the presence of a cytoplasmic membrane, which is surrounded by the cell wall. This mem-

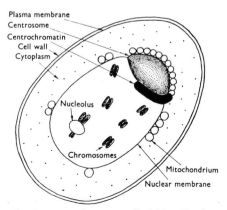

Fig. 59. Diagram of a yeast cell. (*After Lindegren.*)

brane corresponds in function to that found in the bacterial cell (see page 71). It is believed to function as a selectively permeable membrane in determining which substances may enter and leave the cell.

The cytoplasmic membrane is bounded by the cell wall. It is a delicate membrane that is relatively thin in young cells and becomes thicker as the cell ages. The cell wall is composed largely of a carbohydrate known as yeast cellulose although somewhat different from the cellulose found in the cell walls of higher plants.

Chitin is a nitrogenous compound closely related to the polysaccharides. Chemically it is a polymerized acetylated glucosamine. In plants it frequently occupies a corresponding position to cellulose in cell structure.

Chitin is present in the cell walls of molds, in the shells of crabs and lobsters, and in the shards of beetles. Roelofsen and Hoette (1951) reported the presence of chitin in the cell walls of 29 of 30 species of yeasts tested. There is still some question as to its presence in the cell walls of bacteria.

Falcone and Nickerson (1956) isolated an almost homogeneous structural entity of the yeast cell, consisting of a protein-mannan complex in the ratio of 1:12 by weight.

Capsules. The cell walls of some yeasts have been shown to be surrounded by a carbohydrate material similar to the capsular substance of bacteria. Mager (1947) isolated two carbohydrates from capsulated yeasts, notably *Torulopsis rotundata* and *T. neoformans.* One was found to be a zymohexose (starch), and the other a pentosan. The hexose in the zymohexose was shown to be glucose, and the pentose in the pentosan to be D-xylose.

The Cytoplasm and Its Contents. The cytoplasm is a clear fluid rich in ribonucleic acid (RNA). It contains the mitochondria, usually adhering to the surface of the centrosome or the nuclear membrane. The mitochondria contain RNA which may be coated with lipoid, and they vary in appearance from highly refractile lipoidal structures to less refractile organelles with somewhat irregular boundaries. The mitochondria may function as storage reservoirs in the insulation of essential substances inside an oily layer and may assist in establishing dormancy. Granular or fibrous deposits of glycogen may be present which sometimes spread through the entire cytoplasm. The cytoplasm is surrounded by the cytoplasmic membrane.

The Centrosome. This is a rigid structure which stains readily with acid dyes but not with basic dyes. It probably contains largely basic proteins. The centrosome is always attached to the nuclear membrane and plays a leading role in budding, copulation, and meiosis.

The Centrochromatin. This structure is acid in reaction and is attached to the external surface of the centrosome, with some portion of it always in contact with the nucleus. In the resting cell, it may cover most of the centrosome; in division, it is usually present in the form of a long strand.

The Nucleus and Its Contents. Yeast cells differ from the true bacteria in being usually much larger and in possessing well-defined nuclei. The nucleus is difficult to see in hanging-drop preparations but may be seen in stained smears. It contains the chromosomes and the nucleolus. The chromosomes are partitioned between mother cell and bud in a precise and orderly manner without recourse to a spindle. The wall of the nucleus does not break down at any time in the life cycle. It is a permanent cellular structure.

It is well established that the nucleus of yeasts and higher organisms consists largely of nucleoprotein. A nucleoprotein is a high-molecular-weight compound consisting of nucleic acid in combination with a protein. Since nucleic acid is acid in character, it is combined with a basic protein, probably a histone or a protamine. The protamines are proteins that are formed from a few amino acids only, and these are mainly the basic amino acids, arginine, lysine, and histidine. The histones are similar to the protamines but contain a lower concentration of the basic amino acids. A nucleic acid molecule is believed to consist of an unknown number of tetranucleotide units. On hydrolysis each tetranucleotide yields four molecules of phosphoric acid, four molecules of a pentose sugar, two purine bases, and two pyrimidine bases (see page 667).

Two types of nucleic acids have been isolated from living cells, namely, ribonucleic acid (RNA) and desoxyribonucleic acid (DNA). RNA occurs largely in the cytoplasm with smaller amounts in the nucleus; DNA appears to exist entirely within the nucleus.

Vacuoles. Vacuoles are cavities in the protoplasm; they are especially characteristic of plant cells and protozoa but occur also in the cells of higher animals. In plant cells, the vacuoles contain a fluid known as the cell sap, which is commonly an aqueous solution of various organic acids and their salts. In protozoa, they may contain secretions of the protoplasm or substances about to be excreted, or food in various stages of digestion and assimilation.

Granules. The cell contents of yeasts are more clearly differentiated than those of bacteria. Young cells have a very thin cell wall and a relatively homogeneous cytoplasm. As the cells become older, granules and vacuoles appear. The granules in yeast cells consist of metachromatic granules, or volutin, and glycogen. In addition, fat globules are also present.

Metachromatic Granules. Metachromatic granules, or volutin, are widely distributed in fungi and constitute the most important elements found in yeasts. These granules are located almost exclusively in the vacuoles. They are also present in the cytoplasm that surrounds the vacuoles. The granules probably originate in the cytoplasm and localize in the vacuoles later. In old cells, the metachromatic granules may appear in relatively large masses. The granules appear as refractive bodies in unstained preparations and show a great affinity for basic dyes, revealing their acid character.

The granules appear to be composed of metaphosphate or another form of inorganic phosphate, some fat, and possibly small amounts of protein. The granules can be extracted by perchloric and trichloracetic acid. Their presence and size in cells are related to the phosphate concentration of the growth medium in the presence of an energy source and specific divalent ions (Mn and Zn). Older cells possess larger granules. Their basophilic nature does not depend on either ribonucleic acid or desoxyribonucleic acid.

Glycogen. Glycogen is a white, amorphous carbohydrate related to starch and dextrin. It is hydrolyzed to glucose on boiling with dilute mineral acids, and also by the action of amylolytic enzymes. Glycogen is easily recognized by the brown color produced on the addition of a dilute solution of iodine. The color disappears when the solution is heated to 60°C. and reappears when it cools.

Glycogen has been shown to be abundant in well-nourished yeast cells and to disappear during starvation. The concentration increases with age and reaches a maximum after 48 hr. Glycogen is usually localized in the vacuoles distinct from those which contain the metachromatic granules. It accumulates in the asci during sporulation and is absorbed by the spores during their maturity.

Glycogen is believed to be a reserve food material that accumulates in old cells after activity ceases. It disappears when old cells are placed in a new medium and reappears again as the cells increase in age.

Fat. Fat globules of variable size are distributed throughout the cytoplasm of yeast cells. They stain brown with osmic acid. Fat globules are prominent in yeast cells, especially during sporulation, and serve as food for the ascospores. They are considered to be reserve food material.

White and Werkman (1948) reported the following conditions under which relatively large and reproducible increases in the fat content of cells of *Saccharomyces cerevisiae* could be obtained.

1. Cells were grown in an appropriate medium at 30°C. for 24 hr.
2. Cells were harvested by means of a Sharples centrifuge and suspended in a phosphate buffer of pH 7.0 containing acetate. Under such conditions the cells no longer proliferated.
3. The suspension of nonproliferating cells was aerated for 24 hr. During this period the acetate was converted into fat and stored in the cells.

For more information see Agar and Douglas (1957), Klein (1955), Klein and Booher (1955), Lindegren and Townsend (1954), Townsend and Lindegren (1953), Winge (1951), Yuasa and Lindegren (1959).

MULTIPLICATION IN YEASTS

Yeasts multiply by budding, fission, asexual spore formation, copulation or sexual reproduction, and parthenogenesis. However, the usual type of multiplication is by budding. Sometimes thick-walled cells known as chlamydospores are produced. Since only one spore is produced in a cell, this is not a means of increasing the numbers of yeast cells but a method of perpetuating the species.

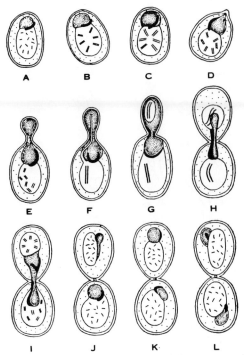

Fig. 60. Multiplication by budding. See text for description. (*After Lindegren.*)

Budding. Multiplication by budding is observed in almost all of the yeasts (Fig. 60). Budding occurs after the organism acquires a certain size. At the first step in budding (Fig. 60D), the centrosome produces a small conical process which forces its way through the cytoplasm and erupts into a new bud (Fig. 60E). The nuclear vacuole puts out a process which enters the bud (Fig. 60F). The bud vacuole finally receives the chromosome complex, after which the connection between the bud and mother vacuole is closed off (Fig. 60G). Cytoplasm passes into the bud, followed by the centrochromatin, which travels along the elongated centrosome (Fig. 60H). The centrochromatin divides transversely, and the mother and daughter cells are held together by a plug of centrosomal material which makes up the bud scar (Fig. 60I). This plug remains at the junction of the bud and mother cells after the bud and mother centrosome have separated (Fig. 60J,K,L). After budding is completed, the nuclei in bud and mother cells reorient themselves so that the centrosome of each is distal to the point of connection between the two cells.

During periods of rapid division, buds may be formed at different points on the surface of the cell. The daughter cells likewise bud at dif-

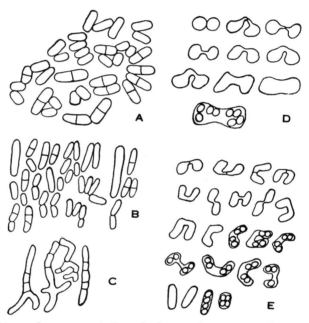

Fig. 61. *Schizosaccharomyces. A, B,* multiplication by transverse fission; *C,* mycelial growth; *D, E,* formation of asci by isogamic copulation. (*From Guilliermond's Clef dichotomique pour la détermination des levures, courtesy of Librairie le François, Paris.*)

ferent points before separation from the mother cell. This results in the formation of a small colony or a chain of yeast cells.

For more information see Agar and Douglas (1955); Hashimoto, Conti, and Naylor (1959); Lindegren, Williams, and McClary (1956).

Transverse Fission. In a few species, multiplication occurs by transverse fission. These yeasts resemble the bacteria in their mode of division.

In *Schizosaccharomyces octosporus,* the spherical or ovoid-shaped cells elongate to a certain size, then form cross walls in the middle. The two cells pull apart, and the ends become rounded. When the two new cells reach maturity, they elongate and repeat the cycle. During periods of rapid multiplication, cells may divide without separating. In this manner a chain of cells is produced, resembling a mycelium, which eventually breaks apart (Fig. 61).

In the genus *Saccharomyces*, a form of division intermediate between budding and fission occurs. Buds are generally produced at the extremities of the cells. The cells first elongate, then a tube puffs out at one end.

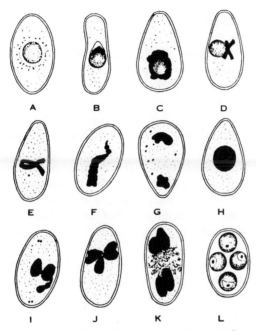

Fig. 62. Sporulation. *A*, unstained cell showing centrally located nuclear vacuole with enlarged centrosome above the vacuole. The latter is surrounded by mitochrondria. *B*, stained cell showing shrunken nuclear vacuole and large centrosome with closely applied chromatin. *C*, cell with large centrosome and conspicuous chromatin complex closely applied to centrosome. Nuclear vacuole not visible. *D*, centrosome with two associated double chromatin rods. Vacuole not visible. *E, F*, paired chromatic strands, probably representing two chromosome complexes. *G*, chromosome complexes separated. *H*, centrosome completely covered with chromatin. *I, J*, division of the chromatin. *K*, division of chromatin completed. *L*, four spores in an ascus, each with a vacuole and darkly stained centrosome. (*After Lindegren.*)

This enlarges and is slowly transformed into a bud, which remains attached to the cell by a collar. Finally a wall is formed which separates the cell from the bud.

Asexual Spore Formation. Although budding is the usual process of multiplication in yeasts, such a method does not perpetuate the species. The usual process for perpetuating the species is by spore formation, which is a form of resistance that permits yeast cells to remain viable after budding has stopped.

According to Lindegren (1952), sporulation may be induced by growing the yeast on a special agar medium, then transferring the cells to the surface of a plaster of Paris block moistened with dilute acetic acid (Fig. 62). On the presporulation medium the cells accumulate enormous reserves of fat and glycogen. The fat is stored on the mitochondria, and the glycogen in the cytoplasm. The nucleus and centrosome assume a central position in the cell in contrast to the eccentric arrangement of the centrosome in the budding cell.

There are at least four pairs of chromosomes which segregate regularly at meiosis. During meiosis, it is believed the chromatin divides first into two long bands, then these divide again to form four structures. At this point neither centrosome nor nuclear vacuole is visible.

At the onset of sporulation the nuclear vacuole becomes indistinct and is not observed clearly again until the spores are fully formed. The most prominent structure in the cell is the chromatin, which occupies a central position in the cell and may be clumped in various patterns around the centrosome. At this stage the chromosomes cannot be distinguished from the chromatin of the centrosome. The chromatin may be arranged over the surface of the centrosome, or it may be at one side, or may surround it completely. Neither the centrosome nor the nuclear vacuole is clearly distinguishable, and the chromatin lies in two or four long granular strands, with the granules of the different strands apparently paired (Fig. 62).

A definite number of spores is usually produced in the cells of each species. The cells bearing spores are called asci (singular, ascus), and the spores are known as ascospores. In the majority of species four spores are produced in a cell. In other species the number in a cell may be one, two, or less frequently, eight.

For more information see Santa Maria (1957).

Sexual Reproduction or Copulation. Sexual multiplication occurs by (1) isogamic copulation, (2) heterogamic copulation, (3) a form of copulation intermediate between isogamy and heterogamy, and (4) copulation of ascospores.

Isogamic Copulation. Isogamic copulation may be defined as the fusion of two similar gametes. *Schizosaccharomyces octosporus* is an example of a yeast that reproduces in this manner. Two cells lying adjacent in a colony are joined by a copulation canal (Fig. 63). The two cells are now known as gametes. The wall that separates the two cells quickly disappears and the nucleus of each passes into the copulation canal. This results in the formation of a single cell or zygospore. The zygospore increases in size, followed by a division of the nucleus. The nuclei become surrounded with cytoplasm, around which are formed the spore walls. The zygospore now becomes an ascus.

Fusion of nuclear material occurs first between the centrosomes (Fig.

64A), which apparently project through the cell walls at the point of contact of the copulating gametes. Next, there is an interchange of cytoplasm between the copulants (Fig. 64B). The strands of centrochromatin from each cell travel along the centrosome to fuse, each retaining contact with its respective nuclear vacuole. Simultaneously, one or both nuclear

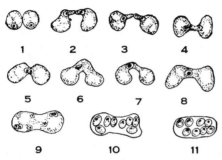

FIG. 63. *Schizosaccharomyces octosporus*. Isogamic copulation of two cells to form an ascus containing eight ascospores. (*From Guilliermond-Tanner, "The Yeasts," John Wiley & Sons, Inc.*)

vacuoles send out processes which also fuse, joining both vacuoles into a single one. The chromosomes pass into the vacuole, which is in contact with fused centrochromatins (Fig. 64C) and pair up (Fig. 64D). The zygospore produces a hybrid diploid bud.

In S. *pombe*, copulation occurs as in S. *octosporus*, except that fusion

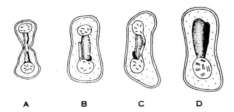

FIG. 64. Isogamic copulation. A, a pair of copulating cells with the centrosomes fused. The centrochromatin elongated preparatory to union. B, incomplete zygote. Centrochromatin fused. Nuclear vacuole putting out a process preparatory to fusion. C, fusion of vacuoles complete. D, completed zygote with chromosomes paired in common nuclear vacuole. (*After Lindegren.*)

usually remains incomplete. Copulation occurs between two adjacent cells in the same colony. The gametes are joined by a canal through which nuclear and protoplasmic fusion occurs. The nucleus resulting from the fusion quickly divides, and the two nuclei migrate to both enlargements of the zygospore. The nuclei undergo a second division, resulting in the formation of four spores. The zygospore becomes an ascus, and the spores are known as ascospores (Fig. 65).

Heterogamic Copulation. Heterogamic copulation may be defined as the fusion of two unlike gametes (Fig. 66). The ascus that develops is composed of two unequal enlargements, the larger representing the mother cell and the other the bud. Because of lack of space in the bud, the spores develop in the mother cell.

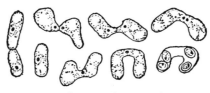

FIG. 65. *Schizosaccharomyces pombe.* Copulation and incomplete fusion of two cells to form an ascus containing four ascospores. (*Reprinted from Guilliermond-Tanner, "The Yeasts," John Wiley & Sons, Inc.*)

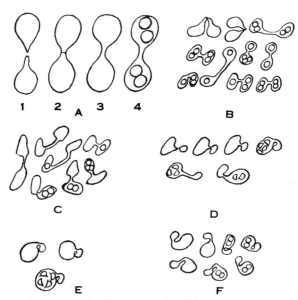

FIG. 66. *Zygosaccharomyces. A, B,* ascus produced by isogamic copulation; *D, E, F,* ascus produced by heterogamic copulation; *C,* ascus produced by copulation intermediate between isogamic and heterogamic. (*From Guilliermond's Clef dichotomique pour la détermination des levures, courtesy of Librairie le François, Paris.*)

In the genus *Nadsonia,* copulation occurs by heterogamy between an adult cell and one of its buds (Fig. 67). After the two cells fuse, the contents of the male gamete or bud pass into the female gamete or mother cell. A new cell then forms by budding, and the contents of the mother cell pass into it. This new cell now becomes an ascus, and it usually contains a single ascospore.

Intermediate Form of Copulation. A rare form of copulation, intermediate between isogamy and heterogamy, has been observed. In these yeasts the two cells or gametes are of the same size and do not show any sexual differentiation. After fusion takes place, the contents of one cell pass into the other. The former may be regarded as the male cell and

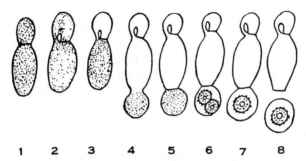

FIG. 67. *Nadsonia.* Formation of an ascus by heterogamic copulation. (*From Guilliermond's Clef dichotomique pour la détermination des levures, courtesy of Librairie le François, Paris.*)

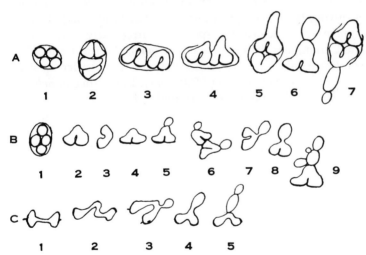

FIG. 68. Conjugation of ascospores. A, *Saccharomycodes ludwigii*; B, *Saccharomyces johannisbergensis*; C, *Hansenula saturnus.* (*From Guilliermond's Clef dichotomique pour la détermination des levures, courtesy of Librairie le François, Paris.*)

the latter as the female cell. The ascospores originate from the female cell and are usually two in number (Fig. 66).

Copulation of Ascospores. In some species, such as in *Saccharomycodes ludwigii*, *S. johannisbergensis*, and *Hansenula saturnus*, an isogamic copulation occurs between the ascospores produced in an ascus (Fig. 68). In the species *S. ludwigii*, an ascus usually contains four spores.

The spores copulate in pairs and are joined by a canal. The nuclear material fuses, resulting in the formation of a zygospore. However, the fusion remains incomplete. The zygospore elongates into a germination tube, from which develop numerous vegetative cells by budding.

Copulation occurs normally between two spores in the same ascus. It has also been observed between ascospores from different asci and even those more distantly related. This may be observed in old asci where many of the spores are dead. Some of the spores can germinate alone; others must fuse in pairs before germination can occur. This means that some of the spores in the latter group are forced to fuse with spores from different asci. The fusion of ascospores is not regarded as a true copulation but as a new process that takes the place of normal sexual fertilization.

Shapes of Spores. Yeast spores assume various shapes (Fig. 69), and some species may be easily recognized by this character. Yeast spores are usually spherical or ovoid. Such spores are found in *Saccharomyces cerevisiae*, the common bread or beer yeast, and in other lesser-known species. The spores in *Hansenula anomala* and in the genus *Hanseniaspora* are hemispherical, and their adjacent surfaces are provided with a projecting border, giving them the appearance of a hat (Fig. 69B). In the species *Pichia membranaefaciens*, the spores are irregularly shaped into ovoid, elongated, triangular, kidney-shaped, or hemispherical forms (Fig. 69C). Cells of *Hansenula saturnus* produce spores that are lemon-shaped and surrounded by a projecting ring (Fig. 69D). In the species *Schwanniomyces occidentalis*, the spores are surrounded by a projecting ring and the membrane is covered with stiff, erect protuberances (Fig. 69E). The spores of *Debaryomyces* are globular and also covered with protuberances (Fig. 69F). Other shapes are shown in Fig. 69G,H,I.

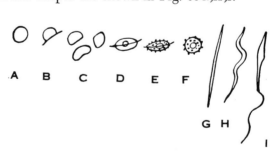

Fig. 69. Various types of ascospores. (*From Guilliermond's Clef dichotomique pour la détermination des levures, courtesy of Librairie le François, Paris.*)

Parthenogenesis. This term may be defined as the development of an organism from an unfertilized cell. Parthenogenesis is a modification of ordinary sexual reproduction and is not to be confused with asexual multiplication.

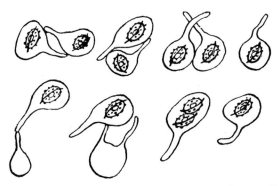

FIG. 70. *Schwanniomyces.* Asci with ascospores. (*From Guilliermond's Clef dichotomique pour la détermination des levures, courtesy of Librairie le François, Paris.*)

In some yeasts, sexuality has not been observed. These yeasts represent parthenogenetic forms derived from primitive sex cells. If the development of an ascus is not the result of copulation, it represents a gamete that has developed by pathenogenesis.

In the *Schwanniomyces,* the cells forming the asci produce projections of different lengths, which attempt to fuse together as in true copulation (Fig. 70). However, fusion fails to occur, and it appears that the cells have retained only a portion of their sexual characteristics. This same phenomenon has been observed in the *Torulaspora* (Fig. 71) and in other yeasts.

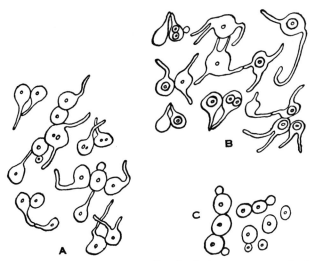

FIG. 71. *Torulaspora.* (*From Guilliermond's Clef dichotomique pour la détermination des levures, courtesy of Librairie le François, Paris.*)

Chlamydospores. Under unfavorable conditions, yeast cells stop multiplying. When this occurs, some cells become filled with reserve food materials, such as fat and glycogen granules, and enclose themselves in a thick wall. These cells are known as durable cells or chlamydospores. When a chlamydospore is placed in a favorable environment, it germinates into a vegetative cell, which multiplies by the usual method of budding. This is sometimes referred to as a method of reproduction. Since only one chlamydospore is formed in a cell, it should not be considered a method of reproduction but rather a method for perpetuating the species.

HAPLOID AND DIPLOID YEASTS

Genes are factors concerned with the transmission and development or determination of hereditary characters. A gene makes up a small part of a chromosome. Haploid yeasts have a single set of genes, whereas the diploid yeasts possess two complete sets of genes.

Haploid yeasts are capable of fusing in pairs to produce diploid yeasts. According to Lindegren (1944), there are two mating types or "sexes" of haploid yeasts, and one haploid cell of one "sex" can fuse with another haploid cell of the opposite "sex" to produce a diploid cell of the type known as a legitimate diploid or *heterozygous* cell. In heterozygous diploids the paired genes in one or more pairs are different from each other, as contrasted to *homozygous* diploids, in which both members of every pair of genes are identical. An "illegitimately" diploid, homozygous cell is formed when fusion occurs between two haploid cells of the same "sex." Most bakers', brewers', and distillers' yeasts which we have examined are illegitimately diploid strains. They were probably produced from wild yeasts by the chance selection of single ascospore cultures homozygous for some desirable modifier of a gene affecting some chemical stage of the fermentation process. Their high stability impressed the manufacturer and led to their selection.

The sexual mechanism of yeasts suggests the possibility of producing many new varieties. For example, no natural yeast is capable of fermenting both lactose and maltose. Some can ferment one and some the other, but none can ferment both. It is conceivable that, if a haploid lactose-fermenter were mated with a haploid maltose-fermenter, the hybrid could ferment both.

Saccharomyces cerevisiae exists in both haploid and diploid forms. The ordinary vegetative cells are diploid, but under certain conditions, diploid cells become converted into asci containing four haploid ascospores. The ascospores germinate to produce four different haploid cultures which are generally easily distinguishable from the diploid cultures.

Lindegren and Lindegren (1943) showed that cultures of the haploid cells, when paired, will copulate to produce diploid cells, provided the haploid cells are of the opposite sexes. The haploid ascospores from the four-spored ascus were designated A, B, C, and D, and the haplophase cultures from them were paired in all possible combinations. They found that A and D belonged to the same mating type, B and C to the complementary type. Copulation tubes and zygotes were produced when A & B, A & C, D & B, and D & C were paired.

A & D
B & C

A & B, A & C, D & B, D & C

When placed in a sporing medium, the diploid cells produced four-spored asci, whereas the A & D and B & C combinations failed to produce spores. Thousands of experiments have confirmed the fact that there are two mating types in *Saccharomyces cerevisiae*. Lindegren designated these different mating types as *a* and *α*. An interpretation of the mating phenomena is schematically represented in Fig. 72. The large diploid zygotes are readily recognized as *S. cerevisiae*, whereas different stabilized haploid cultures are indistinguishable from *Torula* or *Zygosaccharomyces*, depending upon their characteristic morphology.

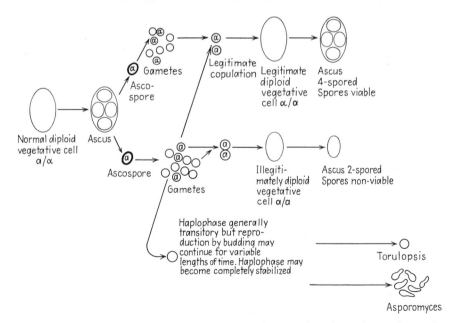

Fig. 72. Life cycle of *Saccharomyces cerevisiae*, showing the relationship with *Torula* and *Zygosaccharomyces*. The ascospores belong to two mating types, *a* and *α*, and the heterozygote is the legitimate diploid. The homozygotes are called illegitimate diploids. (*After Lindegren.*)

To quote from Lindegren (1944),

The legitimate diploids are heterozygous for the a/α genes, while the illegitimate diploids are homozygous, being either aa or $\alpha\alpha$. Legitimately diploid vegetative cells sporulate to produce four haploid ascospores. These ascospores can be separated from each other and each can multiply to produce a culture of haploid cells. Haploid cells are capable of acting as gametes or sex cells. When two of these gametes of opposite sex fuse, a legitimately diploid heterozygous vegetative cell is produced. These cells are generally quite vigorous. When conditions are favorable for sporulation, they produce four spores in each cell. When fusion occurs between two gametes of the same sex, derived from the same ascospore, an illegitimately diploid homozygous cell is formed. This type of cell is often as capable of growth and fermentation as the legitimate diploid, and some illegitimate diploids have some very desirable industrial characteristics. However, illegitimate diploids are often smaller and usually do not produce viable ascospores, and the asci are generally two-spored.

In Fig. 72, the mating types of the haplophase cells are designated as a and α, and cells of each specific mating type are indicated by letter. Diplophase cultures from nature are generally heterozygous for the a/α mating type of genes and are marked a/α in the diagram. Diploid cultures, homozygous for a or α (aa or $\alpha\alpha$), tend to be less vigorous in regard to growth rate, dry weight, yield, and ascospore viability than the a/α heterozygotes.

The superiority of the heterozygote and its normal occurrence in nature has led us to call it a legitimate diploid, while the homozygotes, with their poorly viable spores, have been called illegitimate diploids.

HYBRIDIZATION

A hybrid may be defined as a new organism developed from two cells of different species or different genetic make-up.

Winge and Laustsen (1938, 1939) showed that it is possible to breed new varieties of yeasts by hybridization. They placed two spores of opposite sexes from different species in a drop of culture solution to enable them to copulate. A zygospore was formed from which the hybrid yeast germinated. They succeeded in producing 14 new yeast types from 8 different species and strains of *Saccharomyces* and one of *Zygosaccharomyces*.

Lindegren (1944, 1945, 1949) and Lindegren and Lindegren (1943, 1945) also succeeded in hybridizing yeast spores from different species or strains. They developed a number of new yeast strains strong in characteristics required for special needs or purposes.

While this procedure is in itself very intricate, the even bigger problem is to determine which spore cultures have the specific characteristics required to meet a certain need. The outline drawings in Fig. 73 illustrate four steps in the process of hybridization.

Step 1. Yeast cells from two strains (strains A and B) are shown after they have been induced to form spores. The spores are removed by microdissection by means of a micromanipulator.

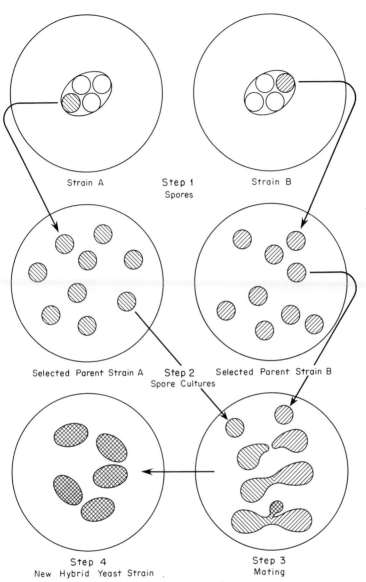

Strain A Step 1 Strain B
Spores

Selected Parent Strain A Step 2 Selected Parent Strain B
Spore Cultures

Step 4 Step 3
New Hybrid Yeast Strain Mating

FIG. 73. Four steps in the process of hybridization. See text for description. (*Courtesy of Anheuser-Busch, Inc.*)

Step 2. Each individual spore is planted into a nutrient medium and allowed to multiply to produce separate spore cultures. After careful testing for the desirable characteristics, two spore cultures of different sexes are selected for mating or cross-breeding.

Step 3. When these two spore cultures are brought together, instead of budding they fuse in pairs and produce a completely new yet stable combination of inherited qualities.

Step 4. The new hybrid strain shown is a combination of the best qualities of strains A and B. The new hybrid grows and reproduces by budding. As it grows, the new inherited qualities are equally transmitted to all cells reproduced.

In Fig. 74, five stages are shown in the use of the microtool for cutting the cell

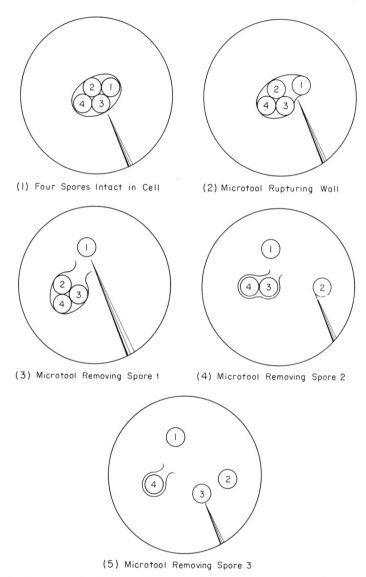

(1) Four Spores Intact in Cell   (2) Microtool Rupturing Wall

(3) Microtool Removing Spore 1   (4) Microtool Removing Spore 2

(5) Microtool Removing Spore 3

Fig. 74. Five stages in the microdissection of yeast spores. See text for description. (*Courtesy of Anheuser-Busch, Inc.*)

wall of an ascus and removing the individual spores. It consists of a high-powered microscope combined with a manipulator that reduces hand movements several thousandfold. When the operator moves a handle $\frac{1}{4}$ in., the micro-needle moves less than $\frac{1}{10,000}$ in.

For more information see Lindegren and Lindegren (1954), Wickerham and Burton (1956a, b), Winge (1952a, b, 1955), Winge and Roberts (1954a, b, 1955).

CLASSIFICATION OF YEASTS

Yeasts have been classified with difficulty, and considerable confusion still exists. The classification given here is taken from the works of Stelling-Dekker (1931), Guilliermond (1928, 1937), and Phaff and Mrak (1948).

Ascosporogenous Yeasts

Family. *Endomycetaceae.* Growth forms mycelium, pseudomycelium, oidia, or yeast cells, together or singly. Multiplication by transverse fission or budding. Asci produced by isogamic or heterogamic copulation or by parthenogenesis. Ascospores spherical, hemispherical, angular, sickle- or spindle-shaped, smooth, warty, or with a projecting border.

Subfamily I. *Eremascoideae.* Growth form entirely mycelial. Multiplication by transverse fission. Spores hat-shaped and formed by isogamic copulation.

Genus. *Eremascus.* Growth form entirely mycelial. Multiplication by fission. Budding not observed. Asci produced by isogamic copulation, and contain eight round ascospores.

Subfamily II. *Endomycoideae.* Growth form either mycelium with oidia or oidia only. Multiplication by transverse fission. Asci formed by isogamic or heterogamic copulation.

Genus I. *Endomyces.* Growth form true mycelium with oidia. Asci formed by heterogamic copulation and contain four spherical or hat-shaped spores.

Genus II. *Schizosaccharomyces.* Oidia formed without mycelium. Multiplication by transverse fission. Asci formed by isogamic copulation and contain four to eight round spores (Figs. 63 and 65).

Subfamily III. *Saccharomycoideae.* Growth form either mycelium with conidial buds and occasionally oidia or only budding yeast cells. Multiplication by transverse fission or budding. Spores spherical, hemispherical angular, or sickle-shaped, or with a projecting border. Asci formed by isogamic or heterogamic copulation or by parthenogenesis. Subfamily divided into three tribes.

Tribe I. *Endomycopseae.* Growth form mycelium with conidial buds, occasionally oidia. Multiplication by transverse fission and by multipolar budding. Ascospores hat-shaped, sickle-shaped, or with a projecting border, and produced by isogamic copulation or by parthenogenesis.

FIG. 75. *Saccharomyces.* Asci and ascospores. A, *S. cerevisiae;* B, *S. ellipsoideus;* C, *S. pastorianus.* (*From Guilliermond's Clef dichotomique pour la détermination des levures, courtesy of Librairie le François, Paris.*)

Genus III. *Endomycopsis.* Growth form mycelium with conidial buds, occasionally oidia. Multiplication by transverse fission and by multipolar budding. Ascospores hemispherical, oval, sickle-shaped, smooth, warty, or with a projecting border, and produced by isogamic copulation or by parthenogenesis.

Tribe II. *Saccharomyceteae.* Growth form yeast cells, no mycelium. Multiplication by multipolar budding. Ascospores produced by isogamic or heterogamic copulation or by parthenogenesis. Spores variously shaped.

Genus IV. *Saccharomyces.* Cells spherical, ovoid, or elongated. Ascospores produced by isogamic or heterogamic copulation or by parthenogenesis. Asci contain one to four spherical, smooth ascospores. Spores germinate by budding (Fig. 75).

Genus V. *Zygosaccharomyces.* Cells spherical, ovoid, or elongated. Asci formed by isogamic or heterogamic copulation or by a process intermediate between the two. Asci contain one to four ascospores (Fig. 66).

Genus VI. *Torulaspora.* Cells spherical, with a large fat globule in the center. Asci show a trace of copulation by development of projections, but union does not occur. Asci produced by parthenogenesis and contain one or two spherical, smooth spores (Fig. 71).

Genus VII. *Pichia.* Cells ovoid or elongated. Sexual process uncertain. Asci contain one to four spherical, hemispherical, or triangular spores (Fig. 76).

Genus VIII. *Zygopichia.* Cells ovoid or elongated. Asci formed by isogamic or heterogamic copulation or by parthenogenesis. Asci contain one to four spherical, hemispherical, or triangular spores.

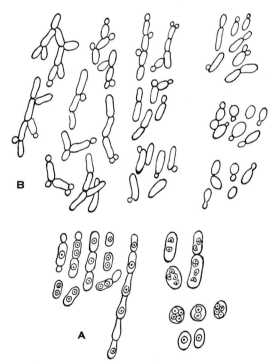

Fig. 76. *Pichia. A,* asci and ascospores; *B,* budding cells. (*From Guilliermond's Clef dichotomique pour la détermination des levures, courtesy of Librairie le François, Paris.*)

Genus IX. *Hansenula.* Cells ovoid or elongated, occasionally spherical. Asci formed by parthenogenesis and contain two to four lemon- or hat-shaped spores (Fig. 77).

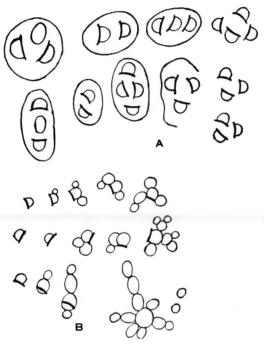

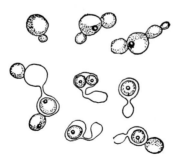

FIG. 77. *Hansenula.* A, asci and ascospores; B, germination of ascospores by budding. (*From Guilliermond's Clef dichotomique pour la détermination des levures, courtesy of Librairie le François, Paris.*)

FIG. 78. *Debaryomyces.* (*Reprinted from Guilliermond-Tanner, "The Yeasts," John Wiley & Sons, Inc.*)

Genus X. *Zygohansenula.* Cells ovoid or elongated, occasionally spherical. Asci formed by isogamic or heterogamic copulation and contain two to four lemon-shaped spores.

Genus XI. *Debaryomyces.* Cells spherical or ovoid. Asci formed by isogamic or heterogamic copulation and contain one or two rough spores (Fig. 78).

Genus XII. *Schwanniomyces*. Cells spherical or ovoid, occasionally show rudimentary mycelia. Asci formed by parthenogenesis and contain one or two spores provided with a projecting collar and with a verrucose wall (Fig. 70).

Tribe III. *Nadsonieae*. Growth form yeast cells, no mycelium. Multiplication by bipolar budding. Ascospores produced by heterogamic copulation or by parthenogenesis.

Genus XIII. *Saccharomycodes*. Cells lemon-shaped and show bipolar budding. Asci formed by heterogamic copulation and contain four spherical, smooth spores. Spores conjugate on germination (Fig. 68).

For additional information see Hjort (1954).

Genus XIV. *Hanseniaspora*. Cells lemon-shaped and show bipolar budding. Asci produced by parthenogenesis and contain two to four smooth, round to hat-shaped spores (Fig. 79).

Fig. 79. *Hanseniaspora*. A, cells; B, C, asci and ascospores. (*From Guilliermond's Clef dichotomique pour la détermination des levures, courtesy of Librairie le François, Paris.*)

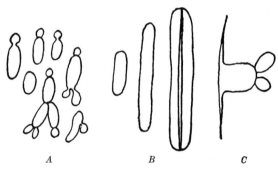

Fig. 80. *Monosporella*. A, budding cells; B, ascus with one ascospore; C, germination of ascospore by budding. (*From Guilliermond's Clef dichotomique pour la détermination des levures, courtesy of Librairie le François, Paris.*)

Genus XV. *Nadsonia*. Cells spherical ovoid, ellipsoidal, or lemon-shaped. Asci produced by heterogamic copulation between a bud and the mother cell. One or two, sometimes up to four spherical, verrucose spores produced in each ascus (Fig. 67).

Subfamily IV. *Nematosporoideae*. Growth form mycelium and budding yeast cells. Multiplication by isogamic copulation. Spores needle-shaped, with or without appendages.

Genus XVI. *Monosporella*. Cells ovoid-shaped. Multiplication by budding and by isogamic copulation. Asci contain one needle-shaped spore (Fig. 80).

Genus XVII. *Nematospora*. Cells oval, long, irregular, or mycelium-like. Multiplication by budding. Asci produced by parthenogenesis and contain four or more spindle-shaped spores with appendage (Fig. 81).

Genus XVIII. *Coccidiascus.* Cells spherical or ovoid-shaped and multiply by budding. Asci produced by isogamic copulation and contain eight spindle-shaped, nonflagellated spores (Fig. 82).

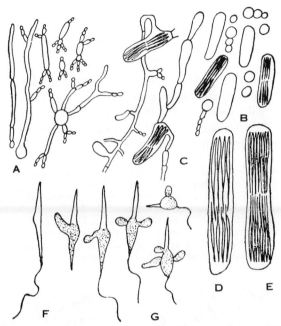

FIG. 81. *Nematospora.* A, mycelial growth; B, C, formation of asci; D, E, asci filled with 8 or 16 ascospores; F, G, germination of ascospores. (*From Guilliermond's Clef dichotomique pour la détermination des levures, courtesy of Librairie le François, Paris.*)

FIG. 82. *Coccidiascus.* Ascus produced by isogamic copulation. Four ascospores in each ascus. (*From Guilliermond's Clef dichotomique pour la détermination des levures, courtesy of Librairie le François, Paris.*)

Saccharomyces. This genus contains almost all the species of industrial importance and is by far the most important group of yeasts. The cells are spherical, ovoid, or elongated. Asci are formed by isogamic or heterogamic copulation or by parthenogenesis and contain one to four spherical, smooth spores.

The most important species is *S. cerevisiae*, the common yeast used by bakers, brewers, and distillers. It is the same species that is extensively employed therapeutically as a natural source of vitamins of the B complex.

Asporogenous Yeasts

The term torulae (singular, torula) is generally applied to the species of yeasts that are not capable of producing spores. They are sometimes called false or wild yeasts. Will (1916) placed all the nonsporing yeasts in the family Torulaceae, and Lodder (1934) recognized two families and a provisional third family containing a single doubtful genus.

Family I. *Rhodotorulaceae*. Produce carotenoid pigments, colonies being yellow, orange, pink, or red. They are commonly found in air and are the frequent cause of contaminations in bacteriological laboratories. All species are non-fermentative and of no practical importance. The family includes only one genus.
    Genus I. *Rhodotorula*. Characteristics same as for the family.
Family II. *Torulopsidaceae*. Do not produce carotenoid pigments. This family includes the remainder of the nonsporing yeasts. It is further divided into the two subfamilies *Torulopsidoideae* and *Mycotoruloideae*.

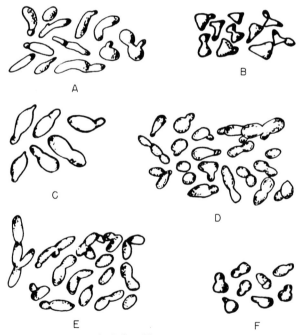

Fig. 83. Asporogenous yeasts. *A, Schizoblastosporion; B, Trigonopsis; C, Kloeckera; D, Torulopsis; E, Mycoderma; F, Pityrosporum.* (*From Mrak, Phaff, and Stadtman, "Taxonomy and Morphology of Yeasts," University of California, Berkeley.*)

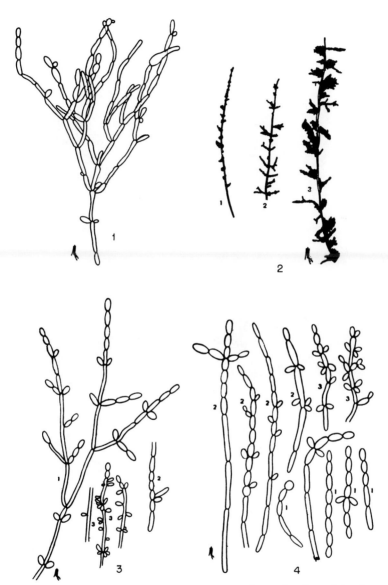

Fig. 84. Asporogenous yeasts. Various types of pseudomycelia formed in the genus *Candida*. (*From Mrak, Phaff, and Stadtman, "Taxonomy and Morphology of Yeasts," University of California, Berkeley.*)

Subfamily I. *Torulopsidoideae.* Do not produce pseudomycelium. The subfamily includes a majority of the wild yeasts common as contaminants in bacteriological procedures.

Genus I. *Kloeckera.* Cells lemon-shaped and show bipolar budding (Fig. 83).

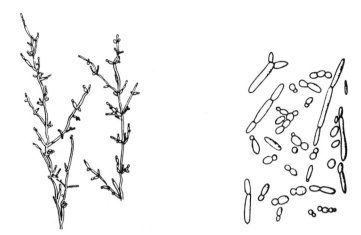

Fig. 85. Asporogenous yeasts. Left and right, *Brettanomyces lambicus*. (*From Mrak, Phaff, and Stadtman, "Taxonomy and Morphology of Yeasts," University of California, Berkeley.*)

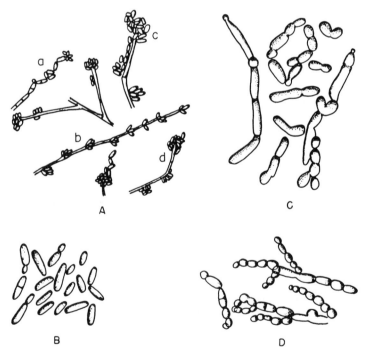

Fig. 86. Asporogenous yeasts. A, B, *Trichosporon capitatum*; C, *T. pullulans*; D, *T. margaritiferum*. (*From Mrak, Phaff, and Stadtman, "Taxonomy and Morphology of Yeasts," University of California, Berkeley.*)

Genus II. *Trigonopsis*. Cells triangular-shaped and show budding at the corners (Fig. 83).

Genus III. *Pityrosporum*. Cells usually flask-shaped and show budding on a broad basis (Fig. 83).

Genus IV. *Mycoderma*. Cells frequently cylindrical and show budding. Rapidly forms dry film on wort. Nonfermentative (Fig. 83).

Genus V. *Schizoblastosporion*. Cells polymorphic. Reproduction by a combination of budding and fission. Rapidly forms dry film on wort (Fig. 83).

Genus VI. *Torulopsis*. Film either absent in wort or forms after several days. Film, if formed, is somewhat slimy (Fig. 83).

Subfamily II. *Mycotoruloideae*. Produce pseudomycelium, with buds at the nodes. The subfamily includes three genera.

Genus I. *Candida*. Cells not ogive or pointed. Pseudomycelium well developed and forms blastospores. Arthrospores absent. Acid production not strong (Fig. 84).

Genus II. *Brettanomyces*. Cells commonly ogive. Pseudomycelium not well developed. Acid production rapid (Fig. 85).

Genus III. *Trichosporon*. Produce pseudomycelium, true mycelium, arthrospores, and blastospores (Fig. 86).

For more information see Lodder and Kreger–Van Rij (1953).

Pityrosporum. A number of species of the genus *Pityrosporum* have been isolated from skin, but they all appear to be sufficiently alike to be considered identical with *P. ovale*. The organism is usually referred to as the bottle bacillus because of its resemblance to a bottle. Since the organism is present on skin, especially of the scalp, it is claimed by some to be the etiological agent of dandruff. However, there appears to be no evidence that it has anything to do with the formation of dandruff or any pathological condition of the skin or scalp.

Brettanomyces. This genus includes a number of species of industrial importance. They are concerned with the afterfermentation of certain English and Belgian beers and ales. The afterfermentation is a secondary fermentation taking place in bottles in which the residual oxygen is utilized and replaced by carbon dioxide. Fermentation under anaerobic conditions is very slow, requiring several months for the reaction to go to completion. Under aerobic conditions, the organisms oxidize alcohol to acetic acid.

The cells are ovoid, or globular, often elongated and pointed at both ends. Budding may occur on all parts of the cell, forming irregular clusters. They show a tendency to form a poorly developed pseudomycelium. Ascospores are not produced. The organisms grow very slowly on culture media.

For information on the use of fermentation reactions in the classification of yeasts see Skinner and Bouthilet (1947) and Wickerham and Burton (1948).

LABORATORY TECHNIQUE

The methods used for the isolation and study of yeasts in pure culture are, in general, the same as those employed for bacteria.

Most species of yeasts grow best at a temperature of about 25°C.

Induced Sporulation. The conditions responsible for sporulation to occur are not clearly understood. Numerous factors are involved, and these seem to vary from species to species. In other words, a set of conditions cannot be laid down that will apply to all species of yeasts.

The following factors are generally believed to be of importance in causing vegetative cells to sporulate:

1. The yeast cells must be vigorous, well nourished, and young.

2. A temperature of about 25°C. is most favorable for sporulation to occur. This generally corresponds to the optimum growth temperature of yeasts. Temperatures somewhat below and above 25°C. are less favorable for sporulation to occur.

3. An abundance of oxygen must be present. Strictly anaerobic suspensions of ascosporogenous yeasts fail to sporulate. Cross sections of yeast colonies reveal sporulating cells only on the extreme outer layer. Stored yeast cakes contain spores only on the outside where oxygen is present.

4. Reports on the effect of pH on sporulation appear to be contradictory. Some maintain that acid or neutral solutions are necessary for sporulation to occur; others claim that slight alkaline conditions are more favorable. It is likely that sporulation is independent of reaction and that a pH of 6 to 7 will give satisfactory results, if the other conditions are satisfied. In this connection it might be of interest to note that Farrer (1953) found the pH of expressed yeast juice to be 5.6 to 6.0 for brewers' yeasts. Values for bakers' yeasts were somewhat lower.

5. An abundance of moisture is necessary for sporulation. Porous materials composed of plaster of Paris, clay, wood, filter paper, agar, gelatin, etc., become soaked up with water or nutrient solution and are satisfactory as carriers of moisture.

6. An appropriate carbon compound in the medium promotes sporulation. The type added varies with the species concerned. Mannose and maltose appear to produce the most asci. Salts of organic acids, especially acetate, give good results.

7. Sporulation may be observed in old cultures where the environmental conditions are less favorable. It is believed that certain specific metabolic products, produced by growing yeasts, shock the vegetative cells into producing spores.

The earlier methods employed to induce sporulation in yeasts made use of vegetable wedges such as carrot, beet, potato, cucumber, and turnip. Of these, carrot appears to give the largest number of positive results.

Engle (1872) employed blocks composed of gypsum. A block is placed in a glass container or Petri dish and water added until the lower portion is immersed. The glass container and contents are sterilized in an autoclave. Then the upper surface of the block is heavily inoculated from a young broth culture and the container incubated at 26°C. for at least one week. This method usually produces satisfactory sporulation.

Hartelius and Ditlevsen (1953) reported that gypsum blocks were unsatisfactory because they would not withstand sufficient heating for adequate sterilization. However, they reported casting blocks from a mixture of diatomaceous earth (kieselguhr) and Portland cement. Also, that such heat-resistant blocks were superior for spore formation. They found that Saccharomyces cerevisiae sporulated profusely after 48 hr. at 26°C.

Gorodkowa (1908) developed a medium containing 1 per cent peptone and 0.25 per cent glucose solidified with agar. Sporulation occurred after 3 to 4 days. A similar medium containing 5 per cent glucose failed to induce sporulation, indicating that the conditions essential to sporulation involved primarily the sugars in the media rather than the other components.

It is generally stated that a starvation medium is more favorable for spore formation, but this does not explain the facts. Welten (1914) found that yeasts sporulated readily on prune-extract agar. More spores were produced in concentrated than in dilute prune extract. He showed that a high acidity was necessary for sporulation to occur. No spores were encountered in an alkaline medium.

Mrak, Phaff, and Douglas (1942) found that agar slants made from a water extract of carrots, beets, cucumbers, and potatoes induced sporulation and, at the same time, served as an excellent stock culture medium. The medium was prepared by grinding equal weights of the vegetables and then mixing with a quantity of water equal to the weight of the ground mass. The mixture was autoclaved at 10 lb. pressure for 10 min., after which the extract was separated from the pulp by passage through a cloth filter. Two per cent agar was dissolved in the extract. The medium was tubed, autoclaved at 15 lb. pressure for 15 min., and slanted.

Nickerson and Thimann (1941) found that copulation and sporulation in a *Zygosaccharomyces* occurred more abundantly when many dead cells were present and postulated that some stimulating substance was derived from the dead cells. They also found that an extract from *Aspergillus niger* increased copulation and sporulation. Later Nickerson and Thimann (1943) showed that riboflavin and sodium glutarate were probably the substances in the extract responsible for the stimulation.

Lindegren and Lindegren (1944) recommended a presporulation medium composed as follows: beet (leaves) extract, 10 ml.; beet (roots) extract, 20 ml.; apricot juice, 35 ml.; grape juice, 16.5 ml.; yeast (dried), 2 gm.; glycerol, 2.5 ml.; agar, 3 gm.; calcium carbonate, 1 gm.; water, to make 100 ml. The medium was steamed for 10 min. and tubed. Tubes were sterilized at 15 lb. pressure for 20 min. and slanted. Most strains of yeasts produced spores directly on the slants if allowed to grow for a few weeks. However, if spores were needed sooner, transfer to gypsum blocks was necessary.

It may be concluded that a specific nutrient is essential for abundant sporulation to occur. If this nutrient is satisfactory and the sugar content of the medium is not too high, sporulation may occur, even on agar slants. If gypsum blocks are used, the water should be acid in reaction and contain by-products of yeast growth, and possibly some substances produced on the death and disintegration of the yeast cells. For more information see Phaff and Mrak (1949).

Isolation of Pure Cultures. Many methods have been recommended for the isolation of yeasts in pure culture. Most of the methods are concerned with the isolation of single cells and their propagation in a suitable culture medium. Such methods require considerable skill and patience. Yeasts may also be isolated in pure culture by the same methods employed for the separation of bacterial species (see page 218).

For more information on yeasts see Cook (1958), Lindegren and Pittman (1953), Palleroni and Lindegren (1953), Pittman and Lindegren (1954).

REFERENCES

Agar, H. D., and H. C. Douglas: Studies of budding and cell wall structure of yeast, *J. Bact.*, 70:427, 1955.
———— and ————: Studies on the cytological structure of yeast: electron microscopy of thin sections, *ibid.*, 73:365, 1957.
Cook, A. H.: "The Chemistry and Biology of Yeasts," New York, Academic Press, Inc., 1958.
Engel, L.: "Les Ferments alcooliques," University of Paris, 1, 1872.
Falcone, G., and W. J. Nickerson: Cell-wall mannan-protein of baker's yeast, *Science*, 124:272, 1956.
Farrer, K. T. H.: Observations on the pH of yeast cells, *Australian J. Exp. Biol. and Med. Sci.*, 31:577, 1953.
Gorodkowa, A. A.: Ueber das Verfahren rasch die Sporen von Hefepilzen zu gewinnen, *Bull. jard. imp. bot. St. Peters.*, 8:163, 1908.
Guilliermond, A.: "Clef dichotomique pour la détermination des levures," Paris, Librairie le François, 1928.
————: "La Sexualité, le cycle de développement, la phylogénie, et la classification des levures d'après les travaux récents," Paris, Masson et Cie, 1937.
Hartelius, V., and E. Ditlevsen: Cement blocks, heat-stable blocks, for ascospore-formation in yeast, *Compt. rend. trav. lab. Carlsberg, Série physiol.*, 25:213, 1953.
Hashimoto, T., S. F. Conti, and H. B. Naylor: IV. Observations on budding *Saccharomyces cerevisiae* by light and electron microscopy, *J. Bact.*, 77:344, 1959.

Hill, D. W., and L. P. Gebhardt: Morphological transformation of *Candida albicans* in tissues of mice, *Proc. Soc. Exp. Biol. Med.*, **92**:640, 1956.

Hjort, A.: Some studies on the genus *Saccharomycodes Hansen, Compt. rend. trav. lab. Carlsberg, Série physiol.*, **25**:259, 1954.

Klein, H. P.: Synthesis of lipids in resting cells of *Saccharomyces cerevisiae, J. Bact.*, **69**:620, 1955.

——— and Z. K. Booher: Synthesis of lipids in cell-free extracts of yeast, *Proc. Soc. Exp. Biol. Med.*, **89**:43, 1955.

Lindegren, C. C.: The improvement of industrial yeasts by selection and hybridization, *Wallerstein Lab. Commun.*, **7**:153, 1944.

———: Yeast genetics: Life cycles, cytology, hybridization, vitamin synthesis, and adaptive enzymes, *Bact. Rev.*, **9**:111, 1945.

———: Yeast of tomorrow, Anheuser-Busch, Inc., St. Louis, Mo., 1949.

———: The structure of the yeast cell, *Symposia Soc. Exp. Biol.*, VI. Structural aspects of cell physiology, 1952.

——— and G. Lindegren: A new method for hybridizing yeast, *Proc. Nat. Acad. Sci.*, **29**:306, 1943.

——— and ———: Sporulation in *Saccharomyces cerevisiae, Botan. Gaz.*, **105**:304, 1944.

——— and ———: Vitamin-synthesizing deficiencies in yeasts supplied by hybridization, *Science*, **102**:33, 1945.

——— and ———: Stability of hybrids in *Saccharomyces, Cytologia*, **19**:45, 1954.

——— and D. D. Pittman: The induction in a *Saccharomyces* sp. of the gene-mutation controlling utilization of galactose by exposure to galactose, *J. Gen. Microbiol.*, **9**:494, 1953.

——— and G. F. Townsend: Methods for distinguishing the spindle, the centrochromatin and the chromosomes of the yeast cell, *Cytologia*, **19**:104, 1954.

———, M. A. Williams, and D. O. McClary: The distribution of chromatin in budding yeast cells, *Antonie van Leeuwenhoek*, **22**:1, 1956.

Lodder, J.: Die Hefesammlung des "Centraalbureau voor Schimmel-cultures." II Teil. Die Anaskosporogenen Hefen. Erste Hälfte, *Verhandel. Koninkl. Akad. Wetenschap. Amsterdam, Afdeel. Natuurk.*, **32**:1, 1934.

——— and N. W. J. Kreger–Van Rij: "The Yeasts—A Taxonomic Study," New York, Interscience Publishers, Inc., 1953.

Mager, J.: Studies on the polysaccharides of capsulated yeasts, *Biochem. J.*, **41**:603, 1947.

Mrak, E. M., H. J. Phaff, and H. C. Douglas: A sporulation stock medium for yeasts and other fungi, *Science*, **96**:432, 1942.

Nickerson, W. J., and K. V. Thimann: The chemical control of conjugation in *Zygosaccharomyces, Am. J. Bot.*, **28**:617, 1941; II. *ibid.*, **30**:94, 1943.

Palleroni, N. J., and C. C. Lindegren: A single adaptive enzyme in *Saccharomyces* elicited by several related substrates, *J. Bact.*, **65**:122, 1953.

Phaff, H. J., and E. M. Mrak: Sporulation in yeasts, Part I, *Wallerstein Lab. Commun.*, **11**:261, 1948; Part II, *ibid.*, **12**:29, 1949.

Pittman, D. D., and C. C. Lindegren: Longterm adaptation to the fermentation of galactose in *Saccharomyces chevalieri, Nature*, **173**:408, 1954.

Roelofsen, P. A., and I. Hoette: Chitin in the cell wall of yeasts, *Antonie van Leeuwenhoek*, **17**:27, 1951.

Santa Maria, J.: Formation by *Saccharomyces cerevisiae* of asci with more than four spores, *J. Bact.*, **74**:692, 1957.

Scherr, G. H., and R. H. Weaver: The dimorphism phenomenon in yeasts, *Bact. Rev.*, **17**:51, 1953.

Skinner, C. E., and R. Bouthilet: Melibiose broth for classifying yeasts, *J. Bact.*, **53**:37, 1947.

Stelling-Dekker, N. M.: Die Hefesammlung des "Centraalbureau voor Schimmel-cultures." Beitrage zu einen Monographie der Hefearten. I. Teil. Die Sporogenen Hefen, *Verhandel. Koninkl. Akad. Wetenschap. Amsterdam, Afdeel. Natuurk.*, **28**:1, 1931.

Townsend, G. F., and C. C. Lindegren: Structures in the yeast cell revealed in wet mounts, *Cytologia*, **18**:183, 1953.

Welten, H.: Wann bildet die Hefe Sporen? *Mikrokosmos*, **8**:3, 41, 1914.

White, A. G. C., and C. H. Werkman: Fat synthesis in yeast, *Arch. Biochem.*, **17**:475, 1948.

Wickerham, L. J., and K. A. Burton: Carbon assimilation tests for the classification of yeasts, *J. Bact.*, **56**:363, 1948.

———— and ————: Hybridization studies involving *Saccharomyces lactis* and *Zygosaccharomyces ashbyi*, *J. Bact.*, **71**:290, 1956a.

———— and ————: Hybridization studies involving *Saccharomyces fragilis* and *Zygosaccharomyces dobzhanskii*, *ibid.*, **71**:296, 1956b.

Will, H.: Beiträge zur Kenntnis der Sprosspilze ohne Sporenbildung, welche in Brauereibetrieben und in deren Umgebung vorkommen. VI. Die Torulaceen, *Centr. Bakt.*, Abt. II, **46**:226, 1916.

Winge, Ö.: The relation between yeast cytology and genetics. A critique, *Compt. rend. trav. lab. Carlsberg, Série physiol.*, **25**:85, 1951.

————: The basis for the present position of yeast genetics, *Wallerstein Lab. Commun.*, **15**:21, 1952a.

————: The genetic situation concerning fermentation in yeasts, *Heredity*, **6**:263, 1952b.

————: On interallelic crossing over, *Compt. rend. trav. lab. Carlsberg, Série physiol.*, **25**:341, 1955.

———— and O. Laustsen: Artificial species hybridization in yeast, *Compt. rend. trav. lab. Carlsberg, Série physiol.*, **22**:235, 1938.

———— and ————: On 14 new yeast types, produced by hybridization, *ibid.*, **22**:337, 1939.

———— and C. Roberts: Causes of deviations from 2:2 segregations in the tetrads of monohybrid yeasts, *ibid.*, **25**:285, 1954a.

———— and ————: On tetrad analyses apparently inconsistent with Mendelian law, *Heredity*, **8**:295, 1954b.

———— and ————: Identification of the maltase genes in some American haploid and European diploid yeasts, *Compt. rend. trav. lab. Carlsberg, Série physiol.*, **25**:331, 1955.

Yuasa, A., and C. C. Lindegren: The integrity of the centriole in *Saccharomyces*, *Antonie van Leeuwenhoek*, **25**:73, 1959.

CHAPTER 6

Molds

Molds are minute saprophytic or parasitic filamentous fungi which reproduce by means of asexual and sexual spores. They constitute a large heterogeneous group of plant-like organisms which form a subdivision of the *Thallophyta,* one of the five divisions of the plant kingdom. The Thallophyta grow in irregular plant masses not differentiated into roots, stems, and leaves like higher plants. Such a mass of plant tissue is known as a thallus.

A thallus consists of branching, filamentous, thread-like growths called hyphae (singular, hypha). A mass of threads taken collectively is spoken of as a mycelium. The filaments or hyphae usually are colorless. Hyphae which are concerned in the production of spores are the fertile hyphae; those which serve to secure nutrients are the vegetative hyphae. The fertile hyphae extend into the air, forming and discharging spores. The vegetative hyphae burrow into the substrate, digesting and absorbing nutrients.

Molds differ from algae in not containing chlorophyll, the green pigment that enables plants to synthesize carbohydrates from carbon dioxide and water in the presence of sunlight as the source of energy. Typical plants are chemosynthetic, being capable of utilizing simple substances and building them up into compounds of greater complexity. They utilize carbon dioxide to form carbohydrates and fats and eliminate oxygen. Generally speaking, animals are chemoanalytic, being capable of breaking down complex organic matter into simple compounds. They differ from plants in that they take in oxygen and eliminate carbon dioxide. Molds resemble plants in structure and in being nonmotile but appear to be more related to animals in requiring oxygen in their metabolism and eliminating carbon dioxide.

Structure of Hyphae. Hyphae may be single-celled (nonseptate) or many-celled (septate). The transverse walls in the septate molds are known as septa (singular, septum). Longitudinal or oblique septa are very rare. Hyphae are more or less branched, continuous tubes (Fig. 87). In most molds, increase in size of hyphae occurs by apical growth. Cells lying back from the tips of hyphae may start to grow and develop into

138

branches. In a few species, all cells may continue to grow and divide. The nonseptate hyphae form one large cell containing many nuclei. This absence of septa makes possible a flowing of protoplasm. The septate hyphae may contain one, two, or many nuclei in each cell. Septa are rare in the Phycomycetes, except in the fruiting bodies, though they may occasionally be present in old cultures.

The nuclei usually are small and, in most fungi, seen only by special staining methods. In young organisms the cytoplasm may nearly fill the cell, whereas in old cells it is often limited to a thin layer lying next to the cell wall. The central portion may show the presence of a large vacuole filled with colorless cell sap. Various reserve food materials such as fat globules, glycogen, and metachromatic granules may also appear (see page 109).

 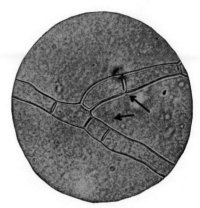

Fig. 87. Mold hyphae. Left, nonseptate; right, septate. (*After Kurung.*)

Cell Wall. The cell wall of molds was formerly thought to be composed of a substance similar to cellulose and referred to as fungus cellulose. More recent investigations indicate that the cell wall is composed largely of a polymerized acetylated glucosamine known as chitin with smaller amounts of cellulose and other substances of an obscure nature. Chitin is also present in the shells of crabs and lobsters and shards of beetles (see page 108).

Classes of Fungi. One of the subdivisions of the Thallophyta includes the fungi. This subdivision is divided into *Eumycetes* (yeasts and molds) and *Myxomycetes* (slime molds). The Eumycetes are further divided into the *Phycomycetes, Ascomycetes, Basidiomycetes,* and *Fungi Imperfecti.* The Myxomycetes consist of naked masses of protoplasm which creep slowly over the surface and ingest solid food. The Fungi Imperfecti include all molds in which a sexual or perfect stage has not been observed. In the Basidiomycetes the sexual spores or basidiospores are borne exogenously and are typically four in number. This class includes in part the

large fleshy fungi such as the mushrooms, the puffballs, and the bracket
fungi which grow on trees. In the Ascomycetes the sexual spores are
endogenous and typically eight in number. In the Phycomycetes sexual
spores are formed which are in some cases single and in others multiple.

MULTIPLICATION IN MOLDS

Most of the common molds may be cultivated by transferring any part
of the plant to fresh medium, but the normal process of development
begins with the germination of a spore. They are of different shapes
and sizes and may be composed of one cell or more than one cell.

FIG. 88. Germination of conidia. (*After Wehmer.*)

A spore consists of an outer wall, the epispore, and an inner wall, the
endospore. The epispore may be smooth, pitted, or roughened by small
projections; the endospore encloses the protoplasm in which may be seen
droplets of oily or fatty material and one or more nuclei. Under favorable
conditions the spore first swells, then throws out one or more germ tubes
(Fig. 88). Each germ tube elongates and becomes branched, forming a
network of hyphae, or a mycelium. Later spore-bearing bodies develop

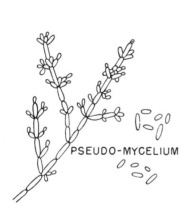

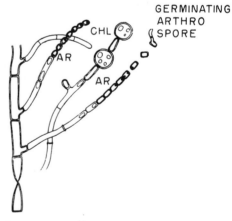

FIG. 89. *Candida*. Fragmentation of
the thallus. Budding of mycelium
to form blastospores. (*After Plunkett and Wilson.*)

FIG. 90. *Geotrichum*. Segmentation of terminal
hyphae to form arthrospores. Rounding up and
thickening of cell walls of a vegetative thallus
to form chlamydospores. (*Courtesy of Plunkett
and Wilson.*)

on the fertile hyphae, or some of the hyphae show the presence of special fruiting bodies in which spores are formed.

Two types of spores are produced: sexual and asexual. An asexual spore is one that is not the result of the fusion of two gametes or sex cells. A few molds produce several kinds of spores corresponding to different stages in their development. Practically all molds commonly encountered produce asexual spores. Some produce both asexual and sexual spores.

Types of Multiplication in Molds. These may be classified as follows:

1. Fragmentation of the thallus.
   a. Reproduction by budding as occurs in yeasts and yeast-like organisms (page 111).
   b. Budding of mycelium to form spores known as blastospores (Fig. 89).
   c. Segmentation of terminal hyphae followed by a rounding up and separation of the segments to form arthrospores (Fig. 90). Segments capable of giving rise to new hyphae.

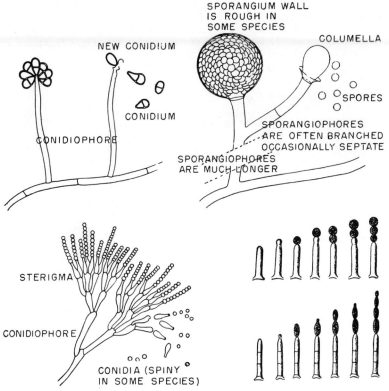

FIG. 91. Asexual spore formation. Upper left, *Trichothecium*. Septate mold that reproduces only by formation of asexual spores known as conidia. Upper right, *Mucor*. Development of a closed structure or sporangium on the tip of a sporangiophore in which are produced sporangiospores. Lower left, *Penicillium*. Development of spores at tip of hyphal branch or conidiophore known as conidia (*courtesy of Plunkett and Wilson*). Lower right, formation of conidia. Upper half, the topmost spore is the oldest; lower half, the topmost spore is the youngest.

    d. Rounding up and thickening of cell walls of a vegetative thallus to form chlamydospores (Fig. 90). Spores may be intercalary or terminal. Occur either simply or in chains in ordinary vegetative hyphae or in special branches. They are resistant bodies and may be considered as resting spores.

2. Asexual spore formation. This represents the imperfect stage of a mold.

    a. Fungi Imperfecti are septate molds which reproduce only by formation of asexual spores (Fig. 91). A sexual stage is unknown. Reproduction occurs by spores developed in various ways. The molds are classified according to types of spores and manner in which they are produced.

    b. Phycomycetes develop asexually by the formation of a closed structure or sporangium on the tip of a sporangiophore in which are produced sporangiospores (Fig. 91).

    c. Ascomycetes develop thin-walled spores at tip of hyphal branch or conidiophore known as conidiospores or conidia (Fig. 91). They may be (1) pinched off from tip of conidiophore or (2) budded off from existing conidiospores instead of directly from conidiophore (Fig. 91). In the former case the topmost spore is the oldest and largest; in the latter case the topmost spore is the youngest and smallest.

3. Sexual spore formation. This represents the perfect stage of a fungus. Spores are the result of nuclear fusion and are formed in or on specialized cells. Hyphal fusion frequently occurs but is not necessarily indicative of sexuality.

    a. Sexual spores of *Phycomycetes.* Fusion of (1) unlike gametes in large cell to form oöspores or (2) like gametes to form zygospores (Fig. 92). Spores are in some cases single and in others multiple.

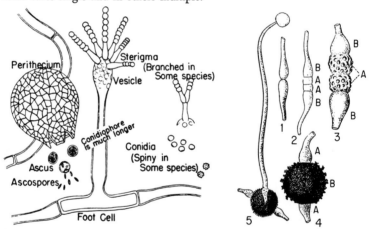

Fig. 92. Sexual spore formation. Left, *Aspergillus.* Ascus is a spore mother cell which arises as a result of nuclear fusion to form ascospores. (*Courtesy of Plunkett and Wilson.*) Right, *Mucor.* Formation of zygospore. 1, two hyphae in terminal contact; 2, articulation into gamete *a* and suspensor *b;* 3, fusion of gametes *a;* 4, ripe zygospore *b* supported by the suspensors *aa;* 5, germination of zygospore. (*After Brefeld.*)

    b. Sexual spores of *Ascomycetes.* Ascus is a spore mother cell which arises as a result of nuclear fusion to form ascospores by reduction division (Fig. 92). Ascospores may be formed (1) by direct conjugation as in yeasts, or (2) by fusion of two mycelial cells, or (3) by fusion of definite sex organs in which oögonium becomes an ascus, or (4) from ascogenous hyphae budded off a binucleate sex organ. In all cases the young ascus is binucleate. The nuclei fuse, and the diploid nucleus undergoes reduction division to yield four haploid nuclei. Haploid nuclei divide to yield typically eight spores.

c. Sexual spores of *Basidiomycetes.* Sexual organs absent. Basidium typically club-shaped, nonsegmented, and bears exogenously four basidiospores. Initially basidia are ends of hyphae composed of binucleate cells. As each terminal cell enlarges, the two nuclei also enlarge. Nuclei fuse to form a diploid fusion nucleus which then divides twice to form four daughter nuclei. Each nucleus is haploid. Four small projections (sterigmata) appear at apex of basidium. These projections expand terminally, and a nucleus passes into each inflated tip. When ripe, the basidiospores are abstricted. Basidium is similar to an ascus except that spores are produced outside rather than inside.

RESISTANCE OF MOLD SPORES

Molds have been responsible for enormous losses in the home and the industries. These losses are due largely to the fact that molds produce spores in great masses which may be spread widely by wind. They are abundant in the atmosphere. Mold spores are very resistant to unfavorable environmental conditions such as heat, cold, desiccation, ultraviolet light, high osmotic pressure, and deficient food supply. They are more resistant to heat than mycelium and generally less resistant than bacterial spores.

Spores are easily disseminated by wind and air currents. They are commonly present in the air of laboratories and are the frequent cause of contaminations of cultures and culture media. Therefore, laboratory windows should be kept closed to prevent the wind from stirring up the dust and spores in the laboratory air.

Molds occur particularly in damp places. Spores will not germinate in a dry environment. Many industrial products, such as paper, leather, textiles, and foods readily absorb moisture from the atmosphere and are susceptible to attack by molds. In order to decrease mold contaminations, laboratories and rooms should be kept as free as possible from excessive moisture.

In general, molds grow more slowly than bacteria. Consequently they are not found growing to any extent in environments where they must compete with bacteria. They are found growing under conditions which are unfavorable to the growth of bacteria. Environments unfavorable to bacterial growth but not to molds include starchy foods, high osmotic salt and sugar solutions, acid materials such as fruit juices and sour milk, salted and smoked meats, butter, and cheese. Richards (1949) reported the isolation and identification of a number of species of molds from the glass surfaces of optical instruments. Unless mold growth is removed from the glass, the moisture will damage the surface and leave it etched or raised where the mold growth occurred.

Generally speaking, molds do not multiply in the absence of oxygen. They are, therefore, unable to grow in commercially canned foods. However, a few species may grow to some extent under reduced oxygen conditions. An example is the mold *Penicillium roqueforti,* which is responsible for the ripening of Roquefort cheese.

CLASSIFICATION OF MOLDS

The general principles followed for the classification of molds are similar to those employed for the classification of bacteria (page 401). A condensed classification of the commonly encountered genera and species of molds is as follows:

Class I. *Phycomycetes.* Vegetative mycelium typically nonseptate. Septations commonly are formed in connection with the development of reproductive structures. They may also appear in old hyphae. Sporangia developed which contain motile or nonmotile sporangiospores, or conidia. Oöspores or zygospores formed, sometimes after fertilization, sometimes without any preliminary fusion of gametes or gametangia. Some are parasitic; others are saprophytic.

Order. *Mucorales.* Accessory multiplication by sporangiospores. Sporangia globose to ovoid, usually contain numerous spores, sometimes one or a few. Zygospores formed from the whole of the two gametangia. Columella present. Zygospores naked or invested by outgrowths from its own wall or from those of the suspensors. Principal sporangia contain numerous spores.

Family. *Mucoraceae.* Sporangiola, if any, developed on lateral branches of principal sporangiophores. Sporangia of one kind. Sporangiophore simple or branched but not repeatedly dichotomous. Suspensors without appendages at maturity.

Genus 1. *Mucor.* Three main types of branching are recognized: the mono-mucors show unbranched sporangiophores; the racemomucors show a main stem with lateral branches; and the cymomucors show sporangiophores typically branched. Stolons absent. Sporangia single and terminal.

Sporangiophores rarely or never branched (monomucors):

M. mucedo. Columella pear-shaped to cylindrical. Sporangium grayish. Arthrospores or chlamydospores not produced.

M. hiemalis. Columella spherical. Sporangium olive to grayish brown when ripe.

M. ramannianus. Columella spherical. Sporangium reddish.

M. piriformis. Columella pear-shaped. Sporangium very large.

Sporangiophores with main stem and secondary lateral branches, racemose (racemomucors):

M. racemosus. Columella ovoid or pear-shaped. Submerged mycelium breaks up into yeast-like cells or arthrospores which germinate by budding. Black chlamydospores formed in aerial mycelium. Yeast-like cells capable of fermenting sugar to alcohol.

M. erectus. Columella spherical. Sporangium gray yellow. Similar to *M. racemosus* except for the form of columella.

M. fragilis. Columella spherical. Sporangium black. Similar to *M. racemosus* except for the form of columella.

Sporangiophores typically branched (cymomucors):

M. spinosus (*plumbeus*). Columella spiny. Spores prickly. Mycelium lead-gray in color.

M. circinelloides. Sporangia in two rows, alternating, spores spherical or ellipsoidal. Submerged mycelium breaks up into yeast-like cells or arthrospores which germinate by budding.

M. alternans. Sporangia in two rows, alternating. Spores longer, ellipsoidal.

M. ambiguus. Sporangia borne irregularly.

M. rouxii. Columella spherical. Spores large and oval. Black chlamydospores appear in aerial mycelium and budding cells in submerged portions. Contains necessary enzymes to convert starch first to sugar and finally to alcohol. Used in manufacture of alcohol.

Genus 2. *Rhizopus.* Stolons present.

R. nigricans. The common black bread mold.

R. oryzae. Employed in the hydrolysis of starch to sugar.

R. japonicus. Also employed in the hydrolysis of starch to sugar.

Class II. *Ascomycetes.* With the exception of the yeasts, all possess a well-developed mycelium of branched and septate hyphae. Cells of mycelium may be uninucleate or may contain several nuclei. Multiplication takes place by conidia and by chlamydospores, but the characteristic method is by means of ascospores. An ascus contains usually eight spores, more rarely a smaller or a larger number. Some of the *Aspergillus, Penicillium,* and *Alternaria* produce ascospores and should be included here (Fig. 93). However, asci have not been identified in the great majority of the species, and for that reason all of them are grouped under the Fungi Imperfecti for convenience.

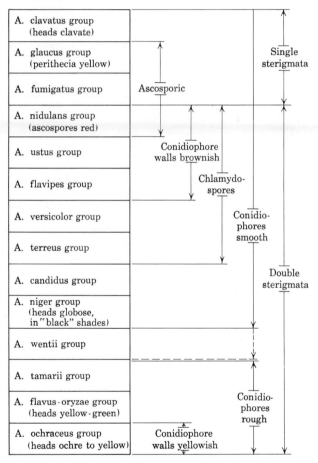

Fig. 93. Natural relationships among the groups of the *Aspergillus.* (*Adapted from Thom and Raper.*)

Class III. *Basidiomycetes.* All possess well-developed mycelium. Basidiospores produced which are borne externally on the mother cell or basidium. The young basidium contains two nuclei that fuse, then divides to provide the nuclei of the spores. The spore is formed on a sterigma through which the nucleus passes from the basidium to enter the developing spore. The basidiospores are unicellular, round or oval, asymmetrically attached to their sterigmata, usually with a smooth, rather thin wall. Echinulate spores occur in a few species.

Class IV. *Fungi Imperfecti.* Characteristic method of reproduction by means of conidia. In some species, arthrospores and chlamydospores may be present. Sporangiospores, ascospores, and basidiospores not produced.

Order. *Moniliales.* Conidiophores free, arising irregularly from the mycelium.

Family 1. *Moniliaceae.* Hyphae colorless or in pale or bright colors.

Genus 1. *Trichothecium (Cephalothecium).* Spores two-celled, in small clusters on ends of erect conidiophores.

T. roseum. A commonly occurring pink mold found on decaying fruit. At times causes contamination of laboratory media.

Genus 2. *Geotrichum.* Reproduction regularly by fragmentation of mycelium into arthrospores. Blastospores rarely, if ever, produced.

G. candidum. Commonly found in milk and cheese. Imparts flavor and aroma to many types of cheese.

Genus 3. *Candida (Monilia).* Reproduction by fragmentation of mycelium into blastospores. Arthrospores not produced.

Colonies dry, flat, and wrinkled on Sabouraud agar; heavy pellicle on liquid media.

C. krusei (M. krusei). Colonies moist and creamy on Sabouraud agar; slight or no pellicle on liquid media.

C. parakrusei (M. parapsilosis). Glucose only carbohydrate fermented.

C. tropicalis (M. candida). Glucose, maltose, and sucrose fermented; lactose and raffinose not fermented.

C. pseudotropicalis (M. mortifera). Glucose, lactose, and sucrose fermented; maltose and raffinose not fermented.

C. guilliermondi (M. guilliermondi). Glucose, sucrose, and raffinose fermented.

C. albicans (M. albicans). Glucose fermented; sucrose not fermented. Blastospores in dense clusters.

Genus 4. *Aspergillus.* Vegetative mycelium consisting of septate hyphae, branching, colorless or colored. Conidiophores arising from specialized foot cells, usually nonseptate, terminating in a swelling which bears the sterigmata. Conidia borne in chains formed by abscission from sterigmata. Conidia vary greatly in color, size, shape, and markings. Perithecia found in some groups (unknown in most species), producing asci and ascospores within a few weeks.

A. clavatus group. Conidial heads clavate, pale blue-green. Conidiophores generally coarse, smooth-walled, uncolored. Conidia elliptical, smooth, thick-walled.

A. glaucus group. Perithecia yellow, thin-walled, suspended in networks of red or yellow hyphae. Asci contain eight lenticular, smooth, or rough-walled ascospores. Conidiophores smooth-walled, terminating in dome-like vesicles. Conidia elliptical to subglobose, uniformly roughened.

A. fumigatus group. Conidial heads columnar, green to dark green. Vesicles flask-shaped. Conidiophores smooth-walled, usually green. Conidia globose, echinulate, green.

A. nidulans group. Conidial heads short columnar, usually dark green. Conidiophores smooth-walled, terminating in dome-like or hemispherical vesicles. Perithecia usually present. Ascospores purple-red. Conidia globose.

A. ustus group. Conidiophores yellow-brown, smooth. Conidial heads irregular. Vesicles hemispherical. Conidia roughened, ranging in color from pale blue-green to deep brown.

A. flavipes group. Conidiophores smooth, yellow, with color often confined to outer layer. Heads barrel-shaped to columnar. Vesicles subglobose to elliptical. Conidia colorless, smooth, thin-walled.

A. versicolor group. Conidial heads hemispherical to almost globose, usually green or blue-green. Conidiophores smooth, colorless, more or less sinuous. Vesicles globose to elliptical. Conidia globose or subglobose, echinulate.

A. terreus group. Heads columnar, pale buff or light flesh shades. Conidiophores smooth, colorless. Vesicles hemispherical with upper portion covered by sterigmata. Conidia small, smooth, globose to slightly elliptical.

A. candidus group. Conidial heads white or becoming cream-colored with age, globose, but approaching columnar in small heads. Conidiophores smooth, colorless, or slightly yellow. Conidia smooth, globose or subglobose.

A. niger group. Conidial heads black, brownish black, or purple-brown. Heads large and globose. Conidiophores smooth, colorless, or slightly yellow-brown. Vesicles globose in large heads, dome-like apices in small heads. Conidia rough, showing mostly bars or bands of brown-black coloring matter.

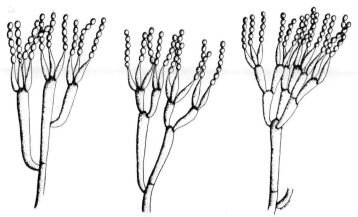

FIG. 94. Branching of spore heads in *Penicillium*. Left, monoverticillate; center, biverticillate; right, polyverticillate. See text for description.

A. wentii group. Conidial heads large, globose, varying greatly in color. Conidiophores smooth-walled or nearly so, often appearing finely roughened. Vesicles globose. Conidia commonly elliptical, smooth, or somewhat roughened, depending upon species.

A. tamarii group. Conidial heads radiate, hemispherical to globose, yellow-brown to olive-brown in color. Conidiophores colorless, roughened throughout a part or all of their length. Vesicles globose to subglobose. Conidia heavy-walled, rough, elliptical, pyriform, or subglobose.

A. flavus-oryzae group. Conidiophores colorless, rough, or pitted. Heads hemispherical to columnar to subglobose. Vesicles hemispherical to dome-shaped in small heads, globose in large heads. Conidia roughened, varying in color.

A. ochraceus group. Conidial heads yellow to ochraceous. Heads globose or radiate with conidial chains commonly adhering into divergent columns. Conidiophores yellowish. Conidia in some series thin-walled and smooth, in others double-walled and echinulate.

Genus 5. *Penicillium*. Conidia produced from sterigmata which in turn are produced from short branches called metulae given off from tips of conidiophores. Penicillia divided into four groups, division being based on nature of branching of spore heads. Branching may be symmetrical about the axis of the conidiophore or unsymmetrical. Symmetrical types separated into (1) monoverticillata, with a single whorl or sterigmata at tip of conidiophore; (2) biverticillata, in which the verticils of sterigmata are produced from two symmetrical branches; and (3) polyverticillata, in which verticils of sterigmata arise from three or more symmetrical branches (Fig. 94).

P. camemberti. Found in Camembert or Brie cheese. Colonies floccose, white or grayish green in color.

P. brevicaule. Found in Camembert or Brie cheese. Yellow-brown areas formed. Spores rough.

P. roqueforti. Found in Roquefort cheese. Forms green streaks inside of cheese.

P. italicum. Produces a soft rot of citrus fruits. Colonies blue-green.

P. digitatum. Produces a shriveling and drying of infected citrus fruits. Colonies dull yellow-green or olive-green.

P. expansum. Produces a soft rot of apples and pears. Colonies blue-green.

P. notatum. Produces penicillin. Used commercially.

P. chrysogenum. Produces penicillin. Used commercially.

Family 2. *Dematiaceae.* Mycelium, spores, or both, dark brown to black. Conidiophores detached, not compacted.

Genus 1. *Cladosporium.* Spores increase by budding, forming branched chains. Spores one-celled but become two-celled in old cultures.

C. herbarum. Found on decaying paper, straw, and similar materials.

Genus 2. *Alternaria.* Spores many-celled, club-shaped, and in chains.

A. tenuis. Found on moldy grains and in soil. Frequently found in laboratory air.

MORPHOLOGY OF THE COMMON MOLDS

Several hundred genera and thousands of species of molds (at least 80,000) have been described. Only a few genera are of common occurrence, and these may be easily recognized. The commonly occurring genera include *Mucor, Rhizopus, Cephalothecium (Trichothecium), Geotrichum, Candida, Aspergillus, Penicillium, Cladosporium,* and *Alternaria.*

Mucor. This is the largest genus of the order Mucorales. The mucors are found in soil and manure, and on fruits, vegetables, bread, and other starchy foodstuffs. The vegetative mycelium penetrates the food material and sends out long, slender threads known as aerial hyphae. The mycelium generally is white in color. A septum forms near the apex of each hypha. The tip cell of the hypha swells into a round, cylindrical, or pear-shaped structure called a columella. Around the columella a globular structure or sporangium then forms, within which develop numerous oval, asexual spores known as sporangiospores. The sporangia are almost black in color. The wall of the ripe sporangium easily breaks, discharging the enclosed spores. Each spore is capable of repeating the cycle (Fig. 91).

Under certain conditions conjugation of two cells from different hyphae precedes spore formation, resulting in the development of a zygospore. This is sexual reproduction. A germ tube arises from the matured zygospore, developing sporangium at the apex (Fig. 92).

Separation of the various species is based on the length and diameter of the sporangiophores, the type of branching if any, the size and color of the sporangia, the character of the sporangial wall, the characteristics of zygospores and chlamydospores if any, the size and shape of the columellae, the size and shape of spores, and general colony characteristics, such as color and height of aerial growth.

Rhizopus. Members of this genus are of common occurrence and the frequent cause of laboratory contaminations. Growth on the usual laboratory media is very rapid. The molds spread widely by means of stolons or runners. Culture tubes and Petri dishes soon become filled with a dense, cottony mycelium. Species of this genus are easily distinguished from the mucors by the presence of stolons. Stolons often reach a length of several centimeters and bear tufts of root-like hyphae or rhizoids, which emerge from the points where the stolons come in contact with the medium or the surface of the glass. The columella is hemispherical, not round, cylindrical, or pear-shaped as in the mucors, and rests in a cup-shaped expansion of the sporangiophore called the apophysis. Spores may be ovoid, polygonal, or striated. The members are usually grayer in color and produce a more luxuriant growth than the mucors (Fig. 95).

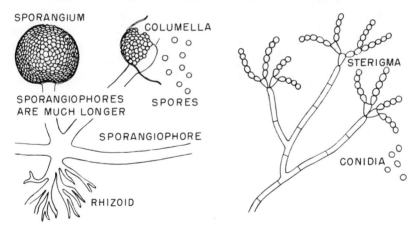

Fig. 95. Left, *Rhizopus;* right, *Cladosporium.* See text for description. (*Courtesy of Plunkett and Wilson.*)

Cephalothecium (Trichothecium). This genus contains several species, but only one, *C. roseum,* is of common occurrence. The colonies are thin, spreading, floccose, at first white in color, then becoming slowly pale pink. The conidiophores bear clusters of spores attached to the tip. The spores are ovoid, with a nipple-like projection at the point of attachment, and are composed of two cells. The cell closest to the conidiophore is the smallest (Fig. 91). This species is widely distributed, being found on fruits, wood, paper, plants and in soil.

Geotrichum. The best-known member is *G. candidum.* It is found in various milk products. It grows readily on milk or wort agar, producing a thin, spreading, slimy growth. Colonies on agar are creamy white in color. In young cultures, long hyphal threads are present, whereas in old cultures, the hyphae break up into short rectangular fragments called arthrospores. Each spore germinates into a new plant (Fig. 90).

Candida. Members of this genus are essentially yeast-like organisms which have a tendency to form mycelium on culture media low in nutrients. Young glucose agar cultures may show a white, pasty growth consisting entirely of round or oval budding yeast cells. In old agar cultures there may be present fine filaments penetrating into the agar. Microscopic examination shows the presence of filaments and budding yeast cells. In a nutrient-gelatin stab culture, yeast-like cells may be present on the surface, whereas tufts of mycelium that radiate into the gelatin may be observed along the line of puncture.

Aspergillus. The species of this genus are relatively common in air. They are found almost everywhere on nearly all types of substrates. The molds are found on decaying fruits, vegetables, grains, bread, and other articles of food. Aspergilli are commonly found in incompletely sterilized culture media. The color may vary considerably. It may appear green, yellow, orange, black or brown. The molds have a powdery appearance. In marked contrast to the mucors, the hyphae are branched and septate. The hyphae enlarge at the apices to form conidiophores. The conidiophores are not branched. Numerous short stalks called sterigmata develop from the apical or swollen ends of the conidiophores. Chains of spores known as conidiospores are produced from the tips of the sterigmata, sometimes developing to a considerable length (Fig.

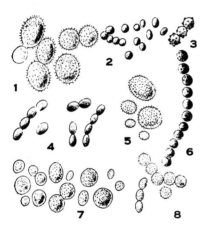

Fig. 96. Conidia of various species of *Aspergillus*. 1, *A. glaucus;* 2, *A. fumigatus;* 3, *A. niger;* 4, *A. clavatus;* 5, *A. tokelau;* 6, *A. varians;* 7, *A. oryzae;* 8, *A. wentii.* (*After Lafar.*)

96). A few species produce perithecia. These are spherical, cylindrical, or flask-shaped, hollow structures, which contain the asci and are usually open by a terminal pore. The asci contain the ascospores (Fig. 92).

For more information on the aspergilli see Thom (1954), Thom and Raper (1945).

Penicillium. The penicillia are closely related to the aspergilli and are also widely distributed in nature. The genus includes the characteristic blue-green-colored mold so often observed on citrus and other fruits, vegetables, grains, hay, organic infusions, cheeses, and other food ma-

terials (Fig. 91). The vegetative mycelium penetrates the food substances, after which aerial hyphae or conidiophores appear. The conidiophores branch one or more times from the same joint, giving rise to a
terminal cluster of parallel hyphae known as sterigmata. A chain of
conidia develops from each sterigma (Fig. 97).

Some species are destructive, whereas others are beneficial. Probably
the most important species are *P. roque-*
forti and *P. camemberti,* which are responsible for the desirable changes occurring in Roquefort, Camembert, Gorgonzola, and similar cheeses. The penicillia are employed in the manufacture
of a considerable number of substances
of commercial importance.

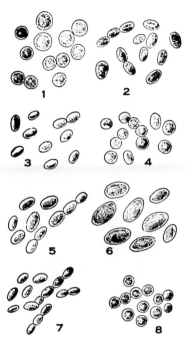

The penicillia are more difficult to
classify than the aspergilli. The conidia
show less variation in color. Most species show some shade of green during
the period of active growth. The colors
vary in shade under different environmental conditions and with age of the
cultures. Also, there are considerably
more species of *Penicillium* than of *As-*
pergillus.

For more information on the pencil-
lia, see Raper and Thom (1949), Stauffer and Backus (1954), and Thom
(1954).

FIG. 97. Conidia of various species
of *Penicillium.* 1, *P. camemberti;* 2,
P. purpurogenum; 3, *P. claviforme;*
4, *P. rubrum;* 5, *P. italicum;* 6, *P.
olivaceum;* 7, *P. luteum;* 8, *P. glaucum.* (*After Lafar.*)

Cladosporium. The most important
species is *C. herbarum.* It is widely
distributed, being found on rubber,
leather, textiles, and foodstuffs; in soil;
and on decaying leaves, straw, and
other vegetation on the surface of the soil (Fig. 95). On culture media it
produces a thick, velvety growth, and the color varies from deep green
to dark gray-green.

The first spores are formed directly from the tips of the conidiophores.
Additional spores are produced by budding of existing conidia. In this
manner a chain of spores is formed in which the terminal spore is the
youngest. Young spores are usually single-celled; old spores frequently
show two cells.

Alternaria. Species of this genus are commonly found on organic matter. Parasitic forms have been isolated from cultivated plants. On culture media the organisms grow rapidly and produce dense, floccose, olive-

green, or brown-colored mycelium. The mycelium is septate and may form large, swollen, greenish-brown to dark-brown conidiospores (Fig. 98). The conidia are composed of more than one cell and vary from oval-shaped to roughly club-shaped forms with a pronounced beak at the tip. The spores are produced in chains, sometimes with short stretches of mycelium between the spores.

For more information see Skinner, Emmons, and Tsuchiya (1947); Wolf and Wolf (1947).

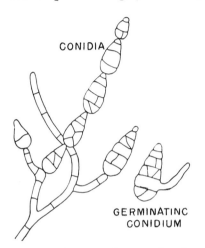

CONIDIA

GERMINATING
CONIDIUM

Fig. 98. *Alternaria.* See text for description. (*Courtesy of Plunkett and Wilson.*)

LABORATORY TECHNIQUE

In order that accurate studies be made on molds, it is necessary to grow them in pure cultures. The methods employed for isolating and studying molds in pure culture are, in general, similar to those used for bacteria (page 218).

Culture Media. Many types of solid and liquid media are employed for the cultivation of molds, but only a few are for general use. Vegetables and vegetable extracts are commonly employed as culture media. These are suitable with or without the addition of sugar. The solid media may be composed of solid substances, such as potatoes, carrots, and beans, or liquid media made solid by the addition of agar or gelatin. Molds generally grow more slowly than bacteria. If both are present in the material to be examined, the bacteria are likely to grow at a faster rate, making it difficult if not impossible to obtain pure culture isolations of the molds. This may be overcome by making the media unfavorable to the growth of the bacteria but favorable to the molds. Since molds can tolerate acid conditions better than bacteria, the procedure generally followed is to make the media highly acid (pH 2 to 5). A useful solid medium for general use is known as Sabouraud's agar. It is composed of 2 per cent glucose, 1 per cent peptone, 2 per cent agar, and adjusted to a pH of 5.6.

Some prefer to use media composed of pure inorganic salts. These are of constant composition and strictly comparable when prepared in different laboratories. One of the simplest synthetic media employed for the cultivation of molds is Czapek's solution. This is easy to prepare and probably is as good as any for general use. A modification of the original formula is as follows: sodium nitrate, 2.0 gm.; potassium chloride, 0.5 gm.; magnesium sulfate, 0.5 gm.; ferrous sulfate, 0.01 gm.; potassium acid phosphate, 1.0 gm.; distilled water, to make 1000 ml.

Various carbohydrates such as glucose and sucrose may be incorporated. Usually 50 gm. of glucose or 30 gm. of sucrose is added. The medium is acid (pH 4.2), which is unfavorable to the growth of most bacteria. The medium may be solidified by the addition of 20 gm. of agar per liter. This is probably the most useful solid medium employed for the cultivation of molds.

Isolation and Purification of Molds. Molds may be easily and satisfactorily purified by the streak-plate and pour-plate methods, as used for the purification of bacterial species (page 219).

Microscopical Methods. Considerable information may be obtained by examining first dry, living cultures under the low-power objective. Petri-dish cultures are placed on the stage of the microscope, with the lids removed, and examined by transmitted or reflected light. Aerial mycelium, conidiophores, fruiting heads, chains of spores, and other structures may be easily examined by this method. This gives a preliminary idea of what to look for when slide preparations are examined, since mold structures are easily broken when disturbed.

For high-power examination, slide preparations are necessary. Mold specimens are very difficult to remove from culture media without being greatly broken. Therefore, great care must be exercised in preparing satisfactory mounts. Water should not be used for the mounting fluid since it rapidly evaporates, produces a shrinkage of the hyphae by osmosis, and causes the various parts to adhere together as a tangled mass. Obviously, such preparations are unsatisfactory for accurate observations.

Probably the most useful mounting fluid is known as lactophenol. It has the following composition: phenol, c.p., crystals, 20 gm.; lactic acid, c.p., 20 gm.; glycerol, c.p., 40 gm.; and distilled water, 20 ml. The solution is prepared by first dissolving the phenol in the water, then adding the lactic acid and glycerol.

This fluid does not cause shrinkage of the cells and does not evaporate, thus permitting permanent preparations to be prepared. A dye may be added to the fluid to stain the various mold structures. This is especially desirable for mounting molds that are to be photographed.

Molds are mounted by first placing a drop of lactophenol in the center of a clean glass slide. A small portion of the mold growth is removed from the culture and placed in the drop of fluid. It is gently teased out with a pair of needles until the various parts are well separated and wetted by the fluid. It is then carefully covered with a cover slip to avoid as far as possible air bubbles being entrapped.

For more information see Foster (1949); Skinner, Emmons, and Tsuchiya (1947); Smith (1942); Wolf and Wolf (1947).

BIOCHEMISTRY OF THE MOLDS

The biochemical activities of molds are of great importance in the industrial world. They probably are not so important in this respect as the yeasts and bacteria, but they do, nevertheless, produce certain changes not carried out by the other two members of the fungi group. A few of the more important biochemical changes induced by molds are the following:

Alcoholic Fermentation. Alcohol is generally produced industrially by the fermentation of various sugars by yeasts (page 371). The fermentable materials used include sucrose, glucose, molasses, pineapple juice and other fruit juices, various starches (potato, corn, wheat), whey, cellulose, etc.

Saccharine materials usually require no special treatment other than proper concentration. Starches, cellulose, and other polysaccharides must first be hydrolyzed to soluble sugars before they can be utilized by yeasts.

In general, the methods of saccharifying complex carbohydrates involve the use of enzymes, or dilute acids, or a combination of both. A number of molds, bacteria, and plants elaborate the necessary enzyme or enzymes that effect the saccharification of the various starches and other polysaccharides, after which certain yeasts are capable of fermenting the sugars to alcohol. Takamine (1914) advocated the use of mold bran

(Taka-koji), an enzyme preparation obtained by growing *Aspergillus oryzae* on moist, sterilized bran (see Underkofler and Fulmer, 1943).

A number of species of *Mucor* are capable of fermenting starch directly to alcohol. The molds secrete both amylase (diastase) and zymase. Amylase is an enzyme that hydrolyzes starch to sugar, and zymase is the name applied to a group of enzymes and coenzymes that converts sugar to alcohol. *Mucor rouxii* produces more alcohol than any other species of this genus and is generally preferred for this purpose. The mold is used in the Orient for preparing alcoholic beverages from rice. It is mixed with rice meal and marketed as Chinese yeast. About 5 per cent alcohol is produced at the end of the fermentation.

Citric Acid. Citric acid is a natural constituent of citrus and other fruits. It was first isolated from lemon juice and crystallized by Scheele in 1784.

Wehmer (1893) showed that two species of *Penicillium* were capable of fermenting sugar with the production of citric acid. Subsequently it was shown that many species of molds were capable of producing citric acid in varying amounts, but in no instance was the yield sufficiently large to enable the process to compete with the extraction of the acid from lemons and other citrus fruits.

Currie (1917) found that the yield could be greatly increased by employing the mold *Aspergillus niger*. This mold is now employed commercially, and in some localities the process competes quite favorably with the production of citric acid from natural sources.

The two most important controlling factors in the production of citric acid are the supply of oxygen and the composition of the medium. The mold is strongly aerobic and requires a plentiful supply of oxygen. Sufficient nitrogen and minerals must be present in the medium for the mold to grow satisfactorily. The highest yield of citric acid is obtained when the medium contains about 15 per cent sucrose.

Currie found the following medium to be most favorable for citric acid production: sucrose, 150 gm.; ammonium nitrate, 2.5 gm.; potassium acid phosphate, 1.0 gm.; magnesium sulfate, 0.25 gm.; distilled water, to make 1000 ml. The medium was adjusted with hydrochloric acid to give a pH of about 3.5.

The fermentation yields oxalic acid and carbon dioxide in addition to citric acid. The fermented medium is concentrated by evaporation, which permits the less soluble oxalic acid to crystallize out, leaving the citric acid in solution.

Foster, Carson, Ruben, and Kamen (1941) found carbon dioxide to be necessary in the formation of citric acid through the Wood-Werkman reaction (pyruvic acid $+ CO_2 \rightarrow$ oxaloacetic acid). Their reaction scheme is as follows:

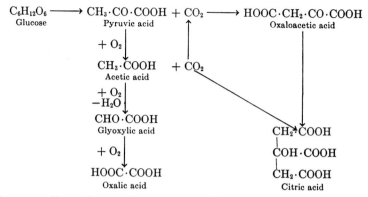

The over-all result may be represented by the equation:

$$C_6H_{12}O_6 + 3O \rightarrow H_3C_6H_5O_7 + 2H_2O$$
$$\text{Glucose} \qquad\qquad \text{Citric acid}$$

According to this scheme: (1) pyruvic acid is probably formed by the same series of reactions as in alcoholic fermentation (page 372); (2) the formation of citric acid is dependent upon the presence of carbon dioxide; (3) the carbon dioxide liberated in the decarboxylation of some pyruvic acid is fixed in the Wood-Werkman reaction, converting other molecules of pyruvic acid to oxaloacetic acid; (4) in unaerated cultures the carbon dioxide arising from respiration accumulates in the vicinity of the mycelium, giving considerably more citric than oxalic acid; (5) in aerated cultures the carbon dioxide is carried away by the air, giving considerably more oxalic acid than citric acid.

For more information see Erkama and Hägerstrand (1949); Erkama, Hägerstrand, and Junkkonen (1949); Erkama, Heikkinen, Hägerstrand, and Junkkonen (1949); Karow and Waksman (1947); Martin, Wilson, and Burris (1950); Shu and Johnson (1947); Tomlinson, Campbell, and Trussell (1950).

D-Gluconic Acid. Molliard (1922) was the first to detect the presence of gluconic acid in mold cultures. He used the organism *Sterigmatocystis nigra* and a culture medium containing sucrose. Later Butkewitsch (1923) identified the same acid in cultures of *Aspergillus niger*. The acid is now known to be produced by a number of aspergilli and penicillia.

Gluconic acid can be more cheaply prepared by means of molds than by chemical methods. Herrick and May (1928) employed the mold *Penicillium purpurogenum* var. *rubrisclerotium* and found that a high yield of gluconic acid could be produced to the exclusion of other acids. They used the following medium: glucose, 200 gm.; magnesium sulfate, 0.25 gm.; disodium phosphate, 0.10 gm.; potassium chloride, 0.05 gm.; sodium nitrate, 1.00 gm.; distilled water, to make 1000 ml.

The medium produced a good yield in about 10 days at 25 to 30°C.

Moyer, May, and Herrick (1936) found that the mold *Penicillium chrysogenum* showed the greatest capacity for producing gluconic acid. However, the mold does not produce large quantities of spores, which are required for the inoculation of media. Wells, Moyer, Stubbs, Herrick, and May (1937) selected a strain of *Aspergillus niger* for gluconic acid production that sporulated readily and produced uniform fermentations.

The over-all reaction for the oxidation of glucose to gluconic acid is as follows:

$$
\begin{array}{ccc}
\mathrm{CH_2OH} & & \mathrm{CH_2OH} \\
| & & | \\
\mathrm{HCOH} & & \mathrm{HCOH} \\
| & & | \\
\mathrm{HCOH} & +\,\mathrm{O}\rightarrow & \mathrm{HCOH} \\
| & & | \\
\mathrm{HOCH} & & \mathrm{HOCH} \\
| & & | \\
\mathrm{HCOH} & & \mathrm{HCOH} \\
| & & | \\
\mathrm{CHO} & & \mathrm{COOH} \\
\text{D-Glucose} & & \text{D-Gluconic acid}
\end{array}
$$

For more information see Porges, Clark, and Gastrock (1940).

Fumaric Acid. Fumaric acid is an unsaturated acid produced by a number of molds, principally by species of the genus *Rhizopus*. It has the formula $COOH \cdot CH{=}CH \cdot COOH$.

The acid is produced from various monosaccharides, and from sucrose, maltose, molasses, and starches. The following medium may be used for good fumaric acid production: glucose, 150 gm.; ammonium sulfate, 5 gm.; magnesium sulfate ($MgSO_4 \cdot 7H_2O$), 0.5 gm.; dipotassium phosphate (K_2HPO_4), 0.5 gm.; zinc sulfate ($ZnSO_4 \cdot 7H_2O$), 0.01 gm.; ferric sulfate [$Fe_2(SO_4)_3$], 0.02 gm.; water, to make 1000 ml. Calcium carbonate is added to the medium to neutralize the fumaric acid as it is formed.

Foster and Davis (1948) proposed the following scheme for the formation of fumaric acid from glucose:

$$
\begin{array}{c}
\mathrm{C_6H_{12}O_6} \\
\text{Glucose} \\
\downarrow -4\mathrm{H}
\end{array}
$$

$$
\underset{\text{Lactic acid}}{\mathrm{CH_3 \cdot CHOH \cdot COOH}} \xleftarrow{+2\mathrm{H}} \underset{\text{Pyruvic acid}}{\mathrm{CH_3 \cdot CO \cdot COOH}} \longrightarrow \underset{\text{Acetaldehyde}}{\mathrm{CH_3 \cdot CHO + CO_2}}
$$

$$
\begin{array}{cc}
\downarrow +\mathrm{CO_2} & \downarrow +2\mathrm{H} \\
\underset{\text{Oxaloacetic acid}}{\mathrm{HOOC \cdot CH_2 \cdot CO \cdot COOH}} & \underset{\text{Ethyl alcohol}}{\mathrm{CH_3 \cdot CH_2OH}} \\
\downarrow +2\mathrm{H} & \\
\underset{\text{Malic acid}}{\mathrm{HOOC \cdot CH_2 \cdot CHOH \cdot COOH}} & \\
\downarrow -\mathrm{H_2O} & \\
\underset{\text{Fumaric acid}}{\mathrm{HOOC \cdot CH{=}CH \cdot COOH}} &
\end{array}
$$

According to this scheme: (1) pyruvic acid, lactic acid, acetaldehyde, and alcohol probably are formed by the same series of reactions as in alcoholic fermentation (page 372); (2) the decarboxylation of some pyruvic acid furnishes CO_2, which reacts with the remainder of the pyruvic acid to give oxaloacetic acid, from which (3) malic acid and finally (4) fumaric acid are produced.

For more information see Rhodes, Moyer, Smith, and Kelley (1959).

Cheeses. A number of cheeses are ripened by molds. These may be placed into two groups: (1) the soft cheeses of the Camembert and Brie types; and (2) the green-streaked cheeses of the Roquefort, Gorgonzola, and Stilton types.

The cheeses in the first group are ripened by the mold *Penicillium camemberti*. The curd is produced by the action of rennase, then allowed to drain without the application of pressure. The soft curd is shaped into cakes, salted on the surface, and inoculated with the spores of the mold. The cakes are placed in a damp room where the mold multiplies rapidly on the surface, then gradually penetrates and softens the entire mass of curd. When complete, about 80 per cent of the nitrogenous matter becomes water-soluble. The process requires about 4 weeks.

The cheeses in the second group are prepared by first inoculating the curd with a pure culture of *P. roqueforti*. The curd is then pressed so as to leave irregular cracks in the cake. The cake is aerated from time to time during the ripening process by piercing it with wires. The mold produces a dense growth along the cracks, giving the finished product a streaked appearance. Salt is periodically applied to the surface of the cheese during the ripening process to decrease the population of undesirable organisms. The ripening process requires 5 to 6 months.

Antibiotics. A large number of molds elaborate certain specific toxic substances which interfere with the metabolism of other organisms to such an extent that they are either killed or prevented from multiplying. These specific toxic compounds are known as antibiotics. The best-known representative of this group is penicillin, produced by the mold *Penicillium notatum*, and other species. This important subject is discussed under Antibiosis (page 457).

Miscellaneous Metabolic Products of Molds. In addition to those already discussed, molds produce a large number of compounds which, with few exceptions, are of minor industrial importance. They are, for the most part, nonnitrogenous metabolic products and probably the result of the action of the molds on carbohydrates or carbohydrate-like compounds. It should be noted that, on the whole, molds produce compounds of greater complexity than do bacteria. The compounds which have been isolated and characterized include organic acids, pigments, polysaccharides, antibiotics, aldehydes, esters, higher alcohols, sterols, etc.

For more information see Arnstein and Grant (1956); Birkinshaw (1937); Bracken, Pocker, and Raistrick (1954); Cochrane (1958); Gould (1947); Lockwood and Moyer (1938); Morton and Broadbent (1955); Prescott and Dunn (1959); and Raistrick (1940).

REFERENCES

Arnstein, H. R. V., and P. T. Grant: The metabolism of the penicillia in relation to penicillin biosynthesis, *Bact. Rev.*, 20:133, 1956.

Birkinshaw, J. H.: Biochemistry of the lower fungi, *Biol. Rev.*, 12:357, 1937.

Bracken, A., A. Pocker, and H. Raistrick: Studies in the biochemistry of microorganisms, *Biochem. J.*, 57:587, 1954.

Butkewitsch, W.: Über die bildung der citronensäure aus Zucker in Kulturen von *Penicillium glaucum* und *Aspergillus niger*, *Biochem. Z.*, 136:224, 1923.

Cochrane, V. W.: "Physiology of Fungi," New York, John Wiley & Sons, Inc., 1958.

Currie, J. N.: The citric acid fermentation of *Aspergillus niger*, *J. Biol. Chem.*, 31:15, 1917.

Erkama, J., and B. Hägerstrand: Studies on the metabolism of *Aspergillus niger*. III. The effect of oxygen tension on the formation of citric and oxalic acids in surface mould cultures, *Acta Chem. Scand.*, 3:867, 1949.

————, ————, and S. Junkkonen: Studies on the metabolism of *Aspergillus niger*. II. Effect of iron on the production of citric and oxalic acids, *ibid.*, 3:862, 1949.

————, I. Heikkinen, B. Hägerstrand, and S. Junkkonen: Studies on the metabolism of *Aspergillus niger*. I. The effect of aeration on the formation of citric and oxalic acids in surface mould cultures, *ibid.*, 3:858, 1949.

Foster, J. W.: "Chemical Activities of Fungi," New York, Academic Press, Inc., 1949.

————, S. F. Carson, S. Ruben, and M. D. Kamen: Radioactive carbon as an indicator of carbon dioxide utilization. VII. The assimilation of carbon dioxide by molds, *Proc. Nat. Acad. Sci.*, 27:590, 1941.

———— and J. B. Davis: Anaerobic formation of fumaric acid by the mold *Rhizopus nigricans*, *J. Bact.*, 56:329, 1948.

Gould, B. S.: Chemical compounds formed from sugars by molds, Scientific Report Series No. 7, Sugar Research Foundation, Inc., New York, 1947.

Herrick, H. T., and O. E. May: The production of gluconic acid by the *Penicillium lutem-purpurogenum* group. II. Some optimal conditions for acid formation, *J. Biol. Chem.*, 77:185, 1928.

Karow, E. O., and S. A. Waksman: Production of citric acid in submerged culture, *Ind. Eng. Chem.*, 39:821, 1947.

Lockwood, L. B., and A. J. Moyer: The production of chemicals by filamentous fungi, *Botan. Rev.*, 4:140, 1938.

Martin, S. M., P. W. Wilson, and R. H. Burris: Citric acid formation from $C^{14}O_2$ by *Aspergillus niger*, *Arch. Biochem.*, 26:103, 1950.

Molliard, M.: Sur une nouvelle fermentation acide produite par le *Sterigmatocystis nigra*, *Compt. rend.*, 174:881, 1922.

Morton, A. G., and D. Broadbent: The formation of extracellular nitrogen compounds by fungi, *J. Gen. Microbiol.*, 12:248, 1955.

Moyer, A. J., O. E. May, and H. T. Herrick: Production of gluconic acid by *Penicillium chrysogenum*, *Centr. Bakt.*, Abt. II, 95:311, 1936.

Porges, N., T. F. Clark, and E. A. Gastrock: Gluconic acid production. Repeated use of submerged *Aspergillus niger* for semi-continuous production, *Ind. Eng. Chem.*, 32:107, 1940.

Prescott, S. C., and C. G. Dunn: "Industrial Microbiology," New York, McGraw-Hill Book Company, Inc., 1959.

Raistrick, H.: Biochemistry of the lower fungi, *Ann. Rev. Biochem.*, 9:571, 1940.

Raper, K. B., and C. Thom: "A Manual of the Penicillia," Baltimore, The Williams & Wilkins Company, 1949.

Rhodes, R. A., A. J. Moyer, M. L. Smith, and S. E. Kelley: Production of fumaric acid by *Rhizopus arrhizus*, *Applied Microbiol.*, 7:74, 1959.

Shu, P., and M. J. Johnson: Effect of the composition of the sporulation medium on citric acid production by *Aspergillus niger* in submerged culture, *J. Bact.*, 54:161, 1947.

Skinner, C. E., C. W. Emmons, and H. M. Tsuchiya: "Henrici's Molds, Yeasts, and Actinomycetes," New York, John Wiley & Sons, Inc., 1947.

Smith, G.: "An Introduction to Industrial Mycology," London, Edward Arnold & Co., 1942.

Stauffer, J. F., and M. P. Backus: Spontaneous and induced variation in selected stocks of the *Penicillium chrysogenum* series, *Ann. N.Y. Acad. Sci.*, **60**:35, 1954.

Takamine, J.: Enzymes of *Aspergillus oryzae* and the application of its amyloclastic enzyme to the fermentation industry, *Chem. News*, **110**:215, 1914.

Thom, C.: The evolution of species concepts in *Aspergillus* and *Penicillium, Ann. N.Y. Acad. Sci.*, **60**:24, 1954.

———— and K. B. Raper: "A Manual of the Aspergilli," Baltimore, The Williams & Wilkins Company, 1945.

Tomlinson, N., J. J. R. Campbell, and P. C. Trussell: The influence of zinc, iron, copper, and manganese on the production of citric acid by *Aspergillus niger, J. Bact.*, **59**:217, 1950.

Underkofler, L. A., and E. I. Fulmer: Microbial amylases for saccharification of starch in the alcoholic fermentation, *Chronica Botan.*, **7**:420, 1943.

Wehmer, C.: Préparation d'acide citrique de synthèse par la fermentation du glucose, *Compt rend.*, **117**:332, 1893.

Wells, P. A., A. J. Moyer, J. J. Stubbs, H. T. Herrick, and O. E. May: Gluconic acid production. Effect of pressure, air flow, and agitation on gluconic acid production by submerged mold growths, *Ind. Eng. Chem.*, **29**:653, 1937.

Wolf, F. A., and F. T. Wolf: "The Fungi," vols. I and II, New York, John Wiley & Sons, Inc., 1947.

CHAPTER 7

Nutrition of Bacteria

Culture media (singular, medium) are solid, semisolid, and liquid nutrient preparations employed for the cultivation of microorganisms. They are artificial environments prepared to simulate natural conditions as far as is necessary.

Strict Autotrophic Bacteria. The strict autotrophs cannot utilize organic matter and may even be harmed by its presence. These organisms are able to synthesize complex compounds composing their protoplasm from simple inorganic salts. They obtain their carbon from carbon dioxide and their energy from the oxidation of certain inorganic compounds or even elements. Because of this fact, they are independent of vegetable and animal life.

Strict Heterotrophic Bacteria. The strict heterotrophs cannot synthesize their complex protoplasm from simple inorganic salts but must have organic compounds, such as proteins, peptones, amino acids, and vitamins, for growth.

Facultative Organisms. The facultative heterotrophic forms show characteristics intermediate between the two, being able to utilize both inorganic and organic compounds. They comprise the great majority of bacteria that have been studied and classified.

At one end of the scale, the organisms exhibit complete independence; at the other end, they show complete parasitism. Fildes (1934) advanced the theory that parasitism involved the loss of enzymes essential for the synthesis of bacterial protoplasm, making it necessary to add certain complex ingredients to the culture medium.

COMMON INGREDIENTS OF CULTURE MEDIA

The ingredients commonly added to culture media and their uses are as follows:

Water. Water is absolutely necessary for the existence of living cells. Tap water may show considerable variation in composition from one locality to another, with the result that uniform culture media cannot always be prepared. The calcium and magnesium in tap water react with the phosphates present in peptones, beef extract, and other ingredients of culture media to give insoluble phosphates. The insoluble phosphates may not form in the cold, but during sterilization such media throw down considerable precipitate, which usually proves objectionable. Since distilled water is of definite composition, it should be used in preference to tap water for the preparation of culture media.

Peptones. Peptones are intermediate products of hydrolysis formed by the action of certain proteolytic enzymes (trypsin, pancreatin, papain, etc.) on native proteins. As hydrolysis proceeds, the large colloidal protein molecules become broken up into a series of smaller fragments which are designated, respectively, as proteoses, peptones, peptides, and finally amino acids. The proteoses still exhibit colloidal properties and it is customary to consider them as the last hydrolytic product still possessing true protein characteristics. In other words, the protein nature of the molecule disappears on further hydrolysis.

The commercial peptones are not the same as the peptone of the chemist, who uses the term in its narrow, chemical sense. The commercial preparations employed by the bacteriologist are composed of proteoses or albumoses, peptones, peptides, and amino acids. The proportions vary, depending upon the type of peptone. The usual commercial preparations contain a high percentage of peptones and amino acids, and only a negligible quantity of proteoses and other nitrogenous constituents. Others contain a higher content of proteoses with small amounts of peptones and amino acids. Still others contain all fractions in more or less well-balanced proportions. Some organisms prefer one type of peptone; others grow better on another type.

A whole protein, such as casein or egg albumin, is probably not attacked by bacteria when incorporated in a medium as the only source of nitrogen and carbon. The molecules are believed to be too large to enter a bacterial cell. If a trace of peptone is added to the medium, it will enter the cell and stimulate the elaboration of an extracellular proteolytic enzyme capable of attacking the whole protein. The protein fractions can then enter the bacterial cell, where they are acted upon by the intracellular enzymes.

The most important function of peptones in culture media is to furnish an available source of nitrogen. Since amino acids are amphoteric compounds, peptones are also excellent buffers.

For more information see Hook and Fabian (1943).

Meat Extract. In its preparation, fresh, lean beef is cut into pieces, placed in a vessel with the appropriate amount of water, and heated for several hours with occasional stirring. The liquid portion is poured off and the solid material subjected to gentle pressure to separate any remaining liquid. The extract is cooled to remove fat, and strained. The clear liquid is evaporated in vacuo to the consistency of a pasty mass.

The constituents removed from muscle by boiling in water are known as extractives. The extractives obtained from fresh muscle tissue by boiling in water amount to about 2 per cent of the weight of the muscle. Two classes of extractives are obtained from meat: the nitrogenous and the nonnitrogenous. The nitrogenous extractives include creatine, xanthine, hypoxanthine, uric acid, adenylic acid, inosinic acid, carnosine, carnitine, glycocoll, urea, glutamine, β-alanine, etc. The nonnitrogenous extractives include glycogen, hexosephosphate, lactic acid, succinic acid, inositol, fat inorganic salts, etc.

The use of beef extract in culture media was introduced by Loeffler (1881) and has been a routine procedure in bacteriology ever since. Meat extract is added to media to supply certain substances that stimulate bacterial activity. It contains enzyme exciters, which cause accelerated growth of microorganisms. McIlwain et al. (1939) showed that glutamine, a constituent of beef extract, was a necessary nutrient for the growth of *Streptococcus pyogenes*. Williams (1941) believed that β-alanine was present in beef extract in small amounts, since it may arise from the hydrolysis of carnosine or in traces from pantothenic acid. Stokes, Gunness, and Foster (1944) analyzed beef extract for the presence of eight members of the B complex, namely, thiamine, riboflavin, pantothenic acid, nicotinic acid, biotin, pyridoxin, folic acid, and p-aminobenzoic acid, and found all of them to be present (see pages 171 to 184 for a discussion of growth factors).

Yeast Extract. Yeast extract is prepared by extracting autolyzed yeast cells with water and evaporating the liquid to dryness in vacuo. The autolysis of the yeast cells is carefully controlled to prevent destruction of the natural-occurring vitamins of the B complex.

Yeast extract is an excellent stimulator of bacterial growth and is frequently used in culture media in place of meat extract. It is a rich source of the B vitamins and is used to supply these factors in culture media. For this reason it is superior to meat extract in most culture media.

Gelatin. Gelatin is a protein and is prepared by the hydrolysis of collagen with boiling water. Gelatin is not soluble in cold water but swells and softens when immersed in it. It is quite soluble in boiling water. On cooling, it solidifies to form a transparent gel.

Gelatin is rarely used as a substitute for agar for the preparation of solid media because (1) it is attacked and decomposed by many bacteria and (2) it melts at 37°C. Gelatin is added to media principally to test the ability of organisms to liquefy it. Some organisms can liquefy it; others cannot. It is of importance in the identification of classification of bacteria.

For more information see Bruckman and Rook (1953), Rook and Bruckman (1953).

Agar. Agar is the dried mucilaginous substance extracted from *Gelidium corneum* and other species of *Gelidium* and closely related algae. The plants are found growing chiefly along the coasts of Japan, China, Ceylon, Malaya, and Southern California.

Agar is the sulfuric acid ester of a linear galactan, insoluble in cold water, but soluble in hot water, a 1 per cent neutral solution of which sets at 35 to 50°C. to a firm gel, melting at 80 to 100°C. Since agar is attacked by very few bacteria, it is used in preference to gelatin as a solidifying agent for the growth and isolation of bacterial species.

Stanier (1941, 1942) described seven well-recognized marine species belonging to the genera *Vibrio, Cytophaga,* and *Pseudomonas,* and several *Actinomyces* capable of liquefying agar. The enzyme responsible for agar digestion has been shown to be extracellular.

For more information see Humm (1946), Humm and Shepard (1946), Kadota (1953), Swartz and Gordon (1959).

Sodium Chloride. Sodium chloride is commonly added to culture media to increase their osmotic pressures, although this is usually not necessary.

Sometimes media containing blood are required for (1) cultivation of bacteria or (2) the recognition of a hemolytic reaction on agar. Red blood cells are hemolyzed when added to water or to media having low osmotic pressures. Obviously such media cannot be used for the recognition of a hemolytic reaction. This may be prevented by the addition of sodium chloride in a concentration approximating that of an isotonic solution.

Sodium chloride does not act as a buffer. Salts such as phosphates and carbonates do possess a strong buffering action and are frequently added to culture media for this purpose (see page 194).

Inorganic Requirements. The inorganic requirements of bacteria are not well understood. The chief obstacle to work of this nature is the difficulty encountered in obtaining media sufficiently free of inorganic contaminants to permit accurate observations to be made. In the absence of accurate information, the following elements are usually supplied: Na, K, Mg, Fe, S, and P; while Cl, C, N, and H are usually obtained from organic matter.

Shankar and Bard (1952) reported the necessity of Ca, Mg, Fe, Na, and K for the growth of *Clostridium perfringens* but not Zn, Mn, Co, or Cu. In the absence of Ca, the bacteria grew in an aggregated state, whereas Mg and K deficiency resulted in the appearance of filaments.

Webb (1948) also found Mg to be necessary for the same organism. Filamentous forms were produced in Mg-free media. Such filaments reverted to cells of normal morphology on subculture to a medium containing the metal. Similar results were reported by MacLeod (1951) in his work on *Streptococcus faecalis,* and Rochford and Mandle (1953) on

Diplococcus pneumoniae. The latter workers believed the phenomenon was not dependent upon the presence of capsular material surrounding the cells but rather appeared related to incomplete separation of morphologic units.

MacLeod and Snell (1948) found that K was necessary for the growth of five lactic acid bacteria. The magnitude of the K requirement was greatly increased by the addition of Na and NH_4. Whether or not these ions inhibited growth depended upon the ratio of their concentrations to that of K, and not upon the absolute amounts present.

Brown and Gibbons (1955) reported that Na, Mg, K, and Fe were essential for the growth of red halophilic (salt-loving) bacteria. In Mg-deficient media the rod forms became coccoid in appearance. Growth did not occur in the complete absence of K in the medium.

The necessity of K for other organisms was shown by Carroll et al. (1950); Friedman and Fox (1954); Haynes, Kuehne, and Rhodes (1954); Lester (1958); Shooter and Wyatt (1956); and Sirny et al. (1954).

Sulfur appears to be a universal constituent of living cells. Cowie, Bolton, and Sands (1950) found that the sulfate ion readily passed through cells of *E. coli* and that the uptake of the element was directly proportional to cellular growth.

The iron requirements of bacteria have been studied by Waring and Werkman (1942, 1943, 1944). They employed an iron-deficient medium and found that cells of *A. indologenes* required a minimum of 0.025 part per million of iron in the culture medium for optimal growth. The organism grown on a medium without the addition of iron contained 0.0031 per cent iron. When grown in the same medium with the addition of its minimal requirement (0.025 part per million), it contained 0.0073 per cent iron. When grown with a large excess, it contained 0.1049 per cent iron. The effect of iron deficiency on the enzyme systems of *A. indologenes* showed that catalase, peroxidase, formic dehydrogenase, hydrogenase, and cytochrome systems were depressed.

For more information see Rothstein (1959).

Fermentable Compounds. Fermentable compounds serve two functions in culture media: (1) they furnish readily available sources of energy, provided the organisms elaborate the enzymes necessary to ferment the compounds; and (2) fermentation reactions are of great help in identifying and classifying organisms.

The fermentable compounds commonly added to culture media include:

Monosaccharides:
  Pentoses: arabinose, xylose, rhamnose.
  Hexoses: glucose, levulose, mannose, galactose.
Disaccharides:
  Sucrose, lactose, maltose, trehalose, melibiose.
Trisaccharides:
  Raffinose, melezitose, gentianose.

Polysaccharides:
  Starch, inulin, dextrin, glycogen, cellulose.
Alcohols:
  Trihydric: glycerol.
  Pentahydric: adonitol.
  Hexahydric: mannitol, dulcitol, sorbitol.
Glucosides:
  Salicin, amygdalin.
Noncarbohydrate compounds:
  Inositol.

TYPES OF CULTURE MEDIA

Culture media employed for the cultivation of microorganisms may be divided into two groups on the basis of the nature of the ingredients entering into their composition: (1) synthetic media and (2) nonsynthetic media.

Synthetic Media. Synthetic media are composed of compounds of known chemical composition. They may be composed entirely of inorganic salts; or mixtures of inorganic salts and organic compounds, such as amino acids, lower fatty acids, hydroxy acids, alcohols, and carbohydrates; or inorganic and organic compounds with added vitamins. The exact chemical make-up of all ingredients is known so that two batches of the same medium can be duplicated to a high degree of accuracy. Synthetic media are employed where it is desired to ascertain what effect an organism will have on a certain compound. The nutritional requirements of bacteria may be accurately determined only by the use of synthetic culture media.

The literature shows an increasing number of synthetic media being recommended for the cultivation of all types of organisms, including the fastidious disease producers. Since the nutritional requirements of organisms are becoming better understood, it appears to be only a question of time until most culture media will be of the synthetic type.

For more information see Erlandson and Mackey (1958); Ginsburg and Grossowicz (1957); Sergeant, Lankford, and Traxler (1957).

Nonsynthetic Media. The nonsynthetic media are composed of ingredients of unknown chemical composition. Some of these are beef extract, yeast extract, various peptones, meat infusion, blood, serum, and casein hydrolysate. It is practically impossible to prepare two identical lots of the same medium from different batches of the ingredients.

The usual culture media employed by the bacteriologist are of the nonsynthetic type.

It is now known that the presence of growth factors in culture media is absolutely necessary for the successful cultivation of most bacteria (page 171). The failure of an organism to grow on a certain medium is probably due to the absence of one or more of the essential growth accessory substances. Media are usually selected for their ability to produce results rather than because they are known to contain the necessary growth substances. It seems highly probable that few media containing all the necessary accessory substances can be successfully employed for the cultivation of bacteria. Until such investigations are made, the bacteriologist will continue to employ many kinds of media, each more or less specific for a particular purpose.

NUTRITIONAL REQUIREMENTS

Sources of Nitrogen. A number of recent studies have shown that many bacteria are able to utilize ammonium salts as their only source of nitrogen. This is true of the autotrophic and probably most of the heterotrophic bacteria. Other heterotrophs grow very poorly or not at all when ammonium salts are present as the sole source of nitrogen. These organisms require nitrogen in the form of amino acids. Since it is believed that the bulk of the amino acids in a medium are dissimilated with the liberation of ammonia, compounds furnishing nitrogen, whether amino acids or inorganic ammonium salts, are generally of equal value as immediately available sources of nitrogen.

The amino acid requirements of bacteria show wide differences. Essential amino acids for one organism may not be necessary for another. No rule can be formulated to apply to all bacteria. This must be determined for each organism.

Fildes, Gladstone, and Knight (1933) showed that the amino acid tryptophan was necessary for the growth of *Salmonella typhosa.* They found that the organism could derive its nitrogen requirement from a mixture of amino acids containing tryptophan, but ordinarily the organisms would not grow in the absence of this essential amino acid. Some strains of *S. typhosa,* which initially required tryptophan, could be trained to grow without it; others could not. They concluded that tryptophan was probably an essential constituent of protoplasm and that, if the organisms could not synthesize the compound, it must be added to the culture medium.

Curcho (1948) succeeded in producing mutant cells of *S. typhosa* capable of growing in the absence of tryptophan. The mutants retained the tryptophan independence through daily transfers for over a year.

Rydon (1948), on the basis of experimental evidence, concluded that anthranilic acid was synthesized by *S. typhosa* and that the compound was a precursor of indole in the biosynthesis of tryptophan. He suggested the following scheme:

$$
\left.\begin{array}{l} \text{Anthranilic acid} \\ \text{Unknown substance} \end{array}\right\} \xrightarrow{A} \left.\begin{array}{l} \text{Indole} \\ \text{Serine} \end{array}\right\} \xrightarrow{B} \left.\begin{array}{l} \text{Tryptophan} \\ \text{Other amino acids} \end{array}\right\} \xrightarrow{C} \text{Protein}
$$

Fildes (1956) showed that strains of S. *typhosa*, in which the indole → tryptophan enzyme was unimpaired, synthesized tryptophan in excess during growth. The amount produced might be so small as to be undetectable by the methods used, but when indole in excess was added

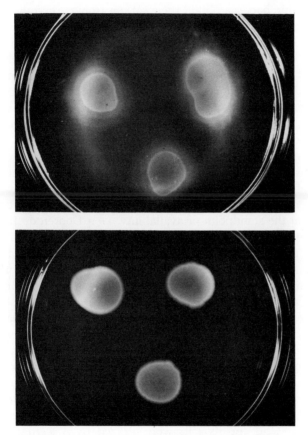

Fig. 99. Two plates of casein agar were flooded with a tryptophan-requiring mutant of *Salmonella typhosa*, and the surfaces dried. Then a few drops of a tryptophan-producing mutant were spotted on the plates. Into the lid of the upper plate was inserted a piece of filter paper carrying a few drops of dilute indole. The S. *typhosa* spotted on the surface synthesized tryptophan from the indole vapors. The tryptophan was utilized by the organisms flooded over the surface of the agar, causing the formation of halos of growth. In the absence of indole (lower plate), the spotted organisms failed to synthesize sufficient tryptophan to produce halos of the organisms flooded on the plate. (*Courtesy of P. Fildes.*)

to a culture, the production of tryptophan was much greater. Experiments with E. *coli* also showed an accumulation of tryptophan in cultures containing indole (Fig. 99). The survival of the tryptophan in this case was due to inhibition of the tryptophanase enzyme by the indole.

For more information see Brenner (1955), Campbell and Frank (1956), Morton and Macmillan (1954), Peters and Snell (1954), Rafelson et al. (1954), Rhuland and Bard (1952), and Yanofsky (1956).

Use of Carbon Compounds. As indicated in the opening paragraphs of this chapter, the carbon requirements of organisms vary considerably. The autotrophic bacteria obtain their carbon from carbon dioxide or carbonates. The heterotrophic bacteria require carbon compounds for energy and cell synthesis. The variety of carbon compounds available to organisms varies considerably from one species to another, which probably accounts for the presence of organisms in specific environments.

Braun and Cahn-Bronner tested a large number of carbon compounds, including formic, acetic, oxalic, lactic, succinic, malic, tartaric, and citric acids and glycerol, glucose, and arabinose. They found that glucose, glycerol, and lactic and citric acids were utilized more than any of the other carbon compounds when tested against *Salmonella schottmuelleri*, *S. enteritidis*, and *S. typhosa*. Acetic and oxalic acids ranked next. Formic and probably tartaric acids were not available as sources of carbon. The amino acids ranked lower than the organic acids, carbohydrates, and glycerol from the standpoint of availability. Den Dooren de Jong (1926) tested about 250 organic compounds for their availability as sources of carbon for a number of organisms. The compounds were added to a synthetic medium containing ammonia as the only source of nitrogen. His conclusions were similar to those of Braun and Cahn-Bronner. He found that carbohydrates and related compounds were most generally utilized; these were followed by malic, citric, succinic, and lactic acids; next came the fatty acids; and last the monohydric alcohols.

Braun and Cahn-Bronner found that anaerobic growth was entirely absent when *S. schottmuelleri* was inoculated into an inorganic medium containing ammonium lactate and glucose. Koser (1923) found the same to be true when the members of the *Escherichia* and *Aerobacter* groups were inoculated into media containing various organic acids as carbon sources. Citric acid and its salts were utilized by *A. aerogenes* but not by *E. coli* (see page 561).

Formation of Lipides. The formation of lipides by bacteria is dependent upon the nature of the carbon compounds added to media. Stephenson and Whetham (1922) employed an inorganic medium containing ammonium salts to which were added (1) lactic acid, (2) lactic and acetic acids, (3) glucose, and (4) glucose and acetic acid. The media were inoculated with *Mycobacterium phlei*, an acid-fast organism. Their results are shown in Table 3. The addition of acetate to the various media produced no increase in protein formation, but did increase the lipide concentration. Increased concentrations of lactate and glucose increased both protein and lipide, usually the former. An organism that normally

TABLE 3. EFFECT OF COMPOSITION OF MEDIUM ON FAT FORMATION BY
Mycobacterium phlei

Constituents of medium	Period of maximum lipide formation, days	Milligrams per 100 ml. medium		Ratio, lipide/nitrogen
		Nitrogen synthesized	Lipides synthesized	
0.68% lactic acid.........	10	19	16	0.84
1.4% lactic acid..........	11	26	20	0.78
1.2% lactic acid ⎫	7	20	35	1.78
0.4% acetic acid ⎭				
1% glucose..............	12	18	28	1.6
1% glucose ⎫	21	18	42	2.34
1% acetic acid ⎭				
1% glucose..............	15	15	19	1.3
2% glucose..............	15	34	21	0.62

synthesizes sufficient lipide material to become acid-fast could be made to grow acid-sensitive by omitting from the culture medium an appropriate carbon source.

Larson and Larson (1922) reported that organisms which fermented glucose or glycerol did not synthesize additional lipide. On the other hand, organisms which did not ferment glucose or glycerol utilized the compounds for fat synthesis. Glycerol was superior to glucose for this purpose.

Geiger and Anderson (1939) inoculated *Agrobacterium tumefaciens* into two synthetic media, one containing glycerol and the other sucrose. The organisms grown on the glycerol-containing medium yielded only 2 per cent of total lipide, whereas those grown on the sucrose-containing medium gave 6 per cent of lipide. The nature of the fatty material synthesized by the organisms on the two media also showed considerable difference (Table 4).

TABLE 4. YIELD OF LIPIDES FROM DRIED *Agrobacterium tumefaciens*

	Medium 1, grams	Medium 2, grams
Bacteria used for extraction..............	364	276
Alcohol-ether-soluble lipides..............	4.85	16.23
Chloroform-soluble lipides...............	2.46	0.63
Total phosphatide......................	3.21	10.90
Total acetone-soluble fat.................	3.35	5.92
Ether-insoluble substance................	0.64	0.03

VITAMINS AND GROWTH FACTORS

Hopkins (1906) was probably the first to point out that compounds other than fat, protein, carbohydrate, minerals, water, and oxygen are necessary in human nutrition. This observation led to the discovery of the vitamins by Funk (1912). Wildiers (1901) reasoned that, since certain factors not known at that time were required in human nutrition, a comparable situation existed in the requirements of fungi. He employed an inorganic medium containing cane sugar and ammonia as sources of carbon and nitrogen, respectively, and found that yeast cells failed to grow unless a certain number of organisms (size of inoculum) were transferred to fresh medium. A larger inoculum carried more growth factors to the new medium, resulting in multiplication. The addition of a boiled suspension of yeast produced the same growth-promoting effect on small inocula as the addition of an emulsion of living yeast. Wildiers named the growth-promoting factor *bios*.

The term *growth factor* was originally applied to any compound that produced a stimulatory effect on the growth of organisms. The term *vitamin* was used in connection with any substance which in minute amount was necessary in the nutrition of animals. Since growth factors and vitamins have been shown to be the same, the terms now are used interchangeably. Williams (1941) coined the term *nutrilite* to include any organic substance, regardless of its nature, which in minute amount is of importance in the nutrition of an organism.

It is now known that bios is a mixture of several of the water-soluble members of the vitamin B complex, including thiamine (vitamin B_1), pantothenic acid, pyridoxin (vitamin B_6), biotin, and inositol.

A large number of vitamins have been studied and their chemical make-up determined. Most of these have been synthesized. Some are simple in structure; others are quite complex.

Response of Bacteria to Growth Factors. The fact that an organism will grow in the absence of a particular growth factor in the medium does not mean necessarily that the factor is not required. Some organisms can synthesize one or more factors, whereas others are unable to do so. Therefore, it is erroneous to conclude that an organism does not require a certain factor because it is absent from the medium in which the cells are growing.

O'Kane (1941) cultivated micrococci on a medium free of riboflavin and found that the organisms synthesized the growth factor. Burkholder and McVeigh (1942) demonstrated that certain intestinal species could synthesize a number of vitamins of the B complex. Actinomycetes were shown by Herrick and Alexopoulos (1943) to be capable of synthesizing thiamine. Miller (1944) reported that *Escherichia coli* synthesized folic acid. Altenbern and Ginoza (1954) showed that smooth cells of *Bru-*

cella abortus possessed an enzyme which coupled pantoyl lactone and β-alanine to produce pantothenic acid.

For more information see Maas and Vogel (1953).

Some bacteria can be adapted to dispense with certain vitamins by repeatedly subculturing to fresh media. For example, strains of *Propionibacterium* can be adapted to grow without riboflavin and thiamine. Koser and Wright (1943) isolated variants of dysentery bacilli capable of growing without added nicotinamide.

VITAMINS REQUIRED BY BACTERIA

The factors most frequently reported as promoting growth of bacteria include thiamine chloride, biotin, pantothenic acid, riboflavin, pyridoxin, nicotinic acid, and *p*-aminobenzoic acid. In addition to these, a number of miscellaneous compounds have been shown to be indispensable for some, but not necessarily for all, bacteria. Some of these are nicotinamide, inositol, pimelic acid, β-alanine, glutamic acid, glutamine, folic acid, purines, pyrimidines, glutathione, hematin, betaine, purine nucleotides, choline, and vitamin B_{12}.

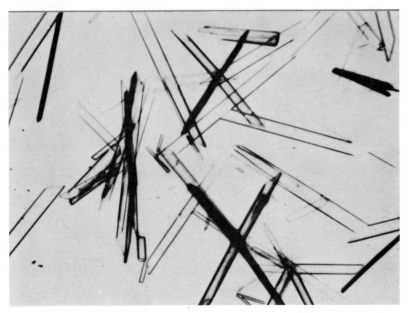

FIG. 100. Thiamine chloride crystals. (*Courtesy of Merck & Company, Inc.*)

Thiamine Chloride (Vitamin B_1). This factor is probably necessary for the growth of all bacteria (Fig. 100). A number of organisms have been shown to be capable of synthesizing the compound. Chemically it is a pyrimidine-thiazole compound having the following structural formula:

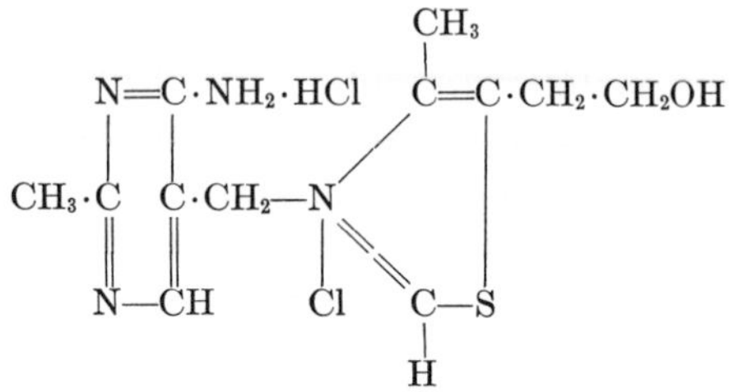

$$\begin{array}{cc}
& CH_3 \\
N{=}C{\cdot}NH_2{\cdot}HCl & C{=}C{\cdot}CH_2{\cdot}CH_2OH \\
CH_3{\cdot}C \quad C{\cdot}CH_2{-}N & \\
N{-}CH \quad Cl \quad C{-}S & \\
& H
\end{array}$$

Thiamine chloride

The pyrophosphate ester (thiamine pyrophosphate) is called cocarboxylase (page 326). It participates in all decarboxylations which lead to the formation of aldehydes and carbon dioxide. It has been shown that cocarboxylase could replace vitamin B_1 in the nutrition of yeasts. It is probable that vitamin B_1 serves as the precursor of cocarboxylase.

Biotin. This growth factor was first isolated by Kögl (1935). It is identical with vitamin H. It has been crystallized as pure biotin and as the biotin methyl ester (Fig. 101).

Du Vigneaud et al. (1942) worked out the structure of the compound and showed it to be 2' keto-3,4-imidazolido-2-tetrahydrothiophene-*n*-valeric acid:

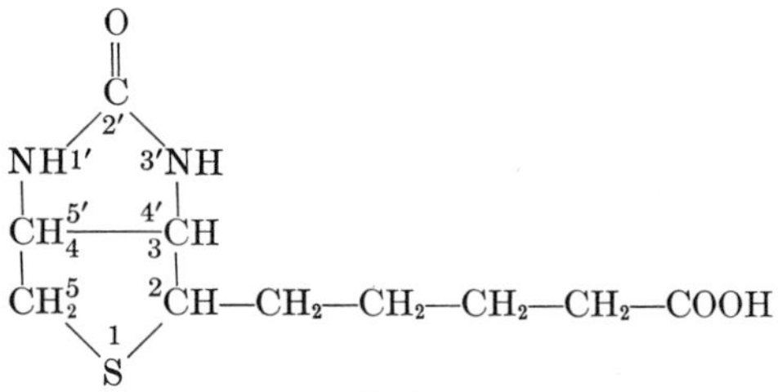

$$\begin{array}{c}
O \\
\| \\
C \\
/2' \quad \backslash \\
NH1' \quad 3'NH \\
CH5'_4 \quad 4'_3 CH \\
CH^5_2 \quad {}^2CH{-}CH_2{-}CH_2{-}CH_2{-}CH_2{-}COOH \\
\backslash 1 / \\
S
\end{array}$$

Biotin

Biotin is present in all living cells in very minute amounts. The fungi (bacteria, yeasts, molds) are the best sources of the vitamin. According to Kögl, an amount as small as 0.00004 microgram added to 2 ml. of a yeast culture caused a 100 per cent increase in growth. This is equivalent to 1 part in 50 billion parts of medium.

The exact function of biotin is not clearly understood. It appears to participate in various enzymatic reactions. Shive and Rogers (1947) believed that biotin functioned as a coenzyme in the carboxylation of pyruvic acid to oxalacetic acid:

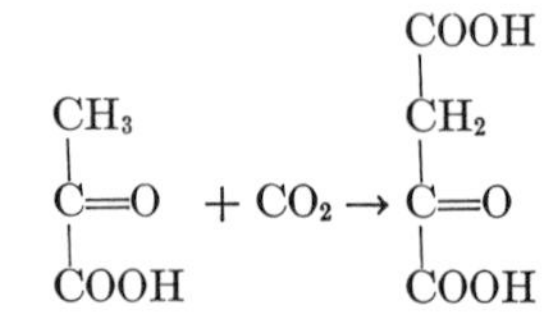

$$\begin{array}{cc}
& COOH \\
CH_3 & CH_2 \\
C{=}O + CO_2 \rightarrow & C{=}O \\
COOH & COOH
\end{array}$$

Pyruvic acid   Oxalacetic acid

The oxalacetic acid, in the presence of glutamic acid or alanine, may be converted into aspartic acid (see page 326).

Stokes, Larson, and Gunness (1947) found that biotin could completely substitute for aspartic acid in the growth of a number of bacteria. They concluded that biotin participated in the synthesis of aspartic acid.

Delwiche (1950) stated that biotin was closely concerned with the decarboxylation of succinic acid to propionic acid by *Propionibacterium pentosaceum*.

FIG. 101. Biotin methyl ester. (*Courtesy of S.M.A. Division, Wyeth Inc.*)

Lichstein (1950) isolated a coenzyme from yeast extract which contained an acid-stable material that replaced biotin for growth of *Saccharomyces cerevisiae*. He believed that this acid-stable component was a derivative of biotin that might be an intermediate in the synthesis of the coenzyme from biotin. This coenzyme was active in the oxalacetate decarboxylase and succinic acid decarboxylase systems.

Carlson and Whiteside-Carlson (1949) found that *Leuconostoc* did not require biotin for the utilization of sucrose, but that the vitamin was essential for growth when the constituent monosaccharides were added to the medium.

Campbell and Williams (1953) reported that all biotin-requiring strains of *Bacillus coagulans* and *B. stearothermophilus* could substitute oxybiotin. Some strains could satisfy their biotin requirement with aspartic acid; some with oleic acid; and some with pimelic acid.

Pantothenic Acid. Williams and Bradway (1931) were the first to show that a growth factor which they called pantothenic acid was neces-

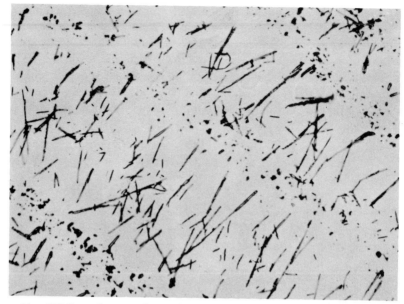

Fig. 102. Pantothenic acid crystals. (*Courtesy of Merck & Company, Inc.*)

Fig. 103. Riboflavin crystals. (*Courtesy of Merck & Company, Inc.*)

sary in the nutrition of yeast (Fig. 102). In a later report, Williams et al. (1933) stated that pantothenic acid was a growth determinant of universal biological importance, being present in all living cells. It was shown to consist of β-alanine united to a saturated dihydroxy acid by a peptide-like combination:

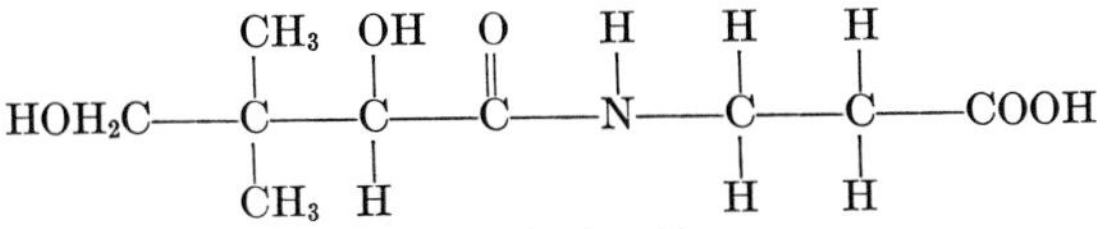

Pantothenic acid

Pantothenic acid is a component of coenzyme A, which is involved in the acetylation of aromatic amines and choline (see page 326). Pantothenic acid is also related to the utilization of other vitamins, especially riboflavin.

For more information see Brown and Snell (1954), Kersey and Porter (1948), King and Cheldelin (1953), and Rowatt (1948).

Riboflavin. This factor has been studied extensively and found to be necessary for the growth of a large number of organisms (Fig. 103). It is sometimes referred to as vitamins B_2, G, lactoflavin (from milk), and ovoflavin (from eggs). Chemically it is 6,7-dimethyl-9-(D-1'-ribityl) isoalloxazine:

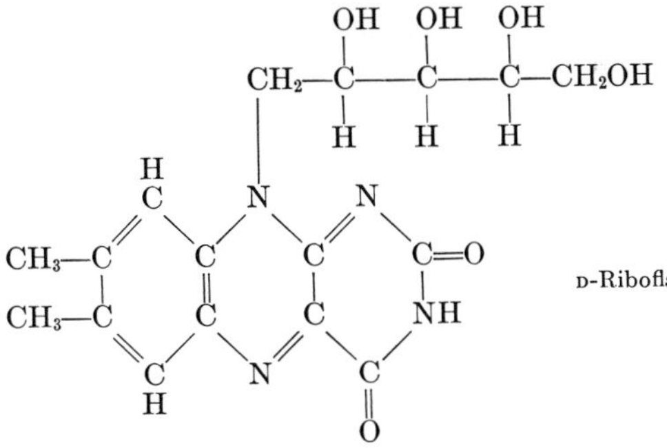

D-Riboflavin

Riboflavin plays an important function in many enzyme systems. It is a component of a number of enzymes known as the flavoproteins. These include Warburg's yellow enzyme (see page 294), diaphorase (see page 325), cytochrome c reductase, xanthine dehydrogenase, D-amino acid oxidase, etc.

Pyridoxin. This growth factor is sometimes called vitamin B_6. It was first recognized as a vitamin by György (1935). Keresztesy and Stevens (1938) and Lepkovsky (1938), working independently, isolated the vitamin in crystalline form (Fig. 104). Harris and Folkers (1939) synthesized the vitamin and showed it to be 2-methyl-3-hydroxy-4,5-di-(hydroxymethyl)-pyridine. Two other important naturally occurring substances with vitamin B_6 activity are pyridoxal, 2-methyl-3-hy-

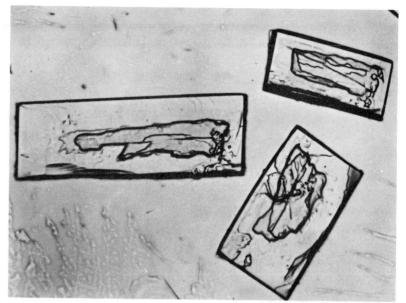

FIG. 104. Pyridoxin crystals. (*Courtesy of Merck & Company, Inc.*)

FIG. 105. Nicotinic acid crystals. (*Courtesy of Merck & Company, Inc.*)

droxy-4-formyl-5-hydroxy-methylpyridine, and pyridoxamine, 2-methyl-3-hydroxy-4-aminomethyl-5-hydroxymethylpyridine:

$$
\begin{array}{ccc}
\text{C} \cdot \text{CH}_2\text{OH} & \text{C} \cdot \text{CHO} & \text{C} \cdot \text{CH}_2\text{NH}_2 \\
\text{HOC} \quad \text{C} \cdot \text{CH}_2\text{OH} & \text{HOC} \quad \text{C} \cdot \text{CH}_2\text{OH} & \text{HOC} \quad \text{C} \cdot \text{CH}_2\text{OH} \\
\text{CH}_3\text{C} \quad \text{CH} & \text{CH}_3\text{C} \quad \text{CH} & \text{CH}_3\text{C} \quad \text{CH} \\
\text{N} & \text{N} & \text{N} \\
\text{Pyridoxin} & \text{Pyridoxal} & \text{Pyridoxamine}
\end{array}
$$

These three vitamins function in the form of a coenzyme. This coenzyme is pyridoxal-5-phosphate; it is also called codecarboxylase, cotransaminase, etc. Pyridoxin, pyridoxal, and pyridoxamine owe their vitamin activity to the ability of the organism to convert them into the active pyridoxal-5-phosphate. It functions as a transaminase for the synthesis of amino acids from their keto analogues. Pyridoxal-5-phosphate has also been reported to function as a glutamate-aspartate transaminase. When combined with protein (apoenzyme), pyridoxal-5-phosphate catalyzes the decarboxylation of amino acids.

Nicotinic Acid (Niacin) and Nicotinamide (Niacinamide). Nicotinic acid was first prepared in 1867, but the nutritional importance of the compound was not recognized until 1937 by Elvehjem et al. (Fig. 105). The structural formulas of nicotinic acid and its amide are as follows:

$$
\begin{array}{cc}
\text{H} & \text{H} \\
\text{C} & \text{C} \\
\text{HC} \quad \text{C} \cdot \text{COOH} & \text{HC} \quad \text{C} \cdot \text{CONH}_2 \\
\text{HC} \quad \text{CH} & \text{HC} \quad \text{CH} \\
\text{N} & \text{N} \\
\text{Nicotinic acid} & \text{Nicotinamide}
\end{array}
$$

Nicotinic acid or its amide is required by all living cells. It is an essential part of coenzymes I and II (see pages 314 ff.). As far as is known, nicotinic acid and its derivatives have no function in living cells other than as parts of the above-named coenzymes.

p-Aminobenzoic Acid. Woods (1940) and Fildes (1941) showed that p-aminobenzoic acid (PABA) was highly active in reversing the bacteriostatic action of the sulfonamides. They reported that sulfanilamide competed with PABA for an enzyme and thus interfered with some essential metabolic reaction. Landy et al. (1943) found that sulfonamide-resistant strains of *Staphylococcus aureus* produced greater amounts of PABA than their parent strains. The quantity of PABA synthesized by resistant strains appeared sufficient to account for their resistance to sulfonamide drugs.

It has the following structural formula:

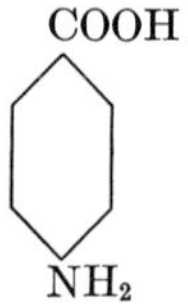

p-Aminobenzoic acid

PABA is a unit in the structure of another vitamin, namely, pteroyl-glutamic acid or folic acid. It is almost universally agreed that the sulfonamides act by inhibiting the conversion of PABA to folic acid.

Folic Acid. Snell and Peterson (1939, 1940) found that *Lactobacillus casei* required a hitherto unrecognized growth substance, which they called the *L. casei* eluate factor. They noted that the factor possessed many of the properties of a purine. Stokstad (1941) found that a mixture of guanine and thymine possessed some of the growth-promoting properties of the eluate factor. Mitchell, Snell, and Williams (1941) concentrated the factor to a state approaching purity and named it *folic acid*.

Chemically, folic acid is pteroylglutamic acid, having the following structure:

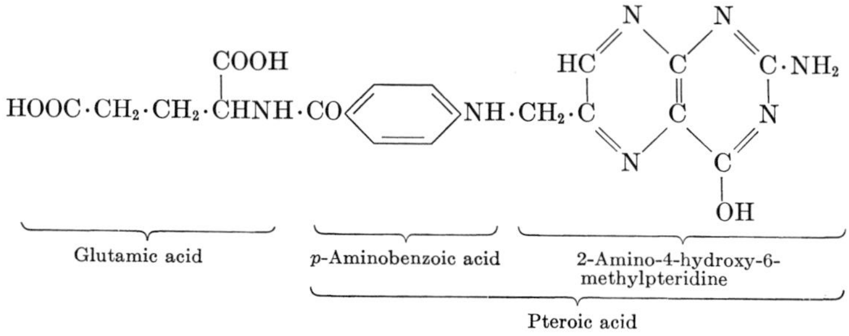

p-Aminobenzoic acid and glutamic acid are components of folic acid. Folic acid appears to be primarily concerned with the synthesis of purines and pyrimidines. It is also believed to be a requirement for the synthesis of certain amino acids which involve the incorporation of a single carbon fragment. It appears that carbon dioxide may serve as the source of the carbon fragment in this experimental system.

For more information see Nickerson and Webb (1956), Stockstad (1954), Walper and Fink (1956).

Inositol. This vitamin was the first pure substance isolated that was found to contribute to bios activity. Inositol was first isolated in pure form by Eastcott (1928) from yeast.

Nine stereoisomeric forms of inositol are possible. Of these, seven are optically inactive or *meso* forms, and two are asymmetric enantiomorphs. The form which is most widely distributed in nature and which is of importance in the nutrition of microorganisms is optically inactive. It has been named *myo*-inositol, and has the following structure:

$$\text{Inositol}$$

Inositol is of widespread occurrence and great abundance in nature. Because of this fact it is believed to act both as a vitamin and as an energy-yielding nutrient. Its exact function in living cells in terms of enzymes and coenzymes is not clearly understood. It has been shown

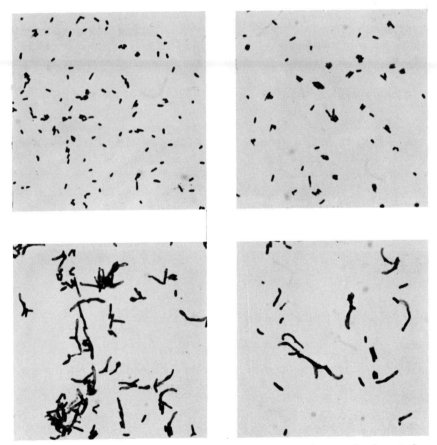

FIG. 106. Effect of various concentrations of vitamin B₁₂ on the growth of an *Arthrobacter* species. Gram stain. Upper left, 2 μgm/ml. Normal cells. Upper right, 1 μgm/ml. Normal cells, slightly larger. Lower left, 0.075 μgm/ml. Cells swollen and elongated with slight branching. Lower right, 0.05 μgm/ml. More pronounced branching. Large Gram-negative areas. (*After Chaplin and Lochhead.*)

to be a constituent of certain phospholipides isolated from bacteria. It combines with phosphate, proteins, fatty acids, glycerol, and galactose.

Vitamin B$_{12}$. This is a cobalt- and phosphorus-containing vitamin, usually produced by microbial fermentation or obtained from liver.

Evidence seems to indicate that the vitamin is a polypyrrole related in some way to hemin or to bile pigments. Its exact chemical structure is not clearly understood.

Vitamin B$_{12}$ affects the phosphorus metabolism of *Lactobacillus leichmannii*. The vitamin increases the uptake of phosphorus in the desoxyribonucleic acid fraction of the cell, which would indicate that it is involved in nucleic acid synthesis.

Chaplin and Lochhead (1956) studied the B$_{12}$ requirements of a species of the genus *Arthrobacter*. They showed that with suboptimal concentrations of the vitamin, growth in liquid medium was flocculent, whereas cultures with adequate amounts were uniformly turbid. Flocculation was associated with abnormal cell morphology. The cells were noticeably swollen, elongated, and irregularly bent and showed rudimentary branching (Fig. 106).

Pimelic Acid and β-Alanine. Mueller (1935) and Mueller and Kapnick (1935) showed that the diphtheria bacillus, *Corynebacterium diphtheriae*, produced a luxuriant growth in a medium composed entirely of amino acids to which were added a purified liver extract and a carbon source, such as glycerol and lactic acid, and suitable inorganic salts. Mueller (1937*a, b*) identified two of the constituents of the liver extract, essential for growth of the diphtheria bacillus, as pimelic acid and nicotinic acid. In a later report, Mueller and Cohen (1937) found β-alanine to be a third growth accessory substance present in liver extract responsible for the luxuriant growth of the diphtheria bacillus in a synthetic medium. The structural formulas for pimelic acid and β-alanine are as follows:

$$
\begin{array}{cc}
\text{COOH} & \text{CH}_2\text{NH}_2 \\
| & | \\
(\text{CH}_2)_5 & \text{CH}_2 \\
| & | \\
\text{COOH} & \text{COOH} \\
\text{Pimelic acid} & \beta\text{-Alanine}
\end{array}
$$

Pimelic acid is one of the degradation products of biotin and has been shown to be capable of serving as a biotin precursor for some microorganisms.

β-Alanine is a component of pantothenic acid, being united to a saturated dihydroxy acid by a peptide-like linkage (page 175).

Glutamic Acid and Glutamine. McIlwain et al. (1939) found that glutamine was an essential nutrient for the growth of some strains of *Streptococcus pyogenes* but not for others. Glutamine is present in beef extract and is probably widely distributed in the animal body. Later

Fildes and Gladstone (1939) and McIlwain (1939) reported that glutamine was indispensable for the growth of many strains of *S. pyogenes*
and other bacterial species. Pollack and Lindner (1942) stated that nine
species of lactic acid-producing bacteria required either glutamine or
glutamic acid for growth. They concluded that bacteria required glutamine or glutamic acid for the construction of cell proteins because the
requirements of these amino acids are of the order of magnitude that
would be expected for this function. Lankford and Snell (1943) found
glutamine to be necessary for the growth of certain strains of *Neisseria
gonorrhoeae*. Glutamic acid is a component of another vitamin, namely,
folic acid.

The structural formulas for glutamic acid and glutamine are as follows:

$$
\begin{array}{ll}
\text{COOH} & \text{CONH}_2 \\
| & | \\
\text{CH}_2 & \text{CH}_2 \\
| & | \\
\text{CH}_2 & \text{CH}_2 \\
| & | \\
\text{CHNH}_2 & \text{CHNH}_2 \\
| & | \\
\text{COOH} & \text{COOH} \\
\text{L-Glutamic acid} & \text{L-Glutamine}
\end{array}
$$

Purines and Pyrimidines. Richardson (1936) found that uracil was
necessary for the growth of *Staphylococcus aureus*. Snell and Mitchell
(1941) reported the necessity of uracil for the growth of *Lactobacillus
plantarum*, thymine for *Streptococcus lactis*, and adenine for *L. plantarum*. Shull, Hutchings, and Peterson (1942) and Pollack and Lindner
(1942) found that adenine, guanine, uracil, and xanthine were necessary
for the growth of *L. casei*. Hutner (1944) and Rogers (1944) reported
the necessity of uracil for *Shigella paradysenteriae* and *S. pyogenes*, respectively.

Chattaway (1944) showed that orotic acid stimulated the growth of
L. casei. Wieland et al. (1950) reported the necessity of orotic acid
for *L. bulgaricus*. Wright et al. (1950, 1953) showed that ureidosuccinic
acid could partially replace the orotic acid requirement, and that both
were precursors of nucleic acid pyrimidines. Snell, Kitay, and McNutt
(1948); Wright, Skeggs, and Huff (1948); and Kitay, McNutt, and Snell
(1950) found that desoxyribosides stimulated growth of lactic acid
bacteria. Pearson (1949) reported the need of a number of purines for
the growth of *Photobacterium fischeri*.

$$
\begin{array}{l}
\text{HN}\!\!-\!\!\!-\!\!\text{C}\!=\!\!\text{O} \\
| \qquad\quad | \\
\text{O}\!=\!\text{C} \quad \text{CH} \\
| \qquad\quad \| \\
\text{HN}\!\!-\!\!\!-\!\!\text{C}\!-\!\text{COOH}
\end{array}
\qquad
\begin{array}{c}
\text{Orotic acid} \\
\text{(Uracil-4-carboxylic acid)}
\end{array}
$$

It is quite likely that purines are utilized in the synthesis of nucleic
acids and related substances. Since folic acid contains a purine-like

component, small amounts are probably utilized in the synthesis of that vitamin.

The formulas of the various purines and pyrimidines may be found on pages 287 *ff.*

For more information see Brooke, Ushiba, and Magasanik (1954); Reynolds, Lieberman, and Kornberg (1955).

V and X Factors. Pfeiffer (1893) reported that the organism *Haemophilus influenzae* would not grow in a broth medium unless blood was added. Thjötta (1921), Thjötta and Avery (1921*a*, *b*), and Fildes (1921, 1922) found that the same organism required the presence of two factors which they named the V and X factors, both of which are present in blood. The V factor is also present in many plant extracts and in a large number of bacteria. It is thermolabile, being destroyed in 15 min. at 90°C., is very sensitive to alkali but not to acid, diffuses through parchment membranes, and is not readily destroyed by atmospheric oxygen. The X factor is found in potatoes and in some bacteria. It is thermostable, resisting a temperature of 120°C. for 45 min.

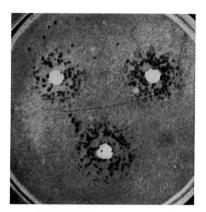

Fig. 107. Satellite colonies of *Neisseria gonorrhoeae*. Agar was streaked with *N. gonorrhoeae*, then spotted with a *Micrococcus*. The colonies of *N. gonorrhoeae* grow as satellites at some distance from the colony of the *Micrococcus*. (*After Lankford et al.*)

H. influenzae is unable to grow on media containing only the X factor. However, it will grow on media in association with an organism, such as *Staphylococcus aureus*, which is capable of producing the V factor. The characteristic arrangement of colonies of *H. influenzae* in such an association is sometimes referred to as the satellite phenomenon. The hemophilic organisms grow as satellites in isolated colonies at some distance from the colonies of *S. aureus*.

Lankford et al. (1943) observed the same phenomenon on agar plates streaked with a mixture of nonpigmented *Micrococcus* and *Neisseria gonorrhoeae* (Fig. 107).

The organism *H. parainfluenzae* requires only the V factor for growth. Lwoff and Lwoff (1937*a*, *b*) isolated the V factor from yeast and added the extract to a culture of the organism. They noted that V activity paralleled the codehydrogenase I concentration of the yeast extract. This substance was found to replace the V factor in extremely low concentration. Codehydrogenases I and II are very similar chemically but are not, as a rule, interchangeable. As growth factors, however, codehydrogenase

II can replace codehydrogenase I. Since one or the other factor must be supplied before growth can occur, they are considered to be true vitamins. Chemically, codehydrogenase I is diphosphopyridine nucleotide and codehydrogenase II is triphosphopyridine nucleotide (see page 323).

X factor requirements are supplied largely by the addition of hemin. Since the addition of a small amount of blood enhances activity of the organism, it is quite likely that other factors are also involved.

For more information see Gingrich and Schlenk (1944).

Putrescine. This putrefactive compound has been shown to be an essential growth factor for *Haemophilus parainfluenzae* and *Neisseria perflava.*

Chemically, putrescine is tetramethylene diamine and may be produced by the decarboxylation of ornithine:

$$NH_2(CH_2)_3 \cdot CHNH_2 \cdot COOH \rightarrow NH_2(CH_2)_3 \cdot CH_2NH_2 + CO_2$$
$$\text{Ornithine} \qquad\qquad\qquad \text{Putrescine}$$

Ornithine in turn may be produced by the hydrolysis of arginine (see page 288).

For more information see Herbst and Glinos (1955).

Glutathione. Gould (1944) reported that glutathione was necessary for the growth of *Neisseria gonorrhoeae.* The factor was found to be present in meat infusion, yeast infusion, and red-blood-cell extract. Freshly isolated strains of the organism were found not to require glutathione, but they showed a tendency to develop dependence on glutathione after some weeks of subculturing on a medium containing meat infusion.

Glutathione possesses several functions: (1) it acts as a carrier of hydrogen; (2) it prevents inactivation of sulfhydryl groups of enzymes; and (3) it is believed to maintain ascorbic acid in the reduced form.

The structural formula of glutathione is given on page 327.

Effect of pH on Growth-factor Requirements. Doede (1945) found that the pH of the medium had a marked influence upon the growth-factor requirements of a number of bacterial species. The amount of nicotinic acid required by *Staphylococcus aureus* for maximum growth was approximately fifteen times greater at pH 8.0 than at pH 6.0. *Shigella paradysenteriae* required nicotinic acid in the medium at pH 7.0 and 8.0 but not at pH 6.0. At pH 6.0 the organisms were capable of synthesizing the factor. *Lactobacillus casei* grew in a medium without pyridoxin at pH 5.0 but failed to grow at pH 6.0 or 7.0 unless supplied with the factor. Folic acid, riboflavin, biotin, nicotinic acid, and pantothenic acid were found to be most effective at pH 6.0.

Bacterial Destruction of Vitamins. A number of bacterial species have been shown to be capable of destroying growth factors. Young and Rettger (1943) found that vitamin C (ascorbic acid) was easily destroyed by the enteric bacteria, including the intestinal streptococci. In the presence of an easily fermentable carbohydrate, such as glucose, the vitamin was protected from decomposition, whereas in the absence of the competitive agents, the ascorbic acid content of the medium became rapidly depleted.

Foster (1944 *a*, *b*) showed that the organism *Pseudomonas riboflavinus* was capable of oxidizing riboflavin to lumichrome according to the reaction

$$C_{17}H_{20}O_6N_4 + 5\tfrac{1}{2}O_2 \rightarrow C_{12}H_{10}O_2N_4 + 5CO_2 + 5H_2O$$

$$\text{Riboflavin} \qquad\qquad \text{Lumichrome}$$

Koser and Baird (1944) reported the destruction of nicotinic acid by bacteria of the *Pseudomonas fluorescens* and *Serratia marcescens* groups. Destruction occurred during periods of active cell multiplication. Metzger (1947) showed that members of the genus *Pseudomonas* utilized pantothenic acid as a growth factor. However, during growth these organisms destroyed 100 per cent of the vitamin within 72 hr. by a process of oxidation.

Bacterial Synthesis of Vitamins. Mayer and Rodbart (1946) reported the synthesis of riboflavin by *Mycobacterium smegmatis* on a synthetic medium. Smith and Emmart (1949) found the same to be true for the tubercle bacillus. Tanner, Vojnovich, and Van Lanen (1949) employed an organic medium and reported the formation of riboflavin by *Ashbya gossypii*.

Vitamin Content of Ingredients of Culture Media. Information concerning the vitamin content of ingredients of culture media should prove of interest and value in the cultivation of microorganisms. Such information could be used to decide whether a particular culture medium satisfies the growth-factor requirements of an organism.

Stokes, Gunness, and Foster (1944) assayed a number of culture media for their content of eight members of the B complex: thiamine, riboflavin, pantothenic acid, nicotinic acid, biotin, pyridoxin, folic acid, and *p*-aminobenzoic acid, and compared the results with the vitamin requirements of various microorganisms that were unable to synthesize these factors. They arranged the various culture-media ingredients in order of descending value on the basis of their content of vitamins of the B complex.

The classification is as follows:

1. Yeast extract.
2. Meat extract, brain infusion, heart infusion.
3. Various peptones.

With the possible exception of thiamine, yeast extract is an excellent source of all vitamins of the B complex. This explains why yeast extract is held in such high favor as an ingredient of culture media.

They concluded that if peptone, meat extract, etc., were used in concentrations of 1 or 2 per cent, singly or in combinations, the resultant media were likely to be deficient in thiamine, riboflavin, pantothenic acid, pyridoxin, and *p*-aminobenzoic acid, but not in nicotinic acid, biotin, and folic acid. They suggested that such growth-factor deficiencies in culture media could be remedied by proper combination of ingredients or by the addition of yeast concentrates or synthetic vitamins.

For more information on growth factors see Cohen and Barner (1956), Hughes and Williamson (1953), Kasai (1953), Mueller (1940), Peterson and Peterson (1945).

Metabolite Antagonists (Antimetabolites). A metabolite may be defined as any substance essential to growth and reproduction of cells. It may be synthesized by the cells or obtained from the environment. A metabolite antagonist is any substance that blocks or inhibits the normal function of the metabolite. The best examples of antimetabolites involve substances structurally related to the substrate.

Inhibition of Succinic Dehydrogenase. The enzyme succinic dehydrogenase is inhibited by malonic acid:

$$COOH \cdot CH_2 \cdot COOH \qquad\qquad COOH \cdot CH_2 \cdot CH_2 \cdot COOH$$

Malonic acid   Succinic acid

The homologous dibasic malonic acid is believed to inhibit the enzyme by competing with the normal metabolite succinic acid. The competitive inhibition between the two compounds results almost in a complete blocking of the enzymic reaction.

Inhibition of p-Aminobenzoic Acid. The close structural relationship between *p*-aminobenzoic acid and sulfanilamide may be shown by the following formulas:

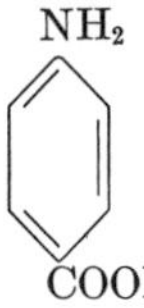

p-Aminobenzoic acid 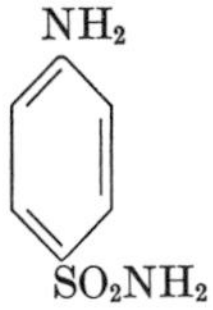   Sulfanilamide

Woods (1940) showed that *p*-aminobenzoic acid (PABA) in high dilutions antagonized the action of sulfanilamide. Fildes reported that PABA is an essential metabolite normally associated with an enzyme. Sulfanilamide displaces PABA from its enzyme, thereby stopping this essential line of metabolism. Other sulfa drugs (sulfonamides) behave in a similar manner.

Inhibition of Arginine. Volcani and Snell (1948) showed that arginine was an essential metabolite for the growth of several species of lactic acid bacteria. None of the species tested could use canavanine in place of arginine:

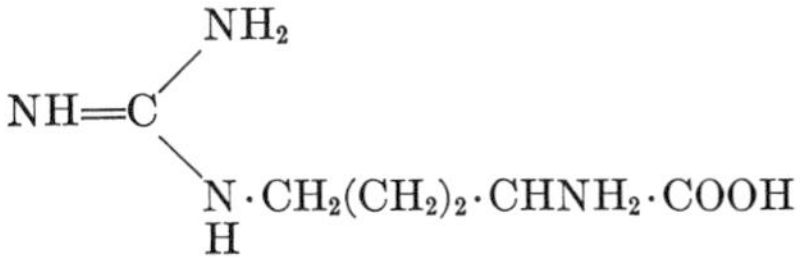

Arginine 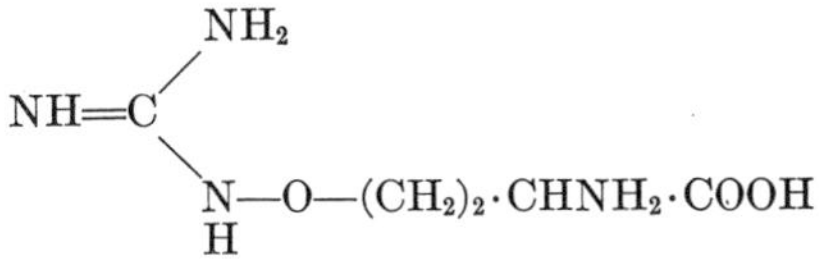   Canavanine

For some of the bacteria tested, canavanine functioned as an effective growth inhibitor. This was true both for organisms which synthesized arginine and for those which required this amino acid preformed.

These are only a few examples of metabolite antagonists. For more information see Grossowicz (1948), Kihara and Snell (1955), Knight (1946, 1949), Pittillo and Foster (1954), Roblin (1949), Webb and Nickerson (1956), and Woolley (1952, 1959).

GROWTH PHASES IN A CULTURE

Most bacteria multiply at a very rapid rate and produce pronounced changes in culture media in a short period of time. Under favorable conditions a single cell of *Escherichia coli* divides into two about every 20 min. If this same rate is maintained, a single organism will give 1 billion new cells after a period of about 10 hr. However, this rate of multiplication is not maintained indefinitely, owing to the exhaustion of the nutrients, to the accumulation of toxic metabolic waste products, and to the fact that many of the cells die. The rate of death increases as the culture ages. The more vulnerable cells die first, leaving the resistant forms in the culture at the end of the incubation period.

When an organism is inoculated into a tube of medium such as nutrient broth, multiplication does not take place in a regular manner. On the contrary, various growth phases may be recognized which are known as the life phases of a culture. Buchanan (1918) recognized seven distinct cultural phases which he designated as follows:

1. *Initial Stationary Phase.* During this phase, the number of bacteria remains constant. Plotting the results on graph paper gives a straight horizontal line (1a) in Fig. 108.

2. *Lag Phase or Phase of Positive Growth Acceleration.* During this phase, the rate of multiplication increases with time (ab).

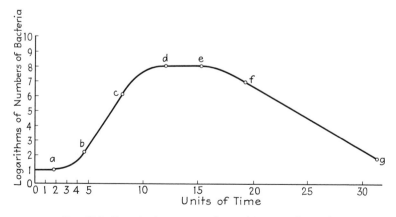

Fig. 108. Growth phases in a culture. (*After Buchanan.*)

3. *Logarithmic Growth Phase.* During this phase, the rate of multiplication remains constant (*bc*). This means that the generation time is the same throughout.

4. *Phase of Negative Growth Acceleration.* During this phase, the rate of multiplication decreases (*cd*). The average generation time increases. The organisms continue to increase in numbers but at a slower rate than during the logarithmic growth phase.

5. *Maximum Stationary Phase.* During this phase, the number of living organisms remains constant, i.e., the death rate equals the rate of increase (*de*).

6. *Phase of Accelerated Death.* During this phase, the numbers fall off with increasing rapidity (*ef*). The average rate of death per organism increases to a maximum.

7. *Logarithmic Death Phase.* During this phase, the rate of death is constant (*fg*).

It is generally believed that the phases in a bacterial culture are due to changes in the environment, such as alteration in pH, exhaustion of food supply, and accumulation of waste products.

Lag Period. When bacteria are transferred from an old culture to a new medium, they exhibit a period of delayed multiplication or lag. Müller (1895) was probably the first to make this observation. He recognized three distinct phases in a culture, which he designated the lag, the logarithmic increase, and the slackened growth phases. Müller found that when cultures of differing ages were used for the inoculation of new medium the generation times in the new cultures showed considerable differences. Transfers from a typhoid culture $2\frac{1}{2}$ to 3 hr. old gave a generation time of 40 min. in the new medium; a culture $6\frac{1}{4}$ hr. old gave a generation time of 80 to 85 min.; and a culture 14 to 16 hr. old gave a generation time of 160 min.

Another characteristic of organisms is that they show considerable variation to harmful influences in the different growth phases. Cultures in the lag and early logarithmic phases exhibit greater sensitivity to heat than those in the older phases of growth. Schultz and Ritz (1910) reported that a 20-min. culture of *E. coli* was more resistant to heat than a 4-hr. culture. Then the resistance showed a steady rise as the culture aged. Sherman and Albus (1923) exposed *E. coli* to various unfavorable conditions and found old cells to be considerably more resistant than very young cells.

If a tube of fresh medium is inoculated from a culture in the logarithmic growth phase (*bc*, Fig. 108), the lag phase will be greatly reduced and in many cases completely eliminated. The organisms in the logarithmic growth phase are multiplying at the maximum rate and continue to do so when transferred to fresh medium. Buchanan (1928) concluded that transfer from any phase of a bacterial culture cycle to a new medium is followed by a continuance of the phase of the parent culture.

Factors Affecting Cell Size. Henrici (1928) showed that organisms increased very markedly in size during the lag phase. He found that the average length of *Bacillus megaterium* was six times that of the inoculated organisms taken from an old culture. This increase generally manifested itself after 2 hr., and the maximum size was usually noted between 4 and 6 hr. During the lag phase, the cells showed considerable fluctuation in form. On passing from the lag phase to the logarithmic death phase, the organisms gradually decreased in size and exhibited a more constant cell form.

It is well known that when a parent culture is inoculated into a new medium, an initially slow rate of increase in bacterial numbers occurs. This slow rate of multiplication cannot be interpreted as indicating a period of lag in the sense of decreased viability and activity. What actually happens is that the rate of multiplication decreases but the individual cells become larger, giving a rapid increase in bacterial mass. During the first 2 or 3 hr., new cultures inoculated from 3-hr.-old parent cultures show a slower multiplication rate than new cultures inoculated from 24-hr. parent cultures, but the increase in protoplasmic growth remains the same. The cells from a young parent culture show the same increase in cell mass as the cells from an old parent culture even though they multiply at a slower rate. The rate of increase in cell mass is nearly constant from the time growth first begins until the maximum population is reached.

The results suggest that conditions in fresh medium favor an increase in cell size but inhibit cell division, with the result that a majority of the cells attain an abnormal size before fission occurs. Inoculation of a large number of cells into new medium tends to produce the reverse effect, i.e., the average size is smaller and attained much sooner than with small inoculations. If cells are removed from a culture before their average maximum size is reached and are transferred to fresh medium, the organisms attain a larger size and the critical point takes place later than in the case of the original culture. This would indicate that the size of the organisms is dependent upon the density of the bacterial culture. The concentration of the nutrients in the medium is another factor. The maximum size of the organisms in a dilute medium is smaller and the critical point is reached earlier. A dilute medium produces a poorer growth than a more concentrated preparation. This means that a more concentrated medium showing a heavy, crowded growth produces the same effect on cell size as a more dilute medium showing a light growth.

Effect of Carbon Dioxide on Growth. In general, bacteria grow better in the presence of an increased concentration of carbon dioxide. Walker (1932) found that the length of the lag phase could be controlled by the concentration of carbon dioxide present. He noted that the multiplication of E. coli could be delayed indefinitely by aeration of the culture with carbon dioxide–free air. Reintroduction of carbon dioxide into the medium caused a rapid increase in bacterial numbers. He concluded that "the phenomenon of lag may be due largely, if not entirely, to the time it takes the culture to build up the CO_2 content of the medium or of the cells themselves to a value essential for growth." Others have come to a similar conclusion. There appears to be no doubt that the amount of carbon dioxide present in a new medium is an important factor in controlling the length of the lag phase, but it is probably not the only factor involved.

Factors Affecting Rate of Reproduction. The rate of multiplication of bacteria is increased by a rise in temperature. This continues until a certain maximum is reached, after which the rate decreases until death finally occurs. The generation times of *E. coli* at different temperatures of incubation are as follows:

°C.	Time	°C.	Time
10	14 hr., 20 min.	35	22 min.
15	120 min.	40	17½ min.
20	90 min.	45	20 min.
25	40 min.	47½	77 min.
30	29 min.		

The composition of the medium also affects the generation times of bacteria. The generation time of *S. typhosa* in a 1 per cent solution of peptone is about 40 min. at 37°C. If the amount of peptone is less than 0.2 per cent, the generation time is almost inversely proportional to its concentration; if more than 0.4 per cent, an increase in the peptone concentration is practically without effect on the growth rate of the organism. The addition of 0.175 per cent of glucose to a medium containing only 0.1 per cent peptone lowers the generation time from about 111 to 50 min. The addition of the same amount of glucose to a 1 per cent peptone solution reduces the generation time only from about 39 to 34 min.

Effect of Age on Cell Morphology. Under some environmental conditions, bacteria show the presence of granules; under other conditions, they do not. It has been observed that when cells are largest (2 to 4 hr. old), intracellular granules disappear and the protoplasm becomes more hyaline and stains more deeply. As the cells age and decrease in size, they become increasingly more granular. Old cells are, in general, very granular, whereas young cells do not exhibit the presence of granules. The development of granules in cells of *Bacillus mycoides* with age is shown in Fig. 109. An exception to this rule is the organism *Corynebacterium diphtheriae*, the causative agent of diphtheria. This organism appears to be smaller in young than in old cultures and to exhibit the presence of granules in both young and old cells.

Effect of Constant Environment on Cell Numbers. Jordan and Jacobs (1944) cultivated *E. coli* in an apparatus that permitted rigid control of temperature, pH, aeration, and culture volume and allowed food to be supplied at a constant rate by means of an automatic syringe mechanism. Determinations of total and viable cell populations were made. Results showed an initial period in which the total and viable counts both increased, followed by a steady phase in which the viable counts remained constant or decreased slightly, while the total cell counts steadily increased. When during the steady phase the food supply was suddenly stopped, the total cell population remained constant, but the viable cells decreased to a constant low level.

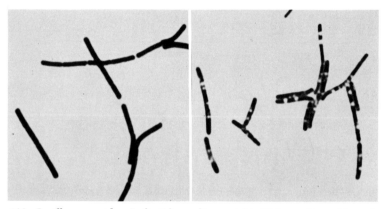

Fig. 109. *Bacillus mycoides*. Left, 6-hr. culture; right, 24-hr. culture. Note the development of granules with age.

For more information see Campbell (1957), De Haan and Winkler (1955), Lichstein (1959), Northrop (1954), Squires and Hartsell (1955).

HYDROGEN-ION CONCENTRATION OF CULTURE MEDIA

Culture media are adjusted to different degrees of acidity or alkalinity, depending upon the requirements of the organisms under cultivation. Some organisms grow best in acid media; others grow best in alkaline media; still others prefer media which are approximately neutral in reaction. This last group includes the great majority of bacteria that have been isolated and studied. Therefore, it is necessary to adjust the reaction of media to the requirements of the organisms being studied.

Two methods are employed for adjusting the reaction of culture media: (1) the determination of the actual numbers of free hydrogen ions and (2) the determination of the net amount of acid- or base-binding groups present. The former is spoken of as the hydrogen-ion (H^+) concentration; the latter as the titratable acidity or alkalinity.

The hydrogen-ion concentration may be determined either colorimetrically or electrometrically. The titratable acidity is determined by titration of a known volume of medium with a standard solution of NaOH to the predetermined endpoint as shown by a glass electrode or by the color of a suitable indicator. Both methods serve very useful purposes in bacteriology. The adjustment of media is more accurately carried out by the hydrogen-ion method. The titratable acidity determination is of great value in learning the buffer content of the medium, i.e., its ability to resist changes in reaction on the addition of acid or alkali.

Measuring the Concentration of Hydrogen (H^+) Ions. Pure water is neutral in reaction because it ionizes into equal numbers of hydrogen and hydroxyl ions.

$$H_2O \rightleftharpoons H^+ + OH^-$$

However, it is dissociated to an extremely small extent.

One liter of $1N$ HCl contains approximately 1 gm. of hydrogen (H^+) ions. One liter of pure water contains approximately 0.0000001 gm. of hydrogen ions. This may be written 10^{-7} gm. per liter. For each H^+ ion, there is a corresponding and neutralizing OH^- ion.

According to the law of mass action,

$$\frac{(H^+)\,(OH^-)}{HOH} = K$$

Since the concentration of undissociated water is very great in comparison to the concentration of free H^+ and OH^- ions, the equation may be written

$$(H^+)\,(OH^-) = K$$

The numbers of H^+ and OH^- ions being equal, each must have a concentration of 1×10^{-7}. The product of the concentrations of hydrogen and hydroxyl ions is equal to 1×10^{-14}. The equation now becomes

$$(H^+)\,(OH^-) = 1 \times 10^{-14}$$

Pure water, which has a hydrogen-ion concentration of 1×10^{-7}, is neutral in reaction. Since the product of the H and OH ion concentrations is constant at 1×10^{-14}, when the H^+ increases, the OH^- decreases. The sum of the two always equals 1×10^{-14}. If the hydrogen-ion concentration of a solution is smaller than 1×10^{-7}, it will be alkaline in reaction; if larger than 1×10^{-7}, it will have an acid reaction.

The term pH may be defined as the logarithm of the reciprocal of the hydrogen-ion concentration. For convenience, only the exponent is used in expressing pH. If a solution has a pH less than 7, it is acid in reaction; if greater than 7, it is alkaline. Most organisms grow best in culture media having a pH of about 7.0.

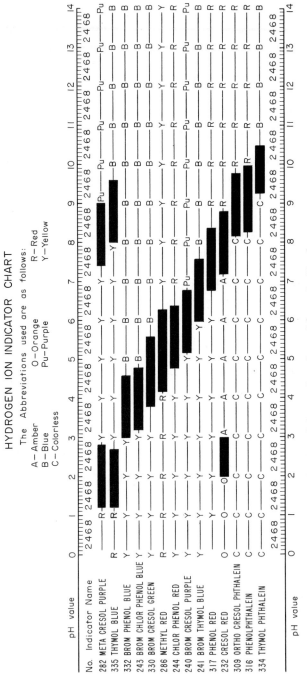

Fig. 110. Selector chart for widely used pH indicators.

192

The relation of pH to H^+ is shown in Table 5.

TABLE 5. THE RELATION OF pH TO H^+

		pH	Normality in terms of hydrogen ions	Normality in terms of hydroxyl ions
		0	1	10^{-14}
		1	10^{-1}	10^{-13}
		2	10^{-2}	10^{-12}
Acid		3	10^{-3}	10^{-11}
		4	10^{-4}	10^{-10}
		5	10^{-5}	10^{-9}
		6	10^{-6}	10^{-8}
Neutral point		7	10^{-7}	10^{-7}
		8	10^{-8}	10^{-6}
		9	10^{-9}	10^{-5}
		10	10^{-10}	10^{-4}
Alkaline		11	10^{-11}	10^{-3}
		12	10^{-12}	10^{-2}
		13	10^{-13}	10^{-1}
		14	10^{-14}	1

Colorimetric Method. The determination of the hydrogen-ion concentration by the colorimetric method depends upon the color changes produced in certain weakly acid or weakly basic dyes by varying the reaction of the medium. Such dyes are called indicators. An indicator changes in color within a short distance each side of that point in the pH scale at which it is 50 per cent dissociated. At that point, one-half of the dye is undissociated and the other half is dissociated. The pH at which this occurs is denoted by the symbol pK.

A short distance each side of the pK point gives a zone which is referred to as the sensitive range of the indicator. Every shade of color of the indicator in this sensitive range corresponds to a definite pH value so that by comparing the shade of the indicator with standards of known reaction, the hydrogen-ion concentration of a solution may be determined. Indicators can be selected displaying a certain amount of overlapping in their sensitive ranges to cover the scale from pH 1.0 to 10.0.

A selector chart for widely used pH indicators is given in Fig. 110.

Potentiometric Method. Most pH determinations by the electrometric method are now made with the glass electrode.

Under suitable conditions, a thin glass membrane separating two solutions of different pH values exhibits an electrical potential that is proportional to the difference in the pH of the solutions. For the construction of the glass electrode, a special type of glass is employed.

The potentiometric method is more accurate than the colorimetric procedure. Also, it can be employed for the determination of the pH values of highly colored solutions which cannot be satisfactorily tested by the use of indicators.

No attempt will be made here to discuss the potentiometric method. For an extensive discussion on the theoretical and practical aspects of the subject, see Clark (1928).

Buffers. The salts of weak acids have the power of preventing pronounced changes in the reactions of solutions on the addition of relatively large amounts of strong acids or alkalies. Substances which possess the power of resisting changes in acidity or alkalinity are spoken of as buffers.

The titration curve of a weak acid is S-shaped. Each end of the curve has a steep slope and the central portion has a gentle slope. This central, almost horizontal portion of the curve expresses the buffer action of the system or its ability to resist pronounced changes in pH on the addition of acidic or basic substances.

The addition of 1 ml. of $N/10$ hydrochloric acid to 1 liter of neutral distilled water (pH 7.0) gives a solution having a pH of about 4.0. The addition of 1 ml. of $N/10$ sodium hydroxide to 1 liter of neutral distilled water gives a solution having a pH of about 10.0. The addition of the same amount of acid or alkali to 1 liter of distilled water in which are dissolved a few grams of sodium phosphate produces very little change in the reaction. Sodium phosphate is classed as a buffer. This may be shown in the following reactions:

The addition of a strong acid:

$$Na_2HPO_4 + HCl \rightarrow NaH_2PO_4 + NaCl$$

The strong acid (HCl) reacts with the weak alkali (Na_2HPO_4) to give the weak acid (NaH_2PO_4) and sodium chloride. In other words, the strong HCl is replaced by the weak acid phosphate, resulting in a relatively small change in the final hydrogen-ion concentration.

The addition of a strong alkali:

$$NaH_2PO_4 + NaOH \rightarrow Na_2HPO_4 + H_2O$$

The strong alkali (NaOH) reacts with the weak acid (NaH_2PO_4) to give the weak alkali (Na_2HPO_4) and water. The strong NaOH is replaced by the weak basic phosphate, resulting in a relatively small change in the final hydrogen-ion concentration.

The important salts commonly added to nutrient media for their buffering action include phosphates and carbonates. These compounds are particularly valuable because they are relatively nontoxic.

Bacteriological peptones contain such substances as proteoses, peptones, peptides, and amino acids, all of which are buffers. These possess both acidic and basic properties, i.e., have the power of uniting with both bases and acids. Therefore, all culture media containing peptone are well buffered, the degree of buffering being dependent upon the amount of peptone added.

Buffers are of special importance in carbohydrate media that are vigorously fermented. In the various fermentations, organic acids are produced. The acidity soon builds up to a concentration that prevents further multiplication of the organisms. In the presence of a buffer, this takes place usually in 24 to 48 hr. In the absence of a buffer, the activity of the organisms may cease after a few hours. A good culture medium, besides containing the necessary nutrients, should also be well buffered.

Buffer Standards. Clark and Lubs (1917) proposed a series of buffer solutions covering the range from pH 1.2 to pH 10.0 at intervals of 0.2 pH. By selection of the proper indicators (Fig. 110), these buffer solutions may be used as standards for the adjustment of the reaction of culture media. For this purpose, comparable concentrations of indicator must be used in both the buffer standards and the medium under adjustment.

For more information see Clark (1928), Cohen (1957), and Hewitt (1950).

REFERENCES

Altenbern, R. A., and H. S. Ginoza: Pantothenic acid synthesis by smooth *Brucella abortus, J. Bact.*, **68**:570, 1954.

Brenner, S.: Tryptophan biosynthesis in *Salmonella typhimurium, Proc. Nat. Acad. Sci.*, **41**:862, 1955.

Brooke, M. S., D. Ushiba, and B. Magasanik: Some factors affecting the excretion of orotic acid by mutants of *Aerobacter aerogenes, J. Bact*, **68**:534, 1954.

Brown, G. M., and E. E. Snell: Pantothenic acid conjugates and growth of *Acetobacter suboxydans, J. Bact.*, **67**:465, 1954.

Brown, H. J., and N. E. Gibbons: The effect of magnesium, potassium, and iron on the growth and morphology of red halophilic bacteria, *Can. J. Microbiol.*, **1**:486, 1955.

Bruckman, H. W. L., and J. J. Rook: On the suitability of gelatin for plate cultures. I. *Antoine van Leeuwenhoek*, **19**:341, 1953.

Buchanan, R. E.: Life phases in a bacterial culture, *J. Infectious Diseases*, **23**:109, 1918.

——: Growth curves of bacteria. From "The Newer Knowledge of Bacteriology and Immunology," edited by E. O. Jordan and I. S. Falk, Chicago, University of Chicago Press, 1928.

Burkholder, P. R., and Ilda McVeigh: Synthesis of vitamins by intestinal bacteria, *Proc. Nat. Acad. Sci.*, **28**:285, 1942.

Campbell, A.: Synchronization of cell division, *Bact. Rev.*, **21**:263, 1957.

Campbell, L. L., Jr., and H. A. Frank: Nutritional requirements of some putrefactive anaerobic bacteria, *J. Bact.*, **71**:267, 1956.

—— and O. B. Williams: Observations on the biotin requirements of thermophilic bacteria, *J. Bact.*, **65**:146, 1953.

Carlson, W. W., and V. Whiteside-Carlson: Biotin-carbohydrate interrelationships in the metabolism of *Leuconostoc, Proc. Soc. Exp. Biol. Med.*, **71**:416, 1949.

Carroll, T. C. N., C. J. Danby, A. A. Eddy, and C. Hinshelwood: The uptake of alkali metals by bacteria, *J. Chem. Soc.*, p. 946, March, 1950.

Chaplin, C. E., and A. G. Lochhead: Abnormal morphology of a bacterium resulting from vitamin B_{12} deficiency, *Can. J. Microbiol.*, **2**:340, 1956.

Chattaway, F. W.: Growth stimulation of L. casei ε by pyrimidines, Nature, 153:250, 1944.

Clark, W. M.: "The Determination of Hydrogen Ions," Baltimore, The Williams & Wilkins Company, 1928.

―――― and H. A. Lubs: The colorimetric determination of hydrogen-ion concentration, J. Bact., 2:1, 109, 191, 1917.

Cohen, B.: The measurement of pH, titratable acidity, and oxidation-reduction potentials. From "Manual of Microbiological Methods," New York, McGraw-Hill Book Company, Inc., 1957.

Cohen, S. S., and H. D. Barner: Studies on the induction of thymine deficiency and on the effects of thymine and thymidine analogues in Escherichia coli, J. Bact., 71:588, 1956.

Cowie, D. B., E. T. Bolton, and M. K. Sands: Sulfur metabolism in Escherichia coli. I. Sulfate metabolism of normal and mutant cells, J. Bact., 60:233, 1950.

Curcho, M. de la G.: Mutation of tryptophan independence in Eberthella typhosa, J. Bact., 56:374, 1948.

De Haan, P. G., and K. C. Winkler: An apparatus for the continuous culture of bacteria at constant generation times, Antonie van Leeuwenhoek, 21:33, 1955.

Delwiche, E. A.: A biotin function in succinic acid decarboxylation by Propionibacterium pentosaceum, J. Bact., 59:439, 1950.

Doede, Dorothy R.: The influence of pH upon the growth-factor requirements of bacteria, Yale J. Biol. Med., 17:595, 1945.

Du Vigneaud, V., D. B. Melville, K. Folkers, D. E. Wolf, R. Mozingo, J. C. Keresztesy, and S. A. Harris: The structure of biotin: A study of desthiobiotin, J. Biol. Chem., 146:475, 1942.

Eastcott, E. V.: The isolation and identification of bios I, J. Phys. Chem., 32:1094, 1928.

Elvehjem, C. A., R. J. Madden, S. M. Strong, and D. W. Woolley: Relation of nicotinic acid and nicotinic acid amide to canine blacktongue, J. Am. Chem. Soc., 59:1767, 1937.

Erlandson, A. L., Jr., and W. H. Mackey: Nutrition of Shigella: growth of Shigella flexneri in a simple chemically defined medium, J. Bact., 75:253, 1958.

Fildes, P.: The nature of the effect of blood pigment upon the growth of B. influenzae, Brit. J. Exp. Path., 2:16, 1921.

―――――: The nature of the action of potato upon the growth of B. influenzae, ibid., 3:210, 1922.

―――――: Some medical and other aspects of bacterial chemistry, Proc. Roy. Soc. Med., 28:79, 1934.

―――――: Production of tryptophan by Salmonella typhi and Escherichia coli, J. Gen. Microbiol., 15:636, 1956.

―――― and G. P. Gladstone: Glutamine and the growth of bacteria, ibid., 20:334, 1939.

―――――, ――――, and B. C. J. G. Knight: The nitrogen and vitamin requirements of B. typhosus, ibid., 14:189, 1933.

Foster, J. W.: Microbiological aspects of riboflavin. I. Introduction. II. Bacterial oxidation of riboflavin to lumichrome, J. Bact., 47:27, 1944a; III. Oxidation studies with Pseudomonas riboflavina, ibid., 48:97, 1944b.

Friedman, S., and C. L. Fox, Jr.: Studies on the relationship of potassium to metabolism and purine biosynthesis in Escherichia coli, J. Bact., 68:186, 1954.

Funk, C.: The etiology of the deficiency diseases, J. State Med., 20:341, 1912.

Geiger, W. B., Jr., and R. J. Anderson: The chemistry of Phytomonas tumefaciens. I. The lipids of Phytomonas tumefaciens. The composition of the phosphatide, J. Biol. Chem., 129:519, 1939.

Gingrich, W., and F. Schlenk: Codehydrogenase I and other pyridinium compounds as V-factor for Haemophilus influenzae and H. parainfluenzae, J. Bact., 47:535, 1944.

Ginsburg, I., and N. Grossowicz: Group A hemolytic streptococci. I. A chemically defined medium for growth from small inocula, Proc. Soc. Exp. Biol. Med., 96:108, 1957.

Gould, R. G.: Glutathione as an essential growth factor for certain strains of *Neisseria gonorrhoeae*, *J. Biol. Chem.*, **153**:143, 1944.

Grossowicz, N.: Glutamine, an antimetabolite for *Staphylococcus aureus*, *J. Biol. Chem.*, **173**:729, 1948.

György, P.: Vitamin B₂ complex. I. Differentiation of lactoflavin and the rat antipellagra factor, *Biochem. J.*, **29**:741, 1935.

Harris, S. A., and K. Folkers: Synthesis of vitamin B₆, *J. Am. Chem. Soc.*, **61**:1245, 1939.

Haynes, W. C., R. W. Kuehne, and L. J. Rhodes: The effect of potassium upon the growth of *Micrococcus pyogenes*, *Appl. Microbiol.*, **2**:339, 1954.

Henrici, A. T.: "Morphologic Variation and the Rate of Growth of Bacteria," Springfield, Ill., Charles C Thomas, Publisher, 1928.

Herbst, E. J., and E. B. Glinos: An analysis of the putrescine requirement of *Hemophilus parainfluenzae*, *J. Biol. Chem.*, **214**:175, 1955.

Herrick, J. A., and C. J. Alexopoulos: A further note on the production of thiamine by *Actinomyces*, *Bull. Torrey Botan. Club*, **70**:369, 1943.

Hewitt, L. F.: "Oxidation-Reduction Potentials in Bacteriology and Biochemistry," Edinburgh, E. and S. Livingstone, Ltd., 1950.

Hook, A. E., and F. W. Fabian: Chemical and bacteriological studies on peptones, *Mich. State Coll. Agr. Exp. Sta. Tech. Bull.* 185, 1943.

Hopkins, F. G.: The analyst and the medical man, *Analyst*, **31**:385, 1906.

Hughes, D. E., and D. H. Williamson: The deamidation of nicotinamide by bacteria, *Biochem. J.*, **55**:851, 1953.

Humm, H. J.: Marine agar-digesting bacteria of the South Atlantic coast, *Duke Univ. Marine Sta. Bull.* 3, 1946.

—— and K. S. Shepard: Three new agar-digesting actinomycetes, *ibid.* 3, 1946.

Hutner, S. H.: A strain of *Shigella paradysenteriae* (Flexner) requiring uracil, *Arch. Biochem.*, **4**:119, 1944.

Jordan, R. C., and S. E. Jacobs: The growth of bacteria with a constant food supply. I. Preliminary observations on *Bacterium coli*, *J. Bact.*, **48**:579, 1944.

Kadota, H.: Studies on the biochemical activities of marine bacteria. II. On the properties of agar-digesting enzyme of *Vibrio purpureus*, *Memoirs College Agr., Kyoto University*, No. 66, 1953.

Kasai, G. J.: Growth response of microorganisms to vitamins at different temperatures, *J. Infectious Diseases*, **92**:58, 1953.

Keresztesy, J. C., and J. R. Stevens: Vitamin B₆, *J. Am. Chem. Soc.*, **60**:1267, 1938.

Kersey, R. C., and J. R. Porter: Pantothenic acid and the metabolism of amino acids by bacteria, *Proc. Soc. Exp. Biol. Med.*, **69**:379, 1948.

Kihara, H., and E. E. Snell: Peptides and bacterial growth. VII. Relation to inhibitions by thienylalanine, ethionine, and canavanine, *J. Biol. Chem.*, **212**:83, 1955.

King, T. E., and V. H. Cheldelin: Pantothenic acid derivatives and growth of *Acetobacter suboxydans*, *Proc. Soc. Exp. Biol. Med.*, **84**:591, 1953.

Kitay, E., W. S. McNutt, and E. E. Snell: Desoxyribosides and vitamin B₁₂ as growth factors for lactic acid bacteria, *J. Bact.*, **59**:727, 1950.

Knight, B. C. J. G.: Growth factors and growth inhibitors for micro-organisms, *Proc. Nutrition Soc.*, **4**:116, 1946.

——: Essential metabolites and antimetabolites, *J. Mt. Sinai Hosp.*, **15**:281, 1949.

Kögl, F.: Über Wuchsstoffe der Auxin- und der Bios-Gruppe, *Ber.*, **68**:16, 1935.

Koser, S. A.: Utilization of the salts of organic acids by the colonaerogenes group, *J. Bact.*, **8**:493, 1923.

—— and G. R. Baird: Bacterial destruction of nicotinic acid, *J. Infectious Diseases*, **75**:250, 1944.

—— and M. H. Wright: Experimental variation of nicotinamide requirement of dysentery bacilli, *J. Bact.*, **46**:239, 1943.

Landy, M., N. W. Larkum, E. J. Oswald, and F. Streightoff: Increased synthesis of *p*-aminobenzoic acid associated with the development of sulfonamide resistance in *Staphylococcus aureus*, *Science*, **97**:2516, 1943.

Lankford, C. E., V. Scott, M. F. Cox, and W. R. Cooke: Some aspects of nutritional variation of the gonococcus, *J. Bact.*, **45**:321, 1943.

—— and E. E. Snell: Glutamine as a growth factor for certain strains of *Neisseria gonorrhoeae, ibid.,* **45:**410, 1943.

Larson, L. W., and W. P. Larson: Factors governing the fat content of bacteria and the influence of fat on pellicle formation, *J. Infectious Diseases,* **31:**407, 1922.

Lepkovsky, S.: Crystalline factor I, *Science,* **87:**169, 1938.

Lester, G.: Requirement for potassium by bacteria, *J. Bact.,* **75:**426, 1958.

Lichstein, H. C.: Further studies on the biotin coenzyme, *J. Bact.,* **60:**485, 1950.

——: III. Physiological aspects of growth initiation, *Bact. Rev.,* **23:**261, 1959.

Lwoff, A., and M. Lwoff: Studies on codehydrogenases: Nature of growth factor V, *Proc. Roy. Soc. (London),* Series B, **122:**352, 1937*a.*

—— and ——: Studies on codehydrogenases; physiological function of growth factor V, *ibid.,* **122:**360, 1937*b.*

Maas, W. K., and H. J. Vogel: α-Ketoisovaleric acid, a precursor of pantothenic acid in *Escherichia coli, J. Bact.,* **65:**388, 1953.

MacLeod, R. A.: Further mineral requirements of *Streptococcus faecalis, J. Bact.,* **62:**337, 1951.

—— and E. E. Snell: The effect of related ions on the potassium requirement of lactic acid bacteria, *J. Biol. Chem.,* **176:**39, 1948.

Mayer, R. L., and M. Rodbart: The production of riboflavin by *Mycobacterium smegmatis, Arch. Biochem.,* **11:**49, 1946.

McIlwain, H.: The specificity of glutamine for growth of *Streptococcus haemolyticus, Biochem. J.,* **33:**1942, 1939.

——, P. Fildes, G. P. Gladstone, and B. C. J. G. Knight: Glutamine and the growth of *Streptococcus haemolyticus, ibid.,* **33:**223, 1939.

Metzger, W. I.: Microbic decomposition of pantothenic acid, *J. Bact.,* **54:**135, 1947.

Miller, A. K.: Folic acid and biotin synthesis by sulfonamide-sensitive and sulfonamide-resistant strains of *Escherichia coli, Proc. Soc. Exp. Biol. Med.,* **57:**151, 1944.

Mitchell, H. K., E. E. Snell, and R. J. Williams: The concentration of "folic acid," *J. Am. Chem. Soc.,* **63:**2284, 1941.

Morton, A. G., and A. Macmillan: The assimilation of nitrogen from ammonium salts and nitrate by fungi, *J. Exp. Bot.,* **5:**232, 1954.

Mueller, J. H.: Studies on cultural requirements of bacteria. VI. The diphtheria bacillus, *J. Bact.,* **30:**513, 1935; X. Pimelic acid as a growth stimulant for *C. diphtheriae, ibid.,* **34:**163, 1937*a.*

——: Nicotinic acid as a growth accessory for the diphtheria bacillus, *ibid.,* **34:**429, 1937*b.*

——: Nutrition of the diphtheria bacillus, *Bact. Rev.,* **4:**97, 1940.

—— and S. Cohen: Beta alanine as a growth accessory for the diphtheria bacillus, *J. Bact.,* **34:**381, 1937.

—— and I. Kapnick: Studies on cultural requirements of bacteria. VIII. Amino acid requirements for the Park-Williams No. 8 strain of diphtheria, *ibid.,* **30:**525, 1935.

Müller, M.: Über den Einfluss von Fiebertemperaturen auf die Wachsthumsgeschwindigkeit und die Virulenz des Typhus-bacillus, *Z. Hyg.,* **20:**245, 1895.

Nickerson, W. J., and M. Webb: Effect of folic acid analogues on growth and cell division of nonexacting microorganisms, *J. Bact.,* **71:**129, 1956.

Northrop, J. H.: Apparatus for maintaining bacterial cultures in the steady state, *J. Gen. Physiol.,* **38:**105, 1954.

O'Kane, D. J.: The synthesis of riboflavin by staphylococci, *J. Bact.,* **41:**441, 1941.

Pearson, W. N.: A purine-requiring strain of *Photobacterium fischeri, J. Bact.,* **58:**653, 1949.

Peters, V. J., and E. E. Snell: Peptides and bacterial growth. VI. The nutritional requirements of *Lactobacillus delbrueckii, J. Bact.,* **67:**69, 1954.

Peterson, W. H., and M. S. Peterson: Relation of bacteria to vitamins and other growth factors, *Bact. Rev.,* **9:**49, 1945.

Pittillo, R. F., and J. W. Foster: Potentiation of inhibitor action through determination of reversing metabolites, *J. Bact.,* **67:**53, 1954.

Pollack, M. A., and M. Lindner: Glutamine and glutamic acid as growth factors for lactic acid bacteria, *J. Biol. Chem.*, 143:655, 1942.

Rafelson, M. E., Jr., et al.: Utilization of acetate-1-C^{14} for the synthesis of tryptophan in *Aerobacter aerogenes*, *J. Biol. Chem.*, 211:725, 1954.

Reynolds, E. S., I. Lieberman, and A. Kornberg: The metabolism of orotic acid in aerobic bacteria, *J. Bact.*, 69:250, 1955.

Rhuland, L. E., and R. C. Bard: The role of anthranilic acid in the nutrition of *Lactobacillus arabinosus*, *J. Bact.*, 63:133, 1952.

Richardson, G. M.: The nutrition of *Staphylococcus aureus*. Necessity for uracil in anaerobic growth, *Biochem. J.*, 30:2184, 1936.

Roblin, R. O., Jr.: Metabolite antagonists, *Chem. Eng. News*, 27:3624, 1949.

Rochford, E. J., and R. J. Mandle: The production of chains of *Diplococcus pneumoniae* in magnesium deficient media, *J. Bact.*, 66:554, 1953.

Rogers, H. J.: Importance of pyrimidine derivatives in the growth of group C (Lancefield) streptococci upon a simplified medium, *Nature*, 153:251, 1944.

Rook, J. J., and H. W. L. Bruckman: On the suitability of gelatin for plate cultures. II. *Antonie van Leeuwenhoek*, 19:354, 1953.

Rothstein, A.: Role of the cell membrane in the metabolism of inorganic electrolytes by microorganisms, *Bact. Rev.*, 23:175, 1959.

Rowatt, E.: The relation of pantothenic acid to acetylcholine formation by a strain of *Lactobacillus plantarum*, *J. Gen. Microbiol.*, 2:25, 1948.

Rydon, H. N.: Anthranilic acid as an intermediate in the biosynthesis of tryptophan by *Bact. typhosum*, *Brit. J. Exp. Path.*, 29:48, 1948.

Schultz, J. H., and H. Ritz: Die Thermoresistenz junger und alter Coli-Bacillen, *Centr. Bakt.*, Abt. I, Orig., 54:283, 1910.

Sergeant, T. P., C. E. Lankford, and R. W. Traxler: Initiation of growth of *Bacillus* species in a chemically defined medium, *J. Bact.*, 74:728, 1957.

Shankar, K., and R. C. Bard: The effect of metallic ions on the growth and morphology of *Clostridium perfringens*, *J. Bact.*, 63:279, 1952.

Sherman, J. M., and W. R. Albus: Physiological youth in bacteria, *J. Bact.*, 8:127, 1923.

Shive, W., and L. L. Rogers: Involvement of biotin in the biosynthesis of oxalacetic and α-ketoglutaric acids, *J. Biol. Chem.*, 169:453, 1947.

Shooter, R. A., and H. V. Wyatt: Mineral requirements for growth of *Staphylococcus pyogenes*. Effect of potassium ions, *British J. Exp. Path.*, 37:311, 1956.

Shull, G. M., B. L. Hutchings, and W. H. Peterson: A microbiological assay for biotin, *J. Biol. Chem.*, 142:913, 1942.

Sirny, R. J., O. R. Braekkan, M. Klungsøyr, and C. A. Elvehjem: Effects of potassium and sodium in microbiological assay medium, *J. Bact.*, 68:103, 1954.

Smith, M. I., and E. W. Emmart: Studies in the metabolism of the tubercle bacillus. I. The production of riboflavin, *J. Immunol.*, 61:259, 1949.

Snell, E. E., E. Kitay, and W. S. McNutt: Thymine desoxyriboside as an essential growth factor for lactic acid bacteria, *J. Biol. Chem.*, 175:473, 1948.

——— and H. K. Mitchell: Purine and pyrimidine bases as growth substances for lactic acid bacteria, *Proc. Nat. Acad. Sci.*, 27:1, 1941.

——— and W. H. Peterson: Properties of a new growth factor for lactic acid bacteria, *J. Biol. Chem.*, 128:94, 1939.

——— and ———: Growth factors for bacteria. X. Additional factors required by certain lactic acid bacteria, *J. Bact.*, 39:273, 1940.

Squires, R. W., and S. E. Hartsell: Measurement of relative lag time, *J. Bact.*, 69:226, 1955.

Stanier, R. Y.: Studies on marine agar-digesting bacteria, *J. Bact.*, 42:527, 1941.

———: Agar-decomposing strains of the *Actinomyces coelicolor* species-group, *ibid.*, 44:555, 1942.

Stephenson, M., and M. D. Whetham: Studies in the fat metabolism of the timothy grass bacillus, *Proc. Roy. Soc. (London)*, Series B, 93:262, 1922.

Stokes, J. L., M. Gunness, and J. W. Foster: Vitamin content of ingredients of microbiological culture media, *J. Bact.*, 47:293, 1944.

Stokes, J. L., A. Larson, and M. Gunness: Biotin and the synthesis of aspartic acid by microorganisms, *ibid.*, **54**:219, 1947.

Stokstad, E. L. R.: Isolation of a nucleotide essential for the growth of *Lactobacillus casei*, *J. Biol. Chem.*, **139**:475, 1941.

——: Pteroylglutamic acid. From "The Vitamins," edited by W. H. Sebrell, Jr., and R. S. Harris, vol. 3, New York, Academic Press, Inc., 1954.

Swartz, M. N., and N. Gordon: Agarase from an agar-digesting bacterium, *J. Bact.*, **77**:403, 1959.

Tanner, F. W., Jr., C. Vojnovich, and J. M. Van Lanen: Factors affecting riboflavin production by *Ashbya gossypii*, *J. Bact.*, **58**:737, 1949.

Thjötta, T.: Studies on bacterial nutrition. I. Growth of *Bacillus influenzae* in hemoglobin-free media, *J. Exp. Med.*, **33**:763, 1921.

—— and O. T. Avery: Studies on bacterial nutrition. II. Growth accessory substances in the cultivation of hemophilic bacilli, *ibid.*, **34**:97, 1921*a*; III. Plant tissue, as a source of growth accessory substances, in the cultivation of *B. influenzae*, *ibid.*, **34**:455, 1921*b*.

Volcani, B. E., and E. E. Snell: The effects of canavanine, arginine, and related compounds on the growth of bacteria, *J. Biol. Chem.*, **174**:893, 1948.

Walker, H. H.: Carbon dioxide as a factor affecting lag in bacterial growth, *Science*, **76**:602, 1932.

Walper, J. F., and R. M. Fink: The utilization of dihydrothymine by *Streptococcus faecalis* in the absence of folic acid and thymine, *J. Bact.*, **72**:105, 1956.

Waring, W. S., and C. H. Werkman: Growth of bacteria in an iron-free medium, *Arch. Biochem.*, **1**:303, 1942.

—— and ——: Iron requirements of heterotrophic bacteria, *ibid.*, **1**:425, 1943.

—— and ——: Iron deficiency in bacterial metabolism, *ibid.*, **4**:75, 1944.

Webb, M.: The influence of magnesium on cell division. I. The growth of *Clostridium welchii* in complex media deficient in magnesium, *J. Gen. Microbiol.*, **2**:275, 1948.

—— and W. J. Nickerson: Differential reversal of inhibitory effects of folic acid analogues on growth, division, and desoxyribonucleic acid synthesis of microorganisms, *J. Bact.*, **71**:140, 1956.

Wieland, O. P., J. Avener, E. M. Boggiano, N. Bohonos, B. L. Hutchings, and J. H. Williams: Orotic acid in the nutrition of a strain of *Lactobacillus bulgaricus*, *J. Biol. Chem.*, **186**:737, 1950.

Wildiers, E.: Nouvelle substance indispensable au développement de la levure, *La Cellule*, **18**:313, 1901.

Williams, R. J.: Growth-promoting nutrilites for yeasts, *Biol. Rev.*, **16**:49, 1941.

—— and E. Bradway: Further fractionation of yeast nutrilites and their relationship to vitamin B and Wildiers' bios, *J. Am. Chem. Soc.*, **53**:783, 1931.

——, C. M. Lyman, G. H. Goodyear, J. H. Truesdail, and D. Holaday: Pantothenic acid, a growth determinant of universal biological occurrence, *ibid.*, **55**:2912, 1933.

Woods, D. D.: The relation of *p*-aminobenzoic acid to the mechanism of the action of sulfanilamide, *Brit. J. Exp. Path.*, **21**:74, 1940.

Woolley, D. W.: "A Study of Antimetabolites," New York, John Wiley & Sons, Inc., 1952.

——: Antimetabolites, *Science*, **129**:615, 1959.

Wright, L. D., C. A. Driscoll, C. S. Miller, and H. R. Skeggs: Dihydroorotic acid in nutrition of lactic acid bacteria, *Proc. Soc. Exp. Biol. Med.*, **84**:716, 1953.

——, H. R. Skeggs, and J. W. Huff: The ability of thymidine to replace vitamin B_{12} as a growth factor for certain lactobacilli, *J. Biol. Chem.*, **175**:475, 1948.

Yanofsky, C.: The enzymatic conversion of anthranilic acid to indole, *J. Biol. Chem.*, **223**:171, 1956.

Young, R. M., and L. F. Rettger: Decomposition of vitamin C by bacteria, *J. Bact.*, **46**:351, 1943.

CHAPTER 8

Sterilization

Sterilization may be defined as the complete destruction of all living organisms in, or their removal from, materials by means of heat, filtration, or other physical or chemical methods.

Plugged test tubes, flasks, bottles, etc., and Petri dishes must be sterilized before use to destroy all living organisms adhering to the inner surfaces. Pipettes are placed in containers and heated to sterilize both inner and outer surfaces. Likewise, all culture media must be sterilized previous to use in order to destroy all contaminating organisms present. Studies on single bacterial species or pure cultures could not be made if the glassware and culture media were contaminated with other organisms previous to use. When once sterilized, glassware may be kept in a sterile condition indefinitely if protected from outside contamination. The same applies to culture media if, in addition to sterility, evaporation can be prevented.

The usual methods employed for the sterilization of laboratory materials involves the use of heat. Three types of heat sterilizers are used in bacteriology for the destruction of living microorganisms: (1) the hot-air sterilizer, (2) the Arnold sterilizer, and (3) the autoclave.

Hot-air Sterilizer. This is a dry-air type of sterilizer (Fig. 111). It is constructed with three walls and two air spaces. The outer walls are covered with thick asbestos to reduce the radiation of heat. A burner manifold runs along both sides and rear between the outside and the intermediate walls. Convection currents travel a complete circuit through the wall space and interior of the oven, and the products of combustion escape through an opening in the top.

The hot-air sterilizer is operated at a temperature of 160 to 180°C. (320 to 356°F.) for a period of 1½ hr. If the temperature goes above 180°C., there will be danger of the cotton stoppers charring. Therefore, the thermometer must be watched closely at first until the sterilizer is regulated to the desired temperature. The necessity of watching the sterilizer may be avoided by having the oven equipped with a temperature regulator.

The hot-air sterilizer is used for sterilizing all kinds of laboratory glassware, such as test tubes, pipettes, Petri dishes, and flasks. In addition, it may be used to sterilize other laboratory materials and equipment that are not burned by the high temperature of the sterilizer. Under no conditions should the hot-air sterilizer be used to sterilize culture media, as the liquids would boil to dryness.

Arnold Sterilizer. It is well known that moist heat is more effective as a sterilizing agent than dry heat. This is believed to be due to the following reasons: (1) moist heat has greater penetrating power; and (2) death of organisms is believed to be caused by a coagulation of the

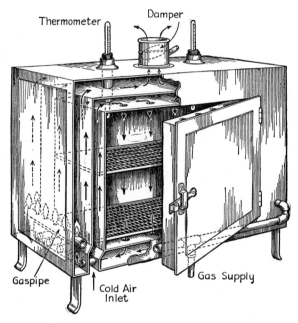

Fig. 111. Hot-air sterilizer. (*From Belding and Marston, "A Textbook of Medical Bacteriology," Appleton-Century-Crofts, Inc.*)

proteins of the protoplasm. An increase in the water content of the protoplasm causes the proteins to coagulate at a lower temperature.

The Arnold makes use of streaming steam as the sterilizing agent (Fig. 112). The sterilizer is built with a quick-steaming base that is automatically supplied with water from an open reservoir. The water passes from the open reservoir, through small apertures, into the steaming base, to which the heat is applied. Since the base contains only a thin layer of water, steam is produced very rapidly. The steam rises through a funnel in the center of the apparatus and passes into the sterilizing chamber.

Sterilization is effected by employing streaming steam at a temperature of approximately 100°C. (212°F.) for a period of 20 min. or longer on three consecutive days. The length of the heating period will depend upon the nature of the materials to be treated and the size of the container. Agar, for example, must be first completely melted before recording the beginning of the heating period.

It must be remembered that a temperature of 100°C. for 20 min. is not sufficient to destroy spores. A much higher temperature is required to effect a complete sterilization in one operation over a relatively short exposure period.

The principle underlying this method is that the first heating period kills all the vegetative cells present. After a lapse of 24 hr. in a favorable medium and at a warm temperature, the spores, if present, will germinate

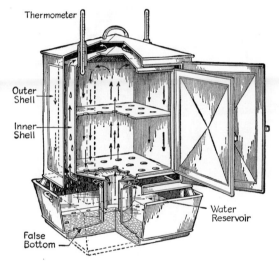

FIG. 112. Arnold sterilizer. (*From Belding and Marston, "A Textbook of Medical Bacteriology," Appleton-Century-Crofts, Inc.*)

into vegetative cells. The second heating will again destroy all vegetative cells. It sometimes happens that all spores do not pass into vegetative forms before the second heating period. Therefore, an additional 24-hr. period is allowed to elapse to make sure that all spores have germinated into vegetative cells.

It may be seen that unless the spores germinate the method will fail to sterilize. Failure may be due to the following causes: (1) The medium may be unsuited for the germination of the spores. Distilled water, for example, is not a favorable environment for the growth of bacteria. Therefore, it will not permit spores to germinate into vegetative cells. (2) Spores of anaerobic bacteria may be present, which will not germinate in a medium in contact with atmospheric oxygen.

The Arnold is used principally for the sterilization of gelatin, milk, and carbohydrate media. Higher temperatures or longer single exposures in the Arnold may hydrolyze or decompose carbohydrates and prevent gelatin from solidifying. Obviously, such media would then be unsatisfactory for use.

Autoclave. The autoclave is a cylindrical metal vessel having double walls around all parts except the front (Fig. 113). It is built to withstand a steam pressure of at least 30 lb. per sq. in.

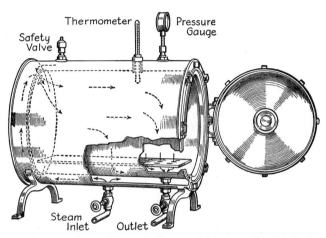

Fig. 113. Autoclave sterilizer. (*From Belding and Marston, "A Textbook of Medical Bacteriology," Appleton-Century-Crofts, Inc.*)

The principle of the method is that water boils at about 100°C., depending upon the vapor pressure of the atmosphere. If the atmospheric pressure is increased, the temperature will be increased. Therefore, if the steam pressure inside the closed vessel is increased to 15 lb. per sq. in. (2 atm.), the temperature will rise to 121.6°C. The relationship between pressure and temperature is shown in Table 6.

The autoclave is operated usually at 15 lb. steam pressure for a period of 15 min., which corresponds to a temperature of 121.6°C. This temperature is sufficient to destroy both vegetative cells and spores in one operation.

Certain precautions must be observed to prevent sterilization failures. The most important single cause is incomplete evacuation of air from the chamber. Observation of the pressure gauge alone is not sufficient. The proper degree of temperature must also be taken into consideration. The temperature figures given in Table 6 are true only if all air is evacuated from the sterilizing chamber.

The temperature of a mixture of steam and air at a given pressure is less than that of pure steam alone. This means that, even though the autoclave is kept at the desired pressure, the temperature may not be

TABLE 6

Pressure, lb. per sq. in.	Corresponding temperature	
	°C.	°F.
5	107.7	227
10	115.5	240
15	121.6	250
20	126.6	260
25	130.5	267
30	134.4	274

high enough to give complete sterilization. The actual temperatures attained in the autoclave under ordinary conditions of proper and improper usage, according to Underwood (1934), are given in Table 7.

TABLE 7. TEMPERATURE WITH VARIOUS DEGREES OF AIR DISCHARGE

Gauge pressure, lb.	Pure steam, complete air discharge		Two-thirds air discharge, 20-in. vacuum		One-half air discharge, 15-in. vacuum		One-third air discharge, 10-in. vacuum		No air discharge	
	°C.	°F.	°C.	°F.	°C.	°F.	°C.	°F.	°C.	°F.
5	109	228	100	212	94	202	90	193	72	162
10	115	240	109	228	105	220	100	212	90	193
15	121	250	115	240	112	234	109	228	100	212
20	126	259	121	250	118	245	115	240	109	228
25	130	267	126	259	124	254	121	250	115	240
30	135	275	130	267	128	263	126	259	121	250

Another important precaution to be observed is that the steam must have access to the materials to be sterilized. If the steam is prevented from penetrating the materials, the method will be of doubtful value. For example, suppose that it is desired to sterilize some cotton contained in a bottle. If the bottle is closed with a rubber stopper, the steam cannot reach the cotton. The process will be no more effective than a hot-air sterilizer kept at 121.6°C. for a period of 15 min. It has already been seen that such a temperature and time interval is insufficient to destroy spores in a dry-air sterilizer. On the other hand, if the mouth of the bottle is covered with one or two thicknesses of muslin, permitting the steam to penetrate, then the cotton will be sterilized.

The autoclave is used to sterilize most types of solid and liquid media with and without carbohydrate, gelatin media, distilled water, normal saline solution, discarded cultures, contaminated media, aprons, rubber tubing and gloves, etc. This is the type of sterilizer employed commercially for processing canned foods.

For more information see Hoyt, Chaney, and Cavell (1938) and Underwood (1937).

STERILIZATION BY FILTRATION

Some solutions cannot be sterilized by heat without being greatly altered in their physical and chemical properties. Serum in culture media is easily coagulated by heat. If the serum content is high enough, the medium becomes changed from a liquid to a solid preparation. Certain physiological salt solutions containing the unstable compound sodium bicarbonate are ruined if heated. The bicarbonate easily loses carbon dioxide and is converted into the more alkaline sodium carbonate. Enzymes and bacterial toxins in solution are easily destroyed by heat. These are but a few examples of many that might be mentioned.

Preparations containing heat-sensitive compounds are best sterilized by the process of filtration. The types of filters employed for this purpose include Chamberland and Jenkins porcelain filters, Berkefeld and Mandler diatomaceous earth filters, fritted-glass filters, asbestos filters, and collodion membranes or ultrafilters.

Porcelain or Chamberland Filters. Porcelain filters are hollow, unglazed cylinders, closed at one end. They are composed of hydrous aluminum silicate or kaolin with the addition of quartz sand and are heated to a temperature sufficiently low to avoid sintering. These filters are prepared in graduated degrees of porosity, from L1 to L13. Cylinders having the largest pores are marked L1; those having the smallest pores are designated L13. The finer the pores, the slower will be the rate of filtration. The L1 and L2 cylinders are preliminary filters intended for the removal of coarse particles and large bacteria. The L3 filter is probably satisfactory for all types of bacterial filtrations. A satisfactory method of assembling a Chamberland filter is shown in Fig. 114.

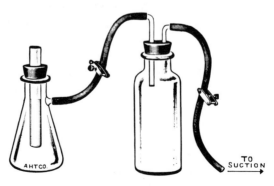

FIG. 114. Chamberland-Pasteur filter assembled in a filter flask and ready for filtration.

Berkefeld Filters. Kieselguhr is a deposit of fine, usually white, siliceous powder composed chiefly or wholly of the remains of diatoms. It is also called *diatomaceous earth* and *infusorial earth.*

Berkefeld filters are manufactured in Germany. They are prepared by mixing carefully purified diatomaceous earth with asbestos and organic matter, pressing into cylinder form, and drying. The dried cylinders are heated in an oven to a temperature of about 2000°C. to bind the materials together. The burned cylinders are then machined into the desired shapes and sizes (Fig. 115).

The cylinders are graded as W (dense), N (normal), and V (coarse), depending upon the sizes of the pores. The grading depends upon the rate of flow of pure filtered water under a certain constant pressure.

Mandler Filters. These filters are similar to the Berkefeld type but are manufactured in this country. They are composed of 60 to 80 per cent diatomaceous earth, 10 to 30 per cent asbestos, and 10 to 15 per cent plaster of Paris. The proportions vary, depending upon the sizes of the pores desired. The ingredients are mixed with water, subjected to high pressure, and then baked in ovens to a temperature of 980 to 1650°C. to bind the materials together.

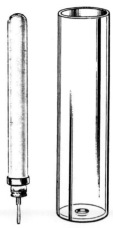

FIG. 115. Left, Berkefeld filter. Right, glass mantle for use with either Berkefeld or Mandler filter.

The finished cylinders are tested by connecting a tube to the nipple of the filter, submerging in water, and passing compressed air to the inside. A gauge records the pressure when air bubbles first appear on the outside of the cylinder in the water. Each cylinder is marked with the air pressure obtained in actual test.

A convenient arrangement of apparatus for filtering liquids through a Mandler or Berkefeld filter is shown in Fig. 116. The reduced pressure is indicated by the manometer. The liquid to be filtered is poured into the mantle, and the filtrate is collected in a graduated vessel, from which it may be withdrawn aseptically. Filtration may be interrupted at any time by stopping the vacuum pump and opening the stopcock on the trap bottle to equalize the pressure.

Fritted-glass Filters. Filters of this type are prepared by fritting finely pulverized glass into disk form in a suitable mold (Morton and Czarnetzky, 1937). The pulverized glass is heated to a temperature just high enough to cause the particles to become a coherent solid mass, without thoroughly melting, and leaving the disk porous. The disk is then carefully fused into a glass funnel and the whole assembled into a filter flask by means of a rubber stopper (Fig. 117). Another arrangement is the coupling of the filter to the flask through a ground-glass joint (Fig. 118), thus eliminating the use of a rubber stopper (Morton, 1944).

The filters are marketed in five degrees of porosity as follows: EC (extra coarse), C (coarse), M (medium), F (fine), and UF (ultrafine).

Bacteriological filters are generally employed under conditions of reduced pressure. Bush (1946) recommended filtration through glass

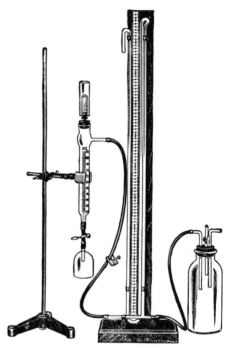

Fig. 116. A convenient arrangement for assembling a Berkefeld or Mandler filter for filtration.

filters by the use of positive pressure. Positive pressure not only reduces or eliminates evaporation of the filtrate, but greatly facilitates the interchange of receivers—particularly important in bacteriological filtrations which must be handled aseptically.

A convenient arrangement is shown in Fig. 119. The main body of the filter *B* contains a fritted-glass disk. A shield *A* protects the receiver from dust, and a pressure head *C* carries a stopcock. An alternate pressure head *C'* contains a built-in mercury manometer. The stopcock on *C* (*C'*) permits the retention of pressure after the apparatus is detached from the source of compressed air. An ordinary rubber pressure bulb is satisfactory for producing pressures up to at least 450 mm. mercury. If the ground-glass joints are well lubricated and the parts held together with strong rubber bands or springs, the apparatus should hold this pressure for days.

Asbestos Filters. The best-known filter employing asbestos as the filtering medium is the Seitz filter (Fig. 120). The asbestos is pressed together into thin disks and tightly clamped between two smooth metal rims by means of three screw clamps. The liquid to be filtered is poured into the metal apparatus, in which the asbestos disk is clamped, and the solution drawn through by vacuum. The filtering disks are capable of effectively retaining bacteria and other particulate matter. At the end of the operation, the asbestos disk is removed, a new one inserted, and the assembled

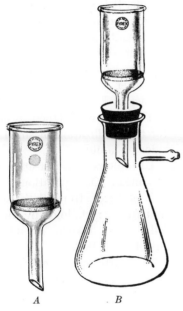

A   . *B*

Fig. 117. *A*, fritted-glass filter. *B*, filter assembled in a filter flask and ready for filtration.

Fig. 118. Fritted-glass filter coupled to a flask through a ground-glass joint. (*Courtesy of Corning Glass Works.*)

filter sterilized. This feature makes the Seitz filter very convenient to use, since no preliminary cleaning is necessary.

A modification of the Seitz filter, utilizing centrifugal force instead of suction or pressure, has been suggested by Boerner (Fig. 121). The filter consists of a cylinder and a funnel-shaped part with stem, which holds the filter pad supported on a wire gauze disk. The cylinder screws into the funnel with the filter disk pressed between them. The assembled filter fits closely into the top of a 15-ml. metal centrifuge tube, with the knurled collar of the funnel portion resting on the top of the metal tube. The filtrate is collected in a glass tube inside the cup. The filter can also be used for vacuum filtration in the conventional manner by inserting the stem through a rubber stopper fitted to a filter flask.

For more information on the composition of the Seitz filter disks, see Webb (1946).

Jenkins Filter. This filter consists of a metal mantle holding a soft rubber sleeve and a porcelain filter block. The porcelain block is held in the rubber sleeve and made watertight by screwing together two metal parts. The filter block is not fragile. It is washed after each use, dried, and inserted in the mantle. The mantle is fitted with a rubber stopper, wrapped in paper, and sterilized in an autoclave. For use, the filter is attached to a flask as shown in Fig. 122.

The filter is designed to be used for the sterilization of small quantities of liquids.

Ultrafilters. Ultrafiltration generally means the separation of colloidal particles from their solvents and from crystalloids by means of jelly filters known as ultrafilters (Bechhold, 1926).

The early jelly filters were composed of gelatin and of silicic acid, but these have been replaced by collodion in membrane or sac form, or collodion deposited in a porous supporting structure. The supporting structure may be filter paper in sheet and thimble form, unglazed porcelain dishes and crucibles, Büchner funnels, filter cylinders, etc.

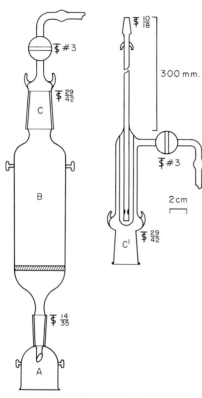

Fig. 119. Arrangement of bacteria filter for positive-pressure filtration. (*After Bush.*)

Collodion. Several types of collodion are employed for ultrafiltration. The earliest type was prepared by dissolving pyroxylin or soluble guncotton in a mixture of 1 part of alcohol and 3 parts of ether. A more popular type is prepared by dissolving pyroxylin in glacial acetic acid. Pore size may be controlled by increasing or decreasing the pyroxylin content or by adding various liquids such as ethylene glycol and glycerol to alcohol-ether collodion. Elford (1931) recommended a new type of collodion for the preparation of a graded series of filters which he termed *Gradocol* membranes. The filters are prepared by incorporating a definite amount of amyl alcohol with an alcohol-ether collodion and then adding graded amounts of water or acetic acid to increase or decrease the permeability of the filters. Since membranes prepared by this procedure are quite strong, it is not necessary to deposit the collodion in a porous supporting structure.

Sacs may be prepared by pouring the collodion into a test tube or beaker, inverting and twirling continuously so that the excess drips out, until a thin, even coating is formed. The tube or beaker is then plunged into cold water to jell the collodion. After most of the solvent has been washed away, the sac can be loosened from the glass mold and removed. Collodion membranes in sheet form may be prepared by cutting the sacs at right angles at the closed end and then lengthwise.

Membranes employing filter paper as the porous supporting structure are usually prepared with acetic collodion. Pore size of the membranes depends upon the strength of the collodion. A strong collodion gives finer pores than a weak collodion. It is a simple matter to prepare a graded

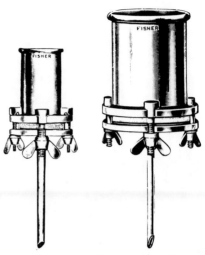

Fig. 120. Seitz filters with asbestos disks in place. These are assembled in filter flasks as shown in Fig. 117.

series of filters. The paper foundation gives the membranes a strength that, under certain conditions, will withstand a pressure of 20 atm. or more.

Collodion filters are extensively used for the isolation of ultramicroscopic viruses and for determination of their diameters.

For more information see Heckly and Watson (1951), Polson and Madsen (1953).

Electrical Charge of Filters. The filtration of solutions of enzymes, toxins, immune bodies, viruses, etc., usually results in a loss of some of the active material. If the active material is present in very low concentration, it may be completely removed from solution.

Filters composed of porcelain (Chamberland), diatomaceous earth (Berkefeld, Mandler), fritted glass, and asbestos (Seitz) consist chiefly of metal silicates and carry negative electrical charges.

The metal (Mg^{++}, Al^{+++}, Ca^{++}, etc.) cations or positive ions are more soluble than the silicate anions or negative ions and show a greater tendency to pass into solution. When a liquid is filtered, positively charged particles will react with the negative silicate ions and negatively charged particles will react with the positive metal ions. Since the metal ions are soluble, they will react with the negatively charged particles and pass through the pores of the filter into the filtrate. On the other hand, the insoluble silicate ions will react with positively charged particles and remain fixed to the walls of the filter pores.

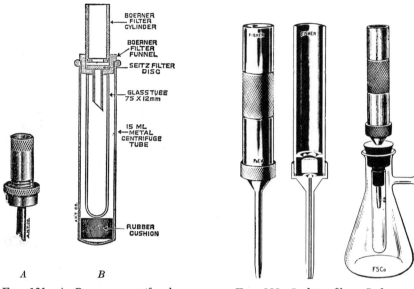

FIG. 121. A, Boerner centrifugal filter; B, Boerner filter assembled in a 15-ml. metal centrifuge tube, with glass collecting tube inside. (*Courtesy of A. H. Thomas Company.*)

FIG. 122. Jenkins filter. Left, completely assembled; center, cross section of filter; right, filter assembled and attached to a filter flask by a rubber stopper. Small tube inside of flask is used to collect the filtrate.

Adsorption of compounds from solution can be very effectively demonstrated by means of basic and acid dyes, such as toluidine blue and picric acid, respectively. Toluidine blue is a thiazine dye having the same chromophore as methylene blue and thionine. It ionizes as follows:

The cation is blue, and the chloride anion is colorless. When a solution of this dye is filtered through one of the silicate filters, the blue cations will react with the negative silicate ions and remain fixed to the pores of the filter. The chloride anions will combine with the metal cations of the silicates to form soluble metal chlorides and pass into the filtrate. If more than sufficient dye is present in the solution to react with all the silicate ions in the filter pores, the excess will pass through, imparting a blue color to the filtrate. If, on the other hand, the amount of toluidine blue is insufficient to take care of all the silicate ions, the dye will be completely removed from the solution and the filtrate will be colorless. The reaction is reversible, however, since the passage of distilled water through the filter saturated with dye results in a blue color in the filtrate.

If a solution of an acid dye is used instead of the basic toluidine blue, the results will be quite different. The dye will not be adsorbed by the filter material but will pass through the pores into the filtrate.

Picric acid or trinitrophenol is an acid dye in which the nitro group is the chromophore. It ionizes as follows:

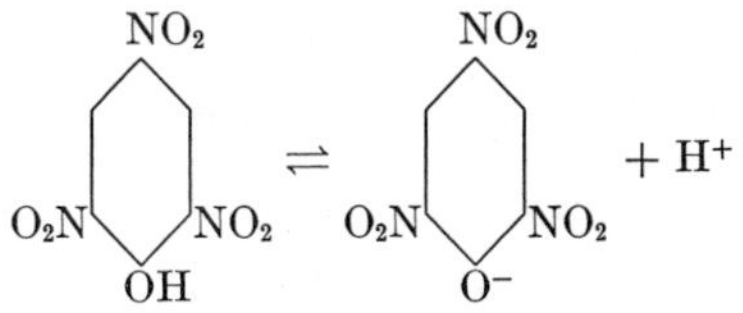

$$
\begin{array}{ccc}
& NO_2 & NO_2 \\
& & \\
O_2N\diagdown\diagup NO_2 & \rightleftharpoons & O_2N\diagdown\diagup NO_2 \quad + H^+ \\
OH & & O^-
\end{array}
$$

In this case, the cation is colorless and the anion is yellow. When a solution of this dye is filtered through one of the silicate filters, not a trace of it will be adsorbed because an exchange of ions results in the formation of soluble picrates, which pass through in the filtrate.

Michaelis (1925) found that collodion filters were nonionogenic but that they also carried a negative charge. Their negative charge was believed to be due to the adsorption of negative ions. Elford (1933) found that proteins in solutions, adjusted to different pH values by hydrochloric acid and sodium hydroxide, were most strongly adsorbed in the isoelectric zone (page 214). On the other hand, proteins in solutions buffered with $M/15$ phosphate, instead of adjusting the pH with hydrochloric acid and sodium hydroxide, are adsorbed on the acid side of the isoelectric zone. The negatively charged collodion now preferentially adsorbs the positively charged proteins. Elford concluded that the effect is probably associated with some specific influence of the phosphate ion.

Amphoteric Nature of Proteins and Amino Acids. An important characteristic of proteins and amino acids is that they contain both acidic (COOH) and basic (NH$_2$) groups. In acid solutions, the compounds act as bases; in basic solutions, they act as acids. Representing the formula of an amino acid as $R \cdot CHNH_2 \cdot COOH$, the reactions with acids and bases are as follows:

With an acid,

$$
\begin{array}{ccc}
R & & R \\
| & & | \\
H-C-NH_2 + HCl \rightarrow & & H-C-NH_3Cl \\
| & & | \\
COOH & & COOH
\end{array}
$$

On ionization, this gives

$$
\begin{array}{ccc}
R & & R \\
| & & | \\
H-C-NH_3Cl \rightleftharpoons & & H-C-NH_3^+ + Cl^- \\
| & & | \\
COOH & & COOH
\end{array}
$$

The acid reacts with the basic amino group. The amino acid molecule has a positive charge and, therefore, behaves as a base.

With a base,

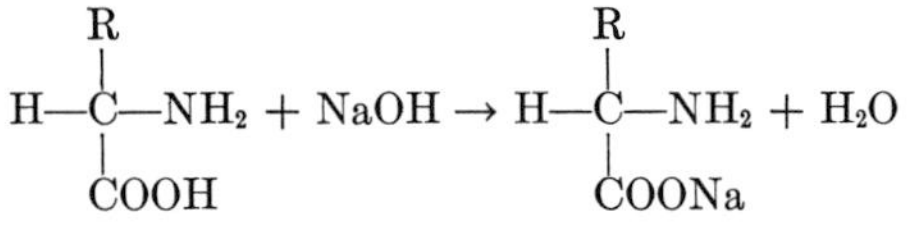

$$\begin{array}{ccc} \text{R} & & \text{R} \\ | & & | \\ \text{H—C—NH}_2 + \text{NaOH} \rightarrow & \text{H—C—NH}_2 + \text{H}_2\text{O} \\ | & & | \\ \text{COOH} & & \text{COONa} \end{array}$$

On ionization, this gives

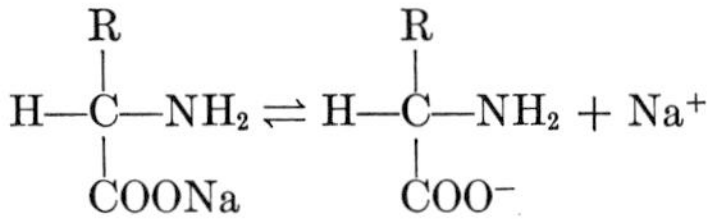

$$\begin{array}{ccc} \text{R} & & \text{R} \\ | & & | \\ \text{H—C—NH}_2 \rightleftharpoons & \text{H—C—NH}_2 + \text{Na}^+ \\ | & & | \\ \text{COONa} & & \text{COO}^- \end{array}$$

The base reacts with the acid carboxyl group. The amino acid molecule has a negative electrical charge and, therefore, behaves as an acid. Compounds of this nature that are capable of reacting with both acids and bases are said to be amphoteric (from the Greek, meaning both).

Isoelectric Point. According to the classical theory, amphoteric compounds are supposed to dissociate into ions on either side of a pH point known as the isoelectric point. The isoelectric point has been defined as that point where the ionization of the amphoteric compound is at a minimum, expressed in pH. Opposed to this concept is the more recently developed view known as the *zwitterion* hypothesis, which states that the isoelectric point is that point where ionization is at a maximum. The difference in the two theories is indicated in the following formulas for isoelectric alanine:

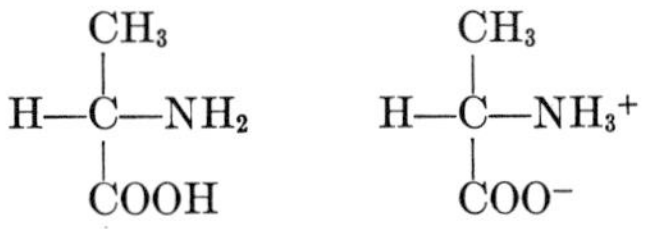

$$\begin{array}{cc} \text{CH}_3 & \text{CH}_3 \\ | & | \\ \text{H—C—NH}_2 & \text{H—C—NH}_3^+ \\ | & | \\ \text{COOH} & \text{COO}^- \\ \text{I. Classical} & \text{II. Zwitterion} \end{array}$$

Formula I represents a molecule that is not dissociated as either an acid or a base. The neutrality of the molecule is assumed to be due to the absence of dissociation. Formula II is also neutral, but the neutrality is assumed to be due to complete ionization of the acidic and basic groups. Regardless of which theory is correct, results obtained on the addition of an acid or a base are the same in both cases.

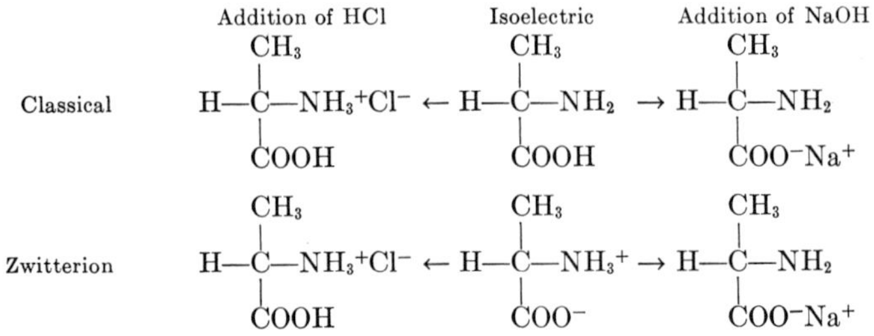

	Addition of HCl	Isoelectric	Addition of NaOH
	CH$_3$	CH$_3$	CH$_3$
Classical	H—C—NH$_3$$^+Cl^-$ ←	H—C—NH$_2$ →	H—C—NH$_2$
	COOH	COOH	COO$^-$Na$^+$
	CH$_3$	CH$_3$	CH$_3$
Zwitterion	H—C—NH$_3$$^+Cl^-$ ←	H—C—NH$_3$$^+$ →	H—C—NH$_2$
	COOH	COO$^-$	COO$^-$Na$^+$

The isoelectric point of a protein is not necessarily the neutral point (pH 7.0). As a matter of fact, most proteins which have been studied have isoelectric points on the acid side of neutrality. The isoelectric points of a few of the common proteins are as follows:

	Isoelectric point (pH)
Casein (milk protein)	4.7
Egg albumin	4.6
Gelatin	4.7
Hemoglobin	6.8
Serum albumin	4.8
Serum globulin	5.6

A knowledge of the isoelectric points is of considerable value in the filtration of solutions containing proteins, amino acids, bacterial toxins, enzymes, viruses, antitoxins, etc. If a solution is acid with respect to its isoelectric point, the active constituent will behave as a base and possess a positive electrical charge. The filtration of such a solution through a silicate filter, which has a negative charge, will result in the complete or partial adsorption of the active constituent on the walls of the filter pores. To avoid this, it would be necessary to use a filter having a positive charge, or to change the reaction of the active constituent to the alkaline side of its isoelectric point.

The adjustment of a solution to correspond to the acidic or basic side of the isoelectric point can be carried out only provided the change in pH will not result in a destruction of the active material. After filtration, the pH of the filtrate should be readjusted to correspond to the optimum pH range of the active component. If the active material is very sensitive to slight changes in pH, a filter having an appropriate electrical charge should be selected instead.

Cleaning Filters. Some filters are discarded after each use and new ones employed; others are intended to be cleaned after each filtration and, with proper care, may be used repeatedly. Collodion membranes are easily prepared, and the Seitz asbestos disks are relatively low in cost. These filters are intended to be used once, then discarded. On the other hand, porcelain, diatomaceous earth, and fritted-glass filters are too expensive to be used only once, but are easily cleaned.

Porcelain filters are cleaned by placing them in a muffle furnace and raising the temperature to a red heat. This burns the organic matter in the pores and restores the filters to their original condition.

Filters of the Berkefeld and Mandler types are cleaned by placing the cylinders in a special metal holder connected to a faucet. The flow of water is reversed by passing through the cylinder from within outward. This should be continued until all foreign matter has been washed away from the filter pores. Albuminous or similar materials remaining in the pores of the filters are likely to be coagulated by heat during the process of sterilization, with the result that the filters will be clogged. Filters in this condition are useless for further work.

Clogged filters may be cleaned in various ways but probably most conveniently by continuous suction of full-strength Clorox, or similar solution, for 5 to 15 min. (Vaisberg, 1938). This treatment quickly dissolves the coagulated material and restores the usefulness of the filter. Thorough washing is necessary to remove the last traces of the oxidizing solution.

Fritted-glass filters may be cleaned by treatment with concentrated sulfuric acid containing sodium nitrate. The strong acid quickly oxidizes and dissolves the organic matter. Thorough washing is necessary to remove the last traces of acid.

Sterilization of Filters. With the exception of collodion membranes, the various filters are assembled in their appropriate holders, wrapped in paper, and autoclaved. Dry heat cannot be used because of the destruction of rubber fittings for the filter flasks.

Since acetic collodion solutions are sterile, it is not necessary to sterilize such membranes in which filter paper is used as the porous supporting structure, if aseptic precautions are observed in their preparation.

REFERENCES

Bechhold, H.: Ultrafiltration and electro-ultrafiltration. From "Colloid Chemistry," edited by J. Alexander, vol. I, New York, Reinhold Publishing Corporation, 1926.

Bush, M. T.: Glass bacteriological filters arranged for positive pressure, *J. Bact.,* **51**:531, 1946.

Elford, W. J.: A new series of graded collodion membranes suitable for general bacteriological use, especially in filterable virus studies, *J. Path. Bact.,* **34**:505, 1931.

————: The principles of ultra-filtration as applied to biological studies, *Proc. Roy. Soc. (London),* Series B, **112**:384, 1933.

Heckly, R. J., and D. W. Watson: An improved ultrafiltration apparatus, *Am. Rev. Tuberc.,* **63**:718, 1951.

Hoyt, A., A. L. Chaney, and K. Cavell: Studies on steam sterilization and the effects of air in the autoclave, *J. Bact.,* **36**:639, 1938.

Michaelis, L.: Contribution to the theory of permeability of membranes for electrolytes, *J. Gen. Physiol.,* **8**:33, 1925.

Morton, H. E.: A new style assembly for fritted filters, *J. Bact.,* **47**:379, 1944.

———— and E. J. Czarnetzky: The application of sintered (fritted) glass filters to bacteriological work, *ibid.,* **34**:461, 1937.

Polson, A., and T. I. Madsen: Optical control of graded collodion membranes, *Biochim. Biophys. Acta,* **12**:584, 1953.

Underwood, W. B.: "Textbook of Sterilization," Erie, Pa., American Sterilizer Company, 1934.

————: "Some Features Relating to Pressure Steam Sterilization of Media and Solutions of Particular Interest to the Laboratory Technician," Erie, Pa., American Sterilizer Company, 1937.

Vaisberg, M.: Method for clearing coagulated serum blocked Berkefeld filters, *J. Lab. Clin. Med.,* **23**:542, 1938.

Webb, H. B.: Composition of Seitz filter pads, *Am. J. Clin. Path.,* **16**:442, 1946.

CHAPTER 9

Technique of Pure Cultures

A pure culture consists of a nutrient medium containing the growth of a single species of organism. Pure cultures are required for studying the morphology and physiology of organisms. All laboratory studies, with few exceptions, are based on the use of pure cultures. Occasionally two species are grown together in making studies of the various types of bacterial associations.

A mixed culture consists of a nutrient medium containing the growth of two or more species of organisms.

A plate culture consists of an organism growing on a solid medium contained in a Petri dish.

A slant culture consists of an organism growing on the inclined surface of a solid medium such as nutrient agar. This is referred to as a nutrient agar slant culture. Other types of solid media include coagulated blood serum, potato wedges, and coagulated egg. Cultures prepared on solid media are sometimes referred to as streak cultures. A nutrient agar slant culture may be called a nutrient agar streak culture; a coagulated blood serum slant culture may be called a coagulated blood serum streak culture; etc. A solid medium prepared in a slanted position increases greatly the surface area exposed to air and gives a much greater growth of organisms.

A stab culture is one prepared by stabbing a solid medium, such as nutrient gelatin or nutrient agar, to a considerable depth with a previously inoculated straight wire needle. Gelatin medium is used for studying the character of liquefaction produced by certain organisms. If an agar medium containing a fermentable carbohydrate is used, the production of gas may be detected by the appearance of gas bubbles in the agar. In some cases, the agar may be split into disks with a layer of gas separating each disk.

A liquid culture consists of a liquid medium, such as nutrient broth, milk, or dextrose broth, containing the growth of organisms.

A shake culture is one prepared by inoculating a liquefied agar medium and rotating or shaking the tube to obtain a uniform suspension of organisms before solidification occurs. A shake culture is valuable for indicating the oxygen requirements of an organism. Obligate anaerobic organisms grow in the deeper portions of the medium; obligate aerobic organisms grow at or near the surface in the presence of free oxygen. All gradations of oxygen tensions will be found in between these two extremes.

PURE CULTURE STUDY OF BACTERIA

This term, as defined here, is restricted to the study of pure cultures of bacteria with the object in view of determining their characteristics and identity. Included are methods of isolation; methods for the preservation of various kinds of bacteria; microscopic study of pure species, either stained or unstained; determination of morphological, cultural, and physiological characters; animal inoculation; and antigenic structure (serology).

Methods Employed for Inoculation of Culture Media. The following procedures are recommended for the inoculation of various types of culture media:

Agar Deep Cultures. Sterilize a wire needle in a flame and allow it to cool for about 5 sec. Remove the cotton stopper from an agar slant culture by grasping it with the small finger of the right hand, and flame the neck of the tube. Hold the tube slanted, not upright, to minimize aerial contamination. Remove a small amount of growth with the sterilized wire needle. Again flame the neck of the agar slant culture, replace the cotton stopper, and set the tube in the test-tube block. Remove the cotton stopper from the tube to be inoculated by grasping it with the small finger of the right hand. Flame the neck of the tube. Stab the straight wire, containing the inoculum, to the bottom of the tube. Withdraw the needle carefully. Again flame the neck of the tube and replace the cotton stopper. Flame the wire needle before setting it down on the table. Mark the tube with a china marking pencil and incubate at the proper temperature.

If a transfer is to be made from a liquid culture, use a wire loop instead of a needle. Remove a loopful of the medium and force the wire loop to the bottom of the tube. Withdraw the loop carefully. The procedure in every other detail is the same as above.

Agar Slant Cultures. Sterilize a wire needle or wire loop in the flame, depending upon whether a solid or a liquid culture is to be used. Allow the wire to cool for about 5 sec. Remove the cotton stopper from the culture, by grasping it with the small finger of the right hand, and flame the neck of the tube. Remove a small amount of the growth with the sterilized wire needle, or remove a loopful of the liquid culture with the wire loop. Again flame the neck of the culture, replace the cotton stopper, and set the tube in the test-tube block. Remove the cotton stopper from the agar slant to be inoculated, by grasping it with the small finger of the right hand. Flame the neck of the tube. Spread the inoculum over the surface of the agar slant by making streaks back and forth a few millimeters apart. Start at the butt of the slant and work up to the top. Withdraw the needle or loop from the tube. Again flame the neck of the tube and replace the cotton stopper. Flame the wire needle or loop before setting it down on the table. Mark the tube with a china marking pencil and incubate at the proper temperature.

Broth Cultures. Follow the same procedure as used for the preparation of agar slant cultures except that the inoculating needle or loop is plunged into broth and shaken to dislodge the inoculum from the wire.

Isolation of Species in Pure Culture. Bacteria are rarely found in nature in pure culture. Mixed species is the rule. Before accurate studies can be made on an organism, it first must be isolated in pure culture. Two different species growing together frequently produce reactions quite different from those given by each organism when studied separately.

A number of methods have been employed for the propagation of cultures from single cells. Most of these are too difficult and time consuming to be of practical value, except in certain special instances.

Plate cultures offer a means of isolating pure species of organisms in a comparatively simple manner. Two methods are generally followed: (1) the streak-plate method, and (2) the pour-plate method.

Streak-plate Method. Melt two tubes of nutrient agar in boiling water or in an Arnold sterilizer. Allow the agar to cool to about 50°C. It is important that the agar be cooled before pouring to minimize steaming; otherwise wetting of the agar surface might occur. A wet surface causes colonies to run together.

Remove the cotton stopper from one of the tubes and flame the neck of the tube. Lift the lid of a sterile Petri dish just high enough to insert the opening of the test tube and pour the melted agar into the plate. In like manner, pour the second tube of melted agar into another sterile Petri dish. Great care must be observed in pouring agar from a test tube into a Petri dish to avoid external contamination. Always flame the neck of the test tube. Also, never raise the lid of the Petri dish any more than is necessary. Set both plates aside until the agar has become firm.

Sterilize the wire loop in the flame of a Bunsen burner and allow it to cool for about 5 sec. Remove the cotton stopper from the broth culture by grasping it with the small finger of the right hand, and flame the neck of the tube. Remove a loopful of the culture with the wire loop. Again flame the neck of the culture tube, replace the cotton stopper, and set the tube in a test-tube block. Raise the lid of the Petri dish high enough to insert the wire loop. With a free arm movement from the elbow, spread the loopful of culture at the upper end of the dish to thin it out; then make streaks back and forth over the surface of the agar about ¼ in. apart. The first streak will contain more of the culture than the second, the second streak more than the third, etc. The last streaks should thin out the culture sufficiently to give isolated colonies. Without reinoculating the wire loop, it is usually advisable to streak a second plate. This gives greater certainty in securing well-isolated colonies. Each colony represents usually the growth from a single organism. Mark the plates with a china marking pencil, and incubate at the proper temperature.

The colonies appear only on the surface of the agar. A pure culture may be obtained from a well-isolated colony by transferring a portion, with the wire needle, to an appropriate culture medium (Fig. 123). It is advisable to make a Gram stain of the colony before transferring a portion to a medium, to ensure greater certainty in the selection of a pure colony.

Pour-plate Method. Place three tubes, each containing 10 ml. of nutrient broth, in a test-tube block, and number them. Inoculate the first tube of broth with 0.1 ml. of the mixed culture, and shake to obtain a uniform suspension of the organisms. Transfer 0.1 ml. of this suspension to the second tube of broth, and mix thoroughly. Finally, transfer 0.1 ml. from the second to the third tube, and mix as before.

Mark three Petri dishes to correspond to the numbers appearing on the culture dilution tubes. Transfer 0.1 ml. of each culture dilution to the Petri dishes.

Melt three tubes of nutrient agar in boiling water or in an Arnold sterilizer. Allow the agar to cool to about 50°C. Pour the melted and cooled agar into the Petri dishes, and tilt from side to side to obtain a uniform suspension of organisms. When firm, invert the plates and incubate at the appropriate temperature for colonies to develop.

In this procedure, most of the colonies are embedded in the agar, only a few appearing on the surface (Fig. 123). The first agar plate usually contains too many organisms, with the result that it is a difficult matter to find a well-isolated colony. The colonies are so crowded that they are unable to develop to their normal size. The second or third plate should show well-separated colonies of normal size. A pure culture may be obtained by removing a portion of a well-separated colony with the wire needle and transferring it to an appropriate medium.

Well-isolated surface colonies are usually round and quite characteristic for each species. On the other hand, colonies embedded in the agar are smaller in size and

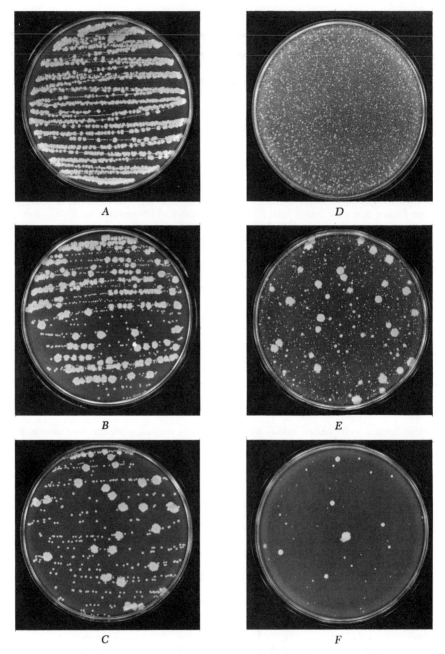

FIG. 123. Isolation of pure species from a mixed culture of *Bacillus subtilis* and *Staphylococcus aureus.* Streak-plate method: *A,* one loopful of culture streaked over the surface of agar. Without recharging loop, a second and third plate (*B, C*) were streaked. Pour-plate method: *D,* tube of agar mixed with one loopful of culture and poured into a Petri dish; *E,* agar mixed with one loopful from tube *A* and poured into a Petri dish; *F,* agar mixed with one loopful from tube *B* and poured into a Petri dish.

usually lenticular in shape. As a rule, it is not possible to distinguish between different species of subsurface colonies by their colonial appearance.

It is usually easier to obtain pure cultures by the pour-plate method because the organisms separate better when mixed with melted agar. Bacteria that produce mucoid colonies are very difficult to separate from nonmucoid organisms by the streak-plate method.

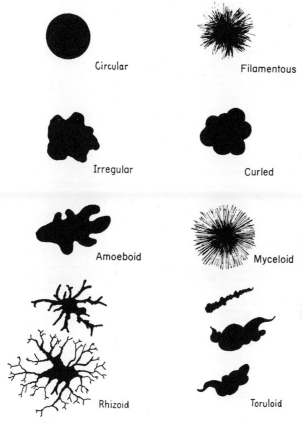

Circular   Filamentous

Irregular   Curled

Amoeboid   Myceloid

Rhizoid   Toruloid

Fig. 124. Shape or form of colonies. (*After Thomas.*)

Identification of Bacterial Species. A descriptive chart, prepared by the Committee on Bacteriological Technic of the Society of American Bacteriologists, will be found on pages 222 to 225. The chart is used for the identification and classification of bacteria. The methods described are intended primarily for the identification of aerobic saprophytes and not for obligate parasites or strict anaerobes.

The most important characteristics of an organism may be entered on the front of the chart, partly in the margin, partly in the larger section at the right, and the fermentation reactions at the bottom. By glancing at the numbers recorded in the right-hand margin and at the bottom edge, a large number of charts may be examined and compared.

Name of organism _____ Source _____
Date of Isolation _____ Habitat _____
Is phase variation observed? _____ Phase on this Chart: S, R, M, G (smooth, rough, mucoid, gonidial) _____

Underscore required terms.	SKETCHES

VEGETATIVE CELLS: Medium used _____
    Reaction (pH) _____ Temp. _____ Age ____ d.
    Size of Majority _____
    Ends, *rounded, truncate, concave, tapering*
MOTILITY: In broth _____ On agar _____
SPORANGIA and **ENDOSPORES:** *present, absent.*
    Medium used _____ pH _____ Temp. _____ Age ____ d.
    Endospore Form: *spherical, ellipsoid, cylindrical*
IRREGULAR FORMS:
    Present on _____ In _____ days at _____ °C.

AGAR COLONIES: Temperature _____ °C. Age ____ d.
    Form, *punctiform* (i.e. under 1 m.m. diam.), *circular* (i.e. over
    1 m.m. diam.), *filamentous, irregular, rhizoid.*
    Surface, *smooth, rough, concentrically ringed, radiately ridged.*
    Edge, *entire, undulate, lobate, erose, filamentous, curled.*
    Elevation of growth, *effuse, flat, raised, convex.*
    Optical Characters, *opaque, translucent, opalescent, irides-cent.*

Surface Colonies	Deep Colonies

GELATIN COLONIES: Temperature _____ °C. Age ____ d.
    Form, *punctiform, circular, irregular, filamentous.*
    Elevation, *flat, raised, convex, pulvinate, crateriform* (lique-fying).
    Edge, *entire, undulate, lobate, erose, filamentous, curled.*
    Liquefaction, *cup, saucer, spreading.*
    Surface, *smooth, contoured, rugose.*
    Optical Characters, *opaque, translucent, opalescent, irides-cent.*

Surface Colonies	Deep Colonies

AGAR STROKE: Temperature _____ °C. Age ____ d.
    Growth, *scanty, moderate, abundant, none.*
    Form of growth, *filiform, echinulate, beaded, spreading, arborescent, rhizoid.*
    Lustre, *glistening, dull.*
    Chromogenesis _____ *photogenic, fluorescent.*
    Odor, *absent, decided, resembling* _____
    Consistency, *butyrous, viscid, membranous, brittle.*
    Medium, *grayed, browned, reddened, blued, greened, un-changed.*

Medium:
Temperature
_____ °C.
Age
_____ d.

NUTRIENT BROTH: Temperature _____ °C. Age ____ d.
    Surface growth, *ring, pellicle, flocculent, membranous, none.*
    Clouding, *slight, moderate, strong, transient, persistent, none,*
    fluid turbid, granular growth.
    Odor, *absent, decided, resembling* _____
    Sediment, *compact, flocculent, granular, flaky, viscid.*
    Amount of sediment, *abundant, scanty, none.*

Medium:
Temperature
_____ °C.
Age
_____ d.

GELATIN STAB: Temperature _____ °C. Age ____ d.
    Growth, *uniform, best at top, best at bottom.*
    Line of puncture, *filiform, beaded, papillate, villous, arbo-rescent.*
    Liquefaction, *none, crateriform, infundibuliform, napiform,*
    saccate, stratiform: begins in _____ d. complete in _____ d.
    Degree of liquefaction in _____ days _____
    Method used _____
    Medium, *fluorescent, browned, unchanged.*

Medium:
Temperature
_____ °C.
Age
_____ d.

Fermentation   Temperature _____ °C

Medium containing _____ _____ and:	Monosaccharides						Disaccharides					Polysaccharides					Alcohols						Glucosides			
	Arabinose	Rhamnose	Xylose	Glucose	Fructose	Galactose	Mannose	Lactose	Sucrose	Maltose	Trehalose	Melibiose	Cellobiose	Raffinose	Melezitose	Starch	Inulin	Dextrin	Glycogen	Glycerol	Erythritol	Arabitol	Adonitol	Mannitol	Sorbitol	Dulcitol	Salicin	Aesculin	Coniferin	a-Methyl Gluc.
Gas in _____ fermentation tube																														
Amt. CO₂ in Eldredge tube																														
Reaction (pH) after _____ d.																														
Titrable acidity in ml. of N/ _____ Na OH																														

Studied by _____ Culture No. _____

Optimum conditions: Media _____ Temp. _____ °C.

Phases recorded on other charts: _____

Brief Characterization

As each of the following characteristics is determined, indicate in proper marginal square by means of figure, as designated below. In case any of these characteristics are doubtful or have not been determined, indicate with the letters U, V, and X according to the following code:

U, undetermined; V, variable; X, doubtful.

Morphological — **VEGETATIVE CELLS**	Form & arrangement: 1, streptococci; 2, diplococci; 3, micrococci; 4, sarcinae; 5, rods; 6, commas; 7, spirals; 8, branched rods; 9, filamentous	
	Diameter: 1, under 0.5μ; 2, between 0.5μ and 1μ; 3, over 1μ	
	Gram stain: 0, negative; 1, positive	
	Flagella: 0, absent; 1, peritrichic; 2, polar; 3, present but undetermined	
	Capsules: 0, absent; 1, present	
	Chains (4 or more cells): 0, absent; 1, present	
	SPORANGIA: 0, absent; 1, elliptical; 2, short rods: 3, spindled; 4, clavate; 5, drumsticks	
	ENDOSPORES: 0, absent; 1, central to excentric; 2, subterminal; 3, terminal	
Cultural — AGAR STROKE	Growth: 0, absent; 1, abundant; 2, moderate; 3, scanty	
	Lustre: 1, glistening; 2, dull	
AGAR COLONIES	Form: 1, punctiform; 2, circular (over 1 mm. diameter); 3, rhizoid; 4, filamentous; 5, curled; 6, irregular	
	Surface: 1, smooth; 2, contoured; 3, rugose	
GELATIN COLONIES	Form: 1, punctiform; 2, circular (over 1 mm.); 3, irregular; 4, filamentous	
	Surface: 1, smooth; 2, contoured; 3, rugose	
Physiological	Biologic relationships: 1, pathogenic for man; 2, for animals but not for man; 3, for plants; 4, parasitic but not pathogenic; 5, saprophytic; 6, autotrophic	
	Relation to free oxygen: 1, strict aerobe; 2, facultative anaerobe; 3, strict anaerobe; 4, microaerophile	
	In nitrate media: 0, neither nitrite nor gas; 1, both nitrite and gas; 2, nitrite but no gas; 3, gas but no nitrite	
	Chromogenesis: 0, none; 1, pink; 2, violet; 3, blue; 4, green; 5, yellow; 6, orange; 7, red; 8, brown; 9, black	
	Other photic characters: 0, none; 1, photogenic; 2, fluorescent; 3, iridescent	
	Indole: 0, negative; 1, positive	
	Hydrogen sulfide: 0, negative; 1, positive	
	Hemolysis: 0, negative; 1, positive	
	Methemoglobin: 0, negative; 1, positive	
PROTEIN LIQUEFAC-TION OR DIGESTION	Gelatin: 0, negative; 1, positive	
	Casein: 0, negative; 1, positive	
	Egg albumin: 0, negative; 1, positive	
	Blood serum: 0, negative; 1, positive	
INDICATOR REDUC-TION	Litmus: 0, negative; 1, positive	
	Methylene blue: 0, negative; 1, positive	
	Janus green: 0, negative; 1, positive	
	Rennet production: 0, negative; 1, positive	

Temperature Relations

Medium _____ pH _____
Optimum temperature for growth _____ °C.
Maximum temperature for growth _____ °C.
Minimum temperature for growth _____ °C.

THERMAL DEATH POINT: Time 10 minutes: _____ °C.

Medium _____ pH _____

THERMAL DEATH TIME:

Medium _____ pH _____

Temp.	Time	Temp.	Time
_____ °C.	_____ min.	_____ °C.	_____ min.
_____ °C.	_____ min.	_____ °C.	_____ min.
_____ °C.	_____ min.	_____ °C.	_____ min.
_____ °C.	_____ min.	_____ °C.	_____ min.
_____ °C.	_____ min.	_____ °C.	_____ min.

Chromogenesis

Gelatin _____
Agar _____
Potato _____

Other Photic Characters

Photogenesis on _____
Iridescence on _____
Fluorescence in _____

Relation to Reaction (pH) of Medium

Medium _____
Optimum for growth: *about pH* _____
Limits for growth: *from pH* _____ *to* _____

Relation to Free Oxygen

Method _____
Medium _____ Temp. _____ °C.
Aerobic growth: *absent, present, better than anaerobic growth, micro-aerophilic*
Anaerobic growth: *absent, occurs in presence of glucose, of sucrose, of lactose, of nitrate; better than aerobic growth*
Additional data: _____

Milk

	Temperature _____ °C.		
Reaction:	___ d. ___;	___ d. ___;	___ d. ___
Acid curd:	___ d. ___;	___ d. ___;	___ d. ___
Rennet curd:	___ d. ___;	___ d. ___;	___ d. ___
Peptonization:	___ d. ___;	___ d. ___;	___ d. ___

Litmus Milk

	Temperature _____ °C		
Reaction:	___ d. ___;	___ d. ___;	___ d. ___
Acid curd:	___ d. ___;	___ d. ___;	___ d. ___
Rennet curd:	___ d. ___;	___ d. ___;	___ d. ___
Peptonization:	___ d. ___;	___ d. ___;	___ d. ___

Reduction of litmus *begins in* _____ *days, ends in* _____ *days*

PATHOLOGY

Animal Inoculation

Medium used _____ Age of culture _____ Amount _____ Incubation period _____

Animal		Whole culture			Cells			Filtrate		
	Subcutaneous	*								
Type of Injection	Intraperitoneal									
	Intravenous									
	Per os									

* In each instance where pathogenicity is observed, indicate location of lesion, and type, *e.g.* edema, histolysis, gas, hemorrhage, ulcer, diphtheritic, etc.

Antigenic Action

Animal _____ Medium used _____ Age of culture _____
Type injection _____ Number of injections _____
Culture causes production of *cytolysins, agglutinins, precipitins, antitoxin.*
Specificity: Antibodies produced effective against other antigens as follows _____

Immune sera from _____
_____ effective against this organism as antigen

This DESCRIPTIVE CHART presented at the annual meeting of the SOCIETY OF AMERICAN
Prepared by a sub-committee consisting

TARY DATA

Action on Erythrocytes

Cells: _____
Method: *plate, broth, filtrate*
Hemolysis: *negative, positive*
Methemoglobin: *negative, positive*

Production of Indole

Medium _____
Test used
Indole *absent, present in* _____ *days*

Production of Hydrogen Sulfide

Medium _____
Test used _____
H$_2$S *absent, present in* _____ *days*

Action on Nitrates

Medium _____ Temp. _____ °C.
Nitrite: __ d. __; __ d. __; __ d. __; __ d. __
Gas (N$_2$): __ d. __; __ d. __; __ d. __; __ d. __
Medium _____ Temp. _____ °C.
Nitrite: __ d. __; __ d. __; __ d. __; __ d __
Gas (N$_2$): __ d. __; __ d. __; __ d. __; __ d. __
Ammonia production (in amino-N-free nitrate medium):
  negative, positive
Complete disappearance of nitrate in _____ medium:
  negative, positive
Disappearance of 2 p.p.m. nitrite in _____ medium:
  negative, positive

Reduction of Indicators

Medium _____ pH _____ Temp. _____ °C.

Indicator	Conc.	Reduction:		
_____	____ %	__ hr. __;	____ hr. __
_____	____ %	__ hr. __;	____ hr. __
_____	____ %	__ hr. __;	____ hr. __
_____	____ %	__ hr. __;	____ hr. __

Staining Reactions

Gram: __ d. __; __ d. __; __ d. __; __ d. __
  Method _____
Spores: Method _____
Capsules: Method _____
  Medium _____
Flagella: Method _____
Special Stains _____

Additional Tests

Methyl red: *negative, positive*
Voges-Proskauer: *negative, positive*
Growth in sodium citrate: *absent, present*
Growth in uric acid: *absent, present*
Hydrolysis of starch: *complete (iodine colorless); partial (iodine reddish-brown); none (iodine blue)*
Nitrogen obtained from the following compounds: _____

SPECIAL TESTS

BACTERIOLOGISTS, Dec. 28, 1934, by the Committee on Bacteriological Technic.
of M. W. Jennison and H. J. Conn.

Colony Formation. Generally speaking, each bacterial species, when grown on a standard solid medium, forms a characteristic type of colony. The colonies differ in size, shape, edge, elevation, and internal structure (Figs. 124 and 125).

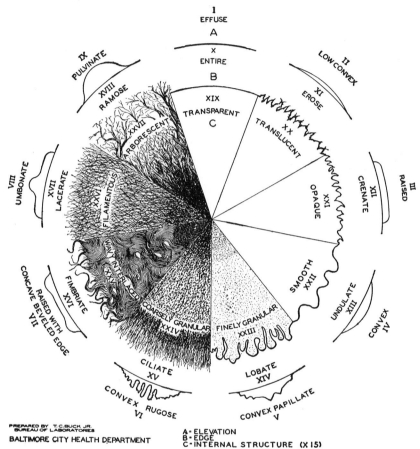

FIG. 125. Bacterial colony formations.

Stab and Streak Cultures. The type of growth on the surface and in the depth of agar media is characteristic for many bacterial species (Figs. 126 and 127). The various characteristics are made use of in the differentiation and classification of bacteria.

Pitfalls in the Use of the Charts. In making routine tests for the identification of bacterial species, the beginner is likely to run into a number of pitfalls, the most important being (1) the danger of contaminated cultures, (2) the variation of species into more than one phase, and (3) differences in methods of study.

Contaminated Cultures. Needless to say, the beginner cannot be too careful in handling and making transfers from cultures to prevent external contamination. Unless a culture is kept pure and viable, results of tests are certain to be misleading.

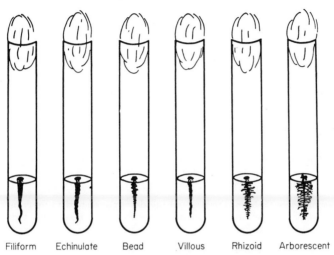

Filiform Echinulate Bead Villous Rhizoid Arborescent

FIG. 126. Growth in agar stab cultures. (*After Thomas.*)

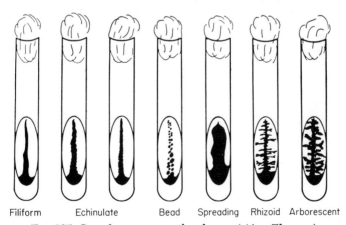

Filiform Echinulate Bead Spreading Rhizoid Arborescent

FIG. 127. Growth on agar streak cultures. (*After Thomas.*)

Bacterial Variation. During the early years of bacteriology most bacteriologists believed that a bacterial species could exist in more than one cell form.

Some years later this concept was altered in favor of a fixed cell form for each species. Forms that departed more or less widely from the normal types were usually dismissed as being involution forms, degenerate cells, or different species present as contaminants.

At the present time sufficient evidence has accumulated to support the original hypothesis of variability in the morphological characters of an organism. As a result of this change in viewpoint, it is easy for a careless beginner to believe that he is observing two phases in a culture when in reality one of the phases observed is a contaminant. Conversely, it is also easy for a beginner to consider a culture composed of two different organisms when actually they are different phases of the same species.

Differences in Methods of Study. In order that results of tests have significance, it is necessary to include the procedure employed. For example, it is not sufficient to state that an organism does or does not produce hydrogen sulfide without including the conditions under which it was investigated. It is necessary to mention the composition of the culture medium, the indicator incorporated in the medium to test for hydrogen sulfide, the temperature of incubation, and the length of the incubation period; otherwise disagreements in results are likely to occur.

Glossary of Terms Used on the Descriptive Chart[1]

A number of scientific terms are used on the descriptive chart to describe the various characteristics of organisms growing on different media. These terms, together with a number of others, are defined as follows:

Acid curd, coagulation of milk due to acid production.
Adherent, applied to sporangium wall, indicates that remnants of sporangium remain attached to endospore for some time.
Aerobic, growing in the presence of free oxygen; strictly aerobic, growing only in the presence of free oxygen.
Agglutinin, an antibody having the power of clumping suspensions of bacteria.
Anaerobic, growing in the absence of free oxygen; strictly anaerobic, growing only in the absence of free oxygen; facultative anaerobic, growing both in presence and in absence of oxygen.
Antibody, a specific substance produced by an animal in response to the introduction of an antigen.
Antigen, a substance which, when introduced into an animal body, stimulates the animal to produce specific bodies that react or unite with the substance introduced.
Antigenic action, behavior as an antigen.
Antitoxin, an antibody having the power of uniting with or destroying a toxic substance.
Arborescent, branched, tree-like in growth.
Aseptically, without permitting microbial contamination.
Autotrophic, able to grow in absence of organic matter.
Bacteriocidal, capable of killing bacteria.
Bacteriostasis, prevention of bacterial growth, but without killing the bacteria.
Beaded (in stab or stroke culture), separate or semiconfluent colonies along the line of inoculation.
Bipolar, at both poles or ends of the bacterial cell.
Bleb, vesicle or blister-like swelling.
Brittle, growth dry, friable under the platinum needle.
Butyrous, showing growth of butter-like consistency.
Capsule, an envelope surrounding the cell membrane of some kinds of bacteria.
Chains, four or more bacterial cells attached end to end.

[1] Taken from "Manual of Microbiological Methods," by the Society of American Bacteriologists. Courtesy of McGraw-Hill Book Company, Inc., 1957.

Chromogenesis, the production of color.

Clavate, club-shaped.

Compact, referring to sediment in the form of a single, fairly tenacious mass.

Complement, a nonspecific enzyme-like substance, destroyed if subjected to heat (56°C. or over for 30 min.), which occurs in blood serum and is necessary, in conjunction with a specific antibody, in order to bring about cytolysis.

Concentrically ringed, marked with rings, one inside the other.

Contoured, having an irregular, smoothly undulating surface, like that of a relief map.

Crateriform, referring to a saucer-shaped liquefaction of the medium.

Cuneate, wedge-shaped.

Curled, composed of parallel chains in wavy strands, as in anthrax colonies.

Cytolysin, an antibody causing cytolysis.

Cytolysis, a dissolving action of cells.

Diastatic action, conversion of starch into simpler carbohydrates, such as dextrins or sugars, by means of diastase.

Diphtheritic, diphtheria-like.

Dissociation, separation of characters, usually referring to phase variation (q.v.).

Echinulate, showing a growth along the line of inoculation with toothed or pointed margins.

Edema, intercellular accumulation of fluid in a part of an animal body.

Effuse, of thin growth, veily, unusually spreading.

Endospores, thick-walled spores formed within the bacteria; i.e., typical bacterial spores like those of B. anthracis or B. subtilis.

Endotoxin, a toxic substance produced within a microorganism and not excreted.

Enzyme, a chemical ferment produced by living cells.

Erose, irregularly notched.

Excentric, slightly to one side of the center, between the positions denoted central and subterminal.

Exogenous, originating outside the organism.

Exotoxin, a toxic substance excreted by a microorganism and hence found outside the cell body.

Facultative anaerobe, see anaerobic.

Filamentous, denoting growth composed of long, irregularly placed or interwoven threads.

Filaments, as applied to morphology of bacteria, refers to thread-like forms, generally unsegmented; if segmented, the organisms are enclosed in a sheath.

Filiform, in stroke or stab cultures, a uniform growth along line of inoculation.

Flagellum (pl. -la), a motile, whip-like attachment; an organ of locomotion.

Flaky, refers to sediment in the form of numerous separate flakes.

Flocculent, containing small adherent masses of various shapes floating in the field.

Fluorescent, having one color by transmitted light and another by reflected light.

Gonidia, asexual spores.

Gonidial, referring specifically to a bacterial phase producing gonidia-like bodies.

Granular, composed of small granules.

Hemolysin, a substance causing hemolysis either alone or in the presence of complement.

Hemolysis, a dissolving action on red blood corpuscles.

Hemorrhage, an escape of blood from the vessels.

Histolysis, breaking down of tissues.

Hydrolysis of starch, destruction of starch by the formation of a chemical union with water; includes diastatic action, but is a more general term.

Immune serum, an animal fluid containing an antibody.

Inactivate, to destroy complement by heat (at 56°C. for 30 min.).

Infundibuliform, in form of a funnel or inverted cone.

Intraperitoneal, within the peritoneum.

Intravenous, within a vein.

Iridescent, exhibiting changing rainbow colors in reflected light.

Lesion, a local injury or morbid structural change.

Lobate, having lobes, or rounded projections.

Maximum temperature, temperature above which growth does not take place.

Membranous, of thin growth, coherent, like a membrane.

Metabolite, a substance produced by metabolism.

Microaerophilic, growing best in presence of small quantities of oxygen.

Minimum temperature, temperature below which growth does not take place.

Mucoid, mucus-like, referring specifically to a bacterial phase producing slimy growth.

Mycelioid, colonies having the radiately filamentous appearance of mold colonies.

Napiform, denoting liquefaction in form of a turnip.

Ontogenetic, pertaining to the life history of an individual.

Opalescent, milky white with tints of color as in an opal.

Opaque, not allowing light to pass through.

Optimum temperature, temperature at which most growth occurs.

Papillate, denoting growth beset with small nipple-like processes.

Parasitic, deriving its nourishment from some living animal or plant upon which it lives and which acts as host; not necessarily pathogenic.

Pathogenic, not only parasitic (*q.v.*) but also causing disease in the host.

Pellicle, bacterial growth forming either a continuous or an interrupted sheet over the culture fluid.

Peptonization, rendering curdled milk soluble by the action of peptonizing enzymes.

Peritrichiate, applied to the arrangement of flagella, indicates that they are distributed over the entire surface of an organism.

Peritrichic, having flagella in peritrichiate arrangement.

Per os, through the mouth.

Persistent, lasting many weeks or months.

Phase variation, separation of a species into strains, having somewhat different characters.

Photogenic, glowing in the dark, phosphorescent.

Polar, at the end or pole of the bacterial cell.

Precipitin, an antibody having the power of precipitating soluble proteins.

Pulvinate, cushion-shaped.

Punctiform, very small, but visible to naked eye; under 1 mm. in diameter.

Raised, denoting thick growth, with abrupt or terraced edges.

Reduction, removal of oxygen or its equivalent from a chemical compound; or addition of hydrogen or its equivalent. Refers to the conversion of nitrate to nitrite, ammonia, or free nitrogen; also to the decolorization of litmus.

Rennet curd, coagulation of milk due to rennet or rennet-like enzymes, distinguished from acid curd by the absence of acid.

Rhizoid, growth of an irregular branched or root-like character, as *B. mycoides.*

Ring, growth at the upper margin of a liquid culture, adhering to the glass.

Rugose, wrinkled.

Saccate, liquefying in the form of an elongated sac, tubular, cylindrical.

Saprophytic, living on dead organic matter.

Sensitize, to render sensitive, usually to a foreign protein.

Sepsis, a state of infection.

Sheath, an envelope similar to a capsule (*q.v.*), but surrounding a filamentous organism.

Spindled, larger at the middle than at the ends. Applied to sporangia, refers to the forms frequently called *clostridia.*

Sporangium (pl. -ia), cells containing endospores.

Spreading, denoting growth extending much beyond the line of inoculation, i.e., several millimeters or more.

Stratiform, liquefying to the walls of the tube at the top and then proceeding downward horizontally.

Strict aerobe, see aerobic.

Strict anaerobe, see anaerobic.

Subcutaneous, under the skin.

Subterminal, situated toward the end of the cell but not at the extreme end, i.e., between the positions denoted excentric (*q.v.*) and terminal.

Synergism, cooperative action of two organisms, resulting in an end product which neither could produce alone.

Thermophilic, growing best at high temperatures, i.e., 50°C. or over.

Toxic, poisonous.

Transient, lasting a few days.

Translucent, allowing light to pass through without allowing complete visibility of objects seen through the substance in question.

Trituration, thorough grinding in a mortar.

Truncate, with ends abrupt, square.

Turbid, cloudy with flocculent particles, i.e., cloudy plus flocculent.

Ulcer, an open sore.

Undulate, wavy.

Villous, having short, thick, hair-like processes on the surface intermediate in meaning between papillate and filamentous (*q.v.*).

Virulence, degree of pathogenicity (referring to infectiousness).

Virus, a self-propagating cause of disease, often referring to one too small to be seen with a microscope.

Viscid, denoting growth that follows the needle when touched and withdrawn; or referring to sediment that on shaking rises as a coherent swirl.

REFERENCES

Breed, R. S., E. G. D. Murray, and N. R. Smith: "Bergey's Manual of Determinative Bacteriology," Baltimore, The Williams & Wilkins Company, 1957.

Committee on Bacteriological Technic, Society of American Bacteriologists, "Manual of Microbiological Methods," New York, McGraw-Hill Book Company, Inc., 1957.

McBee, R. H., C. Lamanna, and O. B. Weeks: Definitions of bacterial oxygen relationships, *Bact. Rev.*, 19:45, 1955.

CHAPTER 10

Effect of Environment upon Bacteria

It is well known that the life activities of organisms are conditioned by their environment. Any marked change in the environment produces a corresponding change in the morphological and physiological characters of organisms. Bacteria are able to withstand great changes in the environment and quickly adapt themselves to the new conditions. In this respect, they differ markedly from higher plant and animal cells. By understanding the various physical factors controlling survival and multiplication, bacterial activity may be increased, decreased, or destroyed completely.

Bacteria multiply normally by binary or transverse fission. The rate at which division takes place can be made to vary widely. Any alteration in the time between consecutive cell divisions (generation time) indicates that one or more environmental factors have changed.

The death time of bacteria by physical agents is related logarithmically to the number of surviving bacteria. This means that the disinfection process does not take place suddenly but is a gradual operation in which the number or organisms killed in unit time is greater at the beginning and becomes less and less as action continues. If the numbers of survivors in unit time are plotted against time and lines drawn, the points lie on smooth curves. On the other hand, if the logarithms of the numbers of survivors are plotted against time, the points fall on a straight line (see page 472). This is a general rule applicable to all agents employed for the destruction of monocellular organisms.

EFFECT OF LOW TEMPERATURE

Bacteria are able to survive wide limits of temperature, but the range in which they can grow and carry on their life activities falls between 0 and 90°C.

When the water surrounding a suspension of cells changes to ice, the intracellular water freezes also. The most important and fundamental concept in biological freezing is that it represents the removal of pure water from solution and its isolation into biologically inert foreign bodies, the ice crystals. In the frozen condition, all metabolic activity ceases. A suspension of *Salmonella typhosa* frozen to $-1°C.$, and kept at that temperature for 5 days, will show many viable cells. On the other hand, alternate freezing and thawing five times will most likely destroy all organisms.

The sensitivity of organisms to freezing damage varies during the growth cycle. Toyokawa and Hollander (1956) reported that the maximum susceptibility of *Escherichia coli* to freezing damage occurred during the period of logarithmic growth (see page 186).

Bacteria in the frozen state die at a very slow rate. They survive for years when frozen, and it is not safe to attempt to sterilize foods, water, or other liquids by freezing. The most common cause of death by freezing is probably due to injury by ice crystals.

There are three requirements for successful preservation by the technique of freezing: (1) very rapid freezing, (2) low-temperature storage, and (3) very rapid thawing. Most failures to obtain survival after rapid freezing can be attributed to insufficient recognition of these requirements.

Luyet and Gehenio (1940) found that rapid freezing of bacteria to very low temperatures, e.g., by immersion in liquid air, proved to be rather harmless. During rapid freezing, the water is not changed to ice crystals but to a glass-like or vitreous, amorphous substance. If cells are vitrified without the formation of ice crystals, they can be held in a viable form at low temperatures for long periods. During slow thawing, the water may change to ice crystals and cause death of the bacteria. On the other hand, rapid thawing may prevent the formation of ice crystals and prove harmless to the bacteria.

Cold Shock. Young bacteria may be sensitive to sudden changes in temperature. If a suspension is quickly cooled from 45 to $10°C.$, as many as 95 per cent of the cells may be killed, whereas gradual cooling produces very little, if any, effect. Hegarty and Weeks (1940) found young cells of *E. coli* to be more susceptible to cold shock than old cells. Mature cells were not affected by either an initial cold shock or a prolonged holding at $0°C.$ They concluded that the sensitivity of young cells to cold appeared to be related in some manner to cell division and to changes within the individual cell.

For more information see Harrison (1955), Harrison and Cerroni (1956), Meryman (1956), Straka and Stokes (1959), Weiser and Hargiss (1946), Weiser and Osterud (1945).

EFFECT OF HEAT

There exists for every organism a maximum, a minimum, and an optimum growth temperature. The temperatures vary with changes in the environmental conditions. Therefore, the values are significant only if the experimental conditions are specified.

Maximum Growth Temperature. The maximum growth temperature may be defined as the highest temperature at which growth and multiplication occur, when the other environmental factors are kept constant. The psychrophilic organisms, i.e., those which grow at low temperatures, do not develop well even at room temperature. Saprophytic mesophilic organisms, i.e., those which live best on dead organic matter, show a maximum at about 30°C. A majority of the pathogenic forms for man fall

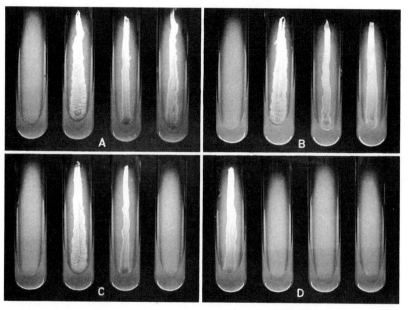

Fig. 128. Effect of temperature of incubation on growth. Organisms from left to right in each illustration: *Bacillus viridulus, B. subtilis, Escherichia coli,* and *Flavobacterium brunneum.* Each set of tubes incubated at the following temperatures: *A,* 15°C.; *B,* 25°C.; *C,* 37°C.; *D,* 55°C.

between 30 and 50°C. The thermophilic or heat-loving bacteria may show growth at temperatures of 60 to 70°C. or even higher.

Optimum Growth Temperature. The optimum temperature is the most favorable temperature for growth. The psychrophilic organisms have an optimum temperature below 20°C. These organisms are found in cold lake and spring waters and in brines kept under cold-storage conditions. This group includes many of the pigment-producing bacteria.

The mesophilic organisms have optimum temperatures of 18 to 45°C. The saprophytic mesophils grow best at temperatures of 18 to 25°C.; the parasitic mesophils grow best at the temperature of the host.

The thermophilic bacteria vary greatly in their temperature optima.

Many possess an optimum temperature of about 55°C. They occur in soil, manure, excreta, decaying organic matter, etc. Owing to their great resistance to heat, they are the source of considerable trouble in the canning industry.

Minimum Growth Temperature. The minimum growth temperature is the lowest temperature at which growth and multiplication occur. This temperature will also show variation when one or more environmental factors are changed.

The multiplication rate of an organism is exceedingly slow at the minimum temperature. As the temperature is lowered from the optimum to the minimum, the rate of multiplication becomes progressively less and less. Beyond the minimum temperature, multiplication ceases entirely.

Growth Temperature Range. This is defined as the number of degrees between the minimum and the maximum growth temperatures. With some organisms this range is very narrow; with others it is very wide.

The effect of different temperatures of incubation on the growth of *Bacillus viridulus, B. subtilis, Escherichia coli,* and *Flavobacterium brunneum* is shown in Fig. 128.

The temperature ranges of the psychrophilic, mesophilic, and thermophilic organisms are as follows:

	Minimum, °C.	Optimum, °C.	Maximum, °C.
Psychrophilic................	0	15	30
Mesophilic.................	5–25	18–45	30–50
Thermophilic................	25–45	55	60–90

Müller (1946) considered only the optimum temperatures in classifying organisms. The psychrophilic were those growing best below 20°C.; the mesophilic growing best between 20 and 40°C.; the thermophilic above 40°C.

Thermal Death Rate. The thermal death rate may be defined as that temperature at which an organism is killed after a period of 10 min. under controlled conditions. This temperature is generally referred to as the *thermal death point.* Since organisms subjected to unfavorable conditions are not all killed in the same period of time, the term *thermal death rate* is more appropriate.

The various factors producing variations in the thermal death rates include (1) water content of the medium, (2) water content of the organisms, (3) hydrogen-ion concentration of the medium, (4) composition of the medium, (5) age of the cells, (6) presence or absence of spores in a culture of a spore-forming organism, and (7) incubation temperature of recovery cultures. A change in one or more factors produces a corresponding change in the thermal death rate.

Water Content of the Medium. Death of bacteria by heat is believed to be due to coagulation of the proteins of the protoplasm. Within limits, the greater the percentage of water in a medium, the lower will be the temperature required to kill bacteria. Moist heat is more effective as a sterilizing agent than dry heat. Dry egg albumin may be heated to a point at which it decomposes without showing any appreciable coagulation. As the percentage of moisture is increased, the temperature of coagulation becomes progressively less. This may be seen in Table 8.

TABLE 8.   RELATION BETWEEN MOISTURE CONTENT AND
TEMPERATURE OF COAGULATION OF EGG ALBUMIN

Amount of water, per cent	Temperature of coagulation, °C.
50	56
25	74– 80
18	80– 90
6	145
0	160–170

Water Content of the Organisms. Yesair, Bohrer, and Cameron (1946) showed that moist or dry micrococci heated under moist conditions were low in resistance. When heated in moist fat, the resistance was higher. The resistance of dry micrococci in dry fat was exceptionally high and approached that obtained under conditions of dry sterilization.

They concluded that (1) dry micrococci might survive sterilization under the usual conditions and (2) the mechanism of fat protection in foods appeared to rest upon the localized absence of moisture.

Similar results were reported by Jensen (1954). He found that dried micrococci suspended in moist butterfat survived only 15 min. at 100°C., but in dry butterfat a period of 50 min. at 115°C. was necessary to achieve the same result.

Hydrogen-ion Concentration of the Medium. The pH of the medium has an important effect on the number of survivors. Most organisms are more easily killed in acid or alkaline solutions than in a neutral environment. In general, the greater the degree of acidity or alkalinity, the lower will be the temperature required to kill bacteria. Acid-fast organisms are exceptions in that they survive heating under acid conditions for periods which kill the cells heated in a slightly alkaline medium. Since the organisms are protected by a waxy capsule (page 60), it seems reasonable to postulate that this covering is destroyed under alkaline conditions, making the cells more vulnerable to attack. The test should be performed in a neutral medium.

Composition of the Medium. The composition of the suspending medium plays a very important role in the results obtained for the thermal death rate. Media containing high concentrations of proteins or albuminous substances usually increase the temperature required to destroy bacteria. The proteins form a film around the organisms, protecting them from unfavorable influences.

The composition of the medium used for the recovery cultures is also very important. Curran and Evans (1937) and Nelson (1943) showed that the number of treated cells which would grow depended to a large extent upon the composition of the medium used for subculture. Stern (1942) came to a similar conclusion on the time required for the germination of spores of a number of putrefactive and thermophilic anaerobic organisms.

Age of Cells. The age of the cells also influences the thermal death rate. Old cells are generally more resistant to adverse environmental conditions than young cells. Cultures 24 hr. old should be used in the test.

Presence of Spores. Non-spore-forming bacteria and the vegetative forms of the spore bearers are generally killed by moist heat at temperatures of 60 to 70°C. Spores can withstand a temperature of 100°C. or higher. In reporting the thermal death rate of a spore-forming organism, care should be taken to make sure spores are present in the culture.

Spores and vegetative cells of different species, and of different strains of the same species, exhibit marked differences in heat resistance. Vegetative cell resistance is not related to spore resistance. Williams and Zimmerman (1951) reported that cultures might contain vegetative cells of high resistance and spores of low resistance, or vegetative cells of low resistance might be associated with spores of high resistance.

According to Curran (1952) spore resistance varies widely from species to species, to a considerable extent within a species, and within a given spore population. It is independent of the luxuriance of growth and of the luxuriance of sporulation.

Spores of *Clostridium botulinum* are most resistant to heat when newly formed, whereas in other species maximum resistance is attained after a certain period of maturation. Among the aerobic sporing bacteria those species with the highest temperature of growth usually show the greatest resistance to heat.

The nature of the nutrients in the medium is important. *Bacillus subtilis* spores produced in vegetable infusions show high heat resistance, whereas the spores formed in certain digest media exhibit low thermal resistance. Spores of *Cl. botulinum* produced in a medium containing certain fatty acids are more heat resistant than spores formed in media from which the fatty acids are previously extracted. Media deficient in certain essential metallic ions, such as magnesium, calcium, and iron, yield spores of low thermal resistance.

Spores show maximum heat resistance when produced at the optimum growth temperature. Any deviation from the optimum yields spores of lowered heat resistance. The pH of the medium affects spore resistance. Spores usually exhibit maximum resistance at or near the neutral point. In strongly acid or alkaline substrates, thermal resistance is materially reduced. Salt in low concentrations increases heat resistance of aerobic and anaerobic mesophilic species, but above 8 per cent the heat tolerance is reduced. On the other hand, as little as 1 per cent salt reduces the thermal resistance of some thermophilic types.

The concentration of moisture in the medium greatly influences the heat resistance of spores. Moist heat at 115°C. for 20 to 30 min. is usually sufficient to sterilize spores, whereas in dry sterilization a temperature of 160 to 180°C. for 1 hr. is generally required. The presence of organic matter in the medium increases the resistance of spores against heat. The presence of added vitamins may alter spore resistance. The addition of 100 p.p.m. of ascorbic acid (vitamin C) to a neutral phosphate buffer increases the spore resistance of a *Clostridium* species. Spores that survive heat treatment are more readily killed by further application of the same treatment than are untreated spores.

Sugiyama (1951) reported that spores of *Cl. botulinum* formed at 37°C. are of higher resistance than those developed at 24, 29, or 41°C.

The thermal resistance of spores suspended in different concentrations of sucrose increases with the concentration of sucrose. With spores suspended in 50 per cent sucrose, the increase in heat resistance is almost immediate and remains high for many hours.

Williams and Robertson (1954) cultivated several strains of *Bacillus stearothermophilus* at increasing temperatures of incubation up to near the maximum. The spores produced increased in resistance to heat as the temperature of incubation was increased.

Spores that survive heat treatment may be more exacting in their nutrient requirements than before treatment. Frank and Campbell (1955) reported that the constitution of the recovery medium exerted an appreciable effect on the apparent thermal resistance of spores of a putrefactive anaerobe.

Falcone (1955) cultivated spores of *B. subtilis* in the presence of L-alanine and showed that the amino acid was metabolized to pyruvate, ammonia, and hydrogen peroxide. In the presence of these compounds, especially the latter, the spores lost their resistance to heat, being killed at 60°C. in 1 hr.

El Bisi and Ordal (1956a) reported that neither the type of nutrient growth medium nor its pH had a significant effect on the death rate of the spores produced. On the other hand, the initial phosphate concentration in the growth medium exhibited a highly significant effect. A higher phosphate level markedly depressed the thermal resistance of the spores.

In a later report (1956b) the same authors determined the effect of sporulation temperatures of 30, 37, and 45°C. on the thermal resistance of B. coagulans and concluded that the higher growth temperature markedly enhanced the thermal resistance of the spores produced.

For more information see Amaha (1953), Amaha and Sakaguchi (1954), Bowen and Smith (1955), Ingraham and Stokes (1959), and Schmidt (1955).

Incubation Temperature of Recovery Cultures. Williams and Reed (1942) found that incubation temperatures of 24 and 27°C. were more favorable for the development of heated spores of Cl. botulinum than was 37°C. and somewhat more favorable than 31°C. A temperature of 27°C. was also found to be more favorable for an unidentified anaerobe than was the higher temperature.

These are the important factors which have been shown to influence the thermal resistance of bacterial spores. Unless the conditions of the test are mentioned, the thermal death rates will be of doubtful value.

Thermal Death Time. In making a determination of the thermal death rate, the time is kept constant and the temperature varied. In finding the thermal death time of an organism, the temperature is kept constant and the time required to kill all cells determined.

Results of thermal death rates and thermal death times are of great value in applied bacteriology and especially in the canning industry. They aid the canner in determining the temperatures and times required to process canned foods.

It is the usual practice to isolate the organism or organisms causing the spoilage of a certain kind of food and to determine their thermal death rates or times under similar environmental conditions. The results may then be used as a guide in determining the temperature and time required to process the food.

The thermal death rates of *Serratia marcescens* and *Bacillus cereus* are shown in Figs. 129 and 130.

For more information see Mattick and Hiscox (1945), McBee and Gaugler (1956), McBee and McBee (1956), and Rahn (1945).

EFFECT OF ULTRAVIOLET IRRADIATION

A few bacteria elaborate a photosynthetic pigment that appears to function in these organisms in a manner similar to chlorophyll in plants. These organisms are benefited by light rays. However, the great majority of bacteria do not contain a photosynthetic pigment and are unable to utilize sunlight as a source of energy. Such organisms are harmed by exposure to ultraviolet rays.

Ultraviolet rays are the invisible components of the sun's radiation. They are short rays and are measured in angstrom units (A.). One milli-

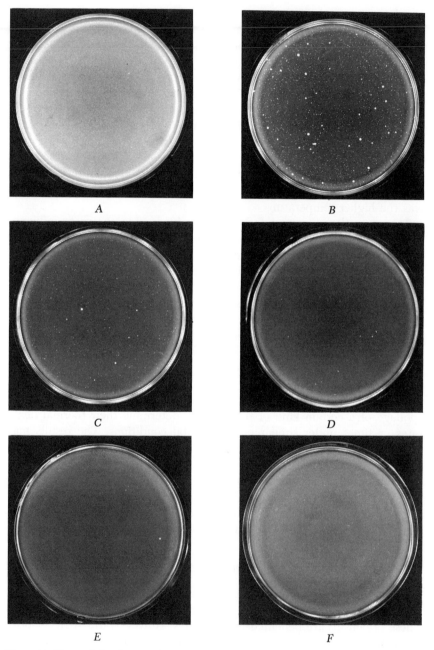

Fig. 129. Thermal death rate of *Serratia marcescens*. Six tubes, each containing 1 ml. of culture, were heated for 10 min. at the following temperatures: *A*, 50°C.; *B*, 55°C.; *C*, 60°C.; *D*, 65°C.; *E*, 70°C.; *F*, 75°C. Then the contents of each tube were transferred to Petri dishes and mixed with melted agar.

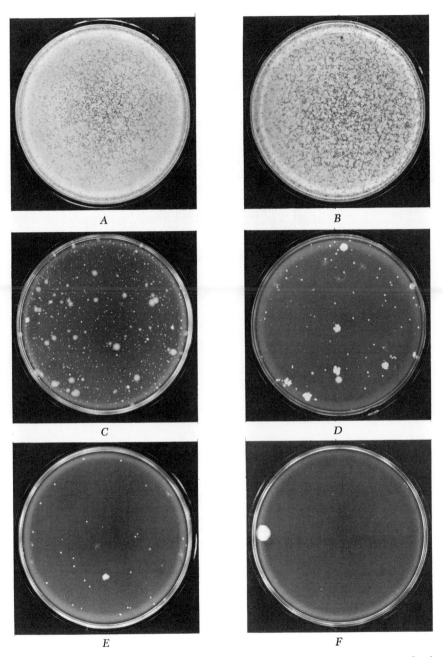

FIG. 130. Thermal death rate of *Bacillus cereus*. Six tubes, each containing 1 ml. of culture, were heated for 10 min. at the following temperatures: *A*, 75°C.; *B*, 80°C.; *C*, 85°C.; *D*, 90°C.; *E*, 95°C.; *F*, 100°C. Then the contents of each tube were transferred to Petri dishes and mixed with melted agar.

meter is equal to 10,000,000 A., or one micron equals 10,000 A. The ultraviolet rays cover the range from 4000 to 400 A., with maximum germicidal activity at 2650 A. (Fig. 131). A wave length of 2537 A. from germicidal tubes is about 10 times more bactericidal than a wave length of 2967 A. from sunlamps, about 4000 times more germicidal than a wave

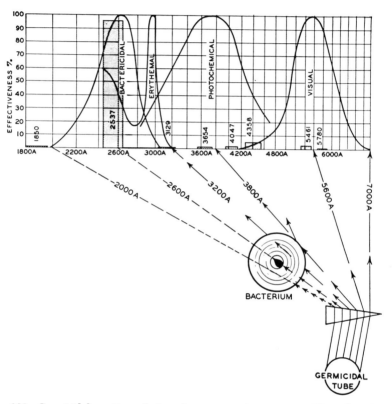

FIG. 131. Germicidal portion of the electromagnetic spectrum. Wave lengths are measured in angstrom units (A.). One angstrom unit is equal to 1/10,000,000 mm., or approximately 1/250,000,000 in. (*Courtesy of General Electric Company.*)

length of 3650 A. from photochemical lamps, and about 30,000 times more germicidal than the most visible wave length from the sun and from artificial light sources. Ultraviolet rays may (1) kill a cell, (2) delay its growth, or (3) change its heredity by causing gene mutation.

Radiations are effective only if they are absorbed. The rays are absorbed by the nucleic acids, especially by the desoxyribonucleic acid of the nucleus. These substances are combined with basic proteins as nucleoproteins and are found in the chromosomes of the nuclear material, and in the cytoplasm as ribonucleic acid (see page 62). Most proteins in solution show marked absorption bands in the ultraviolet region. Ultraviolet rays exert a negligible bactericidal action on bacteria suspended in blood. The proteins in blood absorb the rays, preventing them from reaching the bacteria.

Spores of bacteria and molds are also sensitive to ultraviolet rays, but approximately twice the exposure of vegetative cells is necessary to produce the same percentage reduction in numbers.

Cortelyou, Amundson, and McWhinnie (1956) subjected a 2-hr. culture of *E. coli* to high-intensity ultraviolet irradiation and observed a progressive alteration, disorganization, and disintegration of the chromatinic bodies of the treated cells. The physical changes observed were interpreted as being responsible for the irreversible lethal inactivation by the irradiations.

Viruses and bacteriophages (bacterial viruses) are destroyed by ultraviolet rays. Ingredients of broth associated intimately with bacteriophage particles in the same medium or interposed as a screen between pure phage and light source prevent their destruction.

Protection of Bacteria against Radiation Effects. Thompson, Mefferd, and Wyss (1951) found that the presence of pyruvate in a bacterial suspension protected the cells against the lethal and mutagenic action of ultraviolet rays. Upon prolonged exposure to ultraviolet, pyruvate solutions became toxic and mutagenic. The addition of the pyruvate after exposure of the cells or its presence in the plating medium did not modify the biological response to the radiations.

Berger et al. (1953) reported that the presence of sodium azide during ultraviolet irradiation reduced the sensitivity of three bacterial species to the lethal action of the rays. Blocking or inactivation of heavy metal enzymes by azide was suggested as the mechanism responsible for these effects.

Ogg, Adler, and Zelle (1956) showed that intracellularly synthesized catalase and the related cytochromes protected *E. coli* exposed to ultraviolet light.

Durham and Wyss (1956) noted an increased resistance to ultraviolet light of cells grown in the presence of subinhibitory concentrations of salts of monovalent cations. The addition of salt lowered the absorption of ultraviolet light by desoxyribonucleic acid (DNA). Variation in ultraviolet resistance could be correlated with the concentration of salt in the medium. They believed this was due to a physiological variation in all or most of the cells in the population. It appeared to be associated with the ability of the cell to restrain leakage of nucleotides following radiation damage.

Photoreactivation of Ultraviolet Irradiated Bacteria. Kelner (1949) showed that ultraviolet-"killed" bacteria could be recovered in viable form by exposure to daylight. A suspension of *E. coli* containing 8,000,000 cells per milliliter was irradiated until the viable count was reduced to

100 bacteria per milliliter. A portion of this irradiated suspension was exposed for 30 min. to light of 3600 to 4900 A., then assayed. The suspension now contained 2,000,000 viable cells per milliliter, whereas the original irradiated culture kept in the dark still contained only 100 bacteria per milliliter. Since other organisms examined behaved in a similar manner, the results suggested that the phenomenon was a general one.

The degree of recovery possible for irradiated cells was dependent upon the original dose of ultraviolet light. The greater the dose, the smaller the proportion of inactivated cells that could be revived. Given a sufficiently high dose of ultraviolet, probably not a single cell would recover, regardless of the amount of reactivating light.

A temperature effect was also involved in photoreactivation. The warmer the cells during exposure to visible light, the greater the amount of photoreactivation, up to a temperature of 45 to 50°C. Beyond 50°C., the cells were subject to heat injury.

In a later communication, Kelner (1953) stated that ultraviolet light had no immediate effect on aerobic cellular respiration as measured by oxygen absorption in nutrient broth. Doses of ultraviolet inactivating 90 per cent of the cells stopped cellular division but had little immediate effect on growth measured as cellular enlargement. Greater doses of ultraviolet light inhibited cellular enlargement, but this effect was reversed partially by reactivating light.

Low doses of ultraviolet light had little immediate effect on the synthesis of ribonucleic acid by the cells but stopped immediately and completely the synthesis of DNA. After reactivating light, synthesis of DNA was resumed at an accelerated rate.

Kelner believed that the specific inhibition of DNA synthesis was the basic immediate effect of ultraviolet radiation.

Reactivation by Other Methods. Ellison, Erlanger, and Allen (1955) reversed the lethal and mutagenic effects of ultraviolet light by plating the irradiated bacteria in nutrient agar containing sodium acetate. The degree of reactivation was directly proportional to the acetate concentration.

Heinmetz and Lehman (1955) obtained high numbers of viable cells when irradiated bacteria were incubated with certain combinations of metabolites of the tricarboxylic acid cycle and the coenzymes diphosphopyridine nucleotide and coenzyme A. The combined action of photoreactivation and metabolic reactivation was more effective than the action of a single process alone.

Weatherwax (1956a) reported that survival of E. coli following irradiation was strongly dependent on the pH of the plating medium. With a given dose of radiation, the number of survivors producing colonies on agar was increased as much as a thousandfold when the pH of the plating medium was decreased from 8 to 5. The actual decision for or against survival occurred during the interval of incubation between 2 and 4 hr. after radiation. At any time prior to the end of 2 hr. of incubation, survival could be determined by changing the pH of the medium. This opportunity was rapidly lost during the next 2 hr. of incubation, after which time the radiation damage had become irreversible.

For more information see Barner and Cohen (1956); Charles and Zimmerman (1956); Deering (1958); Goucher, Kamei, and Kocholaty (1956); Jagger (1958); Romig and Wyss (1957); Stuy (1955, 1959); Weatherwax (1956b); Zelle, Ogg, and Hollaender (1957).

Irradiation of Culture Media. The observations already reported are limited to the action of the rays on microorganisms and their spores. It has been shown that culture media, when exposed to ultraviolet light, become less suited for bacterial growth. Bedford (1927), after a series of experiments, concluded that the irradiation of culture media caused the formation of hydrogen peroxide. The presence of this compound in media produced a toxic action on bacteria. The concentration of peroxide that accumulated in media depended upon the wave length of light and the period of exposure.

Similar results were reported by Wyss et al. (1948). They found that the toxic effect of irradiated broth could be negated by the addition of the enzyme catalase, which is capable of decomposing hydrogen peroxide to water and molecular oxygen.

Commercial Uses. Air sanitation is closely analogous to water sanitation. Its purpose is substantially the same, namely, to make the air in confined spaces more safe under the particular circumstances of its use and to guard against the possibility that air-borne organisms may cause clinical infections. This is especially true of the respiratory diseases, because such organisms are caught from breathed air, not because they are diseases of the throat, nose, and lungs. Many hospital rooms and operating rooms are irradiated to sterilize or greatly to decrease the number of organisms in air.

Ultraviolet rays are used commercially for the destruction of bacteria, yeasts, and molds in various foodstuffs such as sugar, meats, and bakery products. Spores of *Bacillus stearothermophilus* are commonly found in sugar and may cause serious losses in many food preparations. The spores may be destroyed by irradiation of the sugar crystals.

Ultraviolet light is effective in destroying bacteria growing on the surfaces of dairy equipment such as milk bottles, tinned dippers, cans, and pasteurizing vats.

Luckiesh, Kerr, and Knowles (1947) found low-pressure mercury-vapor germicidal lamps to be effective in destroying bacteria in water. They recommended their use commercially for the treatment of water intended for drinking purposes.

These are only a few of the commercial applications of ultraviolet rays.

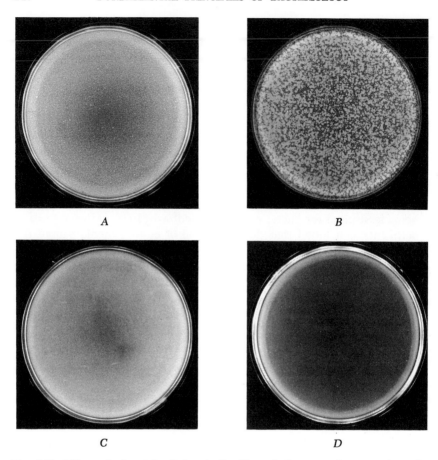

FIG. 132. Effect of ultraviolet light. *A, Bacillus subtilis* exposed to an ultraviolet lamp for 1 hr.; *B,* same exposed for 2 hr. Since the culture contained many spores, a longer exposure was necessary to produce complete sterilization; *C, Staphylococcus aureus* exposed for 1 hr.; *D,* same exposed for 2 hr. Culture was completely sterilized after 2 hr.

The effect of ultraviolet light on the growth of *Bacillus subtilis* and *Staphylococcus aureus* is shown in Fig. 132.

EFFECT OF OSMOTIC PRESSURE

Osmosis may be defined as the diffusion that takes place between two miscible fluids separated by a permeable membrane in which the conditions on the two sides of the membrane tend to become equal.

The term osmotic pressure refers to the unbalanced pressure that gives rise to the phenomena of diffusion and osmosis, as in a solution in which there are differences in concentration.

Plasmolysis. The rate at which water passes into and out of cells is in part determined by the ratio that exists between the concentrations of electrolytes inside and outside the cell membranes. If an organism is immersed in a solution having a higher osmotic pressure, water will leave the cell. This will continue until an equilibrium is established between the osmotic pressures inside and outside the cell. If the initial difference in osmotic pressure between the inside and outside of the cell is sufficiently great, the cytoplasmic membrane will be drawn in with the cytoplasmic contents and collect in the center of the cell. The cell is then said to be plasmolyzed, and the process is called *plasmolysis*. The solution on the outside is hypertonic with respect to the solution on the inside of the cell.

Plasmoptysis. If an organism is immersed in a solution having a lower osmotic pressure, water will enter the cell. This will continue until an equilibrium is established between the osmotic pressures inside and outside the cell. If the initial difference in osmotic pressure between the inside and the outside of the cell is of sufficient magnitude, the cell membranes will burst, releasing their contents. The cell is then said to be plasmoptyzed, and the process is called *plasmoptysis*. In this case, the solution on the outside is hypotonic with respect to the solution on the inside of the cell.

Isotonic Solutions. If the concentrations of ions and molecules on the inside and outside of the cell membranes are equal, there will be no difference in their osmotic pressures. The result will be neither shrinking nor swelling of the cell contents. The two solutions are then said to be isotonic with respect to each other.

Cellular changes during plasmolysis and plasmoptysis can be easily demonstrated in higher plant and animal cells, but it is doubtful that anyone has demonstrated such changes in cells of the true bacteria. Nevertheless, bacteria are sensitive to osmotic effects, but to a lesser extent than plant and animal cells. A great increase in the osmotic pressure of the surrounding solution is necessary before any toxic action is noted on bacteria.

The use of high osmotic pressures finds practical applications in the preservation of some foods from attack by fungi. This principle is employed in the preservation of jams, jellies, and condensed milk by means of sugar; and of meats, corned beef, fish, etc., by the use of salt (Fig. 133).

Iyer and Bhat (1954) found 13 strains and species of the genus *Bacillus* to tolerate salt and sugar concentrations of 10 to 15 per cent and 30 to 60 per cent respectively. The concentrations of these two ingredients as natural preservatives in the food industry may often prove inadequate to prevent spoilage. Such high concentrations will easily destroy higher plant and animal cells.

Barr and Tice (1957a) made a study of the inhibitory concentrations

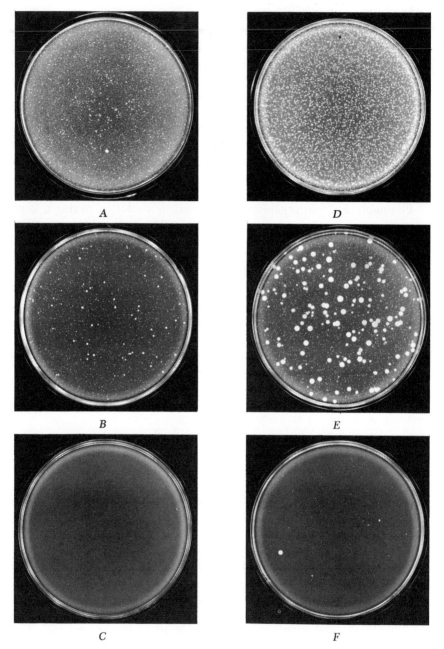

FIG. 133. Effect of osmotic pressure. *Staphylococcus aureus* and *Escherichia coli* exposed to 30 per cent sodium chloride solution, then mixed with melted agar and poured into plates. *A, S. aureus* poured immediately; *B,* same after 24 hr.; *C,* same after 48 hr.; *D, E. coli* poured immediately; *E,* same after 24 hr.; *F,* same after 48 hr.

of various sugars and polyols in aqueous solution using five organisms commonly recognized as being responsible for spoilage in products containing these substances. The inhibitory effect was believed to be largely one of osmotic pressure.

For more information see Barr and Tice (1957b).

Marine Bacteria. Most marine bacteria differ from fresh-water forms in that they are able to tolerate much greater concentrations of salt. ZoBell and Feltham (1933) found that less than 10 per cent of the bacteria isolated from sea water were able to multiply in nutrient fresh-water media and that a smaller number of species isolated from fresh water could multiply in media prepared with undiluted sea water.

ZoBell and Michener (1938) acclimatized marine bacteria to hypotonic solutions by gradually diluting the sea-water medium with each successive transfer of the cultures. The species could be acclimatized to 25 to 30 per cent sea water. Below this concentration, considerable difficulty and delay were encountered in making the bacteria grow. Most of the original cultures which were kept in the refrigerator on undiluted sea-water agar multiplied when transferred to fresh-water medium. The old stock cultures adapted themselves better to hypotonic solutions than did cultures of the same organisms gradually acclimatized to decreasing concentrations of sea-water medium.

Young bacteria are more susceptible to adverse environmental conditions than old cells. Cultures gradually acclimatized to decreasing concentrations of sea water tend to keep the organisms in a physiologically young condition. On the other hand, the parent stock cultures become physiologically old and senescent and less susceptible to environmental changes. These cells are better able to adapt themselves to adverse conditions.

INFLUENCE OF HYDROSTATIC PRESSURE

Hydrostatic pressure has been found to exert a marked effect on the growth of bacteria. ZoBell and Johnson (1949) made a study of the effect of hydrostatic pressure on a large number of representative species of mesophilic terrestrial bacteria and yeasts. They found that at 30°C. the terrestrial organisms developed abundantly within 48 hr. at normal pressure but failed to multiply under 600 atm. (9000 lb. per sq. in.) of pressure. In fact, some of the bacteria were killed by this pressure during the period of incubation. Growth of most of the species was visibly retarded by a hydrostatic pressure of 400 atm., and plate counts indicated that growth was slower and death faster at only 300 atm. than at normal pressure.

On the other hand, marine species, particularly *Bacillus submarinus* and *B. thalassokoites*, which were isolated from depths where the pressure approximated 500 atm., grew readily under 600 atm. at both 30 and 40°C. Other species isolated near the surface of the sea were intermediate, or more nearly resembled terrestrial forms in their sensitivity to pressure. The species *Pseudomonas xanthochrus* developed under 400 to 600 atm. at 40°C. but failed to grow under normal pressure at the same temperature.

In general, the retarding effect of pressure was more marked at low than at high temperatures. The net effect of high temperatures was to oppose the retarding action of hydrostatic pressure.

In subsequent communications Johnson and ZoBell (1949*a, b*) reported that spores of *Bacillus subtilis*, suspended in a buffered salt solution of pH 7.0, slowly lost their viability at 25°C., and this decrease in viability was accelerated by a hydrostatic pressure of 600 atm. At 92.5 or 93.6°C. corresponding suspensions rapidly lost their viability, but this loss was retarded by a hydrostatic pressure of 600 atm.

ZoBell and Morita (1957) demonstrated 1000 to 1,000,000 organisms per gram of wet mud in several samples taken from depths of 7000 to 10,000 meters. Some of the bacteria appeared to be obligate barophiles which grew when compressed to 700 to 1000 atm. Deep-sea bacteria which grew at 1 atm. but not at the high pressures of the environment where found might have been dormant forms from shallower depths, or all of their cultural requirements might not have been satisfied by the laboratory conditions.

Effect of Pressure on Enzymes. Vignais and Vignais (1954) inhibited the action of enzymes by the use of high hydrostatic pressures. The enzyme systems studied were inhibited at different pressures. Morita and ZoBell (1956) inactivated the action of the succinic dehydrogenase system in *E. coli*. Some inactivation occurred at 200 atm. at 30°C. The amount of inactivation increased progressively with time of compression. Approximately half of the enzyme system was inactivated after 4 hr. at 600 atm., and all was irreversibly inactivated after 4 hr. at 1000 atm. The inactivating effects were most pronounced at temperatures either above (40°C.) or below (8°C.) the optimum (30°C.).

PRESERVATION OF BACTERIA

Organisms in the desiccated state are not capable of multiplication. Moisture is absolutely necessary for this to occur. When organisms are dried they gradually die, the rate of death being dependent on several factors. Slow drying destroys bacteria more easily than rapid drying. Death may be due to a denaturation of the proteins of the protoplasm, to the destruction of the essential enzymes, or to other causes.

The percentage of survivors during desiccation may show wide variation, depending upon the species, the age of the culture, the surface on

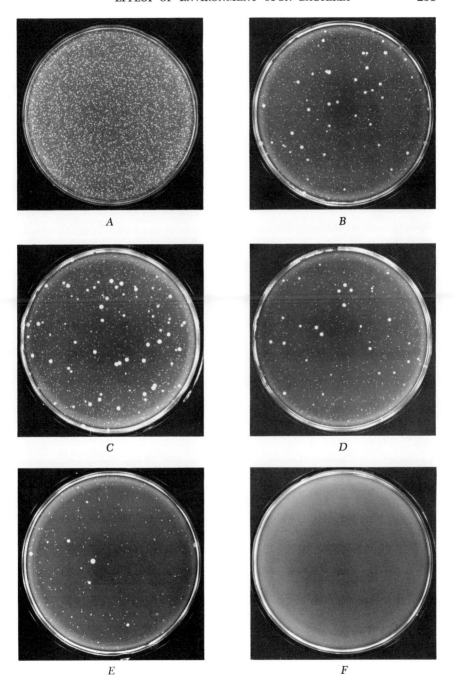

Fig. 134. Effect of desiccation on *Escherichia coli. A*, control, not dried; *B*, dried for 24 hr. at 37°C.; *C*, dried for 48 hr.; *D*, dried for 72 hr.; *E*, dried for 96 hr.; *F*, dried for 216 hr.

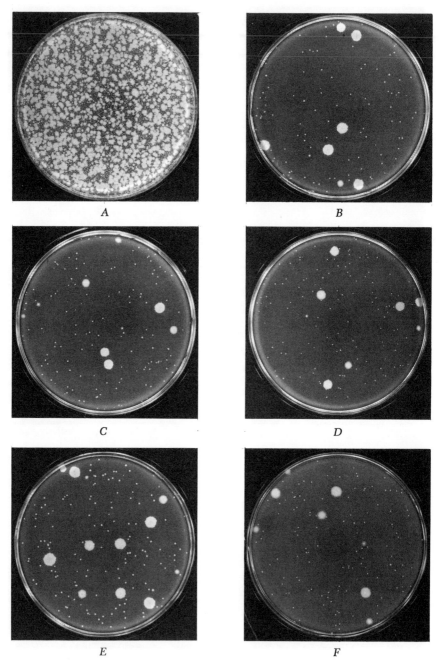

Fɪɢ. 135. Effect of desiccation on *Bacillus subtilis*. *A*, control, not dried; *B*, dried for 24 hr. at 37°C.; *C*, dried for 48 hr.; *D*, dried for 72 hr.; *E*, dried for 96 hr.; *F*, dried for 216 hr. The organism produces spores which were not destroyed in that period of time.

which the cells are dried, the temperature of drying, and the composition of the medium in which the organisms are suspended.

Bacteria growing in culture media composed of broth, milk, and other albuminous fluids survive drying fairly well. The proteins of the medium are believed to protect the cells by acting as protective colloids, which make the drying process more gentle and less abrupt. On the other hand, bacteria suspended in water or saline are easily destroyed by desiccation.

Spores are more resistant to desiccation than the vegetative cells producing them. They are better able to withstand adverse conditions. Likewise, capsulated organisms are more resistant to drying than noncapsulated bacteria. The mucilaginous deposit surrounding the organism acts as a protective layer, decreasing the rate of desiccation.

Desiccated bacteria are more resistant to destructive agencies than the same organisms in the moist state. Much higher temperatures are required to coagulate the protoplasm of partially dried organisms than the same cells under normal conditions. Heat probably does not coagulate the protoplasm of completely dried bacteria. This explains why higher temperatures are required to sterilize glassware by the dry-air sterilizer than by the autoclave. Dried bacterial spores are also more resistant to adverse conditions than spores kept in the moist condition.

Protoplasm in the dry state does not coagulate at 100°C., and dry enzymes retain their activity. Death of bacteria by dry heat is believed to be due to oxidation. The death rate increases with temperature, owing to an increase in the rate of oxidation.

The effect of desiccation at 37°C. on survival of *Escherichia coli* and *Bacillus subtilis* is shown in Figs. 134 and 135.

For more information see Monk and McCaffrey (1957) and Rahn (1945).

Maintenance of Stock Cultures. Bacteria for class use are generally preserved on nutrient agar slants. There are exceptions, such as certain pathogenic organisms that require the addition of serum, blood, and other body fluids to the medium; anaerobic bacteria that must be provided with a reducing environment; and disease-producing streptococci that prefer semisolid media. The toxic metabolic waste products secreted by organisms diffuse into the agar and away from the bacteria. Because of this property of agar, bacteria are able to survive longer than if grown in liquid preparations, where they are in constant contact with the toxic waste products dissolved in the medium. Such cultures, after preparation, are incubated for 24 hr. or more, then stored in a cool, dark room or cupboard and used as needed for the inoculation of transplants. They are referred to as stock cultures.

The maintenance of a large number of stock cultures of bacteria requires frequent attention to prevent loss of the organisms. The method commonly employed for this purpose is to prepare transfers to suitable media at definite intervals before the media become too dehydrated and before the bacteria are destroyed by the accumulation of waste products of metabolism. This requires not only a considerable amount of time but involves also the possible loss of certain biological, immunological, and cultural characteristics of the organisms.

Various methods are employed for preserving bacteria and maintaining them as near as possible in their original state. All methods may be placed into either of two groups: (1) prevention of slow drying; and (2) rapid desiccation.

Preservation by Prevention of Slow Drying. All the methods in this group attempt to preserve cultures by the application of some type of seal to prevent or decrease drying.

Probably the most convenient method of sealing would be to employ screw cap test tubes. However, keeping organisms in sealed tubes does not prevent dissociation. Also, the organisms may undergo changes in colonial forms, virulence, immunological specificities, and in other ways.

The culture tubes may be sealed off as ampules by heating the open end in a blast lamp and drawing out the melted tops with forceps. The disadvantages are (a) the difficulties encountered in opening the ampules, and (b) that the cultures preserved in this manner may also readily dissociate.

Agar slant cultures are prepared, incubated until good growth appears, then covered with sterile mineral oil to a depth of 1 cm. above the agar slant. Transplants are made by removing a loopful of the growth, touching the loop to the glass surface to drain off excess oil, then inoculating fresh medium.

The latter method possesses the following advantages:

1. Practically all organisms tested live longer under oil than in the control tubes.

2. Cultures are available at all times for transplantation without interfering with the preservation of the stock cultures.

3. It is especially advantageous in working with unstable variants where occasional transferring to fresh media or growth in mass culture results in a change in the developmental stage of the strain.

4. No seals, such as paraffin, wax, cement, or rubber caps, are needed for the culture tubes.

5. No special equipment is required, such as a centrifuge, desiccator, or vacuum pump.

Regardless of which method in this group is followed, no one of them will preserve bacteria for an indefinite period. All organisms slowly decrease in viability and finally die unless transfers are made to fresh medium at periodic intervals.

. For more information see Hartsell (1953, 1955).

Preservation by Rapid Desiccation. Kitasato (1889) observed that the organism of cholera, *Vibrio comma,* survived longer when dried in a desiccator than when dried in air. Since that time many workers have desiccator-dried other organisms with similar results.

Shackell (1909) recommended freezing as a preliminary step to rapid desiccation. The cultures may be frozen in salt-ice mixture or, better still, by solid carbon dioxide (dry ice), and then desiccated in a vacuum over sulfuric acid as the desiccant. This method, with its many modifications, is universally employed at present for the preservation of bacteria, viruses, sera, toxins, enzymes, and other biological materials.

Stein and Rogers (1950) designed a simple apparatus for rapid high-vacuum desiccation of frozen suspensions of biologic materials (Fig. 136). The apparatus consists of (1) glass ampule containing frozen suspension, (2) rubber tubing connecting glass vials with multiple glass pipette, (3) multiple glass pipette with 12 prongs, (4) vapor, (5) rubber tubing, (6) rubber stopper, (7) condenser (Pyrex filter flask), (8) refrigerant (dry ice and alcohol) −78°C., (9) vacuum jar, (10) frozen distillate

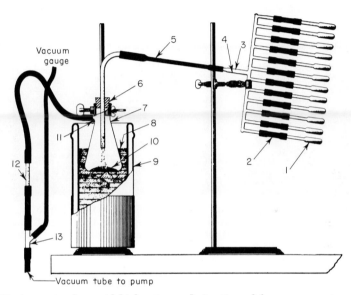

FIG. 136. Apparatus for rapid high-vacuum desiccation of frozen suspensions of biologic materials. See text for description. (*After Stein and Rogers.*)

from vapor, (11) outlet in filter flask, (12) absorbent cotton filter in glass tubing, (13) T-shaped glass tubing for attachment of vacuum gauge and vacuum pump.

Bacteria may be preserved for longer periods by freezing and vacuum drying than is possible by the methods listed in the first group. In fact, some species have remained viable in the desiccated state for at least 20 years. Also, desiccated bacteria do not exhibit any appreciable differences in their morphological, biochemical, and immunological properties as compared with the same organisms prior to drying.

For more information see Christian and Stockton (1956); Collier (1954); Flosdorf (1949); Greaves (1956); Harris (1951); Harrison (1956); Hollander and Nell (1954); Hunt, Gourevitch, and Lein (1958); Rhodes (1957); van Rooyen and Janes (1954).

EFFECT OF HYDROGEN-ION CONCENTRATION

The hydrogen-ion concentration of culture media is of prime importance for the successful cultivation of bacteria. Some organisms grow
best in acid environments; others grow best in alkaline media; still others
prefer substrates approximately neutral in reaction. There exists for each
organism an optimum concentration of hydrogen ions in which it grows
best. The pH values above and below which an organism fails to grow
are known as the minimum and maximum hydrogen-ion concentrations
respectively. The values are true only if other environmental factors are

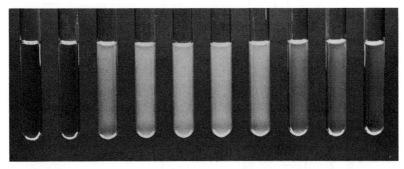

Fig. 137. Effect of pH on the growth of *Escherichia coli*. From left to right, pH 2.8
to 10 at intervals of 0.8 pH. Tubes 1 and 2, no growth; tubes 3 to 6 inclusive, increasing turbidity; tubes 7 to 10 inclusive, decreasing turbidity. Maximum turbidity
occurred in tube 6 at pH 6.8.

controlled. Variations in such factors as composition of the medium,
temperature of incubation, and osmotic pressure of the medium, even
though slight, may produce changes in the minimum, optimum, and
maximum hydrogen-ion values of an organism. The pH range of an
organism is the difference between the maximum and minimum values.
With some organisms this difference is wide; with others it is narrow.

Michaelis and Marcora (1912) noted that *E. coli* fermented lactose
with the production of acids until the pH dropped to about 5.0. This
acidity was sufficient to prevent further growth of the organisms. They
stated that the final hydrogen-ion concentration of cultures of *E. coli*
was a physiological constant. Similar results have been reported for other
organisms. It may be concluded that the growth of any fermentative organism is inhibited upon reaching a rather definite pH value. The final
degree of acidity will vary depending upon the species. These findings
have been used as a basis for differentiating closely related groups and
species of bacteria (see page 559).

The effect of pH on the growth of *E. coli* is shown in Fig. 137.

EFFECT OF SURFACE TENSION

Surface tension may be defined as that property, due to molecular forces, which exists in the surface film of all liquids and tends to bring the contained volume into a form having the least superficial area.

Molecules attract their neighbors and are attracted by them. A molecule situated in a liquid will be in equilibrium by virtue of the equal attractions on all sides. On the other hand, a molecule situated on the surface of a liquid will have equal horizontal attractions but unequal vertical attractions. This results in an unbalanced attraction toward the interior of the liquid. This resultant force reaches a maximum at the surface, and the mass of liquid behaves as if surrounded by an elastic membrane, tending to compress the liquid into the smallest possible volume.

The composition of the surface layer of a culture medium inoculated with an organism may differ appreciably from the composition of the same medium taken as a whole. The surface tension of media may, therefore, play an important role in the growth of an organism. This is especially true in the case of those organisms which have a tendency to grow on the surface of culture media in the form of a film or pellicle.

Organisms growing on the surface of a medium in the form of a pellicle were at one time regarded as strict aerobes. The surface layer, exposed to air, gave the organisms more oxygen than could be obtained from the deeper portions of the medium. It is true that the pellicle-forming bacteria are aerobic but not obligately aerobic. They are capable of growth and multiplication under both aerobic and anaerobic conditions. Bacteria have a density slightly greater than that of the culture medium in which they are grown. If the pellicle produced by a pellicle-producing organism, such as *Bacillus subtilis,* is sedimented, the pellicle will not rise to the surface again but will remain at the bottom of the tube. A new pellicle may develop on the surface of the medium. It is obvious that the surface film is supported in this position by some force in the medium. This force is spoken of as surface tension.

The unit of force in the C.G.S. system of physical units is the dyne. It is such a force that, under its influence, a particle whose mass is 1 gm. would experience during each second an acceleration of 1 cm. per sec. The dyne is approximately the force exerted by a milligram weight under the influence of gravity.

The surface tension of the usual laboratory media varies between 57 and 63 dynes. The surface tension of pure water is 73 dynes. Some substances may be added to culture media to raise the surface tension, among which may be mentioned charcoal and calcium chloride. Charcoal is effective by virtue of its ability to remove some surface-tension depressant from media. The growth of bacteria may, in some cases, raise the surface tension of the media in which they are cultivated. On the other hand, many substances may be added to culture media to lower their surface tensions. Among these may be mentioned ethyl alcohol, soaps, glycerol, and synthetic detergents. The soaps have been almost the only efficient compounds, but they are being gradually replaced by synthetic detergents or wetting agents. The latter compounds can be divided into anionic, cationic, and nonionic detergents (see page 490).

Fig. 138. Effect of surface tension on the growth of *Bacillus subtilis*. Left, growth in nutrient broth. The growth is confined almost entirely to the pellicle. Right, nutrient broth containing 0.05 per cent sodium ricinoleate to lower the surface tension. The growth occurs as a uniform turbidity.

Larson, Cantwell, and Hartzell (1919) found that if the surface tension of nutrient broth was depressed to some point below 40 dynes by means of soap, and then inoculated with *B. subtilis,* the organism grew in a diffuse manner rather than in the form of a pellicle on the surface. The same principle was found to apply to other pellicle-producing organisms. The formation of a pellicle apparently has nothing to do with the oxygen requirements of an organism, but is dependent upon the surface tension of the medium (Fig. 138).

Wetting is a function of surface tension. If bacteria are not wetted by the medium, they will grow on the surface in the form of a film; if they are wetted, they will produce a uniform clouding of the medium. It has been shown that bacteria growing on the surface of media contain a higher content of lipoidal substances than non-pellicle-producing organisms. The organism of tuberculosis has been found to contain as high as 40 per cent lipoidal substances in contrast to nonpellicle producers, which contain about 7 per cent.

Larson and Larson (1922) showed that organisms that ordinarily produced a uniform turbidity of the medium could be made to grow in the form of a pellicle if the lipoid content was increased. The fat content of *Staphylococcus aureus* was greatly increased by growing the organism on a medium containing a carbohydrate or glycerol, neither of which was fermented. The organism produced a pellicle on the surface which resembled the growth of the tubercle bacillus.

For more information see Larson (1928).

ANTAGONISTIC ACTION OF IONS

Winslow and Falk (1923*a*) reported that *E. coli* maintained itself in distilled water at a pH of 6.0 without material reduction in bacterial numbers for nearly 24 hr. At pH 5.0, the reduction was somewhat greater. The viability decreased as the solution was adjusted to more acid or alkaline conditions (Table 9). A heavy line is drawn to indicate the range of time and pH most nearly corresponding to a one-third reduction in bacterial numbers.

On the other hand, NaCl in a strength of 0.0145 *M* exerted a distinctly favorable action on the viability of *E. coli*. Instead of a slight but definite decrease in numbers after 24 hr., as occurred in distilled water at pH 6.0, the bacteria maintained themselves in undiminished numbers. Above a concentration of 0.0145 *M* NaCl, the percentage of living organisms decreased with increasing concentrations of salt.

Similar results were obtained if CaCl₂ was substituted for NaCl. The organisms maintained themselves better in the presence of this salt than in distilled water alone. Here again, a pH of 6.0 appeared to be the most favorable for growth or maintenance of *E. coli*. The most favorable concentration of CaCl₂ appeared to be 0.00145 *M*.

TABLE 9. VIABILITY OF *Escherichia coli* IN DISTILLED WATER

Hours	Per cent alive at pH						
	4.0	5.0	6.0	6.5	7.0	7.5	8.0
1	87	88	84	92	68	77	79
3	39	71	74	66	54	24	52
6	4	48	64	30	24	8	12
9	1	68	82	7	17	5	12
24	0	6	77	2	23	3	10
Number of experiments	2	2	4	2	10	2	4

In another communication, Winslow and Falk (1923*b*) reported that solutions of 0.724 *M* NaCl and over and solutions of 0.435 *M* CaCl₂ and over exhibited distinctly toxic actions on *E. coli* at all hydrogen-ion concentrations. However, in a solution containing a mixture of these two salts in appropriate proportions, an antagonistic action was manifested, which tended to protect the bacteria against the toxic action of each salt if present alone (Table 10). This phenomenon is spoken of as the antagonistic action of ions.

MacLeod and Snell (1950) found that zinc was toxic for *Lactobacillus arabinosus* and that its toxicity could be overcome by manganese. Mag-

TABLE 10. VIABILITY OF *Escherichia coli* IN SOLUTIONS OF NaCL AND CaCL₂, SINGLY AND IN COMBINATIONS

Total isotonic concentration*	Total molar concentration	Percentage of bacteria alive after 9 hr. in			
		Pure NaCl	Pure CaCl₂	NaCl + CaCl₂	Ratio, Na/Ca
0	0	89	89	89	
1	0.145	82	22		
2	0.290	..	...	41	1 : 1
3	0.435	55	0+	28	2 : 1
4	0.580	..	...	40	3 : 1
5	0.725	46	0+	117	4 : 1
6	0.870	33	...	30	5 : 1

* 1 tonicity = 0.145 M.

nesium, calcium, and strontium also counteracted the toxicity of zinc for this organism. On the other hand, the above ions failed to reverse the toxicity of zinc for *Leuconostoc mesenteroides*. They believed that the toxicity of zinc for *L. arabinosus* resulted from the formation of a catalytically inactive zinc protein from this ion and some protein normally activated by manganese, magnesium, calcium, or strontium. The latter ions counteracted the toxicity of zinc by displacing zinc from the protein to form a catalytically active metalloprotein.

Abelson and Aldous (1950) found nickel, cobalt, cadmium, zinc, and manganese to be toxic to *Escherichia coli*. The toxicity of these cations was reduced in the presence of much magnesium. If the magnesium was not present in the medium, the elements were toxic at very low levels.

The addition of cobalt to a medium supporting growth of *Clostridium perfringens* was found by Shankar and Bard (1955) to yield filamentous cells which fermented glucose chiefly to lactic acid. The inhibitory effect of cobalt was quantitative and reversible by magnesium. Metabolic studies indicated that cobalt caused a fermentative shift to the homolactic type by affecting enzyme synthesis during growth.

A practical application of this phenomenon was the development of a physiological salt solution by Ringer before ionic antagonism was clearly understood. Ringer showed that when a beating heart was perfused with a 0.75 per cent solution of sodium chloride, pulsation stopped completely. On the addition of 0.0125 per cent calcium chloride to the solution, the heartbeat was restored, but not in a normal manner. On the further addition of 0.01 per cent potassium chloride and a small amount of alkali, such as sodium bicarbonate to adjust the pH of the solution, the heartbeat became normal. This solution is known as Ringer's solution. Other preparations of this type are Tyrode's and Locke's solutions.

OLIGODYNAMIC ACTION OF HEAVY METALS

Naegeli (1893) noted that silver in very high dilutions produced a toxic action on certain organisms. He found that 1 part of silver in 100,000,000 parts of water killed algae of the genus *Spirogyra*. He believed that silver in such a high dilution could not produce a chemical action on living cells and attributed its toxic effect to an oligodynamic action. The word oligodynamic is compounded from two Greek words, ὀλίγος, *oligo*, few, little, small, and δυναμικός, *dynamic*, powerful. It may be defined as the toxic effect produced by heavy metals on living cells in exceedingly minute quantities.

Other metals also exert a toxic action on organisms. Copper in a dilution of 1 part in 77,000,000 of water is toxic to certain algae. The spores of *Aspergillus niger* fail to germinate in the presence of 1 part of silver in 1,600,000 parts of water. Water distilled from a copper still is toxic to bacteria. This is due to the presence of traces of dissolved copper in the water. Water distilled from stills made of other heavy metals also exhibits the same phenomenon, but to a lesser degree. This is not due to the greater toxicity of copper, as it is known that mercury is probably the most toxic metal, but to the fact that copper is more soluble in water than the other toxic metals. Therefore, metal stills should be avoided for the preparation of distilled water intended for biological use.

ZoBell (1941) found that containers made of copper, zinc, tin, or nickel alloys were not suitable for the collection of samples of sea water for bacteriological analysis owing to the inimical oligodynamic action of the metals. Under certain conditions, most of the bacteria in sea water were killed within a few minutes, and the sea water itself was rendered bacteriostatic by exposure to the metals.

Burrows and Hemmens (1943) reported that bacteria swabbed on the polished surface of a silver chalice died off rapidly. Experiments on the transmission of test organisms from one person to another by common use of the chalice showed that approximately 0.001 per cent of the organisms was transferred, even under the most favorable conditions. When the conditions approximated those of actual use, no transmission could be detected.

Demonstration of Oligodynamic Action. Silver exerts a marked bactericidal or oligodynamic action on bacteria. This may be demonstrated by placing a piece of metallic silver or a silver coin in a Petri dish and pouring over it melted agar, previously inoculated with an organism such as *Sarcina lutea* or *Serratia marcescens*. After incubation for 24 hr. at 37°C., a clear zone will be seen immediately surrounding the silver metal or coin. This is the oligodynamic zone (Fig. 139). Beyond this will appear a narrower zone in which growth is stimulated. Minute amounts of metallic ions stimulate growth, whereas greater concentrations produce an inhibitory effect. Normal growth occurs in the remainder of the agar. The same result is obtained if a piece of copper or a copper coin is substituted for the silver.

Gibbard (1937) came to the following general conclusions regarding the action of silver on bacteria:

1. The width of the oligodynamic zone is increased by treating the silver with nitric acid, and decreased by cleaning the metal mechanically.

2. Pure silver metal shows no bactericidal or oligodynamic action. However, if silver is first treated with nitric acid, a film of silver oxide forms on the surface from which silver ions are produced. If silver oxide is prevented from forming, no inhibitory action occurs. This may be shown by melting silver, allowing a portion to cool in hydrogen and another to cool in air. The silver cooled in hydrogen shows no bactericidal action, while that cooled in air exhibits a pronounced bactericidal effect.

A	*B*

Fig. 139. Oligodynamic action of silver. *A*, agar inoculated with *Sarcina lutea* and poured into a dish containing a silver coin; *B*, same inoculated with *Serratia marcescens*. The zone immediately surrounding the silver coin is the oligodynamic zone. This is followed by a narrow stimulating zone. Normal growth occurs in the remainder of the agar.

3. Silver nitrate, silver oxide, and electrically dispersed colloidal silver, when properly diluted to contain the same concentration of silver, all possess a similar bactericidal action.

4. The bactericidal properties of silver nitrate and silver oxide are greatly reduced in the presence of proteins. Silver proteinates are formed, removing the metal from solution.

Applications of Oligodynamic Action. Silver has been recommended for the treatment of water, milk, vinegar, wine, cider, fruit juices, liquors, etc. Its greatest application appears to be in the treatment of water for drinking purposes. According to Gibbard, three methods are generally used commercially for this purpose:

1. The water is exposed to silver deposited on sand, porcelain, and other solid materials.

2. The silver is applied by electrolysis.

3. Use is made of the difference in E.M.F. that exists between nickel and silver electrodes kept in the material at different temperatures.

In all three methods the objective is the same, namely, to obtain a solution of silver.

Silver Poisoning. There is still considerable discussion as to whether sufficient silver remains in treated water, foods, beverages, etc., to produce silver poisoning or argyria in man and animals. It is important to know how much of the silver ingested will be retained in the body. So far as is known, there are no available data on this point. More work is required before this controversy can be definitely settled.

EFFECT OF SHAKING

Microorganisms can be killed by vigorous agitation. Curran and Evans (1942) agitated bacterial cultures and spore suspensions with abrasives such as glass beads, sand, and carborundum and obtained large decreases in the viable counts. King and Alexander (1948) obtained similar results. The cells were killed by being broken up into small fragments. Recovery of such injured cells was not possible unless damage was slight. It is reasonable to suppose that recovery occurs only when the nucleus or nuclear material remains uninjured.

For more information see Lamanna, Chatigny, and Colledge (1959).

REFERENCES

Abelson, P. H., and E. Aldous: Ion antagonisms in microorganisms: interference of normal magnesium metabolism by nickel, cobalt, cadmium, zinc, and manganese, *J. Bact.*, **60**:401, 1950.

Amaha, M.: Heat resistance of Cameron's putrefactive anaerobe 3679 in phosphate buffer (*Clostridium sporogenes*), *Food Res.*, **18**:411, 1953.

——— and Sakaguchi: Effects of carbohydrates, proteins, and bacterial cells in the heating media on the heat resistance of *Clostridium sporogenes*, *J. Bact.*, **68**:338, 1954.

Barner, H. D., and S. S. Cohen: The relation of growth to the lethal damage induced by ultraviolet irradiation in *Escherichia coli*, *J. Bact.*, **71**:149, 1956.

Barr, M., and L. F. Tice: A study of the inhibitory concentrations of various sugars and polyols on the growth of microorganisms, *J. Am. Pharm. Assoc.*, Scient. Ed., **46**:219, 1957a.

——— and ———: A study of the inhibitory concentrations of glycerol-sorbitol and propylene glycol-sorbitol combinations on the growth of microorganisms, *ibid.*, **46**:217, 1957b.

Bedford, T. H. B.: The nature of the action of ultraviolet light on microorganisms, *Brit. J. Exp. Path.*, **8**:437, 1927.

Berger, H., F. L. Haas, O. Wyss, and W. S. Stone: Effect of sodium azide on radiation damage and photoreactivation, *J. Bact.*, **65**:538, 1953.

Bowen, J. F., and E. S. Smith: Sporulation in *Clostridium pasteurianum*, *Food Res.*, **20**:655, 1955.

Burrows, W., and E. S. Hemmens: Survival of bacteria on the silver communion cup, *J. Infectious Diseases*, **73**:180, 1943.

Charles, R. L., and L. N. Zimmerman: Dark reactivation in ultraviolet irradiated *Escherichia coli*, *J. Bact.*, **71**:611, 1956.

Christian, R. T., and J. J. Stockton: The influence of sealing pressure on survival of *Serratia marcescens* and *Micrococcus pyogenes* var. *aureus* desiccated from the frozen state, *Appl. Microbiol.*, **4**:88, 1956.

Collier, L. H.: The preservation of vaccinia virus, *Bact. Rev.*, **18**:74, 1954.

Cortelyou, J. R., L. M. Amundson, and M. A. McWhinnie: A phase contrast study of the chromatinic bodies of *Escherichia coli* subsequent to ultraviolet irradiation, *J. Bact.*, **71**:462, 1956.

Curran, H. R.: Resistance in bacterial spores, *Bact. Rev.*, **16**:111, 1952.

—— and F. R. Evans: The influence of enrichments in the cultivation of bacterial spores previously exposed to lethal agencies, *J. Bact.*, **34**:179, 1937.

—— and ——: The killing of bacterial spores in fluids by agitation with small inert particles, *ibid.*, **43**:125, 1942.

Deering, R. A.: Studies on division inhibition and filament formation of *Escherichia coli* by ultraviolet light, *J. Bact.*, **76**:123, 1958.

Durham, N. N., and O. Wyss: An example of non-inherited radiation resistance, *J. Bact.*, **72**:95, 1956.

El Bisi, H. M., and Z. J. Ordal: The effect of certain sporulation conditions on the thermal death rate of *Bacillus coagulans* var. *thermoacidurans*, *J. Bact.*, **71**:1, 1956*a*.

—— and ——: The effect of sporulation temperature on the thermal resistance of *Bacillus coagulans* var. *thermoacidurans*, *J. Bact.*, **71**:10, 1956*b*.

Ellison, S. A., B. F. Erlanger, and P. Allen: The chemical reversal of ultraviolet effects on bacteria, *J. Bact.*, **69**:536, 1955.

Falcone, G.: Metabolismo della L-alanina e germinazione delle spore, *Giornale di Microbiologia*, **1**:185, 1955.

Flosdorf, E. W.: "Freeze-Drying," New York, Reinhold Publishing Corporation, 1949.

Frank, H. A., and L. L. Campbell, Jr.: The influence of recovery media on thermal resistance values of spores of a putrefactive anaerobic bacterium, *Appl. Microbiol.*, **3**:300, 1955.

Fricke, H., and M. Demerec: The influence of wave length on genetic effects of x-rays, *Proc. Nat. Acad. Sci.*, **23**:320, 1937.

Gibbard, J.: Public health aspects of the treatment of water and beverages with silver, *Am. J. Pub. Health*, **27**:122, 1937.

Goucher, C. R., I. Kamei, and W. Kocholaty: Ultraviolet inactivation and photoreactivation of *Azotobacter*, *J. Bact.*, **72**:184, 1956.

Greaves, R. I. N.: The preservation of bacteria, *Can. J. Microbiol.*, **2**:365, 1956.

Harris, R. J. C.: A review of laboratory freeze-drying, *Vacuum*, **1**:11, 1951.

Harrison, A. P., Jr.: Survival of bacteria upon repeated freezing and thawing, *J. Bact.*, **70**:711, 1955.

——: Causes of death of bacteria in frozen suspensions, *Antonie van Leeuwenhoek*, **22**:407, 1956.

—— and Cerroni: Fallacy of "crushing death" in frozen bacterial suspensions, *Proc. Soc. Exp. Biol. Med.*, **91**:577, 1956.

Hartsell, S. E.: The preservation of bacterial cultures under paraffin oil, *Appl. Microbiol.*, **1**:36, 1953.

——: Maintenance of cultures under paraffin oil, annotated summary, Laboratories of Bacteriology, Purdue University, March, 1955.

Hegarty, C. P., and O. B. Weeks: Sensitivity of *Escherichia coli* to cold-shock during the logarithmic growth phase, *J. Bact.*, **39**:475, 1940.

Heinmetz, F., and J. J. Lehman: Preliminary studies on the restoration of viability of ultraviolet-inactivated bacteria by metabolites and cofactors, *Arch. Biochem. Biophys.*, **59**:313, 1955.

Hollander, D. H., and E. E. Nell: Improved preservation of *Treponema pallidum* and other bacteria by freezing with glycerol, *Appl. Microbiol.*, **2**:164, 1954.

Hunt, G. A., A. Gourevitch, and J. Lein: Preservation of cultures by drying on porcelain beads, *J. Bact.*, **76**:453, 1958.

Ingraham, J. L., and J. L. Stokes: Psychrophilic bacteria, *Bact. Rev.*, **23**:97, 1959.

Iyer, V., and J. V. Bhat: Growth of spore-forming bacilli in relation to common salt and sugar, *J. Sci. Ind. Res.*, **13B**:336, 1954.

Jagger, J.: Photoreactivation, *Bact. Rev.*, **22**:99, 1958.

Jensen, L. B.: "Microbiology of Meats," Champaign, Ill., Garrard Press, 1954.

Johnson, F. H., and C. E. ZoBell: The retardation of thermal disinfection of *Bacillus subtilis* spores by hydrostatic pressure, *J. Bact.*, **57**:353, 1949a.

—— and ——: The acceleration of spore disinfection by urethan and its retardation by hydrostatic pressure, *ibid.*, **57**:359, 1949b.

Kelner, A.: Photoreactivation of ultraviolet-irradiated *Escherichia coli* with special reference to the dose-reduction principle and to ultraviolet-induced mutation, *J. Bact.*, **58**:511, 1949.

——: Growth, respiration, and nucleic acid synthesis in ultraviolet-irradiated and in photoreactivated *Escherichia coli*, *J. Bact.*, **65**:252, 1953.

King, H. K., and H. Alexander: The mechanical destruction of bacteria, *J. Gen. Microbiol.*, **2**:315, 1948.

Kitasato, S.: Die Widerstandfähigkeit der Cholerabacterien gegen das Eintrocknen und gegen Hitze, *Z. Hyg.*, **5**:134, 1889.

Lamanna, C., M. A. Chatigny, and E. H. Colledge: Pumping as a means for the mechanical rupture of microorganisms mixed with glass beads, *J. Bact.*, **77**:104, 1959.

Larson, L. W., and W. P. Larson: Factors governing the fat content of bacteria and the influence of fat on pellicle formation, *J. Infectious Diseases*, **31**:407, 1922.

Larson, W. P.: The effect of the surface tension of the menstrum upon bacteria and toxins. From "The Newer Knowledge of Bacteriology and Immunology," edited by E. O. Jordan and I. S. Falk, Chicago, University of Chicago Press, 1928.

——, W. F. Cantwell, and T. B. Hartzell: The influence of the surface tension of the culture medium on the growth of bacteria, *J. Infectious Diseases*, **25**:41, 1919.

Luckiesh, M., G. P. Kerr, Jr., and T. Knowles: Killing bacteria in water under pressure, *Gen. Elec. Rev.*, **50**:16, 1947.

Luyet, B. J., and P. M. Gehenio: Life and death at low temperatures, Monograph 1, *Biodynamica*, 1940.

MacLeod, R. A., and E. E. Snell: The relation of ion antagonism to the inorganic nutrition of lactic acid bacteria, *J. Bact.*, **59**:783, 1950.

Mattick, A. T. R., and E. R. Hiscox: Some observations on the resistance of microorganisms to heat, and related phenomena, *Proc. Soc. Appl. Bact.* (Abst.), 1945.

McBee, R. H., and V. H. McBee: The incidence of thermophilic bacteria in arctic soils and waters, *J. Bact.*, **71**:182, 1956.

—— and L. P. Gaugler: Identity of themophilic bacteria isolated from arctic soils and waters, *ibid.*, **71**:186, 1956.

Meryman, H. T.: Mechanics of freezing in living cells and tissues, *Science*, **124**:515, 1956.

Michaelis, L., and F. Marcora: Die Sauereproduktivität des *Bacterium coli*, *Z. Immunitätsforsch.*, Abt. I, Orig., **14**:170, 1912.

Monk, G. W., and P. A. McCaffrey: Effect of sorbed water on the death rate of washed *Serratia marcescens*, *J. Bact.*, **73**:85, 1957.

Morita, R. Y., and C. E. ZoBell: Effect of hydrostatic pressure on the succinic dehydrogenase system in *Escherichia coli*, *J. Bact.*, **71**:668, 1956.

Müller, D.: Psychrophile, mesophile and thermophile Bakterien und die Abgrenzung dieser verschiedenen Gruppen, *Acta Path.*, **23**:384, 1946.

Nelson, F. E.: Factors which influence the growth of heat-treated bacteria, *J. Bact.*, **45**:395, 1943.

Ogg, J. E., H. I. Adler, and M. R. Zelle: Protection of *Escherichia coli* against ultraviolet-irradiation by catalase and related enzymes, *J. Bact.*, **72**:494, 1956.

Rahn, O.: Physical methods of sterilization of microorganisms, *Bact. Rev.*, **9**:1, 1945.

Rhodes, M. E.: The preservation of *Pseudomonas* under mineral oil, *J. Appl. Bact.*, **20**:108, 1957.

Romig, W. R., and O. Wyss: Some effects of ultraviolet radiation on sporulating cultures of *Bacillus cereus*, *J. Bact.*, **74**:386, 1957.

Schmidt, C. F.: The resistance of bacterial spores with reference to spore germination and its inhibition, *Ann. Rev. Microbiol.*, **9**:387, 1955.

Shackell, L. F.: An improved method of desiccation with some applications to biological problems, *Am. J. Physiol.*, **24**:325, 1909.

Shankar, K., and R. C. Bard: Effect of metallic ions on the growth, morphology, and metabolism of *Clostridium perfringens*, *J. Bact.*, 69:444, 1955.

Stein, C. D., and H. Rogers: Recovery of viable microorganisms and viruses from vapors removed from frozen suspensions of biologic material during lyophilization, *J. Vet. Research*, 11:339, 1950.

Stern, R. M.: Comparative studies of the growth of *Clostridium thermosaccharolyticum* and *Clostridium sporogenes* in various anaerobic media, *J. Bact.*, 43:38, 1942.

Straka, R. P., and J. L. Stokes: Metabolic injury to bacteria at low temperatures, *J. Bact.*, 78:181, 1959.

Stuy, J. H.: Photoreactivation of ultraviolet inactivated bacilli, *Biochim. Biophys. Acta*, 17:206, 1955.

———: V. Deoxyribonucleic acid metabolism in ultraviolet irradiated *Haemophilus influenzae*, *J. Bact.*, 78:49, 1959.

Sugiyama, H.: Studies on factors affecting the heat resistance of spores of *Clostridium botulinum*, *J. Bact.*, 62:81, 1951.

Thompson, T. L., Jr., R. B. Mefferd, Jr., and O. Wyss: The protection of bacteria by pyruvate against radiation effect, *J. Bact.*, 62:39, 1951.

Toyokawa, K., and D. H. Hollander: Variation in sensitivity of *Escherichia coli* to freezing damage during the growth cycle, *Proc. Soc. Exp. Biol. Med.*, 92:499, 1956.

van Rooyen, C. E., and C. Janes: A small drying apparatus designed for preservation of viruses, *J. Lab. Clin. Med.*, 43:489, 1954.

Vignais, P., and P. Vignais: Inhibition sélective de quelques enzymes respiratoires chez *Escherichia coli*, *Experientia*, 10:305, 1954.

Weatherwax, R. S.: Reactivations of ultraviolet-irradiated *Escherichia coli*, *J. Bact.*, 72:329, 1956a.

———: Desensitization of *Escherichia coli* to ultraviolet light, *ibid.*, 72:124, 1956b.

Weiser, R. S., and C. O. Hargiss: Studies on the death of bacteria at low temperatures. II. The comparative effects of crystallization, vitro-melting, and devitrification on the mortality of *Escherichia coli*, *J. Bact.*, 52:71, 1946.

——— and C. M. Osterud: Studies on the death of bacteria at low temperatures. I. The influence of the intensity of the freezing temperature, repeated fluctuations of temperature, and the period of exposure to freezing temperatures on the mortality of *Escherichia coli*, *ibid.*, 50:413, 1945.

Williams, O. B., and J. M. Reed: The significance of the incubation temperature of recovery cultures in determining spore resistance to heat, *J. Infectious Diseases*, 71:225, 1942.

——— and W. J. Robertson: Studies on heat resistance. VI. Effect of temperature of incubation at which formed on heat resistance of aerobic thermophilic spores, *J. Bact.*, 67:377, 1954.

——— and C. H. Zimmerman: Studies on heat resistance. III. The resistance of vegetative cells and spores of the same organism, *J. Bact.*, 61:63, 1951.

Winslow, C.-E. A., and I. S. Falk: Studies on salt action. VIII. The influence of calcium and sodium salts at various hydrogen-ion concentrations upon the viability of *Bacterium coli*, *J. Bact.*, 8:215; 1923a; IX. The additive and antagonistic effects of sodium and calcium chlorides upon the viability of *Bacterium coli*, *ibid.*, 8:237, 1923b.

Wyss, O., J. B. Clark, F. Haas, and W. S. Stone: The role of peroxide in the biological effects of irradiated broth, *J. Bact.*, 56:51, 1948.

Yesair, J., C. W. Bohrer, and E. J. Cameron: Effect of certain environmental conditions on heat resistance of micrococci, *Food Research*, 11:327, 1946.

Zelle, M. R., J. E. Ogg, and A. Hollaender: Differential photoreactivation of *Escherichia coli* after exposure to 2650 and 2250 A ultraviolet, *Proc. Soc. Exp. Biol. Med.*, 96:285, 1957.

ZoBell, C. E.: Apparatus for collecting water samples from different depths for bacteriological analysis, *J. Marine Research*, 4:173, 1941.

——— and C. B. Feltham: Are there specific marine bacteria?, *Proc. 5th Pacific Sci. Cong.*, 3:2097, 1933.

———— and F. H. Johnson: The influence of hydrostatic pressure on the growth and viability of terrestrial and marine bacteria, *J. Bact.*, **57**:179, 1949.

———— and H. D. Michener: A paradox in the adaptation of marine bacteria to hypotonic solutions, *Science*, **87**:328, 1938.

———— and R. Y. Morita: Barophilic bacteria in some deep sea sediments, *J. Bact.*, **73**:563, 1957.

CHAPTER 11

Enzymes of Bacteria

Catalysis may be defined as the acceleration of a reaction produced by the presence of a substance known as a catalyst.

A catalyst is an agent that accelerates a chemical reaction without itself being destroyed or used up. It may be recovered practically unchanged at the end of the reaction.

An enzyme or ferment may be defined as a thermolabile organic catalyst elaborated by a living cell and capable of functioning independently of the cell.

Every living cell may be considered a gross catalyst. It converts nutrients to waste products and, in so doing, obtains energy. The reaction

$$6CO_2 + 6H_2O + Energy \rightleftharpoons C_6H_{12}O_6 + 6O_2$$

from left to right is the classical equation for the photosynthetic reaction in green plants; and from right to left in animals, plants, and many microorganisms.

An enzyme acts by catalysis; i.e., it increases the velocity of a chemical reaction without itself being permanently changed. The enzyme may be recovered in an active condition after completion of the reaction. There is a close analogy between inorganic catalysts and enzymes. For example, hydrogen peroxide slowly decomposes into water and oxygen according to the reaction

$$2H_2O_2 \rightarrow 2H_2O + O_2$$

In the presence of an inorganic catalyst, such as platinum, or the enzyme catalase, the decomposition of the peroxide is greatly accelerated and ceases only when the destruction of the compound is complete.

NATURE OF ENZYMES

Enzymes possess the properties of proteins. They form colloidal solutions, dialyze through membranes either very slowly or not at all, are amphoteric, form opalescent solutions, are precipitated from solutions by the same agents which precipitate proteins, and have large molecular weights.

268

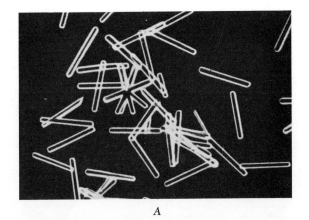

A

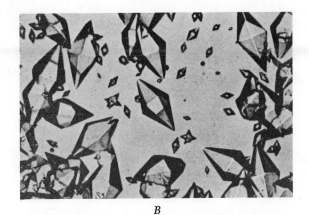

B

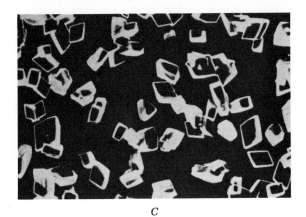

C

FIG. 140. A, trypsin crystals; B, pepsin crystals; C, chymotrypsin crystals. (*From Northrop, Kunitz, and Herriott, "Crystalline Enzymes," Columbia University Press.*)

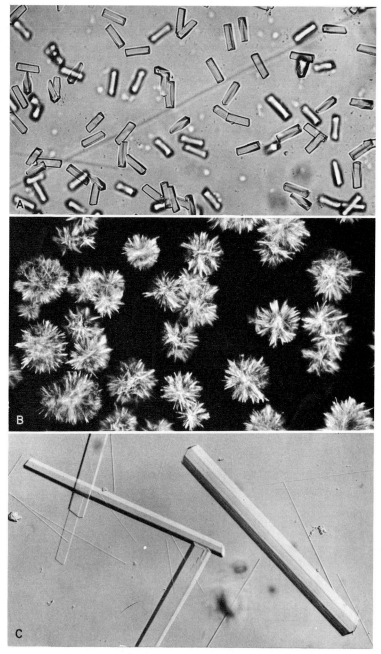

Fig. 141. *A*, desoxyribonuclease crystals; *B*, ribonuclease crystals; *C*, hexokinase crystals. (*Courtesy of M. Kunitz.*)

When enzymes are treated with acids, bases, or proteolytic enzymes, they yield a mixture of α-amino acids.

Over seventy enzymes have been isolated in the crystalline state. These enzymes give positive tests for proteins even after repeated recrystallizations, which indicates that they are pure preparations free from any contaminating proteins.

Photomicrographs of some pure crystalline enzymes are shown in Figs. 140 and 141.

Another indication that enzymes are proteins is their decreased production in culture media containing deficient amounts of nitrogen. Virtanen et al. (1948, 1949a, b) believed it was justifiable to assume that practically all protein in bacterial cells consists of enzyme protein and that the old idea of the distribution of enzymes in various parts of the protoplasm was no longer true. They found that dried cells of *Escherichia coli*, grown in a medium containing an ample supply of nitrogen, showed a nitrogen content of about 13 per cent. When the organisms were grown in a nitrogen-deficient medium, the nitrogen content dropped from 13 to as low as 6.5 per cent. Under these conditions the activity of certain enzymes remained fairly similar to that in normal cells, whereas the activity of other enzymes, such as sucrase, showed a marked decrease.

On the basis of their findings they concluded that the essential enzymes, i.e., those which are necessary for cell activity, regardless of the composition of the medium, retained their activity very well even though the nitrogen content was lowered. On the other hand, the nonessential enzymes, i.e., those which expand the living conditions of the cell, enabling it to utilize several nutrients but not being necessary in all nutritional conditions, lost most or all of their activity when the nitrogen content was decreased.

Union of Enzyme with Substrate. It is generally believed that enzymes combine with the substrates upon which they act. Whether this union is physical (adsorption) or chemical is not clearly understood, but certainly the available evidence points to some type of unstable complex between catalyst and substrate. For example, if hydrogen peroxide is added to catalase, the compound is rapidly decomposed to water and molecular oxygen. If, however, the enzyme is first treated with sodium azide, which inhibits its activity, the peroxide is only slowly decomposed. The catalase-azide complex shows a strong absorption spectrum with bands at 6240, 5440, and 5065 A. On the addition of hydrogen peroxide the spectrum changes with two bands at 5880 and 5470 A. The original spectrum reappears when all hydrogen peroxide has been decomposed, only to change back to the two-banded spectrum again on the addition of more substrate. These results would indicate that the enzyme reacts in some manner with its specific substrate.

Prosthetic Groups. Some enzymes have been shown to consist entirely of protein. Examples are the digestive enzymes pepsin and trypsin. Others contain a nonprotein fraction in their molecules. Enzymes of this type are referred to as conjugate enzymes. The nonprotein fraction is called the prosthetic group and the protein fraction the apoenzyme. The enzyme as a whole, consisting of both apoenzyme and prosthetic group, is known as the holoenzyme.

The prosthetic group is believed to be firmly fixed to the apoenzyme in contrast to the union of enzyme and substrate which is believed to be an unstable complex.

Specificity of Enzymes. Inorganic catalysts, such as nickel, platinum, and palladium, are able to catalyze many reactions. Enzymes, on the other hand, show a greater degree of specificity with respect to the nature of the substrates acted upon.

Enzymes exhibit absolute specificity, group specificity, stereochemical specificity, and relative specificity.

Absolute Specificity. Enzymes in this group act on only a single substrate. Urease, for example, hydrolyzes urea to ammonia and carbon dioxide. This is the only compound acted upon by the enzyme.

Group Specificity. These enzymes are not as specific as those in the preceding classification. Carbohydrases act only on carbohydrates, not on fats and proteins; lipases act on fats, not on carbohydrates and proteins; and proteases act on proteins but have no catalyzing effect on fats and carbohydrates.

Stereochemical Specificity. Maltase catalyzes the hydrolysis of many α-glucosides but has no effect on β-glucosides. Another example of an enzyme of this type is L-arginase, which acts on L-arginine but not on D-arginine.

Relative Specificity. An example of relative specificity is the enzyme β-glucosidase, which hydrolyzes some β-glucosides at much faster rates than other glucosides.

Number of Enzymes. An average cell is said to contain about 10 per cent protein, not including structural protein. Each individual enzyme makes up about 0.01 per cent of the cellular protein. This means that if all protein is in the form of enzymes, the cell could contain up to 1000 different enzymes. From the known facts of the multiplicity of reactions catalyzed by a cell, there could be that many enzymes present.

Localization of Enzymes in the Cell. Considerable interest has developed over the past several years in attempts to associate enzyme activity with certain bodies present in cells. In general, four separate fractions have been isolated and studied: nuclear, microsomal, mitochondrial, and soluble. The four fractions are prepared by differential centrifugation.

The mitochondria have been studied more completely than any of the others. They supply most of the energy for cell metabolism by their ability to carry out oxidative phosphorylation. For this reason they have been termed the "powerhouse of the cell."

In other instances enzyme activity may be associated with the nuclei, the chromosomes, the microsomes, or the soluble fractions of cells.

For more information see Alexander (1956), Darter and Millman (1957), Weibull, Beckman, and Bergström (1959).

FACTORS WHICH INFLUENCE ENZYME REACTION RATES

The rates of enzyme reactions are influenced by a number of factors, the most important being (1) temperature, (2) pH of the solution, (3) ultraviolet light, (4) concentration of enzyme, (5) concentration of substrate, (6) presence of activators, and (7) presence of inhibitors. The same factors which influence the growth and multiplication of bacteria also affect the action of enzymes. However, enzymes are generally more resistant to unfavorable environmental conditions than the cells producing them. For example, dried yeast heated to 100°C. for 6 hr. loses the power of growth and multiplication but still retains the ability to ferment sugar to alcohol and carbon dioxide.

Effect of Temperature. The velocity of an enzyme reaction is accelerated by an increase in temperature. This continues until a maximum is reached, after which the velocity gradually decreases, resulting finally in the destruction of the enzyme. In general, a rise of 10°C. doubles the velocity of an enzyme reaction.

Each enzyme has its own characteristic optimum, maximum, and minimum temperatures. An enzyme displays its greatest activity at the optimum temperature. That temperature above which an enzyme is no longer active is known as the maximum temperature; and that temperature below which it cannot function is known as the minimum temperature. The optimum, maximum, and minimum temperatures are influenced by a number of factors, such as concentration of enzyme, nature and concentration of substrate, pH, and presence of activating and paralyzing substances.

Most enzymes in solution are more or less stable at temperatures below 45°C., but above 50°C. inactivation increases rapidly with a rise in temperature. The majority of enzymes are irreversibly destroyed at temperatures of 70 to 80°C. On the other hand, enzymes in the dry state are more resistant to high temperatures than the same enzymes in solution. For example, dry rennin is only slowly destroyed at 158°C.

Effect of pH. Enzymes are markedly influenced by the hydrogen-ion concentration of the solution. Some enzymes act best in acid solutions; others require alkaline solutions; still others do not function well unless their environments are neutral in reaction. There exists for every enzyme a maximum, an optimum, and a minimum pH. These pH values vary with the substrate, the type of buffer employed, and the length of time the enzyme is allowed to act.

Two different types of behavior may be distinguished in this connection: reversible and irreversible effect. An enzyme can tolerate slight changes in acidity or alkalinity without being destroyed. Readjustment of the reaction to the optimum pH restores fully the activity of the enzyme. On the other hand, if the solution is made strongly acid or strongly alkaline the enzyme undergoes an irreversible loss of activity. Readjustment of the reaction back to the optimum pH does not restore the activity of the enzyme.

Effect of Ultraviolet Light. Ultraviolet light either destroys or modifies the action of enzymes. The rate of destruction is practically independent of temperature but is affected by pH and other environmental conditions.

Purified enzymes are more easily destroyed by light rays than the same enzymes in less purified preparations. Impurities from the culture media, especially proteins and protein split products, may afford considerable protection. In general, the greater the degree of purification of an enzyme, the more susceptible it becomes to the toxic light rays.

Enzymes are sensitive to the same rays which affect living cells. The most toxic rays have a wave length of 2650 A. (see page 239).

Effect of Concentration of Substrate and Enzyme. An increase in the substrate concentration may increase or decrease the velocity of an enzymatic reaction. If the substrate concentration is small in proportion to the amount of enzyme, an increase in the substrate content will increase the velocity of the reaction. For example, the enzyme sucrase hydrolyzes sucrose to glucose and levulose. An increase in the sucrose concentration, up to 4 or 5 per cent, increases the velocity of hydrolysis. Above this concentration, the relative amount of sugar hydrolyzed becomes progressively less as the sugar concentration is increased. It may be concluded that a strong solution of cane sugar diluted to a concentration of about 5 per cent will be more efficiently hydrolyzed by sucrase than one more concentrated.

The time required for sucrose to be hydrolyzed is proportional to the concentration of the enzyme. In general this is true for all enzymes when the amount of enzyme is much smaller than the concentration of substrate so that all of the enzyme can combine with the latter. When an excess of enzyme is used, the velocity appears to be proportional to the square root of the enzyme concentration.

Effect of Activators and Inhibitors. Some substances restore the activity of enzymes, whereas others produce the reverse effect. The former are called activators; the latter, inhibitors. These substances may be either specific or nonspecific.

Heavy Metals. Many enzymes are inactivated by heavy metals such as silver, mercury, and copper. The inactivated enzymes can usually be reactivated by treatment with hydrogen sulfide, which precipitates the heavy metals.

Urease is inactivated by cupric chloride, mercuric chloride, and silver nitrate, and may be reactivated by hydrogen sulfide. This would indicate that the enzyme contains a sulfhydryl group. Urease is inactivated also by fluorides, halogens, borates, quinones, formaldehyde, hydrogen peroxide, and basic dyes. The enzyme is most reactive at about pH 7.0.

Acids. Pepsin is a proteolytic enzyme that acts on peptide linkages by hydrolysis, but it attacks only those links containing the tyrosyl or phenylalanyl group attached to the imino side of the peptide linkage (see page 353).

The enzyme is active only in acid solutions. Its greatest activity occurs at about pH 1.6.

An active pepsin may be inhibited by the addition of alkalies. If the solution is adjusted to a pH higher than 6.8, the enzyme is slowly destroyed.

Alkalies. Trypsin is another proteolytic enzyme that acts on peptide linkages by hydrolysis, but it attacks only those links containing the lysyl or arginyl group attached to the carbonyl side of the peptide linkage (see page 353).

The enzyme is active only in alkaline solutions. It has an optimum pH range of 8 to 9.

Other Chemicals. Peroxidase and catalase are inactivated by hydrocyanic acid, sodium azide, hydrogen sulfide, and hydroxylamine. Removal of these substances restores activity to the enzymes.

Oxidation-Reduction. Papain is a proteolytic enzyme found in the juice of green papaya; it is apparently intermediate in action between pepsin and trypsin. Its optimum pH range is from 4 to 7.

A sulfhydryl group is believed to be an essential part of the active enzyme. Oxidation inactivates the enzyme, and reduction restores its activity. Activation can be effected by hydrogen sulfide, cysteine, glutathione, or hydrocyanic acid.

Proteases. Proteolytic enzymes produce an inhibitory or destructive action on other enzymes. This is another indication that enzymes are proteins.

Pepsin and papain rapidly digest urease at pH 4.3. Trypsin in an alkaline medium readily digests maltose. Pepsin and trypsin rapidly digest rennin. Pepsin at pH 2.0 readily digests trypsin; trypsin at pH 8.0 easily digests pepsin.

CLASSIFICATION OF ENZYMES

The exact chemical structure of any one protein is not known. The same holds true for an enzyme. For this reason enzymes are classified on the basis of what they do rather than on what they are. For example, lactase hydrolyzes lactose to glucose and galactose; arginase hydrolyzes arginine to urea and ornithine; adenase converts adenine to hypoxanthine and ammonia; etc. Also there are general names for groups of enzymes, such as proteases, oxidases, esterases, nucleases, and dehydrogenases. It is customary to name the enzyme after the substance acted upon and to add the suffix -ase. The first discovered enzymes, such as pepsin, trypsin, and rennin, do not follow this terminology, but they are exceptions.

A classification of enzymes is believed to be essential for a clearer understanding of the subject. Table 11 is not complete, but it shows the method followed in naming and classifying enzymes. The chemical reactions are included insofar as it is possible to do so.

TABLE 11.   CLASSIFICATION OF ENZYMES

A. Esterases

The esterases catalyze the reversible reaction

$$R \cdot COOR' + H_2O \rightleftharpoons R \cdot COOH + R'OH$$

The acid may be a higher or lower fatty acid and R'OH may be glycerol or a simple aliphatic or aromatic alcohol or a carbohydrate.

---

1. Butyrases + lower esters → alcohols + lower fatty acids

$$CH_3 \cdot COO \cdot C_2H_5 + H_2O \rightarrow CH_3 \cdot COOH + C_2H_5OH$$

  Ethyl acetate   Acetic acid   Alcohol

---

2. Glyceridases + glycerides → glycerol + higher fatty acids

$$\begin{array}{l}
CH_2OOC \cdot C_{17}H_{33} \qquad\qquad CH_2OH \\
| \qquad\qquad\qquad\qquad\qquad\quad | \\
CHOOC \cdot C_{17}H_{33} + 3H_2O \rightarrow CHOH + 3C_{17}H_{33} \cdot COOH \\
| \qquad\qquad\qquad\qquad\qquad\quad | \\
CH_2OOC \cdot C_{17}H_{33} \qquad\qquad CH_2OH
\end{array}$$

    Triolein   Glycerol   Oleic acid

---

3. Cholinesterase + acetylcholine ⇌ choline + acetic acid

  Acetylcholine   Choline   Acetic acid

---

4. Cholesterol esterase + cholesterol esters → cholesterol + R·COOH

---

5. Chlorophyllase + chlorophyll A + alcohol → ethyl chlorophyllide + phytol

$$C_{32}H_{30}N_4MgO(COOCH_3) \cdot COO \cdot C_{20}H_{39} + C_2H_5OH \rightarrow C_{32}H_{30}N_4MgO(COOCH_3) \cdot COOC_2H_5 + C_{20}H_{39}OH$$

    Chlorophyll A   Alcohol   Ethyl chlorophyllide   Phytol

---

6. Lecithinases

 a. Lecithinase A + lecithin → lysolecithin + oleic acid

    Lecithin   Lysolecithin   Oleic acid

TABLE 11 (Continued)

b. Lecithinase B + lysolecithin → glycerophosphoric ester + stearic acid

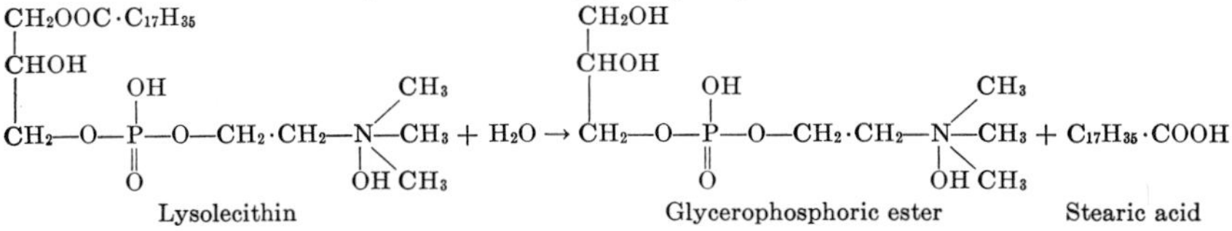

$$CH_2OOC \cdot C_{17}H_{35}$$
$$CHOH$$
with OH and CH₃ phosphocholine group

Lysolecithin + H₂O → Glycerophosphoric ester + $C_{17}H_{35} \cdot COOH$ (Stearic acid)

7. Pectase + pectin → pectic acid + methyl alcohol

$$(R \cdot COOCH_3)_n + (H_2O)_n \rightarrow (R \cdot COOH)_n + (CH_3OH)_n$$
Pectin — Pectic acid — Methyl alcohol

8. Phosphatases

a. Glycerophosphoric + glycerophosphoric → glycerophosphoric + choline
esterase — ester — acid

Glycerophosphoric ester + H₂O → Glycerophosphoric acid + Choline

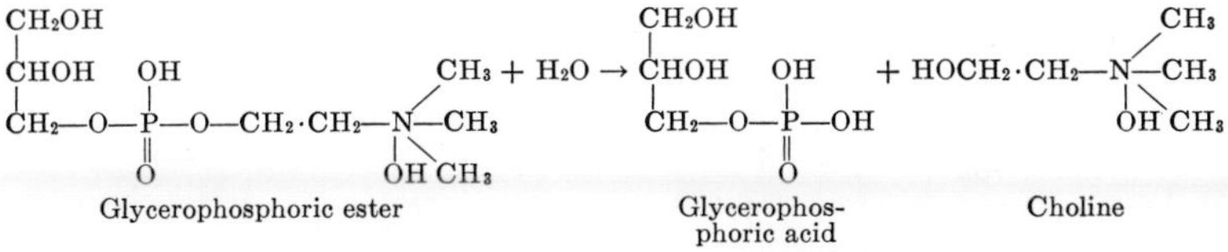

b. The phosphomonoesterases consist of a cophosphatase (coenzyme) and an apophosphatase (carrier). The coenzyme of one enzyme may be combined with the carrier of another to give two new enzymes.

Phosphomono- + monoesters of → alcohol + phosphoric acid
esterases   o-phosphoric acid

Glycerophosphoric acid + H₂O → Glycerol + Phosphoric acid (H_3PO_4)

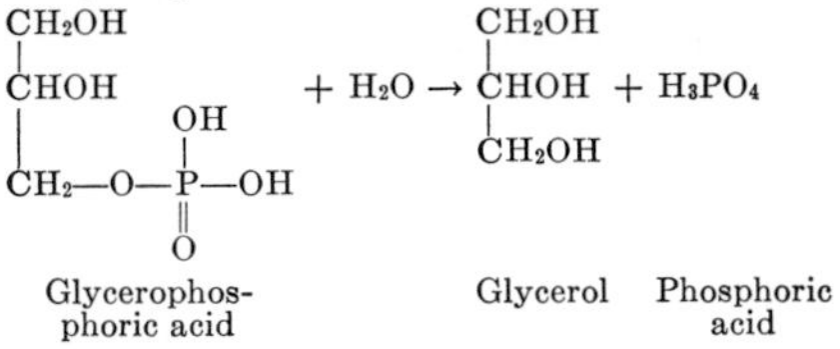

c. Phosphodiesterase + diesters of phosphoric acid → alcohol + monoester

d. Hexose- + hexose- → hexose + phosphoric acid
diphosphatase   diphosphoric acid

Hexose-1,6-diphosphate + 2H₂O → α-D-Glucose (α-D-glucopyranose) + 2H₃PO₄ (Phosphoric acid)

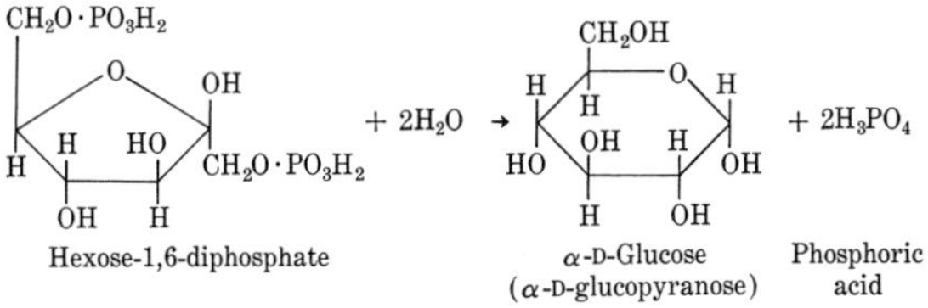

e. Phytase + phytin → inositol + phosphoric acid

Phytin + 3H₂O → Inositol + $6H_3PO_4$

Inositol — Phosphoric acid

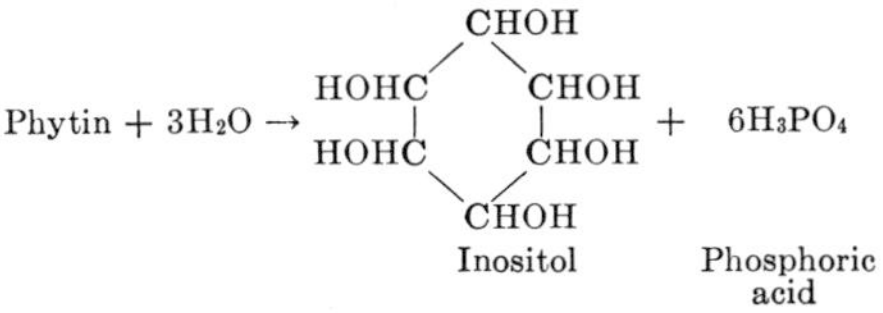

TABLE 11 (Continued)

9. Sulfatases + ethereal sulfates → phenols + potassium bisulfate

$$C_6H_5O \cdot SO_3K + H_2O \rightarrow C_6H_5OH + KHSO_4$$

Potassium   Phenol Potassium
phenyl sulfate   bisulfate

10. Tannase + tannins (esters of polyhydroxy phenols → gallic acid with aromatic acids)

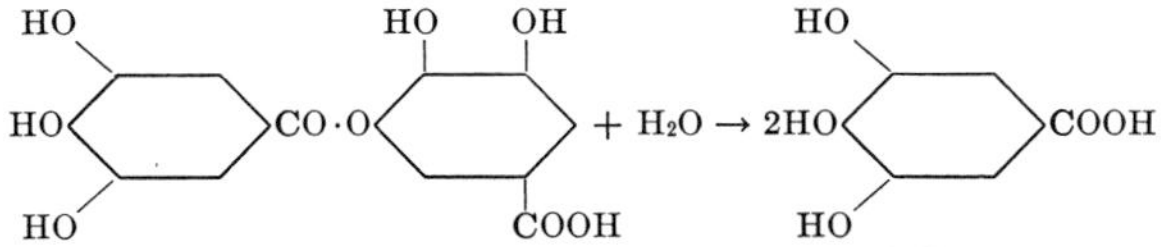

Digallic acid   Gallic acid

11. Adenosine + adenosine → adenosine + H_3PO_4
  triphosphatase triphosphate diphosphate

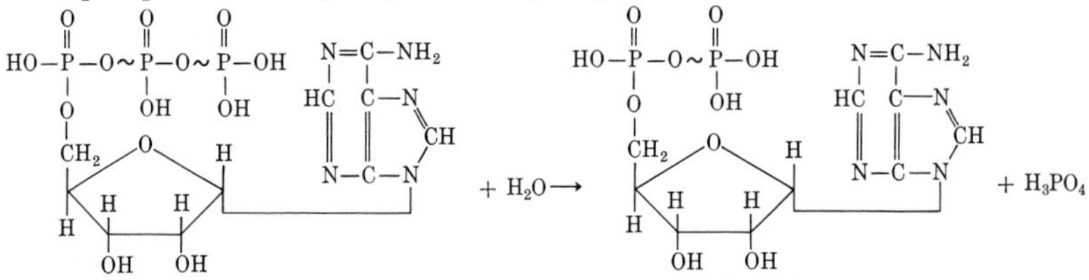

Adenosine triphosphate   Adenosine diphosphate

B. Carbohydrases

The carbohydrases catalyze the hydrolysis of carbohydrates to compounds that are simpler and generally more soluble.

1. Amylases

 a. α-Amylase + starch → dextrin + α-maltose

$$(C_6H_{10}O_5)_x + xH_2O \rightarrow dextrin +$$

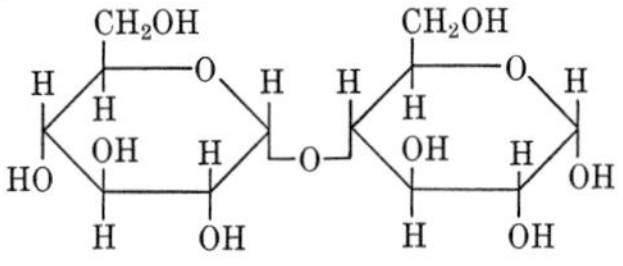

Starch   Maltose
            (4-*O*-α-D-glucopyranosyl-D-glucose)

 b. β-Amylase + starch → maltose

$$(C_6H_{10}O_5)_x + xH_2O \rightarrow maltose$$

 Starch   (see above for formula)

2. Cellulase + cellulose → β-cellobiose

$$(C_6H_{10}O_5)_x + xH_2O \rightarrow$$

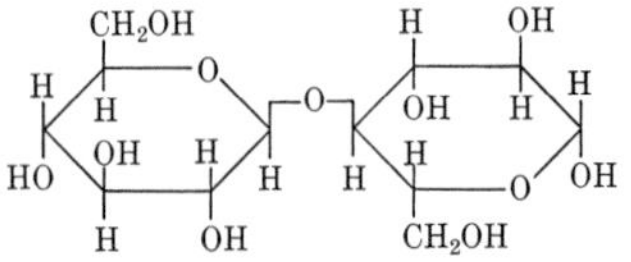

Cellulose   Cellobiose
          (4-*O*-β-D-glucopyranosyl-D-glucose)

3. Cytase + hemicelluloses → simple sugars having formula $C_6H_{12}O_6$

TABLE 11 (Continued)

4. Inulase + inulin → D-fructose (levulose)

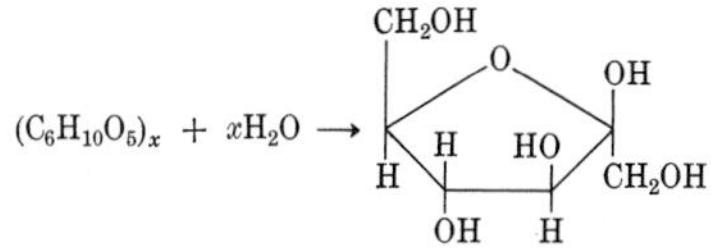

$$(C_6H_{10}O_5)_x + xH_2O \rightarrow$$

Inulin

β-D-Fructose
(β-D-fructofuranose)

5. Pectinase + pectic acid → galactose + galacturonic acid

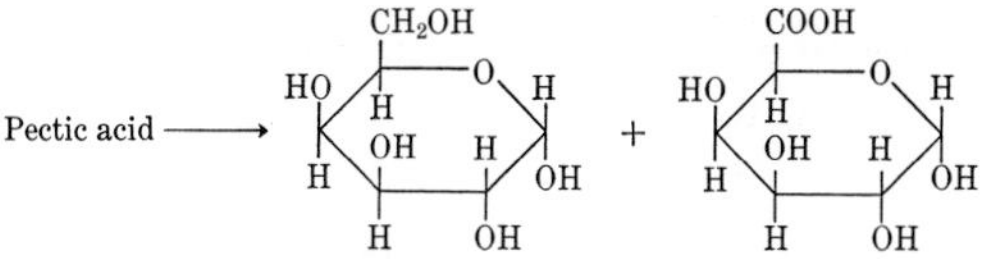

Pectic acid ⟶

D-Galactose
(α-D-galactopyranose)

α-D-Galacturonic acid

6. Raffinase + raffinose → melibiose + β-D-fructose

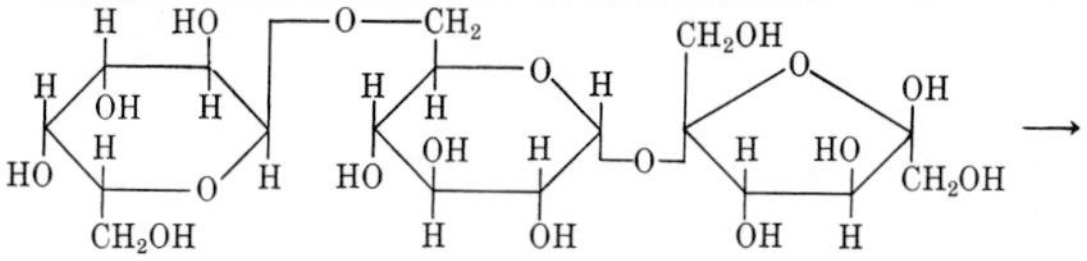

Raffinose
(O-α-D-galactopyranosyl-(1→6)-O-α-D-glucopyranosyl-
(1→2)-β-D-fructofuranoside)

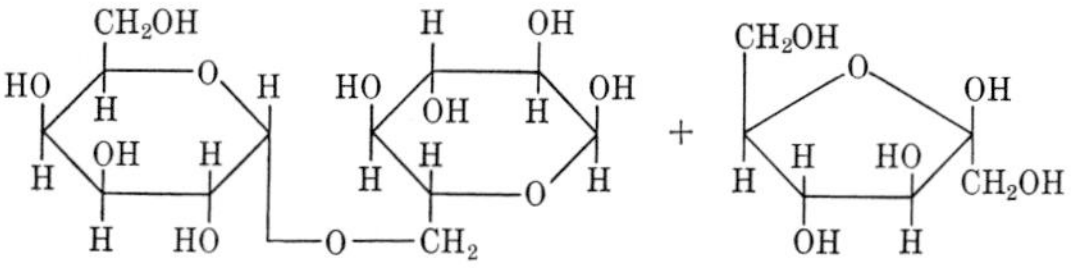

Melibiose
(6-O-α-D-galactopyranosyl-D-glucose)

β-D-Fructose
(β-D-fructofuranose)

7. Gentianase + gentianose → α-gentiobiose + D-fructose

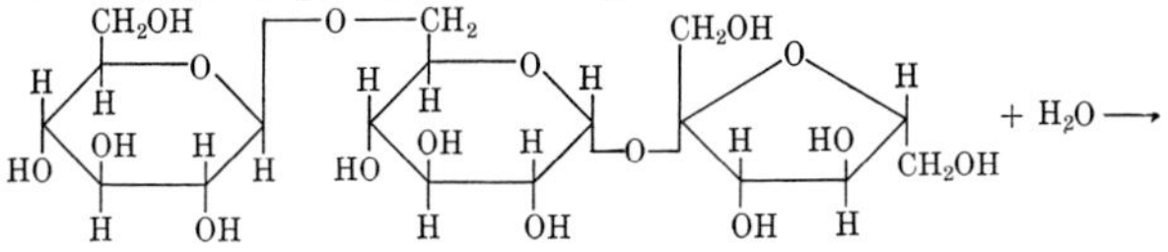

Gentianose
(O-β-D-glucopyranosyl-(1→6)-O-α-D-glucopyranosyl-
(1→2)-β-D-fructofuranoside)

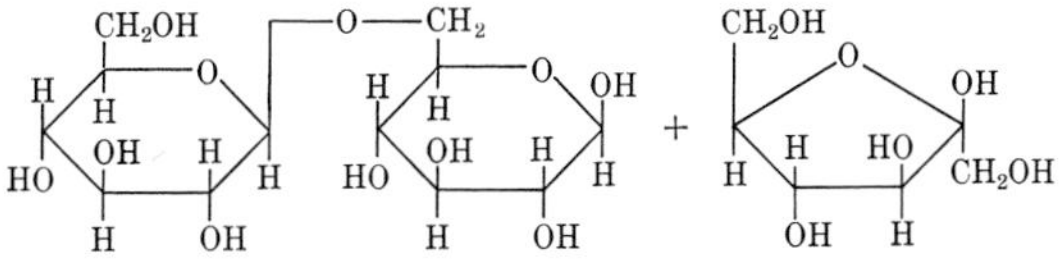

Gentiobiose
(6-O-β-D-glucopyranosyl-D-glucose)

β-D-Fructose
(β-D-fructofuranose)

TABLE 11 (Continued)

8. Sucrase + sucrose → α-D-glucose + β-D-fructose

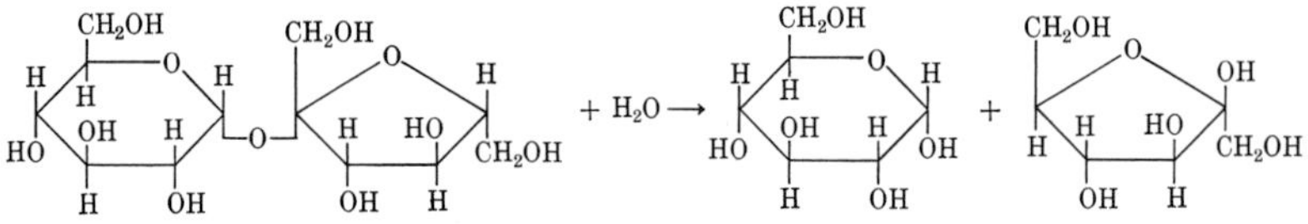

Sucrose
(α-D-glucopyranosyl-β-D-fructofuranoside)

+ H₂O →

α-D-Glucose
(α-D-glucopyranose)

+

β-D-Fructose
(β-D-fructofuranose)

9. Maltase + maltose → α-D-glucose + α-D-glucose

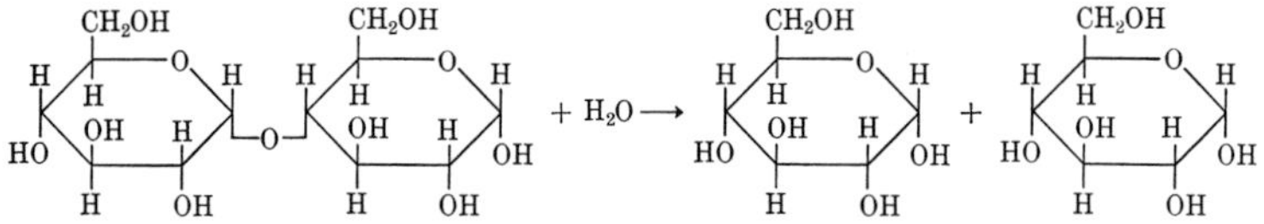

Maltose
(4-O-α-D-glucopyranosyl-D-glucose)

+ H₂O →

α-D-Glucose
(α-D-glucopyranose)

+

α-D-Glucose
(α-D-glucopyranose)

10. Trehalase + α,α-trehalose → α-D-glucose + α-D-glucose

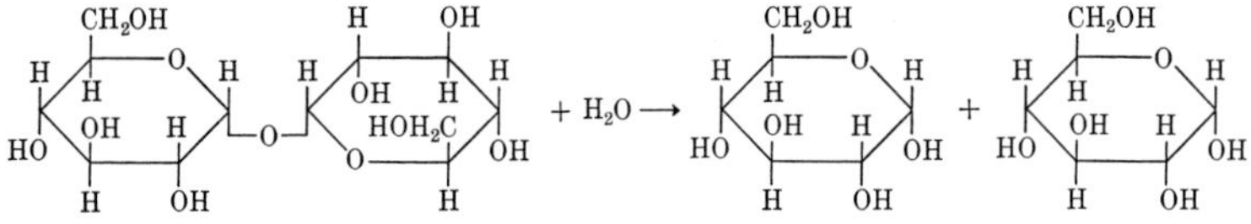

α,α-Trehalose
(α-D-glucopyranosyl-α-D-glucopyranoside)

+ H₂O →

α-D-Glucose
(α-D-glucopyranose)

+

α-D-Glucose
(α-D-glucopyranose)

11. Cellobiase + cellobiose → β-D-glucose + α-D-glucose

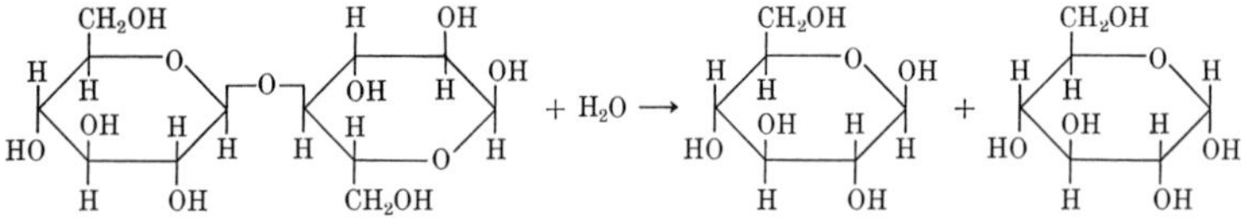

Cellobiose
(4-O-β-D-glucopyranosyl-D-glucose)

+ H₂O →

β-D-Glucose
(β-D-glucopyranose)

+

α-D-Glucose
(α-D-glucopyranose)

12. Gentiobiase + gentiobiose → β-D-glucose + β-D-glucose

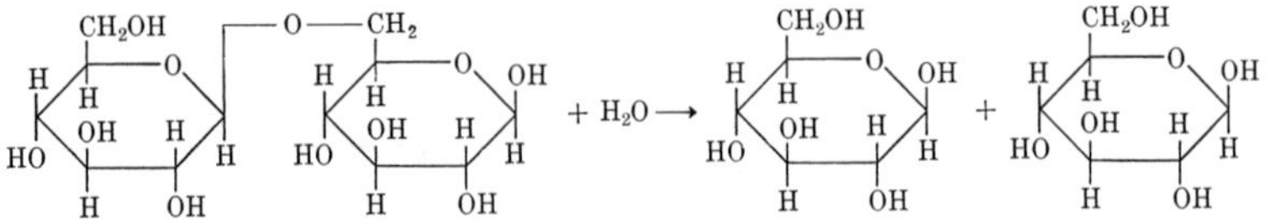

Gentiobiose
(6-O-β-D-glucopyranosyl-D-glucose)

+ H₂O →

β-D-Glucose
(β-D-glucopyranose)

+

β-D-Glucose
(β-D-glucopyranose)

TABLE 11 (Continued)

13. Lactase + lactose → β-D-galactose + α-D-glucose

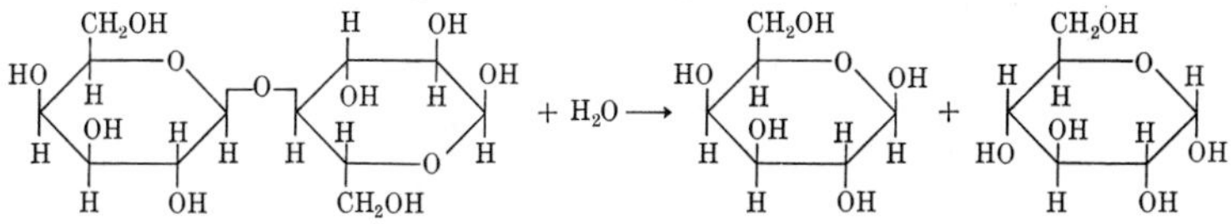

Lactose
(4-O-β-D-galactopyranosyl-D-glucose)

β-D-Galactose
(β-D-galactopyranose)

α-D-Glucose
(α-D-glucopyranose)

14. Melibiase + melibiose → α-D-galactose + β-D-glucose

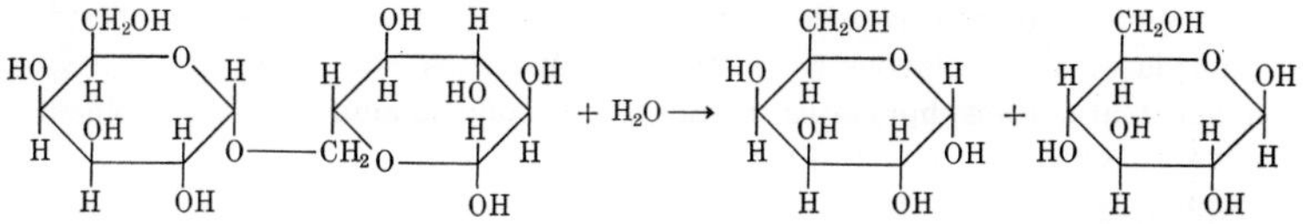

Melibiose
(6-O-α-D-galactopyranosyl-D-glucose)

α-D-Galactose
(α-D-galactopyranose)

β-D-Glucose
(β-D-glucopyranose)

15. α-Glucosidase + α-glucosides → α-D-glucose + alcohol or phenol residue

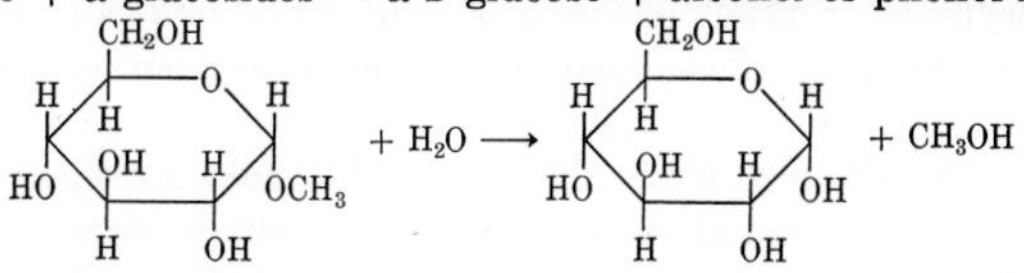

α-Methyl-D-glucoside
(α-methyl-D-glucopyranoside)

α-D-Glucose
(α-D-glucopyranose)

Methyl
alcohol

16. β-Glucosidase + β-glucosides → β-D-glucose + alcohol or phenol residue

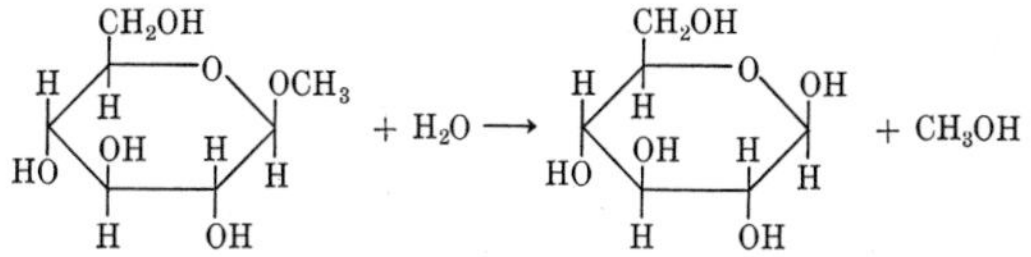

β-Methyl-D-glucoside
(β-methyl-D-glucopyranoside)

β-D-Glucose
(β-D-glucopyranose)

Methyl
alcohol

17. Amygdalase + amygdalin → gentiobiose + benzaldehyde + hydrocyanic acid

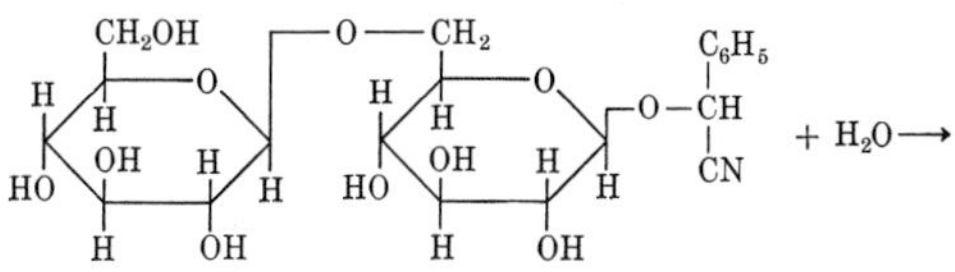

Amygdalin

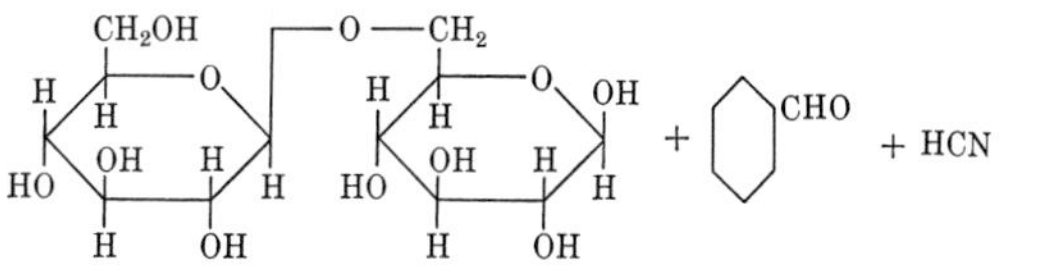

Gentiobiose
(6-O-β-D-glucopyranosyl-D-glucose)

Benz-
aldehyde

Hydro-
cyanic
acid

TABLE 11 (Continued)

18. Emulsin + salicin → β-D-glucose + saligenin

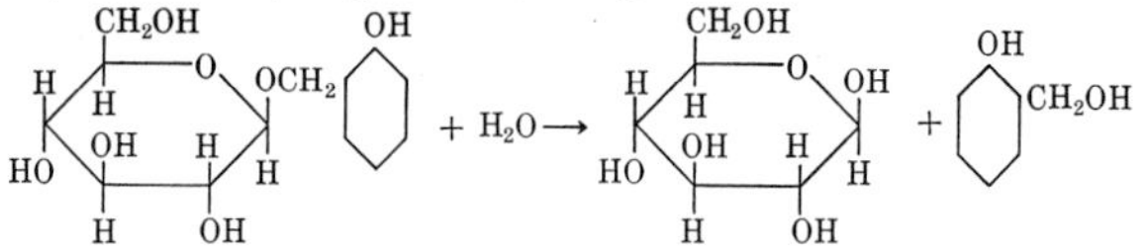

Salicin　　　　　　　　　　β-D-Glucose　　　Saligenin
　　　　　　　　　　　　(β-D-glucopyranose)　(o-hydroxybenzyl
　　　　　　　　　　　　　　　　　　　　　　alcohol)

C. Enzymes of carbohydrate metabolism

These enzymes catalyze reactions involving organic phosphorus compounds. The phosphorylases are analogous to hydrolyzing enzymes, since they cause a splitting of the substrate. Phosphorylases introduce phosphoric acid into the molecule; hydrolyzing enzymes introduce water.

Phosphorolysis:

$$RO \cdot R' + H_3PO_4 \rightarrow RO \cdot PO_3H_2 + R' \cdot OH$$

Hydrolysis:

$$RO \cdot R' + H_2O \rightarrow RO \cdot H + R' \cdot OH$$

Transphosphorylases transfer phosphoric acid from one compound to another. Phosphomutases transfer phosphoric acid from one position to another on the same molecule.

Phospho-isomerases produce other changes in the molecule such as the conversion of a phospho-keto compound into a phospho-aldehyde compound. The organic phosphorus compounds may be divided into two groups: (1) those which have energy-poor phosphate and (2) those which have energy-rich phosphate. Examples of the former group are the hexose phosphates, pentose phosphates, triose phosphates, glycerophosphates, etc. The latter group includes compounds in which the phosphate residue is linked

(a) To another phosphate residue:

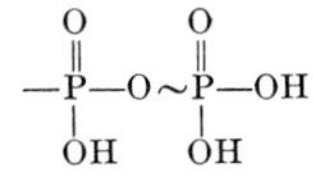

(b) To a carboxyl:

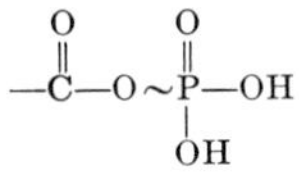

(c) To a guanidine residue:

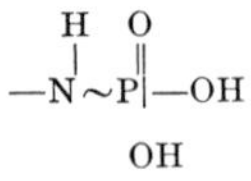

(d) To an acidic enol:

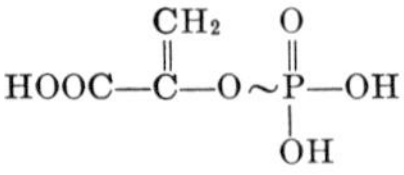

TABLE 11 (Continued)

1. Phosphorylase + glycogen + $H_3PO_4 \rightleftharpoons$ glucose-1-phosphate
(Cori ester)

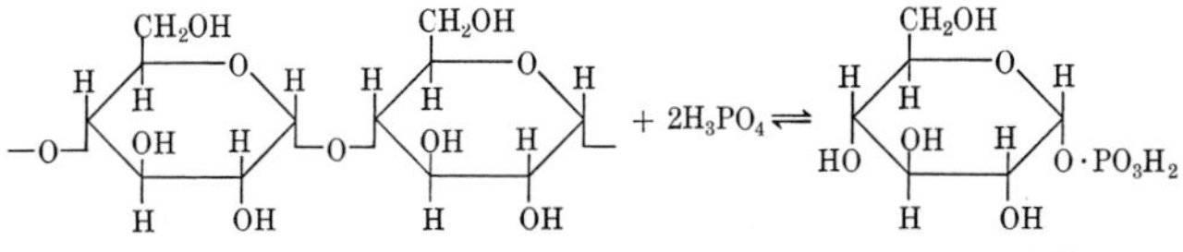

$$+ 2H_3PO_4 \rightleftharpoons$$

Glycogen $(C_6H_{10}O_5)_x$ Glucose-1-phosphate

2. Sucrose phosphorylase + sucrose + $H_3PO_4 \rightarrow$ glucose-1-phosphate + fructose

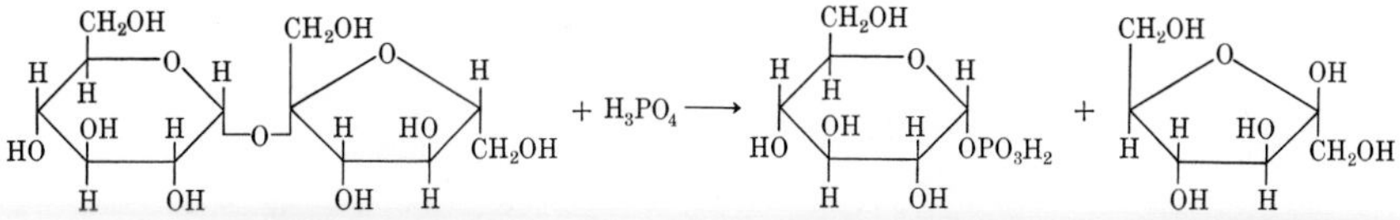

$$+ H_3PO_4 \rightarrow$$

Sucrose
(α-D-glucopyranosyl-β-D-fructofuranoside)   Glucose-1-phosphate β-D-Fructose
(β-D-fructofuranose)

3. Phosphocarboxyl + 1,3-diphospho- + adenosine $\rightarrow$
transphosphorylases   glyceric acid   diphosphate

3-phospho- + adenosine
glyceric acid   triphosphate

These enzymes transfer phosphoric acid residues from a phosphorylated carboxyl group to adenosine diphosphate or adenosine monophosphate (adenylic acid):

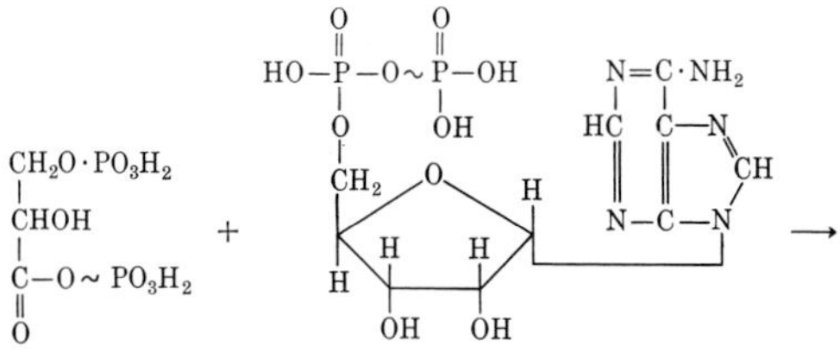

1,3-Diphosphoglyceric acid   Adenosine diphosphate

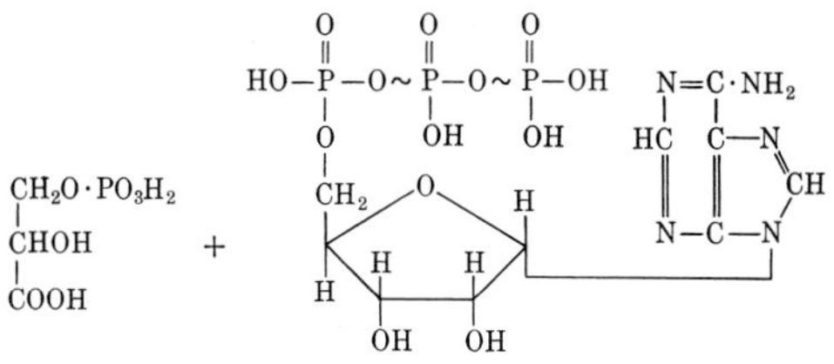

3-Phosphoglyceric acid   Adenosine triphosphate

TABLE 11 (Continued)

4. Phosphoguanidine + arginine + adenosine   → arginine   + adenosine
    transphosphorylase   triphosphate   phosphate   diphosphate

$$
\begin{array}{c}
NH_2 \\
| \\
NH=C \\
| \\
N-(CH_2)_3 \cdot CHNH_2 \cdot COOH \\
| \\
H
\end{array}
\quad + \quad
\text{Adenosine triphosphate}
\quad \longrightarrow
$$

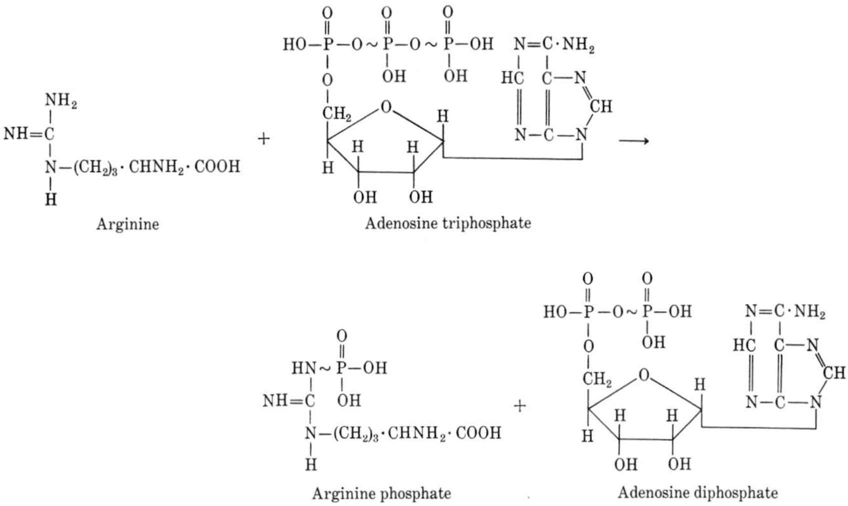

Arginine   Adenosine triphosphate

$$
\begin{array}{c}
O \\
\| \\
HN \sim P-OH \\
| \quad | \\
NH=C \quad OH \\
| \\
N-(CH_2)_3 \cdot CHNH_2 \cdot COOH \\
| \\
H
\end{array}
\quad + \quad
\text{Adenosine diphosphate}
$$

Arginine phosphate   Adenosine diphosphate

5. Phospho-enol   + enol-phospho- + adenylic → pyruvic + adenosine
    transphosphorylase   pyruvic acid   acid   acid   triphosphate

$$
\begin{array}{c}
CH_2 \\
\| \\
2CO \sim POH(OH)_2 \\
| \\
COOH
\end{array}
\quad + \quad
\text{Adenylic acid}
\quad \longrightarrow
$$

Enol-phosphopyruvic acid   Adenylic acid

$$
\begin{array}{c}
CH_3 \\
| \\
2C=O \\
| \\
COOH
\end{array}
\quad + \quad
\text{Adenosine triphosphate}
$$

Pyruvic acid   Adenosine triphosphate

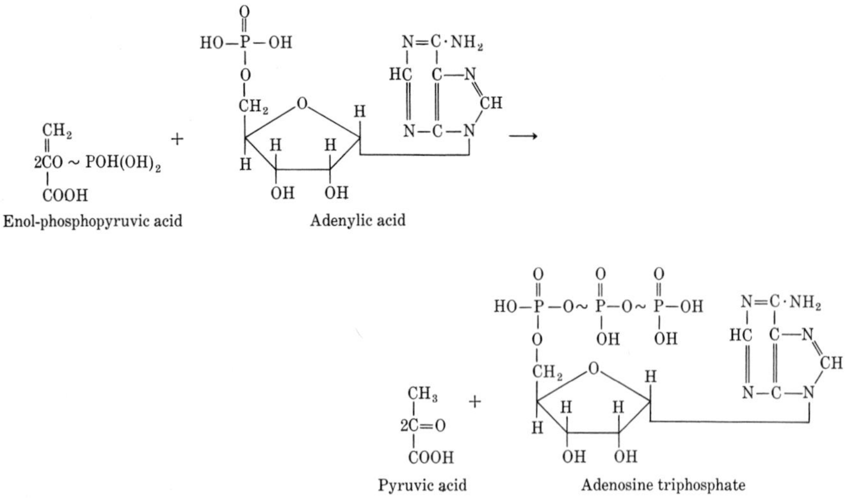

TABLE 11 (Continued)

6. Hexokinase + adenosine triphosphate + glucose → adenylic acid + glucose-6-phosphate

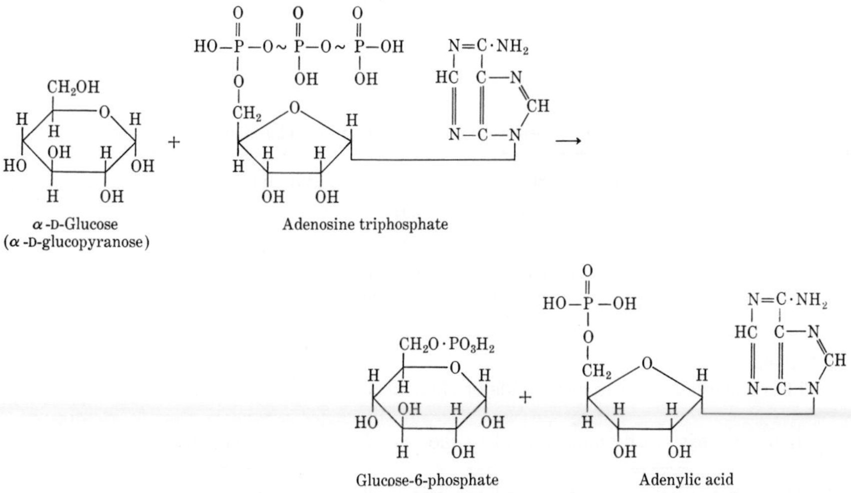

α-D-Glucose
(α-D-glucopyranose)

Adenosine triphosphate

Glucose-6-phosphate

Adenylic acid

7. Phosphoglucomutase + glucose-1-phosphate ⇌ glucose-6-phosphate

Glucose-1-phosphate

Glucose-6-phosphate

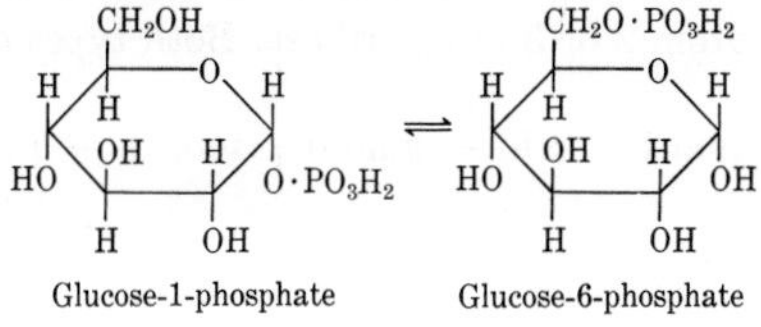

8. Phosphoglyceromutase + 3-phosphoglyceric acid ⇌ 2-phosphoglyceric acid

$$CH_2O \cdot PO_3H_2$$
$$CHOH \qquad \rightleftharpoons \qquad CHO \cdot PO_3H_2$$
$$COOH \qquad\qquad COOH$$

3-Phosphoglyceric
acid

2-Phosphoglyceric
acid

9. Phosphotriose isomerase + 3-glyceraldehyde phosphate ⇌ dihydroxyacetone phosphate

$$CH_2O \cdot PO_3H_2$$
$$CHOH \qquad \rightleftharpoons \qquad C=O$$
$$CHO \qquad\qquad CH_2OH$$

3-Glyceraldehyde
phosphate

Dihydroxyacetone
phosphate

TABLE 11 (Continued)

10. Phosphohexose + glucose-6- ⇌ fructose-6-
    isomerase   phosphate   phosphate

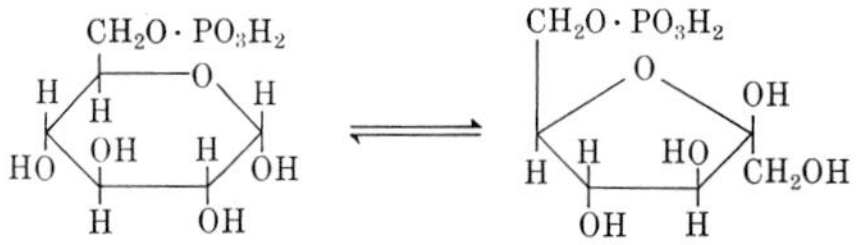

Glucose-6-phosphate   Fructose-6-phosphate

11. Enolase + 2-phosphoglyceric acid ⇌ phosphopyruvic acid (enol)

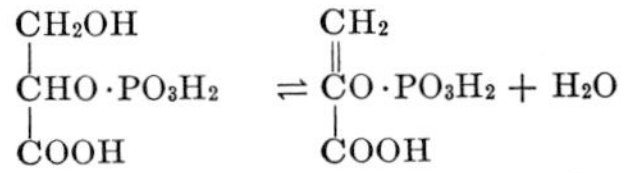

$$\begin{array}{ccc} CH_2OH & & CH_2 \\ | & & \| \\ CHO \cdot PO_3H_2 & \rightleftharpoons & CO \cdot PO_3H_2 + H_2O \\ | & & | \\ COOH & & COOH \\ \text{2-Phosphoglyceric} & & \text{Phosphopyruvic} \\ \text{acid} & & \text{acid (enol)} \end{array}$$

D. Nucleases
   The nucleases attack nucleic acids or their decomposition products.

1. Ribonuclease + ribonucleic acid → mononucleotides (see page 667)

2. Desoxyribonuclease + desoxyribonucleic acid → mononucleotides (see page 667)

3. Nucleotidases acting on nucleotides from ribonucleic acid. The phosphate may
   be united to carbon atom 2 or 3 of the ribose. Both types of molecules have been
   isolated.
   a. Guanylic acid + guanylic acid → guanine riboside + phosphoric acid
      nucleotidase

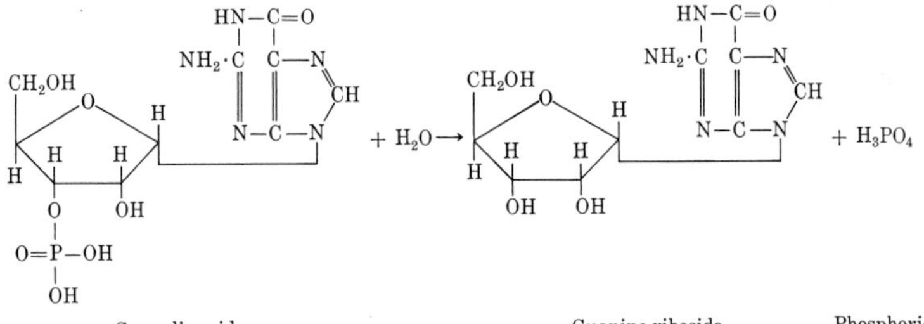

Guanylic acid   Guanine riboside   Phosphoric
                                  (guanosine)   acid

   b. Adenylic acid + adenylic acid → adenine riboside + phosphoric acid
      nucleotidase

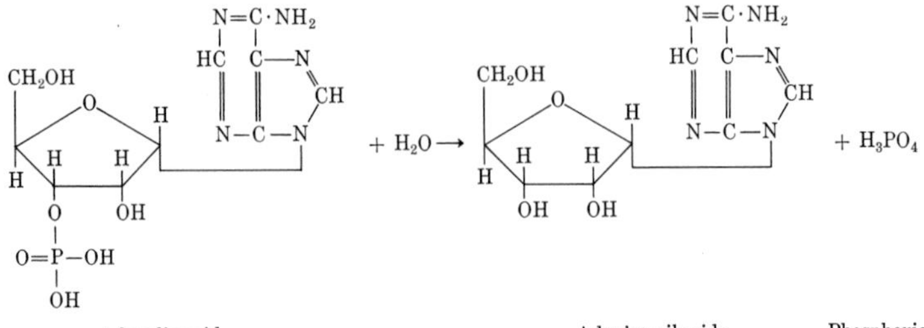

Adenylic acid   Adenine riboside   Phosphoric
                                  (adenosine)   acid

(TABLE 11 Continued)

c. Cytidylic acid + cytidylic acid → cytosine riboside + phosphoric acid
nucleotidase

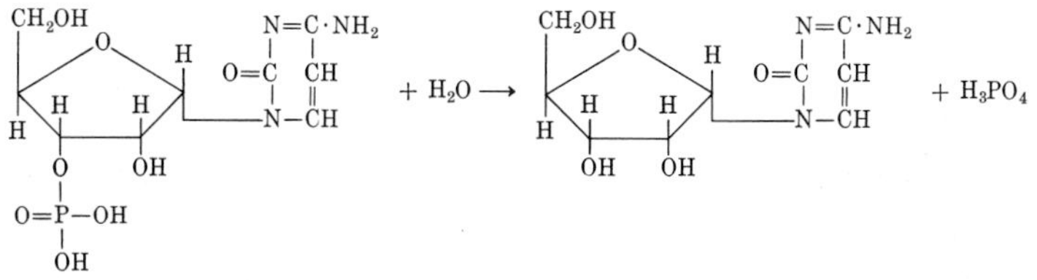

Cytidylic acid   Cytosine riboside   Phosphoric
             (cytidine)   acid

d. Uridylic acid + uridylic acid → uracil riboside + phosphoric acid
nucleotidase

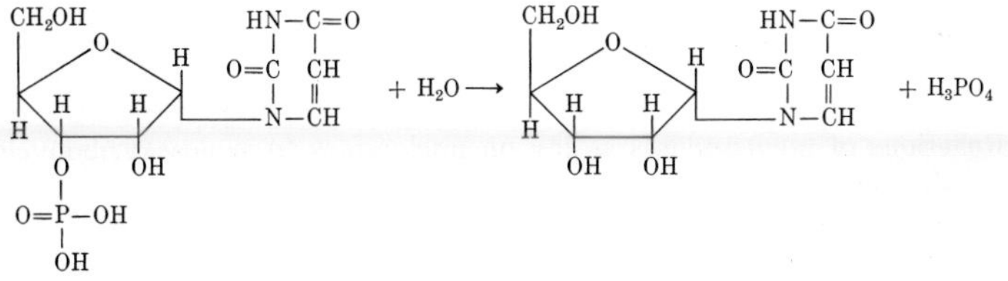

Uridylic acid   Uracil riboside   Phosphoric
              (uridine)   acid

Reactions of nucleotidases acting on nucleotides from desoxyribonucleic acid
are similar to the above except that the phosphoric acid is believed to be linked
to carbon 5 (primary alcohol group) of the sugar molecule instead of to carbon
2 or 3 (see page 667).

4. Nucleosidases acting on nucleosides from ribonucleic acid
   a. Guanine ribosidase + guanine riboside → guanine + β-D-ribose

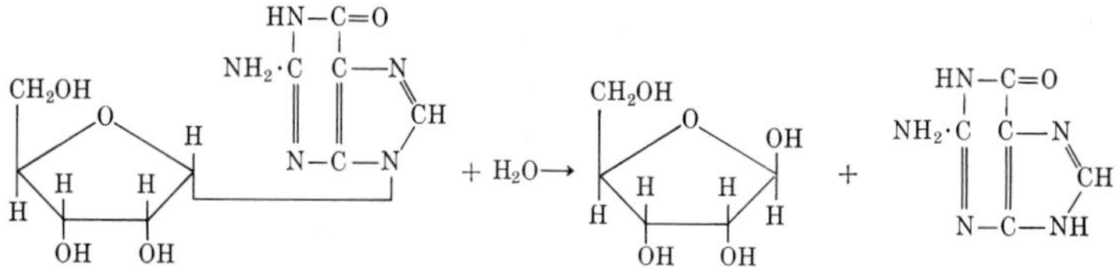

Guanine riboside   β-D-Ribose   Guanine
(guanosine)

   b. Adenine ribosidase + adenine riboside → adenine + α-D-ribose

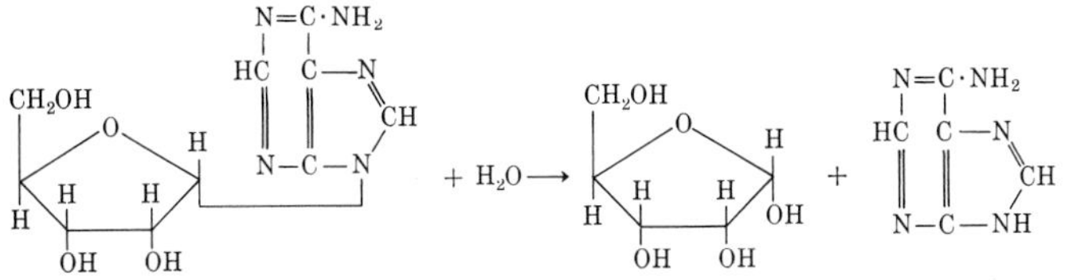

Adenine riboside   α-D-Ribose   Adenine
(adenosine)   (α-D-ribofuranose)

TABLE 11 (Continued)

c. Cytosine ribosidase + cytosine riboside → cytosine + α-D-ribose

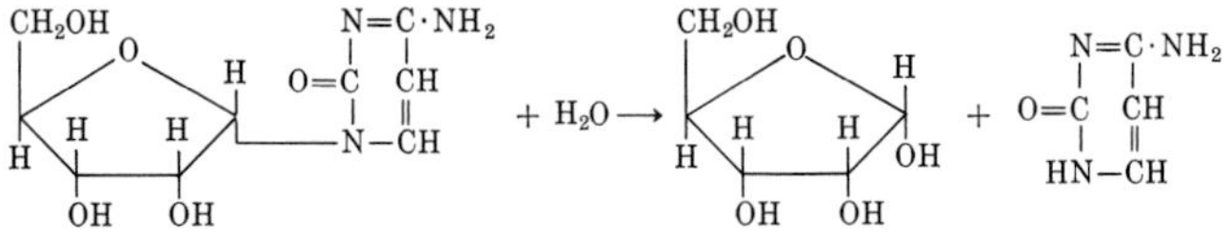

Cytosine riboside (cytidine) — α-D-Ribose (α-D-ribofuranose) — Cytosine

d. Uracil ribosidase + uracil riboside → uracil + α-D-ribose

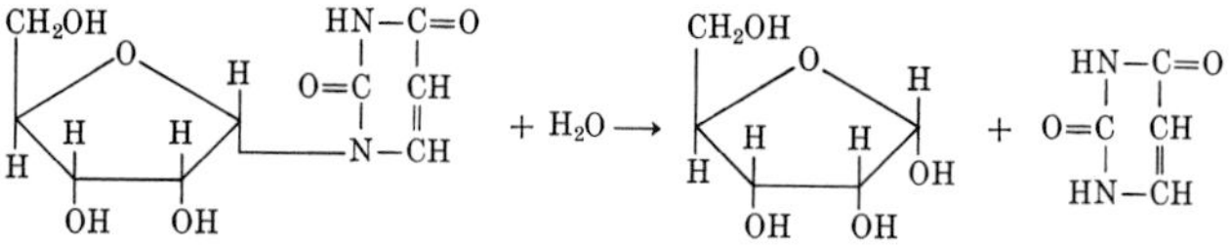

Uracil riboside (uridine) — α-D-Ribose (α-D-ribofuranose) — Uracil

Reactions of nucleosidases acting on nucleosides from desoxyribonucleic acid are similar to the above (see page 667).

E. Enzymes hydrolyzing nitrogen compounds

1. Amidases

a. Arginase + L-arginine → urea + L-ornithine

$$HN{=}C(NH_2){-}N(H)(CH_2)_3{\cdot}CHNH_2{\cdot}COOH + H_2O \rightarrow O{=}C(NH_2)_2 + NH_2(CH_2)_3{\cdot}CHNH_2{\cdot}COOH$$

L-Arginine — Urea — L-Ornithine

b. Asparaginase + L-β-asparagine → L-aspartic acid + ammonia

$$CONH_2{-}CH_2{-}CHNH_2{-}COOH + H_2O \rightarrow COOH{-}CH_2{-}CHNH_2{-}COOH + NH_3$$

L-β-Asparagine — L-Aspartic acid

c. Aspartase + L-aspartic acid ⇌ fumaric acid + ammonia

$$COOH{-}CH_2{-}CHNH_2{-}COOH \rightleftharpoons HC{\cdot}COOH{=}HOOC{\cdot}CH + NH_3$$

L-Aspartic acid — Fumaric acid

TABLE 11 (Continued)

d. Transaminase + glutamic acid → amino group transferred to some reactive carbohydrate residue

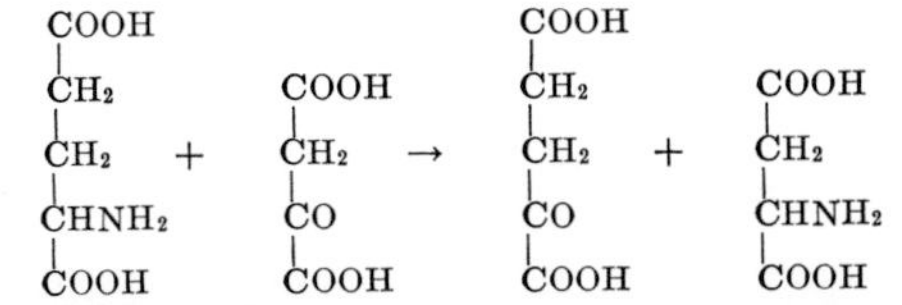

COOH		COOH	
CH₂	COOH	CH₂	COOH
CH₂ +	CH₂ →	CH₂ +	CH₂
CHNH₂	CO	CO	CHNH₂
COOH	COOH	COOH	COOH
L-Glutamic acid	Oxalacetic acid	α-Ketoglutaric acid	L-Aspartic acid

e. Urease + urea → ammonia + carbon dioxide

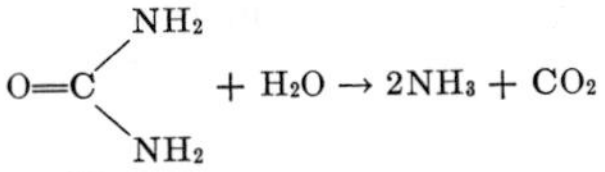

$$O{=}C\underset{NH_2}{\overset{NH_2}{<}} + H_2O \rightarrow 2NH_3 + CO_2$$

Urea

2. Nuclein deaminases

The nuclein deaminases produce an oxidative deamination of purines and pyrimidines, either free or combined

a. Adenase + adenine → hypoxanthine + ammonia

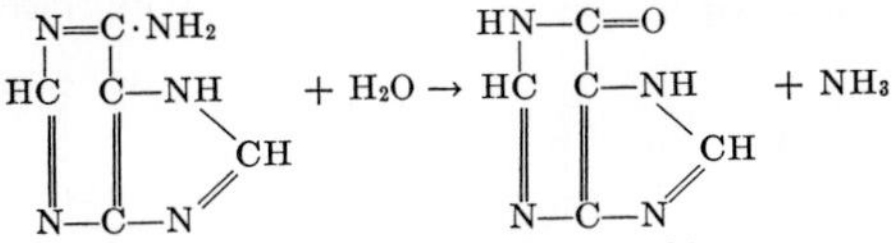

Adenine + H₂O → Hypoxanthine + NH₃

b. Guanase + guanine → xanthine + ammonia

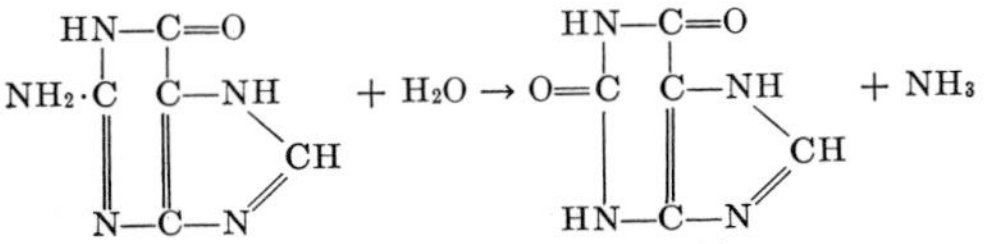

Guanine + H₂O → Xanthine + NH₃

c. Adenosine deaminase + adenosine → hypoxanthosine + ammonia

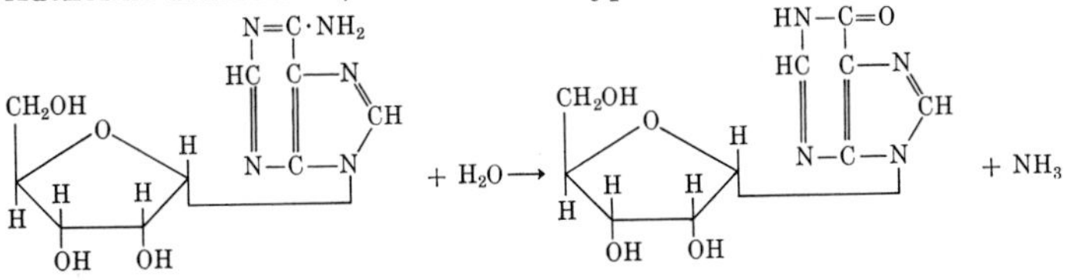

Adenine riboside (adenosine) + H₂O → Hypoxanthine riboside (hypoxanthosine) + NH₃

TABLE 11 (Continued)

d. Guanosine deaminase + guanosine → xanthosine + ammonia

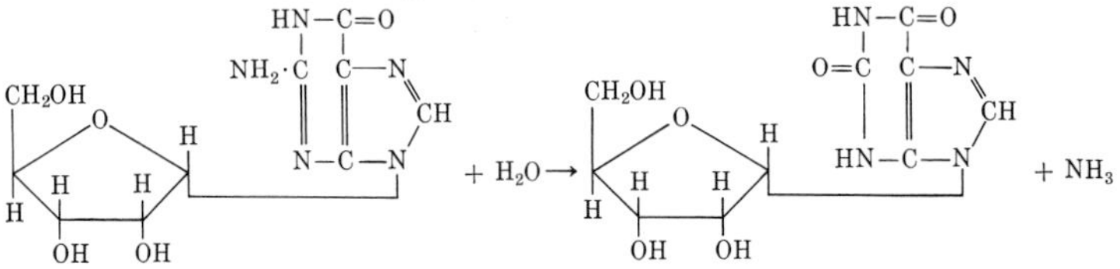

Guanine riboside
(guanosine)

Xanthine riboside
(xanthosine)

e. Cytidine deaminase + cytidine → uridine + ammonia

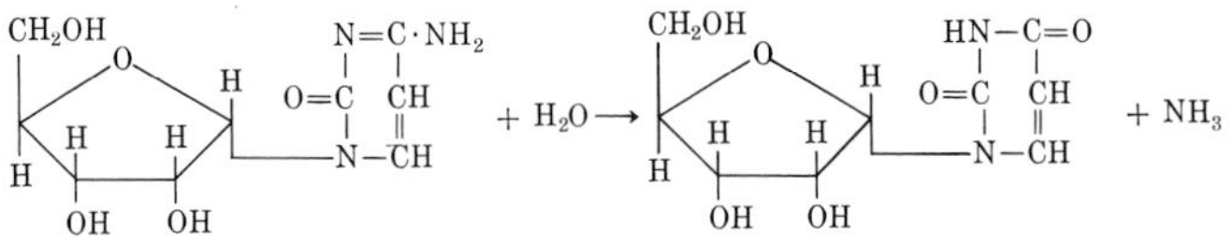

Cytosine riboside
(cytidine)

Uracil riboside
(uridine)

f. Adenylic acid + adenylic acid → hypoxanthylic acid + ammonia
deaminase

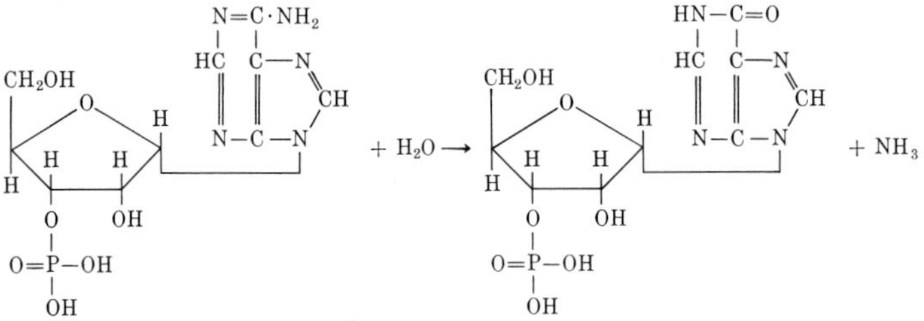

Adenylic acid

Hypoxanthylic acid

g. Guanylic acid + guanylic acid → xanthylic acid + ammonia
deaminase

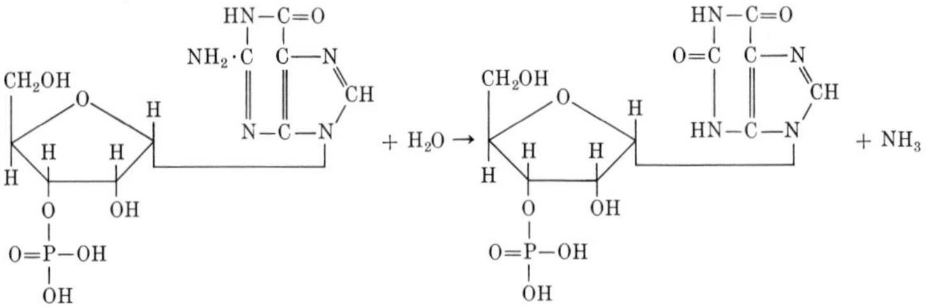

Guanylic acid

Xanthylic acid

3. Proteinases
The proteinases attack the true proteins.

a. Pepsin + native proteins → proteoses + peptones

TABLE 11 (Continued)

b. Rennin + casein → paracasein

c. Trypsin + native proteins, proteoses, → amino acids and
peptones, and peptides   polypeptides

d. Erepsin + proteoses, peptones, and polypeptides → amino acids

e. Papain + native proteins → polypeptides and dipeptides

f. Bromelin + native proteins → polypeptides and dipeptides

g. Protaminase + protamines with terminal → arginine + residue
arginine group

4. Peptidases
The peptidases hydrolyze polypeptides and dipeptides to the stage of amino acids.
They are also capable of attacking the peptide linkages of proteins provided that
certain structural requirements are satisfied.

a. Carboxypeptidase attacks polypeptides having free carboxyl groups. The carboxyl group must be in the neighborhood of the hydrolyzable bond. In the
example,

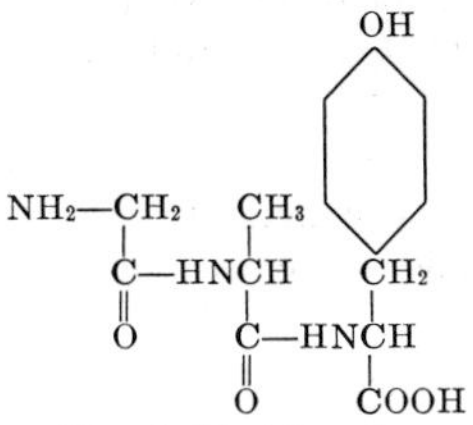

$$NH_2-CH_2 \quad CH_3$$

Glycyl-alanyl-tyrosine

the amino acid tyrosine is liberated on hydrolysis.

b. Leucine aminopeptidase hydrolyzes the amino acid leucine from the end of a
peptide chain if it has a free amino group. In the example,

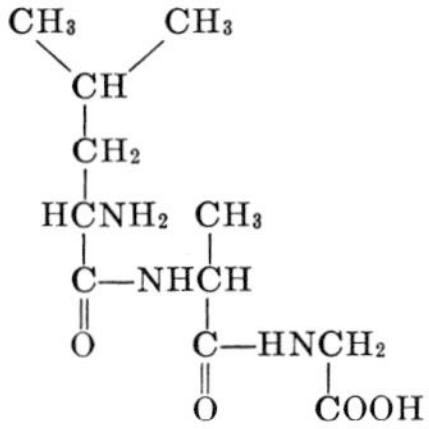

Leucyl-alanyl-glycine

the amino acid leucine is liberated on hydrolysis.

c. Glycylglycine dipeptidase + glycylglycine + H_2O → 2 glycine

$$CH_2NH_2 \cdot CONH \cdot CH_2 \cdot COOH + H_2O \rightarrow 2CH_2NH_2 \cdot COOH$$
Glycylglycine   Glycine

TABLE 11 (Continued)

d. Glycyl-L-leucine dipeptidase + glycyl-L-leucine + H_2O → glycine + L-leucine

$$\underset{\text{Glycyl-L-leucine}}{\overset{\displaystyle \overset{\text{CH}_3 \quad \text{CH}_3}{\underset{\underset{\text{H}_2\text{NCH}_2\cdot\text{CONH}\cdot\text{CH}\cdot\text{COOH}}{|}}{\overset{|}{\underset{\text{CH}_2}{\text{CH}}}}}{}} + H_2O \rightarrow \underset{\text{Glycine}}{CH_2NH_2\cdot COOH} + \underset{\text{L-Leucine}}{\overset{\text{CH}_3\quad\text{CH}_3}{\underset{\underset{\underset{\text{COOH}}{|}}{\overset{|}{\underset{\text{CHNH}_2}{\overset{|}{\text{CH}_2}}}}}{\text{CH}}}}$$

e. Prolidase + glycyl-L-proline + H_2O → glycine + L-proline

$$\underset{\text{Glycyl-L-proline}}{H_2N-CH_2-CO-N\overset{\text{CH}_2-\text{CH}_2}{\underset{\underset{\text{HOOC}}{\diagup}}{\diagdown\;\diagup}}_{\text{CH}-\text{CH}_2}} + H_2O \rightarrow \underset{\text{Glycine}}{CH_2NH_2\cdot COOH} + \underset{\text{L-Proline}}{\overset{\text{CH}_2-\text{CH}_2}{\underset{\text{CH}_2-\text{CH}}{|\qquad|}}\diagdown^{\text{NH}}_{\text{COOH}}}$$

F. Enzymes involved in oxidation-reduction reactions

1. Dehydrogenases

The dehydrogenases produce oxidations by the transfer of hydrogen atoms from the substrate to some acceptor. They cannot transfer the hydrogen directly to molecular oxygen. This type of oxidation is called dehydrogenation.

Two compounds known as coenzyme I and coenzyme II are found associated with the dehydrogenases. Some dehydrogenases are associated with one coenzyme and some with the other. These compounds are the hydrogen acceptors mentioned above.

Dehydrogenases linked with coenzyme I

a. Alcohol   + alcohols + coenzyme I ⇌ aldehydes + coenzyme I·H
    dehydrogenase

$$\underset{\text{Alcohol}}{R\cdot CH_2OH} + \text{coenzyme I} \rightleftarrows \underset{\text{Aldehyde}}{R\cdot CHO} + \text{coenzyme I}\cdot H + H^+$$

---

b. Aldehyde   + aldehydes + coenzyme I + H_2O → correspond- + coenzyme
    dehydrogenase   ing acid   I·H

$$\underset{\text{Acetaldehyde}}{CH_3\cdot CHO} + H_2O \rightarrow \underset{\substack{\text{Acetaldehyde}\\\text{hydrate}}}{CH_3\cdot C\overset{\text{H}}{\underset{\text{OH}}{\diagup\atop\diagdown}}OH}$$

$$\underset{}{CH_3\cdot C\overset{\text{H}}{\underset{\text{OH}}{\diagup\atop\diagdown}}OH} + \text{coenzyme I} \rightarrow \underset{\text{Acetic acid}}{CH_3\cdot COOH} + \text{coenzyme I}\cdot H + H^+$$

---

c. β-Hydroxybutyric + L-β-hydroxy- + coenzyme I ⇌ acetoacetic + coenzyme
    dehydrogenase   butyric acid   acid   I·H

$$\underset{\substack{\text{L-}\beta\text{-Hydroxy-}\\\text{butyric acid}}}{\overset{\text{CH}_3}{\underset{\underset{\underset{\text{COOH}}{|}}{\overset{|}{\underset{\text{CH}_2}{\overset{|}{\text{CHOH}}}}}}{|}}} + \text{coenzyme I} \rightleftarrows \underset{\substack{\text{Acetoacetic}\\\text{acid}}}{\overset{\text{CH}_3}{\underset{\underset{\underset{\text{COOH}}{|}}{\overset{|}{\underset{\text{CH}_2}{\overset{|}{\text{C=O}}}}}}{|}}} + \text{coenzyme I}\cdot H + H^+$$

TABLE 11 (Continued)

d. Glucose   + D-glucose + coenzyme I ⇌ D-gluconic acid + coenzyme I·H
dehydrogenase

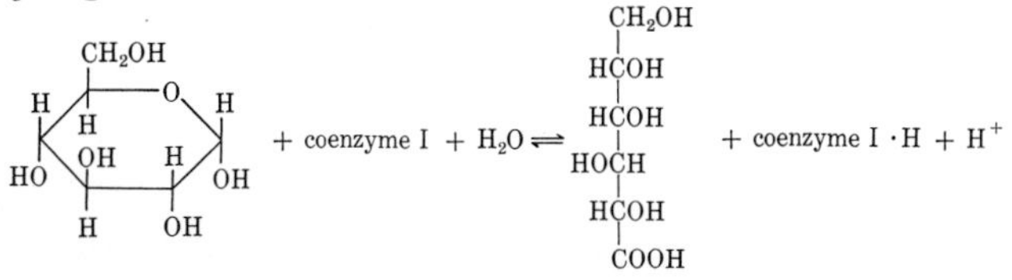

$$CH_2OH$$
$$HCOH$$
$$HCOH$$
+ coenzyme I + H_2O ⇌ $HOCH$ + coenzyme I·H + H^+
$$HCOH$$
$$COOH$$

α-D-Glucose   D-Gluconic acid
(α-D-glucopyranose)

e. Malic   + L(−) malic + coenzyme I ⇌ oxalacetic + coenzyme I·H
dehydrogenase   acid   acid

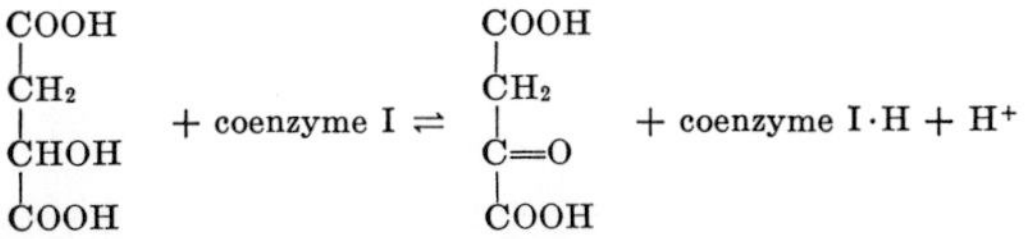

$$COOH$$
$$CH_2$$
$$CHOH$$ + coenzyme I ⇌ $C=O$ + coenzyme I·H + H^+
$$COOH$$

L(−) Malic   Oxalacetic
acid   acid

f. Lactic   + lactic acid + coenzyme I ⇌ pyruvic acid + coenzyme I·H
dehydrogenase

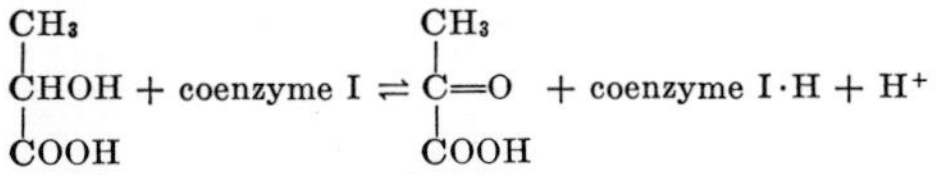

$$CH_3$$
$$CHOH$$ + coenzyme I ⇌ $C=O$ + coenzyme I·H + H^+
$$COOH$$

Lactic   Pyruvic
acid   acid

Scheme for in vitro reduction of methylene blue:
(1) Lactic acid + 2 coenzyme I → pyruvic acid + 2 coenzyme I·H
(2) 2 Coenzyme I·H + diaphorase → 2 coenzyme I + diaphorase·2H
(3) Diaphorase·2H + methylene blue → diaphorase + methylene blue·2H
(4) Methylene blue·2H + O_2 → methylene blue + H_2O_2

g. α-Glycerophos-   + L-α-glycero- + coenzyme I ⇌ dihydroxy + coenzyme I·H
phoric   phosphoric   acetone
dehydrogenase   acid   phosphate

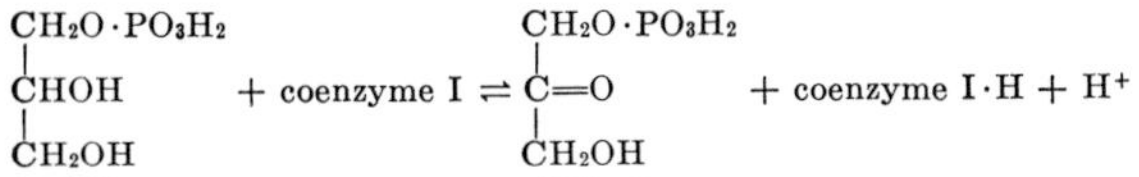

$$CH_2O·PO_3H_2$$
$$CHOH$$ + coenzyme I ⇌ $C=O$ + coenzyme I·H + H^+
$$CH_2OH$$

L-α-Glycero-   Dihydroxy
phosphoric   acetone
acid   phosphate

h. Triosephosphate + 3-glyceraldehyde + H_3PO_4 + coenzyme I ⇌
dehydrogenase   phosphate

                              1,3-diphospho- + coenzyme I·H
                              glyceric acid

$$CH_2O·PO_3H_2$$
$$CHOH$$ + H_3PO_4 + coenzyme I ⇌ $CHOH$ + coenzyme I·H + H^+
$$CHO$$ $CO·PO_3H_2$
                              ‖
                              O

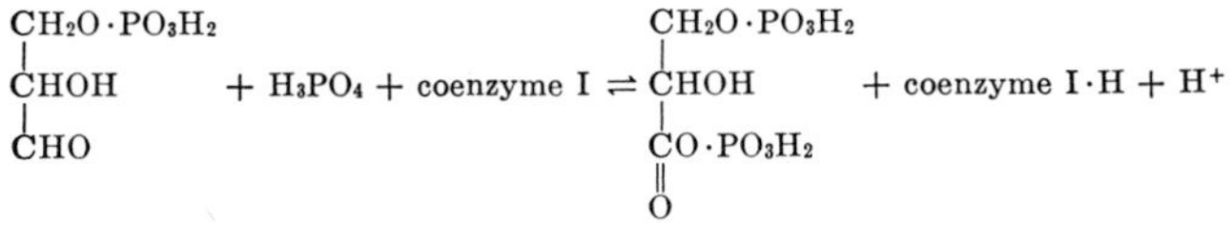

3-Glyceraldehyde   1,3-Diphospho-
phosphate   glyceric acid

TABLE 11 (Continued)

Dehydrogenases linked with coenzyme II

a. Robison ester + hexose-6-phosphate + coenzyme II →
  dehydrogenase

          D-phosphohexonic acid + coenzyme II·H + H⁺

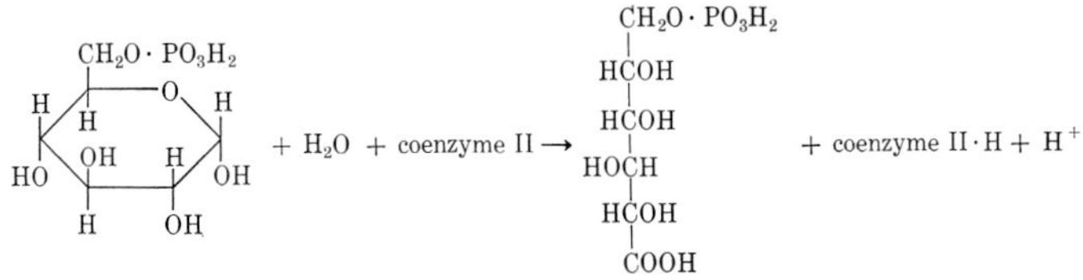

$$\text{CH}_2\text{O}\cdot\text{PO}_3\text{H}_2 \quad + \text{H}_2\text{O} + \text{coenzyme II} \rightarrow \begin{array}{l} \text{CH}_2\text{O}\cdot\text{PO}_3\text{H}_2 \\ \text{HCOH} \\ \text{HCOH} \\ \text{HOCH} \\ \text{HCOH} \\ \text{COOH} \end{array} \quad + \text{coenzyme II}\cdot\text{H} + \text{H}^+$$

  α-D-Glucose-6-phosphate   D-Phosphogluconic acid

---

b. Glutamic + L-glutamic + coenzyme ⇌ α-ketoglu- + coenzyme
  dehydrogenase acid   II   taric acid II·H + H⁺

$$\begin{array}{l} \text{COOH} \\ \text{CH}_2 \\ \text{CH}_2 \\ \text{CHNH}_2 \\ \text{COOH} \end{array} + \text{H}_2\text{O} + \text{coenzyme II} \rightleftarrows \begin{array}{l} \text{COOH} \\ \text{CH}_2 \\ \text{CH}_2 \\ \text{C=O} \\ \text{COOH} \end{array} + \text{NH}_3 + \text{coenzyme II}\cdot\text{H} + \text{H}^+$$

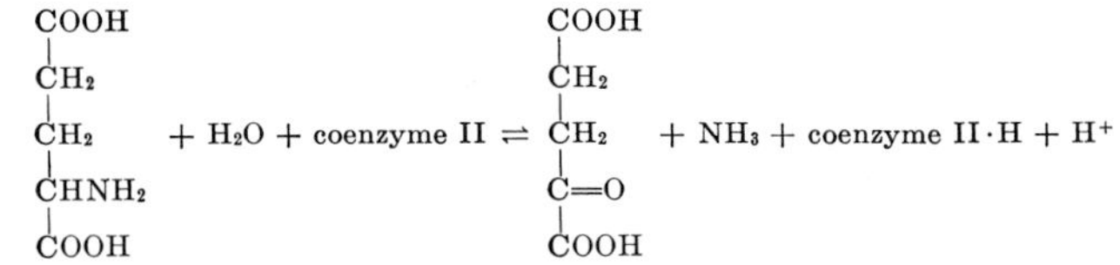

  L-Glutamic   α-Keto-
   acid   glutaric
         acid

---

2. Flavoproteins

The flavoproteins are enzymes which catalyze the transfer of hydrogen atoms from the coenzymes to other acceptors, usually the cytochromes. They are conjugated proteins, the prosthetic groups being nucleotides. Their function may be expressed in the following manner:

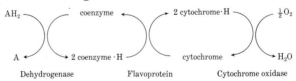

  Dehydrogenase   Flavoprotein   Cytochrome oxidase

---

a. The old yellow enzyme   + O₂ + coenzyme II·H → coenzyme
  (Riboflavinphosphate + protein)   II + H₂O

Example:
1. Hexosemonophosphate + coenzyme II → phosphohexonic acid + coenzyme II·H
2. Old yellow enzyme + coenzyme II·H → old yellow enzyme·H + coenzyme II
3. Old yellow enzyme·H + O₂ → old yellow enzyme + H₂O₂

---

b. Cytochrome c reductase + cytochrome c + coenzyme II·H →
                cytochrome c·H + coenzyme II

Example:
1. Robison ester + glucose-6- + coenzyme II → D-phospho- + coenzyme II·H
  dehydrogenase phosphate   gluconic acid
2. Cytochrome c + cytochrome c + coenzyme II·H → cytochrome c·H + coenzyme II
  reductase

TABLE 11 (Continued)

3. Oxidases

The oxidases include those enzymes which catalyze the transfer of hydrogen directly to molecular oxygen, resulting in the formation of water. They are metalloproteins being inhibited by hydrogen sulfide and potassium cyanide. Some oxidases contain copper; others contain iron. They are active only under aerobic conditions.

---

a. Cytochrome oxidase + cytochrome c·H + O_2 → cytochrome c + H_2O

---

b. Tyrosinase + tyrosine + O_2 → melanin (dark pigment)

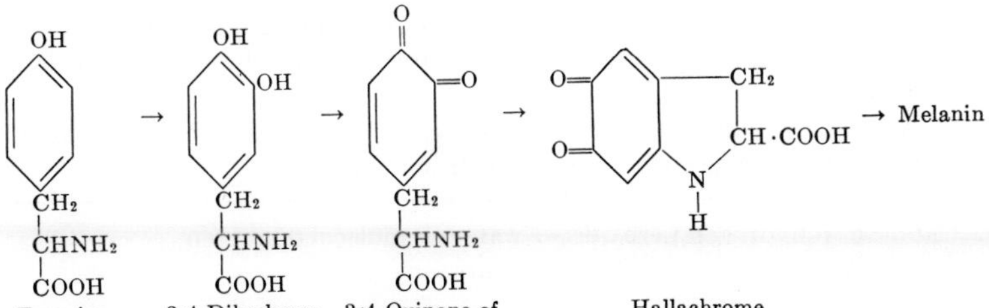

Tyrosine 3:4-Dihydroxy phenylalanine 3:4-Quinone of phenylalanine Hallachrome → Melanin

The enzyme also oxidizes any monohydric phenol to a dihydric phenol in the ortho position, and the o-dihydric phenol to o-quinone. Tyrosine is said to function as follows: cupric copper is reduced to cuprous copper, then reoxidized by molecular oxygen:

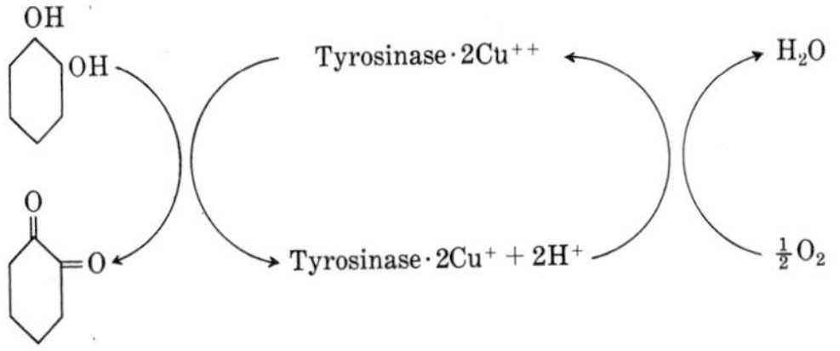

Tyrosinase·2Cu^{++} ← → H_2O

Tyrosinase·2Cu$^+$ + 2H$^+$ ← → $\frac{1}{2}O_2$

---

c. Laccase + di- or polyhydric phenols with hydroxyl groups in o- or p- positions → corresponding quinones

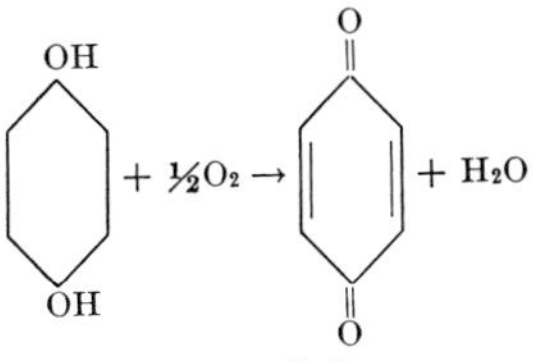

+ $\frac{1}{2}O_2$ → + H_2O

p-Dihydroxy benzene Quinone

TABLE 11 (Continued)

d. Ascorbic acid oxidase + L-ascorbic acid $\rightleftharpoons$ dehydroascorbic acid

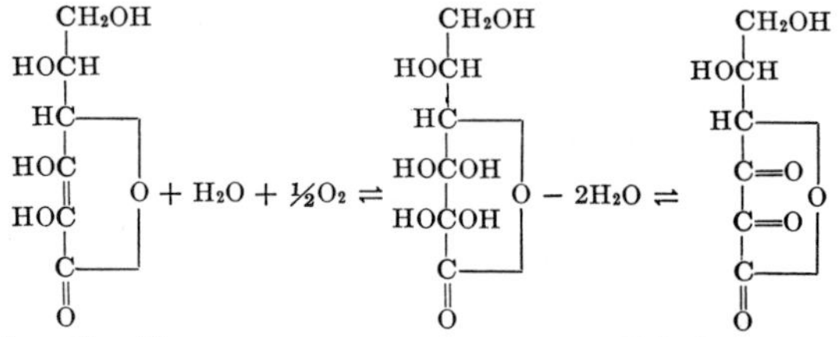

Ascorbic acid
(reduced)

Dehydroascorbic acid
(oxidized)

Hydrogen peroxide is produced in the autooxidation of flavoproteins and other compounds. Obligately aerobic and facultative bacteria contain mechanisms for metabolizing peroxides; anaerobic organisms do not.

Catalase is the name given to the enzyme that destroys peroxides; peroxidases carry out oxidations with various substrates

---

e. Catalase + hydrogen peroxide → water + molecular oxygen

$$2H_2O_2 \rightarrow 2H_2O + O_2$$

This is referred to as the catalatic reaction.

---

f. Peroxidase + hydrogen peroxide + AH_2 → water + A

This is referred to as the peroxidatic reaction. Hydrogen peroxide is not decomposed by peroxidase unless a suitable acceptor is present to accept the oxygen:

$$H_2O_2 + \quad AH_2 \quad \rightarrow 2H_2O + \quad A$$

            Oxidizable   Oxidized
            substance   substance

Miscellaneous oxidases

The enzymes which follow have not been studied in pure preparations. For this reason they are classified separately.

a. Succinic dehydrogenase

This enzyme converts succinic acid to fumaric acid provided an acceptor of hydrogen is present. Under aerobic conditions the hydrogen goes to oxygen by means of the cytochrome–cytochrome oxidase system.

Succinic dehydrogenase + succinic acid $\rightleftharpoons$ fumaric acid + $2H^+$

$$COOH \cdot CH_2 \cdot CH_2 \cdot COOH \rightleftharpoons COOH \cdot CH=CH \cdot COOH + 2H^+$$

2 Cytochrome c + $2H^+$ → 2 cytochrome c·H
2 Cytochrome c·H + $\frac{1}{2}O_2$ → 2 cytochrome c + H_2O

---

b. Monamine (tyramine) oxidase

This enzyme converts primary amines into the corresponding aldehydes, ammonia, and hydrogen peroxide, provided free oxygen is present:

$$R \cdot CH_2NH_2 + H_2O + O_2 \rightarrow R \cdot CHO + H_2O_2 + NH_3$$

      Amine   Aldehyde

---

c. Luciferase + luciferin (reduced) + oxygen → luciferin (oxidized) + light

1. Luciferin + 2H (from some donator) → luciferin·2H
2. Luciferin·2H + luciferase → luciferin + luciferase·2H
3. Luciferase·2H + O_2 → luciferase + H_2O_2 + light

TABLE 11 (Continued)

G. Desmolases
   The desmolases break or form carbon chains

Carboligase links carbon atoms together
1. Carboligase + benzaldehyde + acetaldehyde → acetylphenylcarbinol

$$C_6H_5 \cdot CHO + CH_3 \cdot CHO → C_6H_5 \cdot CHOH \cdot CO \cdot CH_3$$
    Benzaldehyde   Acetaldehyde   Acetylphenylcarbinol

---

2. Tryptophanase + tryptophan + H_2O → indole + pyruvic acid + ammonia

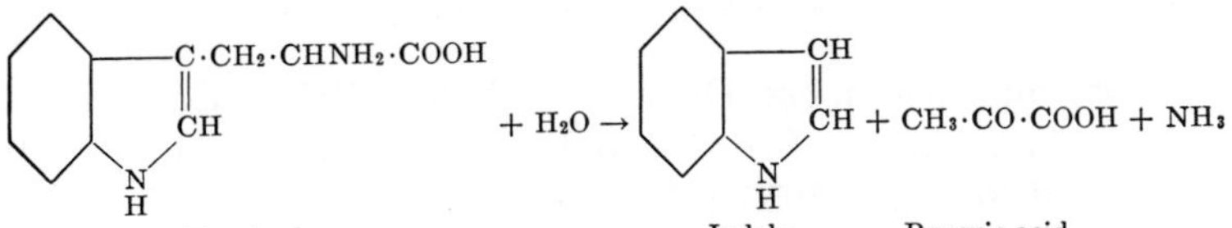

   L-Tryptophan   Indole   Pyruvic acid

---

3. Amines are formed by the action of putrefactive bacteria on proteins. The enzymes involved are amino acid decarboxylases.
   Histidine decarboxylase + histidine → histamine + carbon dioxide

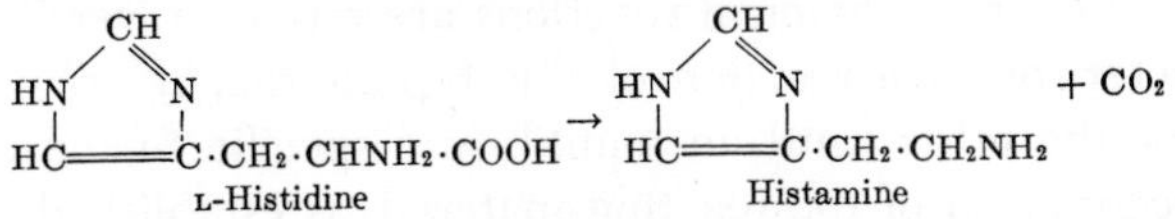

   L-Histidine   Histamine

   Pyridoxal-5-phosphate is the coenzyme involved in the above reaction.

---

4. Aldolase + fructofuranose- ⇌ dihydroxyacetone + 3-glyceraldehyde
   1,6-diphosphate   phosphate   phosphate

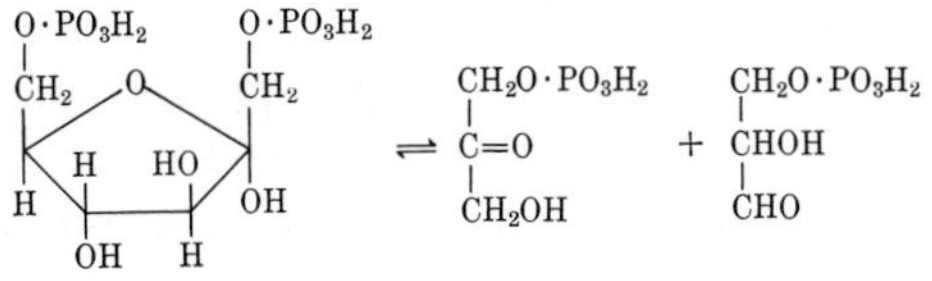

   Fructofuranose-   Dihydroxy acetone   3-Glyceraldehyde
   1,6-diphosphate   phosphate   phosphate

---

5. Pyruvic   + cocarboxylase + pyruvic → acetaldehyde + carbon dioxide
   carboxylase   acid

$$CH_3 \cdot CO \cdot COOH → CH_3 \cdot CHO + CO_2$$
    Pyruvic acid   Acetaldehyde

H. Hydrases
   The hydrases add water to organic compounds without causing a hydrolysis.

---

1. Glyoxalase + coglyoxalase (glutathione) + methyl glyoxal → lactic acid

$$CH_3 \cdot CO \cdot CHO + R \cdot SH → CH_3 \cdot CO \cdot CHOHS \cdot R$$
   Methyl glyoxal

$$CH_3 \cdot CO \cdot CHOHS \cdot R + H_2O → CH_3 \cdot CHOH \cdot COOH + R \cdot SH$$
                          Lactic acid

TABLE 11 (Continued)

---

2. Fumarase + fumaric acid → L-malic acid

$$COOH \cdot CH{=}CH \cdot COOH + H_2O \rightarrow COOH \cdot CHOH \cdot CH_2 \cdot COOH$$

Fumaric acid   L-Malic acid

---

3. Carbonic anhydrase + CO_2 + H_2O ⇌ H_2CO_3

Carbon dioxide is generally believed to be held in the blood as sodium bicarbonate. In the lungs the carbon dioxide is released in the following manner:

$$Protein \cdot COOH + NaHCO_3 \rightleftharpoons protein \cdot COONa + H_2CO_3$$
$$H_2CO_3 \rightleftharpoons H_2O + CO_2$$

For more information see Dixon and Webb (1958); Gaebler (1956); Laidler (1954); Mahler, Baum, and Hübscher (1956); Mehler (1957); Neilands and Stumpf (1958); Pigman (1957); Sierra (1957); Sumner and Somers (1953).

SYNTHETIC ACTIVITIES OF ENZYMES

A great number of chemical reactions are termed reversible reactions. The characteristic of a reaction of this type is that it progresses in one direction or the other until an equilibrium specific to the reaction and to the concentration of the reacting materials is established. Any change in the concentration of the reacting components is immediately followed by a change to a new equilibrium. Many enzymatic reactions are known to be of this type.

Synthesis of Di-, Tri-, and Polysaccharides. Doudoroff et al. (1943, 1944, 1945) found that a dry preparation of a species of *Pseudomonas* contained a phosphorylase capable of phosphorolyzing sucrose to glucose-1-phosphate and fructose. With glucose-1-phosphate and fructose as substrate, the formation of sucrose was demonstrated by the reversal of the reaction:

Adenosine triphosphate + glucose
$$\downarrow$$
Adenosine diphosphate + glucose-6-phosphate
$$\updownarrow$$
Glucose-1-phosphate + fructose ⇌ sucrose + H_3PO_4

In a later report Doudoroff et al. (1949) demonstrated the presence of sucrose phosphorylase, phosphoglucomutase, and phosphohexoisomerase in dry-cell preparations of *P. putrefaciens*.

Polysaccharides containing D-mannose are widely distributed in nature, being found in ivory nuts, orchid tubers, certain algae, yeasts, molds, and some woods. Murphy, Bishop, and Adams (1956) isolated a mannan from a culture of *Bacillus polymyxa* grown in a synthetic medium containing sucrose.

Hestrin and Schramm (1954) reported the synthesis of cellulose from glucose by *Acetobacter xylinum*. Later Hestrin et al. (1956) found that a levansucrase from a species of *Aerobacter* converted sucrose to a levan.

For more information see Bailey et al. (1955); Barker and Bourne (1952); Feingold, Avigad, and Hestrin (1956).

Synthesis of Amino Acids, Peptides, and Proteins. Proteolytic enzymes capable of synthesizing amino acids, peptides, and proteins have been isolated from bacteria.

Rafelson (1955) demonstrated the synthesis of tryptophan by *Aerobacter aerogenes* in the presence of glucose or acetate containing labeled C^{14} and unlabeled glucose as the source of carbon. Tryptophan was isolated from the bacterial proteins and found to contain labeled carbon in the indole ring. In another communication Rafelson, Ehrensvärd, and Reio (1955) cultivated the above organism on glucose containing C^{14} as the only source of carbon. They demonstrated the synthesis of tyrosine, phenylalanine, and tryptophan containing the labeled C^{14} in the benzene rings.

Cameron and Meyer (1955) found that resting cells of *Brucella* oxidatively metabolized the decomposition products of urea. The amino acids synthesized from the urea were chiefly alanine and glutamic acid.

Thorne et al. (1954) demonstrated the production of a glutamyl polypeptide by *Bacillus subtilis* grown on a mineral medium containing L-glutamic acid. Culture filtrates contained an enzyme system capable of degrading the peptide to yield glutamic acid and other products.

For more information see Abelson (1954); Britten, Roberts, and French (1955); Butler, Crathorn, and Hunter (1958); Crathorn and Hunter (1958); Fowler and Werkman (1955); Ory and Lyman (1955).

LYSOZYME

Lysozyme is an enzyme present in nasal mucus and capable of lysing many bacteria. The enzyme is present in egg white, from which it may be easily isolated and crystallized. It is believed to be one of nature's defensive mechanisms.

Welshimer and Robinow (1949) first exposed a lysozyme-sensitive strain of *Bacillus megaterium* to 2 per cent formalin. Killed cells exposed to lysozyme for 5 min., then fixed in Bouin's fluid and stained with Victoria blue 4R, showed a marked increase in the staining intensity of the cytoplasm (Fig. 142). After an exposure of 60 min. to lysozyme, the cells stained delicately and could be observed only with the aid of a suitable contrasting filter. The number of recognizable bacilli was extremely small, and the cells possessed a fragile appearance.

Grula and Hartsell (1954a) treated cells of *Micrococcus lysodeikticus* with lysozyme and reported that lysis was due to enzymatic destruction of the cell wall (Fig. 143). The end results depended upon the ionic

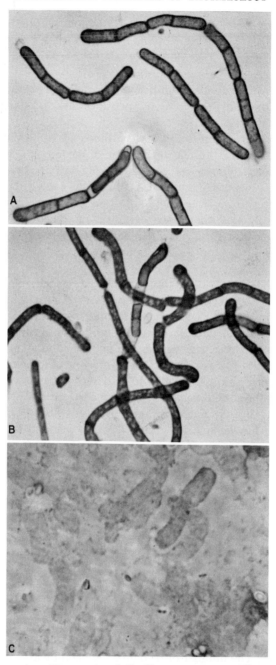

Fig. 142. Lysozyme-sensitive strain of *Bacillus megaterium*. All smears were fixed in Bouin's fluid and stained with Victoria blue 4R. *A*, nonlysozyme treated cells. At lower center of illustration note cells in which protoplasm has shrunk from the cell wall. *B*, cells exposed to lysozyme for 5 min. At upper center of illustration note several cells which have remained resistant to the enzyme. *C*, cells exposed to lysozyme for 60 min. The cells are almost completely lysed by the enzyme. (*After Welshimer and Robinow*.)

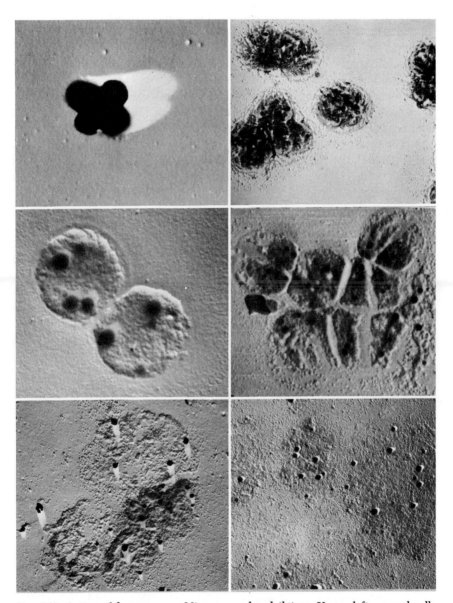

FIG. 143. Action of lysozyme on *Micrococcus lysodeikticus*. Upper left, normal cells after 1 hr. in double distilled water. Upper right, removal of cell wall immediately after addition of lysozyme. Cells appear larger owing to swelling and flattening. Center left, partially solubilized and disrupted protoplasts after cell wall has been removed by lysozyme. Granules exposed from this point on. Center right, protoplasts undergoing plasmoptysis. Lower, end points of lysis in double distilled water. (*Courtesy of Grula & Hartsell.*)

strength of the suspending medium. Following the action of lysozyme, disruption of the protoplast occurred immediately in distilled water, whereas no disruption but rather the formation of ghosts was observed in a medium having an osmotic pressure equal to or similar to an 0.85 per cent sodium chloride solution.

Dense and highly opaque intracellular granules were not destroyed by lysozyme, although desoxyribonucleic acid was liberated from the cells and contributed to the high viscosity of the lysed suspension.

For more information see Becker and Hartsell (1954); Grula and Hartsell (1954b); Peterson and Hartsell (1955); Salton (1957); Skarnes and Watson (1955); Warren, Gray, and Bartell (1955); and Welshimer (1953).

CONSTITUTIVE AND ADAPTIVE ENZYMES

Bacteria elaborate two classes of enzymes, namely, constitutive and adaptive enzymes.

Constitutive Enzymes. Most bacterial enzymes are elaborated irrespective of the presence or absence of the homologous substrates. These are called constitutive enzymes.

Constitutive enzymes have been found to undergo wide fluctuations in the presence and absence of their substrates. Regardless of this fact, constitutive enzymes are believed to be always formed irrespective of the composition of the substrate.

Adaptive Enzymes. Adaptive enzymes are elaborated only as needed. If an organism is grown in a medium containing a substrate not ordinarily attacked, it sometimes happens that the repeated transfer of the organism to fresh medium finally results in the ultilization of the substrate.

The adaptive process involves the formation of a nitrogen compound. A connection has been shown to exist between the adaptive process and the nitrogen metabolism of the cell. Exogenous nitrogen markedly stimulates adaptation both in rate of appearance and in the final amount of enzyme activity. This stimulation is absent if the cells are unable to assimilate the added nitrogen.

It has been shown that a competitive interaction exists between the enzymatic systems of a cell, and that exogenous nitrogen can either abolish this interaction or modify its intensity. This would suggest that the nitrogenous compound formed during enzymatic adaptation is of a protein nature. It further suggests that a new adaptive enzyme is formed at the expense of a previously formed enzyme when the substrate responsible for the first adaptation is replaced by a second substrate.

The activity of adaptive enzymes disappears when the bacteria are cultivated once or twice in nutrient media without the homologous substrate. This is true only when enzymatic adaptation is rapid. If a prolonged period of adaptation is necessary to establish the presence of a new enzyme, a proportionately longer period is required for the loss of the enzyme when the cells are cultivated in the absence of the specific substrate.

For more information see Karström (1938), Pinsky and Stokes (1952).

Lag Period in Adaptive Enzyme Formation. In enzymatic adaptation, a given time interval is necessary for the synthesis of enzyme protein. The lag phase probably represents the period required for the synthesis of the enzyme precursor.

If a small number of cells adapted to a certain substrate is added to unadapted cells in contact with the same substrate, the lag period is greatly reduced. Rotman and Spiegelman (1953) suggested the presence of an unknown substance which was present in a nonfunctional state in nonadapted cells but became converted into positive elements necessary for the elaboration of the adaptive enzyme system.

For more information see Bernheim (1954a, b), Cohen and Barner (1955), De Turk (1955), Inaba et al. (1955), and Magasanik (1953).

Effect of Temperature. It has been shown that ribonucleic acid (RNA) is necessary for adaptive enzyme formation. Bacteria grown at temperatures higher than their normal fail to produce adaptive enzymes. One of the first effects of increased temperatures on bacterial cells is some type of inactivation of RNA. Also, bacteria grown at high temperatures contain a lower content of RNA.

Bernheim (1955) reported that heat apparently damaged at least two general mechanisms involved in enzyme formation: damage to the organizer, probably RNA; and damage to protein synthesis. Heating for 15 min. caused a prolonged delay in the formation of the adaptive enzyme for the oxidation of benzoic acid. This delay was not increased by heating beyond 15 min. or by the presence of benzoic acid during the heating period. Presumably RNA was damaged during the initial heating period, and no further change was manifested by prolonging the heat. However, the rate of enzyme formation, once started, was affected by the heating time.

Enzymatic Deadaptation. The formation of a specific enzyme in response to an inducing substance is called enzymatic adaptation. The reverse process or the loss of an enzyme after removal of the inducing substance has been called enzymatic deadaptation.

Rickenberg, Yanofsky, and Bonner (1953) showed that the enzyme β-galactosidase, once formed by adaptation to lactose, was not subject to destruction by the cell as is generally believed. Enzymatic deadaptation, at least in the case of this enzyme, seemed to consist of a diluting out of preformed enzyme. Furthermore, cell protein was not available for the formation of β-galactosidase and did not serve as a source of free amino acids for β-galactosidase synthesis.

SECRETION OF ENZYMES

Enzymes of bacteria may be divided into two groups, depending upon whether they are secreted into the surrounding culture medium or remain confined within the cell. The enzymes that belong to the first group are known as extracellular enzymes or exoenzymes; those classified in the second group are called intracellular enzymes or endoenzymes.

Extracellular Enzymes. It has been recognized from the time of Pasteur that the changes produced by organisms acting on carbohydrates (fermentation) and on proteins (protein hydrolysis and putrefaction) are brought about by the enzymes they elaborate. Enzymes are capable of producing their specific actions in the complete absence of the living cell. This may be shown in the case of the extracellular enzymes by centrifugating a liquid culture, passing the clear supernatant liquid through a bacteriological filter, and demonstrating enzyme activity by adding the filtrate to the appropriate substrate.

Extracellular enzymes may be demonstrated also by incorporating insoluble, indiffusible compounds into solid media. The presence of caseolytic, hemolytic, amylolytic (diastatic), and lipolytic enzymes may be demonstrated by employing appropriate substrates.

Hydrolysis of Starch. Starch is a polymer of glucose found widely distributed throughout the plant kingdom. It occurs as a reserve material in roots, seeds, fruits, and pith of plants. During periods of active growth, especially in the spring, starch is converted into sugar and transported to where needed for conversion into cellulose or other products.

Starch occurs in the form of granules having characteristic striations. The size, shape, and striations of the granules are typical of many plants and usually enable the skilled microscopist to determine the source of the starch.

Starch granules are insoluble in cold water even after long immersion. After the outer membranes are broken, the contents swell in cold water. Hot water produces a swelling of the intact granules, causing the membranes to burst, after which the contents form viscous solutions or gels. On cooling such solutions, rigid gels may be formed by the crystallization of the dissolved or dispersed starch contents as networks occluding much liquid.

When starch is heated with dilute mineral acids, it is hydrolyzed to dextrins, maltose, and D-glucose. These products are all soluble in water. Concentrated mineral acids hydrolyze the starch molecule completely to D-glucose. Hydrolysis of starch is also effected by the enzymes α- and β-amylases.

Starch can be separated into two fractions possessing different physical properties. These have been designated as amylose (β-amylose) and amylopectin (α-amylose). The amylose is soluble in water and is colored blue with iodine. The amylopectin is insoluble in water and gives a red color with iodine. The amylose is believed to consist of long, straight, unbranched chains of polymerized maltose; the amylopectin of branched chains of polymerized maltose.

Amylose has a lower molecular weight than amylopectin and is hydrolyzed to a much greater extent by β-amylase. The amylose and amylopectin fractions from different sources are heterogeneous both in regard to the size of the molecules and in the degree of branching.

Soluble Starch. Soluble starch consists of altering the molecule so that the product becomes soluble in hot water with the formation of a limpid solution. Soluble starches are produced by treating raw starch with 7.5 per cent hydrochloric acid for 7 days at room temperature. Soluble starch is more satisfactory than raw starch for use in culture media.

Structure of Starch. Starch has the empirical formula $(C_6H_{10}O_5)_x$. On hydrolysis with acid, it yields α-D-glucose, the commercial method for the preparation of the sugar. The starch molecule consists of a chain structure composed of α-D-glucose units joined mainly by glucosidic linkages through the first carbon atom and the fourth carbon atom of the next glucose unit through the sharing of an oxygen atom:

α-Linked glucose units in the amylose fraction of starch

The linkage between any pair of glucose units in starch is the same as in the disaccharide maltose.

The above structure best represents the amylose fraction of starch granules. The structure of the amylopectin is more complicated and may be derived from the above formula by the attachment of side chains through 1,6-glucosidic bonds:

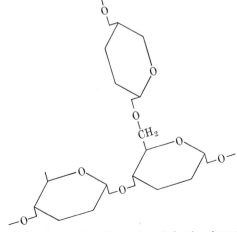

α-Linked glucose units in the amylopectin fraction of starch

α- and β-Amylases. Many organisms elaborate α- and β-amylases which are capable of attacking starch. α-Amylase is known as the liquefying enzyme, being capable of converting starch chiefly to dextrin with some maltose. β-Amylase is known as the saccharifying enzyme, being capable of hydrolyzing starch to maltose units (see page 278).

The amylases are extracellular enzymes secreted by bacteria to convert indiffusible starch into diffusible substances. The diffusible fractions are then capable of entering the cell, where they are utilized by the intracellular enzymes. The fractions are probably further hydrolyzed intracellularly to D-glucose by the enzyme maltase. The products of fermentation of starch are the result of the intracellular utilization of glucose.

Fig. 144. Hydrolysis of starch in the absence of bacteria. Culture filtrates added to tubes of starch broth and incubated at 37°C. for 24 hr. Left, *Bacillus subtilis* filtrate, no color with iodine, indicating hydrolysis. Right, *Escherichia coli* filtrate, blue color with iodine, indicating no hydrolysis.

The presence of amylases may be demonstrated by filtering a broth culture and mixing some of the filtrate with starch. The disappearance of the starch indicates the presence of amylases. This may be detected by adding a few drops of a dilute iodine solution (Fig. 144). A blue color indicates the presence of starch; a brown color indicates the complete hydrolysis of the starch to maltose.

Another method is to streak a loopful of the culture over the surface of a starch agar plate. After incubation, the plate is flooded with a dilute solution of iodine. The absence of a blue color at some distance from the bacterial growth indicates the extracellular hydrolysis of starch (Fig. 145).

For more information see Pigman (1957).

Liquefaction of Gelatin. Gelatin is a protein that possesses the property of forming a gel when dissolved in warm water. Since it is a protein, it can be attacked by many bacteria, resulting in the loss of its property to gel.

The hydrolysis of gelatin is an enzymatic reaction. The enzyme responsible for this change is known as a gelatinase. In the presence of carbohydrates which are rapidly fermented, gelatinase is either not produced at all or only in very minute amounts. In general, noncarbohydrate media should be used to demonstrate the ability of an organism to elaborate a gelatinase.

Bacteria may be divided into two groups on the basis of their action on gelatin. The test is of value in identifying and classifying bacteria.

Hydrolysis of Casein. Casein is the most important protein present in milk. Some organisms possess the power of hydrolyzing the protein to smaller molecular units. This results in the conversion of the insoluble casein into soluble products. This transformation is generally spoken of as peptonization. The enzyme responsible for the hydrolysis of casein is a proteinase and is known as casease.

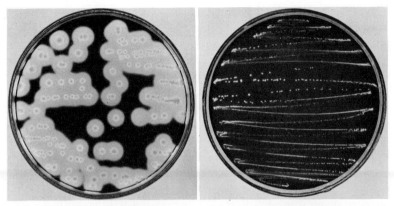

FIG. 145. Hydrolysis of starch in the presence of bacteria. Left, *Bacillus subtilis,* no color with iodine surrounding the colonies, indicating hydrolysis of starch. Right, *Escherichia coli,* blue color with iodine, indicating absence of starch hydrolysis.

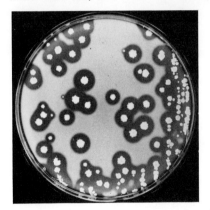 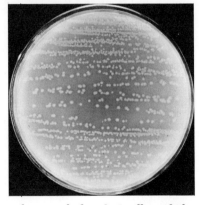

FIG. 146. Hydrolysis of casein. Left, milk agar plate streaked with *Bacillus subtilis.* Clear zones appear around the colonies, indicating hydrolysis of the casein. Right, same medium streaked with *Escherichia coli.* The casein is not hydrolyzed.

The presence of casease may be demonstrated as follows: Agar is mixed with sufficient milk to give it an opalescent appearance. The organism to be tested is then streaked over the surface of the medium. If a culture of *Bacillus subtilis* is used, clear zones will appear around each colony developing on the plate. This indicates that the casein has been digested to soluble compounds by the extracellular enzyme. On the other hand, *Escherichia coli* does not produce an extracellular caseolytic enzyme and is unable to attack the casein (Fig. 146).

The digestion of other compounds may be demonstrated in a similar manner. The tests are of value in identifying and classifying bacteria.

Intracellular Enzymes. The intracellular enzymes are concerned with the respiratory activities of bacteria. They are not secreted outside of cells and cannot, therefore, be demonstrated in culture filtrates. Such enzymes may be detected by employing living, disintegrated, or dissolved bacteria. Cells may be disintegrated by making use of various types of ball mills. Suspensions of pneumococci and other species, when mixed with bile, are dissolved. The disintegrated cells and lysates may be used for demonstrating the presence of various endoenzymes by incorporating such preparations with appropriate substrates.

For more information see Hugo (1954).

Oxidizing and Reducing Enzymes. Oxidation may be defined as (1) the addition of oxygen, or (2) the loss of hydrogen, or (3) the loss of electrons. The term oxidation is the opposite of reduction. The oxidation of one compound is always accompanied by the reduction of another.

The mechanisms involved in intracellular oxidations and reductions are discussed in the chapter that follows.

For more general information on enzymes see Baldwin (1952); Dixon and Webb (1958); Hewitt (1950); Laidler (1954); Mehler (1957); Neilands and Stumpf (1958); Northrop, Kunitz, and Herriott (1948); Sumner and Somers (1953).

REFERENCES

Abelson, P. H.: Amino acid biosynthesis in *Escherichia coli*: Isotopic competition with C^{14}-glucose, *J. Biol. Chem.*, **206**:335, 1954.

Alexander, M.: Localization of enzymes in the microbial cell, *Bact. Rev.*, **20**:67, 1956.

Bailey, R. W., S. A. Barker, E. J. Bourne, and M. Stacey: Enzymatic synthesis of a "branched" trisaccharide, *Nature*, **176**:1164, 1955.

Baldwin, E.: "Dynamic Aspects of Biochemistry," New York, The Macmillan Company, 1952.

Barker, S. A., and E. J. Bourne: The oligosaccharides synthesized from maltose by *Escherichia coli*, *J. Chem. Soc.*, **42**:209, 1952.

Becker, M. E., and S. E. Hartsell: Factors affecting bacteriolysis using lysozyme in dual enzyme systems, *Arch. Biochem. Biophys.*, **53**:402, 1954.

Bernheim, F.: The effect of certain metal ions and chelating agents on the formation of an adaptive enzyme in *Pseudomonas aeruginosa*, *Enzymologia*, **16**:351, 1954a.

———: The effect of certain antibiotics on the formation of an adaptive enzyme in a strain of *Pseudomonas aeruginosa*, *J. Pharm. Exp. Therap.*, **110**:115, 1954b.

———: The effect of temperature on adaptive enzyme formation in a *Mycobacterium*, *Arch. Biochem. Biophys.*, **59**:252, 1955.

Britten, R. J., R. B. Roberts, and E. F. French: Amino acid adsorption and protein synthesis in *Escherichia coli*, *Proc. Nat. Acad. Sci.*, **41**:863, 1955.

Butler, J. A. V., A. R. Crathorn, and G. D. Hunter: The site of protein synthesis in *Bacillus megaterium*, *Biochem. J.*, **69**:544, 1958.

Cameron, H. S., and M. E. Meyer: Synthesis of amino acids from urea by the genus *Brucella*, *Am. J. Vet. Res.*, **16**:149, 1955.

Cohen, S. S., and H. Barner: Enzymatic adaptation in a thymine requiring strain of *Escherichia coli*, *J. Bact.*, **69**:59, 1955.

Crathorn, A. R., and G. D. Hunter: Tracer studies of protein synthesis in sub-cellular fractions of *B. megaterium.* From "Radioisotopes in Scientific Research," New York, Pergamon Press, 1958.

Darter, R. W., and I. Millman: Localization of mycobacterial enzymes, *Proc. Soc. Exp. Biol. Med.,* **95**:440, 1957.

De Turk, W. E.: The adaptive formation of urease by washed suspensions of *Pseudomonas aeruginosa, J. Bact.,* **70**:187, 1955.

Dixon, M., and E. C. Webb: "Enzymes," New York, Academic Press Inc., 1958.

Doudoroff, M.: On the utilization and synthesis of sucrose and related compounds by some microorganisms, *Federation Proc.,* 4:241, 1945.

———, N. Kaplan, and W. Z. Hassid: Phosphorolysis and synthesis of sucrose with a bacterial preparation, *J. Biol. Chem.,* **148**:67, 1943.

———, J. M. Wiame, and H. Wolochow: Phosphorolysis of sucrose by *Pseudomonas putrefaciens, J. Bact.,* **57**:423, 1949.

Feingold, D. S., G. Avigad, and S. Hestrin: The mechanism of polysaccharide production from sucrose. 4. Isolation and probable structures of oligosaccharides formed from sucrose by a levansucrase system, *Biochem. J.,* **64**:351, 1956.

Fowler, E. B., and C. H. Werkman: Synthesis of amino acids by *Aerobacter aerogenes, Arch. Biochem. Biophys.,* **56**:22, 1955.

Gaebler, O. H.: "Enzymes: Units of Biological Structure and Function," New York, Academic Press, Inc., 1956.

Grula, E. A., and S. E. Hartsell: Lysozyme and morphological alterations induced in *Micrococcus lysodeikticus, J. Bact.,* **68**:171, 1954*a*; Lysozyme action and its relation to the Nakamura effect, *ibid.,* **68**:302, 1954*b*.

Hassid, W. Z., M. Doudoroff, and H. A. Barker: Enzymatically synthesized crystalline sucrose, *J. Am. Chem. Soc.,* **66**:1416, 1944.

Hestrin, S., D. S. Feingold, and G. Avigad: The mechanism of polysaccharide production from sucrose, *Biochem. J.,* **64**:340, 1956.

——— and M. Schramm: Synthesis of cellulose by *Acetobacter xylinum.* 2. Preparation of freeze-dried cells capable of polymerizing glucose to cellulose, *ibid.,* **58**:345, 1954.

Hewitt, L. F.: "Oxidation-Reduction Potentials in Bacteriology and Biochemistry," Edinburgh, E. and S. Livingstone Ltd., 1950.

Hugo, W. B.: The preparation of cell-free enzymes from microorganisms, *Bact. Rev.,* **18**:87, 1954.

Inaba, E., N. Kimoto, S. Inoue, and M. Kashimura: On an adaptation-stimulating phenomenon in bacteria, *Med. J. Osaka Univ.,* **6**:173, 1955.

Karström, H.: Enzymatische Adaptation bei Microorganismen, *Ergeb. Enzymforsch.,* **7**:350, 1938.

Laidler, K. J.: "Introduction to the Chemistry of Enzymes," New York, McGraw-Hill Book Company, Inc., 1954.

Magasanik, B.: Enzymatic adaptation in the metabolism of cyclitols in *Aerobacter aerogenes, J. Biol. Chem.,* **205**:1007, 1953.

Mahler, H. R., H. M. Baum, and G. Hübscher: Enzymatic oxidation of urate, *Science,* **124**:705, 1956.

Mehler, A. H.: "Introduction to Enzymology," New York, Academic Press, Inc., 1957.

Murphy, D., C. T. Bishop, and G. A. Adams: A mannan produced by *Bacillus polymyxa, Can. J. Biochem. Physiol.,* **34**:1271, 1956.

Neilands, J. B., and P. K. Stumpf: "Outlines of Enzyme Chemistry," New York, John Wiley & Sons, Inc., 1958.

Northrop, J. H., M. Kunitz, and R. M. Herriott: "Crystalline Enzymes," New York, Columbia University Press, 1948.

Ory, R. L., and C. M. Lyman: Synthesis of tyrosine and phenylalanine by *Lactobacillus arabinosus, J. Bact.,* **69**:508, 1955.

Peterson, R. G., and S. E. Hartsell: The lysozyme spectrum of the Gram-negative bacteria, *J. Infectious Diseases,* **96**:75, 1955.

Pigman, W.: "The Carbohydrates," New York, Academic Press, Inc., 1957.

Pinsky, M. J., and J. L. Stokes: The influence of age on enzymatic adaptation in microorganisms, *J. Bact.,* **64**:337, 1952.

Rafelson, M. E., Jr.: Conversion of radioactive glucose and acetate to tryptophan by *Aerobacter aerogenes, J. Biol. Chem.,* 213:479, 1955.

———, G. Ehrensvärd, and L. Reio: The formation of aeromatic amino acids in *Aerobacter aerogenes, Exp. Cell Res.,* Suppl. 3:281, 1955.

Rickenberg, H. V., C. Yanofsky, and D. M. Bonner: Enzymatic deadaptation, *J. Bact.,* 66:683, 1953.

Rotman, B., and S. Spiegelman: The conversion of negatives to positives in "slow" adapting populations of yeast, *J. Bact.,* 66:492, 1953.

Salton, M. R. J.: The properties of lysozyme and its action on microorganisms, *Bact. Rev.,* 21:82, 1957.

Sierra, G.: Studies on bacterial esterases. Part III. Influence of the composition of the culture media on the production of ali-esterase and lipase of *Pseudomonas aeruginosa, Antonie van Leeuwenhoek,* 23:278, 1957.

Skarnes, R. C., and D. W. Watson: The inhibition of lysozyme by acidic polymers from pathogenic bacteria, *J. Bact.,* 70:110, 1955.

Sumner, J. B., and G. F. Somers: "Chemistry and Methods of Enzymes," New York, Academic Press, Inc., 1953.

Tauber, H.: "The Chemistry and Technology of Enzymes," New York, John Wiley & Sons, Inc., 1949.

Thorne, C. B., C. G. Gómez, H. E. Noyes, and R. D. Housewright: Production of glutamyl polypeptide by *Bacillus subtilis, J. Bact.,* 68:307, 1954.

Virtanen, A. I.: On the adaptive formation of enzymes by micro-organisms, *Särtryck ur Svensk Kemisk Tidskrift,* 60:23, 1948.

———: Dependence of the enzyme activity of cells on their protein content, *Ann. Acad. Sci. Fennicae,* Series A, II, Chem. no. 36, 1949.

——— and U. Winkler: Effect of decrease in the protein content of cells on the proteolytic enzyme system, *Acta Chem. Scand.,* 3:272, 1949.

Warren, G. H., J. Gray, and P. Bartell: The lysis of *Pseudomonas aeruginosa* by lysozyme, *J. Bact.,* 70:614, 1955.

Weibull, C., H. Beckman, and L. Bergström: Localization of enzymes in *Bacillus megaterium,* Strain M, *J. Gen. Microbiol.,* 20:519, 1959.

Welshimer, H. J.: The action of lysozyme on the cell wall and capsule of *Bacillus megatherium, J. Bact.,* 66:112, 1953.

——— and C. F. Robinow: The lysis of *Bacillus megatherium* by lysozyme, *J. Bact.,* 57:489, 1949.

CHAPTER 12

Respiration of Bacteria

The term respiration has undergone several changes in meaning since it was first used. Originally it was used to denote the passage of air into and out of the lungs. Following this the term was extended to include the transference of oxygen to, and of carbon dioxide away from, the tissues. Then the term was employed to include plants and aerobic microorganisms. Since there are some bacteria which multiply in the absence of oxygen, respiration cannot be defined as the intake of air and the release of carbon dioxide. Respiration in its broadest meaning is concerned with the oxidation of metabolites, resulting in the release of energy to the organisms. Only in this sense can the term be used in bacteriology.

During the early years of bacteriology it was believed that free oxygen was necessary for all organisms and that life was not possible in the complete absence of this element. Pasteur demonstrated very early in his studies that such a statement, which was then considered fundamental, had to be abandoned. He showed that there were bacteria that could not grow in the presence of free oxygen. He classified bacteria as aerobic, anaerobic, facultative aerobic, and facultative anaerobic, depending upon their action toward free oxygen.

Pasteur considered all fermentation, i.e., the action of organisms on carbohydrates with the production of acid or of acid and gas, to be anaerobic. The escaping stream of carbon dioxide gas evolved during respiration was capable of driving the dissolved oxygen out of the media. Even though the media were exposed to the air, the conditions in the deeper portions were anaerobic. Yet the cells produced oxidations in the absence of free oxygen.

OXIDIZING-REDUCING ACTIVITIES OF ORGANISMS

A compound may be oxidized by the transfer of hydrogen (or electrons) from a donator to an acceptor. The oxidation of one compound results in the reduction of another. Clark et al. (1923) defined biological oxidations as "the withdrawal of electrons from a substance with or without the addition of oxygen or elements analogous to oxygen; or as the withdrawal of electrons with or without the withdrawal of hydrogen or elements analogous to hydrogen." It is generally believed that oxygen acts as a hydrogen acceptor to form H_2O or H_2O_2. Oxygen as such does not enter the molecule of the substrate. Compounds that are active as hydrogen acceptors take the place of oxygen in various oxidations, being themselves reduced in the reactions. Bacterial oxidations and reductions are associated phenomena and must be studied together.

Wieland (1922) believed that almost all oxidations could be explained on the basis of the removal of hydrogen rather than of the addition of oxygen. Hydrogen acceptors were necessary for the reactions to take place. Oxidations that occurred in this manner were called *dehydrogenations*. A few of the exceptions included the oxidation of aldehydes to acids and of purine bases to uric acid. In these instances, Wieland believed that a preliminary hydration occurred prior to the removal of hydrogen.

1. Oxidation without preliminary hydration:

$$R \cdot CH_2OH \rightarrow R \cdot CHO + 2H + \text{hydrogen acceptor}$$
$$\text{Alcohol} \qquad \text{Aldehyde}$$

2. Oxidation with preliminary hydration:

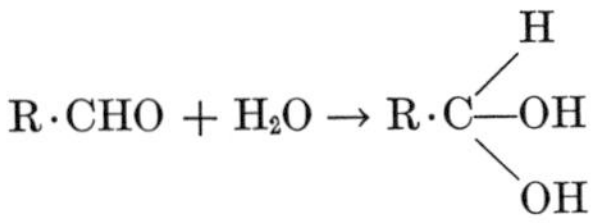

$$R \cdot CHO + H_2O \rightarrow R \cdot \overset{\displaystyle H}{\underset{\displaystyle OH}{C}}\!\!-OH$$
$$\text{Aldehyde} \qquad\qquad \text{Aldehyde hydrate}$$

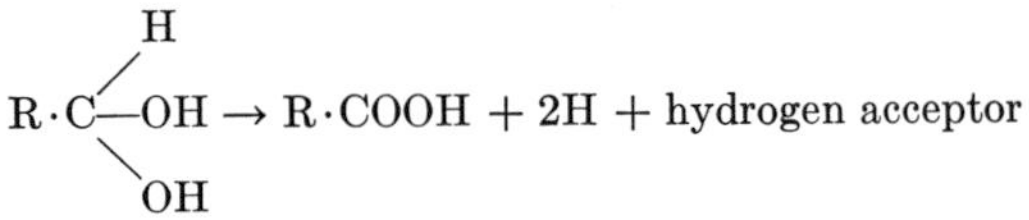

$$R \cdot \overset{\displaystyle H}{\underset{\displaystyle OH}{C}}\!\!-OH \rightarrow R \cdot COOH + 2H + \text{hydrogen acceptor}$$
$$\text{Aldehyde hydrate} \qquad \text{Acid}$$

Theobald Smith was apparently the first to show that anaerobic, facultative, and aerobic organisms possessed the power to reduce methylene blue. Avery and Neill (1924a, b) cultivated the pneumococcus *Diplococcus pneumoniae* under anaerobic conditions and prepared an extract of the organisms by subjecting a suspension to repeated freezing and thawing. The suspension was then centrifugated and the clear supernatant liquid passed through a Berkefeld filter in an atmosphere of nitrogen. The extract prepared in this manner was capable of producing hydrogen peroxide in the presence of oxygen and of reducing methylene blue. Heating the extract to 55 to 60°C. destroyed the power both to reduce and to form hydrogen peroxide.

Other dyes which have been added to culture media to test the reducing activities of bacteria include neutral red, litmus, indigo, and indigo carmine. Methylene blue has undoubtedly been used more than any of the other dyes for this purpose.

Probably all bacteria possess the power to reduce the foregoing dyes. However, there are quantitative differences in their reducing powers. For example, *Escherichia coli* reduces methylene blue twice as fast as *Vibrio comma*, but the reverse is true for litmus.

Bacterial reductions normally occur intracellularly or at the cell surface. The evidence is not very striking to support the statement that bacterial-cell filtrates are capable of actively reducing dyes to their colorless forms. It is true that culture filtrates do possess some reducing power, which is due probably to the enzymes liberated after autolysis of the dead cells. However, the action is very mild compared to the vigorous reduction that occurs when filtrates of disintegrated organisms are used.

The speed of decolorization of dyes is proportional to the number of organisms present. Methylene blue is added to milk to determine its approximate bacterial count. The method is of value where speed is desired. A test based on this principle is known as the reductase test (see page 575).

Reduction of Methylene Blue. Methylene blue acts as a hydrogen acceptor and becomes reduced to the colorless form. If air or oxygen is bubbled through the medium containing the reduced compound, the blue color is restored. The reaction may be represented as follows:

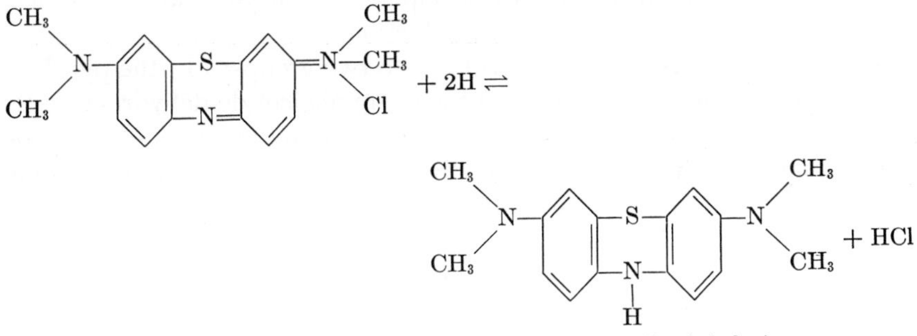

Methylene blue (colored)   Methylene blue (colorless)

One atom of hydrogen is taken up by the double-bonded nitrogen converting the blue-colored compound into the colorless form. The reaction is easily reversible from one form to the other.

By means of the methylene blue technique, Thunberg (1929) demonstrated the presence in animal tissues of respiratory enzymes, which were capable of activating a number of organic compounds. The methylene blue acted as a hydrogen acceptor and became reduced to the colorless or leuco form. The speed of decolorization of the dye was an indication of the rate at which oxidation occurred. The reaction was carried out in an anaerobic environment because the presence of air resulted in a reoxidation of the methylene blue to the colored form.

Thunberg found that methylene blue added to suspensions of minced animal tissue was quickly decolorized because the tissue contained many substances activated by certain enzymes known as *dehydrogenases*. By first extracting minced tissue with water, he was able to remove these substances, but not the dehydrogenases. The tissue had now lost its power to reduce methylene blue. By adding various compounds to the washed tissue, Thunberg succeeded in demonstrating the presence of a large number of dehydrogenases. Such enzymes have been found to be widely distributed in higher plant and animal tissues, yeast cells, bacteria, and other organisms.

Tests for the presence of dehydrogenases in bacteria are performed by (1) placing in a vacuum tube a convenient quantity of the substrate in solution with buffer of the proper reaction, (2) adding a suspension of previously washed bacteria, (3) adding methylene blue, (4) evacuating the tube, and (5) incubating the tube at the proper temperature (usually 37°C.).

The bacteria are grown in pure culture in broth and centrifugated, and the clear supernatant liquid is removed. The bacteria are resuspended in water or salt solution and aerated for 1 hr. to remove easily oxidizable constituents. The suspension is now ready for use in the methylene blue technique.

Dehydrogenases. Among the hydrogen-transferring enzymes, the dehydrogenases make up the largest group. These enzymes are concerned with the processes of oxidation and reduction.

The dehydrogenases may be divided into two groups: (1) the pyridine nucleotide dehydrogenases and (2) the flavin nucleotide dehydrogenases.

Pyridine Nucleotide Dehydrogenases. A pyridine nucleotide dehydrogenase may be defined as an enzyme that removes certain hydrogen atoms from a metabolite and transfers them to a reducible substance. Certain dyes may be used in place of naturally occurring hydrogen acceptors. The metabolite becomes oxidized by the removal of hydrogen. This type of oxidation is termed a dehydrogenation. The dehydrogenase cannot transfer the hydrogen directly to molecular oxygen. However, the hydrogen removed from the metabolite may be transported over several reducible compounds, eventually combining with oxygen in the presence of an oxidase.

This may be represented as follows:

Metabolite → dehydrogenase → diphosphopyridine nucleotide (DPN)
or coenzyme I → flavoproteins → cytochromes → O_2

Diphosphopyridine nucleotide (DPN) or coenzyme I collects hydrogen from the metabolite-dehydrogenase complex and transfers it to a flavoprotein, which in turn passes it on to the cytochromes, and finally to molecular oxygen. The molecular oxygen is reduced to water, thus terminating the chain of reactions.

In the absence of oxygen the reduced DPN cannot be reoxidized through the above chain of carriers. In this case another dehydrogenase functions in place of the oxidase and oxygen. The oxidized DPN is reduced by one dehydrogenase and then reoxidized by another. In this manner the various fermentations are catalyzed.

The pyridine nucleotide dehydrogenases are differentiated according to the first carrier receiving the hydrogen from the metabolite-dehydrogenase reaction.

Pyridine nucleotide dehydrogenases are linked with either diphosphopyridine nucleotide (DPN), also called coenzyme I, or triphosphopyridine nucleotide (TPN), also called coenzyme II (see page 323).

Coenzyme I–linked:
1. Alcohol dehydrogenase.
2. Aldehyde dehydrogenase.
3. β-Hydroxybutyric dehydrogenase.
4. Glucose dehydrogenase.
5. Malic dehydrogenase.
6. Lactic dehydrogenase.
7. α-Glycerophosphoric dehydrogenase.
8. Triosephosphate dehydrogenase.

Coenzyme II–linked:
1. Robison ester dehydrogenase.
2. Glutamic dehydrogenase.

For more information see Dixon and Webb (1958), Neilands and Stumpf (1958), Sumner and Somers (1953).

Flavin Nucleotide Dehydrogenases. In general, the flavoproteins bridge the electron transport gap between the pyridine nucleotides and the various cytochromes.

As an example,

Glucose-6-phosphate + TPN $\rightleftharpoons$ gluconic acid-6-phosphate + TPNH + H$^+$
TPNH + H$^+$ + flavoprotein (oxidized) $\rightleftharpoons$ TPN + flavoprotein (reduced)
Flavoprotein (reduced) + O$_2$ $\rightleftharpoons$ flavoprotein (oxidized) + H$_2$O$_2$

Two important flavin nucleotides are flavin mononucleotide (FMN) and flavin adenine dinucleotide (FAD). See page 324 for a more detailed discussion of these coenzymes. Some reactions they catalyze are given in Table 12.

Oxidases. Oxidases differ from dehydrogenases in that they transfer hydrogen directly to oxygen to form water, whereas the dehydrogenases transfer hydrogen to an acceptor other than oxygen. The enzymes are metalloproteins, containing iron or copper. Iron is quantitatively the most important metal concerned in enzymatic activity. The oxidases are inhibited by potassium cyanide, hydrogen sulfide, and other substances which stabilize the metallic groups. They do not act under anaerobic conditions.

The properties of the iron oxidases are due largely to the presence of the metal. The iron is located in prosthetic groups which are either hematin or a substance closely related to hematin. The hematin is united

TABLE 12. SOME REACTIONS CATALYZED BY FMN AND FAD

Enzyme	Coenzyme	Substrate	Product produced

Type: $R \cdot CHNHR' \cdot COOH$ + flavoprotein (ox) + $H_2O \rightleftharpoons$
$R \cdot CO \cdot COOH + H_2NR'$ + flavoprotein (red)

Enzyme	Coenzyme	Substrate	Product produced
D-Amino acid dehydrogenase	FAD	D-Amino acids	Keto acids + NH_3
Glycine dehydrogenase	FAD	Glycine	Glyoxylic acid
L-Amino acid dehydrogenase	FMN	L-Amino acids	Keto acids + NH_3

Type: $R \cdot CHOH \cdot COOH$ + flavoprotein (ox) $\rightleftharpoons R \cdot CO \cdot COOH$ + flavoprotein (red)

Enzyme	Coenzyme	Substrate	Product produced
L-Hydroxy acid dehydrogenase	FMN	L-Hydroxy acids	α-Keto acids

Type: $\dfrac{DPNH}{TPNH} + H^+$ + flavoprotein (ox) $\rightleftharpoons \dfrac{DPN}{TPN}$ + flavoprotein (red)

Enzyme	Coenzyme	Substrate	Product produced
DPN-cytochrome c reductase	FAD	DPNH	DPN
TPN-cytochrome c reductase	FAD FMN	TPNH	TPN

Type: $-CH_2-CH_2-$ + flavoprotein (ox) $\rightleftharpoons -CH=CH-$ + flavoprotein (red)

Enzyme	Coenzyme	Substrate	Product produced
Fumaric reductase	FAD	Fumarate	Succinate

Miscellaneous reactions

Enzyme	Coenzyme	Substrate	Product produced
Nitrate reductase	FAD	Nitrate	Nitrite
Nitrite reductase	FAD	Nitrite	Hydroxylamine

to various specific proteins, or apoenzymes, to give the complete enzymes. The iron oxidases include catalase and peroxidase.

Catalase. Most bacteria produce hydrogen peroxide in the presence of free oxygen. Since hydrogen peroxide is toxic to living cells, its destruction is of considerable importance. The accumulation of peroxide in cultures is controlled by two factors: (1) bacterial catalase and (2) the degree of sensitiveness of the organisms to the compound.

Catalase is an enzyme that is capable of decomposing hydrogen peroxide to water and molecular oxygen, according to the equation,

$$2H_2O_2 + \text{catalase} \rightarrow 2H_2O + O_2$$

This is sometimes referred to as the catalatic reaction.

The presence of hydrogen peroxide was first detected in the pneumococcus, an organism incapable of producing catalase and only moderately sensitive to the toxic action of H_2O_2. Organisms that do not produce catalase may be protected by being cultivated with certain plant or animal tissues, or with other organisms capable of producing the enzyme.

Catalase is produced by many bacteria. Some produce more of it than others. It is present in largest amounts in the strictly aerobic bacteria. On the other hand, its presence has not been demonstrated in the obligately anaerobic bacteria.

Keilin and Hartree (1945) proposed the following mechanism for the decomposition of hydrogen peroxide by catalase:

$$
\begin{aligned}
1.\ &4Fe^{+++} + 2H_2O_2 \rightarrow 4Fe^{++} + 4H^+ + 2O_2 \\
2.\ &\underline{4Fe^{++} + 4H^+ + O_2 \rightarrow 4Fe^{+++} + 2H_2O} \\
&\phantom{4Fe^{++}+4}2H_2O_2 \rightarrow 2H_2O + O_2
\end{aligned}
$$

In the first reaction the peroxide reduces the ferric iron of catalase to ferrous iron; in the second reaction gaseous oxygen oxidizes the reduced ferrous catalase to the ferric enzyme.

The concentration of catalase may be determined by adding hydrogen peroxide and noting the amount decomposed, or by adding peroxide to bacterial cultures in fermentation tubes and measuring the volumes of oxygen gas evolved (Fig. 147).

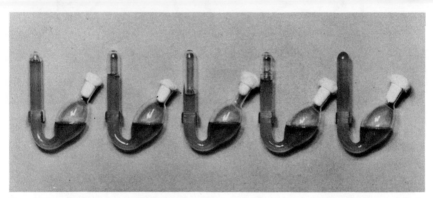

FIG. 147. Reduction of hydrogen peroxide with liberation of oxygen. From left to right: *Bacillus subtilis, Staphylococcus aureus, Pseudomonas fluorescens, Escherichia coli,* and control. *B. subtilis* shows slight decomposition, whereas *P. fluorescens* shows vigorous decomposition. Note absence of gas in the control.

For more information see Isaacs and Scouller (1948), Richardson and Huddleson (1953).

Peroxidase. The function of peroxidase is to transfer oxygen from peroxides to oxidizable substances according to the equation

$$H_2O_2 + \text{organic molecule} + \text{peroxidase} \rightarrow H_2O + \text{oxidized organic molecule}$$

This is known as the peroxidatic reaction.

Peroxidase does not decompose peroxide in the absence of an oxidizable substance. In this respect it differs from catalase, which decomposes peroxide in the absence of an oxygen acceptor. This would indicate that catalase should be classed as a splitting enzyme, and peroxidase as a transferring enzyme.

A large number of compounds may function as oxygen acceptors, thereby permitting the peroxidase to act. Among these may be mentioned glutathione and cytochrome c. Potassium cyanide inhibits completely the action of the enzyme, whereas carbon monoxide has no effect.

The oxidase is widely distributed in nature, being present in vegetables, fruits, many sprouts, sugar beets, wheat flour, bran, brewer's yeast, insects, birds, animals, aerobic bacteria, milk, potatoes, etc. Horseradish is one of the richest sources of peroxidase and is frequently employed for the preparation of the enzyme.

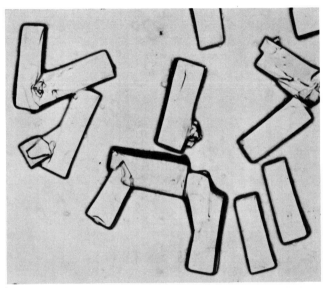

Fig. 148. Ascorbic acid crystals. (*Courtesy of Merck & Company, Inc.*)

Peroxidase is very resistant to heat. It is destroyed at 98°C. in 10 min., but on standing as much as 25 per cent of the original activity is restored.

Two important copper oxidases are ascorbic acid oxidase and tyrosinase.

Ascorbic Acid Oxidase. This enzyme is capable of oxidizing ascorbic acid or vitamin C (Fig. 148) to dehydroascorbic acid:

Ascorbic acid + ascorbic acid oxidase + $O_2 \rightarrow$ dehydroascorbic acid

The oxidase is widely distributed in the plant kingdom, being present in a large number of fruits and vegetables. The enzyme is not present in animal tissues, where ascorbic acid may be oxidized through the cytochrome system.

Ascorbic acid is extremely unstable, being readily oxidized to dehydroascorbic acid (see page 296). Hydrogen peroxide is not produced in the reaction. The oxidized form still displays some antiscorbutic activity which appears to parallel to a remarkable degree its reducing capacity.

It is generally believed that ascorbic acid functions as a hydrogen carrier. It is found in all animal tissues in amounts compatible with hydrogen transport or coenzyme function. Some believe that glutathione is the chief protective substance in cells for maintaining ascorbic acid in the reduced form. It guards the vitamin against irreversible oxidation with a loss of antiscorbutic activity. Glutathione added to a mixture of ascorbic acid and its oxidase maintains the vitamin in the reduced or active form.

For more information see Eddy, Ingram, and Mapson (1954); Ericsson and Lundbeck (1955).

Tyrosinase. The development of a brown, orange, red, or black color around colonies of some bacteria and molds growing on agar is caused by the action of the enzyme tyrosinase on the amino acid tyrosine and related compounds (see page 295). The enzyme is also known as polyphenol oxidase.

Tyrosinase is widely distributed in the plant kingdom. Its presence has also been demonstrated in animal cells. A large number of aerobic streptomycetes are capable of producing dark-colored compounds in nonsynthetic media and in synthetic media to which tyrosine is added.

Some strains of *Bacillus subtilis* growing on peptone media are capable of producing a black pigment. The black compound is produced from the amino acid tyrosine. The addition of glucose to produce a protein-sparing action may inhibit the formation of the pigment. Therefore, noncarbohydrate media containing tyrosine should be used for determining the ability of organisms to produce tyrosinase.

For more information see Behm and Nelson (1944a, b), Burris and Little (1949).

The Cytochromes. Cytochromes are respiratory pigments which were discovered by MacMunn (1886) but were forgotten until 1925, when they were rediscovered by Keilin. The latter worker named the compounds *cytochrome*, which means cellular pigments. They are concerned in the later stages of many biological oxidations. They become reduced by the coenzymes under the action of flavoproteins, and the reduced forms are reoxidized in the presence of cytochrome oxidase.

The cytochromes are widely distributed in nature, being found in higher plants and animals, birds, insects, mollusks, crustacea, bacteria, yeasts, molds, etc. They are absent from most anaerobic bacteria. Exceptions appear to be certain anaerobic photosynthetic sulfur bacteria (Kamen and Vernon, 1955; Newton and Kamen, 1955; Vernon, 1953). It is generally believed that the more aerobic the bacteria, the more fully developed will be the cytochrome system.

Cytochrome is not a single compound but consists of at least twenty known components. They fall into three groups, differing in the nature of the haem prosthetic group. The three types are generally designated cytochromes a, b, and c. Cytochrome c occurs in nature more abundantly than the other cytochromes. Also it is freely soluble in water and was the first to be extracted and purified. For this reason it has been studied in greater detail than the a and b groups of cytochromes. The present knowledge of the cytochromes is based largely on this component.

Chemically, cytochromes are hemoproteins having structures similar to hemoglobin. All of the cytochromes can undergo oxidation and reduction, and most of them serve as carriers of hydrogen. Under normal conditions the cytochromes which function as carriers are present in cells in the oxidized or partly reduced form. During periods of great activity the cytochromes are partly oxidized; during periods of inactivity they are again reduced.

Cytochrome c does not react directly with oxygen. The reduced form is oxidized only by cytochrome oxidase, with which it is closely associated in cells.

Cytochrome Oxidase. Most cytochromes are believed to function as carriers of hydrogen in the complicated bucket brigade leading to the transfer of hydrogen from metabolites to free oxygen. Cytochrome oxidase plays the final role in that it brings about the oxidation, by molecular oxygen, of the reduced forms of cytochromes, leading to the formation of water.

The autooxidizable flavoproteins reduce molecular oxygen to hydrogen peroxide, whereas the cytochrome system converts free oxygen to water. A satisfactory explanation for this difference has not been given.

Cytochrome oxidase has been called indophenolase and indophenol oxidase. The enzyme is widely distributed in nature, being present in higher plants and animals, yeasts, molds, algae, aerobic bacteria, etc.

Cytochrome oxidase is capable of oxidizing p-phenylenediamine to indophenol. The presence of the enzyme is easily detected by pouring a solution of p-phenylenediamine over the surface of an agar plate containing bacterial colonies. In the presence of the enzyme, the p-phenylenediamine is oxidized to indophenol, resulting in the appearance of a blue color. The oxidase is believed to oxidize phenols, amines, etc., not directly, but by oxidizing cytochrome c. The cytochrome c then oxidizes the phenols and amines.

Keilin (1933) reported the following properties for cytochrome oxidase:

1. It oxidizes p-phenylenediamine rapidly.
2. It is thermostable, being destroyed at temperatures above 60°C.
3. It is destroyed on the addition of strong alcohol or acetone.
4. Oxygen uptake during the oxidation of p-phenylenediamine is inhibited by the addition of minute amounts of KCN, H_2S, NaN_3, or CO.
5. p-Phenylenediamine does not require activation by a dehydrogenase to be oxidized by cytochrome oxidase.

Keilin and Hartree (1938) reported that the only property that could be definitely assigned to cytochrome oxidase was the oxidation of reduced cytochrome c, according to the following reactions:

Metabolite·2H + dehydrogenase + cytochrome c → reduced cytochrome c
Reduced cytochrome c + cytochrome oxidase + O_2 → oxidized cytochrome c + H_2O

The flavoproteins are believed to be the reducing agents which bridge the gap between the pyridine nucleotides, which function with the dehydrogenases, and the cytochromes (see page 324). The reduced cytochromes are then oxidized by cytochrome oxidase, which transfers the hydrogen atoms to free oxygen with the formation of water.

For more information on the cytochromes, cytochrome oxidase, and other oxidases see Cooperstein (1959); Dixon and Webb (1958); Kamen and Vernon (1955); Laidler (1954); Mehler (1957); Neilands and Stumpf (1958); Newton and Kamen (1955, 1956); Sih, Hamilton, and Knight (1958); Smith (1954); Sumner and Somers (1953); Tissières (1956); Vernon (1953, 1956); Vernon and White (1957).

Bioluminescence. The emission of light by living organisms is called bioluminescence. The phenomenon is sometimes referred to as phosphorescence. Light of the sea, of fish, flesh, or wood is always caused by the presence of living organisms (Fig. 149).

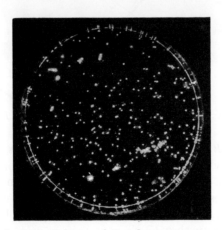

Fig. 149. Luminous bacteria. Colonies of *Pseudomonas toyamensis* growing on agar and photographed by their own light. (*From E. N. Harvey, "Living Light," Princeton University Press, 1940.*)

Luminescent species are found among the animals and the plants. The plant species include the bacteria and molds. Most of the bacterial species are found in the genera *Photobacterium* and *Vibrio*. These are marine forms. Fresh-water luminous bacteria have not been encountered.

Luminescent bacteria may be cultivated on artificial media. They grow best on salt-water media containing 3 to 5 per cent salt as sodium chloride.

Luminescent bacteria and molds may be distinguished from other light-emitting organisms in that the light emitted is of uniform intensity, shining day and night, independent of any stimulation. On the other hand, animals emit light only when disturbed or stimulated.

Since very little heat is produced by luminous organisms, bioluminescence is often spoken of as "cold light." The rise in temperature in some light-producing organisms is less than 0.001°C. The light emitted has properties similar to other kinds of light. It will affect photographic film and can induce chemical reactions. Infrared or ultraviolet radiations are not produced, which means that the luminous efficiency is nearly 100 per cent.

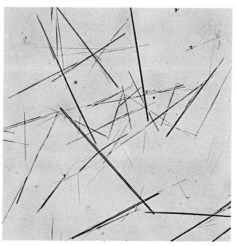

Fig. 150. Crystalline firefly luciferase. (*Courtesy of W. D. McElroy.*)

Mechanism of Bioluminescence. Bioluminescence is a form of chemiluminescence in which specific chemical substances emit light during a chemical reaction. Luciferin and luciferase are names used for these compounds synthesized by luminous organisms, but it is probable that luciferin and luciferase from one species or group may be different chemically from those in another.

Airth, Rhodes, and McElroy (1958), in their studies on pure crystalline preparations of firefly luciferin and luciferase (Fig. 150), proposed the following scheme for the light reaction:

1. Luciferin (LH_2) reacts with adenosine triphosphate (ATP) to form adenyl (AMP)-luciferin (LH_2-AMP) and pyrophosphate (PP).
2. LH_2-AMP in the presence of O_2 gives off light and produces adenyl-oxyluciferin (L-AMP). The L-AMP eventually decomposes into L and AMP.
3. L is a potent inhibitor of the light reaction, and once it has reacted with ATP and luciferase, the latter is incapable of catalyzing the oxidation of LH_2.

4. Coenzyme A (CoA) stimulates light emission by removing L from the enzyme surface. L-CoA can react with cysteine, glutathione, or hydroxylamine to form the corresponding oxyluciferyl derivatives.

5. L-CoA in the presence of luciferase can be split by AMP, and when excess PP is added, ATP and free L are formed.

For more information see Bitler and McElroy (1957); Cormier and Totter (1957); Cormier, Totter, and Rostorfer (1956); Green and McElroy (1956); McElroy and Green (1955, 1956); McElroy and Hastings (1955); McElroy and Strehler (1954); Strehler and Cormier (1953, 1954).

COENZYMES

Enzymes may be defined as organic catalysts elaborated by living cells and capable of functioning independently of the cells. They are heat-labile, nondialyzable, high-molecular-weight compounds. Coenzymes are also catalytic agents produced by living cells and are necessary in enzymatic reactions but they are heat-stable, dialyzable, and have smaller molecular weights.

Pyridine Nucleotides. The two pyridine nucleotide coenzymes are codehydrogenase I and codehydrogenase II.

Codehydrogenase I. This coenzyme consists of one molecule of β-nicotinic acid amide, one of adenine, two of pentose, and two of phosphoric acid. It is also known as coenzyme I and cozymase I. The compound is capable of alternate oxidation and reduction and functions as a carrier of hydrogen. Chemically it is diphosphopyridine nucleotide (DPN), having the following structural formula:

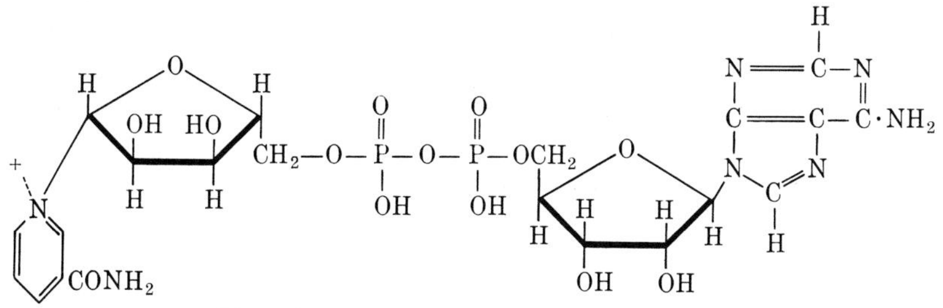

Diphosphopyridine nucleotide (codehydrogenase I)

DPN is universally present in living cells. It is present in high concentration in yeast cells. It functions as a coenzyme in many dehydrogenase reactions. The dehydrogenase transfers hydrogen from the metabolite to the coenzyme. The pyridine ring of the coenzyme accepts an atom of hydrogen, converting a strongly basic quaternary nitrogen to a weakly basic tertiary nitrogen atom:

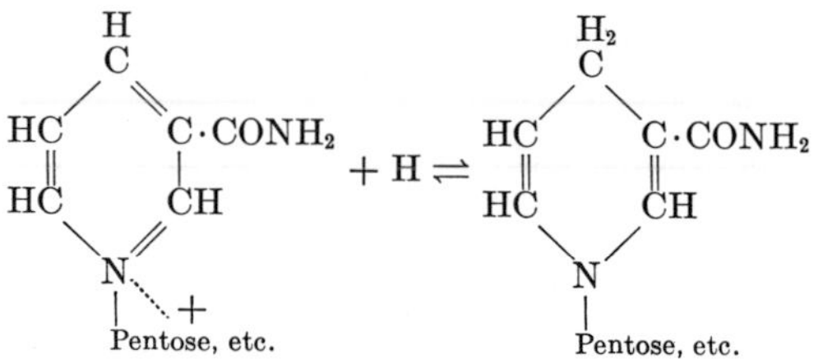

Codehydrogenase II. This catalyst is known also as coenzyme II and cozymase II. Like codehydrogenase I, it is widely distributed in living cells. Codehydrogenase II functions in the same manner as codehydrogenase I and differs from it only in containing one more phosphate radical. Chemically it is triphosphopyridine nucleotide (TPN) having the following structure:

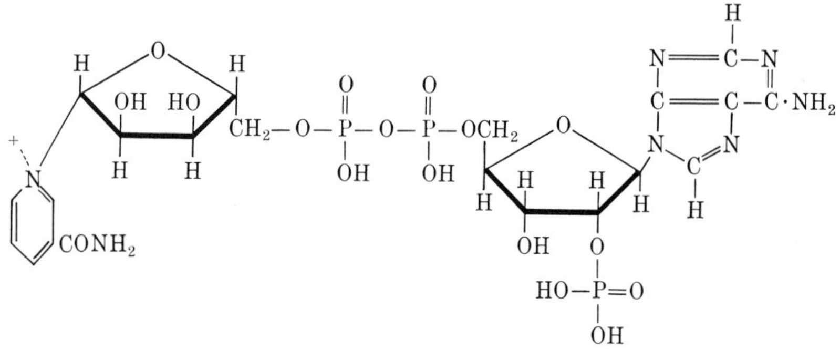

Triphosphopyridine nucleotide (codehydrogenase II)

The two coenzymes are not interchangeable. Some dehydrogenases require codehydrogenase I; others must have codehydrogenase II. Their main function is to transport hydrogen from metabolites to other carriers, usually the flavin nucleotides, and become reoxidized again to accept more hydrogen.

This may be illustrated by the following reactions in which glucose becomes oxidized to gluconic acid:

Glucose + H_3PO_4 $\rightleftharpoons$ glucose-6-phosphate
Glucose-6-phosphate + TPN $\rightleftharpoons$ gluconic acid-6-phosphate + TPNH + H^+
TPNH + H^+ + flavoprotein (ox) $\rightleftharpoons$ TPN + flavoprotein (red)
Flavoprotein (red) + O_2 $\rightleftharpoons$ flavoprotein (ox) + H_2O_2

Flavin Nucleotides. Some important flavin nucleotides include flavin mononucleotide (FMN), flavin adenine dinucleotide (FAD), thiamine pyrophosphate, coenzyme A, and adenosine phosphates. The last named are discussed on page 372.

An important role of the flavoproteins is that of intermediary in the oxidation of reduced pyridine nucleotides.

Flavin Mononucleotide. This coenzyme is the phosphate ester of vitamin B_2 or riboflavin. Chemically it is riboflavin-5-phosphate, having the following structural formula:

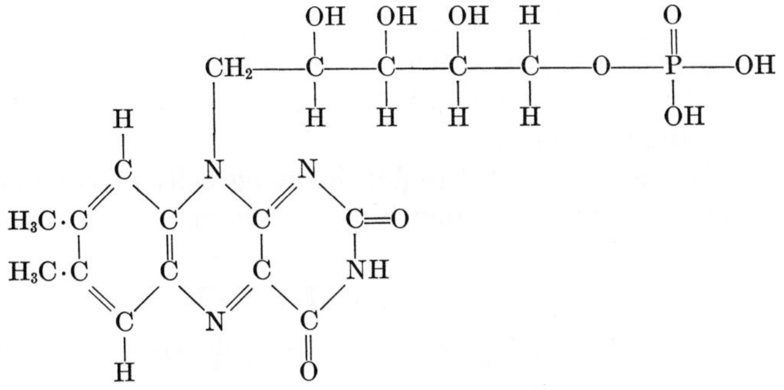

Flavin mononucleotide (FMN)

It is sometimes referred to as the old yellow enzyme because it was the first flavin nucleotide discovered.

Flavin Adenine Dinucleotide. Riboflavin exists also in another coenzyme, namely, flavin adenine dinucleotide (FAD), having the following structure:

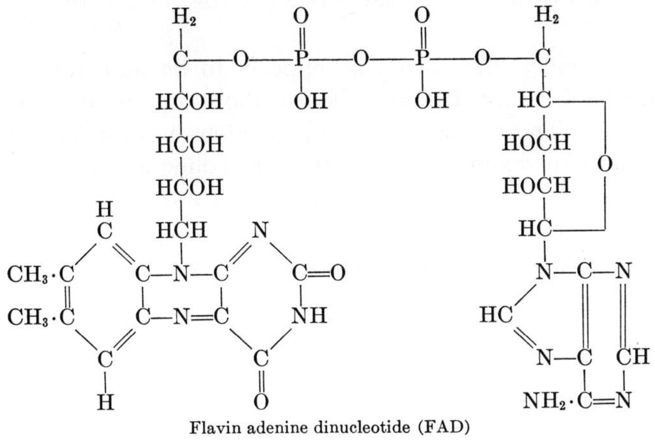

Flavin adenine dinucleotide (FAD)

FMN and FAD act as carriers of hydrogen. The isoalloxazine nucleus is capable of alternate oxidation and reduction in the following manner:

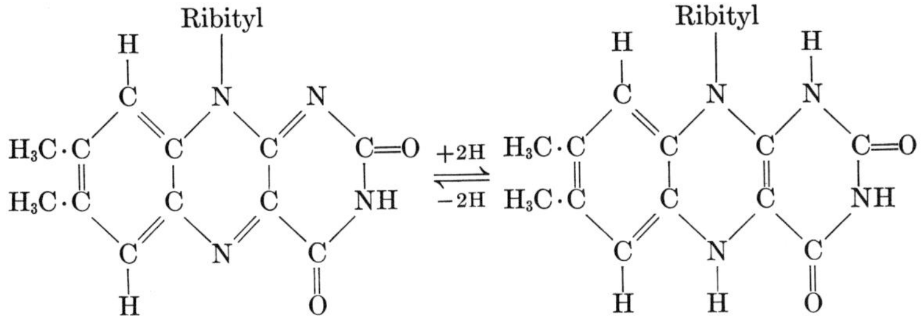

An enzyme has been isolated from yeast that is capable of synthesizing FAD from FMN in the presence of ATP:

$$FMN + ATP \rightarrow FAD + \text{pyrophosphate}$$

Thiamine Pyrophosphate. Carboxylase is an enzyme that catalyzes the decarboxylation of pyruvic acid to acetaldehyde and carbon dioxide. A coenzyme known as thiamine pyrophosphate or cocarboxylase is necessary for the activity of the enzyme.

Cocarboxylase is widely distributed in living cells. It is composed of one molecule of thiamine (vitamin B_1) and two molecules of phosphoric acid:

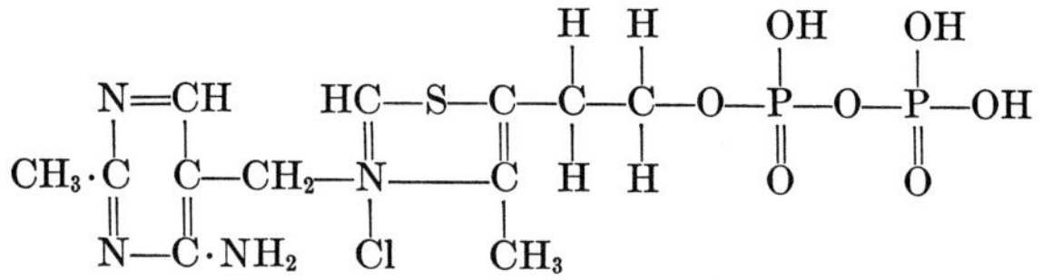

Thiamine pyrophosphate (cocarboxylase)

The decarboxylation of pyruvic acid to acetaldehyde may be represented as follows:

$$\underset{\text{Pyruvic acid}}{CH_3 \cdot CO \cdot COOH} + \text{carboxylase} + \text{cocarboxylase} \rightarrow \underset{\text{Acetaldehyde}}{CH_3 \cdot CHO} + CO_2$$

In animal tissues, the coenzyme appears to be intimately connected with thiamine (vitamin B_1) and the metabolism of pyruvic acid.

Coenzyme A. This coenzyme (CoA) functions as a carrier of the acetyl group. It participates in the acetylation of choline and in the condensation of acetate with oxalacetic acid to form citrate.

The coenzyme is composed of adenylic acid, pantothenic acid, and thioethanolamine having the following structure:

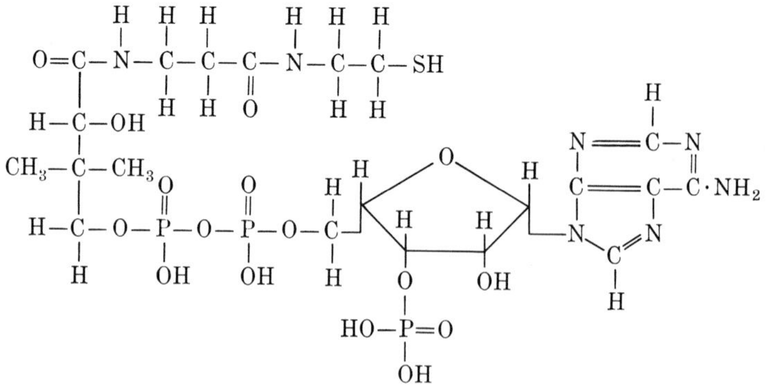

Coenzyme A

For more information on coenzymes see Dixon and Webb (1958), Laidler (1954), Mehler (1957), Neilands and Stumpf (1958).

GLUTATHIONE

Hopkins (1921) isolated a thermolabile substance from extracts of yeast and muscle, which functioned as an oxidation-reduction system. The compound was believed to be composed of one molecule of glutamic acid and one of cysteine united together by a peptide linkage. He named the compound glutathione.

In a later communication, Hopkins (1929) showed that the compound was not a dipeptide, as was at first believed, but a tripeptide composed of glycine, cysteine, and glutamic acid. The structural formula is as follows:

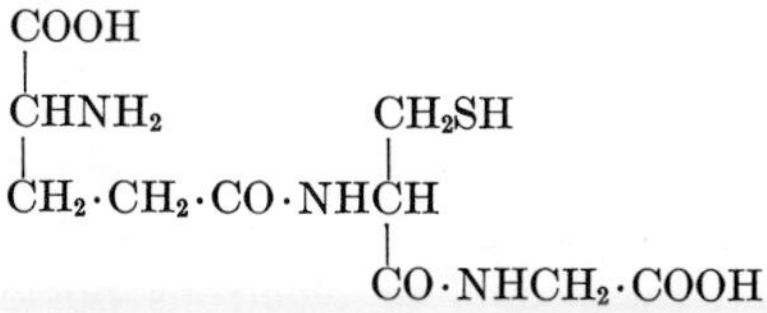

$$COOH$$
$$CHNH_2 \qquad CH_2SH$$
$$CH_2 \cdot CH_2 \cdot CO \cdot NHCH$$
$$CO \cdot NHCH_2 \cdot COOH$$

Glutathione (glutamyl cysteinyl glycine)

Since it is the sulfhydryl group (—SH) which is of importance in reactions of oxidation-reduction, the above formula may be abbreviated to GSH. Two molecules of reduced glutathione readily give up the hydrogen of their sulfhydryl groups and become oxidized to a disulfide:

$$2GSH + B \rightleftharpoons GSSG + BH_2$$

Reduced glutathione   Oxidized glutathione

The disulfide form is readily reduced to the original compound by the addition of two atoms of hydrogen. Cells contain systems which rapidly reduce oxidized glutathione and which quickly oxidize reduced glutathione by means of molecular oxygen.

Glutathione has been shown to be of almost universal occurrence in living tissue where the concentration roughly parallels the metabolic activity of the cells. The concentration is higher in rapidly growing cells than in older cells. Blood is said to contain 34 to 47 mg. of glutathione per 100 gm. It is also present in many species of aerobic and anaerobic bacteria, in yeasts, and in molds.

Since the oxidation-reduction mechanism of glutathione is due to the cystine-cysteine combination, cystine also functions in a similar manner:

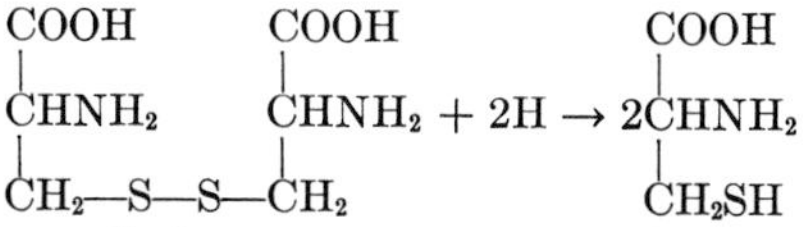

$$COOH \qquad COOH \qquad\qquad COOH$$
$$CHNH_2 \qquad CHNH_2 + 2H \rightarrow 2CHNH_2$$
$$CH_2—S—S—CH_2 \qquad\qquad CH_2SH$$

Cystine   Cysteine

OXIDATION-REDUCTION POTENTIALS

Oxidation-reduction potentials are of great importance in biology. Reactions that occur intracellularly and release energy to the organism involve a study of oxidation-reduction potentials. An oxidation occurs either by the addition of oxygen or by the removal of hydrogen. The oxidation of one compound is accompanied by the reduction of another.

A typical oxidation by the addition of oxygen involves the formation of cupric oxide in the reaction:

$$2Cu + O_2 \rightarrow 2CuO$$

The conversion of alcohol to aldehyde is an example of an oxidation by the removal of hydrogen:

$$CH_3 \cdot CH_2OH \rightarrow CH_3 \cdot CHO + 2H$$

Oxidations occur also by the withdrawal of electrons, and reductions by the addition of electrons. An atom consists of a nucleus of positive electricity surrounded by a shell of electrons possessing negative electrical charges. The sum total of the negative charges must be equal to the positive charge of the nucleus. Some elements easily lose electrons, whereas others add electrons. An oxidation involves the loss of one or more electrons; a reduction involves a gain of electrons.

$$Cu^+ \underset{\text{Reduction}}{\overset{\text{Oxidation}}{\rightleftharpoons}} Cu^{++} + (e)$$

A substance that readily gives up electrons is a good reducing agent; conversely, a substance that readily takes up electrons is a good oxidizing agent.

The transfer of electrons from one compound to another sets up a potential difference between the reactants, which may be measured by an appropriate instrument. The magnitude of this potential difference depends upon the ease with which the electrons are lost or gained. The greater the oxidizing or reducing power of a substance, the greater will be the electrical potential on one side or the other of a zero point. The more highly oxidized a substance, the more positive will be its electrical potential, and the more highly reduced a substance, the more negative will be the electrical potential. The direction in which a reaction proceeds is dependent upon the free electrons in the system. If the number of electrons is increased, the system will produce more of the reductant; if the number is reduced, the system will produce more of the oxidant. The electronic state of the system is a measure of its oxidizing or reducing power.

The oxidation-reduction potential of a system is expressed by the symbol Eh. The greater the proportion of reduced substance present, the lower will be the Eh value; conversely, the greater the proportion of oxidized substance, the higher will be the Eh value. When the concentration of the oxidant is equal to that of the reductant, the term becomes zero and the observed potential is equal to E_0.

Measurement of Oxidation-Reduction Potentials. Two methods may be followed for determining the oxidation-reduction potentials of bacterial cultures: (1) the colorimetric method and (2) the potentiometric method. Each has its advantages and disadvantages, but the potentiometric method is generally preferred for this purpose.

Litmus and methylene blue are used in bacterial cultures as indicators of reduction. For the determination of various degrees of reduction intensity, a selection of a series of indicators is necessary. It is now possible to cover the range from +0.300 to −0.450 volt at pH 7.0 and a temperature of 30°C. Usually the oxidants of the oxidation-reduction systems are colored and the reductants are practically colorless.

For more information see Hewitt (1950) and Society of American Bacteriologists (1957).

ANAEROBIOSIS

Anaerobes are usually defined as organisms which can live and multiply only in the complete absence of oxygen. This statement is not correct as all obligate anaerobes can tolerate some free oxygen. However, they show considerable variation in the amount of oxygen they can tolerate. *Clostridium tetani* can grow in a liquid medium exposed to 5 to 15 mm. air pressure. *Cl. perfringens* produces good growth in an atmosphere containing 200 mm. air pressure and shows slight growth at 380 mm.

The most important anaerobic bacteria are placed in the genus *Clostridium*. Some are obligately anaerobic; others are anaerobic, aerotolerant. They are large, Gram-positive rods producing spores which cause a bulging of the cell wall. Catalase is lacking except in small amounts in certain aerotolerant forms. Some species are strongly fermentative; others are actively putrefactive. A few species are obligately thermophilic. They are commonly found in soil and in human and animal feces.

Mechanism of Oxygen Inhibition. The mechanism involved in the inhibition of growth of anaerobes in the presence of molecular oxygen has been the subject of many investigations. The most important theories appear to be the following:

1. Oxygen is directly toxic to the cell.
2. Hydrogen peroxide is produced, and since the organisms do not elaborate the enzyme catalase, the compound is toxic to the cells.
3. The growth of anaerobes is dependent upon a low oxidation-reduction potential which is not possible in the presence of free oxygen.

1. Free oxygen prevents growth of anaerobic bacteria without killing them. Growth is reestablished when cultures of anaerobes exposed to

air are again placed in an anaerobic environment. The oxygen prevents growth without poisoning the bacteria.

2. McLeod and Gordon (1923) suggested that anaerobes produced small amounts of hydrogen peroxide when exposed to air, and since they are extremely sensitive to the compound, its presence prevented the organisms from growing. This statement was based on certain observations made in connection with the growth of anaerobes in a blood medium. They observed that anaerobic organisms produced a zone of greenish discoloration about $\frac{1}{8}$ in. below the surface of tubes of heated blood (chocolate) agar. The growth was very similar to that produced by the pneumococcus on the same medium and which is known to be a peroxide producer. Others have arrived at the same conclusions.

The function of catalase is to decompose H_2O_2 into water and molecular oxygen. Although catalase is unable to promote growth of anaerobic organisms in contact with air, it raises the level of growth in deep tubes of agar almost to the surface. Also, the appearance of a green-colored ring in chocolate agar cultures of anaerobes is greatly delayed and decreased by the addition of catalase.

It is exceedingly difficult to demonstrate peroxide production by anaerobes since their active life is inhibited by exposure to air before sufficient peroxide has accumulated in cultures to give a positive test. If colonies of Clostridium botulinum on a blood agar plate are treated with benzidine, dark halos appear within an hour after exposure to air. The test indicates the production of peroxide in the presence of oxygen. Since the organisms do not produce catalase, the peroxide becomes toxic to the bacteria.

Gordon, Holman, and McLeod (1953) showed that direct tests for H_2O_2 in oxygenated sediments from liquid cultures of anaerobes gave quite variable and usually negative results. This was due to the fact that the residual medium and metabolic products of the organisms masked the H_2O_2 produced or interfered with the reactions used for its detection. If the organisms were centrifuged in such a way that the residual medium and metabolites were almost completely removed, and the sediment resuspended in peroxide-free distilled water and then oxygenated, positive reactions for H_2O_2 were obtained in almost every case. It was suggested that indirect reactions were less readily obtained with proteolytic anaerobes because this activity increased the concentration of substances capable of masking H_2O_2.

3. Quastel and Stephenson (1926) believed that anaerobic growth was dependent upon a low oxidation-reduction potential, which was not possible in the presence of free oxygen. Reed and Orr (1943) found that some 15 species of pathogenic clostridia grew luxuriantly from small inocula in a simple, slightly alkaline peptone solution, provided that it was poised at a favorable oxidation-reduction potential. The optimum

Eh was in the region −0.2 volt. A low concentration of glucose produced an oxidation-reduction potential that approximated the optimum for the species. Sodium thioglycollate, cysteine, ascorbic acid, and sodium formaldehyde sulfoxylate produced better poised oxidation-reduction potentials than glucose.

For more information see Holman and McLeod (1953), Lieberman and Barker (1954).

Cultivation of Anaerobic Bacteria. A large number of procedures have been devised for the cultivation of anaerobic bacteria. Some employ liquid media; others make use of solid preparations. All the procedures aim to exclude atmospheric oxygen from the environment. In some procedures certain constituents are added to media to reduce the oxygen potential. In other procedures, especially where solid media are employed, the cultures are incubated within closed containers from which the oxygen is either absorbed or removed mechanically.

Use of Reducing Compounds. The addition of reducing compounds such as glucose, cysteine, sodium formaldehyde sulfoxylate, and sodium thioglycollate to liquid media usually permits growth of anaerobes under aerobic conditions. Heavy inocula are more effective than light inocula because of the transfer of reducing substances to the new media.

Brewer (1942) introduced a Petri dish cover, together with an agar medium containing sodium thioglycollate and methylene blue, for the surface cultivation of anaerobic bacteria (Fig. 151). The anaerobic agar is melted, cooled to 50°C., poured into a Petri dish, and allowed to harden. The surface of the agar is streaked with the organism. Then the Petri dish cover is replaced by the Brewer anaerobic lid, which is designed to touch the agar at the periphery and trap a small amount of air (less than 1 mm. in thickness) over the surface of the agar. The sodium thio-

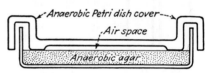

Fig. 151. Technique for using the Brewer Petri dish cover and anaerobic agar.

glycollate in the medium uses up the oxygen in this small amount of air to create anaerobic conditions. The glass rim on the lid forms a seal with the moist agar, preventing the entrance of more atmospheric oxygen. The methylene blue in the agar acts as an indicator, and the center of the dish, which is anaerobic, becomes colorless; the oxygenated edge of the plate, about 5 mm. in diameter, remains blue.

For more information see Skerman (1953).

Use of Aerobe to Absorb Oxygen. Microorganisms have been used to achieve anaerobiosis. This can be handled in two ways: (1) by keeping the aerobe and anaerobe separated and (2) by growing the aerobe and anaerobe together as a mixed culture.

1. A tube of agar is melted and poured into a Petri dish. When the agar has hardened, the plate is divided into two parts by making a line across the bottom with a china-marking pencil. One-half of the plate is streaked with a culture of the anaerobe; the other half is streaked with a culture of an aerobe. The cover is replaced, and the edges of the two halves are sealed with modeling clay. The plate is incubated in the inverted position to prevent accumulation of moisture on the surface of the agar. The moisture may cause the growth to spread and prevent the development of well-isolated colonies.

The aerobe utilizes the free oxygen and eliminates carbon dioxide. The oxygen concentration is soon reduced to a level that permits growth of the anaerobe.

2. Kneteman (1957) proposed a method based on two principles: anaerobiosis was achieved by the addition of an aerobic *Micrococcus* to a liquid medium inocu-

lated with the anaerobe to be cultivated. After anaerobiosis was achieved, the *Micrococcus* gradually died, leaving the anaerobe in a pure state.

If agar plates were used, it was necessary to prevent diffusion of oxygen from the air into the medium. This was effected by covering the agar surface with a very thin film of Saran, which is impervious to oxygen. The plate method is carried out in ordinary Petri dishes. Anaerobic jars are not used.

Use of Activated Iron. Parker (1955) recommended the use of activated iron wool for the removal of oxygen from sealed containers. The iron was activated by immersion in an acid solution of copper sulfate, then drained. Since oxygenated iron absorbs carbon dioxide, more must be added to the closed container; otherwise growth will be seriously affected.

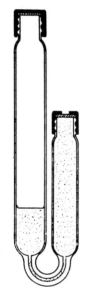

FIG. 152. Anaerobic liquid culture tube. (*After Wilson.*) See text for description.

Use of Living or Dead Tissue. Pieces of kidney, liver, etc., removed aseptically from an animal, or minced and heat-sterilized beef heart or brain tissue have been used for the cultivation of obligate anaerobes.

Minced and sterilized brain medium has been used probably more than any other tissue preparation for the cultivation of anaerobes. It is prepared by suspending cooked and minced sheep brains in glucose broth. Previous to inoculation, the medium is heated for 10 min. in an Arnold sterilizer to drive out as much of the dissolved oxygen as possible. The tube is allowed to cool to a temperature of about 50°C., then inoculated by loop or pipette plunged deep. A surface seal is not necessary because the minced brain tissue is very effective in increasing the reducing power of the medium. Anaerobic growth is first established near the bottom of the tube.

Use of Anaerobic Liquid Culture Tube. Wilson (1950) described a simple device for the cultivation of anaerobic bacteria in a liquid medium without the addition of reducing compounds or pieces of tissue (Fig. 152). It consists of two test tubes, differing in size, which are fitted at the top with screw caps and joined at the bottom with thick-walled capillary tubing. The plastic cap of the small tube is perforated with a small hole, and both caps are supplied with solid, heavy rubber gaskets so that airtight seals are formed when screwed in place.

The tubes are prepared as follows: Broth of the desired composition is added to fill the small arm. It is prevented from running into the large arm by tightening the cap on the latter. After the small arm is filled, its cap is screwed tightly in place. Then the cap in the large arm is removed and about 1 in. of broth added. The cap is replaced loosely on the large arm, and the device with its contained broth is sterilized in an upright position in an autoclave at 121°C. for 20 min. When the tube is removed from the autoclave and allowed to cool, the small arm becomes filled with the medium. The medium in the small arm is maintained in the reduced state, whereas the medium in the large arm becomes oxidized shortly from contact with the air.

The inoculum may be added to the broth in the large arm by a pipette directed at the orifice of the capillary, or it may be introduced into the small arm through the rubber gasket by means of a syringe and needle.

Growth of the anaerobic organisms begins in the small arm, but when growth is particularly vigorous, the medium in both arms will show growth and will be reduced as a result.

Use of Semisolid Agar. The addition of 0.05 to 0.2 per cent agar to an appropriate medium generally provides optimum conditions for the rapid development of anaerobes. The agar creates various degrees of oxygen tension, making possible the growth of anaerobes without special precautions. The medium should be inoculated deep, where the oxygen concentration is very low. The upper portion of the medium is well suited for aerobic growth. Below this the agar develops widely variable degrees of oxygen concentrations, providing a medium suitable for the cultivation of many types of bacteria.

Exclusion of Atmospheric Oxygen. A tube of deep nutrient broth or an appropriate carbohydrate broth is inoculated and then covered with a ½-in. layer of sterile melted vaspar (a mixture of equal parts of petroleum jelly and paraffin). The seal does not prevent entirely the entrance of atmospheric oxygen, but it is usually sufficient in establishing initial growth of the less fastidious anaerobes. After growth has once set in, the elimination of carbon dioxide by the organisms creates optimum conditions for multiplication. It is advisable to heat the medium in an Arnold sterilizer for 10 min. previous to inoculation to drive out as much of the dissolved oxygen as possible.

Agar may be substituted for the broth. A tube of the medium is melted and cooled to about 50°C. The agar is inoculated with the anaerobe, thoroughly mixed by gently shaking and rotating the tube. The medium is allowed to solidify in a vertical position, after which the surface is covered with a ½-in. layer of melted vaspar.

The value of this medium is that it affords a simple means of grading the oxygen tension in the medium. On the surface, the pressure is atmospheric; at the bottom, the conditions are anaerobic. The agar cylinder is removed by cutting the tube in the center, pulling the two halves apart, and collecting the agar in a sterile Petri dish. The colonies can then be fished from the agar and examined.

Absorption of Atmospheric Oxygen. An agar slant is inoculated with the organism to be cultivated. The cotton stopper is cut off flush with the neck of the tube and pushed down about ½ in. below the opening. The surface of the cotton stopper is covered with a layer of pyrogallol crystals, then moistened with a few drops of sodium hydroxide solution. A tight-fitting rubber stopper is inserted into the opening of the tube to exclude atmospheric oxygen. The alkaline pyrogallol absorbs oxygen from the environment, creating conditions compatible with the growth requirements of the anaerobe. This procedure is usually sat-

Fig. 153. Left, Bray anaerobic culture dish; right, Spray anaerobic culture dish.

isfactory for the cultivation of those organisms which are not too exacting in their requirements.

A more convenient arrangement is to employ a Bray or a Spray anaerobic culture dish (Fig. 153). The dish is separated at the bottom by a raised center ridge. In one compartment is placed a solution of pyrogallol and in the other a solution of sodium hydroxide. Melted agar is poured into a Petri dish and allowed to harden. The surface is streaked with the anaerobic organism. The agar plate is then inverted over the top of the culture dish, and the edges are sealed with a suitable material, such as plasticine, to prevent entrance of atmospheric oxygen. Finally, the solutions in the bottom are mixed by gently tilting the dish.

Replacement of Atmospheric Oxygen with Hydrogen. In this procedure the inoculated tubes are placed in a closed jar. The air is evacuated and replaced with hydrogen gas. The jar is then placed in an incubator.

This procedure does not always prove satisfactory, owing to the fact that sufficient oxygen usually remains in the medium to prevent growth. The method becomes considerably more efficient if an alkaline solution of pyrogallol is added to the jar just before the air is removed. This is best performed by placing some pyrogallol crystals on the bottom of the jar, followed by the addition of sufficient solution of sodium hydroxide to dissolve the compound. The lid is replaced immediately and the air removed as quickly as possible. The pyrogallol usually removes any oxygen still remaining in the medium, permitting growth of the strict anaerobes.

A solution of methylene blue is frequently placed in anaerobic jars as an indicator of anaerobiosis. Methylene blue is blue in the oxidized state and colorless when reduced.

A procedure for the preparation of a satisfactory indicator solution is as follows:
Solution A: 6 ml. N/10NaOH solution diluted to 100 ml. with distilled water.

Solution B: 3 ml. of a 0.5 per cent aqueous solution of methylene blue diluted to 100 ml. with distilled water.

Solution C: 6 gm. of glucose dissolved in 100 ml. of distilled water, to which is added a small crystal of thymol as a preservative.

Mix equal parts of the three solutions in a test tube, place the tube in boiling water, and heat until the color of the dye disappears. Transfer the tube to the anaerobic jar containing the organisms to be cultivated and immediately evacuate the

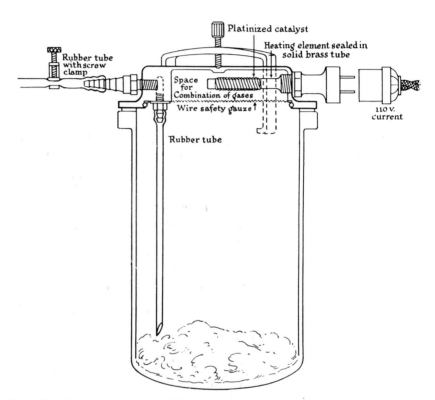

FIG. 154. Cross section of modified Brewer anaerobic jar showing construction. (*After Evans, Carlquist, and Brewer.*)

container. If the solution remains colorless, it indicates that the container is satisfactorily deoxygenated; if the blue color returns, it indicates that conditions are not anaerobic. The mixture of the three solutions should be freshly prepared before use.

Combustion of Oxygen with Hydrogen. Surface colonies are most essential for purifying and identifying anaerobes. The removal of oxygen by combustion with hydrogen is probably the most efficient method for obtaining surface colonies of anaerobes.

The first practical development of a jar of this type was announced by Fildes (1931). A convenient modification by Evans, Carlquist, and Brewer (1948) is shown in Fig. 154.

For more information see Society of American Bacteriologists (1957).

REDUCTION OF NITRATE

The term nitrate reduction includes all processes in which nitrate disappears under the influence of bacterial action and reappears in some less oxidized state. In many cases the reduction does not proceed beyond the stage of nitrite. However, a few organisms are able to convert nitrate to molecular nitrogen.

The reduction of nitrate has long been used as a test for separating bacteria (Fig. 155). The test is of value in identifying and classifying bacteria.

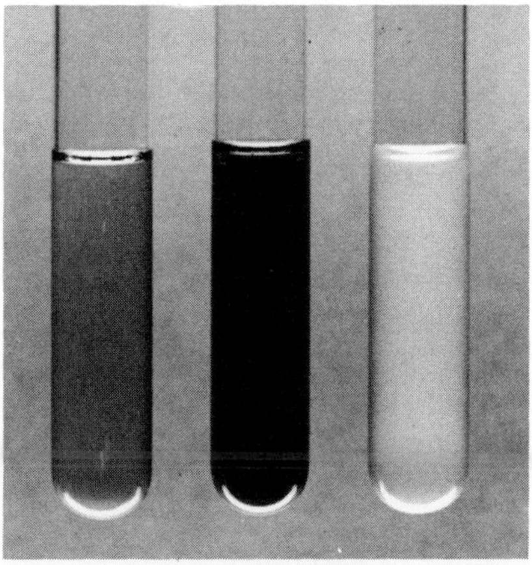

An organism that takes up nitrate from the medium and utilizes it for the synthesis of its cell protein may also be considered a nitrate-reducing organism. However, there are good reasons for separating nitrate-assimilating organisms from those which have the property of reducing the compound and excreting most of the reduction products into the surrounding medium.

FIG. 155. Reduction of nitrate to nitrite. Left, control, uninoculated; center, culture of *Proteus vulgaris* showing reduction of nitrate to nitrite (red color with reagents); right, culture of *Pseudomonas fluorescens* showing no reduction.

From the foregoing considerations, biological nitrate reductions may be classified into the following three types:

1. Assimilatory nitrate reduction, which may be termed nitrate assimilation.
2. Incidental dissimilatory nitrate reduction, in which the nitrate merely acts as a nonessential hydrogen acceptor.
3. True dissimilatory nitrate reduction, in which the nitrate acts as a hydrogen acceptor essential for growth.

In the third type, nitrate is reduced only by aerobic bacteria growing under anaerobic or partial anaerobic conditions. These organisms thrive very well in the absence of nitrate if a suitable nitrogen source is present in the medium. Under anaerobic conditions, nitrate may be substituted for oxygen as a hydrogen acceptor. As a result, the nitrate becomes reduced. On the other hand, if the culture is well aerated, nitrate is not reduced.

Verhoeven (1952, 1956a) and Kluyver and Verhoeven (1954) proposed the following scheme for the reduction of nitrate:

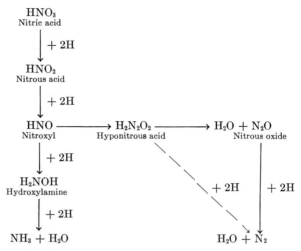

The end products include nitrite, nitrous oxide, ammonia, and nitrogen.

Reduction of nitrate to nitrogen gas may be detected by dispensing nitrate medium in test tubes containing inverted vials. The nitrogen gas is trapped in the vial as it is formed and may be observed.

In making tests for nitrate reduction, observe for (1) the reduction of nitrate to nitrite, (2) the disappearance of nitrite to ammonia, and (3) the presence of nitrogen gas. It is highly important that tests be made for these three products.

The presence of nitrite indicates that nitrate has been reduced. The presence of gas shows that nitrite has been reduced to ammonia and finally to nitrogen. Negative results mean that (1) the organism under examination is unable to reduce nitrate, or (2) the medium is not satisfactory for growth. The medium may be improved by (1) increasing or decreasing the amount of peptone, (2) increasing the concentration of nitrate, (3) adjusting the reaction of the medium to a more favorable pH, (4) adding a readily available carbohydrate to stimulate growth, and (5) incorporating a small amount of agar to increase the viscosity of the medium.

The nitrite test may be negative even though good growth has occurred. This may indicate no action on the nitrate or complete reduction beyond the nitrite stage. Therefore, tests for nitrate should be made in every case where a negative nitrite test is obtained. If tests do not show nitrate reduction, it is probable that the organism is not capable of attacking the compound.

For more information see Allen and van Niel (1952); Collins (1956); Delwiche (1959); Eltinge (1956); Iwasaki, Matsubayashi, and Mori (1956); Kefauver and Allison (1957); Kinsky and McElroy (1958); McElroy and Spencer (1956); Sacks and Barker (1952); Sadana and

McElroy (1957); Skerman and MacRae (1957); Taniguchi, Sato, and Egami (1956); and Verhoeven (1956*b*).

REDUCTION OF SULFATE

Beijerinck (1895) is generally believed to be the first to cultivate an organism from ditch mud that was capable of reducing sulfate to sulfide. He named the organism *Spirillum desulfuricans*.

Van Delden (1904) employed the following isolation medium: gelatin, 10 gm.; sodium lactate, 0.5 gm.; asparagine, 0.1 gm.; $MgSO_4 \cdot 7H_2O$, 0.1 gm.; K_2HPO_4, 0.05 gm.; ferrous ammonium sulfate, trace; tap water, 1000 ml.

The organisms obtained their energy from the anaerobic reduction of the sulfate, accompanied by a simultaneous oxidation of the lactate. The proportion of carbonic acid and hydrogen sulfide produced was in the ratio of 2:1. From this observation van Delden considered the reaction to proceed as follows:

$$2CH_3 \cdot CHOH \cdot COONa + 3MgSO_4 \rightarrow 3MgCO_3 + Na_2CO_3 + 2CO_2 + 3H_2S + 2H_2O$$

A general equation for the reduction of sulfates may be represented as follows:

$$2C + MeSO_4 + H_2O \rightarrow MeCO_3 + CO_2 + H_2S$$

in which C represents an organic substrate and Me a metal.

Baars (1930) showed that a large number of organic compounds could be substituted for the lactate, all of which were oxidized in an appropriate sulfate medium inoculated with the specific organism. The organic compounds were oxidized by the removal of hydrogen, i.e., they acted as hydrogen donors. A few typical examples are the following:

$$H \cdot COOH \rightarrow CO_2 + 2H$$
Formic acid

$$CH_3 \cdot COOH + 2H_2O \rightarrow 2CO_2 + 8H$$
Acetic acid

$$CH_3 \cdot CHOH \cdot COOH + 3H_2O \rightarrow 3CO_2 + 12H$$
Lactic acid

$$CH_2OH \cdot CHOH \cdot CH_2OH + 3H_2O \rightarrow 3CO_2 + 14H$$
Glycerol

In the reduction of sulfate, each molecule required eight atoms of hydrogen for its conversion into hydrogen sulfide. The dehydrogenation of the organic substrate proceeded by steps, followed by a corresponding hydrogenation of the sulfate to produce hydrogen sulfide:

$$H_2SO_4 + 8H \rightarrow H_2S + 4H_2O$$

It was shown that unless the organic compound was present in large excess, complete oxidation did not occur.

Organisms. The sulfate reducers are placed in the genus *Desulfovibrio* (see page 411). The type species is *D. desulfuricans* (Fig. 156). Two other species are recognized. They are strict anaerobes and reduce sulfates to sulfides. The organisms are found in sea water, marine mud, fresh water, and soil.

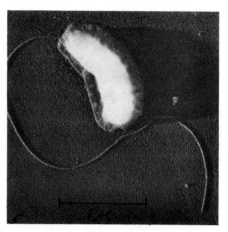

Fig. 156. Electron micrograph of *Desulfovibrio desulfuricans*. (*Courtesy of L. Leon Campbell, Jr.*)

Desulfovibrios may be cultivated by inoculating soil or mud into synthetic media containing 0.5 per cent sodium sulfate and incubating the culture under anaerobic conditions. Isolated colonies may be obtained by streaking a loopful of the liquid culture over the surface of a sulfate agar medium containing a trace of iron salt as an indicator. The hydrogen sulfide produced by the organisms reacts with the iron salt to produce iron sulfide, which imparts a black color to the colonies.

These are the only bacteria that are able to effect the direct reduction of sulfate to sulfide. It is because of this reaction that they are included among the nuisance organisms in water. The sulfide not only makes the water unpalatable and odoriferous, but the bacteria may cause corrosion of steel and cast iron of water-distribution systems.

The organisms are said to contribute to the formation of petroleum and to its modification after formation. It has been claimed that some strains are capable of releasing oil from oil-bearing sediments.

For more information see Butlin, Adams, and Thomas (1949); Davis and Updegraff (1954); LaRivière (1955); Postgate (1951a, b); Updegraff and Wren (1954).

PRODUCTION OF METHANE

Söhngen (1910) showed that salts of various fatty acids could be decomposed by certain soil bacteria to carbon dioxide (CO_2) and methane (CH_4). Using impure cultures, he showed that formate was decomposed according to the equation:

$$4H \cdot COOH \rightarrow CH_4 + 3CO_2 + 2H_2O$$

The impure culture was also capable of synthesizing CH_4 from CO_2 and hydrogen:

$$CO_2 + 4H_2 \rightarrow CH_4 + 2H_2O$$

The important methane-producing bacteria are anaerobes and are found in the genera *Methanobacterium, Methanococcus,* and *Sarcina.* These are characterized as follows:

1. *Methanobacterium:* Straight or slightly curved rods, sometimes united in bundles or long chains. Anaerobic. Chemo-heterotrophic or chemo-autotrophic, oxidizing various organic and inorganic compounds and reducing CO_2 to CH_4. Gram-negative. Found in canal mud and sewage.

2. *Methanococcus:* Spherical cells, occurring singly, in pairs, or in masses. Motile or nonmotile. Gram-variable. Chemo-heterotrophic, fermenting various organic compounds with production of CH_4. Anaerobic. Saprophytes. Found in soil, mud, sewage sludge, and animal feces.

3. *Sarcina:* Spheres, multiplying in packets. Usually nonmotile. Gram-positive. Produce CH_4 from CO_2. Found in mud and fermenting sewage sludge.

For more information see Mylroie and Hungate (1954), Pine (1958), Pine and Barker (1956), Pine and Vishniac (1957), Stadtman and Barker (1951*a, b*).

NECESSITY OF CARBON DIOXIDE FOR BACTERIA

It is well known that bacteria do not grow in the complete absence of carbon dioxide. An accumulation of a definite amount of the gas is necessary to initiate growth. Many bacteria grow better in the presence of an increased concentration of carbon dioxide. Some organisms, when freshly isolated from disease processes, either do not grow or grow very poorly unless the carbon dioxide concentration of the environment is increased to 5 to 10 per cent. After growth on artificial media is once established, an increased concentration of the gas is no longer necessary.

It is now generally accepted that carbon dioxide plays an important role in the metabolism of a variety of heterotrophic organisms. The compound is utilized by these organisms and becomes incorporated in a variety of metabolic products (see page 380).

Tracer Studies with Radioactive Carbon. Slade et al. (1942) employed carbon dioxide ($C^{13}O_2$) as a tracer and found that the assimilation of the gas was a general phenomenon among the heterotrophic bacteria. The radioactive carbon was located in the carboxyl groups of succinic, lactic, and acetic acids. Succinic acid always contained fixed carbon, whereas lactate and acetate did not contain fixed carbon in all cases.

Barker and Kamen (1945) employed carbon dioxide ($C^{14}O_2$) as a tracer and concluded that the acetic fermentation of glucose by *Clos-*

tridium thermoaceticum involved a partial oxidation of the substrate to two molecules each of acetic acid and carbon dioxide, followed by a reduction and condensation of the carbon dioxide to a third molecule of acetic acid:

$$C_6H_{12}O_6 + 2H_2O \rightarrow 2CH_3 \cdot COOH + 8H + 2CO_2$$
$$8H + 2CO_2 \rightarrow CH_3 \cdot COOH + 2H_2O$$

About 94 per cent of the C^{14} from the added carbon dioxide disappeared during the fermentation, and approximately 81 per cent was recovered in the acetic acid.

McLean, Robinson and Purdie (1951) obtained data which indicated that *Serratia marcescens* utilized C^{14}-labeled bicarbonate for the synthesis of protein.

More recently Pine and Barker (1956) found that *Butyribacterium rettgeri* fermented lactate labeled with C^{14} to CO_2 and acetate. The CO_2 originated from the carboxyl group and the acetate from the 2 and 3 carbon positions.

Newton et al. (1954) reported that *Brucella abortus* incorporated $C^{14}O_2$ into the pyrimidines of nucleic acids. Tepper and Wilson (1958) found $C^{14}O_2$ fixed into the amino acid glycine of proteins.

These are only a few of the many reports found in the literature on the necessity of carbon dioxide for living cells.

For more information see Griffin and Racker (1956); Lynch and Calvin (1952); McLean and Purdie (1955); Pine (1956); Prescott, Ragland, and Stutts (1957); Prescott and Stutts (1955); and Wood (1946).

NECESSITY OF OXYGEN FOR BACTERIA

All living plants and animals consume O_2 and eliminate CO_2. Bacteria also utilize O_2 (either free or combined) and eliminate CO_2.

Organisms differ widely in their sensitiveness to free O_2. Some are depressed in growth by a slight increase in the concentration of O_2; others are stimulated in growth by concentrations up to 60 per cent.

The O_2 supply of bacteria in the usual culture methods is generally far from adequate. As an example, *Mycobacterium tuberculosis* is said to require 1.22 per cent O_2 for the complete oxidation of 1 per cent glycerol. The medium at 37°C. contains only 0.00065 per cent O_2. The disproportion between supply and demand is so great that a majority of the cells in a culture probably starve for lack of oxygen.

Smith and Johnson (1954) reported that the per cent yield of *Serratia marcescens* varied directly with aeration efficiency. The cell concentration on a dry-weight basis varied from 9 mg. per ml. at an effective aeration rate of 0.5 mm. O_2 per liter per min., to 23 mg. per ml. at an aeration rate of 9 mm. O_2 per liter per min.

Pirt (1957) found that the fate of glucose in cultures of *Aerobacter aerogenes* depended upon the amount of available O_2 and the O_2 demand of the organisms. Anaerobically, cell synthesis and CO_2 production were at their minimum levels, and most of the glucose carbon was converted to alcohol, formic acid, 2:3-butylene glycol, acetoin, and acetic acid. A small supply of O_2 suppressed the formation of alcohol and formic acid but still permitted the production of butylene glycol and acetoin, and increased the proportion of glucose carbon converted to acetic acid, bacterial cells, and CO_2. With an excess of O_2, all intermediates were oxidized, and complete conversion of glucose carbon into cell material and CO_2 occurred.

Cahn-Bronner (1940) cultivated a number of organisms under partial starvation in tubes containing a deep column of agar and found that the organisms grew in a fine, dense layer below the surface of the medium where the relation between the nutrient content and O_2 was at an optimum. Under increasing starvation (more dilute medium), the bacteria became progressively more sensitive to O_2. The lower the concentration of carbon compounds in the medium which may act as oxygen acceptors, the more inhibitory the action of O_2 on the organisms.

For more information see Finn (1954) and Longmuir (1954).

TRICARBOXYLIC ACID CYCLE

Krebs (1940) pointed out that in most animal tissues investigated, the main pathway of terminal respiration takes place by way of the so-called tricarboxylic acid (TCA) cycle. A schematic drawing of the cycle is given in Fig. 157.

A considerable literature has accumulated since the above date on the demonstration of the cycle in bacteria, yeasts, and molds. This would indicate that the TCA cycle is of universal biological occurrence.

For more information see Ajl and Wong (1955); Campbell and Smith (1956); Delwiche and Carson (1953); DeMoss and Swim (1957); Englesberg and Levy (1955); Pan, Yee, and Gezon (1957); Schatz, Mohan, and Trelawny (1955); Youmans, Millman, and Youmans (1956).

CHROMOGENESIS

A large number of bacteria produce nonphotosynthetic colored compounds known as pigments. This is especially true of the strictly aerobic species. Many colors are produced, covering the entire range of the spectrum.

Conditions Necessary for Pigment Production. It is probable that pigments are produced only in the presence of oxygen.

Pigmented cultures placed in an anaerobic environment slowly lose their color. The color gradually returns when such cultures are again exposed to air.

Certain special media are required for strong pigment production. Yeast extract, glucose, casein hydrolysates, glycerol, and mineral salts appear to be popular constituents of such media. Both solid and liquid media have been used with favorable results. The pH of media influences

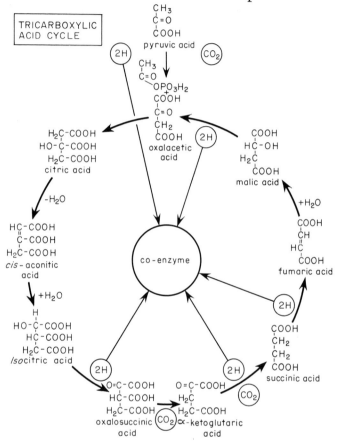

FIG. 157. Krebs's tricarboxylic acid cycle. (*After Kluyver.*)

the color of some pigments. A temperature of 20 to 30°C. appears to be best for the production of most pigments. Pigment production slowly decreases with a gradual rise in temperature.

Some pigments are water soluble and dissolve in the culture media; most pigments are not soluble in water and remain confined within the bacterial cells. The majority of pigments are soluble in fat solvents such as alcohol, acetone, ether, and chloroform.

Effect of Light. With few exceptions (the photosynthetic bacteria), pigment formation takes place best in the dark. Certain strains of acid-fast organisms appear to be exceptions in that pigment is produced only in the presence of light.

Types of Bacterial Pigments. Most bacterial pigments may be classified as carotenoids, anthocyanins, melanins, tripyrrylmethenes, and phenazines.

Carotenoids. These are red, orange, or yellow pigments which are soluble in fat solvents such as alcohol, ether, or chloroform. They derive their name from the unsaturated hydrocarbon carotene, $C_{40}H_{56}$, the same pigment found in butter, egg yolks, flour, and carrots. Oxidized carotene, $C_{40}H_{56}O_2$, is known as xanthophyll. The two pigments are usually found together in nature.

For more information see Courington and Goodwin (1955), Ellinghausen and Pelczar (1955), Goodwin, Land, and Osman (1955), Mathews and Sistrom (1959), and Steuer (1957).

Anthocyanins. The anthocyanins include the red and blue pigments and intermediate shades found in the petals of many flowers and some bacteria. They are soluble in water and alcohol but not in ether. Most, if not all, are natural indicators, changing usually from red in acid solution to green in alkaline solution. They are glucosides and on hydrolysis yield a sugar and some derivative of benzopyrilium:

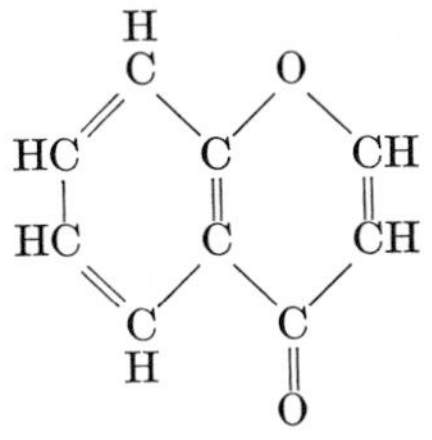

Benzopyrilium

Several species of *Streptomyces* have been reported as being capable of producing anthocyanins.

Melanins. The melanins include certain brown, black, orange, and red pigments which are insoluble in almost all solvents. They are dissolved by concentrated sulfuric acid and reprecipitated by the addition of water. The pigments are produced from the decomposition of proteins by boiling concentrated mineral acids or by the action of the enzyme tyrosinase on the amino acid tyrosine. In addition to tyrosine, the enzyme attacks other compounds, including tryptophan.

Tripyrrylmethenes. *Serratia marcescens* produces the red pigment prodigiosin, which has been characterized as a derivative of tripyrrylmethene. It has been fractionated into four components, each showing a different shade of color. The pigment is generally insoluble in water. An occasional strain has been encountered in which one or more of the components are said to be water soluble.

For more information see Green, Rappoport, and Williams (1956);

Green and Williams (1957); Santer and Vogel (1956); Williams and Green (1956); Williams, Green, and Rappoport (1956); Williams et al. (1958).

Phenazines. *Pseudomonas aureofaciens* and three other species of *Pseudomonas* are capable of producing phenazine α-carboxylic acid:

Phenazine α-carboxylic acid

The pigment is soluble in the medium and imparts to it first an orange-yellow, then a deep orange, and finally a reddish-orange color. For more information see Haynes et al. (1956).

Function of Pigments. Little is known concerning the physiological function of nonphotosynthetic pigments. They are colored when oxidized and colorless when reduced. Since pigment production generally takes place in the presence of oxygen, some believe that they act as respiratory carriers. Evidence available at present is not sufficient to support this view.

For more information see Bancroft (1943) and Williams (1956).

REFERENCES

Airth, R. L., W. C. Rhodes, and W. D. McElroy: The function of coenzyme A in luminescence, *Biochim. Biophys. Acta*, 27:519, 1958.

Ajl, S. J., and D. T. O. Wong: A reappraisal of the tricarboxylic acid cycle in the respiration of *Escherichia coli*, *Arch. Biochem. Biophys.*, 54:474, 1955.

Allen, M. B., and C. B. van Niel: Experiments on bacterial denitrification, *J. Bact.*, 64:397, 1952.

Avery, O. T., and J. M. Neill: Studies on oxidation and reduction by pneumococcus. II. The production of peroxide by sterile extracts of pneumococcus, *J. Exp. Med.*, 39:357, 1924a; III. Reduction of methylene blue by sterile extracts of pneumococcus, *ibid.*, 39:543, 1924b.

Baars, J. K.: "Over Sulfaatreductie Door Bakterien," English translation, dissertation, Delft, 1930.

Bancroft, W. D.: The biochemistry of anthocyanins, *Science*, 98:98, 1943.

Barker, H. A., and M. D. Kamen: Carbon dioxide utilization in the synthesis of acetic acid by *Clostridium thermoaceticum*, *Proc. Nat. Acad. Sci.*, 31:219, 1945.

Behm, R. C., and J. M. Nelson: The activity of tyrosinase toward phenol, *J. Am. Chem. Soc.*, 66:709, 1944a.

——— and ———: The aerobic oxidation of phenol by means of tyrosinase, *ibid.*, 66:711, 1944b.

Beijerinck, M. W.: Über *Spirillum desulfuricans* als Ursache von Sulfatreduktion, *Centr. Bakt., II*, 1:1, 1895.

Bitler, B., and W. D. McElroy: The preparation and properties of crystalline firefly luciferin, *Arch. Biochem. Biophys.*, 72:358, 1957.

Brewer, J. H.: A new Petri dish cover and technique for use in the cultivation of anaerobes and microaerophiles, *Science*, 95:587, 1942.

Burris, R. H., and H. N. Little: Oxidases, peroxidases and catalase. From "Respiratory Enzymes," edited by Henry A. Lardy, Minneapolis, Burgess Publishing Company, 1949.

Butlin, K. R., M. E. Adams, and M. Thomas: The isolation and cultivation of sulfate-reducing bacteria, *J. Gen. Microbiol.*, 3:46, 1949.

Cahn-Bronner, C. E.: Oxygen requirement of pathogenic bacteria under starving conditions, *Proc. Soc. Exp. Biol. Med.*, 45:454, 1940.

Campbell, J. J. R., and R. A. Smith: The enzymes of the tricarboxylic acid cycle of *Pseudomonas aeruginosa, Can. J. Microbiol.*, 2:433, 1956.

Campbell, L. L., Jr., H. A. Frank, and E. R. Hall: Studies on thermophilic sulfate reducing bacteria. I. Identification of *Sporovibrio desulfuricans* as *Clostridium nigrificans, J. Bact.*, 73:516, 1957.

Clark, W. M., B. Cohen, M. X. Sullivan, H. D. Gibbs, and R. K. Cannan: Studies on oxidation-reduction. I. Introduction, *Pub. Health Reports*, 38:443, 1923.

Collins, F. M.: Bacterial denitrification in shaken cultures, *Enzymologia*, 17:291, 1956.

Cooperstein, S. J.: Reduction of cytochrome oxidase by reduced diphosphopyridine nucleotide-cytochrome c reductase, *J. Biol. Chem.*, 234:392, 1959.

Cormier, M. J., and J. R. Totter: Quantum efficiency determinations on components of the bacterial luminescence system, *Biochim. Biophys. Acta*, 25:229, 1957.

————, ————, and H. H. Rostorfer: Comparative studies on different bacterial luciferase preparations, *Arch. Biochem. Biophys.*, 63:414, 1956.

Courington, D. P., and T. W. Goodwin: A survey of the pigments of a number of chromogenic marine bacteria, with special reference to the carotenoids, *J. Bact.*, 70:568, 1955.

Davis, J. B., and D. M. Updegraff: Microbiology in the petroleum industry, *Bact. Rev.*, 18:215, 1954.

Delwiche, C. C.: Production and utilization of nitrous oxide by *Pseudomonas denitrificans, J. Bact.*, 77:55, 1959.

Delwiche, E. A., and S. F. Carson: A citric acid cycle in *Propionibacterium pentosaceum, ibid.*, 65:318, 1953.

DeMoss, J. A., and H. E. Swim: Quantitative aspects of the tricarboxylic acid cycle in baker's yeast, *J. Bact.*, 74:445, 1957.

Dixon, M., and E. C. Webb: "Enzymes," New York, Academic Press, Inc., 1958.

Eddy, B. P., M. Ingram, and L. W. Mapson: Reduction of dehydroascorbic acid by bacteria, *Biochem. J.*, 58:254, 1954.

Ellinghausen, H. C., Jr., and M. J. Pelczar, Jr.: Spectrophotometric characterization of *Neisseria* pigments, *J. Bact.*, 70:448, 1955.

Eltinge, E. T.: Nitrate reduction in the genus *Chromobacterium, Antonie van Leeuwenhoek*, 22:139, 1956.

Englesberg, E., and J. B. Levy: Induced synthesis of tricarboxylic acid cycle enzymes as correlated with the oxidation of acetate and glucose by *Pasteurella pestis, J. Bact.*, 69:418, 1955.

Ericsson, Y., and H. Lundbeck: Antimicrobial effect in vitro of the ascorbic acid oxidation, *Acta Path. Microbiol. Scand.*, 37:507, 1955.

Evans, J. M., P. R. Carlquist, and J. H. Brewer: A modification of the Brewer anaerobic jar, *J. Clin. Path.*, 18:745, 1948.

Fildes, P.: "A System of Bacteriology," vol. 9, London, Medical Research Council, 1931.

Finn, R. K.: Agitation-aeration in the laboratory and in industry, *Bact. Rev.*, 18:254, 1954.

Goodwin, T. W., D. G. Land, and H. G. Osman: Studies in carotenogenesis. 14. Carotenoid synthesis in the photosynthetic bacterium *Rhodopseudomonas spheroides, Biochem. J.*, 59:491, 1955.

Gordon, J., R. A. Holman, and J. W. McLeod: Further observations on the production of hydrogen peroxide by anaerobic bacteria, *J. Path. Bact.*, 66:527, 1953.

Green, A. A., and W. D. McElroy: Crystalline firefly luciferase, *Biochim. Biophys. Acta*, 20:170, 1956.

Green, J. A., D. A. Rappoport, and R. P. Williams: Studies on pigmentation of *Serratia marcescens*. II. Characterization of the blue and the combined red pigments of prodigiosin, *J. Bact.*, 72:483, 1956.

———— and R. P. Williams: Studies on pigmentation of *Serratia marcescens, ibid.*, 74:633, 1957.

Griffin, P. J., and E. Racker: The carbon dioxide requirement of *Neisseria gonorrhoeae*, *J. Bact.*, 71:717, 1956.

Haynes, W. C., F. H. Stodola, J. M. Locke, T. G. Pridham, H. F. Conway, V. E. Sohns, and R. W. Jackson: *Pseudomonas aureofaciens* Kluyver and phenazine α-carboxylic acid, its characteristic pigment, *J. Bact.*, 72:412, 1956.

Hewitt, L. F.: "Oxidation-Reduction Potentials in Bacteriology and Biochemistry," Edinburgh, E. and S. Livingstone, Ltd., 1950.

Holman, R. A., and J. W. McLeod: Observations on Schales' reaction for hydrogen peroxide with special reference to its use in complex solutions containing sugar and peptone, *Brit. J. Exp. Path.*, 34:191, 1953.

Hopkins, F. G.: On an autoxidizable constituent of the cell, *Biochem. J.*, 15:286, 1921.

———: On glutathione: a reinvestigation, *J. Biol. Chem.*, 84:269, 1929.

Isaacs, A., and J. M. Scouller: Catalase production by Gram-positive cocci: A simple test for differentiating enterococci from micrococci, *J. Path. Bact.*, 60:135, 1948.

Iwasaki, H., R. Matsubayashi, and T. Mori: Studies on denitrification. II. Production of nitric oxide and its utilization in the N-N-linkage formation by denitrifying bacteria, *J. Biochem.*, 43:295, 1956.

Kamen, M. D., and L. P. Vernon: Comparative studies on bacterial cytochromes, *Biochim. Biophys. Acta*, 17:10, 1955.

Kefauver, M., and F. E. Allison: Nitrite reduction by *Bacterium denitrificans* in relation to oxidation-reduction potential and oxygen tension, *J. Bact.*, 73:8, 1957.

Keilin, D.: On cytochrome, a respiratory pigment common to animals, yeast, and higher plants, *Proc. Roy. Soc.* (*London*), Series B, 98:312, 1925.

———: Cytochrome and intracellular respiratory enzymes, *Ergeb. Enzymforsch.*, 2:239, 1933.

——— and E. F. Hartree: Cytochrome oxidase, *Proc. Roy. Soc.* (*London*), Series B, 125:171, 1938.

——— and ———: Properties of azidecatalase, *Biochem. J.*, 39:148, 1945.

Kinsky, S. C., and W. D. McElroy: *Neurospora* nitrate reductase: The role of phosphate, flavine and cytochrome c reductase, *Arch. Biochem. Biophys.*, 73:466, 1958.

Kluyver, A. J., and W. Verhoeven: Studies on true dissimilatory nitrate reduction, *Antonie van Leeuwenhoek*, 20:241, 1954.

Kneteman, A.: A method for the cultivation of anaerobic spore forming bacteria, *J. Appl. Bact.*, 20:101, 1957.

Krebs, H. A.: The citric acid cycle, *Biochem. J.*, 34:460, 1940.

Laidler, K. J.: "Introduction to the Chemistry of Enzymes," New York, McGraw-Hill Book Company, Inc., 1954.

LaRivière, J. W. M.: The production of surface active compounds by micro-organisms and its possible significance in oil recovery. II. On the release of oil from oil-sand mixtures with the aid of sulfate reducing bacteria, *Antonie van Leeuwenhoek*, 21:9, 1955.

Lieberman, I., and H. A. Barker: The production of hydrogen peroxide by an obligate anaerobe, *Clostridium kluyveri*, *J. Bact.*, 68:61, 1954.

Longmuir, I. S.: Respiration rate of bacteria as a function of oxygen concentration, *Biochem. J.*, 57:81, 1954.

Lynch, V. H., and M. Calvin: Carbon dioxide fixation by microorganisms, *J. Bact.*, 63:525, 1952.

MacMunn, C. A.: Researches on myohaematin and the histohaematins, *Trans. Roy. Soc.* (*London*), 177:267, 1886.

Mathews, M. M., and W. R. Sistrom: Intracellular location of carotenoid pigments and some respiratory enzymes in *Sarcina lutea*, *J. Bact.*, 78:778, 1959.

McElroy, W. D., and A. A. Green: Enzymatic properties of bacterial luciferase, *Arch. Biochem. Biophys.*, 56:240, 1955.

——— and ———: Function of adenosine triphosphate in the activation of luciferin, *ibid.*, 64:257, 1956.

——— and J. W. Hastings: Biochemistry of firefly luminescence. From "The Luminescence of Biological Systems," edited by F. H. Johnson, Washington, D.C., A.A.A.S., 1955.

—— and D. Spencer: Normal pathways of assimilation of nitrate and nitrite. From "Inorganic Nitrogen Metabolism," edited by W. D. McElroy and B. Glass, Baltimore, Johns Hopkins Press, 1956.

—— and B. L. Strehler: Bioluminescence, *Bact. Rev.*, **18**:177, 1954.

McLean, D. J., and E. F. Purdie: Effect of dicarboxylic acids, amino acids, amides, and carbohydrates on carbon dioxide fixation by *Serratia marcescens, J. Bact.*, **69**:204, 1955.

——, N. H. Robinson, and E. F. Purdie: The influence of the metabolic state and of the medium on carbon dioxide fixation by *Serratia marcescens, J. Bact.*, **61**:617, 1951.

McLeod, J. W., and J. Gordon: The problem of intolerance of oxygen by anaerobic bacteria, *J. Path. Bact.*, **26**:332, 1923.

Mehler, A. H.: "Introduction to Enzymology," New York, Academic Press, Inc., 1957.

Mylroie, R. L., and R. E. Hungate: Experiments on the methane bacteria in sludge, *Can. J. Microbiol.*, **1**:55, 1954.

Neilands, J. B., and P. K. Stumpf: "Outlines of Enzyme Chemistry," New York, John Wiley & Sons, Inc., 1958.

Newton, J. W., and M. D. Kamen: *Chromatium* cytochrome, *Arch. Biochem. Biophys.*, **58**:246, 1955.

—— and ——: *Chromatium* cytochrome, *Biochim. Biophys. Acta*, **21**:71, 1956.

——, A. G. Marr, and J. B. Wilson: Fixation of $C^{14}O_2$ into nucleic acid constituents by *Brucella abortus, J. Bact.*, **67**:233, 1954.

Pan, S. F., R. Yee, and H. M. Gezon: Studies on the metabolism of *Shigella*. I. The occurrence of a tricarboxylic acid cycle in *Shigella flexneri, J. Bact.*, **73**:402, 1957.

Parker, C. A.: Anaerobiosis with iron wool, *Australian J. Exp. Biol. Med. Sci.*, **33**:33, 1955.

Pine, L.: Fixation of carbon dioxide by *Actinomyces* and *Lactobacillus bifidus, Proc. Soc. Exp. Biol. Med.*, **93**:468, 1956.

—— and H. A. Barker: Tracer experiments on the mechanism of acetate formation from carbon dioxide by *Butyribacterium rettgeri, J. Bact.*, **68**:216, 1954.

Pine, M. J.: Methane fermentation of formate by *Methanobacillus omelianskii, J. Bact.*, **75**:356, 1958.

—— and H. A. Barker: Studies on the methane fermentation. XII. The pathway of hydrogen in the acetate fermentation, *J. Bact.*, **71**:644, 1956.

—— and W. Vishniac: The methane fermentations of acetate and methanol, *J. Bact.*, **73**:736, 1957.

Pirt, S. J.: The oxygen requirement of growing cultures of an *Aerobacter* species determined by means of the continuous culture technique, *J. Gen. Microbiol.*, **16**:59, 1957.

Postgate, J. R.: On the nutrition of *Desulphovibrio desulphuricans, J. Gen. Microbiol.*, **5**:714, 1951*a;* The reduction of sulfur compounds by *Desulphovibrio desulphuricans, ibid.*, **5**:725, 1951*b.*

Prescott, J. M., R. S. Ragland, and A. L. Stutts: Effects of carbon dioxide on the growth of *Streptococcus bovis* in the presence of various amino acids, *J. Bact.*, **73**:133, 1957.

—— and A. L. Stutts: Effects of carbon dioxide on the growth and amino acid metabolism of *Streptococcus bovis, ibid.*, **70**:285, 1955.

Quastel, J. H., and M. Stephenson: Experiments on "strict" anaerobes. 1. The relation of *B. sporogenes* to oxygen, *Biochem. J.*, **20**:1125, 1926.

Reed, G. B., and J. H. Orr: Cultivation of anaerobes and oxidation-reduction potentials, *J. Bact.*, **45**:309, 1943.

Richardson, M., and I. F. Huddleson: Study of catalase in erythrocytes and bacteria. IV. Effect of hydrogen peroxide concentration on the catalase activity of bacteria, *Arch. Biochem. Biophys.*, **47**:346, 1953.

Sacks, L. E., and H. A. Barker: Substrate oxidation and nitrous oxide utilization in denitrification, *J. Bact.*, **64**:247, 1952.

Sadana, J. C., and W. D. McElroy: Nitrate reductase from *Achromobacter fischeri.*

Purification and properties: Function of flavines and cytochrome, *Arch. Biochem. Biophys.*, **67**:16, 1957.

Santer, U. V., and H. J. Vogel: Prodigiosin synthesis in *Serratia marcescens:* isolation of a pyrrole-containing precursor, *Biochim. Biophys. Acta*, **19**:578, 1956.

Schatz, A., R. R. Mohan, and G. S. Trelawny: Oxidation of tricarboxylic acid cycle intermediates by *Streptomyces nitrificans, Antonie van Leeuwenhoek*, **3**:15, 1955.

Sih, C. J., P. B. Hamilton, and S. G. Knight: Some properties of the cytochrome oxidase of *Penicillium chrysogenum, J. Bact.*, **75**:623, 1958.

Skerman, V. B. D.: A chemical analysis of Brewer's medium for the aerobic culture of anaerobes, *Australian J. Biol. Sci.*, **6**:276, 1953.

——— and I. C. MacRae: The influence of oxygen availability on the degree of nitrate reduction by *Pseudomonas denitrificans, Can. J. Microbiol.*, **3**:505, 1957.

Slade, H. D., H. G. Wood, A. O. Nier, A. Hemingway, and C. H. Werkman: Assimilation of heavy carbon dioxide by heterotrophic bacteria, *J. Biol. Chem.*, **143**:133, 1942.

Smith, C. G., and M. J. Johnson: Aeration requirements for the growth of aerobic microorganisms, *J. Bact.*, **68**:346, 1954.

Smith, L.: Bacterial cytochromes, *Bact. Rev.*, **18**:106, 1954.

Society of American Bacteriologists: "Manual of Microbiological Methods," New York, McGraw-Hill Book Company, Inc., 1957.

Stadtman, T. C., and H. A. Barker: Studies on the methane fermentation. IX. The origin of methane in the acetate and methane fermentations by *Methanosarcina, J. Bact.*, **61**:81, 1951*a;* X. A new formate-decomposing bacterium *Methanococcus vannielii, ibid.*, **62**:269, 1951*b.*

Steuer, W.: Die Bedeutung verschiedener Umwelteinflüsse auf die Zusammensetzung des Gesamtpigmentes von *Micrococcus pyogenes, Centr. Bakt.*, I Orig., **168**:558, 1957.

Strehler, B. L., and M. J. Cormier: Factors affecting the luminescence of cell-free extracts of the luminous bacterium, *Achromobacter fischeri, Arch. Biochem. Biophys.*, **47**:16, 1953.

——— and ———: Kinetic aspects of the bacterial luciferin-luciferase reaction in vitro, *ibid.*, **53**:138, 1954.

Sumner, J. B., and G. F. Somers: "Chemistry and Methods of Enzymes," New York, Academic Press, Inc., 1953.

Taniguchi, S., R. Sato, and F. Egami: The enzymatic mechanisms of nitrate and nitrite metabolism in bacteria. From "Inorganic Nitrogen Metabolism," edited by W. D. McElroy and B. Glass, Baltimore, Johns Hopkins Press, 1956.

Tepper, B. S., and J. B. Wilson: Fixation and distribution of $C^{14}O_2$ in *Brucella abortus, J. Bact.*, **76**:24, 1958.

Thunberg, T.: "Abderhalden's Handbuch der biologischen Arbeitsmethoden," Lfg. 414, Abt. 4, Tl. 1, Heft 7, 1929.

Tissières, A.: Purification, some properties and the specific biological activity of cytochromes c_4 and c_5 from *Azotobacter vinelandii, Biochem. J.*, **64**:582, 1956.

Updegraff, D. M., and G. B. Wren: The release of oil from petroleum-bearing materials by sulfate-reducing bacteria, *Appl. Microbiol.*, **2**:309, 1954.

van Delden, A.: Beitrag zur Kenntnis der Sulfatreduktion durch Bakterien, *Centr. Bakt.*, II, **11**:81 and 113, 1904.

Verhoeven, W.: Aerobic sporeforming nitrate reducing bacteria, Delft, Holland, Uitgeverij Waltman, 1952.

———: Studies on true dissimilatory nitrate reduction. V. Nitric oxide production and consumption by micro-organisms, *Antonie van Leeuwenhoek*, **22**:385, 1956*a.*

———: Some remarks on nitrate and nitrite metabolism in microorganisms. From "Inorganic Nitrogen Metabolism," edited by W. D. McElroy and B. Glass, Baltimore, Johns Hopkins Press, 1956*b.*

Vernon, L. P.: Cytochrome c content of *Rhodospirillum rubrum, Arch. Biochem. Biophys.*, **43**:492, 1953.

———: Bacterial cytochromes. I. Cytochrome composition of *Micrococcus denitrificans* and *Pseudomonas denitrificans, J. Biol. Chem.*, **222**:1035, 1956.

———— and F. G. White: Terminal oxidases of *Micrococcus denitrificans, Biochim. Biophys. Acta,* **25:**321, 1957.

Wieland, H.: Über den Mechanismus der Oxydationsvorgänge, *Ergeb. Physiol.,* **20:**477, 1922.

Williams, R. P.: Symposium on bacterial pigments, *Bact. Rev.,* **20:**282, 1956.

———— and J. A. Green: Studies on pigmentation of *Serratia marcescens.* III. The characteristics of an orange variant, *J. Bact.,* **72:**537, 1956.

————, ————, and D. A. Rappoport: Studies on pigmentation of *Serratia marcescens.* I. Spectral and paper chromatographic properties of prodigiosin, *J. Bact.,* **71:**115, 1956.

————, W. W. Taylor, D. Hawkins, Jr., and I. L. Roth: A water-soluble, diffusible pigment produced by a strain of *Serratia marcescens, Nature,* **182:**1028, 1958.

Wilson, A. T.: A simple device for the growth of anaerobic organisms in liquid media, *Proc. Soc. Exp. Biol. Med.,* **75:**515, 1950.

Wood, H. G.: The fixation of carbon dioxide and the interrelationships of the tricarboxylic acid cycle, *Physiol. Rev.,* **26:**198, 1946.

Youmans, A. S., I. Millman, and G. P. Youmans: The oxidation of compounds related to the tricarboxylic acid cycle by whole cells and enzyme preparations of *Mycobacterium tuberculosis* var. *hominis, J. Bact.,* **71:**565, 1956.

CHAPTER 13

Hydrolysis and Putrefaction of Proteins

Proteins are naturally occurring, extremely complex combinations of amino acids, being essential constituents of all living cells, both plant and animal. The name protein is derived from the Greek and means preeminence or of first importance.

Almost all soluble proteins form colloidal solutions, which indicates that they are composed of very large molecules or macromolecules (Fig. 158). One of the properties of colloids in solution is their inability to pass through certain membranes such as parchment, collodion, and animal. Most proteins form opalescent solutions, another indication that their molecules are large. They are usually amorphous, although some have been obtained in crystalline form. Colloidal substances are classed as either suspensoids or emulsoids. Suspensoids (lyophobic colloids) do not show any affinity for the dispersion medium. On the other hand, emulsoids (lyophilic colloids) show a strong affinity for the dispersion medium. Proteins form solutions of the emulsoid type. Proteins are precipitated from solution by salts of heavy metals such as mercuric chloride and silver nitrate, by acids such as tannic and phosphotungstic, and by certain dyes and detergents. Proteins are amphoteric compounds, being capable of reacting with both acids and bases to form ionizable salts. Proteins cannot be distilled; they are insoluble in organic solvents. Many are very sensitive to heat and even to the mildest reagents.

Another property of proteins is that they are hydrolyzed rather slowly by (1) strong alkalies; (2) strong acids; and (3) certain groups of specific enzymes. On complete hydrolysis proteins give a mixture of compounds known as α-amino acids.

Alkalies tend to racemize the optically active products of hydrolysis and so are usually avoided. Alkaline hydrolysis also results in the partial or complete destruction of the amino acids cystine, cysteine, and arginine. Acid hydrolysis, especially in the presence of carbohydrate, results usually in the complete destruction of the amino acid tryptophan.

The amino acids are sometimes referred to as the building stones of the protein molecules. The hydrolysis of proteins to the stage of amino acids results in a complete loss of colloidal characteristics.

About 20 amino acids have been recognized as constituents of proteins.

With the exception of glycocoll, all are optically active. They all are soluble in water except tyrosine and cystine. Tyrosine is sparingly soluble in cold water but more soluble in hot water; cystine is sparingly solu-

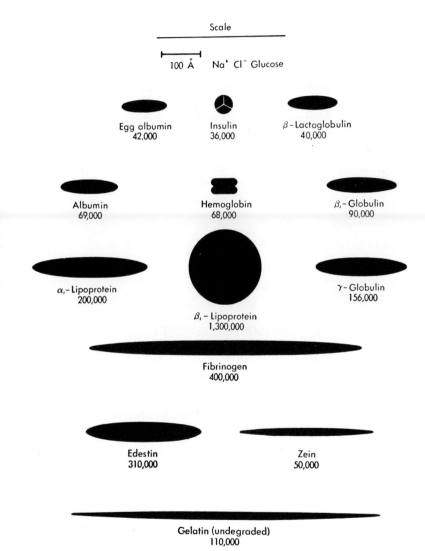

Scale

100 Å   Na⁺ Cl⁻ Glucose

Egg albumin
42,000

Insulin
36,000

β-Lactoglobulin
40,000

Albumin
69,000

Hemoglobin
68,000

β₁-Globulin
90,000

α₁-Lipoprotein
200,000

γ-Globulin
156,000

β₁-Lipoprotein
1,300,000

Fibrinogen
400,000

Edestin
310,000

Zein
50,000

Gelatin (undegraded)
110,000

FIG. 158. Relative sizes of various protein molecules. (*Courtesy West and Todd, "Textbook of Biochemistry," The Macmillan Company.*)

ble in both hot and cold water. They all are soluble in dilute acids and alkalies, with the exception of cystine, which dissolves with difficulty in dilute ammonia water. All of the amino acids possess at least one free amino (NH_2) group and one free carboxyl ($COOH$) group, except proline and oxyproline, which contain an imino (NH) group in place of an amino group. This means that they are amphoteric, being capable of reacting with both acids and bases (page 213). Most of the acids have one free amino group and one free carboxyl group and are neutral in reaction; some have two amino groups to one carboxyl group and are alkaline in reaction; others have one amino to two carboxyl groups and are acid in reaction.

Structure of Protein Molecule. Many theories have been advanced to explain how the amino acids are linked together to produce a protein molecule. It is generally agreed that the amino acids in proteins are linked together principally through their α-amino and carboxyl groups to produce the so-called peptide linkage ($R \cdot CONH \cdot R'$). Other types of linkages probably occur, but from the known facts the peptide linkage is the principal one. For example, if a tripeptide is composed of glycine, alanine, and serine, the amino acids would be joined together in the following manner, according to the peptide linkage:

$$
\begin{array}{c}
\overset{H}{\underset{H}{\mid}}\overset{CH_3}{\mid}\overset{CH_2OH}{\mid} \\
NH_2-\underset{\underset{H}{\mid}}{\overset{\mid}{C}}\overset{}{-}\underset{\underset{O}{\parallel}}{\overset{\mid}{C}}-N-\underset{}{C}-\underset{\underset{O}{\parallel}}{\overset{\mid}{C}}-N-\underset{\underset{H}{\mid}}{\overset{\mid}{C}}-COOH
\end{array}
$$

Glycyl-alanyl-serine

PROTEOLYTIC ENZYMES

The hydrolysis of proteins by proteolytic enzymes results in the formation of the following fractions (with corresponding molecular weights) in the order named:

Proteins ($>$10,000) $\rightarrow$ proteoses ($\sim$5000) $\rightarrow$ peptones ($\sim$2000) $\rightarrow$
      peptides ($\sim$1000 to 500) $\rightarrow$ dipeptides ($\sim$200) $\rightarrow$ α-amino acids ($\sim$100)

Enzymes which open up or hydrolyze peptide linkages are grouped under the proteases (Fig. 159). The proteases are subdivided into the

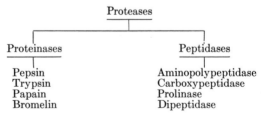

Proteases

Proteinases	Peptidases
Pepsin	Aminopolypeptidase
Trypsin	Carboxypeptidase
Papain	Prolinase
Bromelin	Dipeptidase

Fig. 159. Classification of some proteases.

proteinases and peptidases. The proteinases hydrolyze true proteins, producing chiefly peptides and dipeptides. Sometimes small amounts of amino acids are also released. The peptidases hydrolyze peptides and di-peptides to free amino acids.

Protein Hydrolysis. Protein hydrolysis may be defined as the action of proteinases on a protein, resulting in the disruption of the molecule into diffusible fractions. Many proteinases are known which have in common the power to break the linkage —CO—NH— by the addition of water. This results in the release of free carboxyl (—COOH) and free amino (—NH₂) groups.

The proteinases are probably all extracellular enzymes. Their function is to convert indiffusible proteins into diffusible peptides and dipeptides which can enter the bacterial cell. The compounds produced are largely without odor. The extracellular enzymes play no part in the respiratory activities of the cell, such functions being performed by the intracellular enzymes.

The proteinases attack both proteins and peptides, provided certain conditions are fulfilled. For example, trypsin attacks those links contain-ing the basic arginyl or lysyl group attached to the carbonyl side of the peptide linkage. Likewise, pepsin attacks those links containing the tyrosyl or phenylalanyl group attached to the imino side of the peptide linkage (Fig. 160).

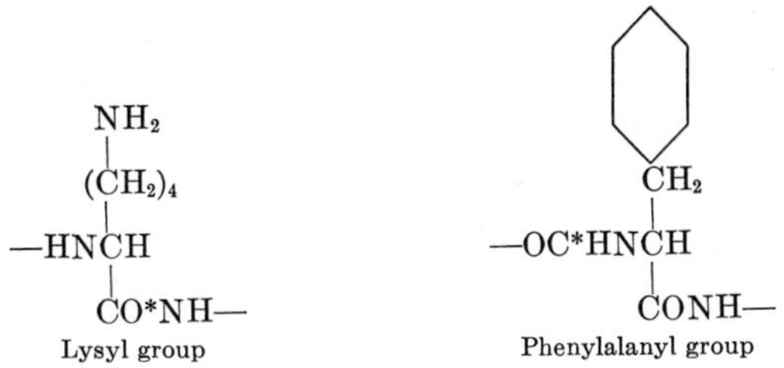

$$
\begin{array}{cc}
\mathrm{NH_2} & \\
| & \\
\mathrm{(CH_2)_4} & \mathrm{CH_2} \\
| & | \\
\mathrm{-HNCH} & \mathrm{-OC^*HNCH} \\
| & | \\
\mathrm{CO^*NH-} & \mathrm{CONH-} \\
\text{Lysyl group} & \text{Phenylalanyl group}
\end{array}
$$

FIG. 160. Left, structure necessary for the action of trypsin; right, structure necessary for the action of pepsin. * Denotes peptide link hydrolyzed.

The peptidases may be both intracellular and extracellular. They at-tack peptides, reducing them to a mixture of smaller units including free amino acids. The peptidases also are capable of attacking the peptide linkages of the protein molecule, provided certain structural requirements are satisfied. For example, leucine aminopeptidase attacks only those links adjacent to a free amino group, provided that leucyl is the amino acid side chain on the carbonyl side of the peptide linkage. Likewise, carboxypeptidase attacks only the peptide linkages adjacent to a free carboxyl group.

These results have been obtained from studies on the proteases of animal origin. Since studies of this nature on the proteases from bacteria are incomplete, it is not possible to draw similar conclusions.

For more information see Castañeda-Agulló (1956), Damodaran et al. (1955), Grob (1946a, b), Laidler (1954), Meister (1957), Springall (1954), Van der Zant and Nelson (1954).

Putrefaction. The term putrefaction may be defined as the anaerobic decomposition of proteins, protein split products, and nitrogenous compounds of a similar nature, resulting in the formation of incompletely oxidized, foul-smelling compounds. The reactions occur inside of the cells by means of the intracellular or respiratory enzymes. The putrefactive changes are the result of the action of organisms on the amino acids. The important compounds produced include sulfides, amines, alcohols, organic acids, hydroxy acids, indole, phenol, cresol, and the gases ammonia, methane, carbon dioxide, and hydrogen.

Bacteria vary considerably in their ability to degrade proteins or protein split products. Organisms are usually designated as putrefactive or fermentative, depending upon whether they act more vigorously on proteins or on fermentable substances. Many of the putrefactive compounds are produced only from specific amino acids; others may be produced from more than one acid.

Decay. Decay may be defined as the aerobic decomposition of proteins in which the products of putrefaction are completely oxidized to stable compounds having no foul odors. The process takes place in nature by aerobic or facultative organisms in the presence of air after the putrefactive changes have occurred. If the substrate is well aerated from the start, the reactions will be aerobic without the formation of foul-smelling end products.

A practical application of this principle is employed in the disposal of sewage. In one process the sewage is first digested under anaerobic conditions, resulting in the liberation of offensive odors. Then the anaerobic digestate is well aerated, after which the aerobic organisms attack the foul-smelling compounds. This results in the disappearance of the offensive odors. In another process the sewage is kept well aerated from the start, thus preventing the formation or accumulation of foul-smelling, incompletely oxidized products.

For more information see Fruton (1938, 1941), Gale (1952), Grob (1946a, b), Laidler (1954), Sumner and Somers (1953).

ACTION OF BACTERIA ON PROTEINS

A pure native protein, when present in a medium as the only source of carbon and nitrogen, is resistant to attack even by the most proteolytic species. If, however, a small amount of peptone is added to the medium, multiplication of the organisms and degradation of the protein occur.

The results would indicate that an extracellular enzyme is necessary to convert the indiffusible protein into diffusible fractions. In the absence of an available nitrogen and carbon source, the organisms are unable to multiply and elaborate the necessary enzyme. However, peptone can enter the cell and stimulate the organisms to produce the necessary proteolytic enzyme. The enzyme is then secreted outside of the cell, where it can attack the indiffusible protein molecules and convert them into diffusible fractions which can enter the cell.

Proteoses are intermediate products in the digestion of proteins by proteolytic enzymes and are also immune to attack by bacteria when present as the only source of nitrogen and carbon. Here again, the addition of a small amount of peptone to the medium prior to inoculation stimulates the organisms to secrete the proteolytic enzyme necessary to attack the proteose.

ACTION OF BACTERIA ON AMINO ACIDS

Bacteria may attack amino acids in a variety of ways. They may remove the amino group (deaminization) and the ammonia utilized as a source of nitrogen; they may destroy the carboxyl groups (decarboxylation) to give basic compounds known as amines. These are only two of a number of reactions produced by bacteria on the amino acids. Other types of changes are discussed below.

1. Oxidative deaminization, resulting in the formation of an α-keto acid:

$$\underset{\text{Alanine}}{\overset{\displaystyle CH_3}{\underset{\displaystyle COOH}{H-C-NH_2}}} + \tfrac{1}{2}O_2 \rightarrow \underset{\text{Pyruvic acid}}{\overset{\displaystyle CH_3}{\underset{\displaystyle COOH}{C=O}}} + NH_3$$

Some organisms may produce an oxidative deaminization of the dicarboxylic aspartic and glutamic acids, resulting in the formation of the corresponding α-keto acids. Others are able to metabolize the compounds to acetic acid, ammonia, and carbon dioxide:

$$\underset{\text{Aspartic acid}}{\overset{\displaystyle COOH}{\underset{\displaystyle COOH}{\underset{\displaystyle |}{\overset{\displaystyle |}{CHNH_2}}}}} \;\; + O_2 \rightarrow \underset{\text{Acetic acid}}{CH_3 \cdot COOH} + NH_3 + 2CO_2$$

where the left structure reads $COOH$–CH_2–$CHNH_2$–$COOH$.

2. Reductive deaminization, resulting in the formation of a saturated acid. This reaction is generally produced by the strict or facultative anaerobes grown under anaerobic conditions:

$$\underset{\text{Alanine}}{\overset{\displaystyle CH_3}{\underset{\displaystyle COOH}{H-C-NH_2}}} + 2H \rightarrow \underset{\text{Propionic acid}}{\overset{\displaystyle CH_3}{\underset{\displaystyle COOH}{H-C-H}}} + NH_3$$

3. Hydrolytic deaminization, resulting in the formation of a hydroxy acid:

$$\begin{array}{ccc}
\text{CH}_3 & & \text{CH}_3 \\
| & & | \\
\text{H--C--NH}_2 + \text{H}_2\text{O} \rightarrow & & \text{H--C--OH} + \text{NH}_3 \\
| & & | \\
\text{COOH} & & \text{COOH} \\
\text{Alanine} & & \text{Lactic acid}
\end{array}$$

Deaminization usually occurs in bacteria grown in a neutral or slightly alkaline medium.

4. Deaminization and desaturation at the α,β-linkage, resulting in the formation of an unsaturated acid:

$$\begin{array}{ccc}
\text{R--CH}_2 & & \text{R--CH} \\
| & & \| \\
\text{H--C--NH}_2 \rightarrow & & \text{CH} \qquad + \text{NH}_3 \\
| & & | \\
\text{COOH} & & \text{COOH} \\
\text{Amino acid} & & \text{Unsaturated acid}
\end{array}$$

5. Hydrolytic deaminization and decarboxylation, resulting in the formation of a primary alcohol with one less carbon atom:

$$\begin{array}{ccc}
\text{CH}_3 & & \text{CH}_3 \\
| & & | \\
\text{H--C--NH}_2 + \text{H}_2\text{O} \rightarrow & & \text{H--C--OH} + \text{CO}_2 + \text{NH}_3 \\
| & & | \\
\text{COOH} & & \text{H} \\
\text{Alanine} & & \text{Ethyl alcohol}
\end{array}$$

6. Decarboxylation or elimination of carbon dioxide, resulting in the formation of an amine with one less carbon atom:

$$\begin{array}{ccc}
\text{CH}_3 & & \text{CH}_3 \\
| & & | \\
\text{H--C--NH}_2 \rightarrow & & \text{H--C--NH}_2 + \text{CO}_2 \\
| & & | \\
\text{COOH} & & \text{H} \\
\text{Alanine} & & \text{Ethylamine}
\end{array}$$

Decarboxylases are generally produced by growing bacteria at a low pH. This is achieved by cultivating the organisms in a fermentable carbohydrate medium.

7. Anaerobic decomposition with the liberation of hydrogen:

$$5\text{COOH} \cdot (\text{CH}_2)_2 \cdot \text{CHNH}_2 \cdot \text{COOH} + 6\text{H}_2\text{O} \rightarrow$$
$$6\text{CH}_3 \cdot \text{COOH} + 2\text{CH}_3 \cdot (\text{CH}_2)_2 \cdot \text{COOH} + 5\text{CO}_2 + 5\text{NH}_3 + \text{H}_2$$

Glutamic acid   Acetic acid   Butyric acid

8. Decomposition by mutase reaction in which one molecule of an amino acid is oxidized and another reduced:

$$3\text{CH}_3 \cdot \text{CHNH}_2 \cdot \text{COOH} + 2\text{H}_2\text{O} \rightarrow 2\text{CH}_3 \cdot \text{CH}_2 \cdot \text{COOH} + \text{CH}_3 \cdot \text{COOH} + 3\text{NH}_3 + \text{CO}_2$$

Alanine   Propionic acid   Acetic acid

9. Transamination reaction in which an amino group from either aspartic or glutamic acid is transferred to the α-position in an α-keto acid:

$$\begin{array}{ccccccc}
\text{COOH} & & \text{COOH} & & \text{COOH} & & \text{COOH} \\
| & & | & & | & & | \\
(\text{CH}_2)_2 & & \text{CH}_2 & & (\text{CH}_2)_2 & & \text{CH}_2 \\
| & + & | & \rightarrow & | & + & | \\
\text{CHNH}_2 & & \text{C=O} & & \text{C=O} & & \text{CHNH}_2 \\
| & & | & & | & & | \\
\text{COOH} & & \text{COOH} & & \text{COOH} & & \text{COOH} \\
\text{Glutamic} & & \text{Oxalacetic} & & \alpha\text{-Keto} & & \text{Aspartic} \\
\text{acid} & & \text{acid} & & \text{glutaric acid} & & \text{acid}
\end{array}$$

10. Mutual oxidation and reduction by pairs of amino acids. Some amino acids (alanine, valine, leucine, phenylalanine) have been shown to be oxidizable by serving as hydrogen donators, whereas others (glycine, proline, hydroxyproline, ornithine, arginine) are reducible by serving as hydrogen acceptors. This reaction takes place by anaerobes cultivated under anaerobic conditions. By mixing together one amino acid from each group, i.e., a hydrogen donator and a hydrogen acceptor, and inoculating the medium with an anaerobe, the former acid becomes oxidized and the latter reduced:

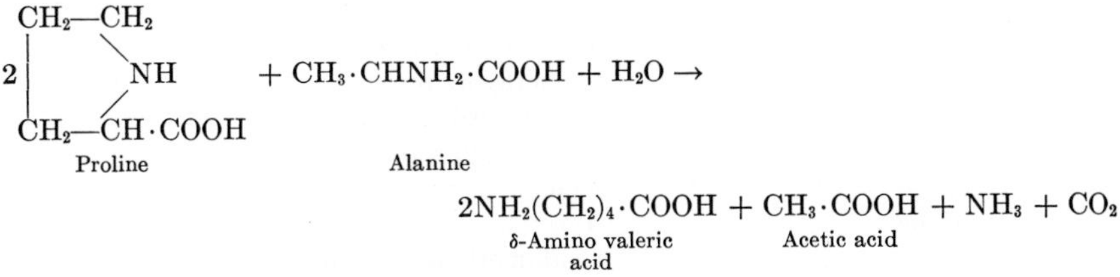

$$2 \begin{array}{c} CH_2\text{---}CH_2 \\ | \qquad \backslash \\ | \qquad \quad NH \\ | \qquad / \\ CH_2\text{---}CH \cdot COOH \end{array} + CH_3 \cdot CHNH_2 \cdot COOH + H_2O \rightarrow$$

Proline   Alanine

$$2NH_2(CH_2)_4 \cdot COOH + CH_3 \cdot COOH + NH_3 + CO_2$$
δ-Amino valeric   Acetic acid
acid

The foregoing types of chemical reactions or their combinations are able to account for nearly all of the products of decomposition and putrefaction formed by bacteria from amino acids.

The names and formulas of the important amino acids present in proteins and the compounds produced from each by bacterial action are given in Table 14. The formulas of the amino acids are given at the top of each division. The table does not include all possible compounds but most of those reported to be produced by the enzymatic reactions already discussed. The numbers refer to the types of reactions given on pages 355 to 357. A few compounds are not preceded by a number, indicating that the mechanism of their formation is not clearly understood.

For more information see Hamdy et al. (1956); Ichihara, Yoshimatsu, and Sakamoto (1956); Kakihara and Ichihara (1953); Møller (1954a, b, 1955); Rosenberger (1959); Stewart and Kallio (1959); Stewart et al. (1959); Thorne, Gomez, and Housewright (1955); Uchida et al. (1953); Umbarger and Brown (1957).

PTOMAINES

Ptomaines may be defined as basic amines and diamines that are formed by the action of putrefactive bacteria on amino acids and organic bases. They are produced from amino acids by decarboxylation (reaction 6, page 356). Ptomaines produced from most of the amino acids are given in Table 13. The organic base choline is included as an example of a nitrogenous compound that is not an amino acid.

PROTEIN-SPARING ACTION

It is well known that bacteria in general prefer a fermentable carbohydrate to protein for energy purposes. In the presence of both types of compounds, protein is utilized for structure only. In the absence of a

TABLE 13. SOME PTOMAINES FORMED BY BACTERIAL ACTION

Amino acid	Ptomaine
Glycocoll (glycine)	Methylamine
Alanine	Ethylamine
Valine	Isobutylamine
Leucine	Isoamylamine
Phenylalanine	β-Phenylethylamine
Tyrosine	p-Hydroxy-β-phenylethylamine (tyramine)
Serine	Hydroxyethylamine
Cystine (cysteine)	Thioethylamine
Methionine	γ-Methylthiolpropylamine
Threonine	β-Hydroxypropylamine
Arginine	δ-Guanidine butylamine (agmatine)
Ornithine	Tetramethylenediamine (putrescine)
Lysine	Pentamethylenediamine (cadaverine)
Histidine	β-Imidazole ethylamine (histamine)
Tryptophan	β-Indole ethylamine (tryptamine)
Choline	Trimethylamine

fermentable carbohydrate, bacteria are forced to utilize protein for both structure and energy.

Organisms like *Escherichia coli* and *Proteus vulgaris,* which ferment carbohydrate very rapidly, exhibit a definite protein-sparing action. The accumulation of a relatively large amount of acid in a short period of time stops the growth of the organisms. Under these conditions only a minimum of action occurs on the protein constituent of the medium.

In the presence of an excess of buffer, such as a mixture of primary and secondary phosphates, the limiting hydrogen-ion concentration is not attained and the course of protein breakdown occurs simultaneously with carbohydrate fermentation. This results in a negative protein-sparing action.

Organisms like *Bacillus subtilis,* which ferment carbohydrate slowly, or those like *Aerobacter cloacae,* which do not produce strongly acid products, fail to show a protein-sparing effect. The limiting hydrogen-ion concentration is never reached, and protein breakdown occurs as though no carbohydrate is present.

It may be concluded that a fermentable carbohydrate exerts a protein-sparing action only when it is rapidly utilized with the accumulation of a high concentration of acid in a short period of time. If steps are taken to neutralize the acid as it is formed (buffering the medium), the inhibitory effect of carbohydrate is prevented.

SOME ROUTINE PHYSIOLOGICAL REACTIONS EMPLOYED FOR THE IDENTIFICATION OF BACTERIA

Many biochemical reactions are employed for the identification and classification of bacteria. Some are based on the breakdown of carbo-

TABLE 14. ACTION OF BACTERIA ON THE AMINO ACIDS

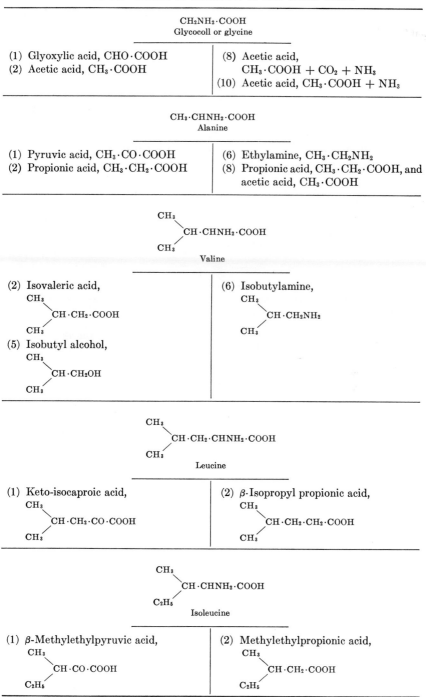

CH₂NH₂·COOH
Glycocoll or glycine

(1) Glyoxylic acid, CHO·COOH	(8) Acetic acid,
(2) Acetic acid, CH₃·COOH	CH₃·COOH + CO₂ + NH₃
	(10) Acetic acid, CH₃·COOH + NH₃

CH₃·CHNH₂·COOH
Alanine

(1) Pyruvic acid, CH₃·CO·COOH	(6) Ethylamine, CH₃·CH₂NH₂
(2) Propionic acid, CH₃·CH₂·COOH	(8) Propionic acid, CH₃·CH₂·COOH, and acetic acid, CH₃·COOH

CH₃
  ⟍
   CH·CHNH₂·COOH
  ⟋
CH₃
Valine

(2) Isovaleric acid, CH₃⟍CH·CH₂·COOH CH₃⟋	(6) Isobutylamine, CH₃⟍CH·CH₂NH₂ CH₃⟋
(5) Isobutyl alcohol, CH₃⟍CH·CH₂OH CH₃⟋	

CH₃
  ⟍
   CH·CH₂·CHNH₂·COOH
  ⟋
CH₃
Leucine

(1) Keto-isocaproic acid, CH₃⟍CH·CH₂·CO·COOH CH₃⟋	(2) β-Isopropyl propionic acid, CH₃⟍CH·CH₂·CH₂·COOH CH₃⟋

CH₃
  ⟍
   CH·CHNH₂·COOH
  ⟋
C₂H₅
Isoleucine

(1) β-Methylethylpyruvic acid, CH₃⟍CH·CO·COOH C₂H₅⟋	(2) Methylethylpropionic acid, CH₃⟍CH·CH₂·COOH C₂H₅⟋

TABLE 14 (*Continued*)

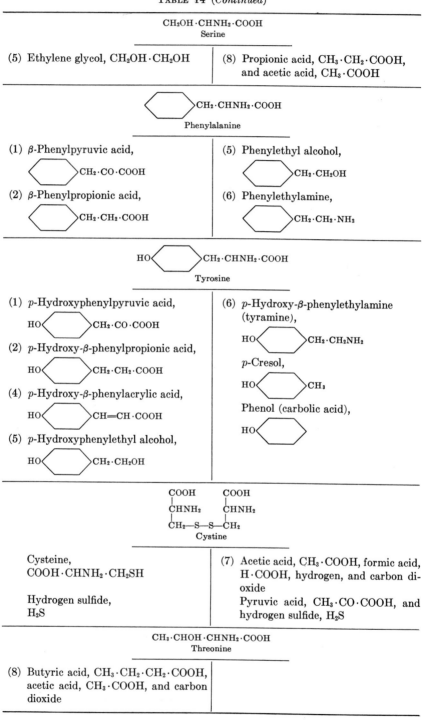

CH₂OH·CHNH₂·COOH
Serine

(5) Ethylene glycol, CH₂OH·CH₂OH

(8) Propionic acid, CH₃·CH₂·COOH, and acetic acid, CH₃·COOH

CH₂·CHNH₂·COOH
Phenylalanine

(1) β-Phenylpyruvic acid,
CH₂·CO·COOH

(2) β-Phenylpropionic acid,
CH₂·CH₂·COOH

(5) Phenylethyl alcohol,
CH₂·CH₂OH

(6) Phenylethylamine,
CH₂·CH₂·NH₂

HO⟨⟩CH₂·CHNH₂·COOH
Tyrosine

(1) *p*-Hydroxyphenylpyruvic acid,
HO⟨⟩CH₂·CO·COOH

(2) *p*-Hydroxy-β-phenylpropionic acid,
HO⟨⟩CH₂·CH₂·COOH

(4) *p*-Hydroxy-β-phenylacrylic acid,
HO⟨⟩CH=CH·COOH

(5) *p*-Hydroxyphenylethyl alcohol,
HO⟨⟩CH₂·CH₂OH

(6) *p*-Hydroxy-β-phenylethylamine (tyramine),
HO⟨⟩CH₂·CH₂NH₂

p-Cresol,
HO⟨⟩CH₃

Phenol (carbolic acid),
HO⟨⟩

COOH   COOH
CHNH₂ CHNH₂
CH₂—S—S—CH₂
Cystine

Cysteine,
COOH·CHNH₂·CH₂SH

Hydrogen sulfide,
H₂S

(7) Acetic acid, CH₃·COOH, formic acid, H·COOH, hydrogen, and carbon dioxide
Pyruvic acid, CH₃·CO·COOH, and hydrogen sulfide, H₂S

CH₃·CHOH·CHNH₂·COOH
Threonine

(8) Butyric acid, CH₃·CH₂·CH₂·COOH, acetic acid, CH₃·COOH, and carbon dioxide

TABLE 14 (*Continued*)

COOH·CH₂·CHNH₂·COOH
Aspartic acid

(1) Oxalacetic acid,
COOH·CH₂·CO·COOH, and acetic
acid, CH₃·COOH
(2) Succinic acid,
COOH·CH₂·CH₂·COOH
(3) Malic acid,
COOH·CH₂·CHOH·COOH
(4) Fumaric acid,
COOH·CH=CH·COOH

(6) β-Alanine, NH₂CH₂·CH₂·COOH
(7) Hydrogen and carbon dioxide
(9) Oxalacetic acid,
COOH·CH₂·CO·COOH, and
alanine, CH₃·CHNH₂·COOH

COOH·CH₂·CH₂·CHNH₂·COOH
Glutamic acid

(1) α-Ketoglutaric acid,
COOH·CH₂·CH₂·CO·COOH
(1) Acetic acid, CH₃·COOH, and carbon
dioxide
(2) Glutaric acid,
COOH·CH₂·CH₂·CH₂·COOH
(5) γ-Hydroxybutyric acid,
CH₂OH·CH₂·CH₂·COOH

(6) γ-Amino butyric acid,
NH₂CH₂·CH₂·CH₂·COOH
(7) Butyric acid, CH₃·CH₂·CH₂·COOH,
acetic acid, CH₃·COOH, carbon dioxide, and hydrogen
(9) α-Ketoglutaric acid,
COOH·CH₂·CH₂·CO·COOH, and
aspartic acid,
COOH·CH₂·CHNH₂·COOH.

NH₂
         /
NH:C
         \
          NH(CH₂)₃·CHNH₂·COOH
Arginine

(1) δ-Guanidine-α-keto-valeric acid,
       NH₂
       /
NH:C
       \
        NH(CH₂)₃·CO·COOH
(6) Agmatine,
       NH₂
       /
NH:C
       \
        NH(CH₂)₃·CH₂NH₂

(10) δ-Guanidine valeric acid,
       NH₂
       /
NH:C
       \
        NH(CH₂)₄·COOH
Ornithine,
NH₂(CH₂)₃·CHNH₂·COOH,
and urea,
    NH₂
     \
      C=O
     /
    NH₂

NH₂(CH₂)₃CHNH₂·COOH
Ornithine

(2) δ-Aminovaleric acid (putridin),
NH₂(CH₂)₄·COOH
(5) γ-Aminobutyl alcohol,
NH₂(CH₂)₃CH₂OH

(6) Tetramethylenediamine (putrescine),
NH₂(CH₂)₃CH₂NH₂

NH₂(CH₂)₄·CHNH₂·COOH
Lysine

(2) ε-Aminocaproic acid,
NH₂(CH₂)₅·COOH

(6) Pentamethylenediamine (cadaver-
ine), NH₂(CH₂)₄·CH₂NH₂

TABLE 14 (*Continued*)

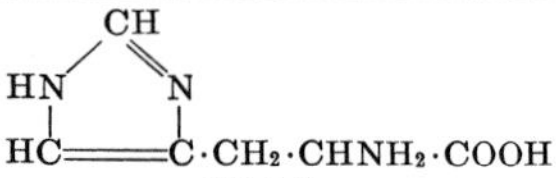

$$
\begin{array}{c}
CH \\
HN \diagdown N \\
HC = C \cdot CH_2 \cdot CHNH_2 \cdot COOH
\end{array}
$$

Histidine

(1) β-Imidazole pyruvic acid, $\begin{array}{c} CH \\ HN \diagdown N \\ HC = C \cdot CH_2 \cdot CO \cdot COOH \end{array}$	(5) β-Imidazole ethyl alcohol, $\begin{array}{c} CH \\ HN \diagdown N \\ HC = C \cdot CH_2 \cdot CH_2OH \end{array}$
(2) β-Imidazole propionic acid, $\begin{array}{c} CH \\ HN \diagdown N \\ HC = C \cdot CH_2 \cdot CH_2 \cdot COOH \end{array}$	(6) β-Imidazole ethylamine (histamine), $\begin{array}{c} CH \\ HN \diagdown N \\ HC = C \cdot CH_2 \cdot CH_2NH_2 \end{array}$
(4) β-Imidazole acrylic acid, $\begin{array}{c} CH \\ HN \diagdown N \\ HC = C \cdot CH = CH \cdot COOH \end{array}$	(7) Hydrogen and carbon dioxide

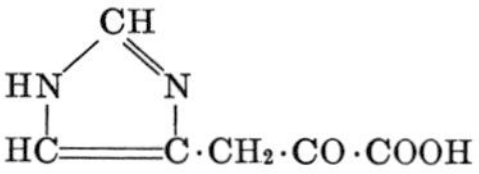

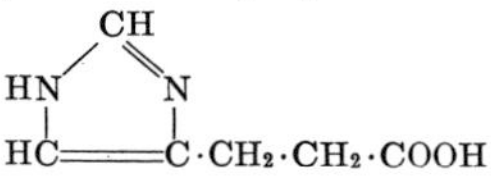

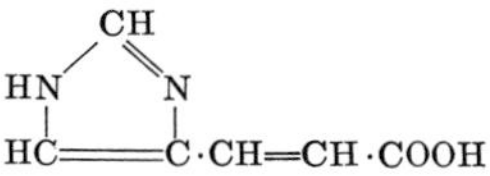

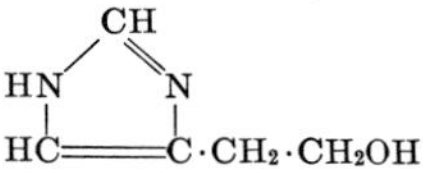

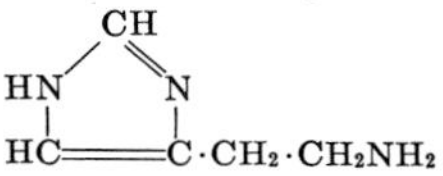

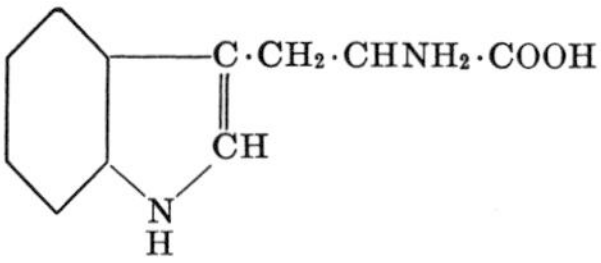

$$
C \cdot CH_2 \cdot CHNH_2 \cdot COOH \\
CH \\
N \\
H
$$

Tryptophan

(1) β-Indole pyruvic acid, —C·CH₂·CO·COOH CH N H	β-Indoleacetic acid, —C·CH₂·COOH CH N H
(2) β-Indole propionic acid (skatole acetic acid), —C·CH₂·CH₂·COOH CH N H	Indole, —CH CH N H
(5) β-Indole ethyl alcohol (tryptophol), —C·CH₂·CH₂OH CH N H	Kynurenic acid, OH COOH N
(6) β-Indole ethylamine (tryptamine), —C·CH₂·CH₂NH₂ CH N H	Anthranilic acid, NH₂ COOH

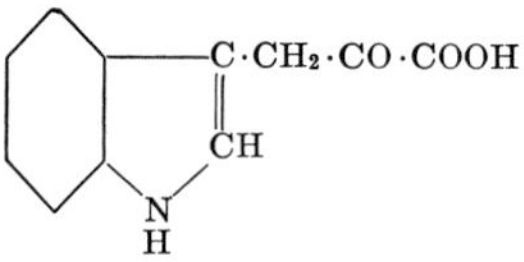

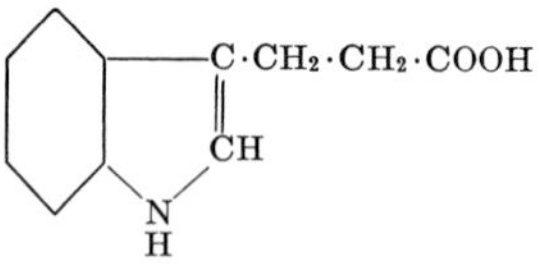

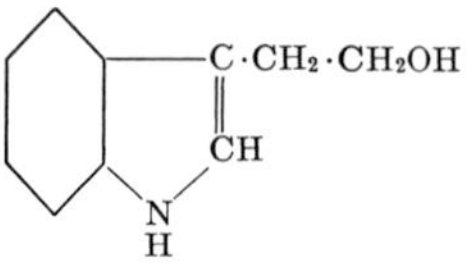

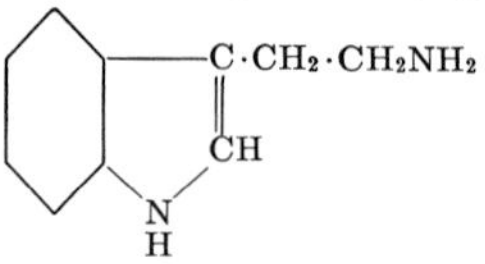

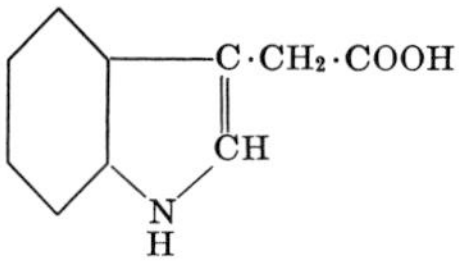

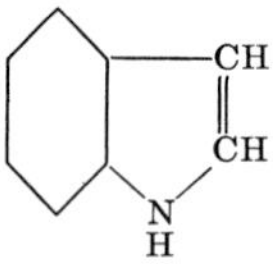

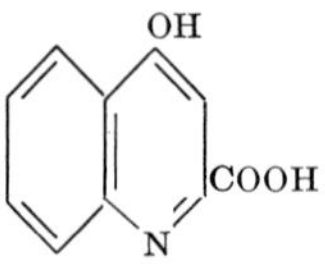

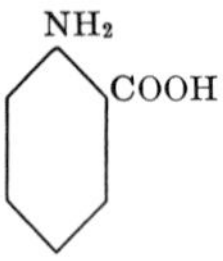

TABLE 14 (*Continued*)

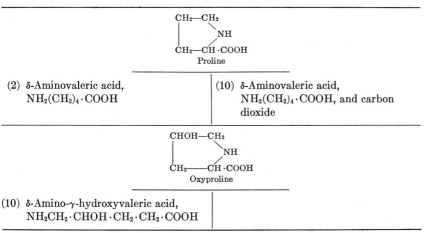

(2) δ-Aminovaleric acid, $NH_2(CH_2)_4 \cdot COOH$	(10) δ-Aminovaleric acid, $NH_2(CH_2)_4 \cdot COOH$, and carbon dioxide

Oxyproline

(10) δ-Amino-γ-hydroxyvaleric acid, $NH_2CH_2 \cdot CHOH \cdot CH_2 \cdot CH_2 \cdot COOH$	

hydrates; others depend upon certain changes in the nitrogenous constituents of the medium.

The following tests are based upon the action of bacteria on proteins or protein hydrolytic products:

Decomposition of Tryptophan. Tryptophan is decomposed by bacteria in a variety of ways, resulting in the formation of β-indole propionic acid, β-indole pyruvic acid, β-indole ethylamine, β-indole ethyl alcohol, β-indole acetic acid, indole, kynurenic acid, anthranilic acid, and indigotin.

Indole. Indole is a putrefactive compound produced by some bacteria from tryptophan, and tests for its presence are frequently made (see page 362). Tryptophan is the only naturally occurring amino acid containing the indole ring. Therefore, the test is also specific for the presence of tryptophan. Some bacteria can produce indole; others cannot. The test is of value in the identification and classification of bacteria.

Tryptophan is not present in all proteins. Manufacturers select only those proteins for peptone production which are certain to yield relatively high concentrations of tryptophan. Casein, the principal protein of milk, is rich in tryptophan and is frequently used for the preparation of peptone where a strong indole test is desirable.

Some organisms are capable of oxidizing the indole ring. The following oxidation products have been reported: isatin, kynurenic acid, formylanthranilic acid, anthranilic acid, salicylic acid, catechol, and indigotin.

In order to prevent the possible occurrence of a protein-sparing action, noncarbohydrate media should be employed for the detection of indole in bacterial cultures.

For more information see Happold (1950); Sakamoto, Uchida, and Ichihara (1953); Uchida, Sakamoto, and Ichihara (1953).

Production of Hydrogen Sulfide. Cystine and methionine are the two sulfur-containing amino acids present in proteins. Practically all of the information available on the effect of bacteria on these acids has been obtained from cystine or its reduction product cysteine.

Some organisms are capable of attacking cystine with the liberation of hydrogen sulfide; others are unable to do so. The test is of value in the identification and classification of bacteria.

Cystine does not occur in all proteins. Manufacturers select only those proteins for peptone production which are certain to contain relatively large amounts of this amino acid.

Under anaerobic conditions the cystine is first reduced to two molecules of cysteine. Then the cysteine is decomposed to hydrogen sulfide, ammonia, acetic acid, and formic acid:

$$
\begin{array}{lll}
\text{COOH} & \text{COOH} & \text{COOH} \\
| & | & | \\
\text{CHNH}_2 & \text{CHNH}_2 + \text{H}_2 \rightarrow 2\text{CHNH}_2 \\
| & | & | \\
\text{CH}_2\text{—S—S—CH}_2 & & \text{CH}_2\text{SH} \\
\quad \text{Cystine} & & \quad \text{Cysteine}
\end{array}
$$

$$
\underset{\text{Cysteine}}{\text{COOH} \cdot \text{CHNH}_2 \cdot \text{CH}_2\text{SH}} + 2\text{H}_2\text{O} \rightarrow \text{H}_2\text{S} + \text{NH}_3 + \underset{\text{Acetic acid}}{\text{CH}_3 \cdot \text{COOH}} + \underset{\text{Formic acid}}{\text{HCOOH}}
$$

Under aerobic conditions cysteine is said to be dissimilated as follows:

$$
\underset{\text{Cysteine}}{\text{HOOC} \cdot \text{CHNH}_2 \cdot \text{CH}_2\text{SH}} + \text{O} \rightarrow \text{HOOC} \cdot \text{CO} \cdot \text{CH}_2\text{SH} + \text{NH}_3
$$

$$
\text{HOOC} \cdot \text{CO} \cdot \text{CH}_2\text{SH} \rightarrow \text{H}_2\text{S} + \text{other products}
$$

Hydrogen sulfide reacts with heavy metals to produce colored compounds. The metal salts are incorporated in solid media. The presence of hydrogen sulfide is detected by a darkening of the medium along the line of inoculation (Fig. 161).

Lead was the first metal used. Since that time other metals have been employed because of their greater sensitivity to hydrogen sulfide. These include iron, bismuth, cobalt, and nickel. The metals may be arranged in the following order on the basis of their sensitivity to hydrogen sulfide:

$$
\begin{array}{l}
\text{Bi} \\
\text{Co} > \text{Fe} > \text{Pb} \\
\text{Ni}
\end{array}
$$

It may be concluded that it is not enough to state that an organism does or does not produce hydrogen sulfide without giving the conditions under which it was investigated.

Liquefaction of Gelatin. The liquefaction of gelatin by bacteria is the result of the action of an enzyme known as gelatinase. It is an extracellular enzyme concerned with the hydrolysis of the indiffusible protein prior to intracellular utilization.

The presence of the enzyme may be demonstrated by inoculating a tube of nutrient gelatin with the organism in question and incubating the culture at the appropriate temperature. If the temperature is above 20°C., the gelatin will melt. Under these conditions, the presence of gelatinase is demonstrated by placing the culture in the refrigerator and noting whether or not hardening occurs. If the gelatin remains liquid, it indicates that the organism under examination secreted a gelatinase into the culture medium.

Another procedure is to streak the organism over the surface of nutrient agar containing 0.4 per cent gelatin. After incubation at the appropriate temperature, the plate is flooded with a solution of mercuric chloride in dilute hydrochloric acid. The reagent forms a white opaque precipitate with the unchanged gelatin, but a liquefier is surrounded by a clear zone.

The extracellular nature of the enzyme may be demonstrated by filtering a bacterial culture and adding some of the filtrate to a tube of gelatin medium. The presence of the enzyme will result in liquefaction of the gelatin.

FIG. 161. Production of hydrogen sulfide. Left, peptone iron agar medium inoculated with *Proteus vulgaris.* Hydrogen sulfide formed which reacted with the iron to give black iron sulfide. Right, same inoculated with *Escherichia coli.* Hydrogen sulfide not produced.

The presence of a fermentable carbohydrate may result in a protein-sparing action. Under these conditions a test for gelatin liquefaction will most likely be negative even though the organism under examination is capable of attacking the protein. Therefore, non-carbohydrate media should be employed to demonstrate the ability of an organism to secrete a gelatinase. The test is of value in identifying and classifying bacteria.

For more information see McDade and Weaver (1959), Smith and Goodner (1958).

Production of Ammonia. The development of ammonia in bacterial cultures containing peptone is largely the result of the deaminization of the amino acids.

Prior to assimilation, amino acids are deaminized to ammonia and a carbon residue. In the absence of a fermentable carbohydrate, bacteria utilize the ammonia for structure and the carbon residue for energy. Since more carbon is required for energy than nitrogen for structure, ammonia accumulates in the medium. In the presence of a fermentable carbohydrate, a protein-sparing action may occur, in which case the bacteria utilize the amino acids for structure but not for energy.

Under these conditions the medium generally shows less free ammonia than the same medium without carbohydrate. This may be attributed to two factors:

1. Organisms prefer carbohydrate to the deaminized carbon residue for energy. Since the carbon residue of amino acids is not required for energy, less ammonia is produced.

2. A fermentable carbohydrate stimulates bacterial growth, resulting in an increased utilization of ammonia. This causes a decrease in the free ammonia of the medium.

It is generally believed that both factors apply. This means that in the case of the strongly fermentative bacteria the addition of carbohydrate results in the accumulation of less free ammonia than in the same medium without carbohydrate. To prevent the possible occurrence of a protein-sparing action, noncarbohydrate media should be employed for the detection of ammonia in bacterial cultures.

Fermentation and Peptonization of Milk. Milk contains the following major constituents: water, carbohydrate (lactose), butterfat, protein (casein), minerals, and vitamins.

The use of milk as a culture medium dates back to the beginning of bacteriology. It is used as a differential medium to demonstrate the ability of an organism to produce a fermentation, or a peptonization, or a simultaneous fermentation and peptonization.

Casein is a protein capable of reacting with both acids and bases (amphoteric). It is present in milk entirely in colloidal suspension. Some bacteria secrete a rennin-like enzyme capable of hydrolyzing casein to soluble paracasein and a peptone-like compound. The soluble paracasein then reacts with the calcium salts in solution to give a precipitate of paracasein or calcium paracaseinate. The clear liquid surrounding the curd of paracasein is known as whey. This may be diagramed as follows:

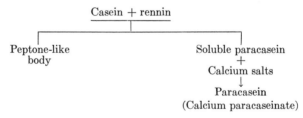

Casein + rennin

Peptone-like body — Soluble paracasein + Calcium salts ↓ Paracasein (Calcium paracaseinate)

Bacteria which ferment lactose very rapidly produce sufficient acid to precipitate or curdle the casein. The clear supernatant liquid that separates from the clot is known as whey. The acid produced is sufficient to stop further growth of the bacteria. Since carbohydrate spares protein, no putrefactive changes occur (Fig. 162).

Bacteria which do not ferment lactose may produce a rennin curd. This is followed by a peptonization of the casein with the formation of various soluble fractions. The milk becomes alkaline in reaction.

Bacteria which ferment lactose very slowly fail to show a protein-sparing effect. The limiting hydrogen-ion concentration is never reached, and protein breakdown occurs simultaneously with carbohydrate utilization. Under these conditions the milk may be acid or alkaline, depending upon which is more vigorous, fermentation or putrefaction.

The indicator litmus is frequently added to milk to detect changes in the pH of the medium. It is a feeble dye and somewhat inaccurate as an indicator. The newer and more brilliant sulfonephthalein indicators, such

Fig. 162. Fermentation and peptonization of milk. Left, litmus milk inoculated with *Bacillus subtilis*. The casein is completely peptonized to a clear purplish solution. Center, litmus milk inoculated with *Escherichia coli*. The lactose is fermented, followed by a curdling of the casein, and the indicator is completely reduced. Right, litmus milk uninoculated.

as bromocresol purple and bromothymol blue, exhibit greater sensitivity and are superior to litmus for detecting changes in reaction. However, litmus also indicates the oxidation-reduction potential of the medium, a property which is not possessed by the synthetic sulfonephthalein indicators and which often is of diagnostic importance. Some bacteria have the ability to reduce the dye to its colorless form. Because of this fact, litmus continues to enjoy popularity as an addition to milk medium.

For more information see Ulrich (1944).

REFERENCES

Castañeda-Agulló, M.: Studies on the biosynthesis of extracellular proteases by bacteria. I. *Serratia marcescens*. Synthetic and gelatin media, *J. Gen. Physiol.*, 39:369, 1956.

Damodaran, M., V. S. Govindarajan, and S. S. Subramanian: The proteolytic system of *Bacillus licheniformis*, *Biochim. Biophys. Acta*, 17:99, 1955.

Fruton, J. S.: Protein structure and proteolytic enzymes, *Cold Spring Harbor Symposia Quant. Biol.*, 6:50, 1938.

————: Proteolytic enzymes as specific agents in the formation and breakdown of proteins, *ibid.*, 9:211, 1941.

Gale, E. F.: "The Chemical Activities of Bacteria," New York, Academic Press, Inc., 1952.

Grob, D.: Proteolytic enzymes. I. The control of their activity, *J. Gen. Physiol.*, 29:219, 1946*a*; II. The physiological significance of the control of their activity, especially with respect to bacterial growth, *ibid.*, 29:249, 1946*b*.

Hamdy, M. K., E. L. Sherrer, C. I. Randles, H. H. Weiser, and W. D. Sheets: Some characteristics of a phenol-oxidizing Pseudomonas, *Appl. Microbiol.*, 4:71, 1956.

Happold, F. C.: Tryptophanase-tryptophan reaction. From "Advances in Enzymology," edited by F. F. Nord, New York, Interscience Publishers, Inc., 1950, vol. 10.

Ichihara, K., H. Yoshimatsu, and Y. Sakamoto: Studies on phenol formation. III. Ammonium and potassium ions as the activator of betatyrosinase, *J. Biochem.*, 43:803, 1956.

Kakihara, Y., and K. Ichihara: Studies on phenol formation. I. Method of the determination of phenol and its microbial formation from tyrosine and tyrosine-derivatives, *Med. J. Osaka Univ.*, 3:497, 1953.

Laidler, K. J.: "Introduction to the Chemistry of Enzymes," New York, McGraw-Hill Book Company, Inc., 1954.

McDade, J. J., and R. H. Weaver: Rapid methods for the detection of gelatin hydrolysis, *J. Bact.*, 77:60, 1959.

Meister, A.: "Biochemistry of the Amino Acids," New York, Academic Press, Inc., 1957.

Møller, V.: Activity determination of amino acid decarboxylases in *Enterobacteriaceae*, *Acta Path. Microbiol. Scand.*, 34:102, 1954*a*; Distribution of amino acid decarboxylases in Enterobacteriaceae, *ibid.*, 35:259, 1954*b*; Simplified tests for some amino acid decarboxylases and for the arginine dihydrolase system, *ibid.*, 36:158, 1955.

Rosenberger, R. F.: Obligate anaerobes which form skatole, *J. Bact.*, 77:517, 1959.

Sakamoto, Y., M. Uchida, and K. Ichihara: The bacterial decomposition of indole. I. Studies on its metabolic pathway by successive adaptation, *Med. J. Osaka Univ.*, 3:477, 1953.

Smith, H. L., Jr., and K. Goodner: Detection of bacterial gelatinases by gelatin-agar plate methods, *J. Bact.*, 76:662, 1958.

Springall, H. D.: "The Structural Chemistry of Proteins," New York, Academic Press, Inc., 1954.

Stewart, J. E., and R. E. Kallio: II. Ester formation from alkanes, *J. Bact.*, 78:726, 1959.

————, ————, D. P. Stevenson, A. C. Jones, and D. O. Schissler: I. Oxidation of *n*-hexadecane by a Gram-negative coccus, *J. Bact.*, 78:441, 1959.

Sumner, J. B., and G. F. Somers: "Chemistry and Methods of Enzymes," New York, Academic Press, Inc., 1953.

Thorne, C. B., C. G. Gómez, and R. D. Housewright: Transamination of D-amino acids by *Bacillus subtilis*, *J. Bact.*, 69:357, 1955.

Uchida, M., Y. Sakamoto, and K. Ichihara: The bacterial decomposition of indole. II. Studies on the enzyme system splitting the pyrrole ring of indole, *Med. J. Osaka Univ.*, 3:487, 1953.

————, Y. Taketomo, Y. Kakihara, and K. Ichihara: Studies on phenol formation. II. β-Tyrosinase and the role of pyridoxal in phenol formation, *Med. J. Osaka Univ.*, 3:509, 1953.

Ulrich, J. A.: New indicators to replace litmus milk, *Science*, 99:352, 1944.

Umbarger, H. E., and B. Brown: Threonine deamination in *Escherichia coli*. II. Evidence for two L-threonine deaminases, *J. Bact.*, 73:105, 1957.

Van der Zant, W. C., and F. E. Nelson: Characteristics of some endocellular peptidases of *Streptococcus lactis*, *J. Dairy Sci.*, 37:795, 1954.

CHAPTER 14

Fermentation of Carbohydrates and Other Compounds

During the early part of the last century, the biological theory of fermentation made slow progress owing to the fact that the majority of scientists of that period were chemists and physicists. Berzelius and his pupils Liebig and Wohler believed that all vital phenomena could be explained on purely chemical grounds. They stated that fermentation and putrefaction were the result of the action of compounds known as ferments (enzymes). The ferments were believed to arise from some constituent of the solution, when exposed to air, but after fermentation had once started, oxygen was no longer required.

Pasteur believed that living yeast cells were always present in fermentation. In their absence, fermentation did not occur.

Later Buchner subjected yeast cells to great pressure and demonstrated that the expressed juice, added to a sugar solution, was capable of inducing alcoholic fermentation. This observation proved that both views were correct, i.e., that fermentation was produced by enzymes but that living cells were necessary for their elaboration.

The term fermentation has undergone many changes in meaning since the time of Pasteur. At present it is generally defined as the incomplete oxidation of carbohydrates and carbohydrate-like compounds by microorganisms. The various types of fermentations result in the formation of many kinds of organic acids, alcohols, carbon dioxide, hydrogen, and other compounds of a nonnitrogenous nature.

Bacterial action on carbohydrates may be either aerobic or anaerobic. In the presence of sufficient oxygen, carbohydrate breakdown may proceed to the final end products carbon dioxide and water. In the partial or complete absence of free oxygen, incomplete combustion or anaerobic breakdown occurs.

Since the discovery of oxygen by Lavoisier, physiologists had familiarized themselves with the idea that oxygen was an essential attribute for the maintenance of life, the slow combustion of the organic nutrients being the source of the vital energy. Under these conditions it is easily understood why Pasteur concluded that the most essential feature of fermenting agents was their ability to utilize the oxygen from organic compounds. In other words, free oxygen was not necessary for oxidations to occur. To use the well-known statement of Pasteur, "*La fermentation est la vie sans air.*"

In anaerobic breakdown, organisms are unable to obtain the maximum amount of energy available in fermentable compounds. In the case of glucose, (1) complete oxidation, (2) partial oxidation, and (3) anaerobic decomposition yield the following number of calories:

1. Complete oxidation:
$$C_6H_{12}O_6 + 6O_2 \rightarrow 6CO_2 + 6H_2O + 674 \text{ Cal.}$$

2. Partial oxidation:
$$C_6H_{12}O_6 + 4\tfrac{1}{2}O_2 \rightarrow 3(COOH)_2 + 3H_2O + 493 \text{ Cal.}$$
Oxalic acid

3. Anaerobic decomposition:

   (a) $C_6H_{12}O_6 \rightarrow 2CH_3 \cdot CHOH \cdot COOH + 22\tfrac{1}{2} \text{ Cal.}$
   Lactic acid

   (b) $C_6H_{12}O_6 \rightarrow 2CH_3 \cdot CH_2OH + 2CO_2 + 22 \text{ Cal.}$
   Ethyl alcohol

   (c) $C_6H_{12}O_6 \rightarrow 3CH_3 \cdot COOH + 15 \text{ Cal.}$
   Acetic acid

FERMENTATION OF NITROGENOUS COMPOUNDS

It is generally stated that in the process of fermentation only carbohydrates or carbohydrate-like compounds are involved, but this is not strictly correct. It is now known that a number of species of anaerobes, or facultative forms growing under anaerobic conditions, are able to satisfy all or part of their energy requirements by the fermentation of single amino acids. The amino group of amino acids is probably first removed as ammonia, followed by the fermentation of the carbon chain.

Clifton (1942) found that *Clostridium tetani* fermented aspartic acid, glutamic acid, and serine with the production of ammonia, acetic acid, lactic acid, butyric acid, alcohol, and carbon dioxide. Essentially, the same products were produced during the dissimilation of pyruvic acid, an intermediary product in the fermentation of carbohydrates.

Cardon and Barker (1946, 1947) isolated from marine mud two obligately anaerobic bacteria which were capable of fermenting single amino acids. *Clostridium propionicum* caused a propionic acid fermentation of alanine according to the equation:

$$3CH_3 \cdot CHNH_2 \cdot COOH + 2H_2O \rightarrow 3NH_3 + 2CH_3 \cdot CH_2 \cdot COOH + CH_3 \cdot COOH + CO_2$$
Alanine   Propionic acid   Acetic acid

The other organism, *Peptococcus glycinophilus*, fermented glycine as follows:

$$4CH_2NH_2 \cdot COOH + 2H_2O \rightarrow 4NH_3 + 3CH_3 \cdot COOH + 2CO_2$$
Glycine   Acetic acid

Dohner and Cardon (1954) found that *Escherichia coli* fermented L-lysine to acetic acid, butyric acid, and ammonia according to the equation:

$$NH_2 \cdot (CH_2)_4 \cdot CHNH_2 \cdot COOH + 2H_2O \rightarrow$$
L-Lysine

$$CH_3 \cdot COOH + CH_3 \cdot CH_2 \cdot CH_2 \cdot COOH + 2NH_3$$
Acetic acid   Butyric acid

Wachsman and Barker (1955) reported the fermentation of L-glutamate by *Clostridium tetanomorphum* to acetate, butyrate, hydrogen, carbon dioxide, and ammonia. Carbon dioxide, acetate, and butyrate originated from carbons 5, 1 and 2, and 3 and 4 of glutamate respectively. Carbon 4 of glutamate was found exclusively in carbon 1 of acetate and in carbons 1 and 3 of butyrate (Fig. 163).

For more information see Barker (1956).

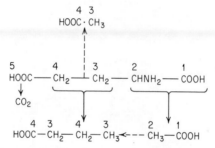

FIG. 163. Origin of products of glutamate fermentation. (*After Wachsman and Barker.*)

ALCOHOLIC FERMENTATION

More than half of all ethyl alcohol is produced by synthesis; the remainder is produced by the fermentation of molasses, grains, potatoes, etc., by the action of yeasts.

The species of yeasts generally used for this purpose is *Saccharomyces cerevisiae*, the common baker's or brewer's yeast. The organism converts approximately 90 per cent of the sugar into equimolecular quantities of alcohol and carbon dioxide. The over-all reaction may be represented as follows:

$$C_6H_{12}O_6 \rightarrow 2C_2H_5OH + 2CO_2$$
D-Glucose   Alcohol

Pasteur Effect. Alcoholic fermentation proceeds in the presence of air as well as in its absence. However, the velocity of the reaction is decreased by aeration. In air the growth of yeast is accelerated while the consumption of sugar is decreased. In the absence of oxygen the reverse is true. Pasteur showed that 1 gm. of yeast was produced from 4 to 10 gm. of glucose in the presence of air, and from 60 to 80 gm. of glucose in the absence of air. This is sometimes referred to as the *Pasteur effect*.

Mechanism of Alcoholic Fermentation. The Meyerhof-Embden scheme for the conversion of sugar to alcohol involves 14 known steps and at least 15 enzymes and 3 coenzyme systems. The entire group of enzymes and coenzymes was formerly called *zymase* by Buchner. The enzymes involved include those for phosphate transfer, oxidation-reduction, decarboxylation, and isomerization; aldolase for the splitting of the carbon chain; and mutase for the shift of phosphate bonds.

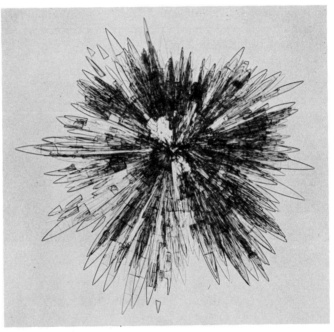

Fig. 164. Crystal of adenosine triphosphate (ATP). (*Courtesy of Sigma Chemical Co.*)

The first step involves the phosphorylation of the hexose sugar by the phosphorylating coenzyme system. This system consists of adenylic acid, adenosine diphosphate, and adenosine triphosphate (Fig. 164). The first two coenzymes pick up phosphate, while the third transfers phosphate. The formulas for adenylic acid and adenosine triphosphate are as follows:

Adenylic acid (adenosine monophosphate)

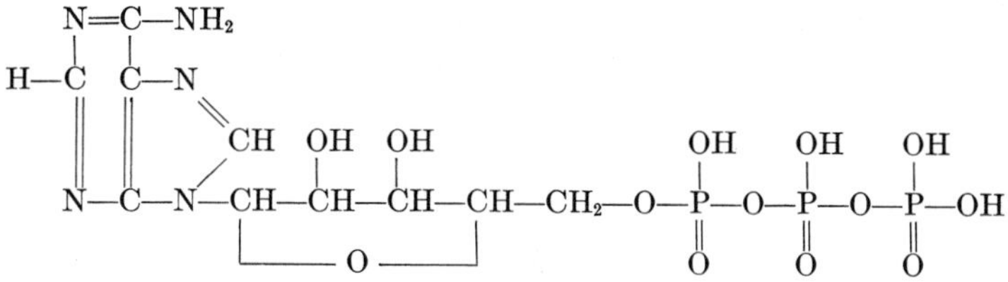

$$\begin{array}{l} N\!=\!C\!-\!NH_2 \\ \ \ |\quad\ | \\ H\!-\!C\quad C\!-\!N \end{array}$$

$$N\!-\!C\!-\!N\!-\!CH\!-\!CH\!-\!CH\!-\!CH\!-\!CH_2\!-\!O\!-\!P\!-\!O\!-\!P\!-\!O\!-\!P\!-\!OH$$

Adenosine triphosphate

The coenzyme system is present in yeast juice and is capable of transferring phosphate to the hexose, converting the sugar first to hexosemonophosphate and then to hexosediphosphate. The loss of one molecule of phosphate converts the coenzyme to adenosine diphosphate. The phosphate is not utilized in the reaction. When the fermentation reaches the pyruvic acid stage, the phosphate is liberated and becomes available again for phosphorylating additional sugar.

The phosphorylation of glucose in the presence of the coenzyme adenosine triphosphate yields first glucopyranose-6-phosphate, then fructofuranose-6-phosphate, and finally fructofuranose-1,6-diphosphate:

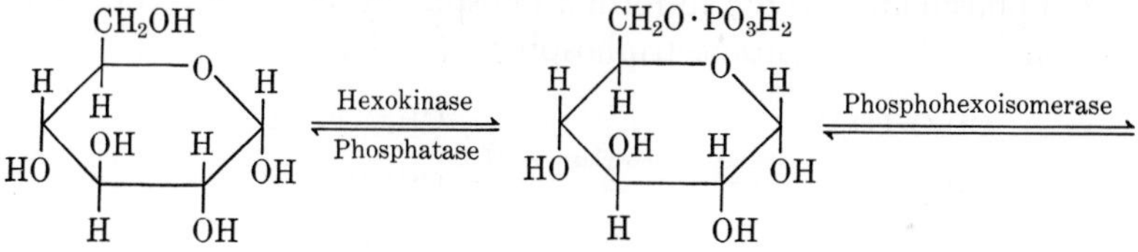

D-Glucose $\xrightarrow[\text{Phosphatase}]{\text{Hexokinase}}$ Glucopyranose-6-phosphate $\xrightarrow{\text{Phosphohexoisomerase}}$

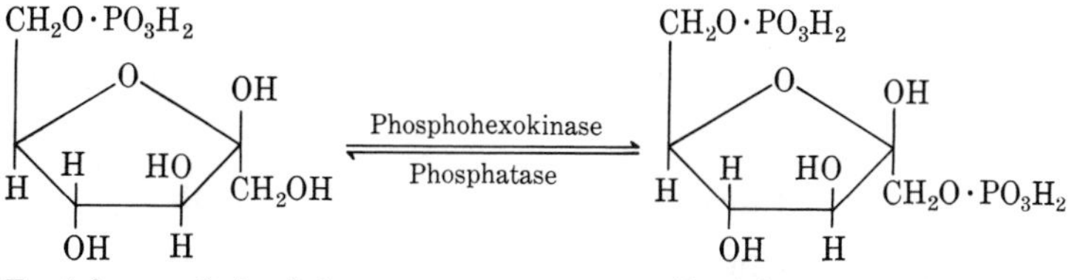

Fructofuranose-6-phosphate $\xrightarrow[\text{Phosphatase}]{\text{Phosphohexokinase}}$ Fructofuranose-1,6-diphosphate

Fructofuranose-1,6-diphosphate splits to form one molecule of 3-glyceraldehyde phosphate and one of dihydroxyacetone phosphate. These two fractions are in equilibrium with each other, being converted largely into the latter:

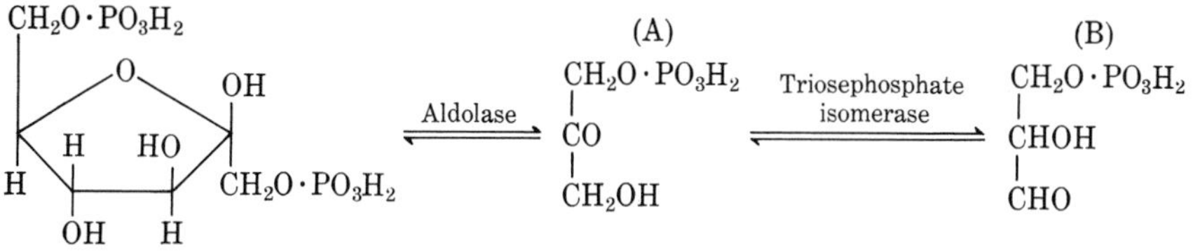

(A) Dihydroxyacetone phosphate
$$\begin{array}{l} CH_2O\cdot PO_3H_2 \\ | \\ CO \\ | \\ CH_2OH \end{array}$$

(B) 3-Glyceraldehyde phosphate
$$\begin{array}{l} CH_2O\cdot PO_3H_2 \\ | \\ CHOH \\ | \\ CHO \end{array}$$

Fructofuranose-1,6-diphosphate $\xrightarrow{\text{Aldolase}}$ (A) $\xrightarrow[\text{isomerase}]{\text{Triosephosphate}}$ (B)

(A) The dihydroxyacetone phosphate becomes reduced to α-glycero-phosphate by reduced coenzyme I (DPNH), and then to glycerol by phosphatase:

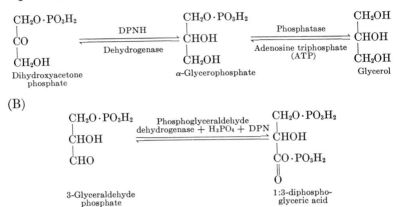

$$
\begin{array}{l}
CH_2O \cdot PO_3H_2 \\
| \\
CO \\
| \\
CH_2OH
\end{array}
\quad
\underset{\text{Dehydrogenase}}{\overset{\text{DPNH}}{\rightleftharpoons}}
\quad
\begin{array}{l}
CH_2O \cdot PO_3H_2 \\
| \\
CHOH \\
| \\
CH_2OH
\end{array}
\quad
\underset{\substack{\text{Adenosine triphosphate} \\ \text{(ATP)}}}{\overset{\text{Phosphatase}}{\rightleftharpoons}}
\quad
\begin{array}{l}
CH_2OH \\
| \\
CHOH \\
| \\
CH_2OH
\end{array}
$$

Dihydroxyacetone phosphate α-Glycerophosphate   Glycerol

(B)

$$
\begin{array}{l}
CH_2O \cdot PO_3H_2 \\
| \\
CHOH \\
| \\
CHO
\end{array}
\quad
\underset{}{\overset{\substack{\text{Phosphoglyceraldehyde} \\ \text{dehydrogenase} + H_3PO_4 + DPN}}{\rightleftharpoons}}
\quad
\begin{array}{l}
CH_2O \cdot PO_3H_2 \\
| \\
CHOH \\
| \\
CO \cdot PO_3H_2 \\
\| \\
O
\end{array}
$$

3-Glyceraldehyde phosphate   1:3-diphospho-glyceric acid

The 1:3-diphosphoglyceric acid loses the high-energy phosphate to adenosine diphosphate (ADP) to form 3-phosphoglyceric acid. The ADP becomes converted to adenosine triphosphate (ATP):

$$
\begin{array}{l}
CH_2O \cdot PO_3H_2 \\
| \\
CHOH \\
| \\
CO \sim PO_3H_2 \\
\| \\
O
\end{array}
\quad
\underset{}{\overset{\text{Transphosphorylase} + ADP}{\rightleftharpoons}}
\quad
\begin{array}{l}
CH_2O \cdot PO_3H_2 \\
| \\
CHOH \\
| \\
COOH
\end{array}
$$

1:3-Diphospho-glyceric acid   3-Phospho-glyceric acid

The 3-phosphoglyceric acid, in the presence of the enzyme phospho-glyceromutase, is in equilibrium with 2-phosphoglyceric acid:

$$
\begin{array}{l}
CH_2O \cdot PO_3H_2 \\
| \\
CHOH \\
| \\
COOH
\end{array}
\quad
\underset{}{\overset{\substack{\text{Phospho-} \\ \text{glyceromutase}}}{\rightleftharpoons}}
\quad
\begin{array}{l}
CH_2OH \\
| \\
HCO \cdot PO_3H_2 \\
| \\
COOH
\end{array}
$$

3-Phospho-glyceric acid   2-Phospho-glyceric acid

The 2-phosphoglyceric acid, in the presence of enolase, loses one mole-cule of water to become phosphopyruvic acid (enol):

$$
\begin{array}{l}
CH_2OH \\
| \\
HCO \cdot PO_3H_2 \\
| \\
COOH
\end{array}
\quad
\underset{}{\overset{\text{Enolase}}{\rightleftharpoons}}
\quad
\begin{array}{l}
CH_2 \\
\| \\
CO \sim PO_3H_2 + H_2O \\
| \\
COOH
\end{array}
$$

2-Phospho-glyceric acid   Phosphopyruvic acid (enol)

The ADP removes the energy-rich phosphate linkage from the 2-phos-phopyruvic acid (enol) to yield pyruvic acid and ATP:

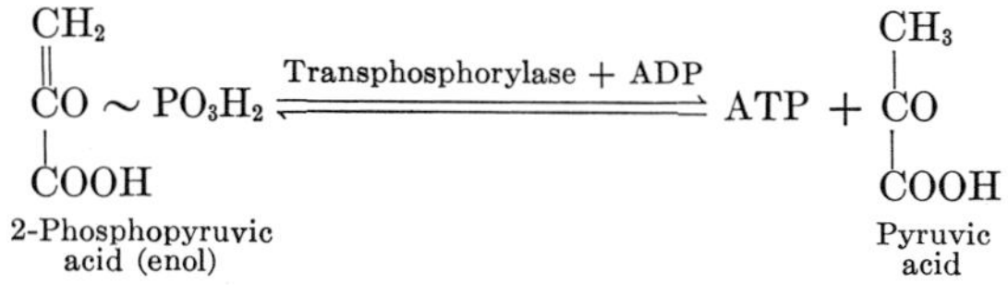

$$CH_2 \atop \overset{\|}{CO} \sim PO_3H_2 \atop \overset{|}{COOH} \quad \underset{\text{Transphosphorylase + ADP}}{\rightleftharpoons} \quad ATP + \overset{CH_3 \atop |}{CO} \atop \overset{|}{COOH}$$

2-Phosphopyruvic acid (enol)   Pyruvic acid

The pyruvic acid is then decarboxylated by the enzyme carboxylase and its coenzyme cocarboxylase to yield acetaldehyde and carbon dioxide:

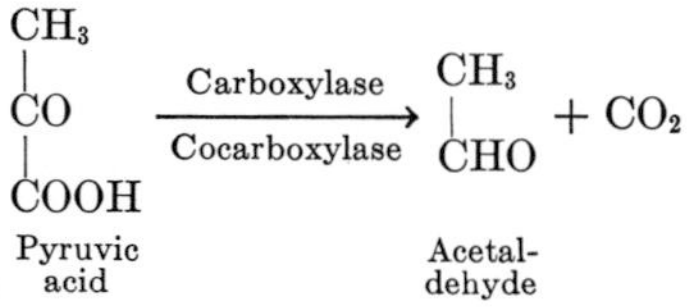

$$\overset{CH_3 \atop |}{CO} \atop \overset{|}{COOH} \quad \underset{\text{Cocarboxylase}}{\overset{\text{Carboxylase}}{\longrightarrow}} \quad \overset{CH_3 \atop |}{CHO} + CO_2$$

Pyruvic acid   Acetaldehyde

Finally, acetaldehyde accepts hydrogen from reduced DPN to yield alcohol:

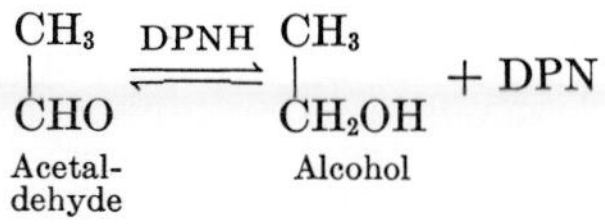

$$\overset{CH_3 \atop |}{CHO} \quad \underset{}{\overset{\text{DPNH}}{\rightleftharpoons}} \quad \overset{CH_3 \atop |}{CH_2OH} + DPN$$

Acetaldehyde   Alcohol

The above steps are diagramed in Fig. 165.

By-products of Alcoholic Fermentation. In addition to alcohol and carbon dioxide, small amounts of D-amyl alcohol, isoamyl alcohol, succinic acid, glycerol, and traces of other compounds are also produced.

D-*Amyl and Isoamyl Alcohols.* A mixture of D-amyl and isoamyl alcohols together with traces of other higher alcohols and compound ethers obtained from fermented liquors is known as fusel oil.

The D-amyl and isoamyl alcohols are derived from the amino acids isoleucine and leucine respectively. These acids may originate from the constituents of the medium or from the protein of dead and autolyzed yeast cells. The alcohols are produced by a deaminization and a decarboxylation of the amino acids:

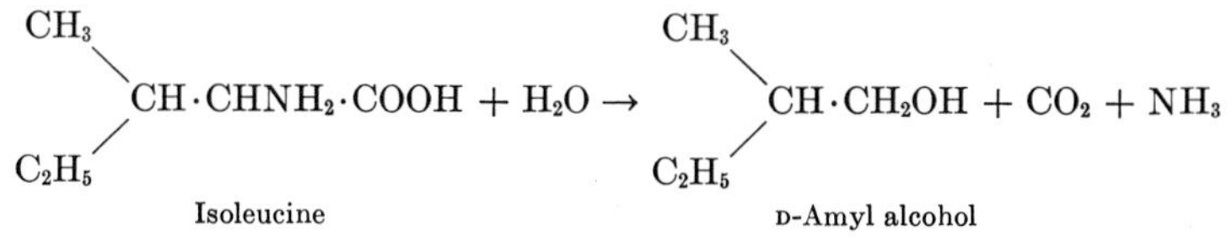

$$\underset{C_2H_5}{\overset{CH_3}{\diagdown}} CH \cdot CHNH_2 \cdot COOH + H_2O \rightarrow \underset{C_2H_5}{\overset{CH_3}{\diagdown}} CH \cdot CH_2OH + CO_2 + NH_3$$

Isoleucine   D-Amyl alcohol

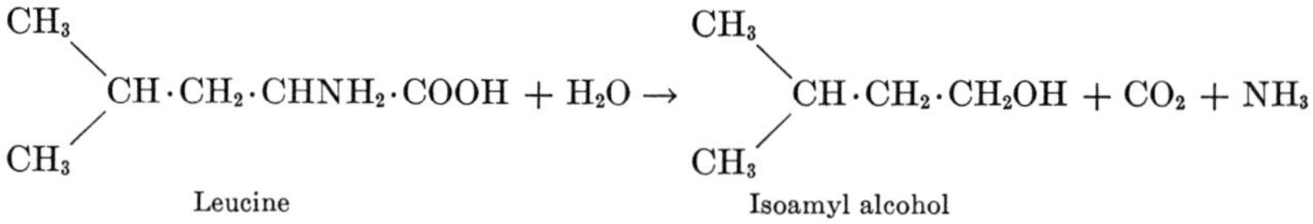

$$\underset{CH_3}{\overset{CH_3}{\diagdown}} CH \cdot CH_2 \cdot CHNH_2 \cdot COOH + H_2O \rightarrow \underset{CH_3}{\overset{CH_3}{\diagdown}} CH \cdot CH_2 \cdot CH_2OH + CO_2 + NH_3$$

Leucine   Isoamyl alcohol

The amounts of the two alcohols produced depend upon the concentrations of the specific amino acids present in the medium, upon the species of yeast employed, and upon the nutritional requirement of the yeast cells. The reaction occurs only in the presence of a fermentable carbohydrate. Small amounts of alcohols are produced from other amino acids, such as tyrosol from tyrosine and tryptophol from tryptophan.

Succinic Acid. Succinic acid is produced from glutamic acid during alcoholic fermentation. It is produced either from the glutamic acid of

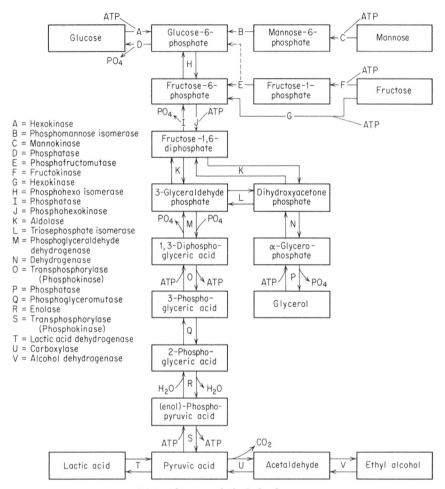

A = Hexokinase
B = Phosphomannose isomerase
C = Mannokinase
D = Phosphatase
E = Phosphofructomutase
F = Fructokinase
G = Hexokinase
H = Phosphohexo isomerase
I = Phosphatase
J = Phosphohexokinase
K = Aldolase
L = Triosephosphate isomerase
M = Phosphoglyceraldehyde
        dehydrogenase
N = Dehydrogenase
O = Transphosphorylase
        (Phosphokinase)
P = Phosphatase
Q = Phosphoglyceromutase
R = Enolase
S = Transphosphorylase
        (Phosphokinase)
T = Lactic acid dehydrogenase
U = Carboxylase
V = Alcohol dehydrogenase

Fig. 165. Mechanism of alcoholic fermentation.

the medium or from the proteins of dead and autolyzed yeast cells. As in the case of fusel oil, the production of succinic acid does not occur in the absence of a fermentable carbohydrate.

Glycerol. Glycerol is prepared commercially chiefly as a by-product in the manufacture of soap. It is produced in small amounts during the alcoholic fermentation of carbohydrates by yeasts. The yield rarely amounts to more than about 3.8 per cent of the sugar fermented. However, it can be increased by the addition of an appropriate alkali or sodium sulfite to the fermenting mixture.

As has already been shown, alcohol results from the reduction of the intermediary compound acetaldehyde by means of hydrogen from reduced DPN. If the hydrogen is prevented from reducing the acetaldehyde, an increased yield of glycerol will result. This is accomplished by adding sodium sulfite to the fermenting mixture. The sulfite reacts with the acetaldehyde to produce an addition product, preventing it from accepting hydrogen from the reduced DPN:

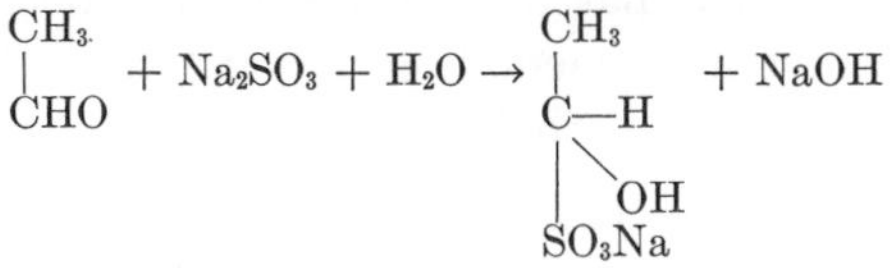

$$\begin{array}{c} CH_3 \\ | \\ CHO \end{array} + Na_2SO_3 + H_2O \rightarrow \begin{array}{c} CH_3 \\ | \\ C-H \\ \diagdown \\ | \quad OH \\ SO_3Na \end{array} + NaOH$$

Acetaldehyde   Aldehyde-bisulfite
compound

A second molecule in the fermenting medium, a triose produced from the hexose sugar, acts as a hydrogen acceptor and becomes reduced to glycerol. Sodium carbonate reacts in a similar manner with the acetaldehyde to prevent its reduction to alcohol.

The yield of glycerol varies, depending upon the concentration of sulfite or carbonate added to the fermenting mixture. In the sulfite process, the yield of glycerol may be as high as 37 per cent of the sugar fermented.

For more information see De Moss (1953), Freeman and Donald (1957a, b, c), Lipmann (1942), Meyerhof (1952), Pigman (1957), Prescott and Dunn (1959), Sumner and Somers (1953), Underkofler et al. (1951a, b, 1954).

The scheme from glucose-6-phosphate through fructose-1,6-diphosphate to pyruvate is the best known of the pathways in the metabolism of glucose and is frequently called the Meyerhof-Embden system. There may be others, but the one given above is believed to be the major pathway in the breakdown of glucose and is widely distributed among the yeasts and bacteria.

The Meyerhof-Embden scheme has been fairly well worked out. However, the pathways of carbohydrate breakdown in some special types of bacterial fermentations are still unsettled. It is generally believed that all types of fermentations pass through the same intermediary steps from hexose to pyruvic acid and branch off only afterward. The most important bacterial fermentations are now discussed.

BUTYRIC ACID FERMENTATION

The organism generally involved in this type of fermentation is the anaerobic spore-forming rod known as *Clostridium butyricum*.

Rods of *Cl. butyricum* are straight or slightly curved, measuring 0.7 by 5 to 7 μ, with rounded ends, occurring singly, in pairs, in short chains, and occasionally in long filaments. Spores are oval and eccentric to subterminal, swelling the cells to clostridial forms. The organism is motile and Gram-positive, becoming Gram-negative in old cultures.

Cl. butyricum and most of the other species of clostridia are able to ferment carbohydrates with the production of butyric and other organic acids. Because of its powerful odor, butyric acid is the most characteristic end product.

It is generally believed that the scheme from glucose to pyruvate is the same as for alcoholic fermentation and diverges at that point. The substitution of pyruvate for carbohydrate produces the same end result:

$$3CH_3 \cdot CO \cdot COOH + H_2O \rightarrow CH_3 \cdot CH_2 \cdot CH_2 \cdot COOH + CH_3 \cdot COOH + 3CO_2 + H_2$$

Pyruvic acid   Butyric acid   Acetic acid

BUTYL ALCOHOL AND ACETONE FERMENTATION

The organism employed is the anaerobic spore-forming rod known as *Clostridium acetobutylicum*. The cells are straight rods, with round ends, occurring singly and in pairs but not in chains. The vegetative cells measure 0.6 to 0.72 by 2.6 to 4.7 μ; the clostridia, 1.3 to 1.6 by 4.7 to 5.5 μ. Spores are ovoid, eccentric to subterminal, swelling the cells to clostridia. Not encapsulated. The cells are motile by means of peritrichous flagella. They are Gram-positive, becoming Gram-negative.

In this type of carbohydrate breakdown, the two chief end products are butyl alcohol and acetone. Other products include ethyl alcohol, isopropyl alcohol, butyric and acetic acids, hydrogen, and carbon dioxide (Fig. 166).

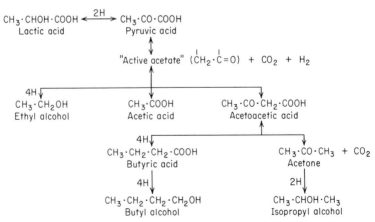

FIG. 166. Reaction scheme for the formation of butyl alcohol and acetone by *Clostridium acetobutylicum.* (*After Kluyver and van Niel.*)

Wood et al. (1944) used heavy carbon (C^{13}) compounds as tracers in an attempt to determine the mechanism of the fermentation. When acetic acid ($CH_3 \cdot C^{13}OOH$) was added to the fermentation, butyl alcohol was formed which contained heavy carbon. Butyric acid, $CH_3 \cdot C^{13}H_2 \cdot CH_2 \cdot C^{13}OOH$, was isolated which contained heavy carbon in the carboxyl and β positions. On the basis of the distribution of the C^{13} in the molecule, they concluded that butyl alcohol was formed by a condensation of acetic acid or its derivative.

ACETONE AND ETHYL ALCOHOL FERMENTATION

The organism responsible for this type of fermentation is *Bacillus macerans*, an aerobic spore-bearing rod.

The cells measure 0.5 to 0.7 by 2.5 to 5 μ, not in chains. They are motile and Gram-variable. Spores measure 1 to 1.5 by 1.2 to 2.5 μ, ellipsoidal, subterminal to terminal. Spore wall is thick and easily stained. Sporangia are swollen and clavate. The organism produces about 2 parts of ethanol to 1 part of acetone.

The reaction scheme is believed to be as shown in Fig. 167.

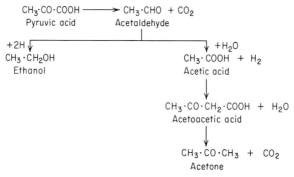

Fig. 167. Reaction scheme for the formation of acetone and ethanol by *Bacillus macerans*.

PROPIONIC ACID FERMENTATION

The propionibacteria are capable of fermenting certain carbohydrates, polyalcohols, lactic and pyruvic acids, etc., to propionic and acetic acids and carbon dioxide.

Propionibacterium. The members of this genus are nonmotile, non-spore-forming, Gram-positive bacteria which grow (1) under anaerobic conditions in neutral media as short, diphtheroid rods, which sometimes resemble streptococci in appearance; and (2) under aerobic conditions in heavy inocula as long, irregular, club-shaped, and branched cells. Metachromatic granules are demonstrable with Albert's stain. As a rule, they are strongly catalase-positive, sometimes weakly so. There is a strong tendency toward anaerobiosis; development is slow, macroscopically visible colonies generally not discernible in less than 5 to 7 days. In an atmosphere containing 5 per cent carbon dioxide, growth is enhanced both aerobically and anaerobically.[1] Nutritional requirements are complex. Development is best in yeast-extract media with the addition of lactates or simple carbohydrates. Vitamin B requirements are relatively simple. Practically all, if not all, species require pantothenic acid, and the majority require biotin. A few require either thiamine or para-aminobenzoic acid in addition. Optimum temperature is 30°C. Found in dairy products, especially hard cheeses.

Formation of Propionic Acid. In a series of investigations, Wood and Werkman (1936, 1938, 1940a, b) showed that propionic acid bacteria utilized carbon dioxide during the fermentation of glycerol. In the absence of carbon dioxide, the fermentation could be represented by the equation:

$$CH_2OH \cdot CHOH \cdot CH_2OH \rightarrow CH_3 \cdot CH_2 \cdot COOH + H_2O$$
$$\text{Glycerol} \qquad\qquad \text{Propionic acid}$$

In the presence of carbon dioxide, the formation of propionic acid was accompanied by the appearance of succinic acid.

Carson and Ruben (1940) and Carson et al. (1941) employed radioactive carbon dioxide as an indicator of its utilization by the propionibacteria. They concluded that propionic and succinic acids contained radioactive carbon only in the carboxyl groups and suggested the following scheme:

$$
\begin{array}{ccc}
& CH_3 & CH_3 \\
& | & \overset{+4H}{\underset{-H_2O}{\rightleftharpoons}} \; | \\
\text{Substrate} \rightarrow & CO & CH_2 \\
& | & | \\
& COOH & COOH \\
& \text{Pyruvic acid} & \text{Propionic acid}
\end{array}
$$

$$
\begin{array}{cccc}
\overset{\pm CO_2}{\updownarrow} & & & \\
COOH & COOH & COOH & COOH \\
| & | & | & | \\
CH_2 & CH_2 & CH & CH_2 \\
| \quad\overset{+2H}{\rightleftharpoons} & | \quad\overset{-H_2O}{\rightleftharpoons} & \| \quad\overset{+2H}{\rightleftharpoons} & | \\
CO & CHOH & CH & CH_2 \\
| & | & | & | \\
COOH & COOH & COOH & COOH \\
\text{Oxalacetic} & \text{Malic} & \text{Fumaric} & \text{Succinic} \\
\text{acid} & \text{acid} & \text{acid} & \text{acid}
\end{array}
$$

On the basis of their results, they came to the following conclusions:

1. Both propionic and succinic acids formed in the presence of $C°O_2$ are radioactive.[2]

2. These acids contain the labeled carbon only in the carboxyl (COOH) groups.

3. Pyruvic acid is an intermediate compound in the propionic acid fermentation.

[1] In a private communication Lichstein and Field also found CO_2 to be necessary for growth initiation of these organisms.

[2] The symbol $C°$ indicates radioactive carbon.

4. A radioactive α-keto acid, besides pyruvic acid, is formed during the fermentation of pyruvic acid in the presence of C^*O_2. This acid contains most, if not all, of the C^* in carboxyl groups.

5. The set of reversible reactions from oxalacetic acid to succinic acid have been found to occur.

Phares, Delwiche, and Carson (1956) reported that during the decarboxylation of succinate to propionate and CO_2 by cell-free extracts of *Propionibacterium pentosaceum*, a 1-carbon fragment (C_1) was produced from the γ-carboxyl carbon of succinyl-CoA, and that CO_2 was subsequently produced from the C_1 fragment by the action of an additional enzyme system (Fig. 168). The data included (1) nonstoichiometry

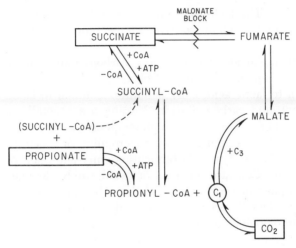

FIG. 168. Scheme for the decarboxylation of succinate to propionate and carbon dioxide by *Propionibacterium pentosaceum* and *Veillonella gazogenes*. (*After Phares, Delwiche, and Carson.*)

of CO_2 and propionate production from succinate; (2) "malonate block" experiments which indicated that the C_1 fragment could be incorporated into the malate carboxyl group; (3) propionate "exchanged" with succinate by combination with a C_1 fragment arising from succinate decarboxylation; (4) CO_2 production from succinate by combinations of cell-free extracts of both organisms, showing that at least two separate enzyme reactions were involved between succinyl-CoA decarboxylation and the production of CO_2; and (5) comparison of the ratios of $C^{14}O_2$ and propionate-1-C^{14} arising from the decomposition of (asymmetrically) labeled succinyl-4-C^{14}-CoA and of (symmetrically) labeled succinyl-1,4-C^{14}-CoA, demonstrating that the C_1 fragment arose from the free carboxyl group of succinyl-CoA.

For more information see Delwiche, Phares, and Carson (1956); Field and Lichstein (1957); Leaver and Wood (1953); Leaver, Wood, and Stjernholm (1955); Wood, Stjernholm, and Leaver (1956).

LACTIC ACID FERMENTATION

Lactic acid was first discovered as one of the products resulting from the souring of milk. It is produced from the milk constituent lactose, which is the precursor of the compound. It is probably the oldest-known acid, having been discovered by Scheele in 1780.

Lactic Acid Bacteria. The designation *lactic acid bacteria* is applied to a group of organisms which ferment lactose to lactic acid as the principal, and often sole, product. The strong acid producers are found in the genera *Lactobacillus* and *Streptococcus* of the family Lactobacillaceae.

Lactobacillus. The lactobacilli are large rods, often long and slender. They are nonmotile, Gram-positive. Pigment production is rare; when present, yellow or orange to rust or brick red. Gelatin is not liquefied. Glucose and similar aldehydic hexoses, carbohydrates which yield these simple sugars, and polyhydroxy alcohols are changed either by homofermentation to lactic acid or by heterofermentation to lactic and acetic acids, alcohol, and carbon dioxide. Nitrates are generally not reduced. Several species grow at relatively high temperatures. Poor surface growth, because members are generally microaerophilic or anaerobic. They do not produce catalase. Found in fermenting dairy and plant products.

Streptococcus. Cells are spherical or ovoid, rarely elongated into rods, occurring in pairs or short or long chains. They are nonmotile, except a few strains in the enterococcus group, and Gram-positive. A fermentable carbohydrate or polyhydroxy alcohol is necessary for satisfactory growth in artificial media. Growth in broth culture is variable in character. Rough variants may show granular growth that tends to settle out quickly, leaving a clear supernatant. Smooth variants may show uniform turbidity with little tendency to settle out. Such variants may be noted within one species. A pellicle is never formed. Growth on agar is usually scanty. Colonies are small, usually less than 1 mm. in diameter. Colony variants within a species may range from rough to smooth to mucoid. Carbohydrate fermentation is homofermentative, with dextrorotatory lactic acid as the dominant end product. Carbon dioxide is produced in very small quantities or not at all from sugar. Ethanol, acetic acid, and formic acid may be produced in appreciable quantities from glucose if allowed to ferment in alkaline media. Cytochrome systems are absent. Catalase-negative. Do not reduce nitrate to nitrite. Facultative with respect to oxygen. All streptococci are fastidious with respect to their nutritional requirements, requiring a number of B vitamins and amino acids for growth. They are commonly found in the mouth and intestine of man and other animals, in dairy and other food products, and in fermenting plant juices.

In their action on glucose, the lactic acid organisms fall into two large groups: (1) the homofermentative species and (2) the heterofermentative species.

Homofermentative Species. The members of this group convert about 95 per cent of glucose and other fermentable hexoses to lactic acid, according to the equation:

$$C_6H_{12}O_6 \rightarrow 2CH_3 \cdot CHOH \cdot COOH$$
$$\text{Glucose} \qquad\qquad \text{Lactic acid}$$

Small amounts of volatile acids and carbon dioxide are also produced. Disaccharides are fermented in a similar manner, e.g., one mole of lactose yields four moles of lactic acid. The lactic acid may be dextrorotatory (D), or levorotatory (L), or a mixture of the two forms (DL) in equal quantities:

The isomer produced is characteristic of the species.

Heterofermentative Species. These differ from the homofermentative species in that lactic acid is only one of several principal products formed from sugar. Other compounds include ethyl alcohol, acetic acid, formic acid, and carbon dioxide.

A large number of carbohydrates, notably glucose, sucrose, and lactose, are employed for the production of lactic acid. Starches of various kinds may first be hydrolyzed to sugars by means of mineral acids or enzymes, then fermented to lactic acid. Molasses and whey are low-priced and serve as excellent sources of carbohydrate for lactic acid production.

For more information see Koser and Thomas (1957) and Snell (1948).

Scheme for Lactic Acid Formation. It is generally believed that the homofermentative species produce lactic acid from carbohydrates by the same pathway as for alcoholic fermentation (page 376, Fig. 165).

On the other hand, the heterofermentative species produce a lower concentration of lactic acid and a number of other products, the most important being ethyl alcohol, acetic acid, formic acid, and carbon dioxide. Gunsalus and Gibbs (1952) and Gibbs, Sokatch, and Gunsalus (1955) showed that glucose fermentation by several heterofermentative species always yielded one mole each of lactic acid, ethyl alcohol, and carbon dioxide.

$$C_6H_{12}O_6 \rightarrow CH_3 \cdot CHOH \cdot COOH + C_2H_5OH + CO_2$$
$$\text{Glucose} \qquad\quad \text{Lactic acid} \qquad\quad \text{Ethyl alcohol}$$

The acetic and formic acids could be produced from the intermediary compound pyruvic acid, according to the equation:

$$CH_3 \cdot CO \cdot COOH + H_2O \rightarrow CH_3 \cdot COOH + HCOOH$$
$$\text{Pyruvic acid} \qquad\qquad\quad \text{Acetic acid} \qquad \text{Formic acid}$$

All or most of the formic acid disappears as carbon dioxide and hydrogen:

$$HCOOH \rightarrow CO_2 + H_2 \rightleftharpoons 2H$$

VINEGAR (ACETIC) FERMENTATION

Vinegar is the product resulting from the oxidation of alcoholic liquids, chiefly to acetic acid, by certain specific bacteria.

Almost any alcoholic liquid may be employed in the manufacture of vinegar. The fermentation of apple cider to hard cider (alcoholic) by means of yeasts, followed by the action of the acetic bacteria, yields a product known as cider vinegar. The oxidation of wines yields a product known as wine vinegar. The alcoholic fermentation of an infusion of barley malt followed by the acetic fermentation gives rise to a preparation known as malt vinegar. Sugar vinegar results from the alcoholic fermentation of sugar, followed by the oxidation of the alcohol to acetic acid. The final product is named after the raw material used in its manufacture. All vinegars are diluted to contain at least 4 per cent acetic acid in the final product. In addition to acetic acid, vinegars may contain traces of other compounds, such as alcohol, glycerol, esters, invert sugar, pentosans, and salts.

When a dilute alcoholic liquid is exposed to the air, a film soon appears on its surface. At the same time the liquid becomes sour, owing to the oxidation of the alcohol to acetic acid. The film is composed of a viscous gelatinous substance, or zooglea, in which are embedded many bacteria. It is commonly known as *mother of vinegar* because a small amount of this material is capable of acting as a starter when added to more alcoholic liquid.

The specific bacteria present in a zoogleal mass are members of the genus *Acetobacter*. They are the so-called acetic acid bacteria.

Acetobacter. Individual cells are ellipsoidal to rod-shaped, occurring singly, in pairs, or in short or long chains. They are motile with polar flagella, or nonmotile. Involution forms may be spherical, elongated, filamentous, club-shaped, swollen, or curved, or may even appear to be branched. Young cells are Gram-negative; old cells often Gram-variable. They are obligate aerobes; as a rule strongly catalase-positive, sometimes weakly so. The cells oxidize various organic compounds to organic acids and other oxidation products which may undergo further oxidation. Common oxidation products include acetic acid from ethyl alcohol, gluconic and 5-ketogluconic acid from glucose, dihydroxyacetone from glycerol, sorbose from sorbitol, etc. Nutritional requirements vary from simple to complex. Development is generally best in yeast infusion or yeast autolysate media with added ethyl alcohol or other oxidizable substrates. Optimum temperature varies with the species. The cells are widely distributed in nature in plant materials undergoing alcoholic fermentation. They are of importance to man for their role in the completion of the carbon cycle and for the production of vinegar.

For more information see Bhat and Rijhsinghani (1955); Brown and Rainbow (1956); Frateur (1950); Hall, Russell, and Tiwari (1954); Leifson (1954); Litsky and Goldman (1953); Rainbow and Mitson (1953); Rao and Stokes (1953).

Aerobic Oxidation of Alcohol. The aerobic oxidation of alcohol to acetic acid is generally believed to occur according to the following scheme:

1. Oxygen acts as a hydrogen acceptor, converting alcohol to acetaldehyde:

$$CH_3 \cdot CH_2OH + O \rightarrow CH_3 \cdot CHO + H_2O$$
$$\text{Ethyl alcohol} \qquad\qquad \text{Acetaldehyde}$$

2. Acetaldehyde takes up water and becomes hydrated:

$$CH_3 \cdot CHO + H_2O \rightarrow CH_3 \cdot C \overset{\displaystyle H}{\underset{\displaystyle OH}{-OH}}$$

$$\text{Acetaldehyde} \qquad\qquad \text{Hydrated}$$
$$\text{aldehyde}$$

3. Oxygen accepts two hydrogen atoms from the hydrated aldehyde to give acetic acid:

$$CH_3 \cdot C \overset{\displaystyle H}{\underset{\displaystyle OH}{-OH}} + O \rightarrow CH_3 \cdot COOH + H_2O$$

$$\text{Hydrated aldehyde} \qquad\qquad \text{Acetic acid}$$

Commercial vinegar contains a minimum of 4 per cent acetic acid. In addition to acetic acid, traces of esters are also present; they are largely responsible for the pleasant odor and flavor of vinegar.

Vinegar may lose its strength on standing, owing to the oxidation of the acetic acid to carbon dioxide and water by some species of *Acetobacter*:

$$CH_3 \cdot COOH + 2O_2 \rightarrow 2CO_2 + 2H_2O$$
$$\text{Acetic acid}$$

This reaction takes place only in the presence of considerable oxygen. The oxidation may be prevented by storing vinegar in well-filled, tightly stoppered bottles or by the destruction of the bacteria by pasteurization.

Methods of Manufacture. To ensure a successful fermentation, the alcohol content should be adjusted to from 10 to 13 per cent. This corresponds to the alcohol concentration of most natural wines. If the alcohol concentration is above 14 per cent, it becomes incompletely oxidized; if too low, much of the vinegar may be lost owing to oxidation of the acetic acid and esters.

Two general methods are employed in the manufacture of vinegar: (1) the Orleans method and (2) the quick method.

Orleans Method. This is the oldest commercial method known for the preparation of vinegar. Barrels or vats are perforated near the top to permit free entrance of air and then filled about two-thirds full with a mixture composed of 2 parts of vinegar and 3 parts of wine. The wine may be raw or pasteurized, the latter being preferable since it greatly reduces the percentage of abnormal fermentations. The acetic acid bacteria grow better in strongly acid solutions. For this reason, vinegar is added to the wine to speed up the reaction, and at the same time to check the growth of undesirable organisms. At definite intervals some of the vinegar is drawn off and fresh wine added. In this manner, the process becomes continuous.

Quick Method. The quick method depends upon the use of large wooden tanks or generators with perforated bottoms through which air enters (Fig. 169). The tanks are filled with beechwood shavings, wood

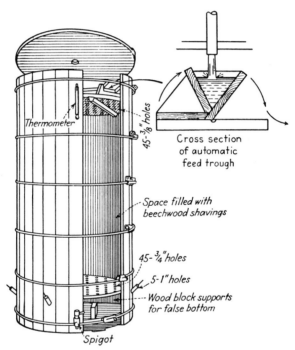

FIG. 169. Generator used in the quick vinegar process. (*From Prescott and Dunn, "Industrial Microbiology."*)

charcoal, corncobs, excelsior, coke, or other supporting media to give greater surface and better aeration of the alcoholic liquid. The supporting medium is first soaked with a culture of the acetic acid bacteria; then the alcoholic liquid (10 to 13 per cent alcohol) is sprayed at the top of the tank and allowed to trickle over the surface of the material. By the time the liquid reaches the bottom of the tank, the alcohol becomes oxidized to acetic acid by the organisms present on the shavings.

The temperature is adjusted to the optimum for the species of organism used, which varies from 28 to 35°C. After completion of the fermentation, the vinegar is drawn off at the bottom of the tank. A generator 10 ft. in diameter and 20 ft. high is capable of producing 80 to 100 gal. of vinegar per day.

Many modifications of the above generator are employed for the manufacture of vinegar. One of these, known as the Frings generator, possesses many advantages. It is cheap and simple to operate. It produces a higher concentration of acetic acid than by other methods. The generator is airtight, thus avoiding loss of vinegar or alcohol by evaporation.

RETTING OF FLAX AND HEMP

Celluloses, hemicelluloses, and pectic substances are polysaccharides which form the framework of plants.

Cellulose is the most abundant cell-wall polysaccharide found in nature. It is probably the most chemically resistant of all substances elaborated by living cells. Complete hydrolysis of pure cellulose by concentrated mineral acids yields D-glucose almost quantitatively as the only constituent sugar (see page 645).

Hemicelluloses are those cell-wall polysaccharides which may be extracted from plant tissues by treatment with dilute alkalies, either hot or cold, but not with water. They may be hydrolyzed to sugar and sugar acid units (D-xylose, D-galactose, L-arabinose, D-glucose, and uronic acids) by boiling with dilute mineral acids.

Pectic substances is a group name for those complex colloidal carbohydrate derivatives which occur in or are prepared from plants and contain a large proportion of anhydrogalacturonic acid units which are believed to exist in a chain-like combination. The carboxyl groups of polygalacturonic acids may be partly esterified by methyl groups and partly or completely neutralized by one or more bases. They always represent mixtures of polygalacturonic acids containing variable numbers of associated units. With the exception of pectic acid, they may also contain different proportions of methyl ester groups in the individual polygalacturonic acids. These may be unevenly distributed on the polygalacturonic acid. Acid salts may contain polymer units with different proportions of metallic ions.

Pectic substances are compounds of a gelatinous consistency which form the middle lamellar layer of plant cells. They act as cement-like substances which bind the cells together. Their hydrolysis by bacteria is of great importance in the retting or rotting of flax and hemp. This may be accomplished by both anaerobic and aerobic methods.

Anaerobic Retting. This method is carried out by immersing the flax or hemp stalks in water and weighting them down. Water is absorbed by the tissues, causing swelling and the extraction of water-soluble substances. The substances extracted amount to about 12 per cent of the weight of the plants and consist of sugars, glucosides, tannins, soluble nitrogenous compounds, and coloring matter. The highly colored water now becomes a good culture medium for the growth of many kinds of organisms. The aerobic organisms reduce the concentration of dissolved oxygen, permitting the growth of the anaerobic species. The anaerobes slowly ferment and dissolve the pectic substances, leaving the fibers intact. During the fermentation, various organic acids, alcohols, and gases are produced. These include acetic, butyric and lactic acids; ethyl and butyl alcohols; acetone; hydrogen; and carbon dioxide. About ten days are required for the reaction to go to completion. The flax or hemp should be removed from the water when the reaction has gone to completion; otherwise overretting will result. The bundles are thoroughly washed to remove the undesirable end products of fermentation, and then spread out in the sun or air to dry. The dried material is now ready for scutching.

Organisms Concerned. A number of organisms have been isolated from fermenting flax or hemp. The most important species are *Clostridium pectinovorum,* anaerobic, spore-forming rods, Gram-positive, found in soil and in naturally retting plant materials; and *C. felsineum,* anaerobic, spore-forming rods, Gram-positive becoming Gram-negative, isolated from retting flax.

A culture of the organism selected is added to the water of the retting vat in the proportion of 1000 ml. to 10,000 gm. of dry tissue. The vat is kept at a temperature of 37 to 38°C. for 50 to 75 hr. or until retting is complete.

Aerobic Retting. An aerobic process known as dew retting is also employed. The stalks are spread out in thin layers on the ground and left exposed to the influence of climatic conditions. If necessary, the materials are turned over once or twice. The flax or hemp is exposed to attack by the aerobic organisms, the process being dependent upon moisture and temperature conditions. Under these conditions, the method cannot be controlled as is possible in the anaerobic process.

A large number of bacteria, molds, and yeasts have been isolated from fermenting materials. Wieringa (1956) concluded that in Holland the mold *Cladosporium herbarum* was the most important retting organism during the summer months, whereas the yeasts *Cryptococcus albidus, Rhodotorula glutinis,* and *R. macerans* were the most important during the winter season. The mold *Pullularia pullulans* might be of some importance in the spring and autumn. Some bacteria such as *Pseudomonas fluorescens* might be important throughout the year. As *Cladosporium* and some other fungi give unfavorable color to the fiber and attack cellulose, the winter season should be recommended for dew retting.

For more information see Pigman (1957), Prescott and Dunn (1959).

SILAGE FERMENTATION

Silage may be defined as the product resulting from the conversion of fodder, either green or mature, into succulent winter feed for livestock through processes of fermentation.

The fodder undergoes an acid fermentation which gives it an agreeable flavor and prevents spoiling. Any farm crop is satisfactory for silage production, provided it contains sufficient sugar to furnish the required amount of acid for its preservation.

Ensilage Process. Fodder (corn, sorghum, sugar cane, legumes, citrus pulp, potatoes, beet pulp, sunflower, etc.) is cut into small pieces and stored in an airtight chamber or silo, where it is compressed to exclude air. Sufficient moisture must be present in the cut pieces; otherwise water is added. Since the surface of the plants contains the required kinds of organisms, inoculation of the fodder is not necessary. Counts show that normally there are present from 10,000 to 400,000,000 bacteria per gram of material.

Because of the presence of carbohydrates in the plant sap, the changes which occur are fermentative rather than putrefactive. The plant cells continue to respire, and within a few hours the free oxygen is utilized and replaced by carbon dioxide. The changes which follow are anaerobic rather than aerobic in character.

Beardsley (1956) recognized five phases in the ensiling process:

1. The continued respiration of the plant cells results in the production of CO_2, the utilization of simple carbohydrate and a flow of water from the mass due to these biochemical changes, and the mechanical compression of the crop. These events are accompanied by the evolution of heat.

2. The production of acetic acid in small amounts by organisms of the coliform group and others. This phase is of short duration and merges into Phase 3.

3. The initiation of a lactic acid fermentation dependent upon the activity of lactic acid organisms (lactobacilli and streptococci) supported by adequate carbohydrate.

4. This is a stage of quiescence in the mass during which the lactic acid production passes its peak and remains constant at 1 to 1.5 per cent of the fresh materials corresponding to a pH of less than 4.2.

These 4 stages take place in about 3 weeks with the first 3 completed in about 3 days. If the material has been properly ensiled, adequate production of lactic acid has been obtained and air is excluded, the silage should remain relatively stable and in good condition for a long time—10 years or more. If, however, the conditions within the silage are unsatisfactory and incomplete production of lactic acid is obtained, a fifth stage may set in.

5. The attack by butyric acid–producing organisms on both the residual soluble carbohydrate and the lactic acid which has already formed. In extreme cases, this is accompanied by a deaminization of amino acids with the formation of higher volatile fatty acids and ammonia; possibly a decarboxylation leading to the formation of amines and carbon dioxide.

The practical aim in the ensiling process is the production of enough lactic acid by certain microorganisms to inhibit further breakdown of the ensiled material by other types of microorganisms.

Characteristics of Good Silage. Good-quality silage has the following characteristics:

1. A pH of 4.5 or less. A lower pH is better.
2. Low volatile base content (0.5 per cent or less, expressed as ammonia).
3. Lactic acid content of 3 to 5 per cent or more.
4. Butyric acid content of 2 per cent or less.

All characteristics are expressed on the basis of dry weight. Silage which possesses these characteristics should (1) have a mild and pleasing odor, (2) have a light to dark green color, (3) be readily accepted by cows, and (4) have a higher feeding value than silage that does not approach these standards.

Bacterial Content of Silage. During active fermentation, each gram of silage may contain as many as 2 billion organisms. Each milliliter of the silage may show a count as high as 4 billion bacteria. If conditions within the silage are satisfactory, the microbial population should consist almost entirely of lactobacilli and streptococci. In the absence of sufficient carbohydrate, preventing the organisms from producing their limiting hydrogen-ion concentration, other species will be present.

For more information see Bryant and Burkey (1956), Rosenberger (1956), Stirling (1953), Thomas (1950), and Wieringa (1959).

TOBACCO FERMENTATION

Tobacco is cured and fermented to improve its color, texture, and aroma. The treatment results in a considerable loss in the nicotine content.

Curing. Tobacco leaves are harvested, tied into bunches, and attached to sticks. They are then ready for curing.

According to Evers (1947), four methods of curing are used: (1) sun-curing; (2) air-curing; (3) fire-curing; and (4) flue-curing.

In sun-curing, the leaf is allowed to wilt for a few days, then exposed to the sun until thoroughly dry. This requires about 1 month and is used principally for Turkish tobaccos.

In air-curing, the tobacco is hung in barns and allowed to undergo a natural process of curing under atmospheric conditions. This requires about 2 months and is used chiefly for "Burley" and cigar tobaccos.

In fire-curing, the tobacco is hung in barns, and curing is effected by means of small open fires kept going at intervals over a period of 3 weeks or more. The smoke and heat impart a peculiar "fired" aroma observed in many dark pipe tobaccos.

In flue-curing, specially designed barns are used, and the rate of curing is controlled by artificial heat generated in small furnaces built on an outside wall of the barn. The heat is distributed by flues running across the floor of the barn so that no smoke contaminates the tobacco. The curing is complete in a few days and in three stages: (1) yellowing of the leaf between 25 and 45°C.; (2) fixing the color between 45 and 50°C.;

(3) drying of the stem between 50 and 75°C. Cigarette tobaccos are generally cured by this method. Increase of temperature must be gradual while relative humidity must fall slowly until the drying stage is reached.

Mechanism of Curing. Tobacco leaves do not cure normally unless subjected to slow drying. The cells of the green leaf remain alive during the yellowing stage, and the processes of respiration and translocation continue as the leaf slowly starves. During slow starvation the stored-up carbohydrates and proteins are gradually consumed, while the chlorophyll changes as the leaf becomes yellow. The insoluble carbohydrates and proteins are hydrolyzed to reducing sugars and amino acids respectively. By further action the reducing sugars may eventually disappear, and the amino acids become deaminized with the release of ammonia. These hydrolytic and oxidative changes occur rapidly during the yellowing stage and gradually disappear as the cells die.

Evers believed that leaf enzymes played an important role in the above changes. Oxidizing enzymes were believed to be responsible for the color changes which occurred in the leaf during curing. If curing proceeded in a normal manner, bacteria and other microorganisms played an insignificant role in the process; otherwise development of bacteria and molds was liable to occur.

Fermentation. After curing is complete, tobaccos are subjected to varying degrees of fermentation.

The cured leaves are moistened with water, packed in containers under pressure, stored in rooms heated to about 45°C. and ±60 per cent relative humidity, and allowed to ferment or "sweat." It is generally agreed that the process is one of oxidation, characterized chiefly by the generation of heat (up to 60°C.) and the evolution of carbon dioxide, ammonia, and other volatile substances. The storage of the tobacco in the heated rooms is periodically interrupted by unpacking and airing the leaves to keep the temperature from exceeding 50°C. This is repeated as often as necessary until fermentation is complete. An easily fermenting tobacco requires only one or two interruptions; a very tough or raw tobacco requires up to 10 or 12 airings.

At the end of the fermentation the leaves have lost the initial "raw" odor and have assumed an aromatic, partly ammoniacal smell. The color has changed to a slightly duller shade. The surfaces have lost the initial glossy appearance and their sticky and gummy feel, and the texture has become considerably more tender and brittle. Also a marked decrease may occur in the nicotine content (6 to 94 per cent). On ignition, well-fermented leaves develop an aromatic smoke that is free of the pungency of the smoke of unfermented tobacco leaves.

Role of Microorganisms. More recent investigations support the possibility that microorganisms may play a subsidiary, if not essential, role in the curing and fermentation of tobacco.

Reid, McKinstry, and Haley (1938a, b) believed that the major changes were brought about by the activity of certain bacteria that usually developed in large numbers during the fermentation process and that leaf enzymes played only a minor role. The predominant forms on cured leaf were bacteria of the *Bacillus megaterium* group and molds of the genera *Penicillium* and *Aspergillus*. A satisfactory fermentation was associated with a rapid increase in numbers of the *Mycococcus albus* and *Bacillus subtilis* types. The predominant types on cured leaf played little part in a satisfactory fermentation, viable molds disappeared entirely in the early stages of the fermentation, and bacteria of the *B. megaterium* group failed to show any significant increase in number during the process. Some cellulose-hydrolyzing species of the genus *Clostridium* were occasionally encountered on cured tobacco; they were usually responsible for the rotting that sometimes occurred during the fermentation process.

For more information see Casida and Rosenfield (1958), Frankenburg and Gottscho (1955), Frankenburg et al. (1955), Frankenburg and Vaitekunas (1955), Jensen (1948), Vickery and Meiss (1953).

FERMENTATIONS BY COLIFORM ORGANISMS

Members of the coliform group and related species ferment glucose and other carbohydrates with the production chiefly of formic, acetic, lactic, and succinic acids; ethyl alcohol; acetylmethylcarbinol; 2,3-butylene glycol; carbon dioxide; and hydrogen. These organisms produce probably the most common types of bacterial fermentations.

The important products produced from the fermentation of glucose by *Escherichia coli* and *Aerobacter aerogenes* are given in Table 15.

TABLE 15. COMPOUNDS PRODUCED IN THE FERMENTATION OF GLUCOSE BY *Escherichia coli* AND *Aerobacter aerogenes*

E. coli	A. aerogenes
Formic acid	Formic acid
Acetic acid	Acetic acid
Lactic acid	Lactic acid
Succinic acid	Succinic acid
Ethyl alcohol	Ethyl alcohol
Carbon dioxide	Carbon dioxide
Hydrogen	Hydrogen
	Acetylmethylcarbinol (acetoin)
	2,3-Butylene glycol (2,3-butanediol)

In the case of *E. coli*, the compounds account for about 99 per cent of the carbon of the fermented glucose. A similar analysis on the same medium inoculated with *A. aerogenes* does not account for such a high percentage of the carbon of the fermented glucose. The discrepancy is due to the production by *A. aerogenes,* but not by *E. coli,* of the two compounds acetylmethylcarbinol (AMC) and 2,3-butanediol.

The production of AMC and 2,3-butanediol is not characteristic of *A. aerogenes* alone. A number of other bacteria and yeasts are also capable of producing the two compounds (see page 594). Since 2,3-butanediol contains two asymmetric carbon atoms, it exists in three isomeric forms: D-2,3-, L-2,3-, and meso-2,3-butanediol.

The mechanism for the formation of AMC and 2,3-butanediol is not clearly understood. The two compounds generally accompany each other in fermentation cultures. Some believe that AMC is formed first, then a part of it is reduced to 2,3-butanediol. Others maintain that 2,3-butanediol is produced first, then some of it is oxidized to AMC. Perhaps AMC and 2,3-butanediol comprise a reversible oxidation-reduction (redox) system. A low redox potential (anaerobic conditions) favors the accumulation of 2,3-butanediol; a high redox potential (aerobic conditions) favors the formation of AMC.

The scheme for the fermentation of glucose by *Aerobacter aerogenes,* according to Kluyver and van Niel (1956), is given in Fig. 170.

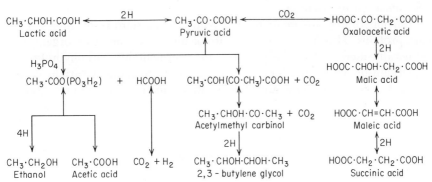

FIG. 170. Reaction scheme for the fermentation of glucose by *Aerobacter aerogenes.* (*After Kluyver and van Niel.*)

Importance of 2,3-Butanediol. The production of 2,3-butanediol by bacteria was first observed by Harden and Walpole (1906). During the Second World War, it was shown that the compound could be used as a precursor for butadiene, the starting point in the synthesis of rubber. Since that time a considerable literature has accumulated on the synthesis of 2,3-butanediol by microorganisms.

Organisms used for this purpose include: (1) *Serratia* species, small, aerobic or facultatively anaerobic, short rods, almost spherical. Motile. Gram-negative. Characteristic red pigment produced. (2) *Aerobacter aerogenes,* small rods, frequently encapsulated. Usually nonmotile. Gram-negative. (3) *Bacillus polymyxa,* large spore-forming rods, sporangia definitely bulged, spindle-shaped or clavate. Rods motile. Gram-variable.

Bacterial Destruction of 2,3-Butanediol. It is well known that all organic compounds elaborated by living cells can be utilized by microorganisms. There are many soil organisms which can use AMC both as a source of carbon and for energy. The breakdown can take place either aerobically or anaerobically. Juni and Heym (1956) suggested a new cyclic pathway involving two intermediates, diacetylmethylcarbinol and acetylbutanediol. They stated that the cycle was a method for generating acetic acid, a compound readily oxidized by these organisms.

For more information see Adams and Stanier (1945), Blackwood et al. (1949), De Ley (1959), Helprin and Sullivan (1954), Juni and Heym (1957), Pirt and Callow (1958), Underkofler and Fulmer (1948), and Wheat et al. (1948).

GENERAL CARBOHYDRATE FERMENTATIONS

Carbohydrates and compounds of a similar nature are generally added to culture media for two important purposes: (1) to serve as readily available sources of energy and (2) to aid in the identification and classification of bacteria.

Carbohydrates are more readily available as sources of energy than are proteins. This means that the rate of multiplication of an organism is generally increased in the presence of a fermentable carbohydrate.

Organisms vary considerably in their ability to ferment various carbohydrates. Some bacteria are able to attack many carbohydrates; others cannot ferment any carbohydrate; all degrees of fermentability occur between these two extremes. Also, some organisms ferment carbohydrates with the production of both acid and gas, whereas others produce acid only (Fig. 171). Such information is of great value in the identification of organisms.

It is not clearly understood why an organism ferments one aldose sugar and not another having the same empirical formula. The sugars differ only in the arrangement of H atoms and OH groups around carbon atoms. There is no method of determining beforehand whether or not a particular organism is capable of fermenting a given carbohydrate. This can be determined only by making the test.

Any change in the structure of the aldose sugars results in a decrease in the frequency of fermentation of the derivatives. For example, D-gluconic, D-mannonic, and D-galactonic acids, as well as D-sorbitol, D-mannitol, and dulcitol, are fermented by fewer organisms than the corresponding aldoses. Similarly, the dicarboxylic mucic and D-saccharic acids are attacked less frequently than the corresponding monocarboxylic D-galactonic and D-gluconic acids.

In general, fermentation becomes less frequent as the complexity of the molecule increases. This means that disaccharides are fermented less frequently than monosaccharides, trisaccharides less frequently than disaccharides, and polysaccharides less than trisaccharides. When tests on the availability of carbohydrates to microorganisms are to be made, always proceed first with the monosaccharides, especially glucose. As a rule, if an organism ferments any carbohydrate, it will most likely be glucose. If glucose is fermented, then other monosaccharides should be tested before proceeding to carbohydrates of greater complexity.

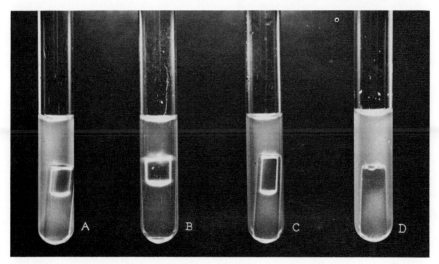

FIG. 171. Fermentation of carbohydrates. A, glucose; B, lactose; C, sucrose, all inoculated with *Escherichia communior*. Acid and gas produced. D, sucrose inoculated with *E. coli*. No acid or gas.

Direct Fermentation of Disaccharides. The fermentation of a disaccharide (maltose, lactose, sucrose, etc.) by bacteria, without action on either of its constituent monosaccharides, has been reported by several investigators. Such observations are not in accord with the generally accepted view of indirect fermentation, which presupposes a hydrolysis of the disaccharide to its constituent monosaccharides before utilization takes place.

For more information see Snell, Kitay, and Hoff-Jorgensen (1948).

SOME ROUTINE FERMENTATION REACTIONS EMPLOYED
FOR THE IDENTIFICATION OF BACTERIA

The ability of an organism to ferment a particular carbohydrate may be determined by incorporating the compound, with an appropriate indicator, in a liquid or solid medium. Gas production is generally detected by placing an inverted vial in a liquid carbohydrate medium to trap any gas as it is evolved.

Importance of Carbohydrate-free Culture Ingredients. Peptones, beef extract, and yeast extract vary considerably in composition.

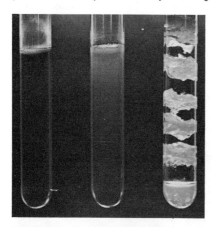

FIG. 172. Action of organisms on lactose litmus agar. Left, *Bacillus* subtilis; center, *Staphylococcus aureus*; right, *Escherichia coli*. *B. subtilis* and *S. aureus* produce neither acid nor gas; *E. coli* produces both acid and gas with the result that the agar is separated into rings and the litmus is decolorized.

In the selection of peptones and other ingredients of culture media for fermentation studies, the presence or absence of intrinsic fermentable components should be considered. Sufficient fermentable material is present in most bacteriological peptones, yeast autolysates, and meat extracts to give rise to false positive results and constitute an important cause of inaccuracy. Routine fermentation tests for identification of microorganisms may be performed with accuracy only when materials free from fermentable components are used as basic substrates.

Litmus Carbohydrate Media. Litmus is a weakly staining dye being employed only as an indicator. Since it is not a delicate detector of changes in reaction, it has been largely replaced by the more sensitive and brilliant sulfonephthalein indicators.

Litmus possesses an important advantage over the newer indicators in that it is sensitive to decolorization by bacteria. It functions as an oxidation-reduction system. Like methylene blue, litmus accepts hydrogen and becomes reduced to the colorless form. The decolorization of the indicator is first noted at or near the bottom of the tube, where the dissolved oxygen is soon exhausted. In the surface layer of media exposed to air, the litmus is seldom completely decolorized because the hydrogen is transferred to oxygen instead of to indicator.

If a tube of agar with indicator is inoculated by deep stab, fermentation is indicated by a change in the color of the agar medium. Gas formation is indicated by a collection of gas bubbles in the medium or by a splitting of the agar. Under some conditions the agar is split in the form of disks with a layer of gas separating each disk (Fig. 172). Sometimes the gas pressure may be sufficient to force some of the disks and cotton stopper out of the tube.

Bromocresol Purple Carbohydrate Media. The ability of an organism to ferment a particular compound may be easily determined by streaking a loopful of the culture over the surface of nutrient agar containing the carbohydrate and indicator. Fermentation is indicated by a change in the color of the indicator (Fig. 173).

If only a few well-isolated colonies appear on the plate, acid production remains confined to areas immediately surrounding each colony. This results in a color change in the vicinity of each colony without affecting the agar free from colonies. The contrast in colors in the acid and alkaline or neutral regions of the agar becomes very striking.

In the presence of a mixed culture composed of two organisms only one of which is capable of fermenting the carbohydrate, isolations of two different colonial forms may be successfully realized. This is possible only if the culture is highly diluted before being streaked, and the two organisms are present in approximately equal numbers.

Bromocresol purple is frequently used as the indicator in carbohydrate media. It is especially valuable for bacteriological use because of its brilliant colors at different hydrogen-ion concentrations and its resistance to decolorization by bacterial action. The sensitive range of the indicator is from pH 5.4 (yellow) to 7.0 (purple). The pK value, i.e., the point at which the dye is 50 per cent dissociated, is pH 6.2. Its pH range makes it suitable for the detection of bacterial fermentations in solid carbohydrate media.

Reversal of Reaction. It sometimes happens that the acid reaction in carbohydrate media turns alkaline, with respect to the indicator employed, if the plates are stored for several days. This may be explained on the basis of (1) insufficient carbohydrate and (2) the oxidation of the organic acids to carbonates. If a medium contains insufficient carbohydrate, an organism will not be able to produce its limiting hydrogen-ion concentration.

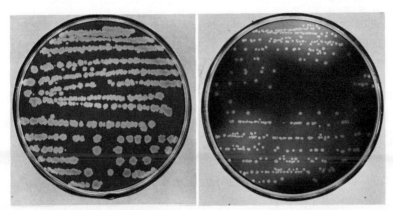

Fig. 173. Bromocresol purple lactose agar. Left, plate streaked with a culture of *Bacillus subtilis*. The organism produced no visible change in the color of the agar in 24 hr. Right, plate streaked with a culture of *Escherichia coli*. The organism produced considerable acid in 24 hr., changing the color of the agar from purple to yellow.

Under these conditions the organism will continue to multiply by utilizing the nitrogenous constituents for both structure and energy. This results in the production of alkaline products, with the consequent reversal in the reaction of the medium.

Reversal in the reaction of a medium sometimes occurs even in the presence of an amount of carbohydrate sufficient for an organism to produce its limiting hydrogen-ion concentration. Under these conditions simultaneous acid and alkaline reactions occur. The carbohydrates are first fermented to organic acids, after which the acids are oxidized to carbonates. The alkaline carbonates are responsible for the reversal in the reaction of the medium. The alkaline changes do not occur after all of the carbohydrate has been converted to acid, but run simultaneously with acid production.

For more information see Gunsalus, Horecker, and Wood (1955); Payne and Carlson (1957); and Wood (1955).

REFERENCES

Adams, G. A., and R. Y. Stanier: Production and properties of 2,3-butanediol, *Can. J. Research*, Sec. B, **23**:1, 1945.

Barker, H. A.: "Bacterial Fermentations," New York, John Wiley & Sons, Inc., 1956.

Beardsley, D. W.: Making and using silage, *Everglades Sta. Mimeo. Rep.* 56-15, Belle Glade, Fla., May 21, 1956.

Bhat, J. V., and K. Rijhsinghani: Studies on *Acetobacter*. I. Isolation and characterization of the species, *Proc. Indian Acad. Sci.*, **41**:209, 1955.

Blackwood, A. C., J. A. Wheat, J. D. Leslie, G. A. Ledingham, and F. J. Simpson: Production and properties of 2,3-butanediol. XXXI. Pilot plant studies on the fermentation of wheat by *Aerobacillus polymyxa*, *Can. J. Research*, F, **27**:199, 1949.

Brown, G. D., and C. Rainbow: Nutritional patterns in acetic acid bacteria, *J. Gen. Microbiol.*, **15**:61, 1956.

Bryant, M. P., and L. A. Burkey: The characteristics of lactate-fermenting spore-forming anaerobes from silage, *J. Bact.*, **71**:43, 1956.

Cardon, B. P., and H. A. Barker: Two new amino-acid-fermenting bacteria, *Clostridium propionicum* and *Diplococcus glycinophilus*, *J. Bact.*, **52**:629, 1946.

———— and ————: Amino acid fermentations by *Clostridium propionicum* and *Diplococcus glycinophilus*, *Arch. Biochem.*, **12**:165, 1947.

Carson, S. F., J. W. Foster, S. Ruben, and H. A. Barker: Radioactive carbon as an indicator of carbon dioxide utilization. V. Studies on the propionic acid bacteria, *Proc. Nat. Acad. Sci.*, **27**:229, 1941.

———— and S. Ruben: CO_2 assimilation by propionic acid bacteria studied by the use of radioactive carbon, *Proc. Nat. Acad. Sci.*, **26**:422, 1940.

Casida, L. E. Jr., and R. Rosenfield: Bacterial oxidation of nicotine, *J. Bact.*, **75**:474, 1958.

Clifton, C. E.: The utilization of amino acids and related compounds by *Clostridium tetani*, *J. Bact.*, **44**:179, 1942.

De Ley, J.: On the formation of acetoin by *Acetobacter*, *J. Gen. Microbiol.*, **21**:352, 1959.

Delwiche, E. A., E. F. Phares, and S. F. Carson: Succinic acid decarboxylation system in *Propionibacterium pentosaceum* and *Veillonella gazogenes*. I. Activation, decarboxylation, and related reactions, *J. Bact.*, **71**:598, 1956.

De Moss, R. D.: Routes of ethanol formation in bacteria, *J. Cell. and Comp. Physiol.*, **41**:207, 1953.

Dohner, P. M., and B. P. Cardon: Anaerobic fermentation of lysine, *J. Bact.*, **67**:608, 1954.

Evers, H. H.: Curing and fermentation of tobacco, *Chemistry & Industry*, **66**:423, 1947.

Field, M. F., and H. C., Lichstein: Factors affecting the growth of propionibacteria, *J. Bact.*, **73**:96, 1957.

Frankenburg, W. G., and A. M. Gottscho: The chemistry of tobacco fermentation. I. Conversion of the alkaloids. B. The formation of oxynicotine, *J. Am. Chem. Soc.*, **77**:5728, 1955.

————, ————, A. A. Vaitekunas, and R. M. Zacharius: The chemistry of tobacco fermentation. I. Conversion of the alkaloids. C. The formation of 3-pyridyl propyl ketone, nicotinamide and n-methylnicotinamide, *J. Am. Chem. Soc.*, **77**:5730 1955.

———— and A. A. Vaitekunas: Chemical studies on nicotine degradation by microorganisms derived from the surface of tobacco seeds, *Arch. Biochem. Biophys.*, **58**:509, 1955.

Frateur, J.: Essai sur la systématique des acetobacters, *La Cellule*, **53**:287, 1950.

Freeman, G. G., and G. M. S. Donald: Fermentation processes leading to glycerol. I. The influence of certain variables on glycerol formation in the presence of sulfites, *Appl. Microbiol.*, **5**:197, 1957*a*; II. Studies on the effect of sulfites on viability, growth, and fermentation of *Saccharomyces cerevisiae*, *ibid.*, **5**:211, 1957*b*; III. Studies on glycerol formation in the presence of alkalies, *ibid.*, **5**:216, 1957*c*.

Gibbs, M., J. T. Sokatch, and I. C. Gunsalus: Product labeling of glucose-1-C^{14} fermentation by homofermentative and heterofermentative lactic acid bacteria, *J. Bact.*, **70**:572, 1955.

Gunsalus, I. C., and M. Gibbs: The heterolactic fermentation. II. Position of C^{14} in the products of glucose dissimilation by *Leuconostoc mesenteroides*, *J. Biol. Chem.*, **194**:871, 1952.

————, B. L. Horecker, and W. A. Wood: Pathways of carbohydrate metabolism in microorganisms, *Bact. Rev.*, **19**:79, 1955.

Hall, A. N., C. Russell, and K. S. Tiwari: The response of certain *Acetobacter* species to the lactone moiety of pantothenic acid, *J. Bact.*, **68**:279, 1954.

Harden, A., and G. S. Walpole: Chemical action of *Bacillus lactis aerogenes* (Escherich) on glucose and mannitol: Production of 2,3-butylene glycol and acetylmethylcarbinol, *Proc. Roy. Soc.* (*London*), Series B, **77**:399, 1906.

Helprin, J. J., and M. X. Sullivan: The production of acetylmethylcarbinol by *Aerobacter* from a variety of carbon sources in a synthetic medium, *J. Bact.*, **67**:90, 1954.

Jensen, H.: Thermal death points for spores and mycelia of moulds on fermented tobacco, *Physiol. Plantarum*, **1**:255, 1948.

Juni, E., and G. A. Heym: A cyclic pathway for the bacterial dissimilation of 2,3-butanediol, acetylmethylcarbinol, and diacetyl. I. General aspects of the 2,3-butanediol cycle, *J. Bact.*, **71**:425, 1956; III. A comparative study of 2,3-butanediol dehydrogenases from various microorganisms, *ibid.*, **74**:757, 1957.

Kluyver, A. J., and C. B. van Niel: "The Microbe's Contribution to Biology," Cambridge, Mass., Harvard University Press, 1956.

Koser, S. A., and J. L. Thomas: Effect of some pentoses on growth of lactobacilli, *Proc. Soc. Exp. Biol. Med.*, **95**:89, 1957.

Leaver, F. W., and H. G. Wood: Evidence from fermentation of labeled substrates which is inconsistent with present concepts of the propionic acid fermentation, *J. Cell. Comp. Physiol.*, **4**:225, 1953.

————, ————, and Stjernholm: The fermentation of three carbon substrates by *Clostridium propionicum* and *Propionibacterium*, *J. Bact.*, **70**:521, 1955.

Leifson, E.: The flagellation and taxonomy of species of *Acetobacter*, *Antonie van Leeuwenhoek*, **20**:102, 1954.

Lipmann, F.: Pasteur effect. From "A Symposium on Respiratory Enzymes," Madison, Wis., University of Wisconsin Press, 1942.

Litsky, W., and C. L. Goldman: The nutritive requirements of Acetobacter. II. The vitamin synthesis of *Acetobacter xylinum*, *Food Research*, **18**:646, 1953.

Meyerhof, O.: Recent advances in the study of metabolic reactions of yeast preparations, *Am. Scientist*, **40**:482, 1952.

Payne, W. J., and A. B. Carlson: Studies on bacterial utilization of uronic acids. II. Growth response and oxidative activity of various species, *J. Bact.*, **74**:502, 1957.

Phares, E. F., E. A. Delwiche, and S. F. Carson: Succinic acid decarboxylation system in *Propionibacterium pentosaceum* and *Veillonella gazogenes*. II. Evidence for an active "C_1" complex, *J. Bact.*, **71**:604, 1956.

Pigman, W.: "The Carbohydrates," New York, Academic Press, Inc., 1957.

Pirt, S. J., and D. S. Callow: I. Production of 2:3-butanediol by *Aerobacter aerogenes* in a single stage process, *J. Appl. Bact.*, **21**:188, 1958.

Prescott, S. C., and C. G. Dunn: "Industrial Microbiology," New York, McGraw-Hill Book Company, Inc., 1959.

Rainbow, C., and G. W. Mitson: Nutritional requirements of acetic acid bacteria, *J. Gen. Microbiol.*, **9**:371, 1953.

Rao, M. R. R., and J. L. Stokes: Utilization of ethanol by acetic acid bacteria, *J. Bact.*, **66**:634, 1953.

Reid, J. J., D. W. McKinstry, and D. E. Haley: Studies on the fermentation of tobacco. I. The microflora of cured and fermenting cigar-leaf tobacco, *Penn. Agr. Exp. Sta. Bull.*, 356, 1938*a*; II. Microorganisms isolated from cigar-leaf tobacco, *ibid.*, 363, 1938*b*.

Rosenberger, R. F.: The isolation and cultivation of obligate anaerobes from silage, *J. Appl. Bact.*, **19**:173, 1956.

Snell, E. E.: Nutritional requirements of the lactic acid bacteria, *Wallerstein Lab. Commun.*, **11**:81, 1948.

————, E. Kitay, and E. Hoff-Jorgensen: Carbohydrate utilization by a strain of *Lactobacillus bulgaricus*, *Arch. Biochem.*, **18**:495, 1948.

Stirling, A. C.: Lactobacilli and silage-making, *Proc. Soc. Appl. Bact.*, **16**:27, 1953.

Sumner, J. B., and G. F. Somers: "Chemistry and Methods of Enzymes," New York, Academic Press, Inc., 1953.

Thomas, R. C.: Microbiology of silage with special reference to grass-legume mixtures, *Ohio Agr. Exp. Sta. Research Circ.*, 2, May, 1950.

Underkofler, L. A., and E. I. Fulmer: The production of 2,3-butylene glycol by fermentation, *Wallerstein Lab. Commun.*, **11**:41, 1948.

———, ———, R. J. Hickey, and T. M. Lees: Production of glycerol by fermentation. I. Fermentation of dextrose, *Iowa State Coll. J. Sci.*, **26**:111, 1951*a*; II. Fermentation of disaccharides and starch, *ibid.*, **26**:135, 1951*b*.

——— and R. J. Hickey: "Industrial Fermentations," New York, Chemical Publishing Company, Inc., 1954.

Vickery, H. B., and A. N. Meiss: Chemical investigations of the tobacco plant, *Conn. Agr. Exp. Sta. Bull.*, 569, 1953.

Wachsman, J. T., and H. A. Barker: Tracer experiments on glutamate fermentation by *Clostridium tetanomorphum*, *J. Biol. Chem.*, **217**:695, 1955.

Wheat, J. A., J. D. Leslie, R. V. Tomkins, H. E. Mitton, D. S. Scott, and G. A. Ledingham: Production and properties of 2,3-butanediol. XXVIII. Pilot plant recovery of L-2,3-butanediol from whole wheat mashes fermented by *Aerobacillus polymyxa*, *Can. J. Research*, F, **26**:469, 1948.

Wieringa, G. W.: Some factors affecting silage fermentation. II. Influence of degree of laceration and of the bacterial flora from the grass, *Netherlands J. Agr. Sci.*, **7**:237, 1959.

Wieringa, K. T.: The micro-organisms decomposing pectic substances in the dew retting process of flax, *Netherlands J. Agr. Sci.*, **4**:204, 1956.

Wood, H. G., R. W. Brown, C. H. Werkman, and C. G. Stuckwisch: The degradation of heavy-carbon butyric acid from the butyl alcohol fermentation, *J. Am. Chem. Soc.*, **66**:1812, 1944.

———, R. Stjernholm, and F. W. Leaver: The role of succinate as a precursor of propionate in the propionic acid fermentation, *J. Bact.*, **72**:142, 1956.

——— and C. H. Werkman: The utilization of CO_2 in the dissimilation of glycerol by the propionic acid bacteria, *Biochem. J.*, **30**:48, 1936.

——— and ———: The utilization of CO_2 by the propionic acid bacteria, *ibid.*, **32**:1262, 1938.

——— and ———: The fixation of carbon dioxide by cell suspensions of *Propionibacterium pentosaceum*, *ibid.*, **34**:7, 1940*a*; The relationship of bacterial utilization of CO_2 to succinic acid formation, *ibid.*, **34**:129, 1940*b*.

Wood, W. A.: Pathways of carbohydrate degradation in *Pseudomonas fluorescens*, *Bact. Rev.*, **19**:222, 1955.

CHAPTER 15

Differentiation and Classification of Bacteria

An organism that has been isolated and studied must be given a name; otherwise reference to it could not be made. Also, it is highly desirable that the name applied to an organism by one person be understood by others.

Two kinds of names are used: (1) common or casual names and (2) scientific or international names.

Usually the common names for the same organism will be different in each language. Because of this fact the common names are responsible for considerable confusion in bacteriology. On the other hand, scientific names are more or less international in meaning. It is better, therefore, to refer to organisms by their scientific names, which are supposed to be the same in all countries.

General Principles of Nomenclature. The method followed in naming plants and animals was first introduced by the Swedish botanist Karl von Linné and is known as the binomial system of nomenclature. The same system is used in naming bacteria.

Each distinct kind of organism is called a species. Each species is given a name which consists usually of two words. The first word is the name of the genus and the second the name of the species. The genus name is taken from the Latin or Greek, or a new word compounded from Latin or Greek roots, or in rare cases from some other language. It is a noun and is always capitalized. It may be masculine (*Bacillus, Micrococcus, Streptococcus*), feminine (*Sarcina, Salmonella, Pasteurella*), or neuter (*Bacterium, Clostridium, Corynebacterium*).

The species name may be (1) an adjective, in which case its ending should agree with the genus in gender, e.g., *Sarcina lutea, Bacillus subtilis, Propionibacterium arabinosum;* (2) an adjective in the form of the present participle of a verb, as *Pseudomonas fluorescens, Bacillus coagulans, Clostridium perfringens;* (3) a noun in the genetive case modifying the generic name, e.g., *Clostridium muelleri, Pseudomonas lindneri, Streptococcus lactis, Brucella abortus;* (4) an explanatory noun that does not

401

agree necessarily with the generic name in gender, as *Rhizobium phaseoli*, *Pseudomonas schuylkilliensis*, *Salmonella oslo*.

Sometimes a species is subdivided into varieties. These are also given Latin designations. Examples of varieties are *Streptococcus faecalis* var. *liquefaciens*. It differs from *S. lactis* in being able to liquefy the acid curd produced in milk.

General Principles of Taxonomy. The term taxonomy may be defined as the classification of plants and animals according to their natural relationships. It is compounded from the two Greek words *taxis*, an arrangement, order, and *nomos*, a law.

A satisfactory development of taxonomy is dependent upon a sound nomenclature. Regardless of whether bacteriologists will ever be able to agree on the exact classification to be employed, they should agree on some of the fundamental characteristics necessary for the development of a satisfactory bacteriological classification.

Species. Each kind of organism is referred to as a species (plural, species). The term is defined in various ways, but it is generally stated to be the lowest member of a classificatory system. A bacterial species is a plant that occupies a position in a classification between the genus and the variety. Since the differences between varieties are often difficult to recognize, it is the species that to the untrained observer usually seem to represent the simplest distinct assemblages or kinds in the plant or animal kingdoms.

The first described specimen of a species is spoken of as the type of the species. It is used as the type for all other species regarded as sufficiently like the type to be placed together in the same group or genus.

The term strain should never be used to indicate a biological character, but rather it should refer merely to source. An organism that is normally flagellated (motile) may be isolated from another source in which flagella are absent (nonmotile). The second form may be considered to be a nonmotile strain of the first organism but not a different species.

Genus. A group of closely related species is spoken of as a genus (plural, genera). It ranks between the family and the species. In some cases a genus contains only one species; in other genera, many species are included.

There is no agreement as to which species should be placed in a particular genus and probably never will be. Much of the confusion in the classification of bacteria may be attributed to this fact. However, as organisms become better known, it seems likely that much of the present confusion may be overcome and a more orderly system of classification established.

Family. Closely related genera are grouped into a family. The word is compounded from the name of the type genus by affixing the suffix

-*aceae* to the root. For example, the name of the family *Micrococcaceae* is formed by combining the root of the genus *Micrococcus* with the suffix -*aceae* (*Micrococc + aceae*).

Order. Closely related families are grouped into an order. An order is usually named by substituting the suffix -*ales* for -*aceae* in the name of the type family. For example, the name of the order *Actinomycetales* is formed by combining the root of the family *Actinomycetaceae* with the suffix -*ales* (*Actinomycet + ales*).

Class. Closely related orders are grouped into a class. There are 3 classes of bacteria and they include 12 orders.

Citation of Authors and Names. It is customary to place after the name of an organism the name of the discoverer, together with the citation to the literature in which the work appeared. When the name of the organism is transferred to another genus, the name of the discoverer is placed in parentheses immediately after the name of the organism, followed by the author of the new name. Citation to the literature in which the work of the new author appeared should also be included. For example, *Salmonella typhimurium* was discovered by Loeffler in 1892 and named *Bacillus typhi murium*. Later Castellani and Chalmers transferred the organism to a new genus and named it *Salmonella typhimurium*. The name of the organism is correctly designated as *Salmonella typhimurium* (Loeffler, 1892) Castellani and Chalmers, 1919. (*Bacillus typhi murium* Loeffler, *Cent. Bakt.*, 11:192, 1892; Castellani and Chalmers, "Manual of Tropical Medicine," 3d ed., page 939, 1919.)

Differentiating Bacteria. Approximately 1500 species of bacteria have been studied and classified. These represent probably only a small percentage of the total number of species in existence.

During the early years of bacteriology, organisms were classified entirely on the basis of morphology. Only a few species were recognized, and their classification was a comparatively simple matter. The morphological characters employed included size and shape of an organism; arrangement of the cells; presence or absence of well-defined capsules; presence or absence of spores; size, shape, and position of the spore in the cell; presence, number, and arrangement of flagella; irregular forms; presence or absence of characteristic granules; acid-fastness; Gram reaction and other differential staining procedures; and cultural and colonial characteristics.

Higher plants are differentiated almost entirely on the basis of morphology. One tree may be easily distinguished from another by differences in such characteristics as the size, shape, and color of the tree; and size, shape, and color of the leaves and seeds. In the case of bacteria, it is quite evident that the problems of classification are more difficult, owing to the fact that such minute organisms are comparatively simple spheres, rods, and spirals.

It soon became apparent that a classification based entirely on morphology was inadequate and that more characteristics were necessary. Physiological reactions were, therefore, introduced into the newer classifications. These include such reactions as temperature relations; chromogenesis or pigment production; effect of a change in the reaction of the environment on growth; production of indole and hydrogen sulfide; reduction of nitrate to nitrite and even to ammonia, and finally to free nitrogen; relation to oxygen; and fermentation of carbohydrates. At the present time physiological reactions are probably more important than morphological differences in the classification of bacteria.

Sometimes it is necessary to resort to animal inoculation and serological reactions to separate similar appearing and reacting organisms. Serological methods are discussed in Chap. 25, Infection and Immunity.

Bacteria are placed in that division of the plant kingdom known as the *Protophyta* (see page 2).

The division Protophyta contains three classes, namely, *Schizophyceae*, *Schizomycetes*, and *Microtatobiotes*.

Class I. *Schizophyceae*, the blue-green algae. Organisms which possess the photosynthetic pigment phycocyanin in addition to chlorophyll.
Class II. *Schizomycetes*, the bacteria. Organisms which usually do not contain photosynthetic pigments. None contains phycocyanin. Reproduce normally by fission.
Class III. *Microtatobiotes*, the viruses and rickettsiae. Minute cells, usually much smaller than the bacteria. All possesss filterable stages.

Purpose of a Classification. The purpose of a classification is to aid in the identification of an unknown organism by comparing its characteristics with one that has already been described. Unfortunately this is not always possible because the unknown may be one that has not been previously studied. Under these conditions the newly isolated organism should be described, named, and the results published so that the material may be made accessible to others. It is quite probable that only a small number of the total bacterial species in existence have been studied and described.

The classification given here was prepared from the unabridged seventh (1957) edition of "Bergey's Manual of Determinative Bacteriology." The book is named in honor of Dr. D. H. Bergey, who was responsible for developing the first edition. The manual is administered by a committee known as the Board of Trustees. The actual work of revision is in charge of the Editorial Committee of the Board of Trustees.

The outline classification is as follows:[1]

Class: *Schizomycetes*. Typically unicellular plants. Cells usually small, sometimes ultramicroscopic. Frequently motile. Presence of true nuclei has been demonstrated. Individual cells may be spherical or straight, curved, or spiral rods. Cells may occur

---

[1] The author is greatly indebted to the Board of Trustees for permission to reproduce this outline classification of the manual.

in regular or irregular masses, or even in cysts. Where they remain attached to each other after cell division, they may form chains or even definite trichomes. The latter may show some differentiation into holdfast cells and into motile or nonmotile reproductive cells. Some grow as branching mycelial threads whose diameter is not greater than that of ordinary bacterial cells, i.e., about one micron. Some species produce pigments. The true purple and green bacteria possess pigments much like or related to the true chlorophylls of higher plants. These pigments have photosynthetic properties. The phycocyanin found in the blue-green algae does not occur in the *Schizomycetes*. Multiplication is typically by cell division. Endospores are formed by some species included in *Eubacteriales*. Sporocysts are found in *Myxobacteriales*. Ultramicroscopic reproductive bodies are found in *Mycoplasmatales*. The bacteria are free-living, saprophytic, parasitic, or even pathogenic. The latter types cause diseases of either plants or animals. Ten orders are recognized.

Order I. *Pseudomonadales.* Straight, curved or spiral, rigid, rod-shaped bacteria. Rarely occur in pairs or chains. Cells in a few species are ellipsoidal and are frequently spoken of as being coccoid or even spherical in form. Usually about 1.0 μ in diameter, but in a few species the individual cell is larger than is normal for bacteria, reaching a size of 3.0 to 14.0 μ in diameter, and as much as 100 μ in length. Cells usually polar flagellate. When motile they sometimes bear a single flagellum; in other cases a tuft of flagella. Flagella are normally found at one or both ends of the cell, but in one genus the curved cells bear a tuft of flagella that is attached in the middle of the concave side (*Selenomonas*). Nonmotile species whose characteristics indicate that they belong in this order with closely related motile species occasionally occur. Cells are Gram-negative. Cells in one suborder contain pigments that have power of photosynthesis. Cells in second suborder lack such pigments, as do all other groups of bacteria. Cells in first suborder are photoautotrophic, while chemoautotrophic species occur in the second suborder. Energy is frequently secured by oxidative processes though there are also many species that show a fermentative physiology. Cells quite frequently occur in zoogloeal masses. No endospores are found, and reproduction is by means of fission. Many species occur in coastal, swamp and pond waters and in soil. Some are parasitic, some even pathogenic, causing diseases of fishes and other cold-blooded vertebrates. Few species cause diseases of warm-blooded mammals, including man.

Suborder I. *Rhodobacteriineae.* Cells contain red, purple, brown, or green photosynthetic pigments. Sometimes also enclose granules of free sulfur.

Family I. *Thiorhodaceae.* Unicellular organisms often developing as cell aggregates or families of variable size and shape. Single cells spherical, ovoids, short rods, vibrios, spirals, long rods, or occasionally chains. Occur in nature in environments containing sulfides and require light for development. Pigments composed of green bacteriochlorophyll and yellow and red carotenoids. Organisms anaerobic or microaerophilic with a photosynthetic metabolism in which carbon dioxide is reduced with the aid of special hydrogen donors without the liberation of molecular oxygen. Where these organisms are found in nature, hydrogen sulfide acts as a hydrogen donor, and sulfur accumulates as sulfur droplets in the cells. Probably all members can utilize a number of organic substances in place of hydrogen sulfide as hydrogen donors for photosynthesis.

I. Cells usually combined into aggregates.

A. Cells grouped as regular sarcina packets.

Genus I. *Thiosarcina.*

B. Cells not in sarcina packets.

1. Aggregates in the form of flat sheet.

a. Cells in regular arrangement, with tetrads as the common structural unit.

Genus II. *Thiopedia.*

aa. Cells in irregular aggregates.

Genus III. *Thiocapsa.*

2. Aggregates in the form of three-dimensional masses.
    a. Cells distinctly rod-shaped and arranged in a net-like structure.
                    Genus IV. *Thiodictyon.*
    aa. Cells not so arranged.
        b. Cells in a common capsule, individuals rather scattered and loosely grouped.
                    Genus V. *Thiothece.*
        bb. Cells in rather dense clumps.
            c. Aggregates embedded in conspicuous common slime capsule.
                d. Aggregates small, compact, often several of them enclosed together in a common capsule.
                    Genus VI. *Thiocystis.*
                dd. Aggregates large and solid, later break up into small clusters.
                    Genus VII. *Lamprocystis.*
        cc. Common capsule lacking or very transient.
            d. Aggregates as a whole exhibit amoeboid movements.
                    Genus VIII. *Amoebobacter.*
            dd. Aggregates devoid of amoeboid movements.
                    Genus IX. *Thiopolycoccus.*
II. Cells usually occurring singly.
    A. Cells clearly spiral-shaped.
                    Genus X. *Thiospirillum.*
    B. Cells not spiral-shaped.
        1. Cells irregular, often swollen, distorted, or composed of long, crooked and bent rods to filaments.
                    Genus XI. *Rhabdomonas.*
        2. Cells regular, spherical to short rods or bean-shaped.
            a. Cells spherical, as a rule nonmotile, and each one surrounded by a rather wide capsule.
                    Genus XII. *Rhodothece.*
            aa. Cells ellipsoidal, ovoid, short rods, or vibrios, actively motile.
                    Genus XIII. *Chromatium.*
Family II. *Athiorhodaceae.* Unicellular organisms of relatively small size, occurring as spheres, short rods, vibrios, long rods and spirals. Motility due to presence of polar flagella. Gram-negative. Produce a pigment system composed of bacteriochlorophyll and one or more carotenoids, coloring the cells yellowish brown, olive-brown, dark brown or various shades of red. Color usually not observable with single cells but only with cell masses. Generally microaerophilic, although many members may grow at full atmospheric oxygen tension. Capable of development under strictly anaerobic conditions, but only in illuminated cultures by virtue of a photosynthetic metabolism. Latter dependent upon the presence of extraneous hydrogen donors, such as alcohols, fatty acids, hydroxy- and keto-acids, and does not proceed with the evolution of molecular oxygen. Members which can grow in presence of air can also be cultivated in darkness, but only under aerobic conditions.
  I. Cells rod-shaped or spherical, not spiral-shaped.
                    Genus I. *Rhodopseudomonas.*
  II. Cells spiral-shaped.
                    Genus II. *Rhodospirillum.*
Family III. *Chlorobacteriaceae.* Green bacteria, usually of small size, occurring singly or in cell masses of various shapes and sizes, developing in environments containing rather high concentrations of hydrogen sulfide and exposed to light. As a rule not containing sulfur globules but frequently depositing sulfur outside the cells. Contain green pigments of a chlorophyllous nature, though not identical with the common green plant chlorophylls

nor with bacteriochlorophyll. Capable of photosynthesis in the presence of hydrogen sulfide; do not liberate oxygen.

I. Free-living bacteria not intimately associated with other microbes.
  A. Bacteria not united into well defined colonies.

                          Genus I. *Chlorobium.*

  B. Bacteria united into characteristic aggregates.
    1. Bacteria without intracellular sulfur globules.

                          Genus II. *Pelodictyon.*

    2. Bacteria with intracellular sulfur globules.

                          Genus III. *Clathrochloris.*

II. Green bacteria found as symbiotic aggregates with other organisms.
  A. Aggregates composed of green bacteria and protozoa.

                          Genus IV. *Chlorobacterium.*

  B. Aggregates composed of two different types of bacteria.
    1. Aggregates small, barrel-shaped, actively motile and consisting of a central, polar flagellate, rod-shaped bacterium with a covering of sulfur green bacteria.

                          Genus V. *Chlorochromatium.*

    2. Aggregates large, cylindrical, nonmotile and composed of a central filamentous bacterium with a more or less extensive covering of sulfur green bacteria.

                          Genus VI. *Cylindrogloea.*

Suborder II. *Pseudomonadineae.* Cells do not contain photosynthetic pigments, although they may produce greenish, brownish, rose or yellow, diffusible, water-soluble pigments or yellow or red non-water-soluble pigments. Free sulfur granules may occur within or without the cells. Ferric hydroxide may be deposited.

Family I. *Nitrobacteriaceae.* Cells without endospores; rod-shaped, ellipsoidal, or even spherical, or spirillar in shape. Flagella polar, occasionally absent. Gram-negative. Organisms derive energy from oxidation of ammonia to nitrite or from nitrite to nitrate. Bacteria depend on this oxidation for growth. Fail to grow on media containing organic matter in the absence of the specific inorganic materials used as sources of energy. Many organic compounds used in standard culture media are toxic to these bacteria. Not parasitic. Commonly found in soil and fresh water.

I. Ammonia oxidized to nitrite.
  A. Zoogloeae not formed. Cells occur separately, free or in dense aggregates.
    1. Cells not spiral-shaped.
      a. Cells ellipsoidal.

                        Genus I. *Nitrosomonas.*

      aa. Cells spherical.

                        Genus II. *Nitrosococcus.*

    2. Cells spiral.

                        Genus III. *Nitrosospira.*

  B. Zoogloeae formed.
    1. Zoogloea surrounded by a common membrane forming a cyst.

                        Genus IV. *Nitrosocystis.*

    2. No common membrane surrounds the cells. The massed cells are embedded in slime.

                        Genus V. *Nitrosogloea.*

II. Nitrite oxidized to nitrate.
  A. Zoogloeae not formed.

                        Genus VI. *Nitrobacter.*

  B. Zoogloeae formed.

                        Genus VII. *Nitrocystis.*

Family II. *Methanomonadaceae.* Rod-shaped organisms deriving their life energy from the oxidation of simple compounds of hydrogen or carbon. Polar flagellate when motile. Gram-negative. Found in soil and water.

I. Organisms deriving their life energy from the oxidation of simple compounds of hydrogen.
 A. Cells capable of securing growth energy by the oxidation of methane.
              Genus I. *Methanomonas*.
 B. Cells capable of securing growth energy by the oxidation of hydrogen.
              Genus II. *Hydrogenomonas*.
II. Organisms deriving their life energy from the oxidation of carbon monoxide.
              Genus III. *Carboxydomonas*.
Family III. *Thiobacteriaceae*. Coccoid, straight or curved rod-shaped bacteria. Oxidize sulfur compounds, usually depositing free sulfur granules within or without the cells. Never filamentous. Colorless bacteria that are sometimes embedded in gelatinous pellicles or in gelatinous bladder-like colonies. Polar flagellate when motile. Presumably Gram-negative. Found where hydrogen sulfide occurs or may oxidize free sulfur, thiosulfates or related compounds.
 I. Free sulfur granules deposited within or without the cells. Usually found in sulfurous waters or soil.
  A. Cells coccoid or straight rods.
   1. Nonmotile so far as known.
            Genus I. *Thiobacterium*.
   2. Motile by means of polar flagella so far as known.
    a. Cells rod-shaped, very large.
            Genus II. *Macromonas*.
    aa. Cells round to ovoid, large.
            Genus III. *Thiovulum*.
  B. Cells large, curved rods, somewhat pointed.
            Genus IV. *Thiospira*.
 II. Oxidize free sulfur, thiosulfates, and related sulfur compounds to sulfates. Autotrophic or facultatively autotrophic.
            Genus V. *Thiobacillus*.
Family IV. *Pseudomonadaceae*. Cells elongate, straight rods, occasionally coccoid. Motile by means of polar flagella which are either single or in small or large tufts. A few species are nonmotile. Gram-negative. May possess either water-soluble pigments which diffuse through the medium or non-water-soluble pigments. Aerobic. Frequently oxidative in their physiology but may be fermentative. Usually found in soil or water, including sea water or even heavy brines. Many plant and a few animal pathogens.
 I. Attack glucose and other sugars either oxidatively or fermentatively.
  A. Genera in which species are either known or are thought to attack glucose oxidatively.
   1. Bacteria which do not produce readily detectable acetic acid though they may oxidize ethanol. May produce a water-soluble pigment which diffuses through the medium.
    a. Cultures may or may not produce a water-soluble pigment which is bluish, greenish, or brownish in color. Rose, lilac- and yellow-colored, diffusible pigments occasionally occur (Fig. 174).
            Genus I. *Pseudomonas*
    aa. Cultures develop a yellow, nonwater-soluble pigment. Cells normally monotrichous. Mostly plant pathogens which cause a necrosis.
            Genus II. *Xanthomonas*.
   2. Bacteria which produce readily detectable amounts of acetic acid by the oxidation of ethanol. The vinegar bacteria.
            Genus III. *Acetobacter*.
  B. Genera in which species ferment glucose, usually with production of H_2 and CO_2.
   1. Cells carry out a fermentation like that of the coliform bacteria. Usually produce acid and gas from glucose.

a. Cells not known to fix free atmospheric nitrogen.
 b. Water organisms. Common species cause diseases of fishes. Also found in leeches. Not luminescent.
        Genus IV. *Aeromonas.*
 bb. Luminescent bacteria commonly found on dead fishes and crustacea on salt-water beaches.
        Genus V. *Photobacterium.*
aa. Cells fix free atmospheric nitrogen.
        Genus VI. *Azotomonas.*
2. Cells carry out an alcoholic fermentation similar to that of yeasts.
        Genus VII. *Zymomonas.*

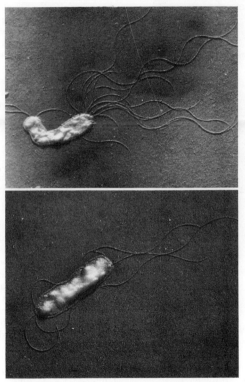

Fɪɢ. 174. Electron micrographs of *Pseudomonas.* Upper, *P. ovalis;* lower, *P. pseudo-mallei.* ×21,000. (*Courtesy of Wetmore and Gochenour, Jr.*)

II. Do not attack carbohydrates or, if so, produce only slight amounts of acid from glucose and similar sugars. Includes certain species which require at least 12 per cent salt for growth.
A. Do not require salt in excess of 12 per cent for growth.
 1. Cells not embedded in a gelatinous matrix.
  a. Cells rod-shaped.
   b. Soil and water bacteria that are known to dissimilate alkylamines.
        Genus VIII. *Protaminobacter.*
   bb. Soil and water bacteria that are known to dissimilate alginic acid.
        Genus IX. *Alginomonas.*

aa. Soil bacteria that are known to utilize phenol and similar aromatic compounds. Cells may be branched.

Genus X. *Mycoplana.*

2. Cells embedded in a gelatinous matrix; this matrix may be of a branching form.

Genus XI. *Zoogloea.*

B. Requires at least 12 per cent salt before growth will take place.

Genus XII. *Halobacterium.*

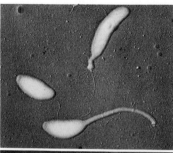

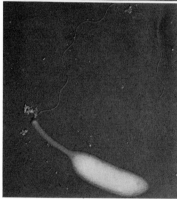

Family V. *Caulobacteriaceae.* Nonfilamentous, rod-shaped bacteria normally attached by branching or unbranching stalks to a substrate. In one floating form the stalks are branched. Cells occur singly, in pairs or in short chains. Cells are asymmetrical in that a stalk is developed at one end of the cell or ferric hydroxide or other material is secreted from one side of the cell to form stalks. Cells are polar flagellate in the free-living state, nonmotile in the attached forms. Gram-negative. Multiply by transverse fission, the daughter cells remaining in place or swimming away as swarm cells. Typically fresh or salt water forms.

I. Long axis of cell coincides with axis of stalk. Stalks slender (Fig. 175).

Genus I. *Caulobacter.*

II. Long axis of cell transverse to long axis of stalk. Stalks may be twisted and branched.

A. Stalks band-shaped or rounded. Contain ferric hydroxide.

1. Stalks band-shaped and twisted. Dumbbell-shaped in cross section.

Genus II. *Gallionella.*

2. Stalks horn-shaped, not twisted. Round in cross section.

Genus III. *Siderophacus.*

B. Stalks lobose, composed of gum. Forming zoogloea-like colonies. Free-floating.

Genus IV. *Nevskia.*

Fig. 175. *Caulobacter,* stalked bacteria. Upper, one cell has not yet grown a stalk. Lower, young cell with one flagellum at base of stalk. (*Courtesy of A. L. Houwink.*)

Family VI. *Siderocapsaceae.* Cells spherical, ellipsoidal or bacilliform. Frequently embedded in a thick, mucilaginous capsule in which iron or manganese compounds may be deposited. Motile stages, where known, are polar flagellate. Free-living in surface films or attached to the surface of submerged objects. Form deposits of iron and manganese compounds. Autotrophic, facultatively autotrophic and heterotrophic species are included in the family. Found in fresh water.

I. Cells surrounded by capsular matter with iron compounds deposited either on the surface or throughout the capsular material.

A. Cells coccoid.

1. Cells in masses in a common capsule.

Genus I. *Siderocapsa.*

2. Cells always in pairs in a gelatinous capsule.

Genus II. *Siderosphaera.*

B. Cells ellipsoidal to bacilliform.
   1. Cells heavily encapsulated but do not possess a torus.
      a. Cells in chains in a gelatinous capsule.
         b. Chains of ellipsoidal cells embedded in a gelatinous capsule, the outlines of which follow the form of the cells.
Genus III. Sideronema.

         bb. Rods in pairs or chains in surface films.
Genus IV. Ferribacterium.

      aa. Coccoid to rod-shaped cells in masses in a gelatinous capsule. Usually show an irregular arrangement of cells.
Genus V. Sideromonas.

   2. Cells with a thin capsule with a torus.
      a. Torus completely surrounds the cells.
Genus VI. Naumanniella.

      aa. Torus open at one pole giving the wall the appearance of a horseshoe.
Genus VII. Ochrobium.

II. Nonencapsulated cells which form deposits of iron compounds in the cell wall, on the surface of the cells or in the surrounding medium.
   A. Cells coccoid.
Genus VIII. Siderococcus.

   B. Cells rod-shaped.
      1. Found in neutral or alkaline waters.
Genus IX. Siderobacter.

      2. Found in acid mine wastes.
Genus X. Ferrobacillus.

Family VII. *Spirillaceae.* Cells simple, curved or spirally twisted rods. These frequently remain attached to each other after transverse division to form chains of spirally twisted cells. Cells are rigid and usually motile by means of a single flagellum (rarely two) or a tuft of polar flagella. Gram-negative. Frequently oxidative in their physiology. Aerobic or facultatively anaerobic, although a few strict anaerobes occur among the vibrios. Largely water forms, although some are parasitic or pathogenic on higher animals and man.

I. Curved, vibrio-like rods that are rarely united into a complete ring.
   A. Cells curved, rods never united at the end into a ring-shaped cell. Usually possess a single polar flagellum.
      1. Curved rods that are not known to attack cellulose.
         a. Aerobic to anaerobic, heterotrophic vibrios.
Genus I. Vibrio.

         aa. Anaerobic, facultatively autotrophic vibrios that produce hydrogen sulfide or methane.
         b. Reduce sulfates to hydrogen sulfide.
Genus II. Desulfovibrio.

         bb. Reduce carbon dioxide to methane.
Genus III. Methanobacterium.

      2. Curved rods that attack cellulose.
         a. Vibrio-like cells.
Genus IV. Cellvibrio.

         aa. Pointed, sickle-shaped cells.
Genus V. Cellfalcicula.

   B. Curved rods that join ends to form a complete ring.
Genus VI. Microcyclus.

II. Crescent-shaped to spiral cells that are frequently united into spiral chains of cells.
   A. Cells not embedded in zoogloeal masses.
      1. Spiral cells with polar flagella.
         a. Possess a tuft of polar flagella.
Genus VII. Spirillum.

aa. Possess a single polar flagellum.
Genus VIII. *Paraspirillum.*
2. Crescent-shaped cells with a tuft of flagella attached to the middle of the concave side of the cell (Fig. 176).
Genus IX. *Selenomonas.*
B. Crescent- to spiral-shaped cells embedded in a spherical mass of jelly. Found in fresh water.
Genus X. *Myconostoc.*
Order II. *Chlamydobacteriales.* Colorless, alga-like bacteria which occur in trichomes. May or may not be ensheathed. May be unbranched or may show false branching. False branching arises from a lateral displacement of the cells of the trichome within the sheath. This gives rise to a new trichome so that the sheath

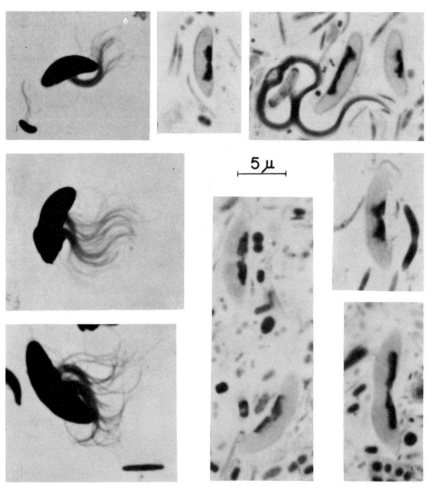

Fig. 176. *Selenomonas palpitans,* showing flagella arising from the middle of the concave side of the cells. Flagella are thicker at the base than at the free end. A highly refractive granule is found on the concave side at the base of the tuft of flagella. This granule stains with nuclear dyes and appears to be a true nucleus, dividing as the cell divides. (*Courtesy of C. F. Robinow.*)

is branched while the trichomes are separate. Sheaths may be composed of an organic matrix impregnated with iron or manganese oxides, or they may be composed of an organic matrix free from these oxides. Gram-negative. Reproduction by flagellate swarm spores or by nonmotile conidia. Endospores never developed. Fresh water and marine forms.

Family I. *Chlamydobacteriaceae*. Bacteria which occur in trichomes and which frequently show false branching. Sheaths, when present, may or may not be impregnated with ferric and/or manganese oxides. Cells divide transversely. Swarm cells, if developed, are usually motile by means of a tuft of flagella. Usually found in fresh water.

    I. Trichomes surrounded by sheaths which are usually not impregnated with iron or manganese oxides and which do not dissolve in hydrochloric acid. Large forms, mostly sessile.

Genus I. Sphaerotilus.

    II. Trichomes surrounded by sheaths impregnated with oxides of iron or manganese which dissolve in strong hydrochloric acid. Free-living or sessile.

        A. Individual trichomes, each with a sheath.

Genus II. Leptothrix.

        B. Sheaths contain more than one trichome; trichomes sometimes in a fan-like arrangement.

Genus III. Toxothrix.

Family II. *Peloplocaceae*. Long, unbranched trichomes usually enclosed in a thin, delicate sheath. Cells within the trichomes, when in the living state, contain false vacuoles which are easily discerned by a reddish gleam of light which they emit; the cytoplasm of the cell appears bluish white. Generally nonmotile, but motile species may occur. Reproduction by transverse fission of the cell. Unattached forms found in fresh-water ponds with decomposing algae.

    I. Trichomes lie parallel to each other in bundles or bands.

Genus I. Peloploca.

    II. Trichomes occur singly.

Genus II. Pelonema.

Family III. *Crenotrichaceae*. Trichomes attached to a firm substrate and show differentiation of base and tip. Unbranched or show false branching. Sheaths may be thin, delicate and not encrusted with oxides of iron or manganese, or they may be plainly visible, thin and colorless at the tip, and thick and encrusted with iron or manganese oxides at the base. Cells disc-shaped to cylindrical, dividing to produce spherical, nonmotile conidia. Individual cells may also slip out of the sheath to grow into new trichomes. Found in fresh and salt waters.

    I. Attached trichomes which are swollen at the free end.

        A. Sheath thick, storing iron or manganese oxides.

Genus I. Crenothrix.

        B. Sheath very delicate, always colorless.

Genus II. Phragmidiothrix.

    II. Attached trichomes which are tapered at the free end.

Genus III. Clonothrix.

Order III. *Hyphomicrobiales*. Multiplication by budding or by budding and longitudinal fission. Buds may be sessile or may be borne at the tip of a slender filament which arises from the pole of a mature cell or from a filament connecting two cells. Cells may occur singly or in pairs but are found more commonly in aggregates. In some types the aggregates consist of groups of cells attached to a surface by stalks which appear to radiate from a common holdfast; in others the aggregates consist of free-floating cell groups in which the cells are attached to one another by the filament engendered in the budding process. Branching of filament may result in groups which contain several hundred cells. Cells ovoid, ellipsoidal, spherical or pyriform. If motile, cells possess a single polar flagellum. Gram-negative so far as known. Metabolism may be heterotrophic or photosynthetic. Found in mud and water of fresh-water ponds and streams; also parasitic on fresh-water crustacea.

Family I. *Hyphomicrobiaceae.* Organisms occur mainly as free-floating groups in which the cells are attached to one another by a slender, sometimes branched, filament. Daughter-cell formation initiated by the outgrowth of a filament from the pole of a mature cell or from some point on a filament connecting two mature cells. Daughter cell is formed by enlargement of the tip of the filament. Gram-negative.

    I. Chemoheterotrophic. Motile.

Genus I. Hyphomicrobium.

    II. Photoheterotrophic. Nonmotile.

Genus II. Rhodomicrobium.

Family II. *Pasteuriaceae.* Stalked bacteria with spherical or pear-shaped cells. If cells elongated, the long axis of the cell coincides with the axis of the stalk. Stalks may be very short or absent, but when present they are usually very fine and at times arranged in whorls attached to a common holdfast. Cells multiply by longitudinal fission and/or by budding. Mostly periphytic; one species parasitic.

    I. Stalks lacking; cells sessile.

Genus I. Pasteuria.

    II. Stalks long and slender, often in whorls.

Genus II. Blastocaulis.

Order IV. *Eubacteriales.* Simple, undifferentiated, rigid cells either spherical or straight rods. Only the simplest forms of branching occur, and these only rarely. Motile and nonmotile species. Flagella are usually arranged peritrichously, but monotrichous species do occur in groups where the flagellation is normally peritrichous; such conditions appear to have been developed from ancestral peritrichous species. Typical endospores occur in one family. All species in certain families are definitely Gram-negative; in other families and groups, where the majority of species are Gram-positive, at least in certain stages of growth, species occur which lose their Gram stain so readily that they are generally classed as Gram-negative. Reproduction by transverse fission; occasionally cells divide in two or three planes perpendicular to each other, thereby forming tetrads or packets of eight cells. Pigments of chromogenic species commonly nonwater-soluble and of a carotenoid nature; other pigments do occur however, some of which show slight powers of diffusion into agar media. Pigments nonphotosynthetic. Order includes saprophytes, parasites, and many pathogenic species; the latter cause diseases of both animals and plants. Found in salt and fresh waters, air, soil, and in the bodies of animals and plants.

Family I. *Azotobacteriaceae.* Relatively large rods or even cocci, sometimes almost yeast-like in appearance. Cells without endospores. Flagellation is peritrichous. Gram-negative. Obligate aerobes, usually growing in a film on the surface of culture media. Capable of fixing atmospheric nitrogen when provided with carbohydrate or other energy source. Grow best on media deficient in nitrogen. Soil and water bacteria.

Genus I. Azotobacter.

Family II. *Rhizobiaceae.* Cells without endospores, rod-shaped, sparsely flagellated; some species nonmotile. Usually Gram-negative. Grow aerobically on ordinary culture media containing glucose. Glucose and sometimes other carbohydrates are utilized without appreciable acid formation. Saprophytes, symbionts and pathogens; the latter are usually plant pathogens forming abnormal growths on roots and stems.

    I. Cells capable of fixing free nitrogen when growing symbiotically on the roots of *Leguminosae.*

Genus I. Rhizobium.

II. Either plant pathogens which attack roots or produce hypertrophies on stems or free-living nonchromogenic soil or water forms. Do not fix nitrogen.

Genus II. *Agrobacterium.*

III. Usually free-living soil and water forms which produce a violet chromogenesis.

Genus III. *Chromobacterium.*

Family III. *Achromobacteriaceae.* Small to medium-sized rods which are usually uniform in shape. Motile by means of peritrichous flagella, or nonmotile. Gram-negative. May or may not liquefy gelatin. Growth on agar nonchromogenic to yellow, orange, brown or even red. Pigment does not diffuse through the agar and apparently is carotenoid in nature. May produce acid but no gas from glucose and sometimes from other sugars; lactose rarely or never attacked. Certain species liquefy agar and/or attack alginates, others digest chitin. May or may not reduce nitrates. Litmus milk may be unchanged, slightly acid, or alkaline. No luminescent species are known. Generally found as salt water, fresh water or soil forms, less commonly found as parasites or pathogens. Some plant pathogens may belong here.

I. Do not attack agar, alginates or chitin. Not active in the production of acid from sugars, especially lactose.

A. Nonchromogenic on ordinary agar media, although the type species of *Achromobacter* produces yellow chromogenesis on potato.

1. Litmus milk alkaline. No acid from carbohydrates.

Genus I. *Alcaligenes.*

2. Litmus milk slightly acid (not enough to be curdled), unchanged, or alkaline. Small amounts of acid usually produced from hexoses.

Genus II. *Achromobacter.*

B. Yellow, orange, brown or red chromogenesis produced on ordinary agar media; pigment nonwater-soluble.

Genus III. *Flavobacterium.*

II. Attack agar, alginates or chitin. Slightly more active in the fermentation of sugars than is the previous group, some even attacking lactose. Nonchromogenic or chromogenic, usually with yellow or orange, always nonwater-soluble pigments.

A. Attack agar and/or alginates.

Genus IV. *Agarbacterium.*

B. Attack chitin and sometimes horny substances.

Genus V. *Beneckea.*

Family IV. *Enterobacteriaceae.* Straight rods. Motile by means of peritrichous flagella, or nonmotile. Gram-negative. Grow well on artificial media. All species attack glucose producing acid or acid and gas. Some species even attack alginates or pectins. Characteristically, nitrites produced from nitrates. Antigenic composition best described as a mosaic which results in serological interrelationships among the several genera, even extending to other families. Many species live in the intestines of man and other animals, frequently causing intestinal disturbances, while others are parasitic on plants, some causing blights and soft rots; still others are saprophytic, causing decomposition of dead organic materials.

Tribe I. *Escherichieae.* Rods, either motile by means of peritrichous flagella, or occasionally nonmotile. Gelatin not liquefied, except slowly by *Aerobacter cloacae* and by *Paracolobactrum arizonae.* Ferment glucose and lactose with production of acid and gas within 24 hr. at 37°C., or within 48 hr. at 25° to 30°C. Some forms produce acid and gas from lactose slowly, occasionally not at all. Do not produce soft rots of vegetables.

I. Alginic acid not decomposed with production of acid and gas.

A. Lactose fermented within 48 hr.

1. Acetylmethylcarbinol not produced; methyl red test positive; salts of citric acid may or may not be used as sole sources of carbon.

Genus I. *Escherichia.*

2. Acetylmethylcarbinol produced; methyl red test negative; salts of citric acid used as sole sources of carbon.
    a. Usually not encapsulated; from feces, milk, dairy products, grain, and other saprophytic sources.

Genus II. *Aerobacter.*

    aa. Usually encapsulated; from respiratory, intestinal, and urogenital tracts.

Genus III. *Klebsiella.*

B. Lactose fermentation consistently delayed, and occasionally lactose is not fermented at all.

Genus IV. *Paracolobactrum.*

II. Alginic acid decomposed with production of acid and gas.

Genus V. *Alginobacter.*

Tribe II. *Erwinieae.* Motile rods which normally do not require organic nitrogen compounds for growth. Produce acid with or without gas from a variety of sugars. In some species the number of carbon compounds attacked is limited, and lactose may not be fermented. May or may not liquefy gelatin. May or may not produce nitrites from nitrates. Invade the tissues of living plants and produce dry necroses, galls, wilts and soft rots.

Genus VI. *Erwinia.*

Tribe III. *Serratieae.* Small, peritrichous rods. Gram-negative. Produce characteristic red pigments; white to rose-red strains that lack brilliant colors are common. Gelatin rapidly liquefied. Milk coagulated and digested. Typical species produce CO_2 and frequently H_2 from glucose and other sugars; acetic, formic, succinic and lactic acids, acetylmethylcarbinol and 2,3-butylene glycol also produced. Coagulated blood serum is liquefied. Nitrates reduced. Aerobic. Saprophytic on decaying plant or even animal materials.

Genus VII. *Serratia.*

Tribe IV. *Proteeae.* Straight rods. Motile by means of peritrichous flagella; generally actively motile at 25°C., but at 37°C. motility may be weak or absent. Gram-negative. Two species, *Proteus vulgaris* and *P. mirabilis,* produce amoeboid colonies which show a swarming phenomenon on solid media devoid of bile salts. On moist agar, remaining species produce colonies which spread to some extent. Spreading colonies can usually be induced to swarm. Pleomorphism is characteristic only of young, actively swarming cultures. Glucose and usually various other carbohydrates, but not lactose, are fermented with the production of acid and usually gas. One species usually produces only acid. Phenylpyruvic acid is produced from phenylalanine by an oxidative deamination, and leucine rendered alkaline by an oxidative decarboxylation. Urea may or may not be decomposed. Trimethylamine oxide is reduced.

Genus VIII. *Proteus.*

Tribe V. *Salmonelleae.* Rods either motile by means of peritrichous flagella or nonmotile. Gram-negative. No spreading growth on agar. Gelatin not liquefied. Milk not peptonized. Numerous carbohydrates attacked with the production of acid or acid and gas. Lactose, sucrose, and salicin not ordinarily attacked. Acetylmethylcarbinol not produced. Urea not hydrolyzed. Found in bodies of warm-blooded animals and man, and occasionally in reptiles; frequently found in the food eaten by these animals.
    I. Motile by means of peritrichous flagella (occasional strains of typhoids are nonmotile, and strains of *Salmonella gallinarum* are frequently nonmotile). Hydrogen sulfide usually produced. Ammonium citrate normally utilized.

Genus IX. *Salmonella.*

    II. Nonmotile. Hydrogen sulfide not produced. Ammonium citrate not utilized.

Genus X. *Shigella.*

Family V. *Brucellaceae.* Small, coccoid to rod-shaped cells which occur singly, in pairs, in short chains or in groups; filamentous and pleomorphic forms occasionally found. Motile and nonmotile species occur, the motile species possessing from 1 to 8 peritrichous flagella. May or may not be encapsulated. May or may not show bipolar staining. Gram-negative. *V* and/or *X* factors sometimes required for growth. Blood serum and similar enrichment materials may be required or may enhance growth. Increased CO_2 tension may also favor growth, especially on primary isolation. Gelatin usually not liquefied. Carbohydrates may or may not be attacked with the production of acid but no gas. Nitrites may or may not be produced from nitrates. Aerobic, facultatively anaerobic. Some invade living tissues; infection in some cases may take place by penetration of the organism through mucous membranes or through the unbroken skin. Parasites and pathogens which affect warm-blooded animals, including man, rarely cold-blooded animals.

I. Nonmotile at 37°C., but may be motile at lower temperatures.
  A. Predominantly occur singly or in masses.
    1. Cells predominantly occur singly and do not occur in masses.
      a. Grow on peptone media but may require blood serum or similar enrichment materials for growth.
        b. Show, or tend to show, bipolar staining.
          c. Attacks carbohydrates.
            Genus I. *Pasteurella.*
          cc. Does not attack carbohydrates.
            Genus II. *Bordetella.*
        bb. Does not show bipolar staining.
            Genus III. *Brucella.*
      aa. Requires *V* and/or *X* factors for growth.
            Genus IV. *Haemophilus.*
    2. Cells predominantly occur singly and show pleomorphism and/or occur in masses.
      a. Growth occurs on ordinary media; increased CO_2 tension enhances growth, especially on primary isolation (Fig. 177).
            Genus V. *Actinobacillus.*
      aa. Growth occurs on infusion media only after growth in chick embryo.
            Genus VI. *Calymmatobacterium.*

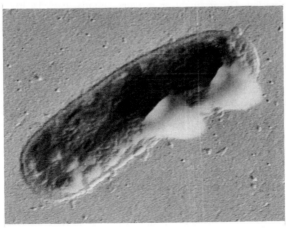

Fig. 177. Electron micrograph of *Actinobacillus mallei.* ×27,400. (*Courtesy of Wetmore and Gochenour, Jr.*)

        B. Predominantly occur as diplobacilli.

Genus VII. Moraxella.

   II. Motile at 37°C.

        A. Optimum temperature for growth, 37°C. Litmus milk becomes strongly alkaline.

Genus II. Bordetella.

        B. Optimum temperature for growth, between 28° and 30°C. Litmus milk unchanged.

Genus VIII. Noguchia.

Family VI. *Bacteroidaceae.* Rods, with rounded or pointed ends, which vary in size from minute, filterable forms to long, filamentous, branching forms. Marked pleomorphism may occur. Motile or nonmotile, the motile species possessing peritrichous flagella (rarely, motility has been observed without demonstrable flagella). Gram-negative. Body fluids frequently required for growth and are always stimulative. Simple carbohydrates usually fermented with the production of acid; gas may be produced in glucose or peptone media. Normally strict anaerobes, but occasionally microaerophilic species occur. Found primarily in the intestinal tracts and mucous membranes of warm-blooded animals. Sometimes pathogenic.

   I. Simple, rarely pleomorphic, rod-shaped cells which are strict anaerobes.

        A. Cells with diameters greater than 0.3 μ.

           1. Cells with rounded ends.

Genus I. Bacteroides.

           2. Cells with pointed ends.

Genus II. Fusobacterium.

        B. Cells with diameters 0.15 μ or less.

Genus III. Dialister.

   II. Highly pleomorphic rods, some of which may be facultative anaerobes.

        A. Strict anaerobes.

Genus IV. Sphaerophorus.

        B. Facultative anaerobes.

Genus V. Streptobacillus.

Family VII. *Micrococcaceae.* Cells in free condition spherical; during division, somewhat elliptical. Endospores not produced (except in *Sarcina ureae* under special conditions). Division primarily in two or three planes; some anaerobic cells divide only in a single plane, producing chains. If cells remain in contact after division, they are frequently flattened in the plane of last division. Occur singly or in pairs, tetrads, packets, irregular masses or even in chains. Motility rare. Gram-positive although the free-living and saprophytic species may be Gram-variable or even Gram-negative. Many species form a nonwater-soluble, yellow, orange, pink or red pigment. Aerobic species produce abundant growth on ordinary culture media and are capable of slight anaerobic growth. Anaerobic to aerotolerant species also occur. Heterotrophic. No visible gas is produced by the aerobic species from carbohydrates, which are frequently fermented. Anaerobic species sometimes produce gas, such as methane, carbon dioxide and hydrogen. Gelatin often slowly liquefied. Free-living saprophytic to parasitic or even pathogenic. The typical aerobic micrococci frequently live on the skin, in skin glands or in the skin gland secretions of *Vertebrata;* however, sea water and soil forms may occur. Anaerobic species live primarily in decomposing organic materials.

   I. Aerobic to facultatively anaerobic species. Also includes some obligate anaerobes that occur in packets (*Sarcina*).

        A. Cells generally found in irregular masses; occasionally they are single or in pairs.

           1. Action on glucose, if any, is oxidative. Aerobic.

Genus I. Micrococcus.

           2. Glucose fermented anaerobically with the production of acid. Facultatively anaerobic.

Genus II. Staphylococcus.

B. Cells normally occur in tetrads or packets of eight cells.
  1. Parasitic species occurring in tetrads. White to pale yellow chromo-
     genesis. Nonmotile.
                                                    Genus III. *Gaffkya.*
  2. Cells occur in packets. White, yellow, orange and red chromogenesis.
     Usually nonmotile.
                                                    Genus IV. *Sarcina.*
II. Obligate anaerobes occurring singly or in pairs, chains or masses but never
    in packets; tetrads rarely formed.
   A. Methane produced from various organic compounds.
                                                Genus V. *Methanococcus.*
   B. Methane not produced.
                                                  Genus VI. *Peptococcus.*
Family VIII. *Neisseriaceae.* Spherical cells occurring in pairs or in masses. Giant
   cells common in young cultures. Nonmotile. Gram-negative. Pigment may or
   may not be produced. Some species grow poorly immediately after isolation
   without mammalian body fluids. Aerobic, facultatively anaerobic, and an-
   aerobic. Optimum temperture, 37°C. All known species are parasitic.
  I. Cells approximately 1.0 μ in diameter, occur in pairs with adjacent sides
     usually flattened. Aerobic or facultatively anaerobic.
                                                    Genus I. *Neisseria.*
 II. Cells usually less than 0.5 μ in diameter, occur in pairs and masses. An-
     aerobic.
                                                  Genus II. *Veillonella.*
Family IX. *Brevibacteriaceae.* Cells without endospores. Rod-shaped, varying
   from a quite short, almost coccoid form to a rather long, straight, unbranched
   rod. Motile or nonmotile, the motile species being peritrichous or, occasionally, monotrichous. Gram-positive. Red, reddish orange, yellow or brown
   pigments may be produced. Carbohydrates may or may not be attacked.
   Aerobic and facultatively anaerobic species occur. Found in dairy products,
   soil, salt and fresh water and decomposing substances of a great variety of
   types.
  I. Short, almost coccoid, unbranched rods which do not form filaments. Acid
     usually produced from simple carbohydrates.
                                               Genus I. *Brevibacterium.*
 II. Long, unbranched rods which may form filaments; filaments may sub-
     divide into coccoid elements. Carbohydrates not utilized.
                                                    Genus II. *Kurthia.*
Family X. *Lactobacillaceae.* Long or short rods or cocci which divide like rods
   in one plane only, producing chains, occasionally tetrads; filamentous as
   well as so-called false branching forms sometimes occur. Usually nonmotile
   but may be motile, the motile species possessing peritrichous flagella. Gram-
   positive. Pigment production rare; a few species produce a yellow, orange,
   red or rusty brown pigment. Gelatin liquefaction rare among the microaerophilic species but is more common among the strict anaerobes. Surface
   growth on all media is poor or absent. Carbohydrates are essential for good
   development; they are fermented to lactic acid, sometimes with volatile
   acids, alcohol, and carbon dioxide as by-products. Nitrites not produced
   from nitrates, but among the strict anaerobes there are a few species that
   are known to reduce nitrates, and some that have not been tested for nitrate reduction. Microaerophilic to anaerobic. Found regularly in the mouth
   and intestinal tract of man and other animals, in food and dairy products,
   and in fermenting vegetable juices; a few species are highly pathogenic.
Tribe I. *Streptococceae.* Cells spherical or elongate, dividing in one plane only,
   usually occurring in pairs or in chains. Gelatin rarely liquefied. None of
   the species grows abundantly on solid media. The microaerophilic species
   attack carbohydrates and polyhydroxy alcohols, producing lactic acid by
   homofermentation or lactic and acetic acids, alcohol, and carbon dioxide
   by heterofermentation; the strictly anaerobic species attack protein decomposition products, organic acids and usually carbohydrates with the

production of carbon dioxide, hydrogen, and other products. Microaerophilic to anaerobic. Catalase-negative. May or may not be pathogenic; some pathogenic species grow poorly without blood serum or other enrichment fluids. Found in various lesions and in the normal mouths and intestines of man and other animals, in food and dairy products and in fermenting plant juices.

I. Facultatively anaerobic to microaerophilic.
  A. Homofermentative, producing only traces of end-products other than lactic acid from carbohydrates.
    1. Produce dextrorotatory lactic acid from glucose.
      a. Parasites which grow poorly on artificial media. Cells usually in pairs, often elongated. Bile-soluble.

Genus I. *Diplococcus.*

      aa. Parasites and saprophytes. Normally form short or long chains. Not soluble in bile.

Genus II. *Streptococcus.*

    2. Produces a racemic mixture of lactic acid from glucose. Occurs singly, as tetrads, pairs, or even short chains.

Genus III. *Pediococcus.*

  B. Heterofermentative, producing considerable amounts of carbon dioxide, ethanol, and acetic acid as well as lactic acid from carbohydrates.

Genus IV. *Leuconostoc.*

II. Strictly anaerobic (one species becomes aerotolerant with repeated transfers).

Genus V. *Peptostreptococcus.*

Tribe II. *Lactobacilleae.* Straight or curved rods usually occurring singly or in chains, sometimes in filaments; so-called false branching may also occur. Usually nonmotile but may be motile, the motile species possessing peritrichous flagella. Gram-positive. Gelatin may be liquefied but only by the strict anaerobes. Carbohydrates usually attacked, the end-products of fermentation including either one or a number of the following: formic, acetic, propionic, butyric, lactic and valeric acids, alcohol, and carbon dioxide. Microaerophilic to anaerobic. Catalase-negative. May or may not be pathogenic. Found in fermenting animal and plant products; also found in the intestinal tracts and in lesions of various warm-blooded animals, including man.

I. Microaerophilic to anaerobic. Glucose fermented with the production of lactic acid or with the production of lactic and acetic acids, alcohol, and carbon dioxide.

Genus I. *Lactobacillus.*

II. Strictly anaerobic.
  A. Nonmotile.
    1. Cells do not show so-called false branching.
      a. Cells do not occur in long chains and/or filaments.

Genus II. *Eubacterium.*

      aa. Cells occur in long chains and/or filaments.

Genus III. *Catenabacterium.*

    2. Cells show so-called false branching.

Genus IV. *Ramibacterium.*

  B. Motile.

Genus V. *Cillobacterium.*

Family XI. *Propionibacteriaceae.* Irregularly shaped rods which tend toward bending or terminal swelling (in *Butyribacterium*) or pleomorphism (in *Propionibacterium*). Nonmotile. Gram-positive. Colonial development on semi-solid media is slow, visible colonies seldom being discernible before two days. Where pigment is produced, it is brownish red. Nonproteolytic; usually saccharolytic. Ferment carbohydrates, usually lactic acid and, in some cases, polyhydroxy alcohols with the production of saturated aliphatic carboxylic acids. Anaerobic to aerotolerant, many strains of *Propionibacterium* being readily adapted to growth under aerobic conditions, with the actual utilization of oxygen. Generally catalase-positive when subjected to the usual laboratory test, but exceptions exist, particularly in *Butyribacterium*. Inhabitants of intestinal tracts of animals; also occur in materials outside the body where suitable foodstuffs are found.

I. Ferment carbohydrates and lactic acid.

    A. Produce propionic and acetic acids and carbon dioxide.

Genus I. Propionibacterium.

    B. Produce butyric and acetic acids and carbon dioxide.

Genus II. Butyribacterium.

II. Carbohydrates fermented. Glucose converted mainly to ethanol and carbon dioxide, with small amounts of acetic and other acids. Lactic acid not fermented.

Genus III. Zymobacterium.

Family XII. *Corynebacteriaceae*. Usually nonmotile rods, frequently banded or beaded with metachromatic granules. May show marked diversity of form. Branching cells have been described in a few species but these are very uncertain. Generally Gram-positive, some species being partially decolorized more easily than others. Where pigment is formed, it is grayish yellow or orange or pink. Gelatin may be liquefied. Nitrites may be produced from nitrates. Aerobic to microaerophilic; a few species are anaerobic. Animal and plant parasites and pathogens; also found in dairy products and soil.

I. Primarily pathogenic on animals and plants.

    A. Aerobic to anaerobic, pleomorphic rods that show the characteristic arrangement produced by snapping division.

        1. Animal species nonmotile but some of the plant pathogens motile.

Genus I. Corynebacterium.

        2. Animal species motile by means of peritrichous flagella. Causes a monocytosis in warm-blooded animals, including man.

Genus II. Listeria.

    B. Microaerophilic rods to long filaments. Nonmotile.

Genus III. Erysipelothrix.

II. Live primarily on decomposing organic matter. Saprophytic.

    A. Found primarily in dairy products. Acid production weak. Lactic acid is the principal acid produced. Nonmotile.

Genus IV. Microbacterium.

    B. Found primarily in soil.

        1. Decomposes cellulose. Motile and nonmotile species.

Genus V. Cellulomonas.

        2. Does not decompose cellulose. Generally nonmotile. Gram-negative rods occur in young cultures, and coccoid, Gram-positive cells develop in older cultures.

Genus VI. Arthrobacter.

Family XIII. *Bacillaceae*. Rod-shaped cells capable of producing endospores which are cylindrical, ellipsoidal or spherical, and which are located in the center of the cell, subterminally or terminally. Sporangia do not differ from the vegetative cells except when bulged by spores larger than the cell diameter; such sporangia are spindle-shaped when spores are central and wedge- or drumstick-shaped when spores are terminal. Motile by means of peritrichous flagella or nonmotile. Usually Gram-positive. Pigment formation rare. Gelatin frequently hydrolyzed. Sugars generally fermented, sometimes with production of gas. Aerobic, facultatively anaerobic; anaerobic; or anaerobic, aerotolerant. Some species capable of growth at 55°C. Mostly saprophytes, commonly found in soil; a few are animal or insect parasites or pathogens.

I. Aerobic or facultatively anaerobic. Catalase-positive.

Genus I. Bacillus.

II. Anaerobic or aerotolerant; catalase not known to be produced.

                                 Genus II. *Clostridium.*

Order V. *Actinomycetales.* Organisms forming elongated cells which have a definite tendency to branch. These hyphae do not exceed 1.5 μ and are mostly about 1.0 μ or less in diameter. In some species the cells are acid-fast. In the *Mycobacteriaceae* the mycelium is rudimentary or absent; no spores are formed. The *Actinomycetaceae, Streptomycetaceae* and *Actinoplanaceae* usually produce a characteristic branching mycelium and multiply by means of special spores (oidiospores, conidia, or sporangiospores) or combinations of these spores. Special spores are formed by the fragmentation of the plasma within straight or spiral-shaped, spore-bearing hyphae; the oidiospores are formed by segmentation or by transverse division of hyphae, similar to the formation of oidia among the true fungi; the conidia are produced singly, at the end of simple or branching conidiophores; the sporangiospores are borne in spherical or variously shaped sporangia. A few species in *Nocardia* are reported to be motile. In *Actinoplanes* the sporangiospores have polar flagella and swim; in *Streptosporangium* the spores are nonmotile. Cell structure like that of the bacteria proper. Cell wall substance is neither chitin nor cellulose. Thus it differs from the cell wall substance of the true fungi, another indication of a closer relationship with the bacteria than with the fungi (molds). Only a few species are pathogenic. Majority found in soil or less commonly in fresh water.

Family I. *Mycobacteriaceae.* Cells spherical to rod-shaped; branching not evident on ordinary media. No conidia. Aerobic. Mesophilic. Gram-positive. Found in soil, dairy products, and as parasites on animals, including man.

    I. Cells usually acid-fast. Rod-shaped cells that do not branch under ordinary cultural conditions.

                                   Genus I. *Mycobacterium.*

    II. Nonacid-fast cells so far as observed. Cells generally spherical, occurring singly, in short chains, or in clumps.

                                   Genus II. *Mycococcus.*

Family II. *Actinomycetaceae.* Mycelium nonseptate during the early stages of growth but later may become septate and break up into short segments, rod-shaped or spherical in shape, or the mycelium may remain nonseptate and produce spores on aerial hyphae. Organisms in culture media are either colorless or produce various pigments. Some species are partially acid-fast. This family distinguished from previous one by formation of a true mycelium.

    I. Obligately aerobic. Colonies are bacteria-like in nature, smooth, rough or folded, of a soft to a dough-like consistency, sometimes compact and leathery in young stages. Most forms do not produce any aerial mycelium; a few produce a limited mycelium, the branches of which also break up into oidiospores or segmentation spores. Some species partially acid-fast.

                                    Genus I. *Nocardia.*

    II. Anaerobic or microaerophilic; parasitic; nonacid-fast, nonproteolytic and nondiastatic.

                                   Genus II. *Actinomyces.*

Family III. *Streptomycetaceae.* Vegetative mycelium does not fragment into bacillary or coccoid forms. Conidia borne on sporophores. Primarily soil forms, sometimes thermophilic in rotting manure. A few species are parasitic.

    I. Conidia produced in aerial hyphae in chains.

                                   Genus I. *Streptomyces.*

    II. Conidia produced terminally and singly on short conidiophores.
       A. No growth between 50° and 65°C.

                                  Genus II. *Micromonospora.*

       B. Growth occurs between 50° and 65°C.

                               Genus III. *Thermoactinomyces.*

Family IV. *Actinoplanaceae.* Vegetative mycelium, usually inconspicuous, is formed in water on a variety of plant and animal parts. The aerial mycelium is lacking as a rule; it is formed in certain species and then much as in *Streptomyces*. Reproduction is by spores formed in sporangia, the spores in *Actinoplanes* possessing flagella and being motile, and those in *Streptosporangium* possessing no flagella and being nonmotile; conidia formed in many species. Culturable on a variety of artificial media and then resembling, in vegetative characters, certain species of *Nocardia, Micromonospora* or *Streptomyces*. Widely distributed in soil and fresh water.

    I. Aerial mycelium usually not formed; coiled conidiophores lacking; sporangiospores motile.

Genus I. Actinoplanes.

    II. Aerial mycelium abundant; coiled conidiophores as well as sporangia are formed in some species; sporangiospores nonmotile.

Genus II. Streptosporangium.

Order VI. *Caryophanales.* Bacteria which occur as trichomes (many-celled filaments) or as shorter structures which function as hormogonia. Individual cells characterized by the presence of a central body or ring-like nucleus which frequently assumes the form of a disc; these bodies are clearly visible in the living cells. The nuclear elements give a clearcut Feulgen reaction. The trichomes are not enclosed in sheaths. Colorless. Each trichome consists of cylindrical or discoidal cells enclosed in a continuous wall. Gonidia are sometimes formed. Found in water, the intestines of arthropods and vertebrates and in decomposing organic materials.

Family I. *Caryophanaceae.* Large trichomes and bacillary structures which do not form spores. Motile with peritrichous flagella or nonmotile. Organisms are found on the mucous membranes of the oral cavity of man and various other animals, in the alimentary tract of ruminants and in decomposing organic materials.

    I. Trichomatous bacteria that are actively motile by means of peritrichous flagella.

        A. Unstained trichomes show alternating light and dark bands, the dark bands being internal crosswalls.

Genus I. Caryophanon.

        B. Trichomes show coenocytic structure. Divide by constriction.

Genus II. Lineola.

    II. Nonmotile trichomes. Found in the buccal cavities of vertebrates.

Genus III. Simonsiella.

Family II. *Oscillospiraceae.* Cells occur in trichomes of varying lengths. Trichomes are partitioned to form narrow cells, each containing a central chromatin body (disc-like nucleus); these bodies give a clear Feulgen reaction and are embedded in hyaline protoplasm. Spores are formed by a fusion of the protoplasms of two to three neighboring cells. Actively motile by means of peritrichous flagella; nonmotile strains may occur. Parasitic in the intestinal tracts of vertebrates.

Genus I. Oscillospira.

Family III. *Arthromitaceae.* Trichomes probably divided into cells although septa (protoplasmic?) disappear during sporulation. Disc-like nuclei alternate with thin protoplasmic segments (septa). Spores form in the distal ends of trichomes. Nonmotile. Trichomes are attached by a spherical body in groups to the intestinal walls of insects, crustaceans, and tadpoles.

Genus I. Arthromitus.

Genus II. Coleomitus.

Order VII. *Beggiatoales.* Cells occur mostly in trichomes in three of the families and singly in the fourth family. When in contact with a substrate, the motile organisms glide over the surface or show a slow, rolling, jerky type of motion. No flagella or other organs of locomotion are known. Nonmotile trichomes may also occur. Trichomes may show bending and flexing. With respect to gliding and oscillating, the trichomes function as distinct units except in the genus *Bactoscilla*, where the trichomes show bending at the joints between the cells. Multiplication is by transverse fission throughout the entire length of the trichomes or of the singly occurring cells; gonidia occur in one family, *Leucotrichaceae*. Do not possess chlorophyll or phycocyanin. Under favorable environmental conditions, sulfur globules, sometimes in accompaniment with calcium carbonate crystals, may be found in or on the cells. Found in fresh water (with or without hydrogen sulfide) and marine habitats, in soil and in decomposing organic matter, especially algae.

Family I. *Beggiatoaceae.* Individual cells, generally not visible without staining, occur in trichomes; within the trichomes the cells are arranged in chains. The trichomes show a gliding motion when in contact with a substrate; they also show flexing movements. When grown in the presence of hydrogen sulfide, the trichomes contain sulfur globules. The structure of these organisms is very similar to that of the *Oscillatoriaceae*, but the cells are devoid of chlorophyll and phycocyanin. Special reproductive structures are unknown.

I. Trichomes are free and motile and are not attached to a substrate.
  A. Trichomes occur singly and are not embedded in a common slime-sheath.
    1. Trichomes straight or somewhat bent, not permanently coiled.
          Genus I. *Beggiatoa.*
    2. Trichomes coiled or spirally wound.
          Genus II. *Thiospirillopsis.*
  B. Trichomes occur in bundles and are surrounded by a slime-sheath.
          Genus III. *Thioploca.*
II. Trichomes attached to substrate at one end; apical segments, when freed, are motile until attached.
          Genus IV. *Thiothrix.*

Family II. *Vitreoscillaceae.* Cells occur in colorless trichomes of varying degrees of flexibility. Trichomes show a gliding motion when in contact with a substrate, the speed of movement varying inversely with the width of the trichome. One end of a trichome may become attached to a surface, the other end then becoming free-swinging. Gram-negative. The gliding habit determines the nature of growth: on agar low in nutrients, wavy, curly or spiral colonies are produced; on rich media, drop-like colonies, resembling those of many bacteria, are formed. Do not possess chlorophyll or phycocyanin. Never contain sulfur granules. Do not hydrolyze genuine proteins. Found in dung, in soil, in water with decaying plant material and almost regularly in myxophycean scum on the surfaces of quiet waters.

I. Trichomes perceptibly septate.
  A. Trichomes divided into cells which are not separated by empty interspaces; the trichomes may bend anywhere along their length.
          Genus I. *Vitreoscilla.*
  B. Trichomes divided into cells separated by empty interspaces; the trichomes bend only at these pliable joints.
          Genus II. *Bactoscilla.*
II. Trichomes not perceptibly septate.
          Genus III. *Microscilla.*

Family III. *Leucotrichaceae.* Short, cylindrical cells arranged in long, colorless, unbranched, nonmotile trichomes tapering from the base to the apex. Sulfur granules may be found on the exterior of the cells under certain conditions. Trichomes commonly attached basally to solid substrates by an inconspicuous holdfast. Multiplication by means of gonidia (single, gliding cells which arise apically from the trichomes). The gonidia may aggregate to form rosettes containing up to 50 cells. The cells in the rosettes become nonmotile, develop holdfasts and elongate to form trichomes; therefore mature trichomes are characteristically arranged in the form of radial colonies, although occasionally gonidia develop singly, forming isolated trichomes. Strictly aerobic. Resemble blue-green algae in many respects but differ from them in that they do not produce photosynthetic pigments. Found in fresh and salt water containing decomposing algal material.

          Genus I. *Leucothrix.*

Family IV. *Achromatiaceae*. Large, unicellular organisms which are spherical to ovoid or shortly cylindrical with hemispherical extremities. Movements, if any, are of a slow, rolling, jerky type and are dependent upon the presence of a substrate; no special organs of locomotion are known. Division of cells is by a constriction in the middle. Do not possess photosynthetic pigments. In their natural habitat, the cells contain sulfur droplets and sometimes additional inclusions, such as large spherules of calcium carbonate. Found in fresh water and marine environments.

Genus I. *Achromatium.*

Order VIII. *Myxobacterales*. Vegetative cells are flexible rods of low refractility which exhibit gliding movement on solid surfaces and which multiply by binary, transverse fission to produce a thin, flat, rapidly extending colony. Actively motile cells at the periphery of the colony commonly occur as groups of 2 or 3 to several hundred individuals in the form of tongue-like extensions or isolated islands whose presence is virtually diagnostic of the order. The moving cells may pave the substrate with a thin layer of slime on which they rest.

Family I. *Cytophagaceae*. Flexible, sometimes pointed rods showing gliding motility. No fruiting bodies or resting cells (microcysts) are formed.

Genus I. *Cytophaga.*

Family II. *Archangiaceae*. Resting cells are shortened rods, never enclosed in larger cysts. Fruiting bodies are irregularly swollen or twisted, or are finger-like structures.

I. Fruiting body depressed, usually irregularly delimited, the interior usually consisting of swollen or intestine-like twisted or inter-twined masses, whose windings may be constricted or may jut out (project) as free ends.

Genus I. *Archangium.*

II. Fruiting body consists of single (separate) columnar or finger-like structures arising from the substrate.

Genus II. *Stelangium.*

Family III. *Sorangiaceae*. The shortened rods of the fruiting body lie in angular, usually relatively small cysts of definite polygonal shape. Often many of these cysts are surrounded by a common membrane. The primary cyst may be differentiated from the angular or secondary cysts. No stalked forms are known.

Genus I. *Sorangium.*

Family IV. *Polyangiaceae*. The resting cells are shortened and usually somewhat thickened rods which are always enclosed in cysts. Cysts may be sessile, occurring either singly or in groups and enveloped in a slime membrane, or they may be raised on stalks (cystophores) which can be either simple or branched. Cysts can occur either singly or in clusters at the tips of the stalks.

I. Cysts embedded in slime; sessile, occurring singly or as loose aggregates.

Genus I. *Polyangium.*

II. Cysts never embedded in slime; either borne on stalks or arranged in tight clusters joined together at the base.

A. Many cysts united at base to form a large disc or rosette; either sessile or stalked.

Genus II. *Synangium.*

B. Cysts not united at base; borne singly or in large numbers on stalks.

1. Cysts borne singly on a stalk.

Genus III. *Podangium.*

2. Numerous cysts on a stalk.

Genus IV. *Chondromyces.*

Family V. *Myxococcaceae*. The rods become shortened when fruiting occurs and develop into spherical or ellipsoidal microcysts. Definite fruiting bodies are produced in three of the genera. In *Sporocytophaga* the microcysts are produced from the vegetative cells without development of fruiting bodies.

I. Definite fruiting bodies formed.

A. Microcysts not enclosed in larger cysts.

1. Fruiting bodies deliquescent.

Genus I. *Myxococcus.*

2. Fruiting bodies firm, not deliquescent.

Genus II. *Chondrococcus.*

B. Microcysts enclosed in larger cysts.

Genus III. *Angiococcus.*

II. No definite fruiting bodies formed.

Genus IV. *Sporocytophaga.*

Order IX. *Spirochaetales.* Slender, flexuous bodies 6 to 500 μ in length, in the form of spirals with at least one complete turn. Some forms may show an axial filament, a lateral crista, or ridge, or transverse striations; otherwise there is no significant protoplasmic pattern. Smaller forms may have a lower refractive index than that of true bacteria, and therefore can be seen only with dark-field illumination. Some forms take aniline dyes with difficulty; Giemsa's stain is uniformly successful. Granules are formed in some species which are found in vector hosts. All forms are motile. In the true bacteria, motility is effected by flagella endowed with a lashing movement; however, no such structures exist among the spirochaetes. Terminal projections, whether derived from the periplast or from the axial filament, may assist in the movements, and it is possible that the crista has a similar function, although neither of these structures can explain the violent motion of spirochaetes. Motility consists of a rapid whirling or spinning about the long axis, which activity drives the organism forward or backward, there being no anteroposterior polarity. In addition the spirochaetes make violent, lashing movements, curling and uncurling their spirals. Multiplication by transverse fission, no sexual cycle being known. Free-living, saprophytic and parasitic forms.

Family I. *Spirochaetaceae.* Coarse, spiral organisms, 30 to 500 μ in length, possessing definite protoplasmic structures. Found in stagnant, fresh or salt water and in the intestinal tracts of bivalve molluscs.

I. No obvious periplast membrane and no cross striations present.

Genus I. *Spirochaeta.*

II. Periplast membrane present. Cross striations present in stained specimens.
A. Free-living in marine ooze.

Genus II. *Saprospira.*

B. Parasitic on lamellibranch molluscs. Cristae are prominent.

Genus III. *Cristispira.*

Family II. *Treponemataceae.* Coarse or slender spirals, 4 to 16 μ in length; longer forms are due to incomplete or delayed division. The spirals are regular or irregular and flexible or comparatively rigid. The protoplasm possesses no obvious structural features. Some cells may show terminal filaments. Some cells are visible only with dark-field illumination. Many of these organisms can be cultivated. With few exceptions, parasitic in vertebrates. Some are pathogenic.

I. Stains easily with ordinary aniline dyes.

Genus I. *Borrelia.*

II. Stain with difficulty except with Giemsa's stain or silver impregnation.
A. Anaerobic.

Genus II. *Treponema.*

B. Aerobic.

Genus III. *Leptospira.*

Order X. *Mycoplasmatales.* Highly pleomorphic organisms which possess a peculiar mode of reproduction characterized by the breaking up of filaments (with a more or less pronounced tendency to true branching) into coccoid, filterable elementary bodies. The cell bodies are soft and fragile; without special precautions they are often distorted or entirely destroyed in microscopical preparations. Nonmotile. Typical endospores are never produced. Gram-negative. Growth occurs in agar media, although most of the species have exacting nutritional requirements. Pathogenic and saprophytic species occur.

Family I. *Mycoplasmataceae.* Characteristics same as for the order.

Genus I. *Mycoplasma.*

Class: *Microtatobiotes*. Includes the smallest of the living things. All are manifested by a dependence on other living organisms for their growth and multiplication. Parasitism is axiomatic since there is no way to determine if there are free-living forms. Most of these organisms occur intracellularly; *Rickettsia quintana* Schmincke of trench fever is an example of extracellular growth in its host, the body louse. A few of the visible forms are known to occur intranuclearly. Characteristic, intracellular inclusion bodies are often associated with the smaller agents. Hosts are represented from the highest members of the plant and animal kingdoms to the lowliest of microbial life. Some species utilize both intermediate and definitive hosts for their propagation. The largest members are the rickettsia-like organisms which are often pleomorphic, including coccoid to filamentous forms, while others show morula-like clusters of elementary bodies occurring as one or up to twenty colonies in an infected cell. Some species show larger ellipsoidal granules with a fairly compact matrix of as much as 2 μ in diameter termed initial bodies from which, in most instances, the groups of smaller elementary bodies are believed to be derived though no life cycle is postulated. At least three of these larger species, visible under the light microscope, have phases which pass through coarse or medium filters, e.g., *Coxiella burnetii* of Q fever.

The small members grade downward to filterable virus particles susceptible to measurement only by physico-chemical techniques and by special preparation under the electron microscope. Special staining procedures are required for forms visible under the light microscope and for studying characteristic pathologic reactions or associated inclusion bodies in the tissues of affected hosts. Special tissue culture techniques have been developed for the more adequate investigation of many of the species.

Order I. *Rickettsiales*. Small, rod-shaped, coccoid and often pleomorphic microorganisms occurring as elementary bodies which are usually intracellular but which may occasionally be facultatively or exclusively extracellular. May also develop larger "initial bodies" as intracellular, spherical or less regular inclusions. Intracytoplasmic forms may be diffuse, compacted into colonies or morulae and may be located in special situations. Usually nonfilterable. Gram-negative. Cultivated outside the host only in living tissues, embryonated chicken eggs or rarely in media containing body fluids. Parasitic organisms almost always intimately associated with not only reticulo-endothelial and vascular endothelial cells or erythrocytes in vertebrates, but also often in invertebrates which may act as vectors. The intracellular parasites of Protozoa and other invertebrates are provisionally assigned here also. May cause diseases in man or other animals or both. Seldom kill the invertebrate hosts.

Family I. *Rickettsiaceae*. Small, rod-shaped, ellipsoidal, coccoid and diplococcus-shaped, often pleomorphic organisms which are often intimately associated with arthropod tissues, usually in an intracellular position. Gram-negative. Species pathogenic for vertebrates have not been cultivated to date in cell-free media. May be parasitic in man and other animals causing disease (typhus and related ills) that may be transmitted by invertebrate vectors (chiefly lice, fleas, ticks, and mites). Information is still inadequate for the systematic assignment of many of the species which inhabit arthropod hosts and which were originally described in this family.

Tribe I. *Rickettsieae*. Small, pleomorphic, mostly intracellular organisms adapted to existence in arthropods and pathogenic for suitable vertebrate hosts.

I. Nonfilterable; produce typhus-like rash and usually Proteus X agglutinins in man.

Genus I. *Rickettsia*.

II. Filterable; produce neither rash nor Weil-Felix agglutinins in man.

Genus II. *Coxiella*.

Tribe II. *Ehrlichieae*. Minute, rickettsia-like organisms pathogenic for certain vertebrate hosts, not including man. Adapted to existence in invertebrates, chiefly arthropods.

I. Transmitted by ticks.

A. Transmitted transovarially; parasites of circulating monocytes of vertebrate hosts.

Genus III. *Ehrlichia.*

B. Not transmitted transovarially; parasites of endothelial cells of vertebrate hosts.

Genus IV. *Cowdria.*

II. Transmitted by parasitic trematodes; pathogenic principally for canines.

Genus V. *Neorickettsia.*

Tribe III. *Wolbachieae.* Includes many species heretofore assigned to the genus *Rickettsia* which are rickettsia-like in growth and in morphological and staining properties and which are mostly intracellular symbiotes or parasites of various species of arthropods, sometimes occupying special tissues or mycetomes. Characterization has often been not so adequate as in the preceding forms that are pathogenic for vertebrates, and differentiation has been arbitrarily assigned chiefly on the basis of presumed host-specificity, in arthropods, though differences in development and morphology are often noted.

I. No known filterability; no reported association with intracellular crystalline inclusions.

A. Symbiotic to highly pathogenic; no mycetomes produced in hosts.

Genus VI. *Wolbachia.*

B. Symbiotic to the point that special mycetomes are developed for harboring the organisms, which are not pathogenic, in the host.

Genus VII. *Symbiotes.*

II. Filterable; cause blue disease of beetle larvae; associated with intracellular, crystalline inclusions; reportedly invade cell nuclei.

Genus VIII. *Rickettsiella.*

Family II. *Chlamydiaceae.* Small, coccoid microorganisms with a characteristic developmental cycle. Stain with aniline dyes. Gram-negative. Have not been cultivated in cell-free media. Obligate, intracytoplasmic parasites or saprophytes. Found in various warm-blooded animals, where they are usually pathogenic.

I. Noncultivable in chicken embryonic tissues.

A. Organisms coccoid; do not exhibit pleomorphism.

Genus I. *Chlamydia.*

B. Organisms usually coccoid or ellipsoidal; exhibit marked pleomorphism.

1. Pleomorphic forms small (200 mμ to 2 μ). Pathogenic.

a. Occur intracytoplasmically as prominent colonies.

Genus II. *Colesiota.*

aa. Occur intracytoplasmically as scattered growth.

Genus III. *Ricolesia.*

2. Pleomorphic forms large (2 μ). Apparently nonpathogenic; may be saprophytic.

Genus IV. *Colettsia.*

II. Cultivable in chicken embryonic tissues.

Genus V. *Miyagawanella.*

Family III. *Bartonellaceae.* Rod-shaped, coccoid, ring- or disc-shaped, filamentous and beaded microorganisms, usually less than 3 μ in greatest dimension. Parasites of the erythrocytes in man and other vertebrates. Not acid-fast. Stain lightly with many aniline dyes but distinctly with Giemsa's stain after methyl alcohol fixation; following this technique the *Bartonellaceae* are readily distinguished from the protozoa which also parasitize erythrocytes in that the former stain with no differentiation into nucleus and cytoplasm. Gram-negative. Cultivation *in vitro* on nonliving media has been achieved in two genera. At least one species bears a single polar flagellum in culture. Arthropod transmission has been established in the majority of genera. Cause bartonellosis in man and haemobartonellosis, grahamellosis, and eperythrozoönosis in lower animals.

I. Multiply on erythrocytes and within fixed-tissue cells. Usually possess a single, polar flagellum when cultivated in or on nonliving media. Provoke a progressive anemia or a cutaneous eruption, usually both in succession, not both coincidentally. Found in man and in *Phlebotomus* spp.

Genus I. *Bartonella.*

II. Not known to multiply in fixed-tissue cells; parasitize erythrocytes and may multiply there. Flagella not demonstrated. Occur in mammals and possibly in other vertebrates, but not known from man.

A. Usually parasitize less than 5 per cent of the total erythrocytes, rarely more. Relatively monomorphic in erythrocytes. Nonpathogenic or only slightly so. Affected little, if at all, by splenectomy. Cultivable on nonliving media. Occur within the red blood cells; epi-erythrocytic forms are problematical.

Genus II. *Grahamella.*

B. Parasitized cells may constitute more than 90 per cent of the total erythrocytes at the peak of infection. Polymorphism is marked when in or on red blood cells. May or may not be pathogenic. Marked increase in numbers following splenectomy. Cultivation on nonliving media not confirmed. Occur on the red blood cells; situation within red cells possible but not proved.

1. Extremely polymorphic; however, rods of varying sizes almost invariably occur, often in chains. Habitat predominantly epi-erythrocytic. Usually pathogenic, provoking a progressive, sometimes fatal, anemia.

Genus III. *Haemobartonella.*

2. Fundamental morphological type is ring- or disc-shaped. Rods are one disc- or ring-diameter in length; composite rods are made of these units. Occur in great numbers in the blood plasma as well as on the erythrocytes. Usually nonpathogenic.

Genus IV. *Eperythrozoon.*

Family IV. *Anaplasmataceae.* Organisms which parasitize red blood cells. There is no demonstrable multiplication in other tissues. In blood smears fixed with May-Grünwald and stained with Giemsa's stain, these organisms appear in the erythrocytes as spherical chromatic granules which stain a deep reddish violet color. Show no differentiation into nucleus and cytoplasm. Occur naturally as parasites of ruminants. Transmitted by arthropods. Situated at or near the margin and/or at or near the center of red blood cells. Position within the erythrocyte and/or host differences serve as bases for differentiating species. Attempts at cultivation in a variety of media have failed. Produce disease in nonsplenectomized and in splenectomized ruminants. The natural and experimental host range is fairly wide, these organisms occurring in members of the families *Bovidae* and *Camelidae.* Influenced by aureomycin and terramycin. Widely distributed throughout the world.

Genus I. *Anaplasma.*

Order II. *Virales.* Viruses are etiological agents of disease, typically of small size and capable of passing filters that retain bacteria, increasing only in the presence of living cells, giving rise to new strains by mutation. A considerable number of plant viruses have not been proved filterable; it is nevertheless customary to include these viruses with those known to be filterable because of similarities in other attributes and in the diseases induced. Some not known to be filterable are inoculable only by special techniques, as by grafting or by the use of insect vectors, and suitable methods for testing their filterability have not been developed; moreover, it is not certain that so simple a criterion as size measured in terms of filterability will prove to be an adequate indicator of the limits of the natural group. Viruses cause diseases of bacteria, plants, and animals.

Our incomplete knowledge of the entities known as viruses has made their classification, and consequently their nomenclature, a difficult matter. It is difficult to describe viruses adequately because of their small size and because they are not cultivable. Electron microscopy has enabled a determination of the size and morphology of some of the viruses. Likewise, serological methods have been developed which are proving to be useful in distinguishing between different species and types of viruses, but in many cases these methods have not been applied.

The useful characteristic that permits recognition of viruses is their capacity to produce specific diseases. Three constituent groups of viruses have come to be recognized, and to some extent named and classified, through the largely separate efforts of bacteriologists, animal pathologists, and plant pathologists. Taxonomic overlapping of the three groups, viruses affecting bacteria, viruses having human and other animal hosts, and viruses invading higher plants, can hardly be justified as yet by available evidence. Nevertheless, it has been shown that a single virus may multiply within, and cause morphological changes in, both a plant host and an insect vector. This seems to dispose of the thought that adaptation to one environment necessarily precludes the utilization of other sources for the materials needed for growth and multiplication.

For the present it seems feasible to continue with the custom, tacitly accepted in the past, of classifying bacteriophages separately as one subgroup, viruses causing diseases in higher plants as a second subgroup, and those causing diseases in man and other animals as a third subgroup. It should be recognized that this may prove to be only a temporary arrangement, necessary because we have little or no evidence to warrant taxonomic overlapping of the three groups and useful while we await critical investigations and possible development of a substitute plan capable of displaying natural relationships to better advantage. It is further possible that there may be discoveries of common physical properties which would aid in formulating an interlocking classification, for which at present we lack any substantial basis.

Because of the rapid expansion of the field by the frequent discovery of new viruses and the development of new methods for their recognition and characterization, together with some uncertainties evidenced by virologists, it does not seem appropriate, therefore, to include a formal classification of *Virales* at this time.

It may be readily seen that a classification of microorganisms is a very difficult task. The work becomes increasingly more difficult as additional species are discovered and studied. Some organisms have been moved from one genera to another and their names changed. Some have had their names changed several times since they were discovered. This is to be expected when the difficulties encountered in studying such minute organisms are considered. Because of the nature of such minute organisms, it is highly probable that no single classification will ever be completely acceptable to all bacteriologists. Nevertheless, a classification, no matter how imperfect, is better than none at all. The one outlined here is undoubtedly the best of those which have been proposed and is in general use throughout the world.

REFERENCES

Alford, J. A., E. E. Wiese, and J. J. Gunter: Heat resistance in *Corynebacterium* and the relationship of this genus to *Microbacterium*, *J. Bact.*, **69**:516, 1955.

Baldacci, E., and A. Grein: Esame della forma delle spore di attinomiceti al microscopio elettronico e loro valutazione ai fini di una classificazione, *Giornale di Microbiologia*, **1**:28, 1955.

Breed, R. S.: The relationships of the bacteria and viruses to other living things, *Can. J. Microbiol.*, 2:201, 1956.

——— and E. F. Lessel, Jr.: The classification of luminescent bacteria, *Antonie van Leeuwenhoek*, 20:58, 1954.

———, E. G. D. Murray, and N. R. Smith: "Bergey's Manual of Determinative Bacteriology," Baltimore, The Williams & Wilkins Company, 1957.

Committee on Bacteriological Technic: "Manual of Microbiological Methods," Society of American Bacteriologists, New York, McGraw-Hill Book Company, Inc., 1957.

Cummins, C. S., and H. Harris: The relationships between certain members of the *Staphylococcus-Micrococcus* group as shown by their cell wall composition, *Int. Bull. Bact. Nom. and Tax.*, 6:111, 1956.

Floch, H.: Etude comparative des genres *Moraxella*, *Achromobacter*, et *Alcaligenes*, *Ann. Inst. Pasteur*, 85:675, 1953.

Gordon, R. E., and M. M. Smith: Proposed group of characters for the separation of *Streptomyces* and *Nocardia*, *J. Bact.*, 69:147, 1955.

Gottlieb, D.: The actinomyces—challenge to the taxonomist, Department of Microbiology, University of Maryland, 1960.

Hansen, H. P.: Correlations and interrelationships in viruses and in organisms. II. The principles of the natural periodical system of plant and animal infecting viruses, *Kgl. Veterinaer- og Land-bohøjskole*, no. 48, 31, 1957.

Houwink, A. L.: *Caulobacter*, its morphogenesis, taxonomy and parasitism, *Antonie van Leeuwenhoek*, 21:49, 1955.

International Committee on Bacteriological Nomenclature: "International Code of Nomenclature of Bacteria and Viruses," Ames, Iowa, Iowa State College Press, 1958.

Keating, S. V.: A biochemical and serological study of the genus *Proteus*, *Med. J. Australia*, Aug. 4, 1956.

Lessel, E. F., Jr., and R. S. Breed: *Selenomonas* Boskamp, 1922—A genus that includes species showing an unusual type of flagellation, *Bact. Rev.*, 18:165, 1954.

Murray, E. G. D.: The story of Listeria, *Trans. Roy. Soc. Can.*, 47:15, 1953.

Philip, C. B.: Comments on the classification of the order *Rickettsiales*, *Can. J. Microbiol.*, 2:261, 1956.

Pijper, A., C. G. Crocker, and N. Savage: Sarcinae: Motility, kind of flagella, and specific agglutination, *J. Bact.*, 69:151, 1955.

Pine, L., and A. Howell, Jr., Comparison of physiological and biochemical characters of *Actinomyces* spp. with those of *Lactobacillus bifidus*, *J. Gen. Microbiol.*, 15:428, 1956.

Smith, N. R., R. E. Gordon, and F. E. Clark: Aerobic sporeforming bacteria, U.S. Department of Agriculture Monograph 16, 1952.

Wetmore, P. W., and W. S. Gochenour, Jr.: Comparative studies of the genus *Malleomyces* and selected *Pseudomonas* species, *J. Bact.*, 72:79, 1956.

Winogradsky, S.: Sur la classification des bactéries, *Ann. Inst. Pasteur*, 82:125, 1952.

CHAPTER 16

Bacterial Genetics[1]

During an early period of bacteriology, microorganisms were assumed to be capable of an almost infinite variety of morphological and physiological changes. Some of the proponents of this concept asserted that only one (or a few) species of bacteria existed and that the diverse morphological forms present in natural material were merely different developmental stages of this basic organism. These morphological changes were thought to be induced in an orderly manner by progressive alterations in the growth medium or by other environmental factors. It is now known that these descriptions of the supposed changes in the morphology of the "organism" under study were actually a series of observations on a mixed culture in which, as a response to the selectively changing growth conditions, first one and then another of the species originally present became the dominant member of the population. The objections to the doctrine of pleomorphism, as this concept was called, were pithily summarized by Brefeld, the German mycologist, who said that unless one works with pure culture, *"da kommt nur Unsinn und Penicillium glaucum heraus."* [2]

The doctrine of pleomorphism, or unlimited morphological variation, was completely discredited after the development of simple pure culture techniques by Robert Koch. In its place the concept of monomorphism was adopted, according to which each bacterium has an absolutely fixed constancy of form and function. Further experience revealed, however, that even when using rigidly controlled pure culture techniques, a certain amount of variation always developed among the bacteria of a given culture. Since most of the early bacteriological work was concentrated on the organisms responsible for diseases in man and animals, it was with this group that the variations were first noted. Upon isolation and repeated subculture of many pathogens, it was found that distinct changes in colonial morphology, antigenicity, and virulence often occurred. These

---

[1] This chapter was written by Dr. W. R. Romig, Department of Bacteriology, University of California, Los Angeles, Calif. The author is greatly indebted to Dr. Romig for his kindness in preparing this material for publication.

[2] "Only nonsense and *Penicillium glaucum* [a common air-borne contaminant] will come of it."

changes could frequently be reversed by appropriate techniques, but under ordinary conditions were quite stable. This phenomenon of reversible variation has been designated *dissociation* and was interpreted to be a natural life cycle analogous to those of some protozoan parasites; or it was thought to be due to a gradual adaptation of the culture to the changed environment within the culture tube.

While it is now accepted that bacteria have definite mechanisms for the transmission of their hereditary traits not greatly different from other living things, the fact has been accepted by most bacteriologists only very recently. This reluctance to assign a genetic basis to the variations which demonstrably occur in bacterial cultures may be attributed to several factors.

Until Robinow published his beautiful pictures of bacterial nuclei (1944), most bacteriologists were of the opinion that bacteria possessed none of the typical structures usually associated with the transmission of genetic information; and even today considerable doubt exists among bacterial cytologists concerning the true nature of the nuclear organization in these organisms (see Knaysi, 1951; and Robinow, 1956). Another barrier to the ready acceptance of a belief in the hereditary origin of bacterial variation was the fact that mutations in bacteria are almost impossible to detect in single cells. One reason for this difficulty is that mutations occur extremely infrequently (about 1 for every 10 million cell divisions), and another is that bacteria lack the many morphological features which facilitate the detection of mutants in higher plants and animals.

For the above reasons there was a tendency to regard all bacterial variation as adaptive responses, which under many conditions were hereditarily transmitted. It is now known that bacterial variations can result from either environmentally induced modifications or from hereditary alterations in the individual cells of a culture. The differences between these two types of variation are typified in the case of pigment production in *Serratia marcescens* discussed below.

PHYSIOLOGICAL AND GENETIC MODIFICATIONS

Pigment production in *Serratia marcescens* is inhibited by incubation at body temperatures, but when the incubation temperature is lowered, normal pigmentation once more appears. Such environmentally induced changes are called *phenotypic modifications* and characteristically occur uniformly in all cells of a given population. Phenotypic modifications differ from *genotypic* changes chiefly in the fact that they simultaneously affect most of the cells in a given culture and they are *not* inheritable. Thus even when pigmentation in *Serratia* is inhibited for many generations by continued high-temperature incubation, all of the cells in the culture will promptly revert to the pigmented condition when the temperature is lowered. In contrast to the transient nature of phenotypic modifications, changes in the genotype of a cell are much more stable and *are* inherited. The *genotype* may be defined as the sum total of all the heritable cell characteristics, and sudden changes in the genotype are called *mutations*. Bunting (1946) has shown that mutations to the nonpigmented condition occur at fairly high rates (about 1 per 10,000 cell divisions) in normally pigmented *Serratia* and that these colorless mutants and their progeny have completely lost the ability to produce pigment, regardless of the incubation temperature or other environmental factors.

Induced Enzymes. The presence of inducible enzyme systems has been shown to cause some of the variations observed in certain bacterial cultures, and their formation and function in *Escherichia coli* have been analyzed in detail (Cohn, 1957; Spiegelman, 1957). An *inducible enzyme* is one which the cell can synthesize in quantity only when its substrate (or a chemically related compound) is present in the environment. Beta-galactosidase, which hydrolyzes lactose to its constituent monosaccharides, glucose and galactose, is an example of an inducible enzyme found in many bacteria. When genotypically lactose-positive (lac$^+$) *E. coli* are grown in media devoid of lactose, β-galactosidase cannot be detected within the cells, and such cultures may be regarded as phenotypically lactose-negative (lac$^-$). However, if lactose is substituted for glucose, the bacteria quickly produce large quantities of the enzyme and can now utilize lactose as their sole carbon source. It should be emphasized that the lactose has in no way altered the genotype of these bacteria. They were all genotypically capable of utilizing lactose, but the enzyme necessary for its utilization is produced only after stimulation by the specific substrate. In this case only the potential for the utilization of lactose is inherited, for when lactose is removed from the environment, the cells rapidly lose the β-galactosidase and revert to a phenotypically lac$^-$ population.

As in the case of pigment production in *Serratia* discussed above, mutations can occasionally occur which alter the genotype of the lac$^+$ cells. In this event, the hereditary potential for β-galactosidase production is lost, and these *fermentation mutants* and their progeny are no longer capable of utilizing lactose, regardless of its presence or absence in the growth medium.

At this point it should be noted that mutations can usually occur in both directions and that cells which have lost the hereditary potential for producing a given enzyme may later mutate again to regain this potential. These mutational changes can be differentiated from phenotypic changes because they occur only under conditions of active multiplication, and even then much more rarely than the latter.

THE MECHANISM OF INHERITANCE

The science of genetics is based primarily on results obtained from breeding experiments with organisms of differing genotypes. It was from a study of the segregation of characters transmitted during sexual reproduction that the concept of the gene as the basic unit of inheritance occupying a definite position on the chromosome was obtained. Although successful breeding experiments have become possible in bacteria only recently, microorganisms other than bacteria have been used as tools for genetic research ever since the pioneering work on the mechanism of inheritance in the bread mold *Neurospora crassa* was performed by Beadle and Tatum (Beadle, 1945).

Neurospora can grow in a minimal medium consisting of a few inorganic salts, a suitable carbon source, and biotin. From these simple compounds it is able to synthesize all of the vitamins, proteins, and other myriad cell constituents necessary for continued growth and division. Following suitable mutagenic treatment, however, strains could be isolated which no longer grew unless specific growth factors, such as preformed amino acids or vitamins, were added to the medium. These strains were shown to be nutritionally deficient mutants of the original strain, and by suitable breeding experiments they were shown to differ from the original at a single gene locus.

From these and similar data, Beadle and Tatum concluded that each gene which the cell inherits functions by controlling in some manner the specificity of a particular enzyme. According to their interpretation, commonly called the "one-gene-one-enzyme" theory, a mutant organism is one in which the ability to form a particular enzyme has been lost because the gene controlling its production has been destroyed or altered in some manner.

Chemical Nature of the Genetic Material. It is now widely believed, although not rigidly proved, that the genetic information which a parent cell transmits to its progeny is contained in the deoxyribonucleic acid (DNA) molecules found in the chromosomes of its nucleus. It seems likely that the hereditary determinants, or genes, are composed of DNA, and for this reason it has been subjected to intensive investigation in recent years (Watson and Crick, 1953; Chargaff, 1955; Wilkins, 1956).

Many of the known chemical and physical data on DNA were incorporated into a model of the molecular structure of this compound by Watson and Crick. One of the main virtues of their model is that it immediately suggested how DNA might produce an exact copy of itself— a prime requisite for a substance assigned the role of the bearer of genetic specificity. According to their model (Fig. 178), DNA consists of two long chains of phosphate and deoxyribose that are connected by their purine and pyrimidine bases. These two chains are wound around each other in a helical fashion and are formed so that at any given point along the helix, the chemical structures of the two chains are exactly complementary to each other. Preceding cell division, the chains separate and each serves as a template for the synthesis of a new complementary chain,

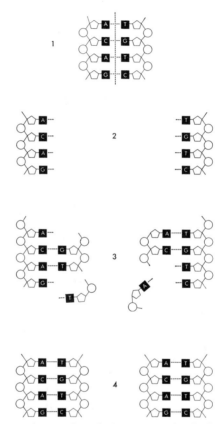

FIG. 178. Replication mechanism by which DNA might duplicate itself. A helix of two DNA chains unwinds and separates (1). Two complementary chains of DNA (2) within the cell begin to attach DNA precursor units floating loosely (3). When the proper bases are joined, two new helixes will build up (4). Letters represent the bases. (*Courtesy of F. H. C. Crick.*)

thus forming two helices, each of which is exactly like the original. Each daughter cell then receives one of these molecules of DNA in which the genetic information of the original cell is incorporated.

It is assumed that the key to the specificity of DNA lies in the order of occurrence of the purine and pyrimidine bases along the helix, so that each chain acts as a template controlling the synthesis of specific enzymes unique to that particular cell. In this context, the purine and pyrimidine bases may be thought of as a sort of genetic pattern analogous to the dots and dashes in the Morse code.

Mutations, or sudden heritable changes, are thought to result when the pattern contained in the DNA molecule is changed. According to the template hypothesis, a change in the order of the purine and pyrimidine bases would result in a loss of enzyme activity, and the progeny bearing the changed pattern would thus perpetuate the mutation.

Factors Affecting Mutation Rates. The cell machinery responsible for replication of DNA is evidently extremely efficient, for under ordinary conditions, spontaneous mutations occur at very low rates. The mutation rate can be greatly increased over the spontaneous level, however, and in general, the treatments which accomplish this increase are also effective in raising the mutation rate in other biological material.

As yet there is no unifying principle to explain the mechanism whereby the many known chemical and physical mutagens exert their mutagenic effect, but it is logical to infer that they primarily affect the chromosomal DNA or the cellular machinery responsible for its manufacture. Agents which have proved effective mutagens include ultraviolet light, X rays and other ionizing radiations, visible light in conjunction with certain dyes, carcinogenic chemicals such as nitrogen and sulfur mustards, various peroxides and epoxides, ultraviolet irradiated media, and purine and pyrimidine analogues. Bacteria have proved quite useful for screening various compounds or treatments for possible mutagenic activity, partly because large populations of them are easily obtained, and also because with these organisms, the problem of chemical diffusion is greatly minimized.

For more information see Zamenhof (1959), Matney et al. (1959), Iyer and Szybalski (1958).

THE MUTATIONAL ORIGIN OF BACTERIAL RESISTANCE

The mode of acquisition of resistance by sensitive bacteria has both practical and theoretical interest and has long been a subject for intensive investigation and heated controversy. The phenomenon of acquired resistance by bacteria was recognized by Ehrlich soon after his discovery of successful chemotherapeutic drugs, but the mechanisms whereby resistance to various toxic agents is acquired were discovered only recently. The experiments which first proved the true nature of this phenomenon were performed by Luria and Delbrück (1943), and are generally conceded to have formed the basis for modern work in the field of bacterial genetics. For this reason their approach will be discussed in some detail.

At the time Luria and Delbrück performed their experiments, two explanations concerning the nature of acquired drug resistance were prevalent. According to one of these, the *direct adaptation* theory, sensitive bacteria become resistant as a result of an interaction between the toxic agent and the sensitive population. According to this theory, then, resistance occurs as a direct adaptive response of the bacteria that is induced by contact with the toxic agent; the theory is identical with the Lamarckian interpretation, which holds that changes in environment cause changes in structure and that acquired characters are transmitted to the new cells.

As an alternative explanation, the *spontaneous mutation* theory suggested that undirected spontaneous mutations occur at a constant rate during normal growth of all bacterial cultures. According to this view, some of these mutations are such that the cells receiving them are endowed with resistance to one or another of a variety of toxic agents. Such cells become resistant in the absence of the agent, and the addition of one of these agents to the medium merely serves as a selective force by eliminating the sensitive parents from the culture.

Unfortunately, direct experimental tests were not available for discriminating between these two conflicting hypotheses. Spontaneous mutations occur at such low frequencies—on the order of 1 per 10 million cell divisions—that it is impossible to isolate directly and test a suspected resistant mutant from a normally growing culture. The only method for detecting the presence of a few resistant cells in a predominantly sensitive population consisted of placing the cell mixture in a growth medium containing the toxic agent. The limitations imposed by this method resulted in a paradoxical situation in which the postulated mutants could be detected only if the agent was added, while by the other hypothesis, addition of the agent evoked resistance by an adaptive process!

The Fluctuation Test. This seeming paradox was resolved by an ingenious experiment called the fluctuation test that may be performed in the following manner:

A young bacterial suspension containing about 500 *E. coli* per milliliter is divided into two cultures, A and B, of 10 ml. each. Culture A is then further subdivided into a series of 50 tubes, each containing 0.2 ml. Both cultures are incubated until a predetermined population density is attained. Under these conditions, the cell concentration in the two cultures will be approximately equal. The number of streptomycin-resistant colonies which develop when the contents of each of the small tubes are poured onto the surface of streptomycin-containing agar plates is then compared with the number which develop when a similar series of 0.2-ml. samples from culture B are pipetted onto the surface of streptomycin-containing agar (Fig. 179).

Luria and Delbrück reasoned that if bacterial resistance developed by direct adaptation to the streptomycin, there should be no significant differences in the numbers of resistant colonies on any of the plates derived from the two cultures. By this theory it should make no difference whether the cultures were incubated in a series of separate tubes or were all grown together in one large tube, since they are all presumed to be sensitive until brought into contact with streptomycin.

If, on the other hand, streptomycin resistance resulted from spontaneous mutations during growth in streptomycin-free medium, there should be a large fluctuation between the numbers of resistant colonies which developed from each of the 50 small tubes. This fluctuation in the numbers of resistant bacteria in a series of parallel cultures is a consequence of the randomness of the occurrence of spontaneous mutations. If the mutation to resistance occurred early during cultural growth, the resistant mutant would pass through a large number of cell divisions, and there would be many resistant bacteria present at the time of testing. If the mutation to resistance occurred just prior to the time the cells were

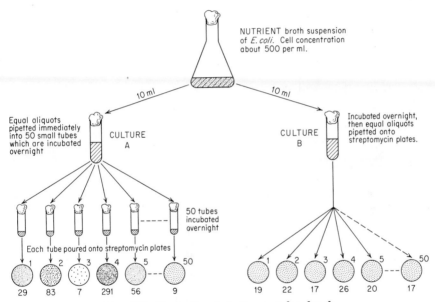

FIG. 179. Fluctuation test. See text for details.

added to streptomycin, only one resistant colony should appear on the plate.

By either hypothesis, the plates derived from the similar series of samples all taken from the same container (culture B) should contain the same number of colonies.

The results obtained from the fluctuation test unequivocally support the spontaneous mutation theory. A large variance was observed in the numbers of resistant colonies derived from the series of small tubes, while on the plates all taken from the single large culture, B, the variance was about equal to the mean and was no larger than would be expected from ordinary pipetting errors.

Indirect Selection. Several other experimental methods have since been devised which more directly support the concept of the spontaneous origin of bacterial resistance. The most unambiguous of these is the method of indirect selection by replica plating developed by the Lederbergs (1952). By this procedure, samples from all of the colonies on a plate may be transferred simultaneously to another plate by means of a velveteen-covered stamp pad. The outstanding advantage of this method is that it allows the spatial relationships between the colonies on the "master" plate and the "copy" to be maintained (Fig. 180).

The replica plating technique was used to verify the spontaneous origin of bacterial resistance in the following manner: Several million streptomycin-sensitive bacteria were spread onto the surface of a strepto-

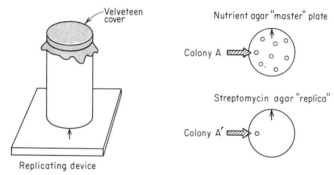

Fig. 180. Replica plating. Colonies on the nutrient agar plate are pressed onto the velveteen stamp pad, and the adhering bacteria are then transferred to a sterile streptomycin agar plate. After incubation, colony A on the nutrient agar plate corresponding to colony A' on the streptomycin plate is located by superimposing the plates over one another. Colony A on nutrient agar may be picked and proved to be resistant to the drug, even though it has never come into direct contact with it. See text for further detail.

mycin-free agar plate and incubated a few hours to allow microcolonies consisting of the descendants of the original cells to be formed. The sterile velveteen stamp was then pressed onto the plate containing these microcolonies so that a few of the bacteria from each of them adhered to the fibers. Next the pad was pressed against the surface of a streptomycin-containing plate, and the bacteria transferred to it were incubated until resistant colonies appeared. These colonies were then superimposed over the original plate, and the bacterial growth in the area corresponding to the resistant colonies was picked into fresh nutrient broth. If this step is carefully performed, there will be almost a hundredfold increase in the proportion of resistant mutants after incubation of this fresh culture.

Following overnight incubation of this new culture, diluted aliquots of it were spread onto the surface of fresh drug-free agar plates, and the same procedure of incubation and replication was repeated as in the previous step. This time more resistant colonies were found on the drug-containing plates than in the first cycle. After one or two more cycles of enrichment, a colony was located on the plain agar plate which exactly corresponded to a colony on the drug-containing replica. The colony on the plain agar was picked and proved to consist entirely of resistant cells. The important point in this procedure is that the resistant colony on the plain agar arose without ever coming directly into contact with the streptomycin, so the drug could not possibly have interacted with it to induce resistance.

As a result of these and similar experiments (Demerec, 1948; Newcombe, 1949; Cavalli-Sforza, 1957), it is now generally held that mutation followed by selection is the main source of variation found among bacteria of the same species. For a discussion of the opposing viewpoint, however, see Dean and Hinshelwood (1957).

Therapeutic Significance of Acquired Resistance. With the advent of widespread, and often ill-advised, antibiotic therapy, the study of mutants resistant to these compounds has assumed great importance. It has been found that organisms which are ordinarily sensitive to any given antibiotic may quickly form resistant mutants completely refractory to the inhibitory action of these substances. Fortunately, it has been found that a mutation to resistance to one antibiotic does not necessarily confer resistance to other antibiotics. Therefore, if two antibiotics are applied simultaneously, the chance that a given organism will become resistant to both of them is exceedingly small. For this reason, dual antibiotic therapy is often preferred to treatment with any single antibiotic.

It has also been shown that resistance to most antibiotics arises as a series of discrete steps, each mutational step conferring a higher degree of resistance to the organism than the one preceding it. It is therefore recommended that these drugs be administered at the highest tolerated level to minimize the chances of selecting mutants resistant to the lower levels of the antibiotic, which may then mutate to progressively more resistant states as antibiotic therapy is continued.

For more information see Bartlett and Hinshelwood (1959) and Braun (1953).

Mutants with Altered Colonial Morphology. Variation in colonial morphology is one of the most common modifications noted in bacterial populations, and the so-called "smooth" to "rough" change is the type most frequently encountered. Smooth colonies are formed by bacteria which produce large amounts of polysaccharide, and it is this material that gives the colonies of these organisms a smooth, glossy appearance when viewed under ordinary conditions. Upon repeated subculture, however, these bacteria may spontaneously lose the ability to produce their polysaccharide capsules, and subsequently their colonies assume a dull, granu-

lar, rough appearance. This type of variation has been of great interest
to bacteriologists because it occurs so readily, and also because other
characters such as virulence, antigenicity, and phage resistance may be
correlated with it (Fig. 181).

In addition to changes in colonial morphology reflected by variations
in polysaccharide production, it has been shown that a change in the

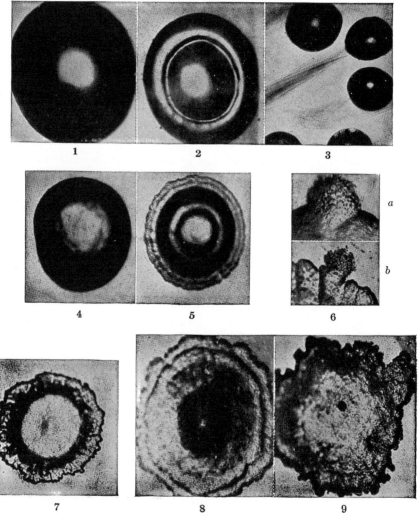

Fig. 181. *Streptococcus hemolyticus.* 1. *M* colony, 18 hr., 37°C.; 2, well-marked
S—M variation, 18 hrs., 37°C.; 3, matt colonies, 18 hrs., 37°C.; 4, *S* colony, 2 days,
37°C.; 5, early *SR* colony, 4 days, 37°C.; 6, *R* variation at margins of *SR* colonies,
6 days, 37°C.; 7, *SR* colony approaching pure *R*, 3 days, 37°C.; 8, *R* colony (possibly
some *SR* elements at center), 3 days, 37°C.; 9, *R* colony, 8 days, 37°C. (*After Dawson,
Hobby, and Olmstead.*)

mode of cell division has a profound effect on the type of colony which bacteria produce. Bisset (1950) has shown that cells comprising smooth colonies divide completely so that their colonies are made up of single, isolated cells. On the other hand, he has shown that some bacteria fail to divide completely, thus forming cell chains of varying lengths. These bacteria form colonies that have a dull, rough appearance.

The factors responsible for changes in colonial morphology are not completely understood at the present time. In many instances they can be shown to be due to mutants which occur spontaneously in the original culture and which become established because they are better fitted than their parent bacteria to grow in the given environment. In addition, certain physiological factors such as temperature, pH, and nutrition may have a profound effect on colonial morphology.

Several kinds of colonial variation other than the smooth (S) and rough (R) types discussed above have been reported. Among these are mucoid (M), G, and L colonies.

Mucoid colonies are formed by bacteria which produce unusually large amounts of capsular material. When growing in liquid medium they frequently produce a stringy mucous material, and if on agar medium, they tend to string out when touched with an inoculating needle. M-type colonies may revert to either S or R colonies upon continued cultivation on laboratory medium.

G-type colonies have been reported for many species of bacteria and may be characterized as follows: Colonies are translucent, do not produce pigment, and vary in size from 0.02 to 1 mm. Stained specimens have revealed microorganisms which were described as normal and uniform, or irregular and small. The most controversial property of G organisms, according to Wise and Spink (1954), is their reported ability to pass through bacteriological filters. They have been reported by some to possess this ability (Hadley, Delves, and Klimek, 1931), but others have not been able to confirm the filterability of these forms.

L-type colonies were first reported in *Streptobacillus moniliformis* (see Dienes and Weinberger, 1951; Tulasne, 1953; Minck, 1955; and Sincovics, 1956, for reviews) and have since been found in many different genera. L-type colonies are characterized, according to Medill and Hutchinson (1953), by a dense center imbedded in the agar and a periphery on the surface of the medium. They contain elements which are spherical in shape and vary in diameter from 0.2 to 7 μ or more. They characteristically appear in normal cultures as a result of deleterious cultural conditions, such as by the addition of penicillin to the medium. These forms have also been reported to possess a filterable stage, but these observations have not been substantiated.

Recent investigations on L forms indicate that they may result from bacteria in which the cell-wall synthesis has been impaired either by deleterious treatment or by mutation. Lederberg and St. Clair (1958) showed that when *E. coli* is grown in the presence of sublethal quantities of penicillin, spherical "protoplasts" are formed which have defective cell walls. They also demonstrated that similar protoplasts develop from mutants which have a genetic block preventing normal synthesis of cell-wall material. These observations strongly suggest that L forms occur under natural conditions as a result of stable mutations which impair cell-wall synthesis.

Nutritional Mutants. Bacterial mutants with inherited nutritional deficiencies similar to those studied by Beadle and Tatum in *Neurospora* are easily isolated and have proved equally valuable for biochemical and genetic studies. As with the *Neurospora* mutants, these nutritional mutants cannot grow unless specific growth factors such as vitamins or amino acids are added to the minimal medium suitable for growth of their parents. These nutritional deficiencies are caused by the mutation of a gene controlling the production of a key enzyme in the biosynthesis of a given growth factor.

By isolating many mutants which require the same compound for growth, it is usually possible to obtain some which are blocked at different points in the biosynthetic pathway of this compound. By judicious analysis of these mutant organisms, it is then possible to determine the mechanism of the synthesis of this compound in normal bacteria.

The usefulness of the technique of mutant analysis for determining biosynthetic pathways was greatly facilitated by the simple methods developed for the isolation of nutritional mutants. In most cases the number of mutants in a nutritionally independent population is increased by treating the bacteria with a mutagenic agent such as ultraviolet light. The numerically superior nutritionally independent parents are then eliminated from the culture by the penicillin method, developed independently by Lederberg and Zinder (1948) and B. Davis (1948). This technique depends upon the fact that penicillin exerts its bactericidal effect only against growing cells, so that when it is added to a mixture of dependent and independent organisms in minimal medium, since only the latter can grow in unsupplemented medium, they will be killed and the mutants will remain unharmed.

For further details on the use of nutritional mutants in biochemical studies see Wagner and Mitchell (1955), Davis (1955), Adelberg (1953).

Nutritional deficiencies have also been extensively used by the bacterial geneticist as specific markers in various genetic studies. The rate at which these nutritionally dependent organisms back-mutate to the nutritionally independent state of their parents is fairly stable and is useful for determining mutation rates under various conditions. This back-mutation rate is greatly increased by various mutagenic treatments and has been used for screening the effectiveness of many mutagens.

The back-mutation rate of any single nutritional mutation is usually quite low, in the neighborhood of 1×10^{-8} per bacterial division. If two of these mutations are carried by the same cell, the chance that both will mutate to the normal condition simultaneously is the product of their separate probabilities, or about 1×10^{-16}, an almost vanishingly low probability. For certain genetic studies, mutants with two separate nutritional deficiencies may be obtained, so that the probability of back mutation to complete nutritional independence is almost nonexistent. The use of these polyauxotrophs is discussed more fully in the section on bacterial recombination.

Mutations Which Affect Virulence. Virulence is defined as the capacity of an organism to produce disease, but is understood to depend not only on properties inherent in the organism, but also on the host defense mechanisms, so that it is not possible to measure virulence without considering the state of the host. At the risk of oversimplification, however, the following discussion will be confined solely to the bacterial properties influencing this relationship.

The ability of a given pathogen to produce capsular material is one of the more obvious properties influencing its degree of virulence. Freshly isolated pathogens are often thickly encapsulated, but upon continued cultivation in vitro lose the ability to form capsules. These nonencapsulated mutants are usually much less virulent than the original isolates. It is generally assumed that the capsule increases virulence by protecting the organism from the macrophages of the host, and possibly from certain of the circulating antibodies and antibacterial drugs.

Some bacteria are virulent solely because of the toxins that they produce. In these organisms, mutations affecting the type or quantity of toxin produced have profound effects on their degree of virulence.

GENETIC EXCHANGE IN BACTERIA

Three modes of genetic exchange are presently recognized in bacteria. In the first of these, *bacterial transformation,* the genetic information is carried from one cell to another by "naked" soluble DNA. Phage acts as the carrier of genetic information from the donor bacterium in which it has developed to a recipient bacterium susceptible to it in *transduction.* In *bacterial recombination,* conjugation occurs between two cells with exchange of nuclear material. These three phenomena are discussed in the order of their discovery.

Bacterial Transformation. Bacterial transformation refers to the hereditary alteration in the properties of one bacterium mediated by soluble DNA obtained from a different bacterium. The phenomenon of transformation was discovered by Griffith (1928) in *Diplococcus pneumoniae,* and has since been reported in several genera (Fig. 182).

Virulent pneumococci characteristically produce appreciable quantities of polysaccharide capsular material, and consequently form smooth, glistening colonies on artificial medium. The kind of polysaccharide which they produce is highly specific to a given strain, and on the basis of its antigenicity, over seventy-five different pneumococci may be recognized. After repeated subculture on laboratory medium, the smooth organisms may lose the ability to form capsular material, and then their colonies assume a rough, granular appearance. These rough strains are usually avirulent and cannot be typed serologically. This change from smooth to rough is now known to be due to the formation of spontaneous non-

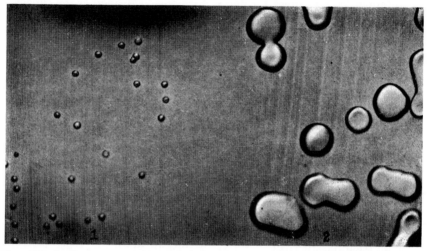

Fig. 182. 1, Pneumococcus Type II (R) colonies; 2, pneumococcus Type II (R) variant grown on agar medium with the addition of active transforming principle isolated from Type III pneumococci. The smooth, glistening, mucoid colonies shown are characteristic of Type III pneumococcus and readily distinguishable from the small rough colonies of the parent R strain. (After Avery, MacLeod, and McCarty.)

encapsulated mutants which have a more favorable growth rate on artificial medium than the original isolates. While back mutations from the nonencapsulated, rough state to the smooth condition may sometimes occur, no cases of mutation from one type to another have ever been reported.

While studying a possible correlation between pneumococcal type specificity and pathogenicity, Griffith injected a mouse with a mixture containing a few living rough pneumococci derived from a Type II culture (Type II-R) and a large number of heat-killed Type III smooth cells (Type III-S). The mouse subsequently died, and living Type III-S pneumococci could be isolated from it.

This phenomenon was confirmed in other laboratories, and it was later found possible to obtain type transformation in vitro by exposing living

Type II-*R* pneumococci to cell-free extracts of the Type III-S cultures (Dawson and Sia, 1931; Alloway, 1933). These newly formed Type III-S bacteria could, in turn, be extracted to obtain more transforming principle, and it used to transform other Type II-*R* cultures into Type III-S. The transforming principle was thus shown to be capable of self-duplication because the quantities extracted from the newly transformed cells greatly exceeded the quantity used to transform them.

Avery, McLeod, and McCarty (1944) demonstrated that transforming principle consisted principally, if not exclusively, of highly polymerized DNA. Their discovery did much to focus the attention of biologists on the importance of nucleic acids, because prior to this report, most of them were of the opinion that the protein portion of the chromosomes determined genetic specificity, while the DNA acted merely as an accessory substance.

Several markers other than type specificity in pneumococci have since been shown amenable to transformation. These include transformation of fermentation and nutritional markers, and transformation from the antibiotic sensitive state to antibiotic resistance. These studies have been reviewed by Austrian (1952), Hotchkiss (1957), Ephrussi-Taylor (1957), and Ravin (1958).

For more information see Austrian et al. (1959), Fox (1959), and Ephrussi-Taylor (1959).

Bacterial Recombination. Sexual recombination in bacteria was first demonstrated by Lederberg and Tatum (1946) using polyauxotrophic mutants of *Escherichia coli* K-12. Normally *E. coli* can synthesize all of its necessary protoplasmic constituents from a simple minimal medium consisting of an inorganic nitrogen source, a few minerals, and glucose. Mutants of this organism can be obtained, however, which have lost the ability to synthesize one or more of the factors which it must have for growth. These mutants are called *auxotrophs,* while the normal cells which can still synthesize these factors are called *prototrophs.*

In order to minimize the likelihood of back mutation to prototrophy, Lederberg and Tatum obtained polyauxotrophic mutants which were deficient in the ability to synthesize several different growth factors. Each deficiency was isolated as a separate mutational event following treatment of the cells with various mutagenic agents.

In their experiments they used two of these polyauxotrophic strains whose genotypes may be represented as $A^+B^+C^-D^-$ and $A^-B^-C^+D^+$, in which the plus sign represents the ability of the organism to synthesize a given growth factor, and the minus sign denotes dependence upon an exogenous source of the factor. These bacteria were tested for the ability to recombine by first growing each culture separately in a "complete" medium to which the required growth factors, A and B in the first case, and C and D in the second case, were present. Both cultures were then washed several times, mixed together, and plated into a medium free of any growth factors (minimal medium). In this environment, only prototrophs, or organisms with the genotype $A^+B^+C^+D^+$, were able to grow, and it was found that colonies of this type were recovered at the rate of about 1 for every million auxotrophic parents in the plating mixture.

The occurrence of prototrophs under these conditions could be explained most simply by assuming that the two dependent organisms conjugated to form a fusion zygote, and that during reduction to the haploid state, portions of their chromosomes were exchanged by a process of crossing over. We can represent this cross as:

$$A^+ B^+ C^- D^- \times A^- B^- C^+ D^+$$

and the fusion zygote as:

$$A^+ B^+ C^- D^-$$
$$A^- B^- C^+ D^+$$

It may be seen that a single crossover between B and C will result in a recombinant chromosome which is prototrophic for all of the factors under consideration.

Since the prototrophs could conceivably arise by a transformation reaction similar to that found in the pneumococci, several experiments were undertaken to test this possibility. One of the most straightforward of these was performed by Bernard Davis (1950). He constructed a culture device consisting of a U tube in which the two arms were separated by a sintered-glass filter with a pore size small enough to hold back the bacteria, but which allowed free passage of the medium and any soluble cellular products that might be present. He inoculated each arm of the U tube with one of the auxotrophic mutants, and during incubation flushed the medium through the filter from one side of the tube to the other. Prototrophs were never recovered from populations placed under these conditions. The results of these and similar experiments indicated that bacterial recombination requires cell-to-cell contact and strengthened the concept that it results from a true sexual fusion.

Lederberg next designed experiments to discover if genetic factors in *E. coli* are transferred between bacteria in the same manner as in other biological material. By the use of nonselective markers, such as resistance to bacteriophage, which confer no selective advantage to bacteria growing on minimal medium, he demonstrated a linkage system in these organisms similar to those in higher plants and animals. By a linkage system, we mean two or more genes which tend to be transferred as a unit rather than randomly; it is a phenomenon occurring with genes located on the same chromosome.

Further experiments indicated that *E. coli* recombinations are controlled by a fertility factor possessed by only one of the recombining pairs. The organism possessing this factor is designated F+ and plays the part of a male in sexual recombination. The receptor strain is designated F−, and it was later shown that these "female" strains contributed more genetic information to the recombinant than the donor F+ did. Soon after the discovery of mating types, mutants of the original F+ strains were isolated which transmit their genetic information to the F− strains at a much higher rate than their parents. These mutants were called "high-frequency recombinants" (Hfr) because they recombine with the receptor F− strains at a rate some 20,000 times higher than the parent F+ strains.

The use of Hfr strains has made it possible to perform crosses on non-selective media and to test the genetic constitution of all colonies which are formed. By this means it has been shown that almost all of the combinations predicted from theory do in fact occur in the recombinants and can be isolated in pure culture. In addition, the use of these strains has made it possible to observe crosses between suitably marked Hfr and F− strains with the phase microscope. These studies have revealed that conjugation between Hfr and F− bacteria occurs soon after they are mixed together. After an hour or so the pairs separate and both exconjugants remain viable. If the progeny of both exconjugants is examined for the occurrence of recombinations, it is found that recombinants are obtained with good regularity in the progeny derived from the F− parents, but that none can be found in those derived from the Hfr strain, thus confirming the concept of a one-way transfer of genetic material from the donor organisms to the F− recipients.

Electron micrographs of the recombining strains have revealed the presence of a thin cytoplasmic bridge between strains of the opposite mating type, but do not reveal enough detail to decide the manner of transfer of genetic material through the bridge.

Some ingenious experiments by Wollman, Jacob, and Hayes (1956) at the Pasteur Institute have shed some light on the manner in which the genetic information passes from the donor strain to the recipient. They mixed Hfr and F− strains together, and at timed intervals after mixing, aliquots removed from the mixture were violently agitated in order to interrupt recombination by breaking the cytoplasmic bridge connecting conjugating pairs. The agitated suspensions were then plated onto the proper medium to determine which genes had been transferred from the Hfr to the F− bacteria prior to agitation. It was found that the genes were transferred into the F− strain in a definite order and at a fixed rate, as if the Hfr was contributing an oriented linear chromosome to the F− recipient. Agitation seemed to break the gene string, so that interruption at any given interval allowed only those genes which had already penetrated the F− organism to participate in recombination.

At the present time our concept of bacterial recombination may be summarized as follows: Upon mixing two organisms of opposite mating type, the cells rapidly collide, and the conjugating pairs form cytoplasmic bridges with each other. A linear-oriented chromosome containing genes arranged in a definite order passes from the donor bacterium into the recipient. After about an hour, the cells separate and the F⁻ bacterium, which has received part of the donor chromosome, may incorporate these genes into its genome by a process analogous to crossing over.

For more information on bacterial recombination see Anderson (1958); J. Lederberg (1957); Wollman, Jacob, and Hayes (1956); Braun (1953); and Cavalli-Sforza (1959).

Transduction. Still another type of unidirectional genetic exchange has been demonstrated in bacteria, one in which a temperate virus (bacteriophage) serves as the vector. This phenomenon, called *transduction*, was discovered by Lederberg and Zinder (1952) while investigating *Salmonella* for evidences of sexual recombination. Two different auxotrophic *Salmonella* were mixed together and were then plated into minimal medium on which only prototrophs can grow. It was found that many more prototrophs than could be accounted for on the basis of back mutation were formed under these conditions. Unlike the experience with recombining *E. coli* K-12 strains described above, when the Davis U-tube experiment was performed with these organisms, prototrophs occurred very readily in one arm of the tube. This, of course, suggested that some soluble products from a donor strain were traversing the sintered-glass filter and transforming the recipient auxotroph to prototrophy.

Further investigation of this phenomenon revealed, however, that a bacteriophage was released from one strain, a *lysogenic* culture, which carried the phage in a hereditary, latent state and only rarely released some of them into the medium. The phage, which can pass through bacterial filters, was then able to infect the other strain (the donor) and lyse it. During intracellular replication of the phage in the second organism, parts of the bacterial chromosome were adventitiously included within the phage, so that when it again traversed the glass filter, it carried back to the recipient strain part of the donor's genetic information.

The genetic information that temperate bacteriophage can transmit from one bacterium to another is quite small, usually only one gene at a time. In some cases, however, when the genes are located very close together on the bacterial chromosome, both of them are included within one phage and are transferred as a unit to the recipient bacterium.

In transduction the phage acts merely as a vector for the transmission of genetic information, the specificity of which is determined by the genotype of the host on which the phage was last grown. A slightly different phenomenon called *lysogenic conversion* has been discovered in

Corynebacterium diphtheriae. All toxigenic diphtheria organisms seem to be infected with a latent phage, and if these organisms are "cured" of their infection they are rendered nontoxigenic. In this system the ability to induce toxin production seems to be a function of the phage itself rather than to depend on the genotype of the host on which it was last grown.

For more information see Bertani (1958), Hartman (1957), Hartman and Goodgal (1959), Luria (1959), Ozeki (1959), and Yanofsky and Lennox (1959).

REFERENCES

Adelberg, E.: The use of metabolically blocked organisms for the analysis of biosynthetic problems, *Bact. Rev.*, 17:253, 1953.

Alloway, J. L.: Further observations on the use of pneumococcus extracts in effecting transformation of types in vitro, *J. Exp. Med.*, 57:265, 1933.

Anderson, T. F.: Recombination and segregation in *Escherichia coli, Cold Spring Harbor Symposia Quant. Biol.*, 23:47, 1958.

Austrian, R.: Bacterial transformation reactions, *Bact. Rev.*, 16:31, 1952.

————, H. P. Bernheimer, E. E. B. Smith, and G. T. Mills: Simultaneous production of two capsular polysaccharides by pneumococcus, *J. Exp. Med.*, 110:571, 1959.

Avery, O. T., C. M. MacLeod, and M. McCarty: Studies on the chemical nature of the substance inducing transformation of pneumococcal types. Induction of transformation by a desoxyribonucleic acid fraction isolated from pneumococcus Type III, *J. Exp. Med.*, 79:137, 1944.

Bartlett, G. W., and C. Hinshelwood: Observations on the drug resistance of bacterial recombinants, *Proc. Roy. Soc. B*, 150:318, 1959.

Beadle, G. W.: Biochemical genetics, *Chem. Rev.*, 37:15, 1945.

Bertani, G.: Lysogeny, *Adv. in Virus Research*, 5:151, 1958.

Bisset, K. A.: "The Cytology and Life-History of Bacteria," Edinburgh, Livingstone, Ltd., 1950.

Braun, W.: "Bacterial Genetics," Philadelphia, W. B. Saunders Company, 1953.

Bunting, M. I.: The inheritance of color in bacteria, with special reference to *Serratia marcescens, Cold Spring Harbor Symposia Quant. Biol.*, 11:25, 1946.

Cavalli-Sforza, L. L.: Indirect selection and origin of resistance, "Drug Resistance in Micro-organisms," edited by G. E. W. Wolstenholme and C. M. O'Conner, London, J. and A. Churchill, Ltd., 1957.

————: Recombination in bacteria. From "Recent Progress in Microbiology," Springfield, Ill., Charles C Thomas, 1959.

Chargaff, E.: Isolation and composition of the deoxypentose nucleic acids and of the corresponding nucleoproteins, "The Nucleic Acids," vol. I, pp. 307–358, New York, Academic Press, Inc., 1955.

Cohn, M.: Contributions of studies on the Beta-galactosidase of *Escherichia coli* to our understanding of enzyme synthesis, *Bact. Rev.*, 21:140, 1957.

Crick, F. H. C.: The structure of the hereditary material, *Scient. Am.*, October, 1954.

Davis, B. D.: Isolation of biochemically deficient mutants of bacteria by penicillin, *J. Am. Chem. Soc.*, 70:4267, 1948.

————: Nonfilterability of the agents of genetic recombination in *Escherichia coli, J. Bact.*, 60:507, 1950.

————: Nutritional and enzymatic studies on microbial mutants, "Perspectives and Horizons in Microbiology," edited by S. Waksman, New Brunswick, N.J., Rutgers University Press, 1955.

Dawson, M. H., and R. H. P. Sia: In vitro transformation of pneumococcal types. I. A technique for inducing transformation of pneumococcal types in vitro, *J. Exp. Med.*, 54:681, 1931.

Dean, A. C. R., and C. Hinshelwood: Aspects of the problem of drug resistance in bacteria, "Drug Resistance in Micro-organisms," edited by G. E. W. Wolstenholme and C. M. O'Conner, London, J. and A. Churchill, Ltd., 1957.

Demerec, M.: Origin of bacterial resistance to antibiotics, *J. Bact.*, 56:63, 1948.

Dienes, L., and H. J. Weinberger: The L forms of bacteria, *Bact. Rev.*, 15:245, 1951.

Ephrussi-Taylor, H.: X-ray inactivation studies on solutions of transforming DNA of pneumococcus, "Chemical Basis of Heredity," edited by W. D. McElroy and B. Glass, Baltimore, Johns Hopkins Press, 1957, pp. 299–320.

———: The mechanism of desoxyribonucleic acid-induced transformations. From "Recent Progress in Microbiology," Springfield, Ill., Charles C Thomas, 1959.

Fox, M. S.: Phenotypic expression of a genetic property introduced by deoxyribonucleate, *J. Gen. Physiol.*, 42:737, 1959.

Griffith, F.: The significance of pneumococcal types, *J. Hyg.*, 27:113, 1928.

Hadley, P., E. Delves, and J. Klimek: The filterable forms of bacteria. A filterable stage in the life history of the Shiga dysentery bacillus, *J. Infectious Diseases*, 48:1, 1931.

Hartman, P. E.: Transduction: A comparative review, "The Chemical Basis of Heredity," edited by W. D. McElroy and B. Glass, Baltimore, Johns Hopkins Press, 1957, pp. 408–467.

——— and S. H. Goodgal: Bacterial genetics (with particular reference to genetic transfer), *Ann. Rev. Microbiol.*, 13:456, 1959.

Hayes, W.: The mechanism of genetic recombination in *Escherichia coli*, *Cold Spring Harbor Symposia Quant. Biol.*, 18:75, 1953.

Hotchkiss, R. D.: Criteria for quantitative genetic transformation in bacteria, "Chemical Basis of Heredity," edited by W. D. McElroy and B. Glass, Baltimore, Johns Hopkins Press, 1957, pp 321–325.

Iyer, V. N., and W. Szybalski: The mechanism of chemical mutagenesis. I. Kinetic studies on the action of triethylene melamine (TEM) and azaserine, *Proc. Nat. Acad. Sci.*, 44:446, 1958.

Knaysi, G.: "Elements of Bacterial Cytology," Ithaca, N.Y., Comstock Publishing Associates, Inc., 1951, pp. 78–113.

Lederberg, J.: Viruses, genes and cells, *Bact. Rev.*, 21:133, 1957.

——— and E. M. Lederberg: Replica plating and indirect selection of bacterial mutants, *J. Bact.*, 63:399, 1952.

——— and J. St. Clair: Protoplasts and L-type growth of *Escherichia coli*, *J. Bact.*, 75:143, 1958.

——— and E. L. Tatum: Gene recombination in *Escherichia coli*, *Nature*, 158:558, 1946.

——— and N. Zinder: Concentration of biochemical mutants of bacteria with penicillin, *J. Am. Chem. Soc.*, 70:4267, 1948.

Luria, S. E.: Lysogeny and lysogenization—studies in infectious heredity. From "A Symposium on Molecular Biology," edited by R. E. Zirkle, University of Chicago Press, 1959.

——— and M. Delbrück: Mutations of bacteria from virus sensitivity to virus resistance, *Genetics*, 28:491, 1943.

Matney, T. S., D. M. Shankel, and O. Wyss: Delayed appearance of induced bacterial mutants, *J. Bact.*, 78:378, 1959.

Medill, M. A., and W. G. Hutchinson: The reversion of the L form of *Proteus mirabilis* into the rod form, *J. Bact.*, 68:89, 1953.

Minck, R.: Organismes du type de la péripneumonie des bovidés et formes L des bactéries, *Rev. Immunol.*, 19:86, 1955.

Newcombe, H. B.: Origin of bacterial variants, *Nature*, 164:150, 1949.

Ozeki, H.: Chromosome fragments participating in transduction in *Salmonella typhimurium*, *Genetics*, 44:457, 1959.

Ravin, A. W.: Bacterial genetics, *Ann. Rev. Microbiol.*, 12:309, 1958.

Robinow, C. F.: Cytological observations on *Bact. coli*, *Proteus vulgaris* and various aerobic spore-forming bacteria, with special reference to the nuclear structure, *J. Hyg.*, 43:413, 1944.

Robinow, C. F.: The chromatin bodies of bacteria, *Bact. Rev.*, **20**:207, 1956.

Sincovics, J.: Die Grundlagen der Virusforschung, Hungarian Academy of Sciences, Budapest, Hungary, 1956.

Spiegelman, S.: Nucleic acids and the synthesis of proteins, "The Chemical Basis of Heredity," edited by W. D. McElroy and B. Glass, Baltimore, Johns Hopkins Press, 1957, pp. 232–267.

Tulasne, R.: Le cycle L et les formes naines des bactéries, Symposium on bacterial cytology, *Sixth Intern. Congr. Microbiol.*, 144, 1953.

Wagner, R. P., and H. K. Mitchell: "Genetics and Metabolism," New York, John Wiley & Sons, Inc., 1955.

Watson, J. D., and F. H. C. Crick: The structure of DNA, *Cold Spring Harbor Symposia Quant. Biol.*, **18**:123, 1953.

Wilkins, M. H. F.: Physical studies of the molecular structure of deoxyribose nucleic acid and nucleoprotein, *Cold Spring Harbor Symposia Quant. Biol.*, **21**:75, 1956.

Wise, R. I., and W. W. Spink: The influence of antibiotics on the origin of small colonies (G variants) of *Micrococcus pyogenes* var. *aureus*, *J. Clin. Investigation*, **33**:1611, 1954.

Wollman, E. L., F. Jacob, and W. Hayes: Conjugation and genetic recombination in *Escherichia coli* K-12, *Cold Spring Harbor Symposia Quant. Biol.*, **21**:141, 1956.

Yanofsky, C., and E. S. Lennox: Transduction and recombination study of linkage relationships among the genes controlling tryptophane synthesis in *Escherichia coli*, *Virology*, **8**:425, 1959.

Zamenhof, S.: "The Chemistry of Heredity," Springfield, Ill., Charles C Thomas, 1959.

Zinder, N. D., and J. Lederberg: Genetic exchange in *Salmonella*, *J. Bact.*, **64**:679, 1952.

CHAPTER 17

Associations of Bacteria

Organisms are rarely, if ever, found growing as pure cultures in their natural habitats. Mixed cultures of two or more species is the general rule. Because of this fact, it is sometimes erroneous to conclude from laboratory studies on pure cultures the true changes that organisms produce in their natural environments.

Associations may exist between (1) different species of bacteria and (2) bacteria and other classes of organisms such as yeasts, molds, algae, protozoa, and even plants. Simple mixtures of two or more bacterial species may exist in which the organisms produce no effect on each other, but this is rare in nature.

SYMBIOSIS

In most cases growth and multiplication are more vigorous in friendly associations than in cultures of each species existing alone. Such a phenomenon is spoken of as symbiosis. This term may be defined as the living together of two or more species of organisms for mutual benefit.

Certain soil bacteria of the genus *Rhizobium* are found growing in tumors or nodules produced on the roots of plants belonging chiefly to the family Leguminosae. These organisms utilize free atmospheric nitrogen and synthesize it into organic compounds. The plants are furnished available nitrogen by the bacteria, and the bacteria derive their nutrients from the plant sap. Apparently a perfect symbiotic relationship exists (see page 648).

Many symbioses reported in the literature are misnomers in that apparently only one of the organisms in the associations is benefited. The favorable influence of an aerobe on the growth of an anaerobe may be mentioned. The aerobe reduces the oxygen tension and creates an environment suitable for the growth of the anaerobe. The anaerobe is benefited by the association, whereas the aerobe either is not affected or is harmed. This should be regarded as an example of commensalism or of antibiosis rather than of symbiosis. True examples of bacteria growing in symbiosis with other bacterial species where both are benefited by the association are rare in nature.

COMMENSALISM

An organism may be unable to grow in the presence of a certain substrate. If, however, another organism is present capable of attacking the substrate with the production of a compound or compounds utilizable by the first organism, growth will occur. Such an association is spoken of as commensalism. The term may be defined as the living together of two species, one of which is benefited by the association, whereas the other is neither benefited nor harmed.

Gale (1940) reported that *Escherichia coli* was capable of decarboxylating arginine to agmatine, and ornithine to putrescine, but was unable to hydrolyze arginine to ornithine. On the other hand, *Streptococcus faecalis* was capable of hydrolyzing arginine to ornithine but was unable to decarboxylate arginine to agmatine, or ornithine to putrescine (Fig. 183).

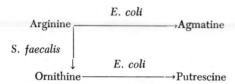

FIG. 183. Action of *E. coli* and *S. faecalis* on arginine and ornithine.

In a medium containing arginine, neither *E. coli* nor *S. faecalis* acting separately could produce putrescine. However, when both organisms were inoculated into the same medium, *S. faecalis* produced ornithine, which was then acted upon by *E. coli* to give putrescine. *E. coli* was definitely benefited by the association, while *S. faecalis* probably was not affected.

Another example of commensalism is the cultivation of an anaerobe in the presence of an aerobe. An agar plate is divided into two equal parts. An anaerobic organism is streaked over one-half of the plate, and an aerobe over the other half. The lid is then sealed to the bottom half of the dish with plasticine or similar material. The aerobe utilizes the free oxygen inside the dish and eliminates carbon dioxide. The oxygen tension is soon reduced to the point where the anaerobe can grow. The anaerobe is definitely benefited by the association, whereas the aerobe is neither benefited nor harmed. A liquid medium may also be used where a mixed culture is desired.

SYNERGISM

Synergism may be defined as the cooperative action of two agencies such that the total effect is greater than the sum of the two effects taken independently. The term is used here to indicate the joint action of two organisms on a carbohydrate medium, resulting in the production of gas that is not formed by either organism when grown separately. This type of association is believed to be of common occurrence in nature.

Sears and Putnam (1923) reported that many pairs of organisms were observed to produce gas from sugar media which was not formed by either organism in pure culture. They found that one of the organisms of the pair was capable of forming acid while the other member produced the gas. The acid former degraded the carbohydrate and released a substance that was utilized by the second organism for the production of gas. The substance attacked by the gas-forming member of the pair was not an end product of the action of the acid producer but an intermediate product of metabolism. Holman and Meekison (1926) confirmed the findings of Sears and Putnam and enlarged on their work. Their results of gas-forming pairs of organisms are given in Table 16.

TABLE 16.   BACTERIAL PAIRS THAT PRODUCE GAS IN ASSOCIATION

Carbohydrate	Organisms
Lactose	*Staphylococcus aureus* + *Salmonella schottmuelleri* *Streptococcus faecalis* + *Salmonella schottmuelleri* *Staphylococcus aureus* + *Proteus vulgaris* *Streptococcus faecalis* + *Salmonella paratyphi*
Sucrose	*Staphylococcus aureus* + *Escherichia coli* *Streptococcus faecalis* + *Escherichia coli* *Streptococcus equinus* + *Salmonella schottmuelleri* *Staphylococcus aureus* + *Salmonella paratyphi*
Mannitol	*Staphylococcus aureus* + *Proteus vulgaris* *Streptococcus pyogenes* + *Proteus vulgaris* *Shigella flexneri* + *Proteus vulgaris* *Salmonella typhosa* + *Proteus vulgaris*

A typical experiment, using sucrose broth and the organisms *Staphylococcus aureus* and *Escherichia coli*, is shown in Fig. 184.

Others who have reported synergic gas from pairs of organisms include Castellani (1926), Greer and Nyhan (1928), Graham (1932), and Atkinson (1935).

The phenomenon of synergism finds its greatest importance probably in the field of bacteriological water examinations. False positive presumptive tests in water analyses are sometimes caused by the associated activities of two or more bacterial species. The opposite effect might also be obtained, namely, the failure of a gas-producing organism to form gas when grown in association with another species.

The general tendency is for one member of a pair to inhibit or out-

Fig. 184. Bacterial synergism. Left, *Escherichia coli* grown in sucrose broth; center, *Staphylococcus aureus* grown in sucrose broth; right, a mixture of *E. coli* and *S. aureus* grown in sucrose broth with gas formation.

grow the other. This may be due to the elaboration by one organism of metabolic products detrimental to the other, to a decrease in the pH of the medium, to a higher growth rate by one of the members, etc. Therefore, the presence or absence of gas does not mean necessarily that *E. coli* is present or absent in a water sample.

ANTIBIOSIS

An organism protects itself against its enemies in various ways. It may produce metabolic waste products which change the conditions in a medium, such as pH, osmotic pressure, and surface tension, making the environment unfavorable to the growth of less tolerant organisms. It may elaborate specific toxic substances which interfere with the metabolism of other organisms to such an extent that they are either killed or prevented from multiplying. These specific toxic substances are called antibiotics, and the phenomenon antibiosis. Antibiosis may be defined as the living together of two organisms one of which is distinctly injurious to the other and which may result finally in the death of the latter.

The phenomenon of antibiosis is not a new discovery. As early as 1877 Pasteur noted that certain air-borne saprophytic organisms were capable of inhibiting the growth of the anthrax bacillus. At about the same time it was shown that pathogenic bacteria disappeared much more rapidly in untreated soil than in soil previously sterilized by heat. Since that time many observations have been recorded of mixed cultures growing on agar plates in which one organism is distinctly antagonistic to another, resulting in the appearance of clear zones around colonies of the former.

On an agar plate culture of *Staphylococcus aureus* Fleming (1929) obtained a mold contaminant which produced a green pigment and prevented bacterial growth for some distance around it. He cultivated the mold in broth and found that a filtrate of the culture had the power, even when greatly diluted, to prevent the growth of a number of pathogenic bacteria. Since the mold proved to be a species of *Penicillium,* Fleming named the antibiotic penicillin. Attempts to isolate and purify the antibiotic failed, and penicillin was almost forgotten by everyone except Fleming, who continued to experiment with cultures of the mold.

Dubos (1939) isolated a spore-bearing bacillus from the soil that was capable of destroying living Gram-positive cocci. Autolyzed cultures of the organism were capable of destroying living micrococci, pneumococci, and certain streptococci. The organism proved to be *Bacillus brevis,* a large Gram-positive spore-producing rod similar to *B. subtilis.* He named the antibiotic *gramicidin.* The addition of gramicidin to nutrient broth prevented the growth of Gram-positive cocci, but failed to retard the multiplication of Gram-negative bacteria.

In 1940 penicillin was isolated in crude form and made available for further study. The crude preparation was shown to be more effective against a number of diseases than the sulfa drugs which were enjoying widespread popularity at the time. The antibiotic was found to be so nontoxic that amounts far beyond the effective curative dose could be safely administered.

Sources of Antibiotics. Many microscopic organisms are carried by air, any one of which might show antibiotic activity in appropriate media.

The soil is perhaps the richest source of microorganisms which exhibit antibiotic action. These include principally the bacteria, actinomycetes, and molds. It has been said that a teaspoonful of soil contains hundreds of millions of bacteria, millions of actinomycetes, hundreds of thousands of mold spores, tens of thousands of protozoa, and hundreds of nematode worms. In such an environment a delicate organism like *Penicillium notatum* needs protection comparable to a tank in human warfare. One of the properties possessed by these organisms is to excrete substances that inhibit or destroy the growth of their neighbors.

Two general techniques are commonly employed in detecting and isolating organisms that give evidence of antibacterial action. The first is based on the assumption that activity against a single test species is a sufficient criterion for the selection of antagonistic organisms. In this method a sample of soil is mixed with an appropriate melted agar medium at a suitable dilution, and the mixture is poured into Petri dishes. After the agar has hardened, the plate is inverted and incubated until scattered colonies appear. The plate is then flooded with a suspension of the test organism and again incubated. The test bacteria form a solid growth on the agar plate except for clear zones of inhibition that appear around some of the colonies of soil organisms capable of producing an antibiotic active against them. The soil colonies surrounded by clear zones are transferred to agar slants and held for further study. By employing a series of soil agar plates each flooded with a different test species, the procedure may be used to isolate forms antagonistic to a wide variety of organisms.

In the second method a culture of an organism is streaked across a segment of an agar plate, then incubated until visible growth develops. Suspensions of several test organisms are then streaked at right angles to the mature culture from its edge, and the plate is again incubated until growth of all test species appears. If an antibiotic substance is formed by the organism that is being screened, the test species are inhibited at varying distances from the original culture, the lengths of the cleared spaces of inhibition being proportional to their sensitivity to the active agent diffusing from the culture producing it.

Production of Antibiotics in Soils. As has already been stated, the majority of organisms known to produce antibiotics are soil inhabitants. There has been considerable speculation whether such organisms actually produce antibiotics in their natural environment. It is generally accepted that if organisms do produce antibiotics in soil, they do so in localized environments where there is a favorable food supply such as in the rhizosphere of certain plants.

Wright (1956) inoculated *Trichoderma viride* into an acid soil containing pieces of wheat straw and demonstrated the presence of high concentrations of the antibiotic gliotoxin. In another report Wright (1955) reported the production by *Penicillium nigricans* of the antibiotic griseofulvin.

The studies indicated that organisms capable of producing antibiotics may have different requirements and that soil conditions favoring the production of one may not be suitable for others. *T. viride* produced gliotoxin in autoclaved soil even if unsupplemented, although the yield increased if the soil was organically enriched. The beneficial effect of autoclaving the soil was believed to be due to the release of nutrients and to the removal of antagonistic organisms. On the other hand, *P. nigricans* produced griseofulvin only when the soil was both autoclaved and supplemented.

Park (1956) found that fungal structures of the mold *Fusarium roseum* were destroyed by the antagonistic organism known as *Bacillus macerans*.

For more information see Jefferys (1952), Stevenson (1954, 1956*a, b*), and Stallings (1954).

Methods of Cultivation. Apparently all antibiotic-producing organisms which have been studied must have free oxygen for normal metabolic activity. Three methods of cultivation are generally employed, all based on the introduction of a plentiful supply of air into the environment: (1) shallow surface cultivation in which the organisms grow on the surface of liquid media and form a firm mat; (2) shallow submerged cultures in which the organisms are inoculated into thin layers of media, air reaching to the bottom of the cultures by diffusion; and (3) deep submerged cultures in which media are inoculated and mechanically agitated throughout the incubation period. The last procedure produces a more abundant growth in a shorter period of time and requires less space and equipment. It is the method that is employed commercially for the preparation of antibiotics.

Measuring Antibiotic Activity. Three methods are commonly employed for measuring antibiotic activity: (1) Oxford cylinder-plate method, (2) agar cup-plate method, and (3) paper-disk method.

In the Oxford cylinder-plate method, melted agar is inoculated with the organism to be antagonized and poured into a Petri dish. When firm, porous clay cylinders, open at both ends, are placed on the surface of the agar and filled with dilutions of the antibiotic. Around the cylinders will appear clear zones where growth has been prevented by diffusion of the antibiotic from the cylinders into the agar (Fig. 185). In the agar cup-plate method, a plate containing inoculated agar is prepared as before. One or more disks are cut in the agar and removed. The cups are filled with dilutions of the antibiotic, and the plate is incubated at the appropriate temperature. After incubation, clear zones will appear around the cups where growth has been prevented by diffusion of the antibiotic into the agar. In the paper-disk method, circles of filter paper about 10 mm. in diameter are used instead of porcelain cylinders. Agar is prepared as before and poured into Petri dishes. Paper disks are placed on the surface of the agar and saturated with measured volumes of antibiotic dilutions. After incubation clear zones will appear around the disks where growth has been prevented by the antibiotic (Fig. 186).

For more information see Balows and Barker (1955); Czerkinsky, Diding, and Ouchterlony (1955); Linton (1958); Streitfeld and Saslaw (1954).

Nature of Antibiotics. Antibiotics possess certain properties which distinguish them sharply from the usual chemical agents employed as antiseptics and germicides. An understanding of the nature, mode of action, and use of antibiotics is possible only after a consideration of their origin, chemical composition, physical properties, and biological effects in vitro and in vivo.

Antibiotics are produced by all classes of organisms such as bacteria, molds, yeasts, plants, and animals. The most useful antibiotics at present are produced from streptomycetes and other bacteria, and from molds. Some are secreted outside of the cells and into the surrounding environment; others are largely retained within the cells and must be separated by extraction.

Antibiotics differ widely in their physical and chemical properties. Some show close similarity, whereas others differ considerably. In support of the former may be mentioned the large number of different penicillins which are produced by incorporating certain related precursors in the culture medium.

Some organisms are capable of producing more than one antibiotic. For example, *Bacillus brevis* produces tyrothricin (a mixture of grami-

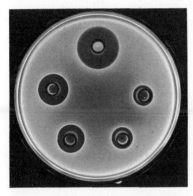 

FIG. 185. Measuring antibiotic activity by the Oxford cylinder-plate method. Melted agar was mixed with *Sarcina lutea* and poured into a Petri dish. Equal volumes of subtilin solutions ranging in concentrations from 1:1000 to 1:1,000,000 were pipetted into the cups. The largest zone was produced by the 1:1000 dilution of subtilin.

FIG. 186. Measuring antibiotic activity by various methods. Melted agar was mixed with *Sarcina lutea* and poured into a Petri dish. A 1:1000 dilution of subtilin was used in all three tests. Top, agar cupplated method; left, Oxford cylinderplate method; right, paper-disk method.

cidin and tyrocidin). *Streptomyces lavendulae* elaborates streptothricin, lavendulin, streptolin, and chloromycetin; and *Aspergillus fumigatus* forms fumigacin, gliotoxin, and fumigatin.

Certain antibiotics are produced by more than one organism. Penicillin is formed by *Penicillium notatum, P. chrysogenum,* and *Aspergillus flavus;* streptomycin is produced by *Streptomyces griseus* and *S. bikiniensis.*

The composition of the medium may or may not have an effect on the antibacterial activities of an antibiotic. Some substrates have no appreciable effect, whereas others may reduce considerably the activity of an antibiotic. For example, the addition of blood may result in the complete inactivation of an antibiotic.

Antibiotics act in various ways. Some interfere with growth and cell division of organisms; others affect the respiration of organisms; still others interfere with the utilization of essential metabolites. Antibiotics may be germicidal in high concentrations or bacteriostatic in more dilute solutions.

Different strains of an organism may vary greatly in their sensitivity to an antibiotic. Sensitive strains are generally able to develop a resistance to an antibiotic if permitted to remain in contact with sublethal concentrations of the agent. The speed at which resistance develops varies with different antibiotics. Bacteria quickly develop a resistance to streptomycin, whereas a gradual development occurs with penicillin.

Chemistry of Antibiotics of Clinical Importance. Antibiotics show great variation in their chemical structures. The structural formulas of the more important clinical antibiotics are included here.

Penicillin. This antibiotic has the following structural formula:

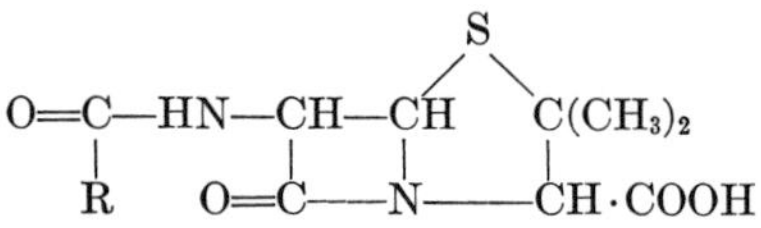

$$O{=}C{-}HN{-}CH{-}CH \overset{S}{\diagup \diagdown} C(CH_3)_2 \qquad \text{Penicillin}$$
$$\underset{R}{|} \qquad \underset{O{=}C{-}-N{-}-CH \cdot COOH}{|}$$

The mold *Penicillium notatum* produces at least six closely related penicillins, depending upon the nature of the side chains (R).

R may be any of the following:

Penicillin	Side chain R
(G) Benzyl	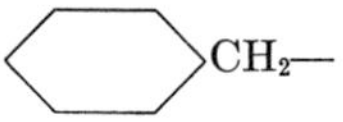 ⬡ $CH_2{-}$
(X) *p*-Hydroxybenzyl	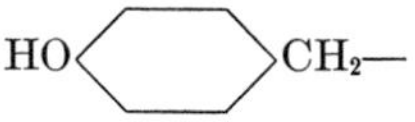 HO ⬡ $CH_2{-}$
(F) 2-Pentenyl	$CH_3 \cdot CH_2 \cdot CH{=}CH \cdot CH_2{-}$
3-Pentenyl	$CH_3 \cdot CH{=}CH \cdot CH_2 \cdot CH_2{-}$
(Dihydro F) *n*-Amyl	$CH_3 \cdot CH_2 \cdot CH_2 \cdot CH_2 \cdot CH_2{-}$
(K) *n*-Heptyl	$CH_3 \cdot CH_2 \cdot CH_2 \cdot CH_2 \cdot CH_2 \cdot CH_2 \cdot CH_2{-}$

The above penicillins are produced in media free of compounds known as precursors. Many other penicillins may be produced by incorporating various precursors in the culture medium. These precursors are capable of introducing different side chains (R) into the penicillin molecule.

All of the penicillins are strongly optically active. They are monocarboxylic acids which readily decarboxylate into biologically inactive derivatives. Benzyl penicillin (G) is the chief product produced by fermentation and the most important marketed form of the antibiotic.

Streptomycin. This antibiotic is a triacidic base having a molecular weight of 581.58.

Its structure is as follows:

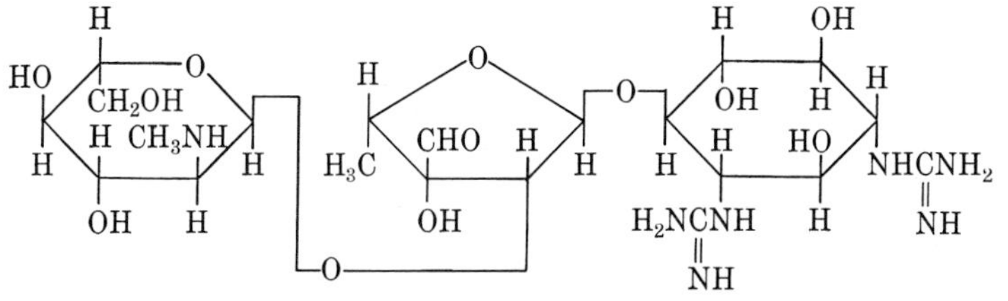

| N-Methyl-L-glucosamine | Streptose | Streptidine |

Streptomycin

Streptomycin is active against certain Gram-positive and Gram-negative bacteria, and the mycobacteria, especially *Mycobacterium tuberculosis*.

The antibiotic forms various salts of which the sulfate, the hydrochloride, the hydrochloride double salt with calcium chloride, and the phosphate are of commercial importance. The salts of streptomycin are readily soluble in water.

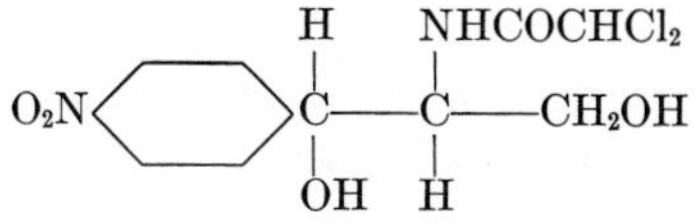

Chloramphenicol (Chloromycetin). This is the first antibiotic to be synthesized on a commercial scale. The synthetic method is competitive with the fermentation process.

Chloramphenicol has the following structure:

Chloramphenicol is effective against a wide variety of microorganisms. Such a substance is known as a broad-spectrum antibiotic. It exerts strong activity against Gram-positive and Gram-negative cocci, bacilli, spirochetes, streptomycetes, certain rickettsiae, and the larger viruses.

Tetracycline, Chlortetracycline, Oxytetracycline. These are amphoteric-crystalline antibiotics which contain a common hydronaphthacene skeleton:

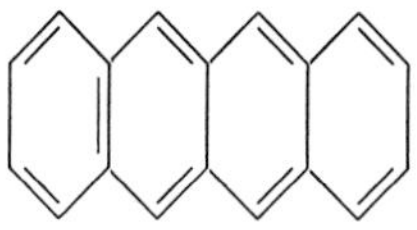

Naphthacene

The chemical structures of the tetracyclines are as follows:

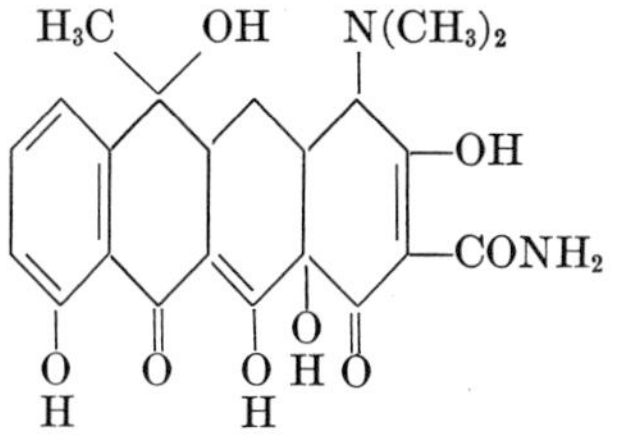

Tetracycline (Tetracyn, Achromycin)

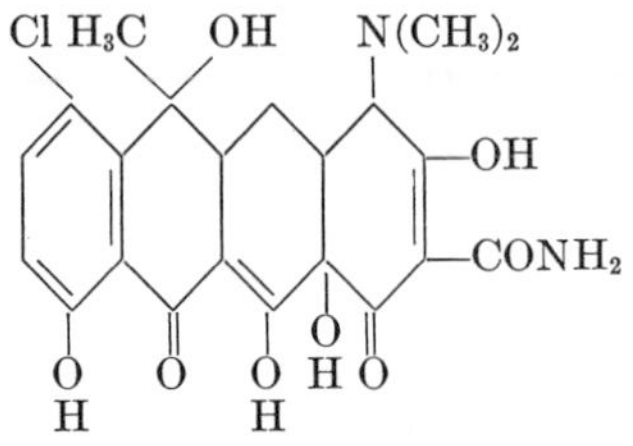

Chlortetracycline (Aureomycin)

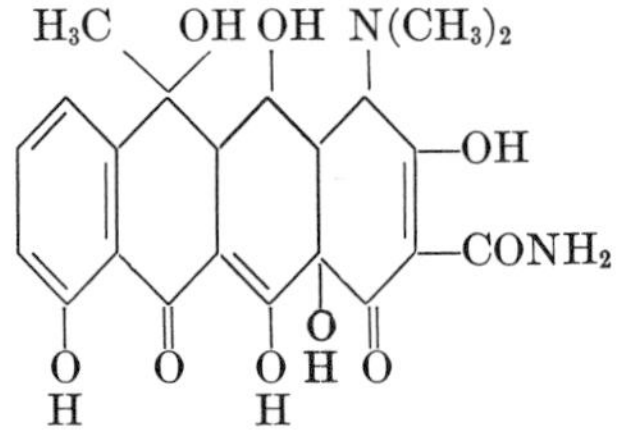

Oxytetracycline (Terramycin)

These antibiotics are only very slightly soluble in water but more soluble in dilute acid and alkali. They form salts readily with strong acids and bases. All three substances are broad-spectrum antibiotics being effective against Gram-positive and Gram-negative bacteria, rickettsiae, and the larger viruses.

Erythromycin and Carbomycin. These two antibiotics have similar antibacterial and chemical properties and were discovered about the same time. Erythromycin is also known as Ilotycin and Erythrocin; and carbomycin as Magnamycin.

Both antibiotics are active principally against Gram-positive bacteria but are also effective against a few Gram-negative organisms such as *Neisseria gonorrhoeae, Haemophilus influenzae,* certain larger viruses, and a few pathogenic protozoa.

Tyrothricin (Gramicidins and Tyrocidins). Tyrothricin has been shown to be a mixture of polypeptide-like compounds possessing antibacterial activity. The antibiotic is composed of a family of polypeptides made up of a mixture of neutral gramicidins and basic tyrocidins. Both groups are active against Gram-positive organisms; in addition, tyrocidin exhibits slight activity against Gram-negative bacteria.

Bacitracin. Bacitracin displays marked activity against Gram-positive bacteria. The antibiotic has merit as a topical agent and has proved useful in certain surgical infections.

Commercial bacitracin appears to be a complex polypeptide composed of at least five components. Acid hydrolysis of the chief component yields a mixture of L-leucine, L-isoleucine, L-cystine, L-histidine, L-lysine, D-phenylalanine, D-ornithine, D-glutamic acid, and DL-aspartic acid.

Polymyxin (Aerosporin). This antibiotic is also a polypeptide and composed of at least five components.

The various polymyxins display a selective but similar spectrum of activity against Gram-negative bacteria. The antibiotic is particularly useful against Gram-negative bacillary infections.

Neomycin. Neomycin has been shown to be a heterogeneous mixture of at least three antibiotics. It is a basic compound and readily forms salts with acids.

Neomycin is effective against many Gram-positive, Gram-negative, and acid-fast bacteria. Its antibacterial spectrum is similar to that of streptomycin. However, bacteria develop resistance to neomycin at a slower rate than to streptomycin.

Viomycin. Viomycin is effective chiefly as a tuberculostatic antibiotic. It is currently in use as an adjunct in the treatment of tuberculosis.

Viomycin is a strong base and reacts readily with acids. It is marketed chiefly as the sulfate.

For more information see Buckwalter (1954) and Regna (1955).

Movement of Antibiotics in Higher Plants. A number of investigations have been conducted on the uptake and translocation of antibiotics in higher plants.

Pramer (1953, 1954) reported that chloramphenicol and streptomycin were absorbed from nutrient solution by the root system of cucumber seedlings and translocated to the leaves. The streptomycin concentration of leaf tissue increased with time to a level above that in the nutrient solution whereas the chloramphenicol concentration remained constant at a level below that in the nutrient solution. On the other hand, the uptake and translocation of Aureomycin, neomycin, and Terramycin could not be demonstrated.

Stokes (1954) grew wheat plants in nutrient solutions containing the antibiotic griseofulvin. The concentration of griseofulvin in the guttation drops was directly related to the concentration in the nutrient solution. There was evidence of griseofulvin accumulation in the leaves, the concentration in the guttation drops being frequently higher than that in the nutrient solution. Atmospheric conditions favoring transpiration increased uptake and translocation of griseofulvin.

For more information see Crowdy et al. (1955, 1956) and Crowdy and Pramer (1955a, b).

Resistance of Organisms to Antibiotics. Bacteria are able to develop resistance to antibiotics. This is characteristic not only of antibiotics but applies to other chemotherapeutic agents as well.

Two types of resistance have been recognized clinically: natural and acquired. Resistance is natural when it occurs among species or strains which have had no previous contact with the antibiotic under consideration. Resistance is acquired when a culture of a normally sensitive species or strain contains a few resistant forms which become predominant under the influence of the antibiotic. This gives rise to strains with acquired resistance. The ability of sensitive bacteria to give rise to antibiotic-resistant forms under the influence of the drug is a demonstration of the biochemical versatility of organisms in their struggle for existence.

The development of antibiotic-resistant forms is essentially an adaptive process since it reflects the ability of organisms to survive by adjusting themselves to adverse environmental conditions.

This form of adaptation falls into two categories:

1. Genetic adaptation, in which resistant mutants arise and overgrow the sensitive population under the influence of the antibiotic. This is called the mutation-selection theory (Fig. 187A).

2. Phenotypic adaptation, in which cytoplasmic alterations, such as adaptive enzyme formation, are induced by the antibiotic, causing at least a few of the bacteria to become more resistant without affecting the genetic apparatus. The phenotypically adapted cells eventually outnumber the sensitive cells under the selective influence of the antibiotic (Fig. 187B).

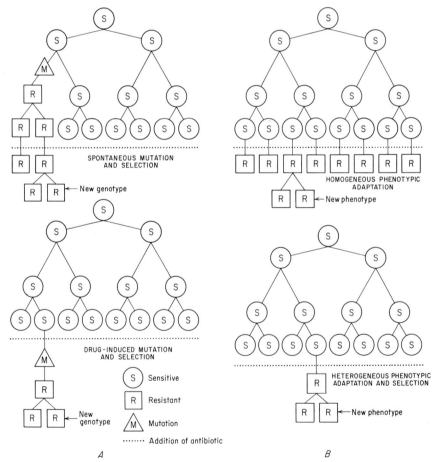

Fig. 187. Theoretical schemes for the origin of drug resistance. (*Courtesy of Eli Lilly and Company.*)

The weight of experimental evidence appears to favor the genetic adaptation concept.

Persistence of Acquired Resistance. Acquired resistance is usually reversible. However, the ease with which resistance reverts to sensitivity depends upon a number of factors such as nature of the organism, nature of the drug, degree of resistance that has been established, and whether the resistance has been acquired by genetic or phenotypic adaptation.

When resistance has been acquired through genetic adaptation, reversion to sensitivity might occur in the absence of the antibiotic as the result of overgrowth by antibiotic-sensitive mutants. Such sensitive mutants are better fitted for survival.

If the resistance is the result of physiological or phenotypic adaptation, removal of the antibiotic should eliminate the primary stimulus for maintenance of the altered phenotype, and rapid reversion to the original phenotype would be expected to occur.

For more information see Bondi (1954), Finland (1956), Florey (1956), and Lilly Research Laboratories Staff (1957).

Antiphage Antibiotics. Bacteriophages are submicroscopic agents which parasitize bacteria (see page 748).

Several antibiotics have been prepared and shown to be active against bacteriophages. Strelitz, Flon, and Asheshov (1955a) isolated from a streptomycete a colorless crystalline antibiotic which exhibited a wide range of activity against bacterial viruses. They named the compound Nybomycin. In another communication (1955b), they reported the isolation from a species of *Streptomyces* of a yellow crystalline antibiotic which also displayed antiphage activity.

For more information see Strelitz et al. (1956).

Importance of Antibiotics. The number of antibiotics is being constantly increased. At present hundreds of them have been isolated and studied. Some are useful clinically; others are not satisfactory for clinical application but are more useful for other purposes. The more important antibiotics for clinical use are listed in Table 17.

The field of antibiotics appears to offer unlimited possibilities in medicine. Powerful antibiotics, such as penicillin, have proved to be of such tremendous importance for the destruction of organisms, especially those capable of producing disease, that an ever-increasing search is going on for more and better ones. Since it is hard to believe that the best antibiotics have already been isolated, we may continue to expect startling discoveries in this field.

For more information see Florey (1951); Massart (1956); Newton (1956); Pratt and Dufrenoy (1953); Rosebury, Gale, and Taylor (1954); Umbreit (1953, 1956); Virtanen (1956); and Waksman (1956).

TABLE 17. SOME IMPORTANT ANTIBIOTICS PRODUCED BY BACTERIA AND MOLDS

Antibiotic	Produced by	Susceptible organisms	Property
Bacitracin	Strain of *Bacillus subtilis*	Principally Gram-positive bacteria	Topical use chiefly
Carbomycin	*Streptomyces halstedii*	Many Gram-positive and a few Gram-negative bacteria, certain large viruses, and some protozoa	Active in vivo
Chloramphenicol (Chloromycetin)	*Streptomyces venezuelae*	Many Gram-positive and Gram-negative bacilli and cocci, spirochetes, rickettsiae, and the larger viruses	Active in vivo
Chlortetracycline (Aureomycin)	*Streptomyces aureofaciens*	Many Gram-positive and Gram-negative bacteria, rickettsiae, the larger viruses, and some protozoa	Active in vivo
Erythromycin	*Streptomyces erythreus*	Many Gram-positive and a few Gram-negative bacteria, certain larger viruses, and some protozoa	Active in vivo
Neomycin	*Streptomyces fradiae*	Many Gram-positive, Gram-negative, and acid-fast bacteria	Active in vivo
Oxytetracycline (Terramycin)	*Streptomyces rimosus*	Many Gram-positive and Gram-negative bacteria, certain rickettsiae, and the larger viruses	Active in vivo
Penicillin	*Penicillium notatum*	Gram-positive bacilli, Gram-negative cocci, and spirochetes	Active in vivo
Polymyxin (Aerosporin)	*Bacillus polymyxa*	Principally Gram-negative bacteria	Active in vivo
Streptomycin	*Streptomyces griseus*	Gram-positive, Gram-negative, and acid-fast bacteria	Active in vivo
Subtilin	Strain of *Bacillus subtilis*	Principally Gram-positive and acid-fast bacteria	Active in vivo
Tetracycline (Tetracyn, Achromycin)	Produced from chlortetracycline chemically	Many Gram-positive and Gram-negative bacteria, and the larger viruses	Active in vivo
Tyrothricin (mixture of gramicidin and tyrocidin)	*Bacillus brevis*	Principally Gram-positive bacteria	Topical use chiefly
Viomycin (Viocin)	*Streptomyces vinaceus, S. puniceus,* and *S. floridae*	Gram-positive and Gram-negative bacteria, especially acid-fast forms	Active in vivo

REFERENCES

Atkinson, N.: Synergic gas production by bacteria, *Australian J. Exp. Biol. Med. Sci.,* 13:67, 1935.

Balows, A., and A. Barker: A comparison of multitipped and conventional disc techniques for determining in vitro antibiotic sensitivity, *Antibiotics & Chemotherapy,* 5:551, 1955.

Bondi, A., F. Pfaff, E. Free, and R. Swerlick: Public health aspects of the development of antibiotic-resistant staphylococci, *Am. J. Pub. Health,* 44:789, 1954.

Buckwalter, F. H.: Antibiotic formulations, *J. Am. Pharm. Assoc.,* 15:694, 1954.

Castellani, A.: Fermentation phenomena when different species of microorganisms are in close association, *Proc. Soc. Exp. Biol. Med.,* 23:481, 1926.

Crowdy, S. H., D. Gardner, J. F. Grove, and D. Pramer: The translocation of antibiotics in higher plants. I. Isolation of griseofulvin and chloramphenicol from plant tissue, *J. Exp. Bot.,* 6:371, 1955.

———, J. F. Grove, H. G. Hemming, and K. C. Robinson: II. The movement of griseofulvin in broad bean and tomato, *ibid.,* 7:42, 1956.

——— and D. Pramer: The occurrence of translocated antibiotics in expressed plant sap, *Ann. Bot.,* 19:79, 1955a.

——— and ———: Movement of antibiotics in higher plants, *Chem. and Ind.,* 1955b, p. 160.

Czerkinsky, G., N. Diding, and O. Ouchterlony: A new method for determination of bacterial sensitivity to chemotherapeutic agents by means of paper strips. *Scand. J. Clin. and Lab. Investigation,* 7:259, 1955.

Dubos, R. J.: Bactericidal effect of an extract of a soil bacillus on Gram-positive cocci, *Proc. Soc. Exp. Biol. Med.,* 40:311, 1939.

Finland, M.: Cross-resistance among five antibiotics, *Giornale di Microbiologia,* 2:371, 1956.

Fleming, A.: On the antibacterial action of cultures of a *Penicillium,* with special reference to their use in the isolation of *B. influenzae, Brit. J. Exp. Path.,* 10:226, 1929.

Florey, Sir H. W.: "Antibiotics," Oxford, Blackwell Scientific Publications, Ltd., 1951.

———: The medical aspects of the development of resistance to antibiotics, *Giornale di Microbiologia,* 2:361, 1956.

Gale, E. F.: The production of amines by bacteria. 3. The production of putrescine from arginine by *Bacterium coli* in symbiosis with *Streptococcus faecalis, Biochem. J.,* 34:853, 1940.

Graham, J. G.: Bacterial synergism—the formation by *B. typhosus* or *B. coli anaerogenes* from mannitol of an intermediate substance from which Morgan's bacillus produces gas, *J. Hyg.,* 32:385, 1932.

Greer, F. E., and F. V. Nyhan: The sanitary significance of lactose-fermenting bacteria not belonging to the *B. coli* group. 3. Bacterial associations in cultures containing lactose-fermenting bacteria, *J. Infectious Diseases,* 42:525, 1928.

Holman, W. L., and D. M. Meekison: Gas production by bacterial synergism, *J. Infectious Diseases,* 39:145, 1926.

Jefferys, E. G.: The stability of antibiotics in soils, *J. Gen. Microbiol.,* 7:295, 1952.

Lilly Research Laboratories Staff: Resistance of micro-organisms to antibiotics, 13:22, 1957.

Linton, A. H.: Influence of inoculum size on antibiotic assays by the agar diffusion technique with *Klebsiella pneumoniae* and streptomycin, *J. Bact.,* 76:94, 1958.

Massart, L.: Antibacterial substances acting as germination inhibitors in plant material, *Giornale di Microbiologia,* 2:33, 1956.

Newton, B. A.: The mode of action of polypeptide antibiotics, *Giornale di Microbiologia,* 2:388, 1956.

Park, D.: Effect of substrate on a microbial antagonism, with reference to soil conditions, *Trans. Brit. Mycological Soc.,* 39:239, 1956.

Pramer, D.: Observations on the uptake and translocation of five actinomycete antibiotics by cucumber seedlings, *Ann. Appl. Biol.*, **40**:617, 1953.

———: The movement of Chloramphenicol and Streptomycin in broad bean and tomato plants, *Ann. Bot.*, N.S., **18**:463, 1954.

Pratt, R., and J. Dufrenoy: "Antibiotics," Philadelphia, J. B. Lippincott Company, 1953.

Regna, P. P.: Chemistry of antibiotics of clinical importance, *Am. J. Med.*, **18**:686, 1955.

Rosebury, T., D. Gale, and D. F. Taylor: An approach to the study of interactive phenomena among microorganisms indigenous to man, *J. Bact.*, **67**:135, 1954.

Sears, H. J., and J. J. Putnam: Gas production by bacteria in symbiosis, *J. Infectious Diseases*, **32**:270, 1923.

Stallings, J. H.: Soil produced antibiotics—plant disease and insect control, *Bact. Rev.*, **18**:131, 1954.

Stevenson, I. L.: Antibiotic production by actinomycetes in soil demonstrated by morphological changes induced in *Helminthosporium sativum*, *Nature*, **174**:598, 1954.

———: Antibiotic activity of actinomycetes in soil and their controlling effects on root-rot of wheat, *J. Gen. Microbiol.*, **14**:440, 1956a.

———: Antibiotic activity of actinomycetes in soil as demonstrated by direct observation techniques, *J. Gen. Microbiol.*, **15**:372, 1956b.

Stokes, A.: Uptake and translocation of griseofulvin by wheat seedlings, *Plant and Soil*, **5**:132, 1954.

Streitfeld, M. M., and M. S. Saslaw: A strip-gradient method for in vitro assay of bacterial sensitivity to antibiotics paired in various concentration ratios, *J. Lab. Clin. Med.*, **43**:946, 1954.

Strelitz, F., H. Flon, and I. N. Asheshov: Nybomycin, a new antibiotic with antiphage and antibacterial properties, *Proc. Nat. Acad. Sci.*, **41**:620, 1955a.

———, ———, and ———: Chrysomycin: A new antibiotic substance for bacterial viruses, *J. Bact.*, **69**:280, 1955b.

———, ———, and ———: Aklavin, an antibiotic substance with antiphage activity, *J. Bact.*, **72**:90, 1956.

Umbreit, W. W.: Mechanisms of antibacterial action. *Pharmacological Rev.*, **5**:275, 1953.

———: Approaches to the mode of action of antibiotics as illustrated by Streptomycin and Cathomycin, *Giornale di Microbiologia*, **2**:398, 1956.

Virtanen, A. I.: Investigations on antimicrobial substances formed in cereals and fodder plants and their importance for the resistance of plants to pathogenic fungi, *ibid.*, **2**:15, 1956.

Waksman, S. A.: The role of antibiotics in natural processes, *ibid.*, **2**:1, 1956.

Wright, J. M.: The production of antibiotics in soil. II. Production of griseofulvin by *Penicillium nigricans*, *Ann. Appl. Biol.*, **43**:288, 1955.

———: Production of Gliotoxin in soils, *Nature*, **177**:896, 1956.

CHAPTER 18

Disinfection and Disinfectants

Various physical and chemical methods are used for the destruction of bacteria.

The common laboratory equipment employed for the killing of bacteria by heat, or their removal by filtration, was reviewed in Chap. 8. The other important physical and chemical methods are discussed here.

A number of terms are used to describe the destruction of bacteria by various processes. These are germicide, bactericide, antiseptic, disinfectant, viricide, fungicide, bacteriostatic agent, sanitizer, and sterilization.

Germicide. A germicide was originally defined as an agent that killed disease organisms. It is now defined as an agent, usually chemical, that kills bacteria (microorganisms) but not necessarily their spores.

Bactericide. A bactericide is an agent that kills both pathogenic and nonpathogenic bacteria but not necessarily their spores. In practice the term is synonymous with germicide.

Antiseptic. The meaning of this term has caused probably more confusion than any of the others. Some define it synonymously with germicide and bactericide; others apply the term to any agent that prevents further bacterial action whether it does so by killing the organisms or merely by preventing them from multiplying. The term antiseptic should be limited to any agent that arrests bacterial growth either by inhibiting their activity or by destroying them.

According to this definition, a germicide may be also an antiseptic, depending upon the strength of the solution, the period of action, and the nature of the organism. A germicide in high dilution may only inhibit the growth of bacteria rather than kill them. Also, an agent that kills in a given period of time may only inhibit growth if the exposure time is shortened. In the former case, the agent would be classed as a germicide; in the latter instance, as an antiseptic. Some organisms are less resistant to toxic agents than others. This means that a substance may be a germicide against one organism and an antiseptic against another. Doubtless, other factors are also involved.

Disinfectant. This term has been used rather loosely and defined in various ways. However, it is generally agreed that it means an agent that

471

destroys disease bacteria and other harmful organisms but not necessarily spores.

From the above definitions, it may be seen that the terms germicide, bactericide, and disinfectant have similar meanings.

Viricide. This term is applied to any agent that destroys or inactivates filterable forms known as viruses. Since viruses are of about the same order of resistance to chemical agents as bacteria, most germicides are also good viricides.

Fungicide. This may be defined as an agent, usually chemical, that destroys both pathogenic and nonpathogenic molds.

Bacteriostatic Agent. This term was coined by Churchman (1912, 1928), in connection with his investigations on dyes, to denote a condition in which bacteria were not necessarily killed but merely prevented from multiplying. He noted that in certain concentrations dyes did not kill bacteria but kept them in a state of suspended animation. Further dilution of the bacteria-dye mixture resulted in growth of the organisms. The dyes were referred to as bacteriostatic agents and the phenomenon as bacteriostasis. Germicidal agents of a nondye nature, such as mercury and silver compounds, also exhibit the same phenomenon and are referred to as bacteriostatic compounds.

Sanitizer. This may be defined as any agent that reduces the bacterial count to safe levels as may be judged by public health requirements. Sanitizers are commonly applied to inanimate objects such as eating and drinking utensils and food-handling equipment.

Sterilization. This term refers to the process of destroying all organisms present including spores. The term sterilization should always be used where reference is made to the destruction of all forms of life, including fungi, viruses, spores, etc.

DYNAMICS OF DISINFECTION

The disinfection process does not take place at once but is a gradual operation in which the number of organisms killed in unit time is greater at the beginning and becomes less and less as the exposure period is increased. If the numbers of survivors in unit volume are plotted against time, the points fall on smooth curves. If the logarithms of the numbers of bacteria surviving in unit volume are plotted against time, a straight line is obtained.

This may be shown in Fig. 188. Anthrax spores were treated with 5 per cent phenol and incubated at $33\frac{1}{3}°C$. The curved line represents the numbers of anthrax spores surviving in unit volume, and the straight line represents the logarithms of the concentration of survivors.

The disinfection process appears to follow the mass-action law and to proceed in accordance with the monomolecular equation, or a reaction of the first order, provided the disinfectant is present in large excess:

$$-\frac{dN}{dt} = KN \quad \text{or} \quad \frac{1}{t_2 - t_1} \log \frac{N_1}{N_2} = K$$

where N_1 and N_2 represent the number of surviving bacteria in unit volume after times t_1 and t_2, respectively.

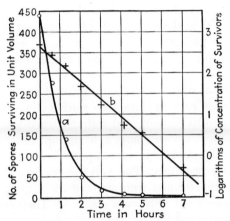

FIG. 188. Disinfection of anthrax spores with 5 per cent phenol. *a*, the number of survivors in unit volume are plotted against time; *b*, logs of concentration of survivors are plotted against time.

Importance of Logarithmic Survivor Curves. In the destruction of bacteria by various agents, the greater the number of cells present, the longer will be the time necessary for complete sterilization. This may be shown in the following example: A suspension contains 200,000 organisms per milliliter. If the bacteria are destroyed at the rate of 90 per cent per minute, the number of survivors at the end of 7 min. will be:

| 200,000 | 20,000 | 2000 | 200 | 20 | 2 | 0.2 | 0.02 |

The last figure means that 2 living bacteria remain in 100 ml. of the suspension. If instead of 200,000 the suspension contains only 200 organisms per milliliter, the time required to reduce the count to 2 bacteria per 100 ml. will be only 4 min.:

| 200 | 20 | 2 | 0.2 | 0.02 |

The relationships between bacterial numbers and the times required to produce complete sterilization are of great value in the canning and dairying industries, in bacteriology, and in surgery.

PHYSICAL AGENTS

The physical agents which have not been discussed in Chaps. 8 and 10 are included here.

Electricity. Beattie and Lewis (1920) employed a current of about 4000 volts and 2 amp. for 4 min. and reported the destruction of over 99.9 per cent of the organisms in milk.

Fabian and Graham (1933) noted the gradual destruction of *Escherichia coli* by exposure to a high-frequency current of 10 megacycles per second and an intensity of 0.8 amp. However, the application of the current for 10 hr. failed to destroy all of the organisms in a suspension. A frequency of 10 megacycles corresponds to a wave length of approximately 30 meters. Gale and Miller (1935) were unable to destroy *Staphylococcus aureus, Salmonella typhosa, Diplococcus pneumoniae,* and streptococci when cultures were exposed to ultrashort waves of 10 meters and 200 watts for 1 hr. on each of three consecutive days.

Ingram and Page (1953) subjected resting suspensions of baker's yeast, *E. coli,* tobacco mosaic virus, and a bacteriophage to high-frequency electric fields in cells which kept the temperature below 30°C., very energetic cooling being necessary. The voltage gradients used were up to 2000 volts per centimeter and were applied for aggregate periods up to 12 min., but no significant kills were observed. They concluded that the lethal effect was too small for any practical value.

Electric current has been employed for the pasteurization of milk and for the destruction of organisms in sewage, water, etc., but the results have been too unreliable to be of practical importance. Its use has been largely abandoned, preference being given to other germicidal agents.

Sonic and Supersonic Waves. Sonic waves are waves of audible frequency of about 8900 cycles per second produced by a nickel tube vibrating in an electromagnetic field and in resonance with a 2000-volt oscillating power circuit. Such waves are capable of destroying bacteria if exposed for sufficient time. Milk has been treated in this manner with a reduction of 99 per cent in the viable count after an exposure period of 40 to 60 min. Williams and Gaines (1930) employed high-frequency audible sound waves of about 8800 cycles per second and reported the destruction of cells of *Escherichia coli.* They concluded that the lethal effects of the waves were due probably to a violent agitation set up within the cell.

Shropshire (1947a, b) subjected dispersed bacteria to intense sonic energy and reported a decrease in the turbidity of the liquid. He proposed the method for the turbidimetric evaluation of bacterial disruption.

Rotman (1956) treated *E. coli* and *Azotobacter vinelandii* to sonic vibrations in a Raytheon 10-kilocycle magnetostrictive oscillator for 10 min. at a temperature below 4°C. and a pH of 6.6, and reported structural damage to the cells (Fig. 189).

Supersonic waves are waves above audible frequency, of 200,000 to 1,500,000 cycles per second, produced by connecting a piezoelectric crystal with a high-frequency oscillator. These waves have also been shown to exert a destructive effect on bacteria and other organisms.

Wood and Loomis (1927) employed sound waves of high frequency and great intensity generated by a piezoelectric oscillator of quartz operated at 50,000 volts and vibrating 300,000 times per second. They noted the fragmentation or the tearing to pieces of organisms such as *Spirogyra* and *Paramecium*. Red blood cells suspended in saline were also broken into small fragments. On the other hand, bacteria were able to survive

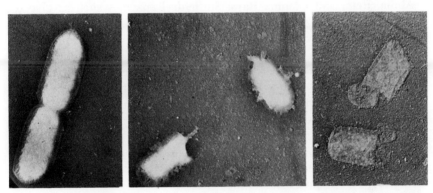

Fig. 189. *Escherichia coli.* Electron micrographs, uranium shadowed. Left, normal cells prior to sonic oscillation; center, cells after 10 min. sonic oscillation; right, same as center but with addition of phosphate buffer pH 7.2 to 1/3000 *M* final concentration. (*Courtesy of Boris Rotman.*)

treatment with high-frequency sound waves of great intensity. Harvey and Loomis (1929) found luminescent bacteria to be destroyed in 1½ hr. by supersonic energy.

Beckwith and Weaver (1936) treated a yeast and several species of bacteria to supersonic waves and reported destruction of the organisms. They concluded that the organisms were usually killed by sufficient application of supersonic radiation. The presence of protein interfered with the action of the sonic energy.

Hamre (1949) found that *Klebsiella pneumoniae* and *Saccharomyces cerevisiae* were destroyed by ultrasonic energy. On the other hand, influenza virus particles were not inactivated by such treatment. Anderson, Boggs, and Winters (1948) found certain large bacteriophages to be sensitive to ultrasonic treatment, whereas the small, compact viruses were relatively resistant to the shearing forces existing during cavitation of the liquid in which they were suspended.

Galesloot (1955) employed ultrasonic waves with a frequency exceeding 20,000 vibrations per second for the destruction of bacteria in milk. The bactericidal effects were disappointing.

Jacobs and Thornley (1954) exposed seven species of bacteria suspended in milk and in nutrient broth to ultrasonic vibrations of a frequency of 1 megacycle per second. *E. coli* was killed fairly rapidly. *Staphylococcus aureus, Streptococcus faecalis,* and other spherical bacteria were considerably more resistant than the rod forms. Under conditions which caused rapid death of *E. coli* suspended in broth, complete protection was afforded by fresh milk, gelatin, and peptone in solution.

For more information see Kinsloe, Ackerman, and Reid (1954); Marr and Cota-Robles (1957); Slade and Vetter (1956); Whitney and Russell (1951).

Alpha, Beta, and Gamma Rays. Sulfhydryl enzymes such as glycerophosphoric dehydrogenase and urease were shown by Barron and Dickman (1949) to be inactivated when dilute solutions were irradiated with small doses of alpha rays from polonium, beta rays from strontium, and gamma rays from radium. Partial reactivation of the enzymes, by addition of glutathione, was obtained after inhibition with the alpha rays. This would indicate that the ionizing radiations inhibit such enzymes by oxidation of the sulfhydryl groups (—SH) which are essential for enzyme activity.

Kempe, Graikoski, and Gillies (1954) inoculated sterilized meat with 40,000 spores of *Clostridium botulinum* and reported that 3,500,000 reps[1] for 24 hr. were required to sterilize the contents.

Morgan and Reed (1954) found that short heat-treatment prior to irradiation was more efficient in the destruction of spores of *Cl. botulinum* than irradiation alone.

For more information see Goldblith et al. (1953), Kempe (1955), Tarpley et al. (1953).

Electrons. Trump and Proctor (1951) employed electrons as a sterilizing agent.

Electrons are very small, negatively charged elementary particles that move about protons or positively charged nuclei of atoms. They are readily released by heating a tungsten filament to several thousand degrees centigrade. When such electrons are acted upon by a high electric field between two metal electrodes, they are accelerated away from the negative electrode or cathode and acquire the energy in volts which produced the field. Electrons may be accelerated to energies of 2, 3, 4 million or more volts.

The penetration of high-energy electrons depends on both the electron voltage and the density of the irradiated material. Electrons accelerated

[1] One rep unit is a dose of ionizing radiation capable of producing energy absorption of 93 ergs per gram of tissue.

to energies of 2 million volts will penetrate water effectively to a depth of about $\frac{2}{3}$ cm. The depth of penetration increases directly with voltage.

Packaged materials containing pharmaceuticals, biologicals, etc., may be effectively irradiated provided they come within the limitations of penetration of the electrons. The rays apparently produce no reduction in potency or increase in toxicity of the irradiated materials.

The effectiveness of high-energy electrons depends upon the excitation and ionization of the atoms of the organism to produce chemical changes which bring about its death.

Cathode Rays. Koh, Morehouse, and Chandler (1956) exposed representative species of non-spore-forming bacteria to cathode rays generated by a 2 million electron volt Van de Graaff accelerator. They reported that all species were susceptible to doses of 0.5 megarep[1] or less. Gram-negative bacteria were more sensitive to irradiation than Gram-positive bacteria. In a later report, Pepper, Buffa, and Chandler (1956) exposed spores to the same cathode rays and found that the resistance of moist spores was greater than frozen spores and dried spores.

X Rays. Haberman (1942) treated *Staphylococcus aureus* with both soft (>1 A.) and hard (<1 A.) X rays. Short wave lengths were more effective in killing the organism than long wave lengths of the same intensity.

Ephrati (1948) destroyed tetanus toxin and *Staphylococcus* hemolysin with X rays. Certain proteins, their split products, reducing amino acids, glutathione, and thioglycollic and ascorbic acids were found to be effective as protective agents, whereas oxidizing substances were ineffective. All observations supported the theory that the effect of X rays on tetanus toxin and *Staphylococcus* hemolysin was an indirect one, the radiation causing the formation of active oxidizing radicals which in turn destroyed the toxins by oxidation.

Barron et al. (1949) reported the destruction of a number of respiratory enzymes by small doses of X rays. These observations were interpreted as being due to oxidation of the sulfhydryl (—SH) groups of the enzymes.

Reduction in the concentration of oxygen in bacterial suspensions has been shown to result in a marked decrease in the X-ray sensitivity of *Escherichia coli*. Stapleton, Billen, and Hollaender (1952) and Burnett et al. (1952) showed that the addition of pyruvate, formate, succinate, serine, alanine, ethanol, and hydrosulfite protected the cells against the lethal action of X rays by virtue of their ability to remove oxygen from the system.

Others who have reported destructive effects with X rays include Gaden, Henley, and Collins (1951); Goucher, Kamei, and Kocholaty

---

[1] 1 megarep = 1 million reps (see footnote, page 476).

(1956); Gunter and Kohn (1956); Kroeger and Kempf (1959); Sherman and Chase (1949a, b); Stapleton (1955); and Woese (1958).

Distilled Water. There appears to be a difference of opinion concerning the action of distilled water on the viability of bacteria and spores. Koch (1881) reported that anthrax spores were able to remain alive for more than 3 months in distilled water; vegetative cells were considerably more sensitive. Some have reported death in a few hours, whereas others have stated that weeks were necessary to destroy all organisms. This discrepancy may be due, in part at least, to the vessel from which the water was distilled. It has already been shown that minute amounts of some metallic ions exert a toxic effect on bacteria. Wilson (1922) reported that water distilled from a copper vessel sterilized a suspension of *Salmonella aertrycke* in a few hours.

The number of organisms introduced in the inoculum has also been shown to be the cause of considerable discrepancy in results. Ficker (1898) showed that, when distilled water was seeded with 60,000,000 cholera organisms per milliliter, viability was present after several months, but when the number was reduced to 10,000 per milliliter, all bacteria were dead after a period of 2 hr. He concluded that the inoculation of large numbers of organisms into distilled water resulted in the transfer of sufficient nutrients to prepare a dilute medium. Such a solution no longer possessed the properties of distilled water. Another cause of conflicting results may be due to variations in the pH of the distilled water. Winslow and Falk (1923a, b) adjusted distilled water to increasing hydrogen-ion concentrations and found that a pH of 6.0 gave the highest percentage of viable organisms after a period of 9 hr. Cohen (1922) showed that the stabilization of distilled water by the addition of buffers gave much more constant results. Spangler and Winslow (1943) reported that washed cells of *Bacillus cereus*, added to distilled water, died out very rapidly. However, the addition of NaCl in concentrations from 0.00001 to 0.3 M protected the organisms for a time against the harmful effects of distilled water. Other factors that affect the final results include traces of alkali dissolved from soft glass, dissolved carbon dioxide from the air, percentage of dissolved oxygen, and temperature of incubation. Whipple and Mayer (1906) found that *Salmonella typhosa* remained viable in distilled water for 2 months under aerobic conditions but only 4 days in an anaerobic environment. Houston placed S. *typhosa* in distilled water kept at different temperatures. At 0°C. the organisms lived for 8 weeks; at 18°C., they lived for 3 weeks; and at 37°C., they lived for only 1 week.

There is no evidence to show that true bacteria, when inoculated into distilled water, are destroyed by the process of plasmoptysis, i.e., the excessive intake of water resulting in the disruption of the cells. Bacterial cells are too resistant to osmotic changes for this to occur.

CHEMICAL AGENTS

Acids. The germicidal efficiency of acids is proportional to the hydrogen-ion concentrations of their solutions. A strong acid (HCl, H_2SO_4) is, therefore, more germicidal than a weak acid (lactic, acetic). Winslow and Lochridge (1906) found that it required a 0.0077 N solution of HCl or a 0.0096 N solution of H_2SO_4 to produce a 99 per cent reduction in an *E. coli* population in 40 min. Since the degree of dissociation is greater with HCl than with H_2SO_4, the final hydrogen-ion concentrations of the two solutions are practically the same.

The hydrogen-ion concentration does not necessarily explain all the disinfecting action of an acid solution. The action of some acids is also dependent upon the nature of the molecule. Winslow and Lochridge showed that either a 0.0812 N solution of acetic acid or a 0.0097 N solution of benzoic acid was required to produce a 99 per cent reduction in the number of *E. coli* after an exposure period of 40 min. The amount of dissociated hydrogen in the acetic acid was equal to 1.2 p.p.m., but in the benzoic acid it was 0.1 p.p.m. On the other hand, 7.49 p.p.m. of HCl were required to produce the same result. It is evident that the acetic and benzoic acids produced a toxic effect in addition to that of the hydrogen ions. This action may be due to the additional effect of the anions, or to the undissociated molecules, or to all three.

Benzoic and salicylic acids are weak acids, almost completely dissociated in neutral or alkaline solution, but almost completely undissociated in strongly acid solution. Rahn and Conn (1944) found that benzoic, salicylic, and sulfurous acids were nearly a hundred times more germicidal in strongly acid solutions than in neutral solutions. Only the undissociated molecules were germicidal; the ions exhibited only a slight germicidal effect.

Alkalies. The disinfecting action of alkalies is dependent upon the presence of hydroxyl ions. The greater the degree of dissociation, the more effective the germicidal action. Alkalies that are especially toxic to bacteria include KOH, $NaOH$, $LiOH$, and NH_4OH. Of these, KOH shows the greatest germicidal action by virtue of its greater degree of dissociation; NH_4OH shows the smallest because it is the least ionized.

There are some exceptions to the above rule. Barium hydroxide, $Ba(OH)_2$, for example, is less dissociated than KOH, yet it is considerably more toxic. This is due to the high toxicity of the barium ion. The combined action of the barium and hydroxyl ions produces a greater germicidal action than that exhibited by either ion acting alone.

Hydrogen ions exert a greater toxic effect than an equivalent number of hydroxyl ions.

Salts. Cations exert a peculiar and characteristic effect on the viability of bacteria. In general, cations in low concentrations tend to stimulate

bacterial growth; in high concentrations, they are inhibitory and ultimately toxic.

Sherman and Holm (1922) found low concentrations of NaCl to produce an accelerating effect on the growth of *E. coli*. The optimum stimulating action occurred at a salt concentration of about 0.2 *M*. The optimum pH for growth in both the control and salt media appeared to be
about 7.8.

They also reported that *E. coli* rarely grew in a 1 per cent peptone
medium at pH 4.8, but grew quite readily in the same medium to which
was added NaCl to make a 0.2 *M* solution. The NaCl produced a widening effect upon the pH limit of growth. This widening effect was even
more pronounced upon the growth of other bacterial species.

Hotchkiss (1923) combined different cations with the same anion
(chloride) and tested their effect on the growth of *E. coli*. The salts
could be divided into two groups on the basis of their toxicity. The salts
in group 1 showed no growth of *E. coli* in concentrations of 2 to 0.05 *M*;
those in group 2 prevented growth in dilutions of 0.01 to 0.00001 *M*. The
salts in group 1 are of common occurrence in the protoplasmic environment and are considered nontoxic. The salts are grouped as follows:

Group 1: Chlorides of Na, K, Li, NH₄, Sr, Mg, Ca, Ba, Mn, Ti, and Sn.
Group 2: Chlorides of Ni, Tl, Cu, Fe, Zn, Co, Pb, Al, Ce, Cd, and Hg.

Studies on the chlorides of Na, K, NH₄, and Li showed that maximum
growth occurred at a salt concentration of 0.25 *M* after an incubation
period of 3 days. Salt concentrations above or below 0.25 *M* showed a
decreased growth of the organisms.

In general, the bivalent salts in group 1 showed a greater toxicity
than the monovalent salts. The optimum growth concentration ranged
from about 0.05 to 0.025 *M*.

The salts in group 2 exhibited a greater degree of toxicity to *E. coli*.

Salts which are toxic become stimulating in higher dilutions. However,
the toxic effects have been studied to a greater extent. Salts of heavy
metals, particularly mercury and silver, are toxic to bacteria in relatively
low concentrations. The toxicity of solutions of $HgCl_2$ is due to the
concentration of Hg ions in solution. The greater the concentration of
free Hg ions, the more efficient the germicidal action. Mercury salts of
the organic acids, e.g., mercury acetate, which show a low degree of
dissociation, exhibit a much weaker germicidal action.

The toxic action of salts of mineral acids may be due to the cation,
to the anion, to the molecule taken as a whole, or to all three. In order
to determine to which component the action is due, tests have been made
in which one cation was combined with different anions and different
cations combined with the same anion.

Winslow and Hotchkiss (1922) tested a number of cations on various bacteria and reported that, in general, the toxicity of cations increased with valence. They arranged the cations in order of increasing toxicity as follows: K, Na, NH$_4$, Li, Sr, Mg, Ba, Ca, Mn, Ti^{+++}, Sn, Ni, Ti$^+$, Zn, Cu, Fe^{++}, Fe^{+++}, Co, Pb, Al, Ce, Cd, Hg.

Holm and Sherman (1921) determined the growth rates of *E. coli* in a peptone solution to which were added various Na salts. They concluded that the chloride ion showed the least toxicity and the fluoride ion the most. The Cl, I, NO$_3$, SO$_4$, PO$_4$, and lactate ions accelerated growth, whereas the oxalate, acetate, citrate, and fluoride ions exhibited an inhibitory effect.

Different species of bacteria vary considerably in their susceptibility to the same ion. Eisenberg (1919) showed that *Bacillus anthracis* was quite resistant to the action of the fluoride, iodide, and oxalate ions; *Corynebacterium diphtheriae* to tellurates, tellurites, nickel, and copper; *Salmonella typhosa* to strontium salt; the pneumococcus to ferricyanides, tellurites; etc. In other words, organisms may be classified on the basis of their susceptibility to the various ions.

Another point to consider in making a study of the action of ions on bacteria is the composition of the culture medium. Salts exhibit a greater germicidal action in distilled water than the same concentration in a protein-containing medium. This is due to a chemical reaction between the salts and the proteins, resulting in a decreased concentration of ions in the medium.

In general, Gram-positive organisms are more sensitive to various ions than Gram-negative bacteria. The same holds true for the action of various dyes on Gram-positive and Gram-negative bacteria (page 486).

Mechanisms of Salt Action. The following conclusions may be drawn on the action of salts on bacteria:

Most salts in high dilutions produce a stimulating action; in more concentrated solutions, a toxic or germicidal effect occurs.

When the toxic range is reached, the germicidal effect is proportional to the concentration of the salt.

The toxic effect of monovalent salts can, in general, be neutralized by the addition of a bivalent salt. Likewise, the toxic effect of a bivalent salt can, in most cases, be neutralized by the addition of a monovalent salt.

In general, divalent cations are more toxic than monovalent cations. Also, the heavier cations are usually more germicidal than the lighter cations. For example, HgCl$_2$ is more toxic than MgCl$_2$.

Salts are more germicidal in distilled water than in solutions containing protein. This is probably true for all germicidal agents. The organic matter greatly inactivates the salts, probably by combining with them and reducing the ionic concentration.

Different bacterial species vary considerably in their susceptibilities to the same salt. In general, closely allied organisms behave in a similar manner.

The Gram-positive organisms are usually more sensitive to the toxic effect of salts than are the Gram-negative bacteria.

The organic acids show only slight dissociation, compared to the inorganic acids; yet some of them exhibit a strong germicidal action. The toxic effect is attributed to the action of the undissociated molecules and not to their ions. Probably the same holds true for the toxicity of the salts of organic acids.

Reducing Agents. Some compounds produce a germicidal action by virtue of their powers of reduction. Sulfurous acid, sulfites, ferrous compounds, and formaldehyde act in this manner. Formaldehyde is a very efficient germicide, being effective against both vegetative cells and spores. A 5 per cent solution of formalin (a 37 per cent solution of formaldehyde gas in water) destroys anthrax spores in 1 to 2 hr.

For more information see Ingram (1948), Lloyd and Foter (1955).

Oxidizing Agents. Compounds that give up oxygen freely or are capable of releasing oxygen from other compounds have been used as germicides. Such agents produce their toxic effects by the process of oxidation. Among these may be mentioned hydrogen peroxide, potassium permanganate, the halogens (chlorine, bromine, iodine), and certain compounds containing these elements, such as hypochlorous acid ($HClO$) and hypochlorites; bleaching powder, $CaCl(OCl)$; chloramine, $CH_3 \cdot C_6H_4 \cdot SO_2NNaCl \cdot 3H_2O$; and dichloramine, $CH_3 \cdot C_6H_4 \cdot SO_2NCl_2$.

Hydrogen peroxide is an active oxidizing agent, being easily decomposed into water and oxygen. The commercial solution of H_2O_2 (3 per cent) is said to be capable of destroying anthrax spores in 1 hr.

Potassium permanganate was at one time employed to a considerable extent for the destruction of bacteria. Its action is increased in acid solution. A solution containing 1 per cent $KMnO_4$ and 1.1 per cent HCl in water is said to destroy anthrax spores in 30 sec. The salt promptly reacts with organic matter, being changed to insoluble MnO_2, a brown-staining compound. For this reason, the use of $KMnO_4$ as a germicide has been largely discontinued.

Bleaching powder is probably the most important oxygen compound of the halogens. When this compound is dissolved in water, it is said to break down as follows:

$$2CaCl(OCl) + 2CO_2 + 2H_2O \rightleftharpoons CaCl_2 + Ca(HCO_3)_2 + 2HClO$$

The HClO then breaks down to hydrogen chloride and oxygen:

$$2HClO \rightleftharpoons 2HCl + O_2$$

If chlorine gas is employed, the reactions are

$$Cl_2 + H_2O \rightleftharpoons HCl + HClO$$
$$2HClO \rightleftharpoons 2HCl + O_2$$

Compounds containing active chlorine attached to a nitrogen atom of the general formula $R_2{=}N{-}Cl$ and $R{-}N{=}Cl_2$ are also strongly germicidal, the activity being directly proportional to the extent to which reactions of hydrolysis proceed in solution:

$$R_2{=}N{-}Cl + H_2O \rightarrow R_2{=}N{-}H + HClO$$

$$R{-}N{=}Cl_2 + H_2O \rightarrow R{-}N\begin{matrix} \diagup H \\ \diagdown Cl \end{matrix} + HClO$$

The active agent is HClO:

$$2HClO \rightleftharpoons 2HCl + O_2$$

Bromine added to water reacts in the following manner:

$$2Br_2 + 2H_2O \rightleftharpoons 4HBr + O_2$$

or

$$Br_2 + H_2O \rightleftharpoons HBr + HBrO$$
$$2HBrO \rightleftharpoons 2HBr + O_2$$

The mechanism of action of iodine appears to be different from that of chlorine and bromine. An aqueous solution of iodine at pH 8 or less contains chiefly two forms of iodine, namely, molecular I_2 and the tri-iodide ion, $I_3{}^-$. The I_2 is only slightly soluble in water. In the presence of an iodide, such as NaI, the solubility is increased several hundred times, the increase being in the tri-iodide form:

$$I_2 + I^- \rightarrow I_3{}^-$$

Carroll (1955) found the tri-iodide ion to have negligible bactericidal activity. Since iodine for bactericidal studies is used in high dilutions, the tri-iodide ion dissociates into diatomic iodine and iodide ion unless the relative concentration of iodide (NaI, KI, etc.) is kept at a high level.

Gershenfeld and Witlin (1949) found that solutions containing free iodine displayed more effective antibacterial activity against *Staphylococcus aureus* than did chlorine or bromine, either in the presence or in the absence of organic matter.

Knox et al. (1948) reported that chlorine, in bactericidal concentrations or less, inhibited various sulfhydryl enzymes and other enzymes sensitive to oxidation. Inhibition of essential enzymes caused death of the cells. Inhibition of glucose oxidation was paralleled by the percentage of bacteria killed. The aldolase of *Escherichia coli* was shown to be one of the essential enzymes of glucose oxidation sufficiently sensitive to chlorine to account for its bactericidal effect.

Iodine is a suitable agent for the emergency disinfection of water supplies. Chang and Morris (1953) reported that iodine in a concentration of 5 to 10 p.p.m. is effective against all types of water-borne pathogenic organisms within 10 min. at room temperature. For this purpose iodine has the following advantages: (1) its germicidal action is less dependent on pH, temperature, and time of contact; (2) nitrogenous impurities do not impair its usefulness; and (3) side reactions leading to consumption of the germicide are less marked for iodine than for chlorinous disinfectants.

For more information see Bogash (1956), Chambers et al. (1952), Friberg and Hammarström (1956), Shelanski and Shelanski (1956).

Phenols and Cresols. The phenols and cresols are very efficient germicides in fairly concentrated solutions. Phenol is soluble in water, but most of the other members of the group are only slightly soluble. However, they may be held in suspension by mixing with soap, by which procedure colloidal solutions are obtained.

The emulsification of disinfectants only slightly soluble in water results in the formation of more potent germicidal preparations. In the emulsified state, the particles of germicide are adsorbed onto the surface of the emulsifying agent (soap), resulting in an increased concentration in the vicinity of the bacteria. The emulsified disinfectants are more active when freshly prepared. After a few days, the activity decreases, probably owing to a change in their colloidal state. An important commercial disinfectant of this type is compound solution of cresol, known under the trade name of Lysol.

It is usually stated that phenols and cresols act on proteins with the formation of insoluble proteinates. This results in a precipitation of the proteins of the protoplasm. Kojima (1931) opposed the theory of direct coagulation of the bacterial proteins. He found that the strength of phenol that was required to destroy bacteria failed to coagulate egg albumin. Reichel (1909) believed that the action was more physical than chemical, the phenol being capable of dissolving in coagulated proteins and in lipoids, fats, and the cytoplasm of bacteria. The germicidal action was due to its ability to penetrate the cell in the form of a colloidal solution.

Alcohols. Absolute alcohol is generally not germicidal or only slightly so. On the addition of water, however, the compound shows a marked germicidal effect. Its maximum germicidal efficiency is exhibited in a concentration of 70 per cent by weight (77 per cent by volume).

Smith (1947) found alcohol to be an effective germicide against *Mycobacterium tuberculosis*. The organism was killed in 15 to 30 sec. by absolute, 95 per cent, and even 70 per cent ethyl alcohol. Ninety-five per cent alcohol was found to be best for wet surfaces, 50 per cent for dry, and 70 per cent for wet or dry.

Tanner and Wilson (1943) reported that the germicidal action of aliphatic alcohols increased with the molecular weight as far as the amyl derivative (5 carbon atoms) and decreased through octyl to undecyl alcohol (11 carbon atoms). Since the alcohols decrease in solubility as the molecular weights increase, the higher members of the series are generally not employed as germicidal agents.

Alcohols are believed to act by denaturing proteins. This occurs more readily in the presence of water than in its absence, which explains why absolute alcohol is less bactericidal than mixtures of alcohol and water.

The addition of absolute alcohol to mercuric chloride reduces greatly the germicidal potency of the latter. Mercuric chloride dissolved in 50 per cent alcohol is more germicidal than a corresponding aqueous solution. The same holds true for silver nitrate. Since the toxicity of these salts is proportional to the concentration of mercury and silver ions, water is necessary for ionization to occur. On the other hand, compounds such as phenol and formaldehyde are less germicidal in the presence of even a small amount of alcohol.

Glycols. Robertson et al. (1948) made a study of a large number of glycols, especially propylene, dipropylene, and triethylene glycols, since these compounds possess certain properties which make them acceptable for use as air disinfectants in atmospheres occupied by human beings.

The formulas are as follows:

Propylene glycol

Dipropylene glycol

Triethylene glycol

They found that the killing effect of the glycols was much less than that of the phenols, halogens, and detergents. Even the most highly bactericidal glycols failed to inhibit the growth of bacteria in concentrations of less than 3 per cent, and the least lethal showed an effect only in solutions above 50 per cent. However, comparison with ethyl alcohol revealed the fact that this compound was only slightly more effective in preventing the growth of microorganisms than was propylene glycol, the most bactericidal of the nontoxic glycols.

In general, the higher the concentration of glycol, the more rapid the bactericidal action. In 98 per cent solution both propylene and triethylene glycol killed in less than 1 min. and probably in a few seconds. Propylene glycol in concentrations of 70 to 80 per cent appeared to produce equally rapid killing and was found to be the most efficient of the three glycols. The action of dipropylene glycol was less regular.

Bazzicalupo, Portella, and Contieri (1951) reported that, in experimentally infected guinea pigs, subcutaneous treatment with propylene glycol inhibited extensive tuberculous alterations and prolonged the survival time. Its in vivo suppression of tuberculosis was equal to that of other substances with in vitro bacteriostatic properties. The antituberculous power of propylene glycol in vivo was greater when the treatment was begun immediately after infection.

Dyes. Certain coal-tar dyes, notably those of the triphenylmethane group, possess the power of affecting the viability of bacteria. This action was first described as bactericidal because it was believed that in the absence of growth the organisms were killed. It was shown later that the organisms were not always killed but merely prevented from multiplying. Churchman (1912, 1928) applied the term bacteriostasis to describe this condition.

In most cases, selective bacteriostatic action parallels the Gram reaction. This means that those organisms which retain the Gram stain (Gram +) are more susceptible to the action of the above dyes than are the Gram-negative bacteria. Conversely, those organisms which do not retain the Gram stain (Gram −) are more resistant to the action of the above dyes than are the Gram-positive bacteria. Notable exceptions to the parallelism between bacteriostatic action and Gram reaction are the acid-fast organisms *Mycobacterium tuberculosis, M. paratuberculosis, M. avium,* etc. These organisms are Gram-positive but comparatively resistant to the action of the triphenylmethane dyes.

An increase in basicity of the solution of a basic dye results in an increase in its germicidal power. A decrease in basicity results in a decrease in its germicidal power. Likewise, an increase in acidity of the solution of an acid dye results in an increase in its germicidal power. A decrease in acidity results in a decrease in its germicidal power.

The effect of crystal violet on *Escherichia coli* and *Bacillus subtilis* is shown in Fig. 190.

Ingraham (1933) believed that the bacteriostatic effect of crystal violet was due to its property of poising the oxidation-reduction potential in a range too high for cell multiplication to occur. Hoffmann and Rahn (1944) agreed with the findings of Ingraham and extended the work. They found that, above a certain concentration, the dye acted like any other germicide. The cells died in logarithmic order and in proportion to the dye concentration. The dye was more toxic to young than to old cells, and its toxicity increased only slightly with an increase in pH. This strict germicidal action was probably due to the combination of dye with some indispensable cell constituents. At lower concentrations, the dye did not give a logarithmic survivor curve and was not influenced by cell age or pH or the dye concentration. Perhaps this unusual effect was due to the unfavorable oxidation-reduction potential poised by the dye. In this range, the cells usually overcame the dye action and multiplied. The dye

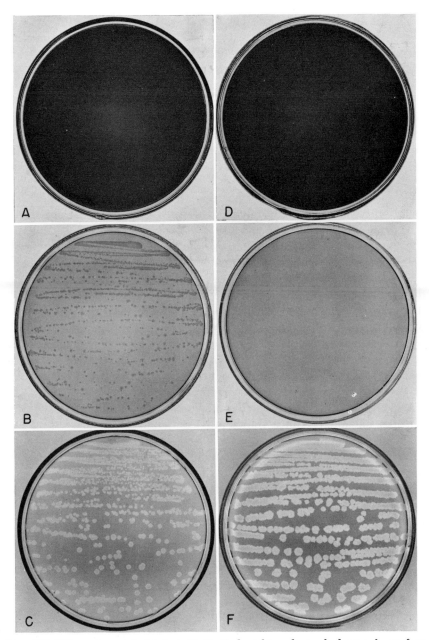

Fig. 190. Effect of crystal violet. A, B, C, *Escherichia coli* streaked over the surface of nutrient agar containing respectively 1:5000, 1:100,000, and 1:2,000,000 concentration of the dye. D, E, F, same streaked with *Bacillus subtilis*. A 1:5000 concentration of crystal violet inhibited both organisms; a 1:100,000 concentration inhibited B. subtilis (Gram +) but not E. coli (Gram −). A 1:2,000,000 concentration was not sufficient to prevent growth of B. subtilis.

produced an abnormally long lag period which increased with the dye concentration. The length of the lag phase was inversely proportional to the logarithm of the number of inoculated cells.

For more information see Fischer et al. (1944) and Tilley (1939).

Mercury Compounds. Mercurial compounds were among the first to be used for the destruction of bacteria. Of these, mercuric chloride (bichloride of mercury) was believed to be the most potent of the germicidal compounds available. At that time Koch (1881) concluded from his experimental results that bichloride of mercury was very effective against the anthrax organism, killing both vegetative cells and spores in one application in a few minutes.

It was shown later that the bacteria were not necessarily killed but merely prevented from multiplying by traces of the chemical present in the medium. In other words, mercury is a strongly bacteriostatic agent and does not necessarily kill all bacteria in the concentrations generally used. To eliminate the bacteriostatic action of the mercury adherent to the bacteria and of the small amount carried into the subculturing medium in the inoculum, ammonium sulfide was used to inactivate the mercury. By this technique many of the bacteria were shown to be living and capable of multiplying in the subculturing medium.

Because of their bacteriostatic action, mercury compounds with dyes or other organic radicals are employed for skin antisepsis. Organomercurials are less toxic and less irritating than the older inorganic chlorides, iodides, and cyanides of mercury.

It is generally believed that the mercurials act by interfering with an essential metabolite. Since compounds containing the —SH radical are essential metabolites, the antibacterial action of mercury may be due to combination with compounds containing the sulfhydryl group. Such action is an inactivation without demonstrable injury to the cell.

Harris, Eisenstark, and Dragsdorf (1954) immersed *Escherichia coli* in a 0.01 M $HgCl_2$, then treated them with hydrogen sulfide. X-ray diffraction studies showed the presence of intracellular crystals of HgS. The results suggested that the site of cation adsorption was the cytoplasmic membrane of the cell.

Morton, North, and Engley (1948) made a study of the organomercurials Metaphen, Merthiolate, and Mercurochrome against *Streptococcus pyogenes* and showed that they possessed many shortcomings as disinfectants. The organisms, placed in a state of bacteriostasis by these agents, were still capable of producing fatal septicemia when introduced into the animal body.

The fact that bacteria are still infectious when in a state of bacteriostasis is sufficient reason for taking precautions to eliminate the bacteriostatic effect of mercury while testing mercurial compounds in vitro for germicidal activity.

For more information on the subject of mercurial compounds see Brewer (1957).

Silver Compounds. The germicidal and antiseptic effects of the simple silver salts (silver nitrate, silver citrate, silver lactate, etc.) are due to the presence in solution of silver ions.

Silver, like mercury, is a strongly bacteriostatic metal. The antiseptic action of the simple silver compounds is complicated by irritation, pain, astringency, and causticity. These effects may be avoided by the use of colloidal preparations of silver.

In contrast to the simple silver salts, the colloidal preparations (silver protein strong, Argyrol, etc.) give only a few free silver ions in solution. Concentrated solutions of organo-silver preparations do not precipitate chlorides or proteins, are noncorrosive, nonastringent, and nonirritant. Nevertheless, the compounds are germicidal and bacteriostatic; this action varies with the different compounds and is not proportional to the total silver content but to the concentration of free silver ions in solution.

The toxic effect of silver compounds for bacteria is generally believed to be due to the precipitation of proteins by the silver ions. The silver proteinates so formed contribute to a sustained antiseptic action by slowly liberating small amounts of silver ions.

For more information see Romans (1957).

Soaps. It has been known since the beginning of bacteriology that both soft and hard soaps are excellent germicides.

Soft soaps are prepared by boiling oils and fats with potassium hydroxide; hard soaps are prepared with sodium hydroxide. The soft soaps are used in preparing liquid soaps and shampoos, whereas the hard soaps are used in preparing soap powders, chips, and bars.

Soap has a number of important physical characteristics. When dissolved in water, it lowers the surface tension, forms colloidal solutions and gels, causes water to wet surfaces more rapidly, gives the solution a soapy or slippery feeling, and has the ability to emulsify and disperse oils and dirt in the solution and thus is able to cleanse.

Various chemicals, such as phenols, cresols, mercuric iodide, mercuric chloride, Metaphen, chloramine, and hexachlorophene, have been incorporated in soaps to enhance their germicidal value. It has been shown that most of these so-called germicidal soaps are no more useful than ordinary soaps for destroying bacteria. In fact, some materials may lose their germicidal effectiveness in the presence of soap and may even decrease the natural antiseptic properties of soap. For example, soaps containing cresol and phenol are less antiseptic than the cresol or the phenol or the soap alone when used in the same concentrations.

McCulloch (1940) tested a large number of commercial soaps for their action on several strains of *Streptococcus agalactiae* and concluded as follows:

Solutions of commercial soaps and soap powders, at 40°C., and in the presence of 5 per cent skim milk and 5 per cent broth culture of the organisms, were found to be between two and three times as effective in killing mastitis streptococci in 1 min. as was phenol and were equally as effective as 100 p.p.m. of the most actively germicidal of several hypochlorites tested.

A soap containing cresols was no more germicidal than were the nonmedicated soaps, and the soaps containing mercury compounds were only slightly more effective.

Soap solutions in the concentrations usually obtained in lathering the hands with soap in warm water are effective disinfectants against mastitis streptococci.

For more information see Fishbein et al. (1945); Morton (1944); Nungester, Thirlby, and Vial (1949); and Rahn (1945a).

Surface-active Agents and Synthetic Detergents. A surface-active agent has the property of orienting itself between two interfaces in such a way that it brings them into more intimate contact. If the function of the agent is to promote wetting and penetration, it is called a surface-active agent. If the two interfaces are immiscible liquids, the surface-active agent lowers the interfacial tension so that emulsions are formed. Under these conditions the agent is called an emulsifier. If the surface-active agent combines both wetting and emulsifying properties to a sufficient degree, it is called a synthetic detergent.

Synthetic detergents, like soaps, consist of a hydrophobic (water-repelling) group and a hydrophilic (water-attracting) group.

The detergent and wetting class of compounds consist largely of anionic agents and possess a negative electrical charge. They ionize in water like soaps:

Soaps	Anionic agents
$R \cdot COONa$	$R \cdot SO_3Na$
Carboxyl group	Sulfonic group

The emulsifiers for the most part are nonionic, i.e., do not ionize in water. A typical nonionic agent is glycerol monostearate, an emulsifying agent used in baking, ice cream, and cosmetics:

$$CH_2 \cdot OOC \cdot C_{17}H_{35}$$
$$|$$
$$CHOH \qquad \text{or} \qquad RCOOR'$$
$$|$$
$$CH_2OH$$

The cationic agents possess a positive electrical charge, being capable of reversing the action of soaps. They are generally substituted ammonium salts. Some well-known cationics are the quaternary ammonium compounds of the form

$$R-N(CH_3)_3Cl$$

Probably 75 per cent of the cationic agents are quaternary ammonium salts. Most of the sanitizing and bactericidal agents belong in this group.

Surface-active agents have a tendency to localize in the surface layer or interface of liquids. A surface-active molecule may be diagrammatically represented by a bar for the hydrophobic (fat-soluble) group and a disk for the polar (water-soluble) group, depending upon whether the polar group is at the end or somewhere along the carbon chain:

Then the surface film can be represented as follows:

The surface of a solution containing a surface-active agent is actually altered, being covered with a hydrocarbon film having the thickness of one molecular layer. When an aqueous solution containing a wetting agent is in contact with a lipoidal surface, the hydrophobic group of the wetter is absorbed and the polar group protrudes:

Such a surface is now capable of being wetted by water. For this reason wetting agents lower the surface tension of water. Such solutions can penetrate into openings and cracks, very small spaces, or even into the center of clumps of bacteria. The same solutions without wetters would simply bridge over openings without showing any appreciable penetration.

Surface-active agents are of great importance as additions to germicidal solutions intended for clinical application. They make it possible for such solutions to penetrate into infected tissues, pus, necrotic debris, bacteria, etc.

A cell surface covered with adsorbed molecules of a wetting agent may be represented as follows:

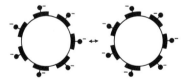

The number of negative charges on the cell surface is much higher in the presence of a surface-active agent than in its absence. This results in immediate dispersion and exposure of living organisms that previously were protected from the action of the bactericidal agent.

Uses of Surface-active Agents. Surface-active agents have a wide variety of uses as manifested by their applications in detergency, solubilization, emulsification, capillary penetration, wetting, spreading, and disinfection.

The quaternary ammonium compounds are widely used as germicidal agents for the destruction of bacteria. They were originally believed to be germicidal in high dilution, but it has since been shown that they are strongly bacteriostatic in high dilution and germicidal only in more concentrated dilutions. The bacteriostatic effect may be eliminated by the addition of an agent capable of neutralizing the action of the germicide. Neutralizing agents include soap, anionic detergents, phospholipides, etc.

The true bactericidal potency of quaternary ammonium compounds seems to be between the two extremes of very high and very low activity. A result indicating unduly high potency is obtained if the adsorbed quaternary compound is not actively removed from the treated organisms. Such inhibited cells will die eventually, but they are not killed immediately as the results seem to indicate.

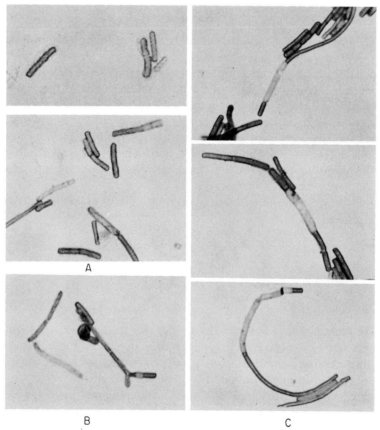

A

B   C

Fig. 191. *Bacillus megaterium,* 6-hr. culture, stained with Victoria blue × 2000. *A,* degeneration of cytoplasmic membrane; *B,* extrusion of cytoplasm; *C,* empty cell walls. (*After Chaplin.*)

The high-grade quaternary ammonium compounds are said to have many advantages over the bactericides with which the medical professions are familiar. They are effective, noninjurious surface disinfectants which are germicidal for many pathogenic nonsporulating bacteria and molds after an exposure of several minutes. They have low surface tensions, and some possess detergent and keratolytic properties. They are said to be emollient and to be relatively nonirritating in effective concentrations.

Chaplin (1952) treated *Bacillus megaterium* with Roccal, a quaternary compound, and reported that three important changes occurred: (1) degeneration of the cytoplasmic membrane; (2) extrusion of the cytoplasm; and (3) a deterioration of the cell wall, in which all rigidity and tensile strength were lost (Fig. 191). Similar results were reported by Tomcsik (1955).

For more information see Curran and Evans (1950), Glassman (1948), Klein and Kardon (1947), Klimek and Bailey (1956), and Lawrence (1948).

Sulfonamides. The sulfonamides is a name given to a group of drugs that exhibit bacteriostatic activity in vitro and a bactericidal effect in vivo. The first important member of this group to be widely used clinically is para-amino benzene sulfonamide (the amide of sulfanilic acid), commonly known as sulfanilamide:

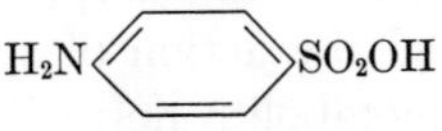

H_2N—〈 〉—SO_2OH
Sulfanilic acid

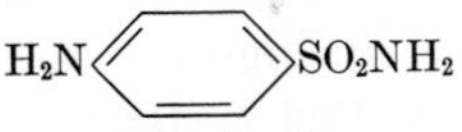

H_2N—〈 〉—SO_2NH_2
Sulfanilamide

A large number of derivatives of sulfanilamide have been prepared by substituting the hydrogen atoms of the amino radicals for other groups or radicals. The names and structures of some of the more common sulfonamides are as follows:

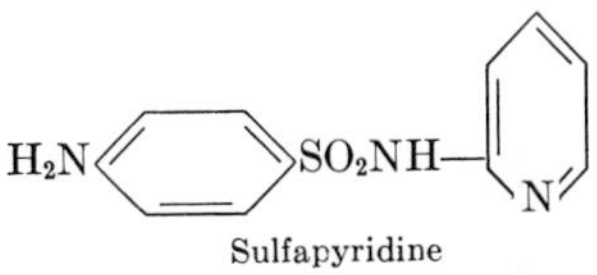

H_2N—〈 〉—SO_2NH—
Sulfapyridine

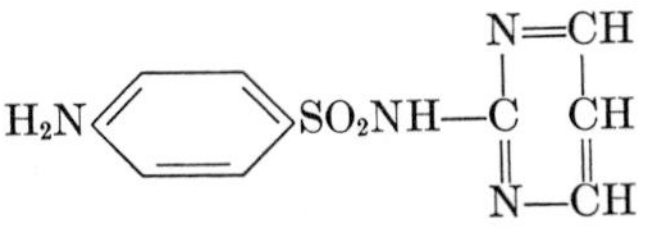

H_2N—〈 〉—SO_2NH—C
Sulfadiazine

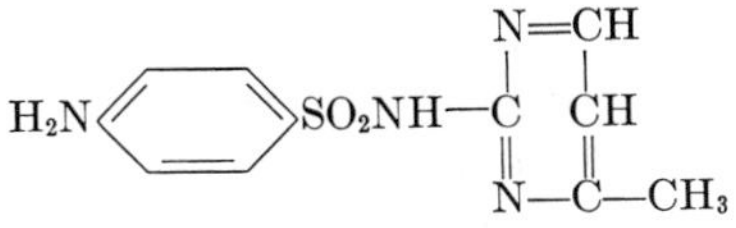

H_2N—〈 〉—SO_2NH—C
Sulfamerazine

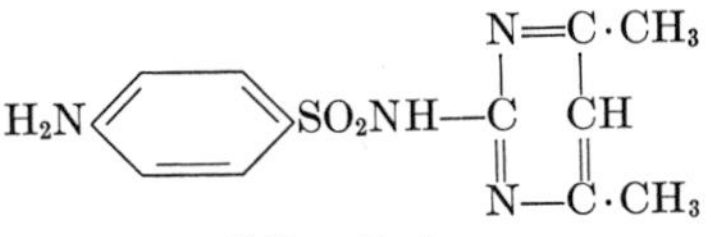

H_2N—〈 〉—SO_2NH—C
Sulfamethazine

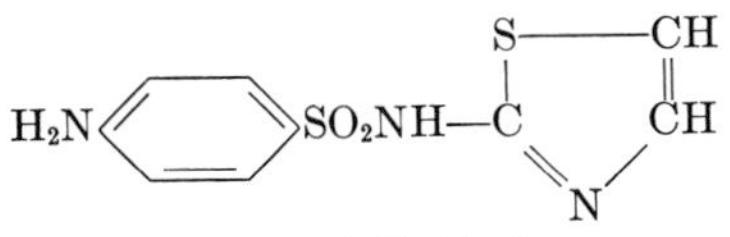

H_2N—〈 〉—SO_2NH—C
Sulfathiazole

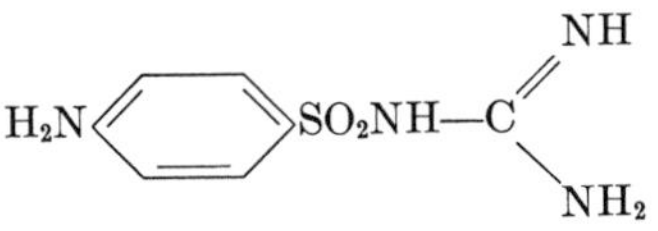

H_2N—〈 〉—SO_2NH—C
Sulfaguanidine

$$H_2N\!\!\diagdown\!\!\diagup\!\!SO_2NH\!-\!\overset{\|}{\underset{S}{C}}\!-\!NH_2$$

Sulfathiourea

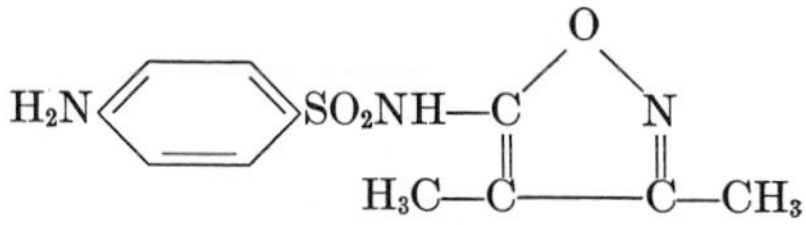

$$H_2N\!\!\diagdown\!\!\diagup\!\!SO_2NH\!-\!C\overset{O}{\diagup}\!\diagdown\!\!N$$
$$H_3C\!-\!C\!-\!\!-\!\!-\!C\!-\!CH_3$$

Sulfisoxazole

$$HOOC\cdot H_2C\cdot H_2COCHN\!\!\diagdown\!\!\diagup\!\!SO_2NH\!-\!C\!\!\diagdown\!\!\diagup\!\!\underset{N}{\overset{S\!-\!-\!-\!CH}{\|}}\!CH$$

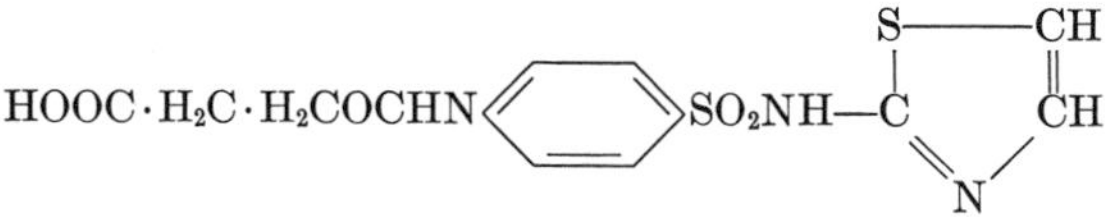

Sulfasuxidine

Clinical Uses. The drugs are useful in a number of diseases and infections, some of which at one time produced a very high mortality rate. Some of these are pneumonia, meningitis, gonorrhoea, infections due to micrococci and hemolytic streptococci, gas gangrene, wound and urinary-tract infections. The derivatives vary in their usefulness to a certain disease. Some may prove to be of great value; others may be useless. Therefore, it is necessary to select the proper derivative for the disease or infection to be treated. As an example, sulfanilamide proved to be of tremendous value to the troops in the Second World War as a dusting powder to wounds to prevent infection. Each soldier carried a supply at all times as an emergency measure.

Mode of Action. From the many theories advanced to explain the mode of action of the sulfonamides, the one advanced by Fildes (1940) appears to be the most logical. Woods (1940) showed that *p*-aminobenzoic acid (PABA) in high dilutions antagonized the action of sulfonamides. Fildes showed that PABA is an essential metabolite normally associated with an enzyme. The sulfonamides displace PABA from its enzyme and thereby stop this essential line of metabolism.

Unless a large enough dose of sulfonamides is administered, the organisms are likely to develop a resistance or fastness to the drug, making it necessary to give much larger doses. Landy, Larkum, and Ostwald (1943) and Landy et al. (1943) found that the development of resistance to sulfonamides by *Staphylococcus aureus* resulted in an increased synthesis of PABA.

For more information see Alimchandani and Sreenivasan (1957), Henry (1943), Roblin (1946), Roblin and Bell (1943), Shannon (1943), Spink et al. (1944).

Urea and Its Derivatives. Urea and some of its derivatives, such as urethane, are highly bacteriostatic and bactericidal for many Gram-negative and a few Gram-positive bacteria. They also potentiate the activity of the sulfonamides, inhibit *p*-aminobenzoic acid moderately, and increase the solubility of sulfanilamide and sulfathiazole. Because of its ability to dissolve necrotic tissue, urea has been used in combination with the sulfonamides in the treatment of wound infections.

Urea or carbamide has the following structure:

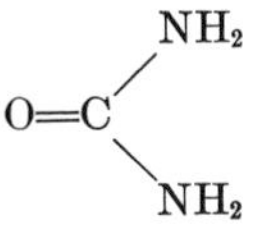

$$O\!\!=\!\!C\!\!\begin{array}{c} \diagup NH_2 \\ \diagdown NH_2 \end{array}$$

Urea

Urethane is the ethyl ester of carbamic acid:

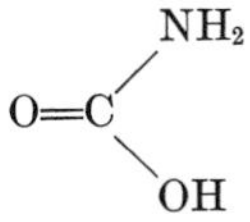

$$O\!\!=\!\!C\!\!\begin{array}{c} \diagup NH_2 \\ \diagdown OH \end{array} \qquad O\!\!=\!\!C\!\!\begin{array}{c} \diagup NH_2 \\ \diagdown OC_2H_5 \end{array}$$

Carbamic acid 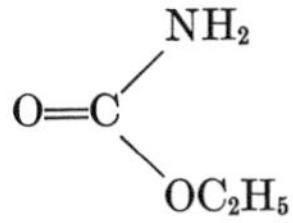   Urethane

Weinstein (1946) reported that the replacement of the $=$O group in urea by $=$S, to give thiourea,

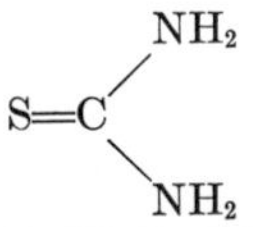

$$S\!\!=\!\!C\!\!\begin{array}{c} \diagup NH_2 \\ \diagdown NH_2 \end{array}$$

increased markedly its antibacterial activity.

For more information see Howe and Weinstein (1947), Klotz and Mellody (1949).

EVALUATION OF GERMICIDES

The method generally employed for the evaluation of germicides is to rate them according to their phenol coefficients. In addition to this, a number of newer methods have been proposed, which are designed to measure the toxicity of germicides for tissue as well as for the test bacteria.

Phenol-coefficient Method. The phenol-coefficient test was first proposed by Rideal and Walker (1903) for comparing and rating substances intended for the destruction of bacteria. Since that time, many modifications of the original method have been recommended. At the present time, the standard procedure in this country is that proposed by Ruehle and Brewer (1931) of the Food and Drug Administration, U.S. Department of Agriculture. The test, in one form or another, is universally employed for examining and rating disinfectants.

Definition. The phenol coefficient may be defined as the killing power of a germicide toward a test organism as compared with that of phenol under identical conditions. The conditions that must be specified include (1) time of action of germicide, (2) temperature of the test, (3) presence and amount of organic matter, (4) organism used in the test, (5) age of the culture, (6) composition and reaction of the culture medium, (7) proportion of disinfectant to culture, and (8) temperature and time of incubation of the transfer tubes or flasks. Variations in one or more of the conditions will affect the final result. It is, therefore, of utmost importance to specify the conditions of the test; otherwise the final result will be worthless.

Time and Temperature. In general, germicidal action is increased with time. This means that a higher dilution may be employed with an increase in the period of action. This applies also to temperature. An increase in temperature increases the effectiveness of a germicide, making higher dilutions possible. Germicides are not affected to the same degree by an increase in time and temperature, and for this reason, no general rule can be made.

An important exception to the rule that germicidal action is increased with time is iodine. This germicide is a vigorous oxidizing agent and acts almost immediately when placed in contact with bacteria.

Organic Matter. Probably all germicides are largely reduced in activity in the presence of organic matter, although some are affected more than others. This is especially true in the presence of proteins, amino acids, and compounds of a similar nature. Results of the evaluation of germicides in aqueous solutions are quite different from those obtained when organic matter is added. The kind and amount of organic matter must be mentioned in reporting the efficiencies of germicidal substances.

Organism. Germicides vary considerably in their action on different bacterial species. Some are more effective against Gram-positive than against Gram-negative bacteria, and vice versa. Still others display approximately the same degree of toxicity toward both groups of organisms. The name of the organism used in the test must be mentioned. The organisms generally used are *Staphylococcus aureus* (Gram +) and *Salmonella typhosa* (Gram −).

Age of the Culture. In general, old organisms are more resistant to adverse environmental conditions than young ones. In practically all procedures for evaluating germicides, 24-hr. cultures are specified. This precaution must be observed in order that constant and comparable results be obtained.

Composition and Reaction of Medium. Variations in composition and pH of culture media also affect the final results. Goetchius (1950) employed beef extract from three different sources and obtained wide variations in the phenol coefficients. Klarmann and Wright (1945) obtained similar results, which led them to propose the use of semisynthetic media for more constant results in phenol-coefficient determinations. In general, an organism is more resistant to adverse conditions at its optimum pH. A change in the reaction of the medium on either side of the optimum pH increases the susceptibility of an organism to a germicide.

Proportion of Disinfectant to Culture. A parallelism exists between the number of organisms employed in the test and the smallest amount of germicide required to destroy them. If the number of organisms is increased or decreased, the concentration of germicide required to destroy them is likewise increased or decreased.

Method. The Food and Drug Administration (FDA) method of Ruehle and Brewer (1931) is as follows: A series of dilutions of phenol and germicide to be compared are prepared in sterile distilled water contained in test tubes measuring 25 mm. in diameter and 150 mm. in length. Each tube must contain not more than 5 ml. of germicidal dilution. The tubes are placed in a rack in a water bath, previously adjusted to a temperature of 20°C., and allowed to remain for at least 5 min. in order to bring the temperature of the germicidal dilutions to that of the water bath.

The test organism should be transferred daily for five successive days previous to use. A 24-hr. culture must be employed in the test. The culture is shaken vigorously to break up small clumps of bacteria and is then placed in the water bath for 15 min. to permit large suspended particles to settle out. One-half milliliter of culture is pipetted into each dilution of the germicide. At intervals of 5, 10, and 15 min. a 4-mm. loopful of material is removed from each tube and transferred to a corresponding tube containing 10 ml. of broth. The subculture tubes are incubated at 37°C. for 48 hr. If the germicide is suspected of being bacteriostatic, the subculture tubes should be incubated for a longer period of time.

If mercurials, silver preparations, dyes, or other compounds exhibiting strong bacteriostatic properties are tested, it is necessary (1) to make secondary subcultures from the first subculture tubes immediately after the test has been completed, or (2) to make the first transfers to 100 ml. amounts of broth contained in flasks, or (3) to make transfers to broth containing substances that combine with or destroy the germicidal agent. For example, bacteria treated with mercuric chloride contain $Hg+$ ions adsorbed to their cell walls. In this condition, the bacteria are not necessarily killed but merely prevented from multiplying. The numbers of $Hg+$ ions may be insufficient to produce death but sufficient to produce a bacteriostatic effect. Sodium thioglycollate contains a sulfhydryl group that is capable of reacting with $Hg+$ ions. If mercury-treated organisms are transferred to a broth medium containing sodium thioglycollate, the germicide is removed from the bacteria by the sulfhydryl groups. This destroys the bacteriostatic effect of the mercury and permits growth of the organisms.

The phenol coefficient is calculated by dividing the highest dilution of germicide killing the test organism in 10 min. but not in 5 min. by the corresponding dilution of phenol. For example, in Table 18 the phenol coefficient would be $\frac{350}{90} = 3.89$. This means that germicide A is 3.89 times more effective than phenol.

Since *Salmonella typhosa* was used as the test organism, the value is referred to as the *S. typhosa* phenol coefficient.

TABLE 18. KILLING DILUTIONS OF PHENOL AND GERMICIDE A
FOR *Salmonella typhosa* AT DIFFERENT TIME INTERVALS

Germicide	Dilution	Time interval, min.		
		5	10	15
Phenol	1 : 70	−	−	−
	1 : 80	−	−	−
	1 : 90	+	−	−
	1 : 100	+	+	+
Germicide A	1 : 325	−	−	−
	1 : 350	+	−	−
	1 : 375	+	+	−
	1 : 400	+	+	+

For more information see Ostrolenk (1950), Stuart, Ortenzio, and Friedl (1955).

Limitations of the Test. The phenol-coefficient test was originally designed to be used for comparing the toxicity of phenol with phenol-like compounds. However, the method has been used to test compounds which are totally unlike phenol in composition and mode of action, as for example, chlorine and its compounds, mercury compounds, iodine, and quaternary ammonium germicides, leading to considerable variation in results.

Another cause of variation has been the liberties which certain investigators have taken with the test itself, modifying it to favor the compounds being tested. For example, water is employed as the diluting agent in the official test procedure; yet alcohol has been substituted for the water to improve the germicidal powers of the compound under examination. Another departure has been the use of water containing alkali for certain germicides which are insoluble in water but soluble in alkaline solutions. Phenol coefficients so obtained do not represent true comparisons of the germicides with phenol.

Still another limitation of the test is that it is of no value in determining the efficiency of a germicide intended for clinical application. A phenol coefficient attempts to compare the toxicity of a germicide for a given organism with that of phenol but gives no information as to its effect on living tissue. It can be seen that a germicide having a high phenol coefficient and a proportionately high toxicity to tissue would have no advantage over one having a low phenol coefficient and a proportionately low toxicity to living tissue.

Tissue-toxicity Method. A number of methods have been proposed for determining the effects of germicides on living tissue cells as well as for their ability to kill bacteria.

Nye (1937), Welch and Hunter (1940), Welch and Brewer (1942), Welch, Slocum, and Hunter (1942), and Hirsch and Novak (1942) tested germicides by using the inhibition of phagocytosis as a criterion of tissue toxicity. Witlin (1942), Green and Birkeland (1942, 1944), and Gershenfeld and Witlin (1947) tested the effect of germicides on the infected chorioallantoic membrane of the developing chick embryo. Nungester and Kempf (1942) swabbed the tails of anesthetized mice with a broth suspension of the test organism and allowed the culture to dry. The tails were next dipped into a solution of the germicide. After a period of drying, the tip of the tail was cut off and inserted into the peritoneal cavity through a small incision. Survival of the animals indicated that the germicide killed the test organism.

Salle and Lazarus (1935), Salle, McOmie, and Shechmeister (1937), Salle et al. (1938, 1939), Shechmeister and Salle (1938), Foord, McOmie, and Salle (1938), and Salle and Catlin (1947) tested germicides for their effect on the viability of chick heart-tissue fragments as well as for their ability to kill bacteria. Paff, Lehman, and Halperin (1945) employed a modification of the method. A number known as the toxicity index may be calculated from the results, which is defined as the ratio of the highest dilution of germicide required to kill the tissue cells in 10 min. to the highest dilution required to kill the test organism in the same time and under similar conditions. Theoretically, an index less than 1 means that the germicide is more toxic to the bacteria than to the tissue; an index greater than 1 means that the germicide is more toxic to the tissue than to the bacteria. The smaller the toxicity index, the more nearly perfect the germicide.

Several germicides and their corresponding toxicity indexes are given in Table 19. Iodine exhibited the highest degree of efficiency of the agents tested by this technique, combining low tissue toxicity with high germicidal potency against *Staphylococcus aureus*.

TABLE 19. TOXICITY OF GERMICIDES FOR EMBRYONIC CHICK HEART TISSUE AND
Staphylococcus aureus AT 37°C.

Germicide	Highest killing dilution for tissue and bacteria and corresponding toxicity index		
	Tissue (A)	Bacteria (B)	Toxicity index, A/B
Iodine, tincture...............	1 : 4000	1 : 20,000	0.2
Mercresin, tincture............	1 : 9000	1 : 19,000	0.5
Merthiolate, tincture..........	1 : 15,000	1 : 4500	3.3
Metaphen, tincture............	1 : 12,000	1 : 1200	10.0

For more information see Rahn (1945*b*), Reddish (1957), and Salle (1955).

REFERENCES

Alimchandani, H. R., and A. Sreenivasan: Inhibition steps in Sulfonamide bacteriostasis of *Escherichia coli*, *J. Bact.*, 73:538, 1957.

Anderson, T. F., S. Boggs, and B. C. Winters: The relative sensitivities of bacterial viruses to intense sonic vibration, *Science*, 108:18, 1948.

Barron, E. S. G., and S. Dickman: Studies on the mechanism of action of ionizing radiations. II. Inhibition of sulfhydryl enzymes by alpha, beta, and gamma rays, *J. Gen. Physiol.*, 32:595, 1949.

———, ———, J. A. Muntz, and T. P. Singer: Studies on the mechanism of action of ionizing radiations. I. Inhibition of enzymes by X-rays, *ibid.*, 32:537, 1949.

Bazzicalupo, C., A. Portella, and M. Contieri: Action of propylene glycol upon experimental tuberculosis in guinea pigs, *Proc. Soc. Exp. Biol. Med.*, 78:671, 1951.

Beattie, J. M., and F. C. Lewis: On the destruction of bacteria in milk by electricity, *Special Report* 49, London, Medical Research Council, 1920.

Beckwith, T. D., and C. E. Weaver: Sonic energy as a lethal agent for yeast and bacteria, *J. Bact.*, 32:361, 1936.

Bogash, R. C.: Polyvinylpyrrolidone iodine, *Bull. Amer. Soc. Hosp. Phar.*, vol. 13, May-June, 1956.

Brewer, J. H.: Mercurials—inorganic and organic. From "Antiseptics, Disinfectants, Fungicides, and Sterilization," edited by G. F. Reddish, Philadelphia, Lea & Febiger, 1957.

Burnett, W. T., Jr., M. L. Morse, A. W. Burke, Jr., and A. Hollaender: Reduction of the X-ray sensitivity of *Escherichia coli* by sodium hydrosulfite and certain other inorganic sulfur compounds, *J. Bact.*, 63:591, 1952.

Carroll, B.: The relative germicidal activity of triiodide and diatomic iodine, *J. Bact.*, 69:413, 1955.

Chambers, C. W., P. W. Kabler, G. Malaney, and A. Bryant: Iodine as a bactericide, *Soap San. Chem.*, 28:149, 1952.

Chang, S. L., and J. C. Morris: Elemental iodine as a disinfectant for drinking water, *Ind. Eng. Chem.*, 45:1009, 1953.

Chaplin, C. E.: Bacterial resistance to quaternary ammonium disinfectants, *J. Bact.*, 63:453, 1952.

Churchman, J. W.: The selective bactericidal action of gentian violet, *J. Exp. Med.*, 16:221, 1912.

———: Staining reactions of bacteria. From "The Newer Knowledge of Bacteriology and Immunology," edited by E. O. Jordan and I. S. Falk, Chicago, University of Chicago Press, 1928.

Cohen, B.: Disinfection studies. The effects of temperature and hydrogen-ion concentration upon the viability of *Bacterium coli* and *Bacterium typhosum* in water, *J. Bact.*, 7:183, 1922.

Curran, H. R., and F. R. Evans: Quaternary ammonium compounds as sterilizing agents for bacterial spores, *J. Dairy Sci.*, 33:1, 1950.

Eisenberg, P.: Untersuchungen über spezifische Desinfektionsvorgänge. II. Mitteilung: Über die Wirkung von Salzen und Ionen auf Bakterien, *Centr. Bakt.*, Abt. I. Orig., 82:69, 1919.

Ephrati, E.: The mechanism of the effect of X-rays on bacterial toxins, *Biochem. J.*, 42:383, 1948.

Fabian, F. W., and H. T. Graham: Influence of high frequency displacement currents on bacteria, *J. Infectious Diseases*, 53:76, 1933.

Ficker, M.: Über Lebensdauer und Absterben von pathogenen Keimen, *Z. Hyg.*, 29:1, 1898.

Fildes, P.: A rational approach to research in chemotherapy, *Lancet*, 238:955, 1940.

Fischer, E., O. Hoffmann, E. Prado, and R. Boné: On the mechanism of bacteriostasis with triphenylmethane dyes, *J. Bact.*, 48:439, 1944.

Fishbein, M., et al.: "Medical Uses of Soap," Philadelphia, J. B. Lippincott Company, 1945.

Foord, D. C., W. A. McOmie, and A. J. Salle: Germicidal efficiency of some silver compounds tested by the improved tissue culture method, *Proc. Soc. Exp. Biol. Med.*, 38:572, 1938.

Friberg, L., and E. Hammarström: The action of free available chlorine on bacteria and bacterial viruses, *Acta Path. Microbiol. Scand.*, 38:127, 1956.

Gaden, E. L., Jr., E. J. Henley, and V. P. Collins: Preservation of milk by radiation, *Food Technol.*, 5:506, 1951.

Gale, C. K., and D. Miller: Bactericidal action of short and ultrashort waves, *J. Lab. Clin. Med.*, 21:31, 1935.

Galesloot, T. E.: Ultra-Geluidsgolven en de mogelijke toepassing ervan in de zuivelindustrie, *Netherlands Milk Dairy J.*, 9:88, 1955.

Gershenfeld, L., and B. Witlin: The egg injection method in the evaluation of bactericides, *Am. J. Pharm.*, 119:156, 1947.

——— and ———: Free halogens. A comparative study of their efficiencies as bactericidal agents, *ibid.*, 121:95, 1949.

Glassman, H. N.: Surface active agents and their application in bacteriology, *Bact. Rev.*, 12:105, 1948.

Goetchius, G. R.: Testing germicides, *Soap San. Chem.*, 26:131, 1950.

Goldblith, S. A., B. E. Proctor, S. Davison, B. Kan, C. J. Bates, E. M. Oberle, M. Karel, and D. A. Lang: Relative bactericidal efficiencies of three types of high-energy ionizing radiations, *Food Res.*, 18:659, 1953.

Goucher, C. R., I. Kamei, and W. Kocholaty: Some results and interpretations of X-irradiation studies with *Escherichia coli*, *Arch. Biochem. Biophys.*, 65:522, 1956.

Green, T. W., and J. M. Birkeland: Use of the chick embryo in evaluating disinfectants, *Proc. Soc. Exp. Biol. Med.*, 51:55, 1942.

——— and ———: The use of the developing chick embryo as a method of testing the antibacterial effectiveness of wound disinfectants, *J. Infectious Diseases*, 74:32, 1944.

Gunter, S. E., and H. I. Kohn: The effect of X-rays on the survival of bacteria and yeast, *J. Bact.*, 71:571, 1956.

Haberman, S.: Lethal and dissociate effects of X-rays on bacteria, Absts., Doctoral Dissertations, No. 36, Ohio State University, 1942.

Hamre, D.: The effect of ultrasonic waves upon *Klebsiella pneumoniae*, *Saccha-*

romyces cerevisiae, Miyagawanella felis, and influenza virus A, *J. Bact.,* **57**:279, 1949.

Harris, J. O., A. Eisenstark, and R. D. Dragsdorf: A study of the location of adsorbed mercuric ions in *Escherichia coli, J. Bact.,* **68**:745, 1954.

Harvey, E. N., and A. L. Loomis: The destruction of luminous bacteria by high frequency sound waves, *J. Bact.,* **17**:373, 1929.

Henry, R. J.: The mode of action of sulfonamides, *Bact. Rev.,* **7**:175, 1943.

Hirsch, M. M., and M. V. Novak: Evaluation of germicides with relation to tissue toxicity, *Proc. Soc. Exp. Biol. Med.,* **50**:376, 1942.

Hoffmann, C. E., and O. Rahn: The bactericidal and bacteriostatic action of crystal violet, *J. Bact.,* **47**:177, 1944.

Holm, G. E., and J. M. Sherman: Salt effects in bacterial growth. I. Preliminary paper, *J. Bact.,* **6**:511, 1921.

Hotchkiss, M.: Studies on salt action. VI. The stimulating and inhibitive effect of certain cations upon bacterial growth, *J. Bact.,* **8**:141, 1923.

Ingraham, M. A.: The bacteriostatic action of gentian violet and its dependence on the oxidation-reduction potential, *J. Bact.,* **26**:573, 1933.

Ingram, M.: The germicidal effects of free and combined sulphur dioxide, *J. Soc. Chem. Ind.,* **67**:18, 1948.

——— and L. J. Page: The survival of microbes in modulated high-frequency voltage fields, *Proc. Soc. Appl. Bact.,* **16**:69, 1953.

Jacobs, S. E., and M. J. Thornley: The lethal action of ultrasonic waves on bacteria suspended in milk and other liquids, *J. Appl. Bact.,* **17**:38, 1954.

Kempe, L. L.: Combined effects of heat and radiation in food sterilization, *Appl. Microbiol.,* **3**:346, 1955.

———, J. T. Graikoski, and R. A. Gillies: Gamma ray sterilization of canned meat previously inoculated with anaerobic bacterial spores, *Appl. Microbiol.,* **2**:330, 1954.

Kinsloe, H., E. Ackerman, and J. J. Reid: Exposure of microorganisms to measured sound fields, *J. Bact.,* **68**: 373, 1954.

Klarmann, E. G., and E. S. Wright: Synthetic and semi-synthetic media for disinfectant testing, *Soap San. Chem.,* January, 1945, p. 113.

Klein, M., and Z. G. Kardon: The "reversal," neutralization, and selectivity of germicidal cationic detergents, *J. Bact.,* **54**:245, 1947.

Klimek, J. W., and J. H. Bailey: Factors influencing the rate of killing of *Escherichia coli* exposed to benzalkonium chloride, *Appl. Microbiol.,* **4**:53, 1956.

Klotz, I. M., and M. Mellody: The inhibition of growth of *Escherichia coli* by some derivatives of urea, *J. Bact.,* **57**:477, 1949.

Knox, W. E., P. K. Stumpf, D. E. Green, and V. H. Auerbach: The inhibition of sulfhydryl enzymes as the basis of the bactericidal action of chlorine, *J. Bact.,* **55**:451, 1948.

Koh, W. Y., C. T. Morehouse, and V. L. Chandler: Relative resistances of microorganisms to cathode rays. I. Nonsporeforming bacteria, *Appl. Microbiol.,* **4**:143, 1956.

Kojima, S.: The effects of peroxidase on the bactericidal action of phenols, *J. Biochem.,* **14**:95, 1931.

Kroeger, A. V., and J. E. Kempf: Inactivation of the influenza virus by low voltage Roentgen rays, *J. Bact.,* **77**:237, 1959.

Landy, M., N. W. Larkum, and E. J. Ostwald: Bacterial synthesis of *p*-aminobenzoic acid, *Proc. Soc. Exp. Biol. Med.,* **52**:338, 1943.

———, ———, ———, and F. Streightoff: Increased synthesis of *p*-aminobenzoic acid associated with the development of sulfonamide resistance in *Staphylococcus aureus, Science,* **97**:265, 1943.

Lawrence, C. A.: Inactivation of the germicidal action of quaternary ammonium compounds, *J. Am. Pharm. Assoc.,* **37**:57, 1948.

Lloyd, R. S., and M. J. Foter: Efficiency of dry heat and formaldehyde in sterilizing used bedding, *Pub. Health Rep.,* **70**:810, 1955.

McCulloch, E. C.: The efficiency of soaps and other disinfectants in destroying mastitis streptococci, *Am. J. Vet. Research,* **1**:18, 1940.

Marr, A. G., and E. H. Cota-Robles: Sonic disruption of *Azotobacter vinelandii*, *J. Bact.*, **74**:79, 1957.

Morgan, B. H., and J. M. Reed: Resistance of bacterial spores to gamma irradiation, *Food Research*, **19**:357, 1954.

Morton, H. E.: "Germicidal" soaps. I. The importance of a clean skin, the action of soaps in freeing the skin of viable microorganisms, and methods for testing the efficiency of germicidal (medicated) soaps, *J. Am. Med. Assoc.*, **124**:1195, 1944.

———, L. L. North, Jr., and F. B. Engley, Jr.: The bacteriostatic and bactericidal actions of some mercurial compounds on hemolytic streptococci, *ibid.*, **136**:36, 1948.

Nungester, W. J., and A. H. Kempf: An "infection-prevention" test for the evaluation of skin disinfectants, *J. Infectious Diseases*, **71**:174, 1942.

———, R. L. Thirlby, and A. B. Vial: Evaluation of hexachlorophene and detergents as substitutes for the surgical scrub, *Surg. Gynecol. Obstet.*, **88**:639, 1949.

Nye, R. N.: The relative in vitro activity of certain antiseptics in aqueous solutions, *J. Am. Med. Assoc.*, **108**:280, 1937.

Ostrolenk, M.: Comparison of in vitro germicide test methods, *J. Am. Pharm. Assoc.*, Sci. Ed., **39**:71, 1950.

Paff, G. H., R. A. Lehman, and J. P. Halperin: Comparison of the toxicity of antiseptics for embryonic tissue and bacteria, *Proc. Soc. Exp. Biol. Med.*, **58**:323, 1945.

Pepper, R. E., N. T. Buffa, and V. L. Chandler: Relative resistances of microorganisms to cathode rays. III. Bacterial spores, *Appl. Microbiol.*, **4**:149, 1956.

Rahn, O.: Physical methods of sterilization of microorganisms, *Bact. Rev.*, **9**:1, 1945*a*.

———: Injury and death of bacteria by chemical agents, *Biodynamica*, 1945*b*.

——— and J. E. Conn: Effect of increase in acidity on antiseptic efficiency, *Ind. Eng. Chem.*, **36**:185, 1944.

Reddish, G. F.: "Antiseptics, Disinfectants, Fungicides, and Sterilization," Philadelphia, Lea & Febiger, 1957.

Reichel, H.: Zur Theorie der Desinfektion: die Desinfektionswirkung des Phenols I, *Biochem. Z.*, **22**:149, 1909.

Rideal, S., and J. T. A. Walker: The standardization of disinfectants, *J. Roy. Sanit. Inst.*, **24**:424, 1903.

Robertson, O. H., E. M. Appel, T. T. Puck, H. M. Lemon, and M. H. Ritter: A study of the bactericidal activity in vitro of certain glycols and closely related compounds, *J. Infectious Diseases*, **83**:124, 1948.

Roblin, R. O., Jr.: Metabolite antagonists, *Chem. Rev.*, **38**:255, 1946.

——— and P. H. Bell: The relation of structure to activity of sulfanilamide type compounds, *Ann. N.Y. Acad. Sci.*, **44**:449, 1943.

Romans, I. B.: Silver compounds. From "Antiseptics, Disinfectants, Fungicides, and Sterilization," edited by G. F. Reddish, Philadelphia, Lea & Febiger, 1957.

Rotman, B.: On the mechanism of sonic lysis of bacteria, *J. Bact.*, **72**:827, 1956.

Ruehle, G. L. A., and C. M. Brewer: U.S. Food and Drug Administration methods of testing antiseptics and disinfectants, *U.S. Dept. Agr. Circ.*, 198, 1931.

Salle, A. J.: An improved tissue toxicity technique for the evaluation of germicidal substances, *Appl. Microbiol.*, **3**:63, 1955.

——— and B. W. Catlin: Profile evaluation of germicides, *J. Am. Pharm. Assoc.*, Sci. Ed., **36**:129, 1947.

——— and A. S. Lazarus: A comparison of the resistance of bacteria and embryonic tissue to germicidal substances. I. Merthiolate, *Proc. Soc. Exp. Biol. Med.*, **32**:665, 1935.

———, W. A. McOmie, and I. L. Shechmeister: A new method for the evaluation of germicidal substances, *J. Bact.*, **34**:267, 1937.

———, ———, ———, and D. C. Foord: An improved method for the evaluation of germicidal substances, *Proc. Soc. Exp. Biol. Med.*, **37**:694, 1938.

———, ———, ———, and ———: The evaluation of a group of germicides by the tissue culture technique, *J. Bact.*, **37**:639, 1939.

Shannon, J. A.: The relationship between chemical structure and physiological disposition of a series of substances allied to sulfanilamide, *Ann. N.Y. Acad. Sci.*, **44**:455, 1943.

Shechmeister, I. L., and A. J. Salle: Germicidal efficiency of synthetic phenolic compounds tested by the improved tissue culture method, *Proc. Soc. Exp. Biol. Med.*, **38**:295, 1938.

Shelanski, H. A., and M. V. Shelanski: PVP-iodine: history, toxicity and therapeutic uses, *J. Inter. Coll. Surg.*, vol. 25, June, 1956.

Sherman, F. G., and H. B. Chase: Effects of ionizing radiations on enzyme activities of yeast cells. I. Relation between anaerobic CO_2 production and colony production at intervals after X-radiation, *J. Cell. Comp. Physiol.*, **33**:17, 1949*a*; II. Influence of dilution on X-ray induced inhibition of anaerobic CO_2 production and colony formation, *ibid.*, **34**:207, 1949*b*.

Sherman, J. M., and G. E. Holm: Salt effects in bacterial growth. II. The growth of *Bacterium coli* in relation to H-ion concentration, *J. Bact.*, **7**:465, 1922.

Shropshire, R. F.: Turbidimetric evaluation of bacterial disruption by sonic energy, *J. Bact.*, **53**:685, 1947*a*.

———: Bacterial dispersion by sonic energy, *ibid.*, **54**:325, 1947*b*.

Slade, H. D., and J. K. Vetter: Studies on *Streptococcus pyogenes*. I. Observations on the microscopical and biological aspects of the disintegration and solubilization of a type 6 strain by sonic oscillation, *J. Bact.*, **71**:236, 1956.

Smith, C. R.: Alcohol as a disinfectant against the tubercle bacillus, *Pub. Health Reports*, **62**:1285, 1947.

Spangler, C. D., and C.-E. A. Winslow: The influence of the sodium ion on the viability of washed cells of *Bacillus cereus*, *J. Bact.*, **45**:373, 1943.

Spink, W. W., L. D. Wright, J. J. Vivino, and H. R. Skeggs: Para-aminobenzoic acid production by staphylococci, *J. Exp. Med.*, **79**:331, 1944.

Stapleton, G. E.: Variations in the sensitivity of *Escherichia coli* to ionizing radiations during the growth cycle, *J. Bact.*, **70**:357, 1955.

———, D. Billen, and A. Hollaender: The role of enzymatic oxygen removal in chemical protection against X-ray inactivation of bacteria, *J. Bact.*, **63**:805, 1952.

Stuart, L. S., L. F. Ortenzio, and J. L. Friedl: The phenol coefficient number as an index to the practical use-dilution for disinfection. *J. Assoc. Off. Agr. Chem.*, **38**:465, 1955.

Tanner, F. W., and F. L. Wilson: Germicidal action of aliphatic alcohols, *Proc. Soc. Exp. Biol. Med.*, **52**:138, 1943.

Tarpley, W., J. Ilavsky, B. Manowitz, and R. V. Horrigan: I. The effect of high energy gamma radiation from kilocurie radioactive sources on bacteria, *J. Bact.*, **65**:305, 1953.

Tilley, F. W.: Bactericidal efficiency of certain aniline dyes, *J. Agr. Res.*, **58**:941, 1939.

Tomcsik, J.: Effect of disinfectants and of surface active agents on bacterial protoplasts, *Proc. Soc. Exp. Biol. Med.*, **89**:459, 1955.

Trump, J. G., and B. E. Proctor: Sterilizing with electrons, *Modern Packaging*, July, 1951.

Weinstein, L.: Action of urea and some of its derivatives on bacteria. V. Antibacterial activity of methyl- and thiourea, *Proc. Soc. Exp. Biol. Med.*, **63**:506, 1946.

Welch, H., and C. M. Brewer: The toxicity-indices of some basic antiseptic substances, *J. Immunol.*, **43**:25, 1942.

——— and A. C. Hunter: Method for determining the effect of chemical antisepsis on phagocytosis, *Am. J. Pub. Health*, **30**:129, 1940.

———, G. G. Slocum, and A. C. Hunter: Method for determining the toxicity of antiseptics as measured by the destruction of human leucocytes, *J. Lab. Clin. Med.*, **27**:1432, 1942.

Whipple, G. C., and A. Mayer, Jr.: On the relation between oxygen in water and the longevity of the typhoid bacillus, *J. Infectious Diseases*, Supp. **2**:76, 1906.

Whitney, R. McL., and L. A. Russell: An experimental approach to problems of control in quantitative studies of ultrasonic bactericidal effects, *Food Research*, **16**:205, 1951.

Williams, O. B., and N. Gaines: The bactericidal effects of high frequency sound waves, *J. Infectious Diseases*, **47**:485, 1930

Wilson, G. S.: The proportion of viable bacteria in young cultures with especial reference to the technique employed in counting, *J. Bact.*, **7**:405, 1922.

Winslow, C.-E. A., and I. S. Falk: Studies on salt action. VIII. The influence of calcium and sodium salts at various hydrogen ion concentrations upon the viability of *Bacterium coli*, *J. Bact.*, **8**:215, 1923*a*; IX. The additive and antagonistic effects of sodium and calcium chlorides upon the viability of *Bacterium coli*, *ibid.*, **8**:237, 1923*b*.

—— and M. Hotchkiss: Studies on salt action. V. The influence of various salts upon bacterial growth, *Proc. Soc. Exp. Biol. Med.*, **19**:314, 1922.

—— and E. E. Lochridge: The toxic effect of certain acids upon typhoid and colon bacilli in relation to the degree of their dissociation, *J. Infectious Diseases*, **3**:547, 1906.

Witlin, B.: Evaluation of bactericides by egg injection method with special reference to development of technic, *Proc. Soc. Exp. Biol. Med.*, **49**:27, 1942.

Woese, C. R.: Comparison of the X-ray sensitivity of bacterial spores, *J. Bact.*, **75**:5, 1958.

Wood, R. W., and A. L. Loomis: The physical and biological effects of high-frequency sound waves of great intensity, *Phil. Mag.*, Series 7, **4**:417, 1927.

Woods, D. D.: The relation of para-aminobenzoic acid to the mechanism of the action of sulfanilamide, *Brit. J. Exp. Path.*, **21**:74, 1940.

CHAPTER 19

Bacteriology of Air

The atmosphere consists of a mixture of permanent gases and variable quantities of water and solid particles. Its gaseous content, vapor pressure, and suspended matter are not constant in composition.

According to Landsberg (1951), air has the following composition:

Element	Volume, per cent	Range
Nitrogen	78.03	
Oxygen	20.99	
Argon	0.94	
Carbon dioxide	0.03	
Hydrogen	0.01	
Neon	0.0012	
Krypton	0.0010	
Helium	0.0004	
Xenon	0.0001	
Ozone	Very variable	2 to 20×10^{-7}
Water vapor	Very variable	0 to 4
Dust	Very variable	0 to millions of particles per ml.

The composition shows slight variation with latitude and to a lesser extent with altitude. The ozone owes its existence in the atmosphere to photosynthesis from oxygen under the influence of solar ultraviolet radiation. This process takes place at heights of 15 to 22 miles, where the ozone concentration is much greater than at the surface. Most of the water vapor is concentrated in the lower atmosphere. The amount is usually about 1.2 per cent by volume, but in cold weather this quantity may fall almost to zero. Almost any sample contains suspended matter consisting of dust, bacteria, yeasts, molds, pollen grains, etc. Unlike the gaseous content, the suspended matter shows considerable variation.

Air is not a natural environment for the growth and reproduction of microorganisms. It does not contain the necessary amount of moisture and kinds of nutrients in a form utilizable by bacteria and other microscopic organisms. Therefore, air does not possess a flora. Yet organisms are found in air, and their presence is of considerable importance from the standpoint of economy and public health.

Bacteria are introduced into air by various forces, the principal source being from dust particles containing dry vegetative cells and spores. The organisms for the most part are saprophytes, i.e., forms which live on dead organic matter. They are of great importance to the canner and in sugar refineries, dairies, biological laboratories, etc. In short, they are the organisms responsible for contaminations from the air.

The species vary somewhat, depending upon the locality. However, certain forms are quite uniformly present. Molds and yeasts are quite commonly found in the air and in some localities even outnumber the bacteria. These organisms produce spores which are capable of resisting unfavorable conditions for long periods of time. The aerobic spore-forming bacilli from the soil are found quite frequently in the air. The best-known member of this group is *Bacillus subtilis*. It is known as the hay bacillus and is one of the most common bacterial organisms found in nature. Its natural habitat is in the soil and on vegetation. Since it is a spore-forming organism, it is very resistant to drying and other unfavorable environmental conditions. Sarcinae and micrococci also are found in air. The spherical, saprophytic, chromogenic organisms found in air usually belong to these two genera.

NUMBER AND KINDS OF BACTERIA IN AIR

The number of organisms in air is dependent upon the activity in the environment and upon the amount of dust stirred up. An active environment shows a higher bacterial count than a less active one. The numbers in dirty, untidy rooms are greater than in clean rooms.

A rich, fertile, cultivated soil shows a higher viable count than a sandy, or clay, uncultivated soil. It follows that the air above the fertile, cultivated soil will contain more organisms than the air above the poor soil. Likewise, the air above a bare surface contains more organisms than the air above land covered with vegetation. This means that, where the earth is bare, the organisms can be blown more easily into the air, because the earth is not protected from air currents.

Microorganisms have been isolated from the air over the ocean. However, marine air contains usually fewer organisms than terrestrial air.

Kelly and Layne (1957a, b) collected air samples over the Atlantic Ocean at altitudes of 8000 to 9000 ft. The organisms isolated were common types that could be found by sampling soil at random. The organisms were placed in the following genera: *Achromobacter, Bacillus, Corynebacterium, Flavobacterium, Micrococcus, Sarcina,* and *Staphylococcus.* They concluded that the organisms isolated from air over the ocean were very similar to those found over land. The ratio of the types of bacteria could be used to some extent to trace the history of an air mass. The tropical air tended to show a higher percentage of Gram-negative rods and Gram-positive pleomorphic rods than micrococci and sporeformers, whereas arctic air tended to show the opposite.

Bacteria remain in air for varying periods of time, depending upon the speed of the air current, the size of the particles on which they are attached, and the humidity of the air. Bacteria are slightly heavier than air and settle out slowly in a quiet atmosphere. A gentle air current is capable of keeping them in suspension almost indefinitely. This applies to organisms not attached to particles but existing in the free state. Bacteria attached to dust particles or in droplets of water settle out at a much faster rate.

A damp or humid atmosphere contains fewer organisms than a dry one, owing to the fact that the organisms are carried down by the droplets of moisture. The air of a refrigerator is usually free from all organisms. Therefore, air during the dry summer months contains many more organisms than during the wet winter months. Gently expired air from the lungs is sterile. The moist passages of the upper respiratory tract remove the bacteria from the air. Cotton stoppers in pipettes are not necessary as far as contamination of the contents is concerned. They are inserted as a protection against aspirating infectious or other material into the mouth.

ALTITUDES ATTAINED BY MICROORGANISMS

Organisms are able to attain considerable altitudes. According to Proctor and Parker (1935, 1938),

The ability of these living microorganisms to attain altitudes of 20,000 ft. or more through the chance action of air currents is particularly significant as it suggests the almost limitless possibilities of travel in a horizontal direction. The survival of such forms despite the many influences which are unfavorable to their existence is also significant in view of the length of time for which they may remain viable.

The presence of pollen at high altitudes also indicates the importance of air as a vehicle for the transmission of wind-borne pollens over wide areas.

The high dust counts obtained in comparison to the numbers of microorganisms is interesting in view of the various possible sources of dust, some of which, as from soil, might be also associated with high bacterial counts, while in other cases particles from smokestacks and industries might be sterile.

METHODS EMPLOYED FOR ENUMERATION OF BACTERIA IN AIR

Koch (1881) employed solid media in plates and exposed them to air for varying periods of time. The plates were then incubated and the colonies counted.

This is one of the simplest procedures used for air examinations but is of no value from a quantitative standpoint. It does not indicate the

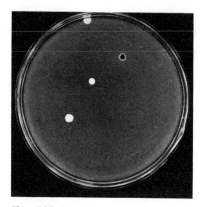 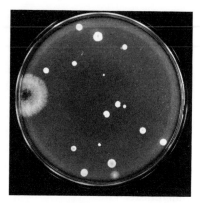

FIG. 192. Bacteria in air. Left, colonies developing on an agar plate exposed to a quiet atmosphere (office) for 10 min.; right, colonies developing on an agar plate exposed to an active atmosphere (laboratory) for the same period of time.

number of organisms present in a known volume of air. However, the method does give relative results and is commonly employed for this purpose.

The results of plates exposed to different environments for the same period of time, then incubated at 37°C. for 24 hr., are shown in Fig. 192. It may be seen that the bacterial population increases in proportion to the activity of the atmosphere.

A.P.H.A. Method. In 1917 the American Public Health Association adopted the filter shown in Fig. 193 as the standard procedure for the quantitative bacterial analysis of air. A layer of fine sand is supported by a plug of cotton resting on the shoulder at the junction of the small and large tubes. The upper end of the sand filter is closed with a stopper through which passes a tube 6 mm. in diameter and bent at a 45° angle. After a known volume of air has been drawn through the filter, the sand is shaken into 10 ml. sterile water, and aliquot parts are plated out in nutrient agar.

FIG. 193. A modification of the Petri sand filter adopted by the American Public Health Association, 1909.

Wells Air Centrifuge. Wells (1933) utilized the principle of the centrifuge for the separation of bacteria from air (Fig. 194).

The centrifuge consists of a head assembly with exhaust fan, air inlet tube, and aluminum chamber to contain sample tube. The variable-speed motor is mounted in an aluminum housing and equipped with a 300-step rheostat providing a range of speeds from 2000 to 4500 r.p.m. Air flow is measured by a manometer tube with reservoir bottle and rubber connecting tube. The head assembly fan and sample chamber are driven by the motor through a hub on which rests the sample tube. The air inlet tube, which is suspended from the case top by means of a rubber disk and clamp, serves as upper shaft.

An auxiliary case is provided for carrying 12 sample tubes and melted agar.

In use, the culture medium in a fluid state is poured into the sample tube. The tube is then inserted in the centrifuge and the current switched on. The incoming air is mixed with the agar, and the medium is spread as a thin film on the walls of the sample tube by the centrifugal force of

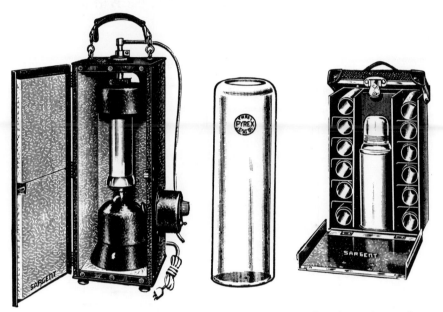

FIG. 194. Wells air centrifuge. Left, centrifuge; center, sample tube; right, auxiliary case containing sample tubes and melted agar. See text for description.

rotation. The bacteria are deposited in the film and may be counted after incubation.

Wells stated that four independent operations are combined in one compact instrument:

1. Air flow is created and regulated.
2. The amount of air is measured.
3. The bacteria are collected.
4. The bacteria grow and can be counted on the collection medium without separate plating.

The Wells centrifuge is simple to operate, quickly manipulated, and portable. All testing is carried out in one step. The apparatus has a wide range of application, and any type of solid medium may be used, depending upon the types of organisms to be cultivated.

Funnel Impinger. Hollaender and Dalla Valle (1939) described a funnel impinger for sampling air-borne bacteria (Fig. 195). The sampling device consists of a brass container with a removable bottom. The container is fitted with an inverted 60° 3-in. glass funnel which sits approximately 1 cm. from the bottom of a standard-type Petri dish. The latter is placed in the lower portion of the container before use and is then screwed tightly against the washer as shown in the figure. The inside of the funnel and the rim are swabbed with alcohol before use. The air sample passes through the funnel stem, and the air-borne organisms and dust are impinged upon the medium placed in the Petri dish. The air

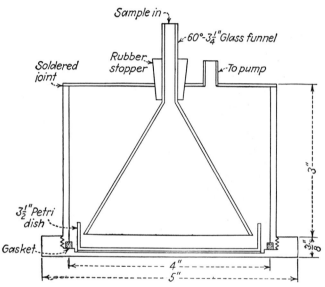

Fig. 195. Funnel device used for sampling air-borne bacteria. (*After Hollaender and Dalla Valle.*)

sample is drawn by means of an ordinary impinger pump in series with a flowmeter. A sampling rate of 1 cu. ft. per min. was found to be the most effective. They found their funnel device to be efficient and to compare favorably with the Wells centrifuge, giving slightly higher results when the bacterial population was low. The method is simple and portable, and all testing is carried out in one operation.

Radial-jet Sampler. Luckiesh, Taylor, and Holladay (1946) recommended the use of the radial-jet sampler (Fig. 196), utilizing the principle of the slit sampler first employed by Bourdillon, Lidwell, and Thomas (1941). The air is drawn through the sampler by means of a vacuum pump attached to the outlet. The air enters a closed metal drum, as shown, passes through a radial slit in the bottom of the drum, and impinges at high velocity on the culture medium in the Petri dish below.

It then passes over the edge of the dish and out through an opening below, as shown. At an air rate of 1 cu. ft. per min., the velocity of air through the slit is approximately 100 ft. per sec. The Petri dish is rotated at a rate of 2 r.p.m. to spread the colonies uniformly over the surface of the culture medium.

The efficiency of the sampler has been evaluated by connecting other

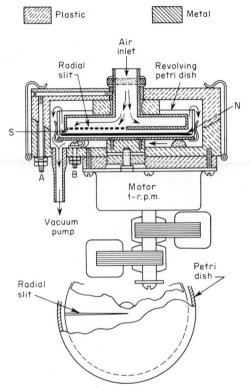

Fig. 196. A vertical section of the radial-jet air sampler. At the bottom is a plan view of the radial slit in relation to the Petri dish. (*After Luckiesh, Taylor, and Holladay.*)

samplers of different types in series with it. Apparently the radial-jet sampler collects more than 95 per cent of the air-borne bacteria.

Electrostatic Air Sampler. The same authors also applied the technique of the electrostatic principle to the collection of bacteria and devised a sampler which they named the duplex electrostatic air sampler (Fig. 197). The two Petri dishes are placed in the two plastic units, which have removable covers. A small electrically operated blower draws air at equal rates through the two units. One of these has the lower electrode negative and the upper electrode, a fairly flat metal cone, positive. In the other unit the electrical conditions are reversed. The applied voltage of approximately 7000 volts is derived from a half-wave rectifier employ-

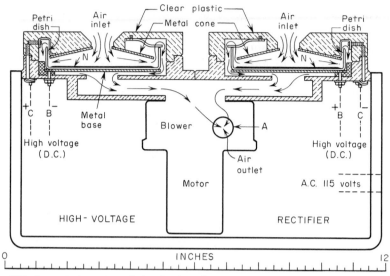

FIG. 197. A vertical section of the duplex electrostatic air sampler. (*After Luckiesh, Taylor, and Holladay.*)

ing a high-voltage transformer and an $^{87}\!\!\%_2 \times 2$ rectifier tube. The air rate through each unit is 0.5 cu. ft. per min.

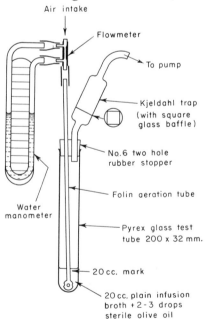

FIG. 198. Device for the collection of air-borne bacteria. (*After Lemon.*)

Both positively and negatively charged bacteria exist simultaneously in the air. Those having a positive charge will be collected on the negative electrode (or the Petri dish placed on it), and those negatively charged will be collected on the positive electrode. Consequently, one unit collects on the Petri dish those which are positively charged and the other those which are negatively charged.

Lemon Air Sampler. Lemon (1943) recommended a simple device for the collection of organisms from air (Fig. 198). The apparatus consists of a glass Folin aeration tube with a bulb at one end perforated by six holes. The tube is passed through a two-hole rubber stopper, and the bulb is centered near the bottom of the containing test tube. The Kjeldahl trap with square glass baffle is shortened at both ends for convenience, and a slight bend made in the intake, so that this may be inserted into the remaining hole of the stopper. A small flowmeter measures the rate of air flow entering the upper open end of the Folin tube. An air pump is attached to the exhaust end of the Kjeldahl trap.

The entire bubbler can be sterilized by autoclaving or by rinsing with 70 per cent alcohol and drying. Air drawn in at a rate of 25 to 30 liters per minute is dispersed through 20 ml. of broth containing two to three drops of olive oil to prevent foaming. Room-air samples generally require about 300 liters of air for satisfactory results.

Capillary Impinger. Kluyver and Visser (1950) made a comparison of a number of air-sampling devices and concluded that the capillary impinger type as used by Rosebury (1947) was the most satisfactory (Fig. 199). The air is brought in contact with water through a capillary tube. The purpose of the capillary is to break up clumps of bacteria. For best results, the capillary orifice must be placed about 5 mm. above the bottom of the flask and at least 5 mm. below the upper level of the water. Then an aliquot part of the water is mixed with melted nutrient agar and the number of colonies that develop are counted. The device recovered at least 99 per cent or more of the spores of *Bacillus cereus* from artificially contaminated air.

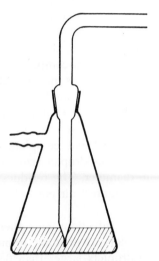

Fig. 199. Capillary impinger. See text for description. (*After Kluyver and Visser.*)

Solberg, Shaffer, and Kelley (1956) made a comparison of the all-glass impinger, the electrostatic air sampler, and the funnel impinger. They found the all-glass impinger and the electrostatic air sampler to be about equally effective in the collection of air-borne microorganisms from air streams. Both types had an efficiency of about 99 per cent.

For more information see Andersen (1958); Cown, Kethley, and Fincher (1957); du Buy and Hollaender (1945); du Buy, Hollaender, and Lackey (1945); Griffin et al. (1956); O'Connell, Wiggin, and Pike (1960); Rosebury (1947); Wells et al. (1947).

IMPORTANCE OF STATE OF SUSPENSION

Organisms in air are seldom in a free state but are usually attached to floating particles such as dust, saliva, or carbon. The state of suspension plays a very important role on the settling velocity of bacteria in air. It is of great importance to distinguish between ubiquitous saprophytic soil organisms raised as dust and those from body tissues introduced into the air during the processes of coughing, sneezing, talking, and singing. The former probably do not have any pathogenic significance; the latter do.

The state of suspension of bacteria introduced into the air under these conditions is different. Organisms in the free state are slightly heavier than air and settle out very slowly in a quiet atmosphere. A gentle current is capable of keeping them in suspension almost indefinitely. Dust particles laden with bacteria settle out rapidly and remain in a quiet atmosphere for a relatively short period of time. Droplets expelled into the air during coughing and sneezing do not necessarily fall immediately to the ground within a short distance from their source. As droplets decrease in size, the surface exposed to air resistance becomes relatively greater when compared to the weight or gravitational attraction toward the earth. This means that the droplets remain suspended longer as their size becomes smaller.

The rate of evaporation also depends upon surface area and becomes more rapid as the droplets are reduced in size. Some droplets are of such size that complete evaporation occurs in falling the height of a man. This droplet size has been estimated to be approximately 0.1 mm. in diameter. The residues of droplets of this size will float or drift with the slightest air currents and become in effect a part of the atmosphere itself.

Air infections may then be said to occur by means of two types of droplets, depending upon their size. Droplet infection proper applies to droplets larger than 0.1 mm. in diameter, which rapidly settle out a short distance from their source before drying occurs. The other type of droplet infection may be called air-borne; this term applies to the dried residues of infected droplets (droplet nuclei) derived from droplets less than 0.1 mm. in diameter. The time they remain suspended in air depends upon the activity of the atmosphere. Droplet infection may become air-borne infection when large droplets evaporate in settling to the ground and then are lifted into the air as dust. It can be seen that droplet infection remains localized and concentrated, whereas air-borne infection may be carried long distances and is dilute.

Dust in hospital wards, army barracks, and other places where people congregate has been shown to become highly contaminated with certain pathogenic bacteria associated with diseases of the respiratory tract, particularly streptococcal infections. The dispersion of these organisms into the air from floors, bedclothes, and clothes of the room occupants at the time of floor sweeping, bedmaking, and dressing results in a general contamination of the environment, providing many opportunities for the spread of disease from direct or indirect contact with the infected dust. Recent studies suggest that the spread of respiratory-tract diseases in this manner is more important than by the direct inhalation of infectious droplets or droplet nuclei.

For more information see Duguid and Wallace (1948) and Loosli (1947, 1948).

AIR-BORNE DISEASE ORGANISMS AND THEIR CONTROL

Newer techniques developed during the past few years have stimulated a renewed interest in air bacteriology. It was formerly supposed that air played an insignificant role in transferring infection from one person to another. This view is no longer tenable since it has been definitely established that air is capable of transmitting infections, especially those of the respiratory tract, and that infections transferred in this manner could be of frequent occurrence. This is especially true in closed spaces such as in rooms, offices, theaters, and halls.

Wells (1935, 1938), in his researches on air-borne infections, came to the following conclusions:

1. During coughing and sneezing, minute droplets containing microorganisms from infected surfaces may be ejected into the air.
2. Most of these droplets are sufficiently small to evaporate before they can settle to the ground, leaving suspended in the air minute residues.
3. These nuclei, in which the microorganisms remain viable for considerable periods, may drift in air currents like particles of cigarette smoke.
4. The air breathed commonly by the various persons congregated in a room or other enclosed space can thereby transfer organisms from one person to another and plant them upon the susceptible tissues of the respiratory tract.

Jennison and Edgerton (1940) and Jennison (1941), by means of high-speed photography, showed that the distance the majority of respiratory droplets were actually expelled was not more than 2 or 3 ft. and often was less. However, droplets discharged during coughing and sneezing could move at a velocity as fast as 152 ft. per sec. Such a speed in dry air would result in almost instantaneous evaporation, producing droplet nuclei. They showed also that the great majority of sneeze droplets, before appreciable evaporation occurred, measured 0.1 to 2 mm. in diameter.

Duguid (1946) made droplets visible by introducing a dye into the mouth just prior to each test. The dyes used were congo red, eosin, or fluorescein. Following solution of the dye in the mouth, droplet spray was produced by sneezing, coughing, or speaking. The spray was directed at a celluloid-surfaced slide held 3 in. in front of the mouth in tests of speaking and 6 in. in front of the mouth in tests of coughing and sneezing. The slides were examined under the microscope and the diameters of 12,000 droplet marks measured with the aid of a micrometer eyepiece. The droplets ranged from 0.001 to 2 mm. in diameter, with 95 per cent falling between 0.002 and 0.1 mm. The smaller droplets were relatively more numerous after sneezing than after coughing or talking.

Boyland, Gaddum, and McDonald (1947) described an apparatus for determining the penetration of particulate air-borne material through the nose. They measured the penetration of particles of a liquid spray in rats, rabbits, goats, sheep, and men. Penetration was found to be inversely proportional to the rate of flow through the nose. Particles of the order of 0.001 mm. in diameter penetrated the nose at all rates of flow, whereas very few particles larger than 0.015 mm. penetrated except at low rates of flow.

The results would indicate that the smaller particles constitute a greater health hazard than the larger particles because they are able to penetrate into the pulmonary depths more readily.

Walter and Hucker (1942) found pathogenic β-streptococci to be relatively widespread in the floor sweepings of public places, particularly schools. Isolated streptococci were found to survive for more than 5 days when artificially inoculated into sterile, dry dust, and also to survive for more than 31 hr. when spread over the surface of floor boards and left at room temperature.

Hamburger, Green, and Hamburger (1945a, b) made nose and throat examinations of patients at two army hospitals and reported that approximately two-thirds of those with streptococcal tonsillitis-pharyngitis or scarlet fever had positive nose cultures. In 95 per cent of the cases, β-hemolytic streptococci persisted longer in the throat than in the nose. Many more hemolytic streptococci were recovered from the air of wards housing patients with positive nose cultures than from wards where the patients' nose cultures were negative but whose throat cultures were positive. Concomitant with the disappearance of organisms from the nose was a diminution of the numbers recovered from the environment. Carriers of β-hemolytic streptococci whose nose cultures were strongly positive represented a definitely more dangerous group than those in whom only the throat cultures were positive.

Hamburger (1947) made quantitative cultures of the hands of nasal carriers of hemolytic streptococci and of individuals who shook hands with these carriers. Results showed that as many as 49,900 of these pathogens could be transferred by ordinary handshakes. The greatest numbers were transferred by carriers who had just blown their noses into sterile handkerchiefs.

Hamburger and Robertson (1948) determined the numbers of streptococci discharged into the air of an experimental room during sneezing, coughing, and talking. They were able to differentiate between streptococci expelled in large, rapidly falling droplets and those discharged as droplet nuclei which remained in the air for at least several minutes.

They recognized four dispersion patterns by sneezing (Fig. 200). In the most common pattern, moderate numbers were expelled in large droplets which fell rapidly to the floor 1½ ft. from the sneezer, but very few or none in droplet nuclei. In one of two less common patterns, small numbers of streptococci were sneezed as droplet nuclei but none in large droplets; in the other, no streptococci were recovered from the air. In the rarest pattern, large numbers of streptococci were expelled both as droplet nuclei and in large droplets; many were collected as far as 9½ ft. from the sneezer.

Loosli et al. (1948) and Lemon, Loosli, and Hamburger (1948) made a study of dust from floors, beds, wearing apparel, and air in the barracks of an army camp. The streptococcal contamination of the barracks was low during the winter and summer months and high during the spring months, when the incidence of respiratory disease among the personnel was highest.

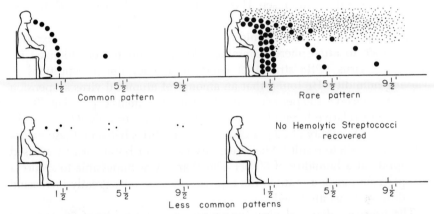

FIG. 200. Patterns of expulsion of hemolytic streptococci by carriers during sneezing. The exaggerated heavy dots represent large droplets which fall rapidly to the ground and were collected by settling plates. The small dots represent "droplet nuclei" which remained suspended in the air for longer periods of time. (*After Hamburger and Robertson.*)

Individuals with positive nose and throat cultures for hemolytic streptococci showed far greater numbers of the corresponding types in their bedding than did those with these organisms only present in their throats. In the barracks in which the majority of the positive bed, dust, and air cultures showed the same type of *Streptococcus,* this same type was more prevalent in the positive nose and throat cultures of the barrack personnel.

The greatest number of positive air cultures were obtained in barracks in which the beds and floor dust were heavily contaminated with hemolytic streptococci. The highest streptococcal counts per cubic foot of air and the most frequently positive cultures were obtained during the time of maximum activity, such as getting up, dressing, floor sweeping, and bedmaking.

Wells, Ratcliffe, and Crumb (1948) added homogeneous suspensions of single cells of *Mycobacterium tuberculosis* to the air breathed by rabbits. They found that nuclei settling less than 0.1 ft. per min. in still air penetrated quantitatively to the lung and were planted upon the alveolar surfaces throughout the lung. In 4 to 5 weeks visible tubercles developed where the organisms had been planted. Less than 10 per cent of nuclei settling a foot per minute reached the lung; organisms in the remainder apparently did not affect the rabbit. More than 10,000 bacilli from a culture producing tubercles in the lung were ingested without observable effect. They concluded that inhalation of few tubercle bacilli in the nuclei of droplets coughed or sneezed into the atmosphere is of greater consequence than far larger numbers of organisms in coarse particles which are strained out in the upper respiratory passages and ingested.

For more information see Hare and Thomas (1956), Ratcliffe and Merrick (1957).

Effect of Atmospheric Humidity on Survival. Lester (1948) exposed white mice to atmospheres containing known amounts of atomized influenza A virus (PR8 strain) of constant potency under conditions of varying humidity. He found that an amount of atomized virus suspension which produced a 100 per cent mortality rate in animals exposed at 30 and 80 per cent relative humidity resulted in the death of only 22.5 per cent of mice at a humidity of 50 per cent. The humidities between these values gave intermediate results. The infectivity of the air-borne virus decreased so rapidly at a humidity of 50 per cent that it was impossible to secure a 100 per cent mortality rate in the exposed mice even by greatly increasing the dose of virus atomized.

The use of a dialyzed virus suspension at a humidity of 50 per cent resulted in the death of all exposed mice. This suggested that the deleterious influence of humidity was related to the presence of sodium chloride in the atomized suspension.

Dunklin and Puck (1948) reported similar results with pneumococci, streptococci, and micrococci, which would suggest that the factor responsible for the lethal effect of humidity is common to moist particles containing either the above-named bacteria or influenza A virus.

Lidwell and Lowbury (1950a) observed that the bacteria of dust survived longer in samples kept in a cupboard than those stored at 4°C. in a refrigerator, where the relative humidity was found to vary between 75 and 90 per cent. The disadvantage of high humidity had evidently outweighed the advantage of low temperature.

Certain pathogens may actually multiply in dust when the atmospheric humidity approaches the saturation point. Such conditions are uncommon indoors, but may occur in unheated rooms during the winter, or on floors which are kept moist.

Against the general assumption of the superior healthiness of a dry climate it must be emphasized that many bacteria and probably also viruses tolerate a dry atmosphere better than a moist one.

For more information see Abramson (1956); Ames and Nungester (1949); Habel (1945); Hodes et al. (1945); Kethley, Fincher, and Cown (1957); Lurie (1945); Phair and Schoenbach (1945).

Potential Infectious Hazards of Laboratory Techniques. Infections have occurred among laboratory workers handling disease organisms such as *Brucella abortus, B. melitensis,* and *Pasteurella tularensis.* In most cases the source of these infections has been obscure and has not been related to known accidents in handling cultures. Many laboratory tech-

Fig. 201. Blowing last drop from pipette. Pipette was allowed to drain, then last drop was blown out with moderate force. (*After Johansson and Ferris.*)

niques have been accepted with little consideration to the role they may play in the dissemination of organisms into the air.

The addition of the finest safety device to a laboratory does not ensure against the possibility of laboratory infections. Equipment is not a substitute for careful laboratory technique. All laboratory workers should be instructed to follow safe procedures to guard against the possible dissemination of disease organisms.

Johansson and Ferris (1946), by means of high-speed photographic and air-sampling techniques, showed that certain accepted bacteriological laboratory operations, such as pipetting, pouring, and vigorous agitation of dilution blanks, often produced bacterial contaminations of the surrounding air and environment (Fig. 201). Slightly more than one-half of the laboratory operations revealed droplet aerosols formed by blowing the last drop out of pipettes or removing the stoppers from dilution blanks that had been vigorously agitated. The dangers in handling some of the highly infectious agents with the commonly used laboratory equipment were apparent.

During the past decade, the preservation of bacteria and viruses by drying (lyophilization) has increased to such an extent that almost every laboratory has occasion to treat organisms by this technique. Organisms in the desiccated form are easily disseminated into the air. It has been shown by Reitman et al. (1954a, b, c) that the lyophilizer becomes heavily contaminated during its operation and should be treated as carefully as any other piece of contaminated equipment. Danger to the operator appears to lie in the contamination of the hands from the manifold outlets. Heavy contamination of the apparatus precludes disassembling before sterilization.

For more information see Phillips and Novak (1956); Reitman and Wedum (1956); Wedum, Hanel, and Phillips (1956).

AIR SANITATION

Methods for the continuous disinfection of air of enclosed spaces have been employed and found to be practicable. These may be classified as follows:

1. Suppression of dust, particularly through application of oil emulsions to floors, blankets, and bed linen.
2. Inactivation of organisms by mists and vapors.
3. Inactivation of organisms by ultraviolet rays.

Dust Control. As has already been said, pathogenic, parasitic, and saprophytic organisms are found in dust, and their removal or destruction is of great importance economically and to public health.

According to Loosli (1947),

The bacterial content of dust found in homes, schools, factories, offices, and hospitals varies with the different environments. Saprophytic organisms usually predominate but parasitic and pathogenic agents may be found in large numbers. Both healthy and ill individuals more or less continually extrude bacteria into their environments in secretions and excretions from: (a) the respiratory tract (nose and throat secretions, sputum, ear, mastoid and sinus discharges); (b) the gastrointestinal and urinary tracts (feces, vomit, urine); (c) skin (scales and hair, septic skin lesions, mucous membrane, conjunctiva and vagina); and (d) wounds (discharges from septic wounds, burns and abscesses). While dust in the outside atmosphere may not be dangerous, that which is found in intramural environments inhabited by human beings should always be considered a potential source of disease agents.

Dust as a vehicle for the spread of disease agents has been studied particularly in relation to respiratory tract infections, skin infections, and secondary infections of burns and wounds. Large numbers of hemolytic streptococci, staphylococci, pneumococci, diphtheria bacilli, and tubercle bacilli have been demonstrated in the floor dust of hospital wards. These organisms have been shown to survive in the environment for long periods of time. Little is known concerning the survival of viruses in dust. Influenza A virus, however, has been shown to survive in floor dust up to ten days without loss of its ability to produce infection in susceptible animals. The great proportion of organisms expelled from the respiratory tract in droplets and droplet nuclei eventually settle to form a part of the bacterial component of dust.

Oiling floors, bedclothes, and other textiles is a highly effective procedure for the control of dust, lint, and dust-borne bacteria. The action of the oil is a mechanical one only. Methods are now available for the treatment of surfaces and fabrics with oil which fall within the range of practicability with respect to simplicity of application and cost. Although the most important environmental reservoirs of pathogens found in hospital wards are the floors and bedclothes, all surfaces (floors, tables, desk tops, etc.), as well as textiles (blankets, sheets, pajamas, clothes of attending nurses and doctors, etc.), should be oiled to bring about the maximum dust control.

Studies thus far indicate that oiling floors, bedclothes, and other textiles can effect a significant reduction in the incidence of respiratory-tract infections of streptococcal etiology in hospital wards and army barracks.

For more information see Loosli (1948); Miller et al. (1948); Shechmeister and Greenspan (1947); and Willmon, Hollaender, and Langmuir (1948).

Effect of Hypochlorites. Edward and Lidwell (1943) showed that it was possible to obtain a 90 to 99 per cent or more destruction of suspended influenza virus in an atmosphere to which sufficient hypochlorous acid was added to produce a final concentration of 1:2,000,000. Similar results were obtained from the use of sodium hypochlorite.

Challinor (1943) sprayed a 1 per cent solution of sodium hypochlorite in air and reported a marked reduction in the bacterial content. He suggested that the application of this simple, practical method of air disinfection of occupied places would reduce the spread of air-borne infections.

Elford and van den Ende (1945) reported that the effectiveness of hypochlorites and hypochlorous acid aerosols, in concentrations of 0.1 to 0.3 p.p.m. HClO against air-borne organisms, depended upon the amount of moisture present. The degree of inactivation of streptococci and staphylococci sprayed as aerosols was found to be slight if the relative humidity fell below 50 per cent. If the relative humidity was maintained between 70 to 90 per cent, the organisms were very rapidly killed.

Effect of Glycols. Robertson et al. (1942) and Puck, Robertson, and Lemon (1943) atomized propylene glycol (see page 485) in air and reported that a concentration of 1 gm. of the vaporized compound in 2,000,000 to 4,000,000 ml. of air produced immediate and complete sterilization of air into which pneumococci, streptococci, staphylococci, *Haemophilus influenzae,* and other organisms as well as influenza virus had been sprayed. The killing process was found to be most effective at a temperature below 27°C. and an atmospheric relative humidity of 45 to 70 per cent.

Bigg (1943) believed glycols exerted their bactericidal action by the chief physical property of glycol, namely, hygroscopicity. The glycol molecules dissolved in the film of moisture about each bacterial cell. When the glycol concentration became sufficiently great, moisture was drawn out of the cell, which resulted in its death.

Loosli et al. (1947) made a study of the effect of triethylene glycol vapor in hospital wards. They found that a concentration of glycol vapor between 55 and 70 per cent produced a 31 to 70 per cent reduction in the bacterial content of the environment.

Krugman and Swerdlow (1949) found triethylene glycol vapor in saturated concentration to be rapidly lethal for air-borne mumps virus and Newcastle disease virus.

Lester et al. (1949) made a study of the rate at which freshly atomized bacteria were killed by triethylene glycol under varying conditions of atmospheric humidity and per cent saturation of the air with glycol vapor. They found that under optimum conditions (15 to 40 per cent relative humidity and 40 to 100 per cent saturation of glycol vapor at room temperature) bactericidal action was very rapid. Eighty to ninety per cent of the bacteria were killed within the first minute or two of exposure, and by 3 or 4 min. the air samples were essentially sterile. The rate of kill at any relative humidity between 5 and 55 per cent rose progressively with increasing per cent saturation of glycol vapor. As the relative humidity was increased beyond 50 per cent, a rapid diminution in the rate of bacterial killing occurred with any given per cent saturation of glycol vapor. At 60 per cent relative humidity the rate of kill was one-fifth to one-sixth that of the optimum occurring at lower humidities.

For more information see Johnson (1950), Personnel of United States Naval Medical Research Unit No. 4 (1952), Puck (1947a, b), Rosebury (1947), Rosebury et al. (1947).

Effect of Ultraviolet Light. Ultraviolet rays of sunlight or of various types of lamps centering around 2537 angstrom units (A.) exert a pronounced destructive action on bacteria, viruses, and other microorganisms suspended in air (see page 239). Ultraviolet wave lengths from 2900 to 3600 A. are also germicidal but considerably less potent. Radiant disinfection of air depends on type of infection, state of suspension, humidity of the atmosphere, volume of space, quality of the radiation, strength of ray, length of ray, total exposure, uniformity of exposure, and air motion (Wells, 1942).

Low-pressure mercury-vapor lamps have been used extensively for this purpose. According to Luckiesh and Holladay (1942a, b) and Luckiesh, Taylor, and Knowles (1947) these lamps emit about 99 per cent of their ultraviolet flux in a narrow spectral region near 2537 A. However, the highly bactericidal range is between 2000 A. and 2967 A., with a maximum at 2650 A. (Fig. 202).

Edward, Lush, and Bourdillon (1943) reported that at least 99 per cent and probably more of influenza and vaccinia viruses sprayed in air were killed in a few seconds by exposure to an ultraviolet lamp. Such lamps are particularly valuable in preventing the spread of virus infections of the upper respiratory tract.

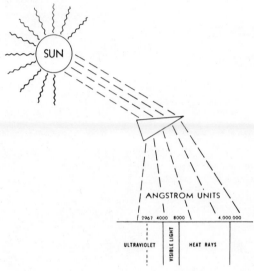

FIG. 202. Radiant energy from the sun may be divided into three broad groups: long-wave energy, such as heat, which is invisible; visible energy which produces light and color; and short-wave energy such as invisible ultraviolet. It is the invisible ultraviolet that produces the germicidal effect. (*Courtesy of General Electric Company.*)

Miller et al. (1948) applied ultraviolet radiations to the floors and upper air in barracks housing recruits and reported a 19.2 per cent reduction in total respiratory disease. *Streptococcus* disease rates were at a very high level, and a 24 per cent reduction was obtained.

Room Sanitation. Outdoor air practically never contains hazardous numbers of human disease-producing organisms. Air of outdoor purity is an essential part of man's environment, and the need for it is well recognized. Air sanitation is inherent in the dispersion and dilution provided by a large volume of air. The amount of air needed indoors depends upon the volume of the room, and the number of normal and sick individuals present.

The development of the germicidal tube has made it possible to obtain air sanitation indoors which is equivalent to that of outdoor air. To provide outdoor benefits to indoor air, it would be necessary to change the air in a room about 60 times per hour. Germicidal tubes properly installed make it possible to achieve the equivalent of 100 or more air changes per hour.

Intensities of germicidal ultraviolet sufficient to kill air-borne organisms before they have had time to travel from one person to another would be very irritating to the face and eyes. For this reason the rays must be limited to the upper and lower parts of rooms where the faces of people

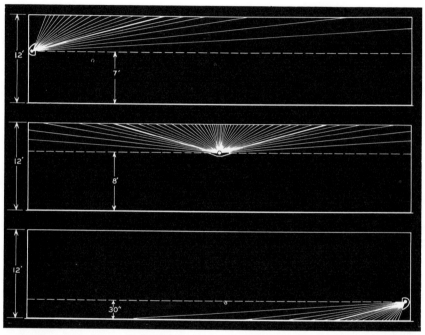

Fig. 203. Three basic methods for installing germicidal lamps. Upper, side wall; center, ceiling; lower, above floor. (*Courtesy of General Electric Company.*)

would not be exposed for more than a few minutes per day. These limitations lead to three basic methods of installing germicidal lamps: (1) on the side wall or (2) from the ceiling of a room to irradiate the air above the 7-ft. level, and (3) on the side wall to irradiate the floor and the air below the 30-in. level (Fig. 203).

Air warmed by heat sources such as radiators and floor lamps rises upward to the ceiling (Fig. 204). This forces cooler air down along the cool outside walls to the floor, where it is again warmed and rises. This normal air circulation is utilized in diluting contaminated air with disinfected air. Disinfected air from above the head level and below the 30-in. level is as good as outdoor air for room sanitation by ventilating dilution.

Operating-room Sanitation. The problem in the surgery is chiefly that of protecting tissues exposed during the operation. Debilitated tissues

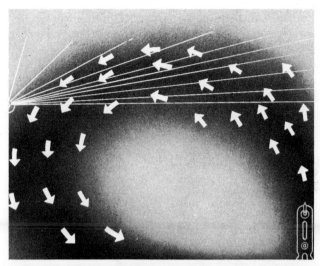

FIG. 204. How air circulates. Air warmed by radiators, floor lamps, etc., rises toward the ceiling. This forces cooler air down along cool outside walls to the floor, where it is again warmed and rises. Germicidal units are mounted on the walls so that the radiation from the tubes disinfects the room's upper air. (*Courtesy of General Electric Company.*)

exposed during long operations may become contaminated with pus-forming and fever-producing organisms not ordinarily a hazard. This is especially serious during brain surgery and thoracoplasty operations, during which the tissues may be exposed for hours.

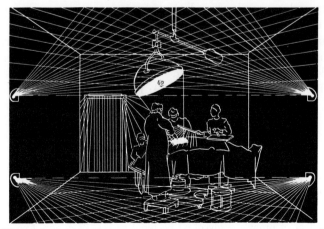

FIG. 205 Ultraviolet air sanitation in the operating room. See text for description. (*Courtesy of General Electric Company.*)

Although the aseptic techniques in the operating room are superior to those in other parts of the hospital, the practice can be further improved by the application of floor and air irradiation. In order to protect the hands, arms, and face of the operating personnel, the air should be irradiated above the 7-ft. level and below the 2½- to 3-ft. level (Fig. 205).

Product Sanitation. Product sanitation includes the application of ultraviolet rays to the protection of food and pharmaceutical products; the sterilization of instruments and towels by the barber or beautician; the washing and sterilization of dishes, cutlery, and drinking glasses used in restaurants and other public places (Fig. 206); the treatment of foods

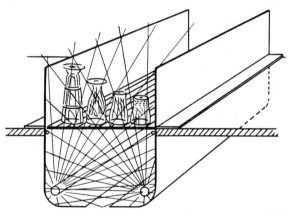

Fig. 206. Sanitary storage of drinking glasses combined with germicidal ultraviolet treatment. (*Courtesy of General Electric Company.*)

in domestic refrigerators to reduce odors and to provide some protection by the disinfection of the enclosed air; and the treatment of meats in storage to reduce spoilage and to make it less necessary to use lower temperatures.

For more information see du Buy et al. (1948); General Electric (1950, 1953); Jarrett, Zelle, and Hollaender (1948); Langmuir, Jarrett, and Hollaender (1948); Lidwell and Lowbury (1950*b*); Lurie (1947); Perkins, Bahlke, and Silverman (1947); Robertson (1947); Wells (1945); Willmon, Hollaender, and Langmuir (1948).

REFERENCES

Abramson, S.: Experimental air-borne infection, *Am. Rev. Tuberc.*, **73**:315, 1956.
Ames, A. M., and W. J. Nungester: The initial distribution of air-borne bacteria in the host, *J. Infectious Diseases*, **84**:56, 1949.
Andersen, A. A.: New sampler for the collection, sizing, and enumeration of viable airborne particles, *J. Bact.*, **76**:471, 1958.
Bigg, E.: Effect of propylene glycol on bacterial spores, *Proc. Soc. Exp. Biol. Med.*, **53**:120, 1943.

Bourdillon, R. B., O. M. Lidwell, and J. C. Thomas: A slit sampler for collecting and counting air-borne bacteria, *J. Hyg.*, **41**:197, 1941.

Boyland, E., J. H. Gaddum, and F. F. McDonald: Nasal filtration of air-borne droplets, *J. Hyg.*, **45**:290, 1947.

Challinor, S. W.: Bacteriological observations on the air of occupied premises. I. Air disinfection with hypochlorites. A simple practical method of disinfecting the air of occupied premises, *J. Hyg.*, **43**:16, 1943.

Cown, W. B., T. W. Kethley, and E. L. Fincher: The critical-orifice liquid impinger as a sampler for bacterial aerosols, *Appl. Microbiol.*, **5**:119, 1957.

du Buy, H. G., J. E. Dunn, F. S. Brackett, W. C. Dreessen, P. A. Neal, and I. Posner: An evaluation of ultraviolet radiation of sleeping quarters as a supplement of accepted methods of disease control, *Am. J. Hyg.*, **48**:207, 1948.

——— and A. Hollaender: Sampling devices, *Am. J. Med. Sci.*, **209**:172, 1945.

———, ———, and M. D. Lackey: A comparative study of sampling devices for air-borne microorganisms, *Pub. Health Reports*, Suppl. 184, 1945.

Duguid, J. P.: The size and the duration of air-carriage of respiratory droplets and droplet-nuclei, *J. Hyg.*, **44**:471, 1946.

——— and A. T. Wallace: Air infection with dust liberated from clothing, *Lancet*, Nov. 27, 1948, p. 845.

Dunklin, E. W., and T. T. Puck: The lethal effect of relative humidity on air-borne bacteria, *J. Exp. Med.*, **87**:87, 1948.

Edward, D. G., and O. M. Lidwell: Studies on air-borne virus infections. III. The killing of aerial suspensions of influenza virus by hypochlorous acid, *J. Hyg.*, **43**:196, 1943.

———, D. Lush, and R. B. Bourdillon: Studies on air-borne virus infections. II. The killing of virus aerosols by ultra-violet radiation, *ibid.*, **43**:11, 1943.

Elford, W. J., and J. van den Ende: Studies on the disinfecting action of hypochlorous acid gas and sprayed solution of hypochlorite against bacterial aerosols, *J. Hyg.*, **44**:1, 1945.

General Electric Company: Ultraviolet air sanitation, Bull. LD-11, Cleveland, Ohio, 1950.

———: Ultraviolet product sanitation, Bull. LD-14, Cleveland, Ohio, 1953.

Griffin, C. W., H. L. Kantzes, P. M. Ludford, and M. J. Pelczar, Jr.: Studies of aerosols with a simple cloud-chamber technic, *Appl. Microbiol.*, **4**:17, 1956.

Habel, K.: Mumps and chickenpox as air-borne diseases, *Am. J. Med. Sci.*, **209**:75, 1945.

Hamburger, M., Jr.: Transfer of beta hemolytic streptococci by shaking hands, *Am. J. Med.*, **2**:23, 1947.

———, M. J. Green, and V. G. Hamburger: The problem of the "dangerous carrier" of hemolytic streptococci. I. Number of hemolytic streptococci expelled by carriers with positive and negative nose cultures, *J. Infectious Diseases*, **77**:68, 1945a; II. Spread of infection by individuals with strongly positive nose cultures who expelled large numbers of hemolytic streptococci, *ibid.*, **77**:96, 1945b.

——— and O. H. Robertson: Expulsion of Group A hemolytic streptococci in droplets and droplet nuclei by sneezing, coughing and talking, *Am. J. Med.*, **4**:690, 1948.

Hare, R., and C. G. A. Thomas: The transmission of *Staphylococcus aureus*, *Brit. Med. J.*, **11**:840, 1956.

Hodes, H. L., F. F. Schwentker, B. M. Chenoweth, and J. L. Peck, Jr.: Scarlet fever as an air-borne infection, *Am. J. Med. Sci.*, **209**:64, 1945.

Hollaender, A., and J. M. Dalla Valle: A simple device for sampling air-borne bacteria, *Pub. Health Reports*, **54**:574, 1939.

Jarrett, E. T., M. R. Zelle, and A. Hollaender: Studies of the control of acute respiratory disease among naval recruits. II. Limitations of ultraviolet irradiation in reducing air-borne bacteria in barracks with low ceilings, *Am. J. Hyg.*, **48**:233, 1948.

Jennison, M. W.: The dynamics of sneezing—studies by high-speed photography, *Sci. Monthly*, **52**:24, 1941.

———— and H. E. Edgerton: Droplet infection of air: Highspeed photography of droplet production by sneezing, *Proc. Soc. Exp. Biol. Med.*, **43**:455, 1940.

Johansson, K. R., and D. H. Ferris: Photography of air-borne particles during bacteriological plating operations, *J. Infectious Diseases*, **78**:238, 1946.

Johnson, E. P.: Triethylene glycol in the control of air-borne dissemination of pneumoencephalitis (Newcastle Disease), *Virginia J. Sci.*, **1**:123, 1950.

Kelly, C. D., and S. Layne: Bacteria found in the air over Canada and the American arctic, *Can. J. Microbiol.*, **3**:447, 1957*a*.

———— and ————: Bacteria found in the air over the Atlantic Ocean, *ibid.*, **3**:457, 1957*b*.

Kethley, T. W., E. L. Fincher, and W. B. Cown: The effect of sampling method upon the apparent response of airborne bacteria to temperature and relative humidity, *J. Infectious Diseases*, **100**:97, 1957.

Kluyver, A. J., and J. Visser: The determination of microorganisms in air, *Antonie van Leeuwenhoek*, **16**:299, 1950.

Koch, R.: Zur Untersuchung von pathogenen Organismen, *Mitt. Kaiser Gesundh.*, **1**:32, 1881.

Krugman, S., and B. Swerdlow: Lethal effect of triethylene glycol vapor on air-borne mumps virus and Newcastle disease virus, *Proc. Soc. Exp. Biol. Med.*, **71**:680, 1949.

Landsberg, H.: Origin and physics of the atmosphere, *Trans. N.Y. Acad. Sci.*, **13**:154, 1951.

Langmuir, A. D., E. T. Jarrett, and A. Hollaender: Studies of the control of acute respiratory diseases among naval recruits. III. The epidemiological pattern and the effect of ultraviolet irradiation during the winter of 1946–1947, *Am. J. Hyg.*, **48**:240, 1948.

Lemon, H. M.: A method for collection of bacteria from air and textiles, *Proc. Soc. Exp. Biol. Med.*, **54**:298, 1943.

————, C. G. Loosli, and M. Hamburger, Jr.: The transmission and control of respiratory diseases in army barracks. II. The spread of hemolytic streptococcal infections among enlisted personnel, *J. Infectious Diseases*, **82**:72, 1948.

Lester, W., Jr.: The influence of relative humidity on the infectivity of air-borne influenza A virus (PR8 strain), *J. Exp. Med.*, **88**:361, 1948.

————, O. H. Robertson, T. T. Puck, H. Wise, and M. Smith: The rate of bactericidal action of triethylene glycol vapor on microorganisms dispersed into the air in small droplets, *Am. J. Hyg.*, **50**: 175, 1949.

Lidwell, O. M., and E. J. Lowbury: The survival of bacteria in dust. II. The effect of atmospheric humidity on the survival of bacteria in dust, *J. Hyg.*, **48**:21, 1950*a*; IV. Atmospheric humidity and the bactericidal action of ultra-violet irradiation, *ibid.*, **48**:38, 1950*b*.

Loosli, C. G.: Dust and its control as a means of disinfection of air, *Am. J. Pub. Health*, **37**:353, 1947.

————: Problem of dust control for the disinfection of air, *ibid.*, **38**:409, 1948.

————, H. M. Lemon, H. Wise, and O. H. Robertson: Studies on the transmission and control of respiratory disease within army barracks. I. Hemolytic streptococcal contamination of the environment, *J. Infectious Diseases*, **82**:59, 1948.

————, M. H. D. Smith, R. L. Gauld, O. H. Robertson, and T. T. Puck: Control of cross-infections in infants' wards by the use of triethylene glycol vapor, *Am. J. Pub. Health*, **37**:1385, 1947.

Luckiesh, M., and L. L. Holladay: Tests and data on disinfection of air with germicidal lamps, *Gen. Elec. Rev.*, **45**:223, 1942*a*.

———— and ————: Designing installations of germicidal lamps for occupied rooms, *ibid.*, **45**:343, 1942*b*.

————, A. H. Taylor, and L. L. Holladay: Sampling devices for air-borne bacteria, *J. Bact.*, **52**:55, 1946.

————, ————, and T. Knowles: Killing air-borne respiratory microorganisms with germicidal energy, *J. Franklin Inst.*, **244**:267, 1947.

Lurie, M. B.: Experimental air-borne tuberculosis, *Am. J. Med. Sci.*, **209**:156, 1945.

————: Experimental air-borne tuberculosis and its control, Am. Rev. Tuberc., 55:124, 1947.

Miller, W. R., E. T. Jarrett, T. L. Willmon, A. Hollaender, E. W. Brown, T. Lewandowski, and R. S. Stone: Evaluation of ultraviolet radiation and dust control measures in control of respiratory disease at a naval training center, J. Infectious Diseases, 82:86, 1948.

O'Connell, D. C., N. J. B. Wiggin, and G. F. Pike: New technique for the collection and isolation of airborne microorganisms, Science, 131:359, 1960.

Perkins, J. E., A. M. Bahlke, and H. F. Silverman: Effect of ultraviolet irradiation of classrooms on spread of measles in large rural central schools, Am. J. Pub. Health, 37:529, 1947.

Personnel of U.S. Naval Medical Research Unit No. 4: The use of triethylene glycol vapor for control of acute respiratory diseases in Navy recruits. I. Physical factors and the effect of air-borne bacteria; II. Effect on acute respiratory diseases, Am. J. Hyg., 55:203, 215, 1952.

Phair, J. J., and E. B. Schoenbach: The transmission and control of meningococcal infections, Am. J. Med. Sci., 209:69, 1945.

Phillips, G. B., and F. E. Novak: Applications of germicidal ultraviolet in infectious disease laboratories. II. Appl. Microbiol., 4:95, 1956.

Proctor, B. E.: The microbiology of the upper air. II. J. Bact., 30:363, 1935.

———— and B. W. Parker: Microbiology of the upper air. III. An improved apparatus and technique for upper air investigations, ibid., 36:175, 1938.

Puck, T. T.: The mechanism of aerial disinfection by glycols and other chemical agents. I. Demonstration that the germicidal action occurs through the agency of the vapor phase, J. Exp. Med., 85:729, 1947a; II. Analysis of the factors governing the efficiency of chemical disinfection of the air, ibid., 85:729, 1947b.

————, O. H. Robertson, and H. M. Lemon: The bactericidal action of propylene glycol vapor on microorganisms suspended in air. II. The influence of various factors on the activity of the vapor, ibid., 78:387, 1943.

Ratcliffe, H. L., and J. V. Merrick: Tuberculosis induced by droplet nuclei. Its development pattern in guinea pigs and rats in relation to dietary protein, Am. J. Path., 33:1121, 1957.

Reitman, M., R. L. Alg, W. S. Miller, and N. H. Gross: Potential infectious hazards of laboratory techniques. III. Viral techniques, J. Bact., 68:549, 1954a.

————, M. L. Moss, J. B. Harstad, R. L. Alg, and N. H. Gross: I. Lyophilization, ibid., 68:541, 1954b; II. The handling of lyophilized cultures, ibid., 68:545, 1954c.

———— and A. G. Wedum: Microbiological safety, Pub. Health Reports, 71:659, 1956.

Robertson, O. H.: The dispersal of respiratory pathogens in relation to the occurrence and control of air-borne infections, Am. Rev. Tuberc., 55:109, 1947.

————, E. Bigg, T. T. Puck, and B. F. Miller: The bactericidal action of propylene glycol vapor on microorganisms suspended in air. I. J. Exp. Med., 75:593, 1942.

Rosebury, T.: "Experimental Air-borne Infection," Baltimore, The Williams & Wilkins Company, 1947.

————, G. Meiklejohn, L. C. Kingsland, and M. H. Boldt: Disinfection of clouds of meningopneumonitis and psittacosis viruses with triethylene glycol vapor, J. Exp. Med., 85:65, 1947.

Shechmeister, I. L., and F. S. Greenspan: The relation of the oil treatment of floors and bedding to the control of respiratory diseases among naval personnel, Am. J. Hyg., 46:376, 1947.

Solberg, A. N., H. C. Shaffer, and G. A. Kelley: The collecting of air-borne microorganisms, Ohio J. Sci., 56:305, 1956.

Walter, W. G., and G. J. Hucker: Pathogenic bacteria in public places, Soap San. Chem., February, 1942.

Wedum, A. G., E. Hanel, Jr., and G. B. Phillips: Ultraviolet sterilization in microbiological laboratories, Pub. Health Reports, 71:331, 1956.

Wells, W. F.: Apparatus for study of the bacterial behavior of air, Am. J. Pub. Health, 25:58, 1933.

————: Air-borne infection and sanitary air control, *J. Ind. Hyg.*, **17**:253, 1935.

————: Air-borne infections, *Modern Hosp.*, **51**:66, 1938.

————: Radiant disinfection of air, *Arch. Phys. Therapy*, **23**:143, 1942.

————: Measurement of air-borne infection by the disinfection of air, *Am. J. Med. Sci.*, **209**:177, 1945.

————, C. T. Butterfield, F. W. Gilcreas, E. C. Robertson, and C.-E. A. Winslow: Bacteriological procedures in sanitary air analysis, *Am. J Pub. Health*, **37**:1023, 1947.

————, H. L. Ratcliffe, and C. Crumb: On the mechanics of droplet nuclei infection. II. Quantitative experimental air-borne tuberculosis in rabbits, *Am. J. Hyg.* **47**:1, 1948.

Willmon, T. L., A. Hollaender, and A. D. Langmuir: Studies of the control of acute respiratory diseases among naval recruits. I. A review of a four-year experience with ultraviolet irradiation and dust suppressive measures, 1943 to 1947, *Am. J. Hyg.*, **48**:227, 1948.

CHAPTER 20

Bacteriology of the Sea[1]

The ocean, which covers nearly three-fourths of the earth's surface, is the home of numerous species of bacteria and allied microorganisms. Living bacteria have been detected in sea water and marine bottom deposits from the greatest depths sampled.

Bacteria are believed to play an important role in the economy of the sea, where they function as biochemical, geological, and hydrobiological agents. Although preponderantly beneficial, certain bacteria are pathogenic for marine plants and animals, some cause spoilage of fish or other marine foods products, others contribute to the corrosion or biofouling of man-made structures, and a few species are responsible for the harmful vitiation of water in localized areas.

CHARACTERISTICS OF MARINE BACTERIA

Morphologically, marine bacteria resemble those found in other environments, although statistically there are relatively more Gram-negative rods and vibrios in the sea than in soil or other fresh-water habitats. Likewise, a larger percentage of marine bacteria are motile and pigmented. Cocci and actinomycetes are of more limited occurrence in the sea than on the land.

On the average, marine bacteria are smaller than those which occur in milk, manure, sewage, soil, or other fresh-water sources. Among the exceptions are representatives of marine Rhodobacteriineae, Chlamydobacteriales, and Spirochaetales, many of which are quite large.

In general, marine bacteria grow more slowly and the colonies are smaller than those formed by most bacteria from soil or sewage. As a group, marine bacteria are strongly proteolytic and not so commonly saccharolytic as soil or fresh-water forms. Facultative aerobes predominate in the sea, there being relatively few obligate aerobes.

Most agar-liquefying bacteria come from the sea. Stanier (1941) and Humm (1946) have described a large number of marine agar digesters.

[1] This chapter was written by Dr. Claude E. ZoBell of the Scripps Institution of Oceanography, University of California, La Jolla, Calif. The author is greatly indebted to Dr. ZoBell for his kindness in preparing this material for publication.

531

Agar is a galactan found in marine algae, *Gelidium* species being the principal algae of commercial significance.

Bioluminescence is also preponderantly a property of marine organisms (Harvey, 1940). ZoBell (1946a) has compiled a list of 34 species of photogenic bacteria which have been isolated from the sea by various workers.

Reference is made to other unique characteristics of marine bacteria by ZoBell and Feltham (1934) and ZoBell and Upham (1944).

Salinity Requirements. Unless diluted by heavy rainfall, melting ice, or rivers, sea water generally contains 3.3 to 3.6 per cent solids, 85 per cent of which is sodium chloride with lesser quantities of magnesium sulfate and traces of virtually all known cations and anions (Sverdrup et al., 1942). Thus it should not be surprising to find that most marine bacteria grow best or only in media prepared with sea water or similar salt solutions.

Though sometimes characterized as halophilic or salt-loving, marine bacteria are not nearly so halophilic as bacteria found in Great Salt Lake (ZoBell et al., 1937), in the Dead Sea (Elazari-Volcani, 1940), in strong brines (Hof, 1935), or in marine salterns which may contain nearly ten times as much salt as sea water. This may be illustrated by the data in Table 20, which gives the comparative counts obtained by plating samples from various habitats in nutrient agar prepared with balanced mineral solutions of different salinities.

TABLE 20. AVERAGE GROWTH INDEX IN PER CENT OF BACTERIA FROM DIFFERENT SOURCES PLATED IN NUTRIENT AGAR HAVING DIFFERENT SALT CONCENTRATIONS

Source of bacteria	Salt concentration of nutrient agar					
	0.5%	2.0%	3.5%	7.0%	15%	30%
Sea water..........	19.2	61.7	*100.0*	38.3	7.4	0.0
Marine mud........	23.9	54.2	*100.0*	43.5	6.1	0.2
Marine saltern.......	4.3	12.6	19.6	30.4	84.9	*100.0*
Great Salt Lake.....	1.7	8.0	14.1	26.3	92.2	*100.0*
Garden soil........	*100.0*	56.1	25.2	9.8	4.6	0.4
Sewage............	*100.0*	44.8	13.5	5.7	2.7	0.0
River water........	*100.0*	47.3	22.8	6.2	1.9	0.0

Neither artificial sea water nor isotonic salt solutions have proved to be so good as natural sea water for the cultivation of marine microorganisms. Korinek (1927) claimed that marine bacteria could be distinguished from fresh-water forms upon a basis of their specific salinity requirements.

Temperature Tolerance. Most marine bacteria grow best at temperatures ranging from 12 to 25°C. Very few of them grow at temperatures as high as 30°C., and as shown by ZoBell and Conn (1940), 37°C. may be lethal. Hess (1934) noted that many species are physiologically active at −3 to 6.5°C. Nearly all species of marine bacteria multiply slowly at 0 to 4°C., this being the temperature range of approximately 80 per cent of the ocean by volume.

Effect of Hydrostatic Pressure. The activities of bacteria in the sea are influenced by hydrostatic pressure, which increases approximately 0.1 atm. per meter of depth. Nearly 90 per cent of the ocean ranges in depth from 1000 to 10,000 meters, which means that the hydrostatic pressure ranges roughly from 100 to 1000 atm. ZoBell and Johnson (1949) found that, unlike barophilic or pressure-loving bacteria from great depths, very few terrestrial bacteria in the logarithmic phase of growth tolerate pressures exceeding 300 atm. Marine bacteria from shallow depths tolerate no higher hydrostatic pressures than barophobic (pressure-sensitive) forms found in soil, sewage, or other surface sources. On the other hand, barophilic bacteria in abundance were demonstrated in several abysses ranging in depth from 7200 to 10,460 meters (ZoBell, 1952a).

According to ZoBell and Oppenheimer (1950), hydrostatic pressures, such as occur in the deep sea, affect the morphology as well as the multiplication and metabolism of marine bacteria in nutrient media. The effects of pressure are influenced by the species, growth phase, composition of the medium, time of exposure, and temperature.

Hydrogen-ion Concentration Requirements. Most marine microorganisms grow best at pH 7.2 to 7.6. This is somewhat less alkaline than sea water, which ranges from pH 7.5 to 8.5. Living bacteria have been found in marine sediments throughout the range of pH 6.4 to 9.4.

INTERCHANGE OF BACTERIA BETWEEN THE LAND AND SEA

Very few of the terrestrial fresh-water bacteria that are being continually carried into the sea by rivers, sewage outfalls, the wind, migratory waterfowl, and other agencies survive very long in the sea except in badly polluted or diluted near-shore areas (Burke and Baird, 1931). A rapid diminution in numbers of both *Salmonella typhosa* and *Escherichia coli* in sea water was observed by Beard and Meadowcroft (1935).

Natural sea water was found by Carpenter et al. (1938) to kill about 80 per cent of the bacteria in sewage within half an hour. The results of sanitary surveys conducted by Rittenberg et al. (1958) show that the number of sewage bacteria decreases with distance from outfalls far faster than can be accounted for by dilution. Water from the Black Sea was reported by Krassilnikov (1938) to be germicidal for terrestrial bacteria, but boiling destroyed the germicidal principle. Literature reviewed by Greenberg (1956) shows how the survival of enteric organisms in sea water is influenced by toxic substances, antibiotics, bacteriophage, sunlight, sedimentation, adsorption, predators, and available nutrients.

Typhoid and other coliform bacteria may survive in marine shellfish for several weeks, according to Hunter and Harrison (1928).

ZoBell (1942a) has shown that large numbers of bacteria from the sea are carried considerable distances inland by the wind, but they soon disappear among the more abundant terrestrial ones. Except in marine fish or in the media of the microbiologist, marine bacteria do not survive very far inland beyond the shore line.

ABUNDANCE OF BACTERIA IN THE SEA

Comprehensive reviews by Benecke (1933) and ZoBell (1946a) indicate that bacteria are widely distributed in the sea. Plating procedures, which detect only a small percentage of viable organisms, reveal the presence of a few cells per milliliter to several hundred thousand per milliliter of sea water. The largest bacterial populations occur in waters richest in organic matter near shore or near the mud-water interface.

In the open ocean, the abundance of bacteria generally increases with depth from the surface down to a depth of 40 or 50 meters and then decreases with depth. The bacterial population below the photosynthetic zone, which is 10 to 50 meters below the surface, is believed by ZoBell (1947a) to be restricted primarily by the low concentration of organic matter.

The abundance of bacteria in the sea appears to be more closely related to the abundance of phytoplankton than to any other single ecological factor. A parallelism between the abundance of bacteria and plankton in sea water was noted by Waksman et al. (1933), in the Pacific Ocean by Kriss (1959), and in Lake Alexander by Henrici (1938).

The beneficial effect of plankton is due partly to the organic matter which they provide for bacteria and partly to solid surfaces. Bacteria occur only to a limited extent floating free in water, most of them being attached to suspended solids such as the bodies or remains of plankton organisms. As pointed out by ZoBell (1943), solid surfaces tend to concentrate organic nutrients, retard the diffusion of bacterial enzymes, and provide a resting place for sessile forms.

The sessile habit of aquatic bacteria is the basis of the submerged-slide technique employed by Henrici (1933), Hotchkiss and Waksman (1936), ZoBell (1943), and others for estimating the abundance of bacteria by the direct microscopic method. Waksman and Vartiovaara (1938) found most of the bacteria in marine bottom deposits to be adsorbed on or attached to particles of sediment. According to Kriss (1959), the bacterial biomass ranges from 0.01 mgm. per cubic meter of water at great depths to 10 or more mgm. near the surface.

Bacteria in Bottom Deposits. Drew (1912) found an average of 160,-000,000 bacteria per gram of mud from the sea floor near Andros Island in the West Indies. Lloyd (1931) found 300,000 per gram of mud from the Clyde Sea off the west coast of Scotland. Bavendamm (1932) detected up to 16,800,000 bacteria per gram of calcareous mud from around the Bahama Islands. From plate counts Mare (1942) estimated that mud collected in the English Channel contained 0.3 to 2 mgm. of living bacteria per gram.

Lloyd (1931), Reuszer (1933), and others have noted a gradual decrease with core depth in the abundance of bacteria in marine mud. This may be illustrated by the data in Table 21 obtained by ZoBell (1942b) from three mud cores collected from the floor of the Pacific Ocean off the coast of Southern California.

TABLE 21. NUMBER OF BACTERIA PER GRAM OF MARINE MUD FROM DIFFERENT CORE DEPTHS

Core depth, inches	Station number		
	14:37	14:45	14:53
0–1	38,000,000	7,500,000	840,000
1–2	940,000	250,000	102,000
4–5	88,000	160,000	63,000
9–10	36,000	23,000	19,000
14–15	2,400	8,700	1,500
19–20	400	2,100	2,200
39–40	330	200	190
79–80	130	100	140
99–100	290	150	140

Viable bacteria have been found at the bottom of the longest cores examined, some exceeding 25 ft. in length and consisting of sediments several thousand years old. Evidence for the occurrence of bacteria in ancient marine sediments has been summarized by ZoBell and Rittenberg (1948).

Most of the bacteria found in marine bottom deposits prove to be facultative or strict anaerobes. Some of them are able to oxidize molecular hydrogen as an energy source (ZoBell, 1947b):

$$4H_2 + CaSO_4 \rightarrow CaS + 4H_2O; \quad \Delta F_{298} = -56,750 \text{ cal.}$$
$$4H_2 + CO_2 \rightarrow CH_4 + 2H_2O; \quad \Delta F_{298} = -31,030 \text{ cal.}$$

Energy obtained from such reactions may provide for the synthesis of bacterial cell substance from the reduction of carbon dioxide:

$$2H_2 + CO_2 \rightarrow (CH_2O) + H_2O; \quad \Delta F_{298} = +6,740 \text{ cal.}$$

where (CH_2O) represents the primary building block for the synthesis of organic matter.

BACTERIA AS GEOLOGICAL AGENTS

Bacteria in marine bottom deposits promote many processes involving organic compounds, inorganic constituents, and physicochemical conditions. One of the first geochemical processes to be studied by microbiologists was calcium carbonate precipitation, which Drew (1912) attributed to the activities of denitrifying bacteria in subtropical seas. The extensive observations of Bavendamm (1932) established that calcium carbonate precipitation in tropical seas is partly a microbiological process.

The solubility or precipitation of calcium carbonate in the sea is primarily a function of the pH. The pH of marine sediments may be increased by microorganisms which (1) form ammonia, (2) reduce nitrate or nitrite, (3) reduce sulfate, (4) destroy or decarboxylate organic acids, or (5) utilize carbon dioxide. On the other hand, the (1) production of carbon dioxide or organic acids, (2) oxidation of hydrogen sulfide or sulfur, (3) formation of nitrate, (4) assimilation of ammonia, and (5) liberation of phosphate from organic compounds are microbial processes that tend to decrease the pH.

Deposition of Iron and Manganese. Harder (1919) and Cholodny (1926) have outlined several ways in which bacteria are instrumental in the deposition and transformation of iron in sediments. The microbial precipitation of manganese in marine muds has been studied by Thiel (1925). Iron and manganese concretions in the White Sea were attributed to bacterial activity by Butkevich (1928), who found species of *Gallionella* to be abundant.

Whether iron or manganese in marine sediments occurs in the oxidized or reduced state is influenced by the oxidation-reduction potential, or Eh. Bacteria appear to be the principal dynamic agents that influence the oxidation-reduction potential of marine sediments. In the presence of organic matter, bacteria create reducing conditions by consuming oxygen and by producing hydrogen sulfide or other reducing agents.

The oxidation-reduction potential is believed by ZoBell (1946b) to have a pronounced effect upon the composition, chemical reactivity, diagenesis, color, biological population, and other properties of recent sediments. Reducing conditions are also believed to be conducive to the formation and preservation of petroleum hydrocarbons.

Origin of Oil. It is generally agreed by geologists that petroleum has been formed in marine sediments from the transformation of the organic remains of plants and animals. Bacteria may contribute to the process by modifying sedimentary conditions (ZoBell, 1952b).

In highly reducing environments, the microbial modification of organic matter may result in residues relatively richer in hydrogen and poorer in oxygen, nitrogen, sulfur, and phosphorus. This results in the accumulation of organic complexes that are more petroleum-like than their predecessors, since petroleum consists largely of gaseous, liquid, and solid hydrocarbons.

The microbial formation of methane is a common property of marine sediments, and there is evidence for the production of higher hydrocarbons by marine bacteria. While it is not to be concluded that bacteria produce petroleum, it is generally agreed that bacteria may contribute to early phases of the process.

Petroleum hydrocarbons may be modified by bacteria in marine sediments. Virtually all classes of hydrocarbons are susceptible to microbial attack under favorable aerobic conditions (ZoBell, 1946c).

ACTION OF MARINE BACTERIA ON ORGANIC MATTER

The most important activity of bacteria in the sea is the mineralization or modification of organic matter (Waksman, 1934). Although large quantities of organic matter are washed into the sea from the land and much more is produced in the sea by photosynthetic plants, the organic content of sea water is rarely more than 5 mgm. per liter. Most marine bottom deposits contain less than 5 per cent organic matter. Because of the effectiveness of bacteria in decomposing organic matter, the ocean has been described as being the world's largest and most efficient septic tank.

The bacterial decomposition of dead organisms in the sea is accompanied by oxygen utilization, ammonia production, carbon dioxide formation, and phosphate liberation. Waksman and Renn (1936) observed that approximately 60 per cent of the organic matter attacked was mineralized and the remaining 40 per cent was converted into bacterial cell substance.

Simple carbohydrates and amino acids are rapidly attacked by marine bacteria; complex polysaccharides, lipides, and proteins are decomposed more slowly. Several species of marine fungi studied by Barghoorn and Linder (1944) utilized xylose, galactose, maltose, starch, cellulose, or pectin.

Cellulose Decomposers. Waksman, Carey, and Reuszer (1933) found cellulose-decomposing bacteria to be generally present in sea water and quite abundant in bottom deposits and plankton tows. Most marine cellulose decomposers are aerobic, but some anaerobic ones were demonstrated by Kadota (1956). A large variety of sugars were utilized by the cellulose decomposers.

Bavendamm (1932) found cellulose-digesting bacteria in all marine mud samples examined. Stanier (1941) isolated from marine materials four new species of bacteria that digest cellulose and also agar.

Agar Digestion. Humm (1946) has described all known marine agar digesters, including 17 new species. Along the coast of North Carolina he found from 2 to 150 agar digesters per milliliter of sea water and from 80,000 to 20,000,000 per gram of mud. All of Humm's agar digesters utilized glucose, fructose, galactose, mannose, cellobiose, and maltose; 90 per cent utilized xylose and lactose; 85 per cent utilized sucrose and salicin; and 53 per cent utilized arabinose, raffinose, and glycerol. About 70 per cent of them attacked alginic acid, 20 per cent attacked cellulose, and 25 per cent attacked chitin.

Chitin Decomposition. Carbon dioxide, ammonia, acetic acid, and reducing sugars were among the products resulting from the decomposition of chitin by marine bacteria studied by ZoBell and Rittenberg (1938). Chitin is a complex glucosamine having the empirical formula $C_{32}H_{54}O_{21}N_4$. Being the chief constituent of the exoskeleton of arthropods and occurring commonly in mollusks, coelenterates, protozoa, and fungi, large quantities of chitin are produced in the ocean. Copepods alone are believed to produce several tons of chitin annually.

Hock (1940) isolated chitinoclastic bacteria from marine sands, mud, sea water, decomposing crabs, and the intestinal contents of several marine animals. Such bacteria in the gut of animals probably digest for the animals the ingested chitin. Hess (1937) found large numbers of chitinoclastic bacteria in lesions on the carapace of lobsters having a shell disease. From marine mud Campbell and Williams (1951) isolated 29 strains of bacteria that were able to obtain their carbon and nitrogen requirements from chitin.

Proteolytic Bacteria. Most marine bacteria are actively proteolytic, rapidly attacking nitrogenous compounds with the liberation of ammonia and carbon dioxide. All the 60 pure cultures of marine bacteria studied by ZoBell and Upham (1944) liberated ammonia from peptone, 47 liquefied gelatin, and 30 hydrolyzed casein.

Fish protein is extremely susceptible to bacterial decomposition as manifested by the rapid production of ammonia, indole, trimethylamine, histamine, hydrogen sulfide, and other protein-decomposition products (Beatty and Gibbons, 1937). Waksman et al. (1938) noted that plankton organisms, particularly zooplankton rich in proteinaceous material, undergo rapid decomposition in sea water.

Asparagine, aspartic acid, glutamic acid, alanine, propionamide, acetamide, hippurate, urea, and creatinine were assimilated by most of the marine bacteria studied by Ostroff and Henry (1939). From 2 to 4 mgm. of glycine, alanine, phenylalanine, glutamic acid, tyrosine, and asparagine per liter of sea water were found by Waksman and Renn (1936) to be almost quantitatively decomposed by bacteria in 2 to 5 days at 20°C. with the liberation of ammonia.

Marine bacteria that liberated ammonia from gelatin and urea were found by Rubentschik (1925) to be active at temperatures as low as −2.5°C.

NITROGEN CYCLE IN THE SEA

As in the soil, bacteria transform nitrogen and its compounds in the sea (Wood, 1958). There is also a cycle of nitrogen compounds from the soil into the sea with drainage from land. Except for the insignificant amount of nitrogenous compounds removed by man (in the form of fish) and fish-feeding birds (guano deposits), nitrogen escapes from the sea primarily in the gaseous state.

Nitrification. Although data compiled by Rakestraw (1936) indicate that relatively large quantities of ammonia must be oxidized in the sea by bacteria, conventional enrichment culture procedures generally fail to demonstrate the presence of nitrifying bacteria in sea water except near land. Carey (1938) concluded that marine nitrifiers are confined primarily to water in the photosynthetic zone and to the topmost portions of marine bottom deposits.

Most attempts to demonstrate in the sea bacteria that oxidize nitrite to nitrate have yielded negative results, although such organisms do occur in marine bottom deposits.

Nitrate Reduction. Numerous investigators have demonstrated a great variety of marine bacteria that reduce nitrate in nutrient media. Studies summarized by Bavendamm (1932) and Waksman, Hotchkiss, and Carey (1933) indicate, however, that except in localized environments there is generally inadequate organic matter in the sea to provide energy for bacterial denitrification.

Nitrogen Fixation. Evidence for the occurrence in the sea of nitrogen-fixing species of *Azotobacter* and *Clostridium* has been reviewed by Bavendamm (1932), Benecke (1933), and Waksman, Hotchkiss, and Carey (1933). The extent to which nitrogen fixation occurs in the sea, however, is still unknown. In fact, the whole problem of the nitrogen cycle in the sea is very incompletely understood, although bacteria are believed to play an important part.

PHOSPHATE REGENERATION

The rapid liberation of phosphate from marine plankton undergoing bacterial decomposition has been observed by Seiwell and Seiwell (1938). Renn (1937) has investigated the part played by bacteria in this process that makes phosphorus available as a plant nutrient in the sea.

SULFUR CYCLE IN THE SEA

Most saprophytic bacteria found in the sea decompose albuminous material with the liberation of hydrogen sulfide. Under anaerobic conditions, organic sulfur is converted almost quantitatively into hydrogen sulfide by mixed cultures of heterotrophs. Aerobes also liberate H₂S from organic compounds containing sulfur, but the sulfide may be abiogenetically oxidized as fast as it is liberated in oxygenated sea water.

In stagnant water basins, hydrogen sulfide may accumulate in concentrations high enough to be lethal for marine animals. Under such conditions much hydrogen sulfide may result from the reduction of sulfate.

Sulfate Reduction. As shown by ZoBell and Rittenberg (1938), sulfate reducers occur abundantly in marine bottom deposits. Being strict anaerobes, such bacteria are only infrequently found in sea water. *Desulfovibrio aestuarii* is the principal marine sulfate reducer, although there may be other genera and species.

Sulfate-reducing bacteria utilize a large variety of organic compounds. Certain cultures described by Sisler and ZoBell (1950) can utilize molecular hydrogen as an energy source. Their common occurrence in oil-well brines suggests that sulfate reducers may be associated with the formation of petroleum (ZoBell et al., 1957).

Sulfur Bacteria. Several genera of achromic sulfur bacteria that oxidize sulfide, elementary sulfur, sulfite, thiosulfate, or other inorganic sulfur compounds have been found in the sea. Some of these appear to be exclusively marine species, whereas others live in both marine and nonmarine habitats.

Baas-Becking (1925) and Bavendamm (1924) found achromic sulfur bacteria, along with purple forms, to be abundant in shallow water where hydrogen sulfide is formed. Whether the hydrogen sulfide is oxidized to free sulfur or to sulfate depends upon the bacterial species, oxygen tension, concentration of hydrogen sulfide, light penetration, and other factors (van Niel, 1936).

In localized regions investigated by Gietzen (1931), purple sulfur bacteria sometimes occur in sufficient abundance to color the water. According to Baas-Becking (1925), such bacteria occur in water ranging in salinity from 0.05 to 7.5 per cent sodium chloride. They prefer diffuse or subdued sunlight, a low oxygen tension, and the presence of hydrogen sulfide, which is commonly provided by sulfate reducers. Further information on the physiology of this group of bacteria is given in treatises by van Niel (1931, 1936), Gietzen (1931), and Starkey (1956).

BACTERIOLOGY OF MARINE FISH

Escherichia coli and allied coliform bacteria are not normal inhabitants of the intestines or viscera of marine fish. The occurrence of such bacteria in the intestines or flesh of fish indicates either that the fish has been taken from polluted water or that contamination has occurred during transportation, handling, or marketing (Griffiths, 1937).

The normal bacterial flora of the intestine and viscera depend largely on the feeding habits of the fish and the type of food being ingested. The intestinal tract of nonfeeding fish is often found to be free of bacteria. Numerous marine bacteria are associated with the surface slime and gills of fish. Whether the muscle tissue of living or recently killed fish is always sterile is questionable, but shortly after fish are caught, invasion occurs. Predominating are species of *Achromobacter, Pseudomonas, Flavobacterium, Proteus, Bacillus, Serratia,* and *Micrococcus.* The bacterial population of dead fish increases rapidly at a rate that is influenced primarily by the temperature. Bacteria growing in fish may cause discoloration or other undesirable changes (Beatty and Gibbons, 1937).

Bacteriology of Shellfish. Though normally free from pathogenic bacteria in clean water, oysters, clams, mussels, and other shellfish may become contaminated in polluted water or by careless handling. Nearly all outbreaks of typhoid fever or Asiatic cholera traced to infected shellfish resulted from oysters that had been "floated" or "fattened" in brackish water near sewage outfalls or polluted rivers (Prescott et al., 1946).

Inasmuch as human pathogens may survive in oysters for several weeks (Hunter and Harrison, 1928), shellfish of questionable origin should be cooked before they are eaten.

Large numbers of saprophytic bacteria are ordinarily associated with shellfish. These are of little sanitary significance except that they may promote the decomposition of shellfish during storage. Methods for the bacteriological examination of shellfish have been summarized by Perry (1939) and by Wilson and McCleskey (1951).

Oysters and other shellfish may themselves be susceptible to diseases. The large-scale death of oysters in an epidemic pattern has been attributed to microbial infections. A protistan parasite, *Dermocystidium marinum,* has been incriminated by Mackin (1951), and the "pit disease" of oysters is caused by the flagellate *Hexamita* accompanied by bacteria as secondary invaders (Mackin et al., 1952). Spirochetes, ostensibly parasitic in the gut, were found in the majority of market oysters examined by Dimitroff (1926).

EFFECT OF BACTERIA ON MARINE ANIMALS

Marine animals appear to be susceptible to microbial infections, although very few observations have been made except in aquariums (ZoBell, 1946a).

The vast majority of the bacteria in the sea are beneficial to the animal population. Many species that live normally in the gut of animals aid in the digestion of food. Bacterial enzymes catalyze the hydrolysis of cellulose, chitin, and other complex chemical substances eaten by marine animals.

Being highly nutritious and usually readily digestible, bacteria constitute an important part of the diet of many marine animals. MacGinitie (1935) and Mare (1942) have stressed the importance of bacteria as food for bottom-dwelling animals.

Photogenic or luminescent bacteria on the integument and growing in the light organs of certain marine animals sometimes cause the latter to glow in the dark (Harvey, 1940).

BACTERIA IN INLAND SEAS

Although the Dead Sea, having a salt content of about 30 per cent, has the popular reputation of being lifeless, Elazari-Volcani (1940) found numerous bacteria in water and mud samples. The organisms thrived in nutrient media containing 3 to 30 per cent salt.

An abundant bacterial flora representing several genera was observed on glass slides submerged by Smith and ZoBell (1937) in Great Salt Lake, an inland sea almost as saline as the Dead Sea. The development of microcolonies on the submerged slides proved that the bacteria multiplied in the brine and were not merely passive inhabitants.

Its high content of sulfide renders nine-tenths of the Black Sea virtually uninhabitable by any form of life except bacteria. Bacteria are also the predominant form of life in the Caspian Sea (Butkevich, 1938).

REFERENCES

Baas-Becking, L. G. M.: Studies on the sulfur bacteria, *Ann. Botany* (*London*), 39:613, 1925.

Barghoorn, E. S., and D. H. Linder: Marine fungi: their taxonomy and biology, *Farlowia*, 1:395, 1944.

Bavendamm, W.: "Die farblosen und roten Schwefelbakterien des Suss- und Salzwassers," Jena, Germany, Gustav Fischer Verlagsbuchhandlung, 1924.

————: Die mikrobiologische Kalkfällung in der tropischen See, *Arch. Mikrobiol.*, 3:205, 1932.

Beard, P. J., and N. F. Meadowcroft: Survival and rate of death of intestinal bacteria in sea water, *Am. J. Pub. Health*, 25:1023, 1935.

Beatty, S. A., and N. E. Gibbons: The measurement of spoilage in fish, *J. Biol. Board Can.*, 3:77, 1937.

Benecke, W.: Bakteriologie des meeres, "Abderhalden's Handbuch der biologischen Arbeitsmethoden," Abt. 9, Tl. 5, 717, 1933.

Burke, V., and L. A. Baird: Fate of fresh water bacteria in the sea, *J. Bact.*, 21:287, 1931.

Butkevich, V. S.: Die Bildung der Eisenmangan-Ablagerungen am Meeresboden und die daran beteiligten Mikroorganismen, *Ber. wiss. Meeresinst.*, *Moscow*, 3 (3):5, 1928.

————: On the bacterial population of the Caspian and Azov seas, *Mikrobiologiya*, 7:1005, 1938.

Campbell, L. L., and O. B. Williams: A study of chitin-decomposing microorganisms of marine origin, *J. Gen. Microbiol.*, 5:894, 1951.

Carey, C. L.: The occurrence and distribution of nitrifying bacteria in the sea, *J. Marine Research*, 1:291, 1938.

Carpenter, L. V., L. R. Setter, and M. Weinberg: Chloramine treatment of sea water, *Am. J. Pub. Health*, 28:929, 1938.

Cholodny, N.: "Die Eisenbakterien," Jena, Germany, Gustav Fischer Verlagsbuchhandlung, 1926.

Dimitroff, V. T.: Spirochaetes in Baltimore market oysters, *J. Bact.*, 12:135, 1926.

Drew, G. H.: Report of investigations on marine bacteria carried on at Andros Island, Bahamas, British West Indies, in May, 1912, *Carnegie Inst. Wash. Yearbook*, no. 11, p. 136, 1912.

Elazari-Volcani, B.: Studies on the microflora of the Dead Sea, dissertation, Hebrew University, Jerusalem, 1920.

————: Studies on the microflora of the Dead Sea, résumé of thesis published by Daniel Sieff Research Institute, Rehovoth, Palestine, 1940.

Gietzen, J.: Untersuchungen über marine Thiorhodacean, *Centr. Bakt.*, II Abt., 83:183, 1931.

Greenberg, A. E.: Survival of enteric organisms in sea water, *Pub. Health Reports*, 71:77, 1956.

Griffiths, F. P.: A review of the bacteriology of fresh marine-fishery products, *Food Research*, 2:121, 1937.

Harder, E. C.: Iron-depositing bacteria and their geologic relations, *U.S. Geol. Survey, Prof. Papers*, 113:1, 1919.

Harvey, E. N.: "Living Light," Princeton, N.J., Princeton University Press, 1940.

Henrici, A. T.: Studies of freshwater bacteria. I. A direct microscopic technique, *J. Bact.*, 25:277, 1933; IV. Seasonal fluctuations of lake bacteria in relation to plankton production, *ibid.*, 35:129, 1938.

Hess, E.: Cultural characteristics of marine bacteria in relation to low temperatures and freezing, *Can. Biol. Fish Contr.*, N.S., 8:459, 1934.

————: A shell disease in lobsters (*Homarus americanus*) caused by chitinovorous bacteria, *J. Biol. Board Can.* 3:358, 1937.

Hock, C. W.: Decomposition of chitin by marine bacteria, *Biol. Bull.*, 79:199, 1940.

Hof, T.: Investigations concerning bacterial life in strong brines, *Rec. trav. botan. néerl.*, 32:92, 1935.

Hotchkiss, M., and S. A. Waksman: Correlative studies of microscopic and plate methods for evaluating the bacterial population of the sea, *J. Bact.*, 32:423, 1936.

Humm, H. J.: Marine agar-digesting bacteria of the South Atlantic coast, *Duke Univ. Marine Sta. Bull.* 3, p. 45, 1946.

Hunter, A. C., and C. W. Harrison: Bacteriology and chemistry of oysters, with special reference to regulatory control of production, handling, and shipment, *U.S. Dept. Agr. Tech. Bull.* 64, p. 1, 1928.

Kadota, H.: A study of marine aerobic cellulose-decomposing bacteria, *Mem. Coll. Agric. Kyota Univ., Japan*, 74:1, 1956.

Korinek, J.: Ein Beitrag zur Mikrobiologie des Meeres, *Centr. Bakt.*, II Abt., 71:73, 1927.

Krassilnikov, N. A.: The bactericidal action of sea water, *Mikrobiologia*, 7:329, 1938.

Kriss, A. E.: "Marine Microbiology (Deep Water)." Academy of Science SSSR, Moscow, 425 pp., 1959 (in Russian).

Lloyd, B.: Muds of the Clyde Sea Area. II. Bacterial content, *J. Biol. Assoc.*, 17:751, 1931.

MacGinitie, G. E.: Ecological aspects of a California marine estuary, *Am. Midland Naturalist*, 16:629, 1935.

Mackin, J. G.: Histopathology of infection of *Crassostrea virginica* (Gmelin) by *Dermocystidium marinum*, *Bull. Marine Sci.*, 1:72, 1951.

————, P. Korringa, and S. H. Hopkins: Hexamitiasis of *Ostrea edulis* and *Crassostrea virginica,* *ibid.*, 1:266, 1952.

Mare, Molly: A study of a marine benthic community with special reference to the microorganisms, *J. Marine Biol. Assoc., United Kingdom*, 25:517, 1942.

Ostroff, Rose, and B. S. Henry: The utilization of various nitrogen compounds by marine bacteria, *J. Cellular Comp. Physiol.*, 13:353, 1939.

Perry, C. A.: A summary of studies on pollution in shellfish, *Food Research*, 4:381, 1939.

Prescott, S. C., C.-E. A. Winslow, and M. H. McCrady: "Water Bacteriology: with

Special Reference to Sanitary Water Analysis," New York, John Wiley & Sons, Inc., 6th ed., 1946.

Rakestraw, N. W.: The occurrence and significance of nitrate in the sea, *Biol. Bull.*, **71**:133, 1936.

Renn, C. E.: Bacteria and the phosphorus cycle in the sea, *Biol. Bull.*, **72**:190, 1937.

Reuszer, H. W.: Marine bacteria and their role in the cycle of life in the sea. III. The distribution of bacteria in the ocean waters and muds about Cape Cod, *Biol. Bull.*, **65**:480, 1933.

Rittenberg, S. C., T. Mittwer, and D. Ivler: Coliform bacteria in sediments around three marine sewage outfalls, *Limnol. & Oceanogr.*, **3**:101, 1958.

Rubentschik, L.: Über die Lebenstätigkeit der Urobakterien bei einer Temperatur unter 0°C., *Centr. Bakt.*, II Abt., **64**:166, 1925.

Seiwell, H. R., and Gladys Seiwell: The sinking of decomposing plankton in sea water and its relationship to oxygen consumption and phosphorus liberation, *Proc. Am. Phil. Soc.*, **78**:465, 1938.

Sisler, F. D., and C. E. ZoBell: Hydrogen utilizing sulfate reducing bacteria in marine sediments, *J. Bact.*, **60**:747, 1950.

Smith, W. W., and C. E. ZoBell: Direct microscopic evidence of an autochthonous bacterial flora in Great Salt Lake, *Ecology*, **18**:453, 1937.

Stanier, R. Y.: Studies on marine agar-digesting bacteria, *J. Bact.*, **42**:527, 1941.

Starkey, R. L.: Transformations of sulfur by microorganisms, *Ind. Eng. Chem.*, **48**:1429, 1956.

Sverdrup, H. U., M. W. Johnson, and R. H. Fleming: "The Oceans," Englewood Cliffs, N.J., Prentice-Hall, Inc., 1942.

Thiel, G. A.: Manganese precipitated by microorganisms, *Econ. Geol.*, **20**:301, 1925.

van Niel, C. B.: On the morphology and physiology of the purple and green sulphur bacteria, *Arch. Mikrobiol.*, **3**:1, 1931.

————: On the metabolism of the *Thiorhodaceae*, *ibid.*, **7**:323, 1936.

Waksman, S. A.: The role of bacteria in the cycle of life in the sea, *Sci. Monthly*, **38**:35, 1934.

————, Cornelia Carey, and H. W. Reuszer: Marine bacteria and their role in the cycle of life in the sea. I. Decomposition of marine plant and animal residues by bacteria, *Biol. Bull.*, **65**:57, 1933.

————, Margaret Hotchkiss, and Cornelia Carey: Marine bacteria and their role in the cycle of life in the sea. II. Bacteria concerned in the cycle of nitrogen in the sea, *ibid.*, **65**:137, 1933.

————, ————, ————, and Yvette Hardman: Decomposition of nitrogenous substances in sea water by bacteria, *J. Bact.*, **35**:477, 1938.

———— and C. E. Renn: Decomposition of organic matter in sea water by bacteria. III. Factors influencing the rate of decomposition, *Biol. Bull.*, **70**:472, 1936.

————, H. W. Reuszer, Cornelia Carey, Margaret Hotchkiss, and C. E. Renn: Studies on the biology and chemistry of the Gulf of Maine. III. Bacteriological investigations of the sea water and marine bottoms, *ibid.*, **64**:183, 1933.

———— and Unto Vartiovaara: The adsorption of bacteria by marine bottom, *ibid.*, **74**:56, 1938.

Wilson, T. E., and C. S. McCleskey: Indices of pollution in oysters, *Food Research*, **16**:313, 1951; also see **16**:377.

Wood, E. J. F.: The significance of marine microbiology, *Bact. Rev.*, **22**:1, 1958.

ZoBell, C. E.: Microorganisms in marine air, *Aerobiology*, Am. Assoc. Advance, Sci., Publ. 17, p. 55, 1942a.

————: Changes produced by microorganisms in sediments after deposition, *J. Sediment. Petrol.*, **12**:127, 1942b.

————: The effect of solid surfaces upon bacterial activity, *J. Bact.*, **46**:39, 1943.

————: "Marine Microbiology," Waltham, Mass., The Chronica Botanica Co., 1946a.

————: Studies on redox potential of marine sediments, *Bull. Am. Assoc. Petroleum Geol.*, **30**:477, 1946b.

————: Action of microorganisms on hydrocarbons, *Bact. Rev.*, **10**:1, 1946c.

————: Marine bacteriology, *Ann. Rev. Biochem.*, **16**:565, 1947a.

————: Microbial transformation of molecular hydrogen in marine sediments, with particular reference to petroleum, *Bull. Am. Assoc. Petroleum Geol.*, **31**:1709, 1947*b*.

———: Bacterial life at the bottom of the Philippine Trench, *Science*, **115**:507, 1952*a*.

———: Part played by bacteria in petroleum formation, *J. Sediment. Petrol.*, **22**:42, 1952*b*.

———, D. Q. Anderson, and W. W. Smith: The bacteriostatic and bactericidal action of Great Salt Lake Water, *J. Bact.*, **33**:253, 1937.

——— and Jean E. Conn: Studies on the thermal sensitivity of marine bacteria, *ibid.*, **40**:223, 1940.

——— and Catharine B. Feltham: Preliminary studies on the distribution and characteristics of marine bacteria, *Bull. Scripps Inst. Oceanogr., Univ. Calif., Tech. Ser.*, **3**:279, 1934.

——— and F. H. Johnson: The influence of hydrostatic pressure on the growth and viability of terrestrial and marine bacteria, *J. Bact.*, **57**:179, 1949.

——— and C. H. Oppenheimer: Some effects of hydrostatic pressure on the multiplication and morphology of marine bacteria, *ibid.*, **60**:771, 1950.

——— and S. C. Rittenberg: The occurrence and characteristics of chitinoclastic bacteria in the sea, *ibid.*, **35**:275, 1938.

——— and ———: Sulfate reducing bacteria in marine sediments, *J. Marine Research*, **7**:602, 1948.

——— and H. C. Upham: A list of marine bacteria including descriptions of sixty new species, *Bull. Scripps Inst. Oceanogr., Univ. Calif.*, **5**:239, 1944.

———, et al.: Sulfate reducing bacteria—Their relation to the secondary recovery of oil. Symposium, St. Bonaventure Univ., N.Y., 81 pp., 1957.

CHAPTER 21

Bacteriology of Water

Water receives its bacterial content from air, soil, sewage, organic wastes, dead plants and animals, etc. This means that at times almost any organism may be found in water. Most of the bacteria find conditions unfavorable and soon die. Those species which survive and are constantly present constitute the natural flora of water.

The great majority of the bacteria found in nature live on dead or decaying organic matter. They are called saprophytes (*sapro*, rotten; and *phyte*, plant) and belong to the so-called metatrophic group of organisms. Saprophytes are commonly present in large numbers in humus, a brown or black material found in the surface layer of soil, formed by the partial decomposition of vegetable or animal matter.

Natural waters are commonly grouped into four well-marked classes: (1) atmospheric waters, (2) surface waters, (3) stored waters, and (4) ground waters.

Atmospheric Waters. Rain and snow are included under the atmospheric waters. Sometimes these may contain considerable numbers of bacteria, owing chiefly to the high content of dust in the air. After a snow or heavy rain the atmosphere is washed nearly free of organisms so that many sterile plates, each inoculated with 1 ml. of water, may be obtained.

Surface Waters. As soon as the raindrops and snowflakes touch the earth, they become quickly contaminated by the microorganisms in the soil. These are then known as surface waters. The extent of the contamination is dependent upon the numbers of organisms in the soil and, also, upon the kinds and quantities of food materials dissolved out of the soil by the water. The bacterial counts of surface waters are apt to show great variations. This is particularly true in the fall and spring, the seasons of heavy rains and melting snows. The washoff from the soil may upset the existing equilibrium in the surface water, resulting in considerable variation in the flora and bacterial content.

The first result of a mild rain is to increase greatly the bacterial contamination of a body of water. A prolonged rain exerts an opposite effect, owing to the fact that after the main impurities have been removed from the upper layers of the soil, the subsequent rainfall acts merely as a diluent of the body of water. Rivers usually show their highest count during the rainy period.

Stored Waters. The effect of storage is to decrease greatly the numbers of organisms in water. The forces which tend to produce bacterial self-purification now come into play. These are sedimentation, activities of other organisms, ultraviolet light, temperature, food supply, and perhaps osmotic effects.

Bacteria have a specific gravity slightly greater than that of distilled water, which means that they will slowly settle in a still body of water. However, the greatest factor responsible for the sedimentation of bacteria is their attachment to suspended particles. The suspended particles in settling mechanically remove the organisms from the upper layers of the water.

Predatory protozoa present in waters play an important role in decreasing the number of bacteria. Protozoa require living or dead bacteria for food and easily engulf large numbers of these organisms, provided the water contains sufficient dissolved oxygen. In the absence of bacteria and dissolved oxygen, the protozoa gradually disappear.

Direct sunlight is toxic to vegetative bacterial cells and even to spores if the action is sufficiently prolonged. Diffuse light is less effective as a sterilizing agent. In a water supply, the toxicity of ultraviolet rays is inversely proportional to its turbidity. In other words, the light rays are practically without action in a turbid water. In a clear water ultraviolet rays may be effective for a depth of 1 to 3 meters.

Increasing temperatures exert a harmful effect upon the survival of some organisms in water, especially those capable of producing disease. On the other hand, multiplication of certain soil and intestinal forms may actually occur when the temperature of the water is increased. Bigger (1937) showed that *Escherichia coli* was capable of multiplying in water from various sources that had been autoclaved previous to inoculation and then incubated at 37°C. In some instances the numbers of organisms present were more than 10,000 times the original count. Cultures in autoclaved water kept at 22°C. showed higher counts and a greatly prolonged period of positive cultures as compared to those kept at 37°C. Raw waters also showed an increase in bacterial numbers when stored at 22 and 37°C., but not so great as when autoclaved water was used.

An increase in the food supply usually results in an increase in bacterial numbers. On the other hand, certain toxic substances such as acids and bases produce marked reductions in the numbers of viable organisms. Various dissolved gases such as carbon dioxide and hydrogen also show a toxic effect. Environmental factors generally produce marked fluctuations in the bacterial counts. Apparently this is not due to any one factor but to a group of factors acting as a whole.

Obviously, all the factors that operate to decrease the numbers of bacteria in water will be more effective with an increase in time. This may be represented mathematically as follows:

$$\log \frac{N_1}{N_2} = kt$$

where N_1 = number of organisms at the beginning
$\quad N_2$ = number of organisms at the end
$\quad t$ = time
$\quad k$ = a constant that varies with temperature and other environmental factors

Ground Waters. Ground waters are, in general, relatively free from bacteria because of the filtering action of the earth through which the waters have penetrated. This filtering action removes not only most of the bacteria but also any suspended organic food particles. Deep wells contain usually fewer organisms than water from shallow wells, owing to the deeper layers of filtering material. The distance that bacteria travel through soil depends upon a number of factors, including the permeability of the soil, the hydraulic gradient of the ground water, and the climatic conditions.

The majority of bacteria found in soil belong to the following groups: (1) fluorescent bacteria, (2) chromogenic rod forms, (3) coliform bacteria, (4) organisms of the genus *Proteus*, (5) spore formers of the *Bacillus* subtilis type, and (6) chromogenic and nonchromogenic cocci.

QUANTITATIVE BACTERIOLOGICAL EXAMINATION OF WATER

The sample of water to be examined is collected in a clean, sterile 100-ml. glass-stoppered or screw-cap bottle. The neck and top of the bottle are covered with a parchment paper cap and tied in place with string. The bottle is then sterilized in an autoclave at 15 lb. pressure (121°C.) for 30 min. The purpose of the covering is to keep the neck and stopper of the bottle free from contaminating bacteria.

Bottles for the collection of waters containing residual chlorine should contain a dechlorinating agent such as sodium thiosulfate. This should be added to the bottle before sterilization in a concentration of 100 mg. per liter of water.

In order to obtain a representative sample from a tap, the water should be allowed to run for at least 5 min. to remove any contaminating organisms present around the opening of the faucet. Also changes in bacterial content are liable to occur in small pipes; some species tend to die, others to multiply. The bottle is grasped with the right hand. The stopper is removed with the left hand, holding it by the paper covering. The bottle is filled to within ½ in. of the stopper to permit mixing of the contents. After the sample is collected, the stopper with covering is carefully replaced to avoid contamination, and the paper tied in place with string. The fingers must not touch the inside of the neck or stopper; otherwise contamination of the contents may occur and lead to an erroneous result.

In sampling a still body of water, the cap is first removed with the left hand. The bottle is plunged mouth downward to a depth of about 1 ft., then inverted. When filled, it is removed and stoppered. If any current exists, the mouth of the bottle should be directed against it in order to avoid the introduction of bacteria from the fingers.

After a sample of water has been collected and stored, a rapid change in the bacterial content takes place. The numbers of organisms usually show marked increases. In some cases, the increase in numbers is gradual; in others, it is very rapid. The increase in numbers is due to a multiplication of the typical water bacteria. Disease and other organisms whose natural habitat is the intestinal tract of man and animals tend to die very rapidly.

An increase in bacterial numbers is greatly accelerated by an increase in temperature. Because of the rapid bacterial changes which may take place in bottled waters, even when stored at a temperature as low as 10°C., all samples should be examined as quickly as possible. Samples which are to be kept for any length of time should be stored at temperatures between 6 and 10°C.

Method. The bottle containing the sample is shaken vigorously at least 25 times to obtain a uniform distribution of the organisms. Measured amounts are transferred to Petri dishes and mixed with melted agar. After the agar has solidified, the plates are inverted and incubated at 35°C. for 24 ±2 hr. The colonies are counted, and the count is expressed in numbers per milliliter of sample.

Only plates showing from 30 to 300 colonies should be counted. If more than 300 organisms per milliliter are present, many of them will fail to develop owing to the inhibitory action of the waste products secreted by those organisms which develop first.

Various factors influencing the numbers of colonies developing on agar plates include the composition and reaction of the medium, temperature and period of incubation, presence of an abundant supply of oxygen and moisture. Unless such factors are controlled, variable counts will be obtained.

The above method and its many modifications give only a fraction of the total count. The nitrifying and other autotrophic bacteria are cultivated on synthetic media composed of inorganic salts. They are unable to grow on the usual nonsynthetic culture media. The obligate anaerobic bacteria fail to multiply in the presence of air. Certain parasitic bacteria do not grow in the absence of rich animal fluids. Sulfate-reducing bacteria require the presence of sulfates for growth to occur. Cellulose-dissolving bacteria either do not grow or grow very poorly unless cellulose is present in the medium. The result is that most of the bacteria found in water escape detection. Twenty to seventy times more organisms have been enumerated by the direct or microscopic method than with the usual agar-plate procedure.

No great error is introduced by failure to obtain the total bacterial count of water. The sanitary bacteriologist is not interested in such organisms as the anaerobic spore formers, the nitrifying and other autotrophic forms, and the pathogenic organisms, but in a group of rapidly growing, rich-food-loving bacteria found in sewage. Most of these organisms are members of the coliform group.

The plate method is also useful in judging the efficiency of operation of various water treatment methods.

WATER-BORNE DISEASE

The most important bacterial diseases transmitted by water are dysentery, cholera, and typhoid. Since they are intestinal diseases, the causative agents are found in the intestinal contents. Therefore, the presence of sewage in a water supply means that one or more of these disease organisms may be present and that the water is potentially dangerous for human consumption.

Theoretically it would be better to examine water for the presence of disease organisms to determine its potability from a sanitary standpoint. However, several difficulties enter into such a procedure. Chief among these are (1) the length of time that disease organisms remain viable in water, and (2) the number encountered in a water supply.

Natvig and Nilsen (1955) reported that the longevity of *Escherichia coli* was greatly reduced outside the animal body. In soil under outdoor conditions, the numbers dropped markedly during the first month. However, a few organisms remained viable for up to 14 months. In soil stored indoors, the numbers increased during the first 4 to 6 months, then disappeared rapidly. A few remained viable up to 24 months. The bacteria did not lose their characteristics during the period of their residence outside of the animal organism.

Kelly and Arcisz (1954) found *Salmonella schottmuelleri* and S. *typhosa* to survive for 15 to 60 days in shell stock. S. *schottmuelleri* persisted at least as long as *E. coli*. The reduction of both organisms in stored soft clams proceeded much in a parallel fashion. There was little evidence that multiplication of either organism occurred during the storage period.

Kelly, Winsser, and Winkelstein (1957) reported the frequent isolation of poliomyelitis virus during the summer and fall months from both untreated and treated sewage.

The numbers of disease organisms encountered in a water supply are usually exceedingly small. If only one person in a community is suffering from typhoid fever and the discharges from that individual are mixed with the sewage from all individuals, the high dilution would make it practically impossible to isolate the disease organisms from a convenient sample of water. If, on the other hand, many persons are suffering from typhoid fever, the concentration of bacilli in sewage might be high enough to make isolations relatively easy, but special culture media would be required for this purpose. For these reasons, attempts to isolate disease organisms directly from water supplies are rarely practiced.

Salmonella typhosa–coliform Ratio. Kehr and Butterfield (1943) concluded, from the findings of others, that it is unlikely that a single individual would imbibe more than one typhoid organism, or at most only a few. They advanced the theory that a single typhoid organism is infective to a small percentage of the general population. They assumed that a drinking water showed a *Salmonella typhosa–coliform* ratio of 10 per million, which corresponded roughly to that found in the Thames and in London sewage. If the drinking water contained 500 coliform bacteria per 100 ml., then the chance of an individual obtaining one S. *typhosa* in a daily portion of 1 liter of water would be about 1 chance in 20. Two S. *typhosa* cells from a liter of water would presumably be imbibed by 1 in 400 persons and three by 1 in 8000 according to the laws of probability and assuming uniform distribution of bacteria. The presence of 500 coliform organisms per 100 ml. of drinking water, in the absence of any knowledge concerning the concentration of S. *typhosa*, would probably give rise to outbreaks of gastroenteritis followed by a few cases of typhoid fever in the majority of instances.

These studies of Kehr and Butterfield of the available data in the literature emphasize the basic value of the coliform test as an indicator of the possible presence of pathogens and indicate that a very real danger may exist when coliform bacteria, in even moderately high concentrations, are present.

Presence of Escherichia coli in Sewage. E. *coli* was first isolated by Escherich (1885) from the feces of an infant. It was shown later to be a normal inhabitant of the intestinal tracts of man and animals. Since it is present in the discharges from all individuals with rare exceptions (Parr, 1938), tests for the potability of a water supply are generally based on the presence or absence of this organism. Its presence in water does not mean necessarily that disease organisms are present but that they may be present. In other words, all sewage-polluted waters are potentially dangerous.

The procedures employed for the bacteriological examination of water make no attempt to distinguish coliform bacteria indicative of fecal contamination from coliforms of nonfecal contamination. Such a differentiation is of little importance in determining the suitability of a water for human consumption. Contamination with either type of waste renders the water potentially unsatisfactory from a sanitary standpoint.

For more information see Litsky, Mallmann, and Fifield (1955).

PRESUMPTIVE TEST

The first step in water examinations is known as the presumptive test, which consists in placing graduated amounts of water in a series of tubes containing lactose broth of proper strength. It is the usual practice to employ five fermentation tubes each containing 10 ml. of water, one tube containing 1 ml. of water, and another with 0.1 ml. of water. The tubes are incubated at 35°C. and examined at the end of 24 and 48 hr. The

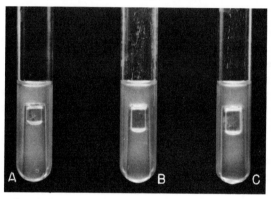

Fig. 207. Lactose broth fermentation tubes. A, 1-ml. water sample; B, 0.5-ml. water sample; C, 0.1-ml. water sample. All tubes show fermentation of the lactose with the production of acid and gas.

formation of gas in any of the tubes within 48 ± 3 hr., regardless of the amount, constitutes a positive presumptive test (Fig. 207).

The absence of gas at the end of 48 hr. constitutes a negative presumptive test, and no further tests need be performed. The water may be considered satisfactory from a bacteriological standpoint.

All tubes showing gas in any amount shall be subjected to the confirmed test.

Conditions Necessary for Gas Production. Chambers (1950) showed that 40 to 390 million coliform organisms per milliliter were required to produce visible gas in lactose broth. The average of all determinations was 170 million per milliliter. Different coliform cultures varied in the population density required to produce gas. In most cases coliform counts of 75 million or more per milliliter were required to produce the first visible gas. The number of coliform bacteria originally inoculated into lactose broth had relatively little effect on the population density required to produce gas but did have a marked effect on the time necessary for gas production. The results from the cultures studied indicated that when the ratio of noncoliforms to coliforms was high, visible gas might not be produced at all, even though coliforms were present in considerable numbers in the original sample. This probably explains why coliforms are isolated occasionally from lactose broth tubes which show growth but no gas production.

False Positive Presumptive Tests. A positive test does not mean necessarily that members of the coliform group are present. In most cases it is true, but there are exceptions. False positive presumptive tests may be produced by the presence of other organisms capable of fermenting lactose with the formation of acid and gas.

Also, positive presumptive tests are frequently caused by a type of association known as synergism. Bacterial synergism may be defined as the joint action of two organisms on a carbohydrate, resulting in the production of gas that is not formed by either organism when grown separately (see page 455).

Elimination of False Presumptive Tests. Probably the most important procedure employed for the elimination of false positive presumptive tests is to incorporate an appropriate amount of a suitable triphenyl-methane dye in the lactose broth medium. Synergism is frequently caused by a Gram-positive and a Gram-negative organism growing together. A concentration of dye just sufficient to prevent the growth of Gram-positive organisms will have no effect on the Gram-negative bacteria. This will result in the elimination of a synergistic reaction. False presumptive tests caused by the presence of gas-forming Gram-positive aerobes and anaerobes will also be eliminated by this procedure.

For more information see Folpmers (1948) and Wattie (1948).

CONFIRMED TEST

All lactose broth fermentation tubes showing gas at the end of 24- or 48-hr. incubation at 35°C. shall be utilized in the confirmed test.

Eosin methylene blue or Endo agar plates or brilliant green lactose bile broth fermentation tubes may be used in the test.

Eosin Methylene Blue Agar Medium. This medium is prepared by adding definite quantities of the two dyes eosin and methylene blue to a melted lactose agar base, and pouring about 15 ml. into each Petri dish.

A loopful of the culture from each tube is streaked over the surface of an E.M.B. agar plate. The plate is inverted and incubated at 35 ± 0.5°C. for 24 ± 2 hr.

Three types of colonies will develop on the medium:

1. Typical nucleated, with or without metallic sheen.
2. Atypical unnucleated after 24-hr. incubation, opaque, pink.
3. Negative, all others.

If typical coliform colonies appear on the plate after 24 hr. at 35°C., the confirmed test may be considered positive (Fig. 208).

If only atypical colonies appear on the plate, the confirmed test cannot be considered negative, since some coliform organisms fail to produce

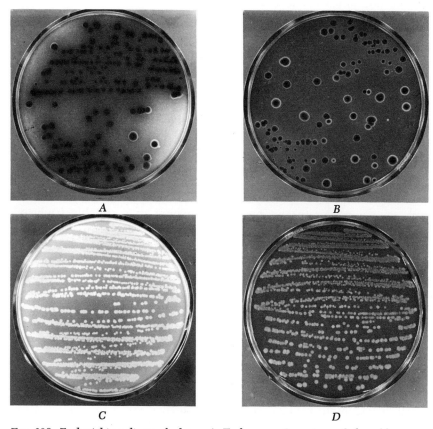

FIG. 208. *Escherichia coli*, streaked on: *A*, Endo agar; *B*, eosin methylene blue agar. The colonies have dark centers and a metallic sheen. *Aerobacter aerogenes*, streaked on: *C*, Endo agar; *D*, eosin methylene blue agar. The colonies do not have dark centers or a metallic sheen.

typical colonies on this medium, or the colonies develop slowly. Regardless of whether typical or atypical colonies appear, it is necessary to complete the test as directed below (page 556).

If only negative colonies appear on the plate, the confirmed test may be considered negative and no further tests need be made.

Wynne, Rode, and Hayward (1942) found that the color of coliforms on this medium depended on two factors: (1) the reaction of eosin (an acid dye) with methylene blue (a basic dye) to form a dye compound of either acidic or neutral nature and (2) the production, by lactose-fermenting organisms, of sufficient acid to cause this dye compound to be taken by individual cells of a colony. Non-lactose-fermenting organisms were not colored because the compound was not taken up in alkaline solution.

The medium is relatively stable. Prepared plates may be kept in the refrigerator for a week or longer before use. The plates should not be exposed unnecessarily to the light; otherwise toxic substances might be formed in the medium (see page 245).

Endo Agar Medium. Endo agar medium is prepared by adding basic fuchsin, previously decolorized with sodium sulfite, to a melted lactose agar base, and pouring about 15 ml. into each Petri dish.

The basic fuchsin of commerce is a mixture of pararosaniline (magenta O), rosaniline (magenta I), and magenta II. On the addition of sodium sulfite, the compounds are decolorized. The dyes react with sulfite as follows:

Pararosaniline:

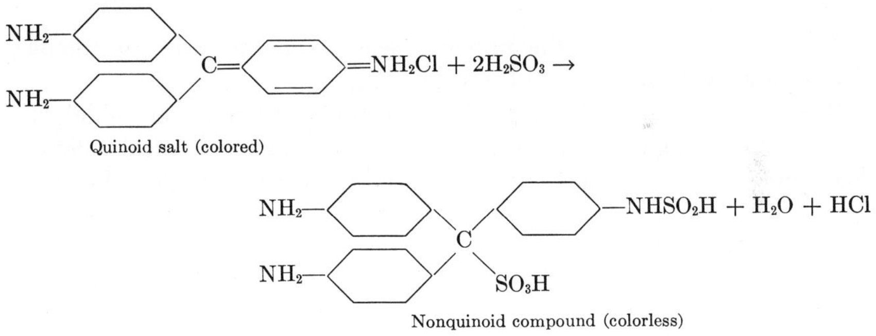

Quinoid salt (colored)

Nonquinoid compound (colorless)

Rosaniline:

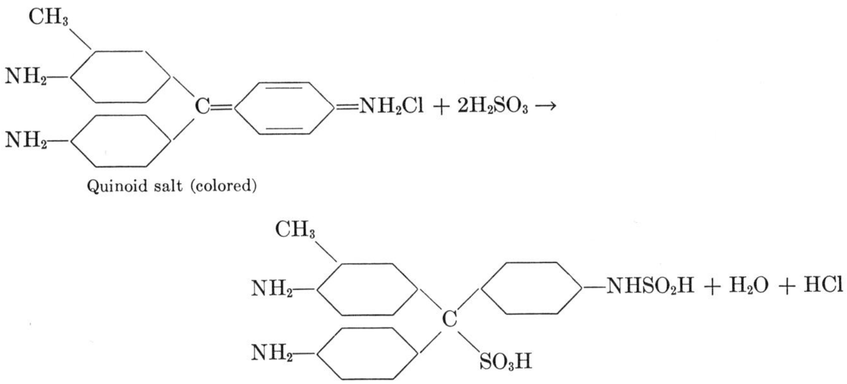

Quinoid salt (colored)

Nonquinoid compound (colorless)

Magenta II:

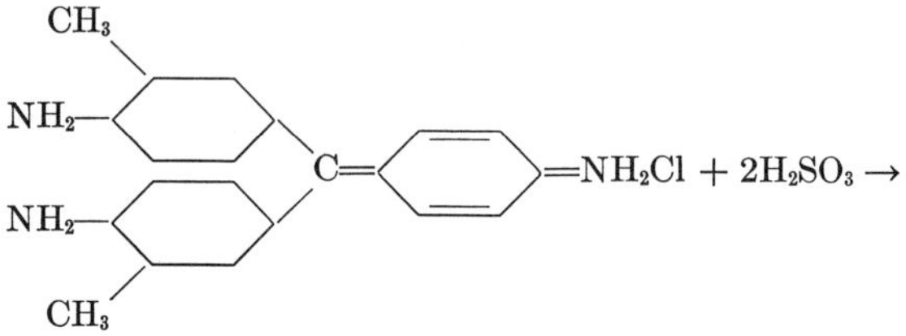

Quinoid salt (colored)

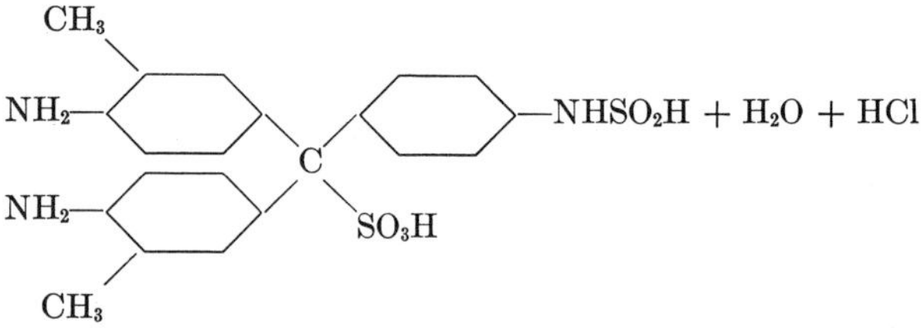

$$\text{...} =NH_2Cl + 2H_2SO_3 \rightarrow$$

$$\text{...} -NHSO_2H + H_2O + HCl$$

Nonquinoid compound (colorless)

A loopful of the culture from each tube is streaked over the surface of an Endo plate and incubated in the inverted position at $35 \pm 0.5°C$. for 24 ± 2 hr.

The remarks made in the previous section on the types of colonies developing on E.M.B. agar also apply here.

It is believed that Endo agar acts as a trapping agent for acetaldehyde, which is the compound responsible for the reaction of typical colonies. Acetaldehyde is an intermediary compound in the fermentation of lactose.

As the aldehyde is produced, it reacts with the sulfite to form an addition compound. Then the dye is released from the combination, resulting in the restoration of the red color to the medium. The metallic gold-like sheen imparted to the surface of typical colonies is due to the precipitation of the liberated dye.

Margolena and Hansen (1933) showed that the restored dye was different chemically from the original compound, being more purple in color. The process appears to be more complicated than just the removal of the sulfite and the liberation of the basic fuchsin dye.

Brilliant Green Lactose Bile Broth. A loopful of culture from each positive presumptive tube is transferred to brilliant green lactose bile broth fermentation tubes. The primary tubes are gently shaken before making the transfers. The tubes are incubated at $35 \pm 0.5°C$. for 48 ± 3 hr.

A positive test is indicated by the presence of gas in any amount in the inverted vial within the incubation period.

COMPLETED TEST

The completed test may be performed on the typical or atypical colonies developing on Endo or E.M.B. agar plates, or on the brilliant green lactose bile broth tubes showing gas in the confirmed test. If the latter medium is used in the confirmed test, one or more Endo or E.M.B. agar plates are streaked from tubes showing gas. The plates are incubated at $35 \pm 0.5°C$. for 24 ± 2 hr.

The purpose of the completed test is to determine if (1) the colonies developing on Endo or E.M.B. agar plates are again capable of fermenting lactose with the production of acid and gas, and (2) the organisms transferred to agar slants show the morphological and tinctorial picture of members of the coliform group.

At least one typical colony or, if no typical colonies are present, at least two atypical colonies considered likely to be members of the coliform group are each transferred to lactose fermentation tubes and to agar slants. All tubes are incubated at $35 \pm 0.5°C$. for a period not to exceed 48 ± 3 hr. Gram stains are prepared from the cultures on agar slants.

The formation of gas in any amount in the fermentation tubes and the demonstration of Gram-negative, non-spore-forming rods on the agar slants shall constitute a positive completed test for members of the coliform group. The absence of gas or failure to show the presence of rods answering to the above description in a gas-forming culture shall constitute a negative completed test.

For more information see American Public Health Association (1960) and Henriksen (1955).

The above procedures make no distinction between so-called fecal and nonfecal types. The American Public Health Association feels that any attempt to evaluate a drinking water on the basis of a distinction between the above two types is unwarranted. Contamination with either type of waste renders the water potentially unsatisfactory and unsafe from a sanitary standpoint.

However, the procedures which follow make an attempt to distinguish between fecal and nonfecal types. The tests are employed in many laboratories, but they are not to be regarded as official in any sense of the word.

DIFFERENTIATION OF FECAL FROM NONFECAL MEMBERS OF THE COLIFORM GROUP

Studies of recent years have emphasized the complexity of the coliform group. The general practice is to classify the members into fecal *Escherichia coli*, nonfecal *Escherichia freundii*, and nonfecal *Aerobacter aerogenes*. The classification is based on the results of four tests, namely, indole, methyl red, Voges-Proskauer, and sodium citrate.

Parr (1936) coined the mnemonic IMViC to designate these four reactions. The term is one of convenience. The I is for indole, M for methyl red, V for Voges-Proskauer, and C for citrate. The letter i between the V and C is added solely for euphony.

Using these four tests, the members of the coliform group may be classified as shown in Table 22.

TABLE 22. A SIMPLIFIED REACTION CLASSIFICATION OF MEMBERS OF THE COLIFORM GROUP

Organism	Indole	Methyl red	Voges-Proskauer	Sodium citrate	Commonly designated source
Escherichia coli					
Variety I.............	+	+	–	–	fecal
Variety II...........	–	+	–	–	fecal
Escherichia freundii					
(Intermediates)					
Variety I.............	–	+	–	±	nonfecal
Variety II...........	+	+	–	+	nonfecal
Aerobacter aerogenes					
Variety I.............	–	–	+	±	nonfecal
Variety II...........	±	–	+	+	nonfecal

Probably all types of coliform organisms may be found in feces. *E. coli* will most likely be found in fresh pollution derived from several sources, but other types, without *E. coli,* may sometimes be present in a fresh pollution from a single source.

There is little evidence that any of the coliform organisms multiply on grasses, on grains, or in soils. Therefore, it is questionable whether grasses, grains, and soils can be considered normal habitats of the members of the coliform group.

However, there is evidence that coliforms do multiply on such organic materials as leather washers, wood, swimming-pool ropes, and jute packing, and even in water pipes. The presence of large numbers of coliforms of a single type in water obtained from wells, springs, or a single distribution system is suggestive of multiplication on the above materials.

When members of the coliform group are inoculated into lactose broth fermentation tubes, some cultures produce more gas than others. Typical strains of *E. coli* rarely produce more than 25 per cent of gas in the inverted vial, whereas typical strains of *A. aerogenes* produce 75 to 100 per cent of gas. This indicates distinct differences in the carbohydrate metabolism of the two subgroups.

Rogers, Clark, and Davis (1914), Rogers, Clark, and Evans (1914, 1915), and Rogers, Clark, and Lubs (1918) found that typical strains of *E. coli* produced carbon dioxide and hydrogen in approximately equal amounts, whereas typical members of the *A. aerogenes* subgroup produced about twice as much carbon dioxide as hydrogen. The former are known as the low-ratio organisms ($CO_2/H_2 = 1$) and the latter as the high-ratio organisms ($CO_2/H_2 = 2$).

The high-ratio organisms (*Aerobacter*) are only occasionally found in the intestinal contents of man and animals (about 6 per cent). They are normally present in the soil. For this reason very little sanitary significance is attached to their presence in a water supply. On the other hand, the low-ratio organisms (*Escherichia*) are rarely found in the soil but constitute the predominating organisms found in the intestinal contents of man and animals. They are only occasionally found in localities not showing recent fecal pollutions.

For more information see Medrek and Litsky (1960), Thomas and Hobson (1955).

Methyl Red Test. Cultures of *Escherichia* ferment lactose with the formation of acids until the pH drops to about 5.0. This acidity is sufficient to prevent further growth of the organisms. The same principle applies to any fermentative organism.

Clark (1915) and Clark and Lubs (1915) stated that the metabolism of members of the coliform group can be controlled so that the final hydrogen-ion concentration of cultures of one subgroup can be made to diverge widely from the final pH of another subgroup. From a given amount of sugar, the *Escherichia* produce more acid than the *Aerobacter*. This is due largely to the fact that the *Escherichia* do not produce 2:3-butylene glycol and acetylmethylcarbinol, whereas the *Aerobacter* do. The amount of fermentable carbohydrate that is just sufficient for the *Escherichia* to produce their maximum acidity is inadequate for the *Aerobacter* to produce their limiting hydrogen-ion concentration. The result is that the *Escherichia* will be stopped in their growth, whereas the *Aerobacter* will exhaust the sugar, without producing their limiting pH, and continue to grow, utilizing the nitrogenous constituents for both structure and energy. The reaction of the medium becomes progressively less acid.

The amount of buffer present greatly influences the final hydrogen-ion concentration attained by an organism when grown in the presence of a fermentable substance. As the buffer content increases, the final acidity decreases. This means that as fermentation is prolonged, metabolic waste products other than acids accumulate to produce an increased toxic effect on the organisms.

The medium used for the test contains 0.5 per cent glucose and is sufficiently buffered with dibasic potassium phosphate and peptone to give a limiting hydrogen-ion concentration of about pH 5.0 when inoculated with typical *Escherichia*. The final hydrogen-ion concentration of cultures of typical *Aerobacter* will be at a much higher pH. The methyl red indicator used in the test is turned red by cultures of *Escherichia* and yellow by *Aerobacter*.

Voges-Proskauer Test. Voges and Proskauer found that the addition of potassium hydroxide to cultures of organisms of the hemorrhagic septicemia (*Pasteurella*) group resulted in the development of a pink color if allowed to stand for 24 hr. or longer.

The chemistry of the reaction was worked out by Harden and Walpole (1906), Harden (1906), and Harden and Norris (1912*a, b*). They found that distinct differences existed in the carbohydrate metabolism of typical *E. coli* and *A. aerogenes*. The fermentation of glucose by the two organisms yielded the products shown in Table 23.

TABLE 23

Product	Per cent by weight of glucose fermented	
	A. aerogenes	E. coli
Alcohol..........................	17.10	12.85
Acetic acid......................	5.10	18.84
Succinic acid....................	2.40	5.20
Formic acid.....................	1.00	0.00
Lactic acid......................	5.50	31.90
Carbon dioxide..................	38.00	18.10
Total........................	69.10	86.89
Ratio, CO_2/H_2.................	2.40	0.83

The figures show that 87 per cent of the carbon is accounted for in the case of *E. coli*, but only 69 per cent in cultures of *A. aerogenes*. Harden and Walpole found that the discrepancy was due to the formation by *A. aerogenes* of 2:3-butylene glycol ($CH_3 \cdot CHOH \cdot CHOH \cdot CH_3$) and acetylmethylcarbinol ($CH_3 \cdot CO \cdot CHOH \cdot CH_3$), but not by *E. coli*. The acetylmethylcarbinol in the presence of potassium hydroxide and air is further oxidized to diacetyl ($CH_3 \cdot CO \cdot OC \cdot CH_3$) which, in the presence of peptone, gives an eosin-like color. The constituent of peptone responsible for the eosin-like color is the guanidine nucleus [$NH:C(NH_2)$ $NH \cdot R$] of the amino acid arginine.

The Voges-Proskauer test appears to possess considerable sanitary significance because it distinguishes to a high degree between fecal *Escherichia* and nonfecal *Aerobacter*.

The presence of acetylmethylcarbinol (acetoin) may be easily detected in bacterial cultures. The organism being studied is inoculated heavily into a tube of glucose broth and incubated at 30°C. for 24 to 48 hr. Then 0.6 ml. of α-naphthol (5 gm. α-naphthol in 100 ml. 95 per cent alcohol) is added, followed by 0.2 ml. of 40 per cent potassium hydroxide solution. A positive reaction is indicated by the appearance of a red color in from 2 to 4 hr. Results should be read not later than 4 hr. after addition of the reagents.

Sodium Citrate Test. Koser (1923, 1924) found that the coliform organisms could be separated into two groups on the basis of their action on sodium or potassium citrate.

Typical fecal *Escherichia* were unable to utilize citrate when added to a synthetic medium as the only source of carbon. Typical nonfecal *Aerobacter* utilized citrate readily.

Koser showed that the test for citrate utilization correlated more closely with the source of the organisms than did any of the other differential tests.

Lara and Stokes (1952) observed that living cells of typical *Escherichia* could not oxidize citrate, whereas dried cells were able to do so. This would indicate that perhaps impermeability of living cells of *Escherichia* to citrate might be responsible for their inability to grow in Koser's medium.

Brewer and Werkman (1939) and Dagley and Dawes (1953a, b) showed that citrate was dissimilated by *Aerobacter* to acetate, pyruvate, and carbon dioxide, according to the reactions:

1. Citrate → oxalacetate + acetate
2. Oxalacetate → pyruvate + CO_2

The reactions occurred in an anaerobic environment. Results indicated that the enzyme was adaptive and suppressed by aerated growth.

For more information see Ferlin and Karabinos (1954).

Eijkman Test. Eijkman (1904) found that cultures of *Escherichia* produced acid and gas from glucose broth at 46°C., whereas *Aerobacter* failed to do so.

Stuart et al. (1942) found that *Aerobacter* and intermediates seldom produced gas from lactose at 45.5°C., whereas *Escherichia* seldom failed to do so. In their Eijkman characteristics, the intermediates were more closely related to *Aerobacter* than to *Escherichia*.

Taylor (1945) reported that 97 per cent of cultures of typical or type I *E. coli* (Table 24) examined fermented lactose with the production of

TABLE 24. PRODUCTION OF ACID AND GAS IN LACTOSE BROTH BY VARIOUS TYPES OF COLIFORM BACTERIA AT DIFFERENT TEMPERATURES

Type	No. of cultures tested	Percentage of cultures forming acid and gas at						
		37°C.	40°C.	42°C.	43°C.	44°C.	45°C.	46°C.
E. coli, type I.........	96	100	97	97	97	97	93	52
E. coli, type II........	50	100	64	36	32	28		
Intermediate type I....	78	100	78	56	23	0		
Intermediate type II...	53	100	55	4	2	0		
A. aerogenes, type I (or A. cloacae)	80	100	83	53	35	15	2	
	52	100	..	..	..	15		
A. aerogenes, type II...	25	100	80	12	0	0		

acid and gas between 40 and 44°C. The number was not appreciably reduced at 45°C. but was markedly reduced at 46°C. On the other hand, 15 per cent of cultures of typical or type I *Aerobacter* were found to be positive at 44°C. but only 2 per cent at 45°C.

COMPUTING THE MOST PROBABLE NUMBERS
OF COLIFORM ORGANISMS

Table 25 is based on the general formula of Hoskins (1934) for calculating the numbers of coliform organisms present in 100 ml. of a water sample. The figures are based on the employment of five tubes each con-

TABLE 25.   MOST PROBABLE NUMBERS OF COLIFORM ORGANISMS PRESENT IN 100 ML.
OF A WATER SAMPLE

Number of positive lactose broth tubes			Number of coliform organisms	Number of positive lactose broth tubes			Number of coliform organisms
10 ml.	1 ml.	0.1 ml.		10 ml.	1 ml.	0.1 ml.	
0	0	0	0	3	0	0	7.8
0	0	1	1.8	3	0	1	11
0	1	0	1.8	3	1	0	11
0	1	1	3.6	3	1	1	14
1	0	0	2	4	0	0	13
1	0	1	4	4	0	1	17
1	1	0	4	4	1	0	17
1	1	1	6.1	4	1	1	21
2	0	0	4.5	5	0	0	23
2	0	1	6.8	5	0	1	31
2	1	0	6.8	5	1	0	33
2	1	1	9.2	5	1	1	46

taining 10 ml. of water sample, one tube containing 1 ml. of water sample, and another tube containing 0.1 ml. of water sample.

For information on the general formula for the derivation of the above results see the report by Hoskins.

For more information see Levine et al. (1955); Litsky, Rosenbaum, and France (1953).

Paracolon Bacteria. The paracolon bacteria occupy a position intermediate between the coliforms (*Escherichia*—intermediates—*Aerobacter*) and the *Salmonella*. Borman, Stuart, and Wheeler (1944) proposed the genus name *Paracolobactrum* for this group.

The *Paracolobactrum* have some of the cultural characteristics of the coliforms and some of the pathogenicity of the *Salmonella*. They are characterized as short rods, Gram-negative. Fermentation of lactose is consistently delayed; occasionally lactose is not fermented. Certain forms attack carbohydrates charactistically at 20 to 30°C. but not at 37°C. The production of acetylmethylcarbinol may likewise be influenced by incubation temperature. Antigenic relationships to other genera in the family (see page 415) are common, even with respect to major antigens. They are found in surface water, soil, grains, and the intestinal tracts of animals, including man.

West and Edwards (1954) combined the Ballerup group and the Bethesda group of paracolons. They are generally believed to be identical with *Paracolobactrum intermedium*.

The paracolons, like the coliform bacteria, can be divided into three subgroups: paracolon *Escherichia*, paracolon intermediates, and paracolon *Aerobacter*, according to their IMViC reactions. A frequent property of the paracolons is that they either do not ferment lactose or attack it very slowly. For this reason plate colonies on differential media are often mistaken for pathogenic nonlactose fermenters. The organisms are frequently the cause of food poisoning and have been mistaken for members of the *Salmonella*.

For more information see Cooper and Ramadan (1955); Ewing et al. (1956); Gainey and Lord (1952); Moran and Bruner (1949); Mushin (1949, 1950); Parr (1939); Prescott, Winslow, and McCrady (1946); Schwabacher (1949); Sears and Brownlee (1952); Slanetz and Bartley (1955); Stuart, Galton, and McGann (1948).

THE MILLIPORE FILTER METHOD

Goetz and Tsuneishi (1951) described a new method for the enumeration of coliform bacteria in water, which they named the molecular filter technique. It is now generally referred to as the millipore filter method.

A sterile millipore filter is placed in the holding apparatus as shown in Fig. 209. The bacteria are collected by passing the water sample through the membrane with the aid of a partial vacuum. The membrane and side of the funnel are rinsed with a small amount of sterile distilled water. The membrane is then placed on an absorbent disk previously saturated with culture medium, and contained in a Petri dish. The nutrient solution passes through the membrane and nourishes the bacteria present thereon. Each organism will grow and produce a visible colony on the membrane after sufficient incubation (Fig. 210). The incubation time and temperature depend on the organism to be grown and the medium used.

According to Goetz and Tsuneishi, the millipore filter possesses the following advantages in water examinations:

It permits the concentration of a small number of organisms from large quantities of water, thereby increasing the accuracy and reliability of such determinations.

It minimizes spreading of colonies and allows the combination of any number of

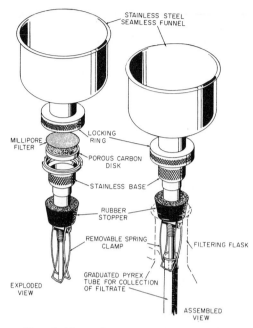

FIG. 209. Millipore filter holder. The unit consists of a funnel of stainless steel clamped to a base containing a molecular filter. The stem of the base is inserted into a filter flask through a rubber stopper. (*After Goetz and Tsuneishi.*)

bacteria, from a few to 5000 at one time. This has the advantage of reducing the number of laboratory dilutions and duplicate incubations.

It permits separation of the organisms from their nutrient at any time, for the purpose of either changing the medium or partially or totally inhibiting further development.

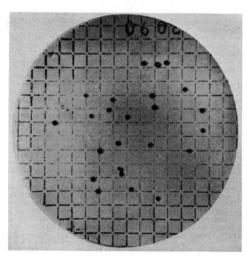

FIG. 210. Culture of *Escherichia coli* on molecular filter. (*After Goetz and Tsuneishi.*)

It gives a direct count instead of a determination of the most probable number from positive fermentation tubes (Table 25, page 562).

It saves time in comparison with the approved standard procedure.

It permits better and faster differentiation of bacteria.

It gives a permanent record in the form of the preserved filter disks.

On the other hand, studies by others have indicated that there is no readily apparent relationship between results secured by the millipore filter and the standard dilution tube procedure for computing the most probable numbers. According to Kabler (1954), the two procedures do not measure precisely the same group of organisms and the sanitary significance of the differences in the results of the methods is yet to be determined.

Lieber (1955) reported that in its present state of development the membrane filter procedure has many characteristics which prevent it from supplanting the A.P.H.A. Standard Methods test. Its limitations are the large volumes of potable ground-water samples necessary for routine examinations, the increased cost per analysis by the millipore method as compared with the Standard Methods procedure, and the undesirable concentration of laboratory activity resulting from the routine use of the membrane filter.

For more information see American Public Health Association (1960), Geldreich et al. (1955), McCarthy (1955), Shipe and Cameron (1954).

PURIFICATION OF WATER

Sewage organisms, especially the pathogenic forms, do not live long in water. The temperature and food conditions are not conducive to survival for any length of time. Also many protozoa are present in water at times, and these depend largely on bacteria as a source of food.

However, a municipal water supply must usually pass through a series of purification steps to make it safe for human consumption. In some cases the water may be sufficiently pure to require only the addition of a disinfectant. In other instances the condition of the water is such as to require three stages of purification, namely, sedimentation, filtration, and disinfection.

Sedimentation. In this stage the water is run into large tanks where it is allowed to stand for the suspended matter to settle out. Since this is a very slow process, it may be hastened by the addition of a chemical coagulant, such as aluminum sulfate, which reacts with the alkaline salts to produce insoluble gelatinous aluminum hydroxide. The insoluble material rapidly settles out, carrying with it bacteria and other particulate matter in suspension.

Filtration. In the second stage the water is passed through sand filters. These are of two types: the slow sand filter and the rapid sand filter. When the slow filter is employed, it is usually not necessary to add a chemical coagulant. A slimy or gelatinous film soon forms on the surface of the sand; the film acts as a filtering medium, removing bacteria and other suspended matter. The filtering surface eventually becomes too thick and must be removed.

In the rapid method the coagulant forms a mat or floc on the surface of the sand which acts as a filtering medium. It should remove bacteria and particles of similar size. Since this type of filter can handle more water per surface area than the slow type, it is more extensively used.

Disinfection. Since not all bacteria are removed by the sand filters, the remaining ones can be destroyed by the addition of a suitable disinfectant. Chlorine has been shown to be effective in minute amounts and is generally used for this purpose. Automatic machines are available which feed chlorine gas directly into the water. Usually sufficient chlorine is added to provide a residual concentration of one part of available chlorine per million parts of water.

For more information see Chang and Morris (1953) and Ricks et al. (1955).

REFERENCES

American Public Health Association: "Standard Methods for the Examination of Water and Wastewater," New York, 1960.

Bigger, J. W.: The growth of coliform bacilli in water, *J. Path. Bact.*, **44**:167, 1937.

Borman, E. K., C. A. Stuart, and K. M. Wheeler: Taxonomy of the family *Enterobacteriaceae*, *J. Bact.*, **48**:351, 1944.

Brewer, C. R., and C. H. Werkman: The anaerobic dissimilation of citric acid by *Aerobacter indologenes, Enzymologia*, **6**:273, 1939.

Chambers, C. W.: Relationships of coliform bacteria to gas production in media containing lactose, *Pub. Health Reports*, **65**:619, 1950.

Chang, S. L., and J. C. Morris: Elemental iodine as a disinfectant for drinking water, *Ind. Eng. Chem.*, **45**:1009, 1953.

Clark, W. M.: The final hydrogen ion concentrations of cultures of *Bacillus coli, J. Biol. Chem.*, **22**:87, 1915.

―――― and H. A. Lubs: The differentiation of bacteria of the colon-aerogenes family by the use of indicators, *J. Infectious Diseases*, **17**:160, 1915.

Cooper, K. E., and F. M. Ramadan: Studies in the differentiation between human and animal pollution by means of faecal streptococci, *J. Gen. Microbiol.*, **12**:180, 1955.

Dagley, S., and E. A. Dawes: Dissimilation of citric acid by extracts of *Aerobacter aerogenes, Proc. Biochem. Soc.*, **55**:16, 1953*a;* Citric acid metabolism of *Aerobacter aerogenes, J. Bact.*, **66**:259, 1953*b*.

Eijkman, C.: Die Gärungsprobe bei 46°C. als Hilfsmittel bei der Trinkwasseruntersuchung, *Centr. Bakt.*, I Orig., **37**:742, 1904.

Escherich, T.: Die Darmbakterien des Neugeborenen und Säuglings, *Fortsch. Med.*, **3**:515, 547, 1885.

Ewing, W. H., H. W. Tatum, B. R. Davis, and R. W. Reavis: Studies on the serology of the *Escherichia coli* group, U.S. Department of Health, Education, and Welfare, Public Health Service, Atlanta, Ga., August, 1956.

Ferlin, H. J., and J. V. Karabinos: Differential media for *Escherichia coli* and *Aerobacter aerogenes, J. Washington Acad. Sci.*, **44**:303, 1954.

Folpmers, T.: Is it justified to use lactose broth for the detection of *B. coli* in the

Presumptive Test of routine water analysis?, *Antonie van Leeuwenhoek*, **14**:58, 1948.

Gainey, P. L., and T. H. Lord: "Microbiology of Water and Sewage," Englewood Cliffs, N.J., Prentice-Hall, Inc., 1952.

Geldreich, E. E., P. W. Kabler, H. L. Jeter, and H. F. Clark: A delayed incubation membrane filter test for coliform bacteria in water, *Am. J. Pub. Health*, **45**:1462, 1955.

Goetz, A., and N. Tsuneishi: Application of molecular filter membranes to the bacteriological analysis of water, *J. Am. Water Works Assoc.*, **43**:943, 1951.

Harden, A.: On Voges and Proskauer's reaction for certain bacteria, *Proc. Roy. Soc.* (London), Series B, **77**:424, 1906.

—— and D. Norris: The bacterial production of acetylmethylcarbinol and 2:3-butylene glycol from various substances, *ibid.*, **84**:492, 1912*a;* II. *ibid.*, **85**:73, 1912*b*.

—— and G. S. Walpole: Chemical action of *Bacillus lactis aerogenes* (Escherich) on glucose and mannitol: Production of 2:3-butylene glycol and acetylmethylcarbinol, *ibid.*, **77**:399, 1906.

Henriksen, S. D.: A study of some modifications of methods for detection of coliform bacteria in water, *Acta Path. Microbiol. Scand.*, **37**:267, 1955.

Hoskins, J. K.: Most probable numbers for evaluation of coli-areogenes tests by fermentation tube method, *Pub. Health Reports*, **49**:393, 1934.

Kabler, P.: Water examinations by membrane filter and most probable number procedures, *Am. J. Pub. Health*, **44**:379, 1954.

Kehr, R. W., and C. T. Butterfield: Notes on the relation between coliforms and enteric pathogens, *Pub. Health Reports*, **58**:589, 1943.

Kelly, C. B., and W. Arcisz: Survival of enteric organisms in shellfish, *Pub. Health Reports*, **69**:1205, 1954.

Kelly, S., J. Winsser, and W. Winkelstein: Poliomyelitis and other enteric viruses in sewage, *Am. J. Pub. Health*, **47**:72, 1957.

Koser, S. A.: Utilization of the salts of organic acids by the colonaerogenes group, *J. Bact.*, **8**:493, 1923.

——: Correlation of citrate utilization by members of the colonaerogenes group with other differential characteristics and with habitat, *J. Bact.*, **9**:59, 1924.

Lara, F. J. S., and J. L. Stokes: Oxidation of citrate by *Escherichia coli*, *J. Bact.*, **63**:415, 1952.

Levine, M., R. H. Tanimoto, H. Minette, J. Arakaki, and G. B. Fernandes: Simultaneous determination of coliform and *Escherichia coli* indices, *Appl. Microbiol.*, **3**:310, 1955.

Lieber, M.: A critique on the membrane filter, *Water & Sewage Works*, September, 1955, p. 400.

Litsky, W., W. L. Mallmann, and C. W. Fifield: Comparison of the most probable numbers of *Escherichia coli* and enterococci in river waters, *Am. J. Pub. Health*, **45**:1049, 1955.

——, M. J. Rosenbaum, and R. L. France: A comparison of the most probable numbers of coliform bacteria and enterococci in raw sewage, *Appl. Microbiol.*, **1**:247, 1953.

McCarthy, J. A.: Comparative coliform densities in water by membrane filter test and by multiple tube technic, *Am. J. Pub. Health*, **45**:1569, 1955.

Margolena, L. A., and P. A. Hansen: The nature of the reaction of the colon organism on Endo's medium, *Stain Technol.*, **8**:131, 1933.

Medrek, T. F., and W. Litsky: Comparative incidence of coliform bacteria and enterococci in undisturbed soil, *Appl. Microbiol.*, **8**:60, 1960.

Moran, A. B., and D. W. Bruner: Further studies on the Bethesda group of paracolon bacteria, *J. Bact.*, **58**:695, 1949.

Mushin, R.: Studies on paracolon bacilli, *Australian J. Exp. Biol. Med. Sci.*, **27**:543, 1949.

——: Bacteriological aspects of gastro-enteritis in infants, *ibid.*, **28**:493, 1950.

Natvig, H., and B. F. Nilsen: Experimental study of the longevity and viability of

Escherichia coli outside the animal organism, *Acta Path. Microbiol. Scand.,* 37:111, 1955.

Parr, L. W.: Sanitary significance of the succession of coli-aerogenes organisms in fresh and in stored feces, *Am. J. Pub. Health,* 26:39, 1936.

———: Organisms involved in the pollution of water from long stored feces, *Am. J. Pub. Health,* 28:445, 1938.

———: Coliform bacteria, *Bact. Rev.,* 3:1, 1939.

Prescott, S. C., C.-E. A. Winslow, and MacH. McCrady: "Water Bacteriology," New York, John Wiley & Sons, Inc., 1946.

Ricks, H. C., J. R. Cortelyou, T. D. Labecki, M. A. McWhinnie, F. J. Underwood, J. E. Semrad, and G. R. Reeves: Practical application of ultraviolet radiation in purification of naturally contaminated water, *Am. J. Pub. Health,* 45:1275, 1955.

Rogers, L. A., W. M. Clark, and B. J. Davis: The colon group of bacteria, *J. Infectious Diseases,* 14:411, 1914.

———, ———, and A. C. Evans: The characteristics of bacteria of the colon type found in bovine feces, *ibid.,* 15:99, 1914.

———, ———, and ———: The characteristics of bacteria of the colon type occurring on grains, *ibid.,* 17:137, 1915.

———, ———, and H. A. Lubs: The characteristics of bacteria of the colon type occurring in human feces, *J. Bact.,* 3:231, 1918.

Schwabacher, H.: A serological investigation of the paracolon group of organisms, *J. Path. Bact.,* 61:63, 1949.

Sears, H. J., and I. Brownlee: Further observations on the persistence of individual strains of *Escherichia coli* in the intestinal tract of man, *J. Bact.,* 63:47, 1952.

Shipe, E. L., Jr., and G. M. Cameron: A comparison of the membrane filter with the most probable number method for coliform determinations from several waters, *Appl. Microbiol.,* 2:85, 1954.

Slanetz, L. W., and C. H. Bartley: Evaluation of membrane filters for the determination of numbers of coliform bacteria in water, *Appl. Microbiol.,* 3:46, 1955.

Stuart, C. A., M. M. Galton, and V. McGann: Antigenic relationships of 765 *Paracolobactrum intermedium* cultures, *J. Bact.,* 56:411, 1948.

———, A. Zimmerman, M. Baker, and R. Rustigian: Eijkman relationships of the coliform and related bacteria, *ibid.,* 43:557, 1942.

Taylor, C. B.: The effect of temperature of incubation on the results of tests for differentiating species of coliform bacteria, *J. Hyg.,* 44:109, 1945.

Thomas, S. B., and P. M. Hobson: Coli-aerogenes bacteria isolated from ears and panicles of cereal crops, *J. Appl. Bact.,* 18:1, 1955.

Wattie, E.: Relative productivity of newer coliform media, *Pub. Health Reports,* 63:269, 1948.

West, M. G., and P. R. Edwards: The Bethesda-Ballerup group of paracolon bacteria, *Pub. Health Monograph* 22, 1954.

Wynne, E. S., L. J. Rode, and A E. Hayward; Mechanism of the selective action of eosin-methylene-blue agar on the enteric group, *Stain Technol.,* 17:11, 1942.

CHAPTER 22

Bacteriology of Milk and Milk Products

MILK

Milk is considered to be the most satisfactory single food substance elaborated by nature. It contains fat, protein, carbohydrate, inorganic salts, and vitamins.

The United States Public Health Service (1956) defines milk as follows:

Milk is hereby defined to be the lacteal secretion, practically free from colostrum, obtained by the complete milking of one or more healthy cows, which contains not less than 8¼ per cent milk solids-not-fat and not less than 3¼ per cent milk fat.

The food value of milk depends upon its milk fat and its solids-not-fat content. If either of these is reduced below the range for normal market milk, the proteins, carbohydrate, minerals, and certain vitamins are also reduced. Practical experience shows that 3¼ per cent milk fat and 8¼ per cent solids-not-fat are reasonable minima for mixed-herd milk. Colostrum tends to produce intestinal disturbance in children.

The constituents of milk may be placed into three groups on the basis of their solubilities: (1) some of the constituents are in true solution, (2) some are partly in solution and partly in suspension or colloidal solution, and (3) some are present entirely in colloidal solution (see page 366).

Color of Milk. The color of milk is due largely to the presence of carotene. Carotene exists in at least three isomeric forms: α-carotene, β-carotene, and γ-carotene. Another pigment closely related to carotene is cryptoxanthin, which occurs in yellow corn. All these pigments are precursors of vitamin A. One molecule of β-carotene is capable of yielding two molecules of vitamin A; one molecule of each of the others yields only one molecule of vitamin A.

Carotene is found in hay, grass, green leaves, some fruits, carrots, etc. The carotene content of cow's milk is dependent upon the carotene content of the·ration. Not all the carotene of the ration is converted into vitamin A. When cows consume carotene-containing foods, some of the pigment is converted into vitamin A and some is found unchanged in the milk. Vitamin A is colorless, whereas carotene is yellow.

Milk also contains ascorbic acid and riboflavin. Holmes and Jones (1945) exposed bottled milk to sunshine and found that the ascorbic acid content was destroyed after 30 min. and the riboflavin almost completely destroyed after 2 hr. The results indicated that milk should not be allowed to stand in strong sunlight for any appreciable length of time.

NORMAL SOURING OF MILK

Reaction of Fresh Milk. Milk when freshly drawn may show considerable variation in reaction. As a general rule, the pH is slightly acid, ranging from about 6.3 to 7.2, with an average at about 6.75. The pH fluctuates at different stages of the milking operation. The fore milk is usually the lowest in acidity, the middle milk the highest, and the strippings between the two.

Changes in the Reaction of Milk. On standing, unsterilized milk rapidly ferments, with the production chiefly of lactic acid from the lactose of the medium. The first stage is believed to be a hydrolysis of the lactose to one molecule of glucose and one of galactose. In the second stage, the hexoses are fermented to lactic acid.

It is generally stated that acidity in milk is first detected by taste when the pH drops to about 6.0. As the acid concentration continues to increase, it eventually causes a precipitation of the casein. This is said to occur when the pH reaches 4.78 to 4.64. Boiling produces a curdling of milk at a much higher pH (lower acidity). The acidity continues to rise until the concentration is sufficient to prevent growth of the bacteria producing the fermentation. The lactic acid produced in the milk prevents the growth of most types likely to be present and thus acts as a preservative.

Molds and yeasts are capable of growing in soured milk. They utilize some of the acid and produce a corresponding decrease in the acidity. Conditions now become favorable for the rapid decomposition of the milk proteins by the growth of putrefactive bacteria. As a rule, several weeks are required for putrefactive changes to occur. The utilization of the acid occurs at a faster rate if the milk is placed in shallow, well-aerated layers. This is the general cycle of changes that occur in raw milk when allowed to stand at ordinary temperature.

Lactic Acid Bacteria. A number of organisms are concerned in the production of lactic acid from the lactose sugar in milk. Some produce relatively large amounts of lactic acid; others form smaller amounts together with other products.

The principal lactic acid–producing bacteria include (1) *Streptococcus lactis* and related species and (2) *Lactobacillus* species.

Streptococcus lactis. This organism is responsible for the normal souring of milk. It is of widespread occurrence in dairy products. Several varieties of the organism are recognized which show differences in flavor produced, character of the fermented milk, rate of acid formation, and rate of litmus reduction, and in other ways. Proof of the similarities of the different varieties or strains of S. *lactis* was furnished by Sherman, Smiley, and Niven (1940). They produced species-specific grouping sera and found that such sera gave good pre-cipitation reactions with extracts of all strains of S. *lactis* tested.

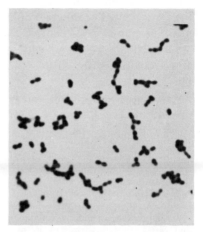

Cells of S. *lactis* are ovoid in shape and elongated in the direction of the chain, measuring 0.5 to 1 μ in diam-eter. They occur mostly in pairs or short chains, sometimes in long chains (Fig. 211), and are Gram-positive.

Distinctive Characteristics. Homo-fermentative, fermenting a number of carbohydrates with the production chiefly of dextrolactic acid; gas not formed; growth at 10° or below and at 40° but not at 45°C.; rapid and complete reduction of litmus before curdling milk; growth in presence of

Fig. 211. *Streptococcus lactis*, the cause of normal souring of milk.

4 per cent but not 6.5 per cent sodium chloride; growth at pH 9.2 but not pH 9.6.

S. *lactis* is a common contaminant of milk and milk products. It seldom occurs in the udders of cows. Hay and grains are believed to be the natural habitat of the organism. Since these are consumed by cows, the or-ganisms are found in manure. S. *lactis* can be obtained from the coat of the cow. It is generally believed that the organism finds its way into milk from manurial contamination.

Streptococcus cremoris. The characteristics of this organism are similar to S. *lactis.*

Distinctive Characteristics. Ferments several carbohydrates with the production of acid but no gas; growth of 10° and below but not at 40°C.; optimum temperature below 30°C.; litmus completely reduced before milk curdled; no growth in presence of 4 per cent sodium chloride; com-monly employed in commercial dairy starters. Readily distinguished from S. *lactis* by its inability to grow at 40°C., in 4 per cent NaCl broth, or in a medium adjusted to pH 9.2.

S. *cremoris* is commonly found in raw milk and milk products, com-mercial starters for butter and cheese manufacture. Probably of plant origin.

Lactobacillus Species. These are characterized as rod-shaped organisms, often long and slender. They are nonmotile and Gram-positive. A large number of carbohydrates are fermented to acid. The homofermentative species yield lactic acid with traces of other end products; the heterofermentative species produce considerable amounts of end products other than lactic acid. Several species grow at relatively high (50 to 65°C.) temperatures. Organisms produce poor surface growth because they are generally microaerophilic or anaerobic. They are found in fermenting animal (especially dairy) and plant products.

Lactobacilli are found widely distributed in milk, butter, cheese, sour and aromatic foods, cattle feed, normal saliva, gastric juice, fermented milk, soil, feces, etc.

The important species are homofermentative and are found in dairy products. They include *L. casei, L. acidophilus, L. bulgaricus, L. helveticus,* and *L. plantarum.*

L. casei, isolated from milk and cheese. Utilizes casein and is important in cheese ripening. Isolated from compressed yeast and fermenting milk. Found in dairy and plant products.

L. acidophilus, isolated from feces of milk-fed infants. Also found in feces of older persons on diets rich in milk, lactose, or dextrin.

L. bulgaricus, originally isolated from yogurt. Optimum temperature between 45 and 50°C. Probably present in many milk products if held at high temperature.

L. helveticus, isolated from sour milk and cheese. Widely distributed in dairy products.

L. plantarum, isolated from cheese, butter, kefir, fermenting potatoes, beets, corn, sauerkraut, cucumber pickles, spoiled tomato products, feces, etc. Widely distributed in nature, particularly in fermenting plant and animal products.

QUANTITATIVE EXAMINATION OF MILK

Normal udders of cows are probably never sterile. Organisms are present in abundance in freshly drawn milk. The first milk drawn shows the highest count, the middle milk shows a smaller count, and the strippings the least of all. The comparatively high count of the fore milk is the result of the washing out of the easily removable organisms present in the milk passages. The numbers washed out become less and less during the milking process. It is the general practice to discard the first few streams of milk which contains the highest count. This may decrease the bacterial count as much as 5 per cent.

A high bacterial count means that the milk has come from diseased udders, has been collected or handled under undesirable conditions, or has been kept warm enough to permit bacterial growth. It would seem, therefore, that the contamination of milk by bacteria is largely preventable.

The methods commonly employed for enumerating the bacterial population of milk include (1) the agar plate method, (2) the direct microscopic method, (3) the methylene blue reduction method, and (4) the resazurin method.

Agar Plate Method. The agar plate method is used more than any other for the enumeration of the number of bacteria in milk.

The method consists of preparing a series of dilutions of the milk sample, transferring 1-ml. amounts to Petri dishes, mixing with melted agar cooled to 45°C., incubating the plates at 35°C. for 48 hr., and counting visible colonies (bacteria) developing on the medium. The result is expressed as the number of bacteria per milliliter of undiluted milk.

The factors which influence plate counts include temperature of incubation, period of incubation, composition of plating medium, amount of oxygen, etc. Unless a standard procedure is followed, the results from different laboratories may show wide variation.

Advantages of the Plate Method. The agar plate method is especially suited to determinations where bacterial numbers are low. The method is generally used for testing pasteurized milk and the higher-grade raw milk. It is the only method approved by the American Association of Medical Milk Commissions for examining samples of certified milk.

Objections to the Plate Method. Objections to the method are numerous. Pathogenic bacteria usually are not detected. If the organisms grow, they cannot be distinguished from nonpathogenic forms by appearance. The number of colonies appearing on agar do not represent all organisms present in the milk. Many of the organisms fail to develop. Anaerobic organisms do not find conditions favorable for growth. This means that no single medium or given set of conditions is capable of giving growth of all viable organisms likely to be found in milk. A temperature of 35°C. is not the optimum for the growth of all organisms. Shaking the sample does not break up all clumps or groups of bacteria. Chains of streptococci usually remain intact and record as only one colony. The colony counts represent only a fraction of the total bacterial content of milk. Agar counts should be regarded as estimates rather than exact numbers.

Because of the long incubation period, the milk is usually consumed before information on the number of bacteria present is available. However, the quality of a milk supply cannot be determined on the basis of one bacterial count. A series of counts are necessary to establish the quality of the milk source.

Direct Microscopic Method. This method consists of spreading 0.01 ml. milk sample uniformly over a ruled area of 1 sq. cm. on a glass slide, allowing the film to dry, removing the fat, staining the film with methylene blue, and examining under the oil-immersion objective previously calibrated to determine the area of the field.

Advantages of the Microscopic Method. The method possesses a number of advantages over the plate procedure. Results can be obtained quickly, usually in about 10 or 15 min. Since less work is required, more samples can be examined by this procedure than by the plate method. The amount of equipment necessary is much less. The slides may be preserved as a permanent record and examined whenever occasion arises, whereas plates must be examined and discarded. Some idea of the morphological types can be obtained from slide preparations. This is frequently of great value in determining the cause of the bacterial count. Microscopic examination reveals the presence of leucocytes and other body cells in milk. An excessive number of leucocytes indicates a diseased condition of the udder. The slide method gives a better quantitative determination than the agar plate method.

Some believe that the method is less useful for pasteurized milk because most of the bacteria are dead. This is not necessarily so. It has been shown that bacteria killed by heat-treatment usually disintegrate and gradually lose their ability to stain within a few hours after pasteurization. Even if the bacteria remain intact, they are usually distinguished from living forms by their inability to stain intensely.

Objections to the Microscopic Method. Unless the milk sample contains a high count, the microscopic method may be the source of considerable error. A large factor is used for converting the number of bacteria per field to the number per milliliter of milk. Significant errors in the average number of organisms per field are not likely to be of great importance when bacteria are numerous in milk. However, in low-count milk a considerable error may be introduced. This is especially true where many fields show no bacteria and some fields show a chain or cluster of organisms to produce great variation in the count per field. Other objections involve inaccuracies in measurement of 0.01-ml. quantities, faulty preparation and staining of slides, failure of bacteria to stain, and errors in observation and calculation.

Comparison of Counts by the Two Methods. The microscopic method gives much higher individual cell counts than the agar method. The differences between the counts by the two methods are considerably greater on samples showing low bacterial counts than on those showing high counts. The organisms in low-count milk generally represent external contaminants that fail to develop on agar, whereas those organisms in high-count milk are forms which have developed in the milk. Also, low-count milk usually shows a greater percentage of clumps than high-count milk.

Bacterial standards are generally based on microscopic clump counts or agar plate counts, the standards being the same by either method. However, if individual cells are counted, the slide method gives higher results, the ratio being 3.33 to 1. Therefore total cell counts by the slide method are approximately 3.33 times greater than counts by the plate method. The word clumps refers to isolated cells as well as to groups of bacteria.

Methylene Blue Reduction Method. The method depends upon the ability of bacteria in milk to grow and to consume the dissolved oxygen, which reduces the oxidation-reduction potential in the medium. Certain enzymes present in bacteria, known as dehydrogenases, are then able to produce oxidations by the removal of hydrogen. The methylene blue accepts the hydrogen and becomes reduced to the colorless or leuco compound. The speed of decolorization is an indication of the rate at which oxidation takes place.

Methylene blue is of value in making a rapid survey of the quality of raw milk. The rate of decolorization depends upon the number of organisms present. The test can be employed to determine, in a rough way, the bacterial population of a milk sample. The procedure is quickly and easily carried out and with a minimum of expense. It is particularly valuable in making rapid inspections of large numbers of samples to determine if the milk received by companies answers the requirements prescribed by law.

The test is expressed as the period of time required for a known concentration of methylene blue in milk to lose its color when incubated at 35.5 to 37.5°C. Under some conditions the blue color does not disappear uniformly. In such cases the end point is taken as the time required for the milk to show no blue color after it is mixed.

There is not always good agreement between the methylene blue reduction time and the agar plate count because (1) some organisms fail to grow on nutrient agar; (2) a clump of organisms records as only one colony, whereas the rate of decolorization is due to the combined effect of each member of the mass; (3) the rate of decolorization of the dye is not the same for all organisms; and (4) the test becomes less accurate as the reduction time is increased, freshly drawn milk requiring at least 10 hr. to decolorize methylene blue.

Milk may be classified on the basis of the methylene blue reduction time as follows:

Class 1. Excellent milk, not decolorized in 8 hr.
Class 2. Good milk, decolorized in less than 8 hr., but not less than 6 hr.
Class 3. Fair milk, decolorized in less than 6 hr., but not less than 2 hr.
Class 4. Poor milk, decolorized in less than 2 hr.

Resazurin Method. Resazurin (diazoresorcinol) is an oxidation-reduction indicator having a pH range between 3.8 and 6.5. At pH 3.8 and below, the indicator is pink; at pH 6.5 and above, it is purple. A gradual color change occurs between these two extremes. The dye is capable of being reduced by bacteria. Because of this fact, it may be used to estimate the number of bacteria in milk. The greater the bacterial count, the quicker the dye is reduced. The resazurin test provides results in less time than the methylene blue reduction method. The test is quickly performed and with a minimum of expense. Since resazurin is also sensitive to the reducing action of leucocytes, the dye reveals the presence of the udder disease known as mastitis.

The test is performed as follows:

The milk sample is thoroughly mixed and 10 ml. pipetted into a ⅝- by 6-in. test tube. One milliliter of a 1:20,000 dilution of resazurin is added to the milk, and the tube is inverted three times slowly to mix well. The tube is placed in a 35.5 to 37.5°C. water bath and is examined at end of each of 3 successive hourly intervals. The color of the milk should be compared with a series of standard disks prepared for the purpose. If the color remains blue or lilac (disk 6 or 5) for 1 hr., the milk is normal in bacterial content. If mauve or mauve-pink (disk less than 5), the bacterial content is high and the milk should be regarded as abnormal. If a disk number less than 3 is obtained in ½ hr., the milk is grossly abnormal. If the dye is completely reduced (disk 0) in 1 hr. or less, the milk contains many pus cells and is probably teeming with mastitis organisms.

For more information see American Public Health Association (1960); Davis (1943); Galesloot (1948, 1949); Morgan, MacLeod, and Anderson (1952); Nelson and Baker (1954); and U.S. Public Health Service (1956).

GRADING OF MILK

According to the Milk Ordinance and Code of the U.S. Public Health Service (1956), milk and certain milk products are graded on the basis of their bacterial counts for the following reasons:

It is widely accepted that the bacterial count of milk and certain milk products is an index of the sanitary quality. A high count does not necessarily mean that disease organisms are absent; but a high bacterial count does mean that the milk has come from diseased udders, or has been milked or handled under undesirable conditions, or has been kept warm enough to permit bacterial growth. This means, in the first two cases, that the chances of infection have been increased, and, in the last case, that any bacterial contamination which may have reached the milk has been permitted to increase to more dangerous proportions. In general, therefore, a high count means a greater likelihood of disease transmission. On the other hand, a wrong interpretation of the significance of low bacterial counts should be avoided, since low-count milk can be obtained from cows with brucellosis or tuberculosis, or can have been handled by typhoid carriers or under unclean conditions.

When coliform organisms are present in pasteurized milk, they usually indicate that the milk has been contaminated after pasteurization. The phosphatase test is an index of the efficiency of pasteurization.

Collection of Samples. Samples for bacteriological examinations are collected by inspectors or other officials. At least 10 ml. of well-agitated milk is collected and placed in a sterile sample bottle, which should be of such size that only about two-thirds of it is filled. This provides sufficient air space for vigorous agitation to ensure a suspension of organisms of uniform turbidity before plating the milk. The sample must be kept at

32 to 40°F. until plated. The average bacterial plate count is expressed as the logarithmic average of the plate counts of the last four consecutive samples taken on separate days.

Milk Standards. The numbers of organisms permissible in different grades of milk vary somewhat, depending upon standards set up by local public health authorities.

The highest grade of milk is known as certified milk, which is safeguarded at every step in its production, collection, and distribution. Milk collected under conditions not so carefully controlled is graded as A, B, or C. The ratings are based upon the bacterial count of milk and also upon the hygienic conditions under which it was produced. The standards of the various grades reported here are those set up by the U.S. Public Health Service Milk Ordinance (1956). They are as follows:

Certified Milk—Raw. Raw milk which conforms with the latest requirements of the American Association of Medical Milk Commissions in force at the time of adoption of this ordinance, and which is produced under the supervision of a medical milk commission reporting monthly to the health officer, and of the state health authority. These vary depending upon localities, but the usual standard is that the count must not go above 10,000 organisms per milliliter. All milk having a count in excess of this number must be placed in one of the following grades.

Grade A Raw Milk for Pasteurization. Raw milk from producer dairies conforming with certain items of sanitation. The bacterial plate count or the direct microscopic clump count of the milk, as delivered from the farm, shall not exceed 200,000 per milliliter.

All milk for pasteurization shall be from herds which are located in a modified accredited tuberculosis-free area, as determined by the U.S. Department of Agriculture, and which have been tested for tuberculosis not more than 6 years prior to the adoption of this ordinance and at least every 6 years after such test.

Grade B Raw Milk for Pasteurization. Raw milk which does not meet the bacterial standard for Grade A raw milk for pasteurization, but which conforms with all other requirements. The bacterial plate count or the direct microscopic clump count of the milk, as delivered from the farm, shall not exceed 1 million per milliliter.

Grade C Raw Milk for Pasteurization. Raw milk which does not meet the requirements for Grade B raw milk for pasteurization.

Certified Milk—Pasteurized. Certified milk (raw) which has been pasteurized, cooled, and bottled in a milk plant which conforms with the requirements for Grade A pasteurized milk.

Grade A Pasteurized Milk. Grade A raw milk for pasteurization which has been pasteurized, cooled, and placed in the final container in a milk plant which conforms with certain items of sanitation. In all cases the milk shall show efficient pasteurization as evidenced by satisfactory phosphatase test (see page 590), and at no time after pasteurization and before delivery shall the milk have a bacterial plate count exceeding 30,000 per milliliter, or a coliform count exceeding 10 per milliliter. The raw milk shall have at no time between dumping and pasteurization a bacterial plate count or direct microscopic clump count exceeding 400,000 per milliliter.

Grade B Pasteurized Milk. Pasteurized milk which does not meet the bacterial-count standard for Grade A pasteurized milk, but which conforms with all other requirements for grade A pasteurized milk, and has been made from raw milk for pasteurization of not less than Grade B quality, and has a bacterial plate count after pasteurization and before delivery not exceeding 50,000 per milliliter.

For more information see Nilsson (1959).

INFLUENCE OF TEMPERATURE ON THE KEEPING QUALITY OF MILK

The numbers of organisms in milk at the outset depend upon the degree of care exercised in its collection, handling, and storing. For a period after collection, the bacterial count tends to remain constant or decrease somewhat. Then the numbers increase rapidly unless milk is stored at low temperatures. The temperature at which it is stored determines to a large extent the bacterial count and the microflora of milk.

Germicidal Property of Milk. Freshly drawn milk contains substances which are capable of exerting a bactericidal action. These substances are destroyed by heat, but the temperature required varies for different organisms.

Morris (1945) heated raw milk to temperatures of 52 and 53°C. for 30 min., then inoculated the samples with a young culture of coliform organisms. Plate counts were made immediately after inoculation and after holding the milk for 4 hr. at 37°C. From the results (Table 26), it would

TABLE 26.   EFFECT OF HEAT ON THE GERMICIDAL PROPERTY OF MILK

Temperature to which milk was heated for 30 min. before inoculation	Count per ml. immediately	Count per ml. after 4 hr. at 37°C.
Culture No. 1:		
52°C.	1,328,000	1,000
53°C.	848,000	40,000,000
Culture No. 2:		
52°C.	316,000	31,000
53°C.	640,000	28,000,000

appear that the bactericidal substances are completely destroyed by heating the milk at 53°C. for 30 min. and that this destruction is critical to within 1°C.

The bactericidal property is of little practical importance unless milk is stored at a low temperature immediately after collection. Milk cooled promptly to 4°C. and held at this temperature for 10 hr. retained to a large extent its bactericidal action. On the other hand, the germicidal property was almost completely lost when a temperature of 16°C. was used.

Milk Held Below Freezing Point. When milk is frozen to −0.55°C. and held at that temperature, no multiplication of organisms occurs. The methods by which bacteria obtain their nutrients preclude growth as long as the milk is frozen throughout. In fact, milk treated in this manner may show a decrease in bacterial numbers. When frozen milk is thawed, the bacteria present start multiplying again, the temperature determining the rate of multiplication and the type of change occurring.

Milk Held Just Above Freezing. If raw milk, or milk pasteurized at temperatures below 70°C., is kept at 0 to 5°C. for 24 hr., the plate count decreases. After about one week there is an increase over the original plate count. At the same time the number of organisms capable of lique-fying gelatin increases. This continues until enormous numbers are present. Some of the organisms are acid formers; others are neutral types; still others are strongly proteolytic forms.

This is followed by decomposition and putrefaction of the casein. Under these conditions, toxic waste products may be present, rendering the milk unfit or even dangerous for human consumption. Milk is generally stored at 0°C. but the time it may be kept at this temperature should not be over 10 days, for the above reasons.

The bacterial flora of milk kept at different temperatures is as follows:

0 to 5°C. *Pseudomonas* spp. predominate.

5 to 10°C. *Pseudomonas* spp., *Proteus vulgaris, Micrococcus* spp., *Alcaligenes viscolactis, A. marshallii.*

10 to 15°C. *Streptococcus acidominimus, S. agalactiae, S. cremoris, S. durans, S. dysgalactiae, S. faecalis, S. lactis, S. uberis.*

15 to 30°C. Streptococci, especially *S. lactis.*

30 to 40°C. *Aerobacter aerogenes, Escherichia coli,* lactic acid–forming rods including *Lactobacillus brevis, L. bulgaricus, L. casei, L. caucasicus, L. fermenti, L. helveticus, L. lactis, L. leichmannii, L. plantarum, L. thermophilus,* and a few streptococci.

40 to 50°C. Lactic acid–forming rods including *Lactobacillus bulgaricus, L. caucasicus, L. fermenti, L. helveticus, L. lactis, L. thermophilus, Streptococcus faecalis, S. thermophilus,* and yeasts.

The smaller the initial plate count, the greater will be the time required to sour the milk. As has already been shown, the fluorescent bacteria (*Pseudomonas*) found in the soil are able to multiply at a temperature as low as 0°C. If milk is to be kept for any length of time, it should be frozen. At somewhat higher temperatures, organisms of the *Proteus* group develop, with the result that putrefactive compounds accumulate in the milk.

Coagulation seldom takes place in milk stored below 10°C. Above this temperature, a coagulum forms in a few days owing to the combined action of rennin and acid-producing organisms. At a temperature of 20°C., the bacterial flora is composed of about 90 per cent streptococci. This results in a rapid coagulation of the milk. The acidity produced is sufficient to inhibit the growth of most other species of organisms likely to be present. Above 30°C., rod-shaped bacteria predominate, which are capable of producing still higher concentrations of lactic acid. Also, this is the most favorable temperature range for the growth of the butyric acid–producing anaerobes.

The aerobic organisms grow best near the surface of milk, where there is an abundant supply of dissolved oxygen. The organisms predominating near the bottom include the anaerobes and S. *lactis*. This means that the spontaneous curdling of milk usually starts at the bottom.

For more information see Abd-el-Malek and Gibson (1948a, b), Yotis and Teodoro (1957).

UNDESIRABLE ORGANISMS IN MILK

Great care must be exercised during the milking process; otherwise a great variety of additional bacteria may enter the milk. Since particles of manure and soil are always found adhering to the skin of the cow, they may be an important source of contamination. Additional organisms may enter the milk from the milker, the air of the barn, improperly cleaned utensils, milking machines, etc.

A number of undesirable organisms may be recovered from milk. These are discussed below.

Coliform Organisms. Isolated instances are on record in which coliform organisms have been recovered from milk taken directly from the udder. However, this is unusual; for all practical purposes, normal milk as it comes from the udder is entirely free from coliform bacteria.

The presence of *Escherichia coli* in milk usually represents contamination from manure. Since *Aerobacter aerogenes* is found in water and soil, on hay, grains, and other foods consumed by cows, its presence in milk does not necessarily indicate fecal contamination. As milk leaves the farm, it almost always contains members of the coliform group regardless of the care exercised in its production. Under careful conditions raw milk usually contains less than 100 coliforms per milliliter. Under careless conditions of production the number may run as high as 2000 per milliliter. Regardless of the conditions of production, milk always contains coliform organisms in varying numbers.

The examination of water for the presence of *E. coli* is a standard procedure for the determination of the healthfulness of a water supply. On the other hand, it is controversial as to whether the *E. coli* test should be used for the determination of the healthfulness of dairy products. In the former case, the presence of *E. coli* indicates fecal pollution and the possible presence of intestinal pathogens. In the latter case, coliforms may indicate manurial pollution, which is not subject to the intestinal infections common to man.

Coliforms are generally completely destroyed in the pasteurization process. Only occasionally are coliform bacteria encountered which are capable of resisting pasteurization. However, the presence of coliform bacteria in milk immediately after pasteurization indicates that (1) the milk was not processed properly or (2) it became contaminated after pasteurization. Under these conditions, the *E. coli* test should prove valuable for control work.

The procedures followed for the identification of the coliforms in milk are similar to those employed for the bacteriological examination of water (see page 552).

Sackett and Gralak (1950) found no correlation between the standard plate count and the coliform count in raw milk. A low plate count did not mean necessarily that raw milk would have a low coliform count; a high standard plate count did not indicate a high coliform count. In other words, the standard plate count did not give any indication of the coliform count. Because pasteurized milk having a low plate count still could contain an undesirable number of coliform organisms, they believed that a coliform count was a more consistent indication of the sanitary conditions and that it should be performed routinely on all samples of pasteurized milk.

Importance in Dairy Products. Coliform organisms are undesirable in dairy products. In addition to acid and gas production, they may produce objectionable odors and flavors. When such products are used in the manufacture of butter and cheese, the objectionable qualities are commonly carried over, producing off-flavors in the products. Also, the gas produced may give cheese a blown appearance.

For more information see Thomas (1955).

Ropy or Slimy Milk. A number of organisms are capable of producing a condition in milk known as ropiness. The milk becomes ropy or slimy and may be pulled out into long threads. Sometimes the change is very slight; at other times the ropy consistency may be so pronounced that the milk may be drawn out into threads 3 ft. or more in length.

Generally the ropy condition does not manifest itself immediately when milk is produced or processed but only after 24 or 48 hr. of incubation. A milk dealer does not know he has a ropy-milk problem until after the milk is delivered to the home.

Several organisms are capable of producing this condition in milk. Probably the most important species is *Alcaligenes viscolactis*. The organism produces its maximum amount of ropiness at a temperature of about 25°C.

Alcaligenes viscolactis is a small rod measuring 0.6 to 1.0 by 0.8 to 2.6 μ, occurring singly, in pairs, or in short chains. It is frequently found as almost spherical cells. It is nonmotile and Gram-negative. The organism produces both ropiness and a pellicle in milk. The pellicle is the result of the aerobic character of the organism. This explains why the ropy condition is frequently noted only in the cream layer. The organism produces an alkaline reaction in milk with no coagulation of the casein.

Jones (1954a, b, c) found *A. viscolactis* to be a pleomorphic Gram-variable rod that produced ropiness and an alkaline reaction in milk. Loss of smoothness or mucoid colony characteristic was accompanied by a decrease or loss of the ability to produce ropiness in milk and most likely occurred during prolonged storage of cultures without transfer.

Ropiness was found to result from attack on the albumin of the milk. No evidence of polysaccharide synthesis was obtained. Therefore the slime is neither capsular material nor carbohydrate gum.

Some members of the coliform group have been responsible for producing the ropy condition of milk. Most strains are unable to do so, but occasionally a strong ropy producer is encountered. *Aerobacter aerogenes* is of more frequent occurrence than *Escherichia coli.*

Organisms causing ropiness are commonly found in pools, wells, and streams. Water from such sources contaminates the dairy utensils and equipment. The organisms must be removed as quickly as possible; otherwise great economic losses may result. All utensils and equipment coming in contact with the milk should be sterilized. The barns should be thoroughly cleaned and disinfected. The flanks of the cows should be washed with an appropriate disinfectant. The organisms causing ropiness should be destroyed by pasteurization, but outbreaks sometimes occur in pasteurized milk. They are the result of recontamination from the plant equipment after pasteurization.

Slime-producing lactic acid organisms have been used in the manufacture of cheese, but such practice has been largely discontinued, owing to the fact that it is difficult to separate the whey from the cheese. Also, the presence of the organisms in cream results in a poor yield of butter. The property of producing slime appears to be lost by growing the organisms at higher temperatures. Conversely, some organisms that ordinarily do not produce slime can be made to do so if cultivated at lower temperatures.

For more information see Gainor and Wegemer (1954), Wegemer and Gainor (1954).

Clostridium perfringens in Milk. *Clostridium perfringens* is an anaerobic, spore-forming organism of widespread occurrence in nature. It is present in the intestinal tract of man and animals, in fish, mollusks, milk, cheese, water, etc. It occurs abundantly in soil. The organism is generally considered to be the most important etiological agent of gas gangrene.

Cl. perfringens is a short, thick rod, measuring 1.0 to 1.5 by 4.0 to 8.0 μ, occurring singly, in pairs, or less frequently in short chains. Spores are ovoid, central to eccentric, not swelling the cells. The rods are encapsulated, nonmotile, and Gram-positive.

The organism is strongly saccharolytic, being capable of fermenting all of the common sugars with the production of acid and gas. *Cl. perfringens* produces a characteristic stormy fermentation of milk (Fig. 212). The curd becomes torn to shreds by the vigorous fermentation and gas formation. Under these conditions the milk proteins are not attacked.

Since the organism is present in the intestinal contents of cows, the presence of *Cl. perfringens* in milk generally indicates a manurial contamination.

Colored Milk. Several organisms have been isolated which are capable of imparting brilliant colors to milk. These changes occur only occasionally and are of minor importance economically.

Many organisms isolated from milk produce colored colonies, but they should not be confused with certain species which elaborate brilliant colors in milk. Organisms in the latter group are strongly aerobic. This means that pigment formation is first observed in the surface layer of milk.

Blue Milk. Blue milk is caused by the growth of the pigmented organism *Pseudomonas syncyanea*. It is a rod-shaped organism measuring 0.7 by 2.0 to 4.0 μ. It is motile, with two to four polar flagella, and Gram-negative.

FIG. 212. Stormy fermentation of milk. Left, fermentation of a sample of milk free from *Clostridium perfringens*; right, fermentation of a sample of milk containing *Cl. perfringens*. The vaspar seal is pushed up by the gas pressure, and the curd is riddled with bubbles.

The organism produces a gray color in neutral or alkaline milk. In association with lactic acid bacteria, the milk takes on a deep blue color. The organism grows best at a temperature of 25°C.

Red Milk. Serratia marcescens imparts a red color to milk. It is a small rod, sometimes almost spherical, measuring 0.5 by 0.5 to 1.0 μ, occurring singly and occasionally in short chains. It is motile, by means of peritrichous flagella, and Gram-negative.

The organism produces an acid reaction in milk accompanied by a red surface growth. The casein is not attacked. Optimum temperature is 25 to 30°C. The natural habitat of the organism is water and soil, from which it gains entrance to milk.

Yellow Milk. Pseudomonas synxantha produces a canary yellow pigment in milk. It is rod-shaped, measuring 0.5 to 0.6 by 1.3 to 2.2 μ, occurring singly and in pairs. It is motile, with polar flagella, and Gram-negative.

Acid is produced in milk with coagulation. Casein is slowly digested. The organism produces an intense diffusible yellow to orange color in cream or in the cream layer of milk. Optimum temperature is about 20°C.

Psychrophilic Bacteria. These are cold-loving organisms capable of growing at temperatures below 16°C.

Psychrophiles are widely distributed in raw milk. They grow at refrigeration temperatures (about 5°C.) and produce many off-flavors characterized as fruity, stale, musty, bitter, rancid, and even putrid.

Psychrophilic bacteria are killed by pasteurization, but they are sometimes found in pasteurized milk. Contamination takes place after pasteurization from equipment, cans, bottles, and water. Organisms growing at refrigeration temperatures are members of the genera *Achromobacter*, *Alcaligenes*, *Flavobacterium*, and *Pseudomonas*.

Achromobacter species are small rods, usually uniform in shape. They are motile by peritrichous flagella, or nonmotile. The rods are Gram-negative and are generally found in salt or fresh water, in soil, or less commonly as plant pathogens.

Members of the *Alcaligenes* are rods, motile by means of peritrichous flagella, or nonmotile. They are Gram-negative and are generally found in intestinal tracts of vertebrates or in dairy products.

Flavobacterium species are rods, motile by means of peritrichous flagella, or nonmotile. They are Gram-negative and are found in water and soil. Some species are pathogenic.

Pseudomonas members are monotrichous, lophotrichous, or nonmotile rods. They are Gram-negative. Many species are found in soil and water, including sea water. Many are plant pathogens; very few are animal pathogens.

For more information see Andrey and Frazier (1959); Atherton, Doan, and Watrous (1954); Hadfield (1956); Lawton and Nelson (1954); Olson, Parker, and Mueller (1955).

PASTEURIZATION

The destruction of all organisms in milk is called sterilization. The high temperature required to achieve this result would impart a cooked flavor to the milk. Such milk is objectionable for two reasons: (1) the cooked flavor is not so pleasant as that of unheated milk, and (2) heating to such a high temperature might result in a decrease in the vitamin content. These objections are largely overcome by heating milk to temperatures lower than that required to sterilize completely but sufficiently high to destroy all disease organisms likely to be present.

The destruction of disease and most other organisms in milk without attempting complete sterilization is called pasteurization.

According to the U.S. Public Health Service (1956):

The terms pasteurization, pasteurized, and similar terms shall be taken to refer to the process of heating every particle of milk or milk products to at least 143°F. (62°C.), and holding at such temperature continuously for at least 30 min., or at least

161°F. (72°C.), and holding at such temperature continuously for at least 15 sec., in approved and properly operated equipment: Provided, that nothing contained in this definition shall be construed as barring any other process which has been demonstrated to be equally efficient and which is approved by the State health authority.

Public-health Reason. The public-health value of pasteurization is unanimously agreed upon by health officials. Long experience conclusively shows its value in the prevention of diseases which may be transmitted through milk. Pasteurization is the only practical, commercial measure which, if properly applied to all milk, will destroy all milk borne disease organisms. Examination of cows and milk handlers, while desirable and of great value, can be done only at intervals and, therefore, it is possible for pathogenic bacteria to enter the milk for varying periods before the disease condition is discovered. Disease bacteria may also enter milk accidentally from other sources, such as flies, contaminated water, utensils, etc. It has been demonstrated that the time-temperature combinations of 143°F. for 30 min., and 161°F. for 15 sec., if applied to every particle of milk, will devitalize all milk borne pathogens. Compilations of outbreaks of milk borne disease by the U.S. Public Health Service, over many years, indicate that the risk of contracting disease from raw milk is approximately 50 times as great as from milk labeled pasteurized.

A note of caution is in order. Although pasteurization devitalizes the organisms, it does not destroy the toxins that may be formed in milk when certain staphylococci are present (as from udder infections), and when the milk is not properly refrigerated before pasteurization. Such toxins may cause severe illness.

Numerous studies and observations clearly prove that the food value of milk is not significantly impaired by pasteurization.

The pasteurization process generally reduces the bacterial count 99 to 100 per cent (Fig. 213), depending upon the kinds and numbers present at the time of heating.

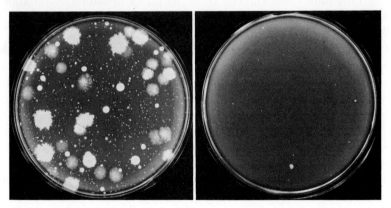

FIG. 213. Pasteurization of milk. Left, 1 ml. of a 1:10 dilution of milk before heating; right, 1 ml. of a 1:10 dilution after heating.

For more information see Doetsch (1949), Druce and Thomas (1959), Galesloot (1955), Kaufmann and Tobias (1955), Overcast and Skean (1959), and Read et al. (1957).

MILK-BORNE INFECTION

Milk is an excellent culture medium for the growth of a great variety of organisms. Pathogenic as well as saprophytic forms may remain viable and even multiply in milk. For this reason it is difficult to obtain pure milk and to keep it pure. The prevention of milk-borne disease is one of the most important problems of public health.

Pathogenic organisms of both bovine and human origin have been isolated from milk. Many serious epidemics were caused by the consumption of such products before this fact was clearly recognized. This is to be expected when one takes into consideration the enormous quantities of milk and its products that are consumed daily. Even today, epidemics are spread through milk, but they are of rare occurrence compared with the number reported during the early years of public health.

The abnormal changes that occur in milk are usually easily detected by appearance, taste, and smell. However, the presence of disease organisms cannot be detected in that manner. Milk containing disease bacteria looks and tastes normal and gives no warning to the consumer. The disease organisms present in milk may be derived from (1) diseased cows or (2) persons collecting and handling milk.

Diseases of Bovine Origin. The health of the cow is a very important consideration, because a number of diseases of cattle, including tuberculosis, brucellosis, Q fever, salmonellosis, staphylococcic infection, streptococcic infection, and foot-and-mouth disease, may be transmitted to man through the medium of milk. The organisms of most of these diseases may get into the milk either directly from the udder or indirectly through infected body discharges which may drop, splash, or be blown into the milk.

Tuberculosis. Tuberculosis of cattle is produced by the organism *Mycobacterium bovis.* The disease has been practically eradicated in this country but is still common in other parts of the world. The organism is very similar in appearance to the human type. Adults are not very susceptible to infection by the bovine species, but children, especially those under five years of age, may become infected by drinking milk from tuberculous cows. If the udders of cows are infected with the organisms, contamination of milk cannot be avoided.

If cows are suffering from tuberculosis of the lungs, the sputum is swallowed, with the result that the organisms appear in the feces. Since most milk may contain some excreta, it is likely to show the presence of such organisms. It is doubtful that the organism multiplies in milk, but it can live and may retain its virulence for a considerable time.

The great reduction in the incidence of bovine tuberculosis in man in recent years indicates that the practice of good sanitation in animal husbandry, the testing of cattle and removal of the reactors from the herds, and the pasteurization of milk have been effective in the control of this disease. The reservoir of bovine tuberculosis still exists, however; hence, constant vigilance against this disease must be continued by industry and health agencies.

For more information see page 724.

Brucellosis. Another disease organism frequently found in cows' milk is *Brucella abortus,* which produces contagious abortion in cows. The organisms may produce the same effects in mares, sheep, rabbits, and guinea pigs. Organisms producing similar results are *B. melitensis* from goats and *B. suis* from hogs. *B. melitensis* may also infect cows and hogs and be excreted in the milk. *B. suis* produces abortion in swine and frequently attacks horses, dogs, cows, monkeys, and laboratory animals.

All three of the organisms are pathogenic for man, producing the disease known as Malta fever, so named because it has been prevalent for centuries on the island of Malta, where humans become infected from drinking contaminated goats' milk. The disease is now generally referred to as undulant fever or brucellosis (after Bruce, who first isolated the organism from a fatal case of the disease).

Brucellosis may be contracted by drinking raw milk or, less frequently, certified milk. Pasteurized milk should be safe, since the organism is destroyed in the heat process. Because of this fact, many public health authorities believe that all milk should be pasteurized before it reaches the consumer.

The incidence of brucellosis in man is increasing at the present time, and a greater effort is required to reduce the extent of infection in cattle and its transmission to man through milk.

For more information see page 709.

Q Fever. This is a relatively newly recognized disease of cattle which may be transmitted to man through the use of milk. The causative agent is the rickettsial organism *Coxiella burnetii.*

Within the last few years, this disease has reached endemic proportions in man in some parts of this country. Although no means of controlling Q fever in cattle has yet been developed, pasteurization of the milk is the most practical safeguard against its transmission to man through milk.

For more information see page 791.

Salmonellosis. Members of the genus *Salmonella* produce a variety of infections in man and animals. In man the organisms may give rise to food poisoning, enteric fever, or other types of gastroenteric disturbances.

Some species are natural pathogens for cattle and other domestic warm-blooded animals, being present in the intestinal contents. Outbreaks of salmonellosis have occurred from drinking contaminated milk.

Staphylococcic Infection. Some strains of *Staphylococcus aureus* are capable of elaborating a potent exotoxin. The consumption of milk containing a toxin-producing strain may result in severe gastroenteritis.

For more information see pages 625 and 739 and Smith (1957).

Streptococcic Infection. The disease known as mastitis refers to an inflammatory and, generally, highly communicable disease of the bovine udder. A number of organisms may be the inciting factor, but the species generally associated with the disease is *Streptococcus agalactiae*. It is found in the udders of nearly all milch cows. Frequently it remains latent, but sooner or later it may start an active infection, resulting in an inflammation of the udder. If the mastitis is severe, pus and blood may appear in the milk. Milk containing appreciable numbers of the organisms and blood cells must be regarded as unfit for human consumption. All organisms associated with mastitis are killed by pasteurization.

For more information see De Vries and Strikwerda (1956); Hale, Plastridge, and Williams (1956); Plastridge and Hale (1956); Simon and Hall (1955).

Foot-and-mouth Disease. This is a highly contagious viral disease of domestic animals (Fig. 214). It produces fever, digestive disturbances, and a vesicular eruption on the mucous membranes of the mouth, on the

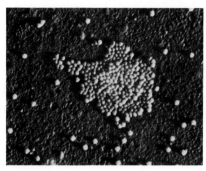

Fig. 214. Electron micrograph of foot-and-mouth disease virus particles. ×79,000. The particles are approximately 22 mμ in diameter. (*Courtesy of Bachrach and Breese.*)

skin between the toes, and on the udder and teats of the cow. From the vesicles, the virus may gain entrance to saliva, urine, feces, and milk.

The virus produces a high death rate among cattle. The infection may be transmitted by feeding and drinking troughs, stalls, cattle cars, etc. In man the disease runs a mild course.

For more information see Bachrach and Breese (1958).

Diseases of Human Origin. Some of the diseases of human origin that have been disseminated by milk are (1) typhoid fever, (2) scarlet fever, (3) diphtheria, (4) septic sore throat, (5) infantile diarrhea, and (6) infantile paralysis. The organisms may be transferred to milk by contaminated hands of the workers; by droplets expelled during coughing, sneezing, and talking; by moistening the hands with saliva during wet milking; and in other ways.

Typhoid Fever. Many typhoid epidemics that have occurred in recent years have been traced to the consumption of contaminated milk. Further investigation usually revealed the fact that only one dairy supplying the milk was responsible for the spread of the infection. The organisms were introduced into the milk by a typhoid carrier or an unrecognized case of typhoid fever among the workers at the dairy. The isolation of this individual resulted in a disappearance of new typhoid cases in the community. Typhoid epidemics have been traced not only to milk but to a lesser extent to ice cream, cheese, and butter.

For more information see page 732.

Scarlet Fever and Septic Sore Throat. Both diseases are probably produced by *Streptococcus pyogenes,* a pus-producing organism. Epidemics have been caused by the consumption of milk containing this organism. The milk may become contaminated by handlers or by infected udders of cows. Usually a milker suffering from scarlet fever or sore throat infects the udders with the organisms by means of contaminated hands. The organisms rapidly multiply in the milk in the udders. Abscesses form in the udders, from which the milk becomes heavily contaminated. The contaminated milk may produce septic sore throat or scarlet fever in persons who consume the raw milk.

For more information see page 740.

Diphtheria. Diphtheria is spread principally by direct contact with human sources through either active cases of the disease or carriers of the organism.

Dairy workers may also disseminate the organisms in milk. Although outbreaks of milk-borne diphtheria are comparatively rare, a few outbreaks have been traced to infected milk handlers.

For more information see page 715.

THERMODURIC BACTERIA

Bacteria growing best at temperatures of 25 to 40°C. are termed mesophilic organisms.

Some mesophilic forms are capable of surviving pasteurization, although they cannot grow at such temperatures. These resistant species are called thermoduric bacteria (*thermo*, heat; and *durans*, to endure).

The most common thermoduric bacteria are found in the genera *Bacillus, Microbacterium, Micrococcus,* and *Streptococcus.* The important species are:

Bacillus. *B. brevis, cereus, coagulans, licheniformis, polymyxa, pumilis,* and *subtilis.* All members of this genus are aerobic or facultative anaerobic spore-forming rods.

Microbacterium. *M. flavum, lacticum.* Members of this genus are among the most heat-resistant, non-spore-forming bacteria known, surviving a temperature of 72°C. for 15 to 30 min. in skim milk.

Micrococcus. *M. caseolyticus, conglomeratus, flavus, freudenreichii, luteus,* and *varians.* Optimum growth temperature of all species ranges from 20 to 25°C.

Streptococcus. *S. bovis, cremoris, durans, faecalis, faecalis* var. *liquefaciens, faecalis* var. *zymogenes, thermophilus,* and *uberis.*

Source of Thermoduric Organisms. The major factor in high counts of thermoduric bacteria in pasteurized milk is the presence of such organisms in the raw product. Sanitary conditions on the farm and in the processing plant must be high to prevent the entrance of such organisms in milk.

Thermodurics are sometimes found in infected udders and find their way into pails, cans, milking machines, and other equipment used for handling milk. Unless pieces of equipment are properly sterilized after each use, they will continue to contaminate each new lot of milk.

Excessive numbers of thermoduric bacteria in milk make it difficult to meet grading standards. Their presence in milk is generally indicative of insanitary conditions on the farm.

THERMOPHILIC BACTERIA

Some organisms present in milk are able to survive pasteurization and can grow at such temperatures. They have an optimum range of 50 to 55°C. These high-temperature forms are referred to as thermophilic bacteria (*thermo,* heat; and *phile,* to like).

Thermophilic bacteria grow well at the temperatures used in pasteurization, especially when the low-temperature method is followed. For the most part the thermophilic forms encountered in milk are sporeformers. They are found in two genera, namely, *Bacillus* (aerobic) and *Clostridium* (anaerobic). In addition, there are some thermophilic species which do not produce spores.

The thermophilic species are found in soil, air, manure, and improperly cleaned milking machines, and on utensils and pasteurizing equipment; they undoubtedly get into milk from these sources. If the utensils and equipment are not thoroughly scrubbed daily, the organisms collect in the milk films and act as focuses for seeding new lots.

Significance of Thermoduric and Thermophilic Bacteria. Thermoduric and thermophilic bacteria are not pathogenic and are of no importance from the standpoint of public health. The organisms indicate improper care in cleaning milking utensils and pasteurizers. The organisms may be controlled by proper care of utensils and equipment.

For more information see Fabian (1946a).

PHOSPHATASE TEST

The phosphatase test is employed to determine the efficiency of the pasteurization process. The test is based on the property of the heat-labile enzyme phosphatase, present in raw milk, to liberate phenol from phenyl phosphoric ester. Then the phenol is measured quantitatively by adding 2,6-dibromoquinonechloroimide (BQC) to form an indophenol blue. Any blue color developed in the test tube is extracted with butyl alcohol and compared with a series of permanent standards.

The enzyme is always present in raw milk. When milk is heated to a temperature of 143°F. for 30 min., 96 per cent of the phosphatase is destroyed; when heated above 145°F. (63°C.) for 30 min., all of the enzyme present is destroyed.

The presence of the enzyme indicates either faulty pasteurization or subsequent addition of raw milk. The amount of phosphatase present may be easily and quickly measured colorimetrically. Disease organisms likely to be present in milk are killed at a temperature lower than that required to destroy the enzyme. Therefore, a heat-treatment adequate to destroy the phosphatase should ensure a milk that is free from the common pathogenic bacteria.

Several organisms have been shown to be capable of elaborating phosphatase in milk. The organisms are members of the genera *Aerobacter, Klebsiella,* and *Micrococcus.* This observation may explain many positive phosphatase tests attributed to manual and mechanical defects in the dairy, when in reality the false tests have been the result of phosphatase produced by bacteria.

For more information see Hetrick and Tracy (1948), Sanders and Sager (1948).

ANTIBIOTICS IN MILK

Antibiotics have been used chiefly to combat mastitis infections in the udders of cows. The antibiotics which have been used include penicillin, streptomycin, and aureomycin. The antibiotic selected for treatment depends upon the type of organism producing the infection.

Probably most of the antibiotic is excreted in the first milking after administration of the drug. Smaller and smaller quantities are excreted in subsequent milkings, unless more injections of the drug are given.

It is generally advisable to discard the milk from several milkings after completion of the antibiotic treatment; otherwise the drug may interfere with the lactic fermentation of milk. Penicillin, for instance, is effective chiefly against Gram-positive organisms. The concentration in milk may be sufficient to interfere with the growth of *Streptococcus lactis* but not high enough to affect the growth of Gram-negative forms which may produce some undesirable defects in the milk.

Galesloot (1956), in his studies on yoghurt (a fermented milk prepared from a mixture of *Streptococcus thermophilus* and *Lactobacillus bulgaricus*), found penicillin to eliminate selectively the cocci without exhibiting any appreciable effect on the lactobacilli (Fig. 215). This resulted in a modified type of fermentation.

Presence of antibiotics in milk is undesirable for another important reason. Many disease-producing bacteria may be capable of developing resistance to antibiotics. The frequent presence of such drugs in milk might result in the development of resistant forms of potential disease-producing organisms in the human body. Under these conditions the antibiotics would not be effective if, at a later date, such organisms produced a disease process in the host. It would then be necessary to switch

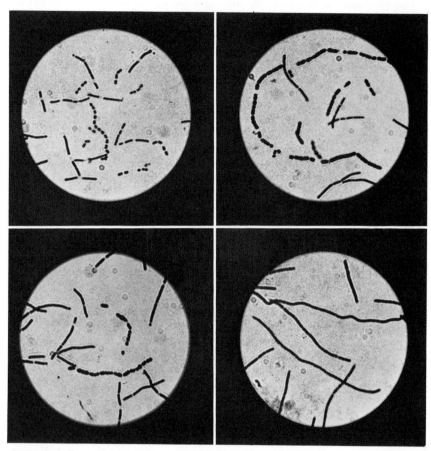

Fig. 215. Effect of penicillin on *Streptococcus thermophilus* and *Lactobacillus bulgaricus* in yoghurt. Upper left, no penicillin added. Upper right, 0.01 μg penicillin added. Lower left, same as in preceding. Lower right, 0.03 μg penicillin added. The streptococci gradually disappear, leaving the more resistant lactobacilli. This gives a modified type of fermentation. (*Courtesy of Galesloot.*)

to a different antibiotic not present in the milk, or to resort to some other type of treatment.

The addition of antibiotics to milk as preservatives has not been approved by the U.S. Public Health Service.

For more information see Blackburn (1956); Nutting and Barber (1956); Welch, Jester, and Burton (1956).

BUTTER

Butter consists of about 80.5 per cent butterfat, 16.5 per cent water, 2 per cent salt (sodium chloride), 1 per cent curd, and traces of lactose. The amount of casein and lactose present depends upon the extent to which butter is washed during manufacture. Since the salt is completely dissolved in the water, the liquid portion of butter consists of about a 30 per cent salt solution.

Butter is prepared by churning fresh, sweet cream, either raw or pasteurized, to separate the fat globules from the other constituents. This method necessitates churning daily while the milk or cream is still fresh. A more popular method is to allow the cream to sour first, after which the butterfat may be more easily separated from the casein.

The cream may be soured naturally or by the addition of a culture of organisms known as a starter. Many starters are used, depending upon the type of organism desired. The advantages of first souring the cream are: (1) the yield of butter is increased, owing to a better separation of the butterfat, and (2) the aroma and flavor may be greatly improved.

Before a starter is added, it is necessary to destroy practically all of the bacteria already in the milk or cream. For this purpose a pasteurization temperature of 71°C. is applied for a period of 30 min. Such treatment results in the destruction of at least 99.9 per cent of the organisms present.

Butter Cultures. Butter cultures consist of a mixture of two types of organisms: (1) those producing a high acidity (lactic acid) and (2) those imparting the characteristic aroma and flavor to butter.

Lactic Acid Type. The lactic acid type consists generally of *Streptococcus lactis*, the organism responsible for the normal souring of milk. Another organism of this type is *S. cremoris*. These organisms produce fairly large amounts of lactic acid from the lactose of milk together with small amounts of secondary products. Growth of the organisms in milk does not result in the product having a butter-culture flavor. However, the compounds formed by the lactic bacteria greatly influence the action of the flavor organisms, resulting in a product having a more pronounced aroma and flavor.

The lactic acid organisms produce from 0.7 to 1 per cent lactic acid in milk with a maximum of about 1.2 per cent. These figures correspond to a pH range of 4.0 to 4.6 approximately.

Cells of *S. cremoris* are spheres or ovoid-shaped, elongated in the direction of the chain, measuring 0.6 to 1.0 μ in diameter; they usually form long chains in milk. The cells are Gram-positive. Optimum growth temperature is below 30°C. They may survive 60°C. for 30 min. The organism fails to grow in 4 per cent salt solution. It is commonly employed in commercial starters for butter and cheese manufacture. Plants are believed to be its natural habitat.

Characteristics of *S. lactis* are given on page 570.

Aroma and Flavor Type. Organisms responsible for the aroma and flavor of butter generally consist of a mixture of *Leuconostoc dextranicum* and *L. citrovorum.*

Cells are normally spherical, but under some conditions, such as in acid media, organisms may lengthen and become pointed or even elongated into a rod. Spheres measure 0.6 to 1.0 μ in diameter, occurring in pairs and in short chains. They are Gram-positive. Optimum temperaure is 21 to 25°C. The organisms are isolated from dairy starters. Their habitat is on plant materials and in milk products.

The aroma and flavor of butter are dependent upon the citric acid content of milk. Milk normally contains about 0.18 per cent citric acid. *L. citrovorum* is capable of attacking the citric acid with the formation of acetic acid, possibly some formic and propionic acids, carbon dioxide, and acetylmethylcarbinol ($CH_3 \cdot CO \cdot CHOH \cdot CH_3$). The addition of more citric acid to milk results in a proportionate increase in the content of acetylmethylcarbinol. Under conditions of high acidity, some acetylmethylcarbinol is oxidized to diacetyl ($CH_3 \cdot CO \cdot OC \cdot CH_3$). Under conditions of low acidity and suitable temperature, some acetylmethylcarbinol is reduced to 2,3-butylene glycol ($CH_3 \cdot CHOH \cdot CHOH \cdot CH_3$).

The citric fermentation, according to van Beynum and Pette, is given in Fig. 216.

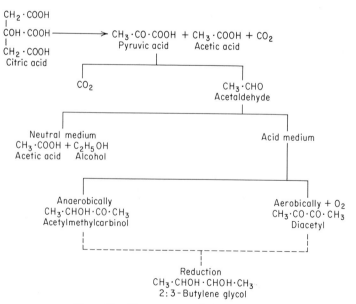

FIG. 216. The citric acid fermentation.

Diacetyl in high dilution suggests the odor of butter. Acetylmethylcarbinol in pure form is odorless; in the impure state, it gives off an odor not unlike that of diacetyl. Cultures having a satisfactory aroma and flavor contain relatively large amounts of these two compounds. Milk is rarely curdled by the flavor and aroma organisms.

Preparation and Use of Butter Culture. The butter culture is generally prepared as follows: The milk or cream is pasteurized at a temperature of 70 to 85°C. for 30 min. to diminish foreign bacteria, then inoculated with the desired organisms. After the starter is prepared, it should be handled with great care to prevent entrance of organisms likely to produce undesirable changes. Butter cultures are commonly ripened at a temperature of 21.1 to 22.2°C. for maximum development of aroma and flavor. The flavor compounds are not produced in significant amounts until the butter culture has an acidity of about 0.8 per cent. Usually 0.25 to 1 per cent butter culture is added to cream that is to be ripened for the preparation of butter.

Elliker (1945) showed that the loss of aroma of butter, butter substitutes, and other food products was caused by the action of certain organisms on the diacetyl content. Some members of the genus *Pseudomonas* (*fluorescens, fragi, putrefaciens,* etc.) were found to be active in destroying diacetyl with accompanying loss of flavor. The results emphasized the importance of keeping butter and other products containing diacetyl free from contaminating organisms.

Undesirable Changes in Butter. Butter prepared from sweet unpasteurized cream contains the same microflora as the cream from which it was prepared. Also the bacterial changes which take place during storage are the same as those which occur in the milk or cream under the same conditions. Butter prepared from cream previously pasteurized at high temperatures, and then inoculated, generally contains only those organisms which were added to promote ripening. Some molds and yeasts may be present which result from air contamination. Since molds are generally aerobic, they grow chiefly on the surface of butter.

Undesirable changes which take place after butter has been manufactured are produced largely by the growth of organisms. Many of the organisms are present as a result of contamination of butter after its manufacture. Therefore, the same precautions followed in handling milk and cream also apply to butter. The extent of recontamination is roughly an indication of the care exercised in handling and storing butter.

Some butter defects and their causes are the following:

Surface Taint. Caused by *Pseudomonas putrefaciens,* commonly found in raw milk and cream, butter, water, soil, and creamery equipment.

Rancidity. The first stage is believed to be a hydrolysis of the butterfat into glycerol and fatty acids. During this stage butter acquires a strong odor of butyric and caproic acids. A lipase capable of doing this is normally present in raw milk or is secreted by various contaminating organisms such as *Pseudomonas fragi* and *P. fluorescens*. Since the enzyme is destroyed in the pasteurization process, the defect can be controlled by heat-treatment.

Malty Flavor. Produced by a variety of *Streptococcus lactis*. The organism may be isolated from raw milk. It is easily destroyed by pasteurization.

Skunk-like Odor. A defect produced by the contaminant *Pseudomonas mephitica*.

Black Discoloration. Caused by *Pseudomonas nigrifaciens*, a black pigment–producing organism.

Surface Discoloration. Produced by molds of the genera *Cladosporium, Alternaria, Aspergillus, Mucor,* and *Rhizopus.*

Yeasty Flavor. Caused by the yeasts *Torula cremoris* and *T. sphaerica.*

Metallic Flavor. Various organisms, including a strain of *Streptococcus lactis.*

Tallowiness in Butter. A tallow-like odor is produced by oxidation. This may result from the action of ultraviolet rays of sunlight or to oxidases naturally present in milk. Certain mold enzymes are capable of producing a similar effect. Changes may be prevented by high-temperature pasteurization, which destroys the oxidases.

Quantitative Bacteriological Examination of Butter. Butter is not a favorable medium for bacterial growth. Multiplication usually occurs only in the minute droplets of water containing salt and traces of casein and lactose. Since the high salt content makes this an unfavorable medium, butter never shows bacterial counts as high as those of milk. The count is highest in freshly prepared butter and becomes less and less as the butter ages.

The bacterial flora of the surface of butter differs from that of the interior, owing to contamination from the air and differences in the oxygen concentration. For these reasons it is difficult to obtain representative samples for examination. A sample is usually obtained by removing a cylinder of butter from a cake by means of a sterile sampler. The butter is then melted on a water bath at a temperature not to exceed 40°C., and dilutions are prepared in sterile dilution blanks previously heated to the same temperature.

For more information see Bång (1949); Breed, Murray, and Smith (1957); De Man (1956); Elliker (1949); Foster et al. (1957); Hammer and Babel (1957); Richards and El-Sadek (1949).

ICE CREAM

Ice cream is a frozen dairy product composed of cream and other milk derivatives, stabilizers, sugar, flavoring materials, and coloring.

The milk derivatives consist of sweetened condensed skim milk, non-fat dry milk, butter oil, etc.

Stabilizers are added to give ice cream a smooth texture by preventing the formation of large ice crystals. These include sodium alginate, Irish moss, locust bean gum, cellulose gum, karaya gum, gelatin, etc.

Unlike the preparation of butter and certain cheeses, bacteria play no part in the manufacture of ice cream.

Bacterial Counts of Ice Cream. The bacterial content of ice cream depends largely upon (1) the number present in the cream at the time of preparation and (2) the number of organisms present in the various ingredients employed in its manufacture.

High total counts usually indicate neglect and unsanitary conditions. These may result from (1) poor quality of ingredients used in its manufacture, (2) improper pasteurization of the finished product, (3) contamination after pasteurization, (4) improper aging, (5) unsanitary equipment, and (6) negligent and untrained personnel.

Organisms which may be found in ice cream include coliform bacteria, micrococci, streptococci, spore-forming rods, yeasts, and molds. Some are of dairy origin, whereas others are from the ingredients used in its manufacture.

Ice cream is stored at temperatures of -17.8 to $-28.9°C$. At these temperatures, there is a gradual but slow decrease in the bacterial population. The lactic acid organisms, i.e., those responsible for the souring of cream, fail to multiply. The presence of disease-producing organisms in ice cream is generally the result of using contaminated cream in its manufacture. Cold is not a sterilizing agent and should not be depended upon to destroy all disease organisms in ice cream.

CHEESE

According to the standards of the Food and Drug Administration of the U.S. Department of Agriculture, cheese may be defined as

. . . the product made from the separated curd obtained by coagulating the casein of milk, skimmed milk, or milk enriched with cream. The coagulation is accomplished by means of rennet or other suitable enzyme, lactic fermentation, or by a combination of the two. The curd may be modified by heat, pressure, ripening ferments, special molds, or suitable seasoning.

The name "cheese" unqualified means cheddar cheese (American cheese, American cheddar cheese).

Two general processes are used for the preparation of curd. One method depends upon the addition of an appropriate enzyme; the other, on the activities of organisms. Since the changes produced by organisms are dependent upon the presence of enzymes, the latter is also an enzymatic process. The cheeses in the first group are known as rennin-curd cheeses; those in the second group as acid-curd cheeses.

Steps in Cheese Making. Five steps are followed in the preparation of cheese. These are (1) inoculating pasteurized milk with lactic acid bacteria, (2) curdling the milk, (3) draining the curd and pressing it into desired shapes, (4) adding salt, and (5) ripening.

Starter cultures may consist of one or a combination of two or more of the following organisms: *Streptococcus lactis, S. cremoris, S. thermophilus, Lactobacillus bulgaricus, L. helveticus, L. lactis,* etc. These organisms are capable of fermenting lactose with the production of sufficient acid to curdle the milk.

Casein is dispersed in milk as calcium caseinate. Lactic acid, as it is formed, reacts with the calcium to give calcium lactate. When the calcium content is reduced to a certain low point, the casein precipitates. The clear straw-colored liquid that separates from the curd is known as whey.

Curd may also be prepared by adding the enzyme rennin to milk. The enzyme reacts with the calcium caseinate to form calcium paracaseinate. Then the calcium paracaseinate reacts with free calcium ions to give a curd. The insoluble curd is produced at the pH of milk.

The curd is separated from the whey by draining, with or without the use of pressure. Draining without pressure results in the production of soft cheeses; draining with pressure results in the formation of hard cheeses.

The solid curd is molded into various shapes according to the variety of cheese being manufactured. Sodium chloride is added by (1) floating the cheese in a strong brine solution or (2) rubbing the surface with dry salt. The salt slowly diffuses throughout the cheese.

Freshly prepared and molded curd is known as green cheese. In order that it be made satisfactory for consumption, it must be set aside to ripen. Certain conditions, such as temperature and moisture, are carefully controlled during the ripening process. The cheese changes considerably during this stage. The insoluble casein is rendered soluble, and the digestibility is greatly improved. The consistency changes to give a softer product. Also the flavor, characteristic of the finished product, develops during the ripening period.

As has already been stated, the changes which occur during ripening are largely enzymatic. However, this does not explain all of the changes which occur during the long aging period. The flavors which develop are not the result of enzymatic action but of the associated activities of bacteria, yeasts, and molds. The enzymes improve the consistency and digestibility of cheeses but play no part in improving the aromas and flavors. These depend upon the kinds and numbers of organisms present.

Hard Cheeses. Hard-curd cheeses are prepared from curd subjected to heavy pressure to remove as much of the whey as possible. This gives a very hard, tough curd that does not become softened to any extent during the ripening period. Since the curd is very compact and tough, the ripening stage requires a considerable period of time to produce a satisfactory product. Enzymatic and bacterial changes proceed simultaneously.

Examples of hard-curd cheeses include Cheddar, Edam, Parmesan, Provolone, Romano, and Swiss.

Soft Cheeses. Soft cheeses are prepared by allowing the whey to drain from the curd without the application of pressure. Cheeses prepared in this manner contain more moisture than the hard-curd cheeses, which results in a much softer finished product.

Examples of soft-curd cheeses include brick, Brie, Camembert, Limburger, and Roquefort.

Camembert cheese is made by shaping the curd into the desired size and form. The surface is inoculated with spores of the mold *Penicillium camemberti*. Enzymes secreted by the mold growth act upon the surface of the cheese to produce a slow liquefaction of the casein. The enzymes gradually penetrate the product until the entire curd is affected. The result is the formation of a soft, creamy mass at the completion of the ripening period. The enzymes are responsible for the consistency of the product, while the growth of the mold contributes to the flavor and aroma.

In cheeses of the Roquefort type, spores of the blue-green mold *Penicillium roqueforti* are inoculated into the curd. Since the mold is aerobic, holes are punched into the curd to facilitate development of the mold throughout the curd. The enzymes elaborated by the organism soften the casein, while certain metabolic products impart the characteristic aroma and flavor to the cheese.

Desirable Organisms. Many organisms are responsible for the aromas, flavors, and characteristics of the various types of cheeses. Apparently each type has its own characteristic flora. Some of the organisms which have been isolated from cheeses are (1) *Streptococcus cremoris* (see page 593); (2) *S. faecalis*, ovoid cells elongated in direction of chain, occurring mostly in pairs or short chains, Gram-positive, some strains actively motile, some strains fermenting citric acid; (3) *S. lactis* (see page 570); (4) *S. thermophilus*, spherical to ovoid cells, occurring in pairs to long chains, Gram-positive, optimum temperature 50°C., extremely sensitive to salt; (5) *Lactobacillus bulgaricus*, slender rods with rounded ends, often in chains, nonmotile, Gram-positive, forming high acidity in milk, optimum temperature 50°C., originally isolated from yoghurt; (6) *L. casei*, short or long rods, occurring in short or long chains, nonmotile, Gram-positive, optimum temperature 30°C., producing 1.5 per cent lactic acid; (7) *L. helveticus*, large rods, occurring singly and in chains, nonmotile, Gram-positive, optimum temperature 40 to 42°C., widely distributed in dairy products; (8) *L. lactis*, rods with tendency to grow into threads, often strongly curling, occurring singly or in pairs in young cultures, Gram-positive, producing 1.7 per cent lactic acid in milk, optimum temperature 40°C.; (9) *L. plantarum*, large rods, occurring singly or in short chains, with rounded ends, cells tending to become longer in acid media, Gram-positive, optimum temperature 30°C.; (10) *Leuconostoc citrovorum* (see page 594); (11) *L. dextranicum* (see page 594); (12)*Propionibacterium shermanii*, small cells, occurring mostly in pairs and short chains, non-motile, Gram-positive, producing propionic acid from carbohydrate, isolated from dairy products, also Swiss cheese.

Undesirable Organisms. The presence of undesirable organisms is responsible for numerous types of faulty cheeses. Some faults affect the taste; others are concerned with the appearance of the finished product. The milk becomes contaminated through carelessness in its collection and handling. Considerable losses are experienced at times by cheese manufacturers. For this reason it is generally advisable to use milk previously pasteurized and then inoculated with a desirable organism rather than to start with raw milk.

One of the most common faults is swollen or blown cheese, the result of the fermentation of the lactose with the formation of acid and gas. The gas bubbles cause the cheese to swell until it may actually burst. Unpleasant flavors are also produced by organisms; Galesloot (1947*a*, *b*) reported that *Aerobacter* types and certain yeasts were involved.

The presence of putrefactive organisms may be responsible for putrid odors and flavors. The bacteria grow and become active when the acidity of the cheese is reduced during the ripening period. The presence of chromogenic organisms may be responsible for discolorations in cheese. This may be caused also by various chemical reactions with metals, such as copper and iron from the utensils used in handling the raw materials. Red and brown spots in Emmentaler cheese are caused by the growth of chromogenic *Propionibacterium. Lactobacillus brevis* is responsible for the appearance of rusty spots in cheddar cheese. Surface discolorations are produced by many molds, such as *Penicillium casei, Cladosporium herbarum, Monilia niger,* and *Oöspora crustacea.* Red and yellow torulae (false yeasts) play some part in the process.

For more information see Babel (1953); Hood and Smith (1951); Lubert and Frazier (1955); Yates, Irvine, and Cunningham (1955).

Cheese and Its Relation to Disease. Many epidemics have been traced to the consumption of cheese contaminated with disease organisms. According to Fabian (1946*b*, 1947), the organisms most commonly associated with cheese-borne infections are *Brucella melitensis, Clostridium botulinum, Staphylococcus aureus, Salmonella choleraesuis, S. schottmuelleri, S. typhimurium,* and *S. typhosa.*

Gilman and Marquardt (1951) recovered *Brucella abortus* from 5 out of 6 Italian cheese curds made from raw milk. After pasteurization, they were unable to recover the organisms from either the milk or the curd prepared from the same lot.

From available evidence, it appears that if cheese made from raw milk is allowed to ripen for at least 90 days, all pathogenic organisms present are either dead or attenuated. A ripening period of 120 days should eliminate all viable disease bacteria. However, a combination of pasteurization and a 90-day ripening period should be more nearly ideal, as well as economically sound, in the preparation of a safe and mature cheese.

FERMENTED MILK

Milk is probably the most important article of food among many pastoral tribes of Europe and Asia. Because of the primitive sanitary conditions under which the people live, milk is usually allowed to ferment before it is consumed. The high acidity produced preserves the milk for an indefinite period.

The consumption of sour milk preparations is widespread because of their supposedly therapeutic value. The fact that they appear under various names does not mean necessarily that each product is fermented with a different organism. The names identify the country or region where they are produced. Some preparations contain only one organism; others result from the combined action of two or more organisms. The latter preparations furnish excellent examples of associations.

Yoghurt. The sour milk preparation of Bulgaria and Turkey is known as yoghurt. This is usually prepared from camel's or mare's milk. The fermentation is produced by acid-forming organisms of the *Lactobacillus bulgaricus* type. Sometimes *Streptococcus thermophilus* is also present. The organisms produce from 1.5 to 2.5 per cent acid calculated as lactic acid.

Matzoon. This is the sour milk preparation of Armenia and is similar to yoghurt in flavor and flora.

Gioddu. Gioddu is the sour milk product prepared on the island of Sardinia. It is similar to yoghurt in its method of preparation.

Leban. The Egyptian drink known as leban is prepared by the action of lactic acid bacteria and yeasts on cow's, goat's, or buffalo's milk. The lactose of the milk is attacked by both organisms, the former producing lactic acid and the latter alcohol accompanied by carbon dioxide. It is a sour effervescent preparation containing alcohol.

Kumiss. Kumiss is a Russian product prepared by the fermentation of mare's or cow's milk by yeasts, lactobacilli, and lactic streptococci. The yeasts produce alcohol and carbon dioxide, and the bacteria produce lactic acid.

Kefir. Kefir is prepared by inoculating milk with kefir grains. These resemble minute cauliflowers and are composed of *Saccharomyces kefir*, *Lactobacillus bulgaricus*, and *Streptococcus lactis*. The yeast produces alcohol and carbon dioxide; the bacteria produce lactic acid.

Curds. The fermented milk preparation of Ceylon is usually referred to as curds. It is manufactured from cow's or buffalo's milk. The milk is boiled, cooled, and while still warm, inoculated with a piece of curd from the previous lot. The milk is allowed to ferment for at least 36 hr. The organisms involved include yeasts, *Streptococcus lactis*, and a *Lactobacillus*. In most samples, the yeast and *S. lactis* predominate. The preparation is similar to kefir and kumiss.

This is only a partial list of the various fermented milk preparations.

Bulgarian and Acidophilus Milk

Yoghurt is consumed in large quantities as an article of diet by the people of Bulgaria. Metschnikoff (1908) noted that centenarians were more numerous in Bulgaria, in proportion to population, than in other countries. He believed that the increase in the life span was due to the ingestion of large quantities of sour milk, produced by the action of the rod-shaped, Gram-positive organism *L. bulgaricus* (see page 599). Because of this fact, Metschnikoff advocated the consumption of Bulgarian milk for the prolongation of life.

According to Metschnikoff, growth of *L. bulgaricus* in the intestinal tract produced a high percentage of lactic acid, which was capable of inhibiting the growth of the putrefactive bacteria. Disorders that were supposed to be associated with autointoxication (absorption of putrefactive metabolic waste products from the intestinal tract) would be prevented.

Later Hull and Rettger (1915) found the conclusions of Metschnikoff to be incorrect. They reported that *L. bulgaricus* was not a normal inhabitant of the intestinal tract of man and, therefore, did not become acclimated to the new environment. They showed that the consumption of Bulgarian milk stimulated the growth of *L. acidophilus*, an organism normally present in the intestinal tract of adults.

L. acidophilus was first isolated from the feces of breast-fed infants. It is present in the intestinal contents of adults. On a mixed diet, the numbers are small. If the diet is supplemented with large quantities of milk or carbohydrates, such as lactose or dextrin, the numbers are greatly increased. The organisms ferment the carbohydrate with the production of a high concentration of lactic acid (about 3 per cent), which is sufficient to inhibit the growth of the putrefactive types (*Escherichia coli*, etc.). In the absence of a high carbohydrate diet, the flora again becomes predominantly putrefactive in character. The numbers are also increased by the ingestion of milk fermented by *L. acidophilus*, especially when taken with lactose or dextrin to increase the fermentable constituents in the intestinal tract.

For more information see Nilsson (1949) and Olsen (1949).

REFERENCES

Abd-el-Malek, Y., and T. Gibson: Studies in the bacteriology of milk. I. The strepto-cocci of milk, *J. Dairy Research*, 15:233, 1948a; II. The staphylococci and micro-cocci of milk, *ibid.*, 15:249, 1948b.

American Public Health Association: "Standard Methods for the Examination of Dairy Products," New York, 1960.

Andrey, J., Jr., and W. C. Frazier: Psychrophiles in milk held two days in farm bulk cooling tanks, *J. Dairy Sci.*, 42:1781, 1959.

Atherton, H. F., F. J. Doan, and G. H. Watrous, Jr.: Changes in bacterial popula-tion and characteristics of bottled market milk during refrigerated holding, *Penn. State Univ. Agr. Exp. Sta. Bull.* 575, March, 1954.

Babel, F. J.: The role of fungi in cheese ripening, *Econ. Bot.*, 7:27, 1953.

Bachrach, H. L., and S. S. Breese, Jr.: Purification and electron microscopy of foot-and-mouth disease virus, *Proc. Soc. Exp. Biol. Med.*, 97:659, 1958.

Bång, Von F.: Über den Stoffwechsel von *Streptococcus citrovorus*, *Arkiv Kemi*, 1:27, 1949.

Blackburn, P. S.: Antibiotic treatment of mastitis and its effect on the cell content of the milk, *J. Dairy Research*, 23:225, 1956.

Breed, R. S., E. G. D. Murray, and N. R. Smith: "Bergey's Manual of Determinative Bacteriology," Baltimore, The Williams & Wilkins Company, 1957.

Davis, J. G.: The technique for the resazurin tests, *Dairy Ind.*, 8:167, 1943.

De Man, J. C.: Over de wijze waarop diacetyl in culturen van *Betacoccus cremoris* ontstaat, *Ned. Melk-en Zuiveltijdschrift*, 10:38, 1956.

De Vries, J., and R. Strikwerda: Een geval van Listeria-mastitis ("Uier-Listeriose") bij het rund, *Tijdschrift voor Diergeneeskunde*, 81:833, 1956.

Doetsch, R. N.: The problem of thermophilic and thermoduric bacteria in milk, *Milk Plant Monthly*, December, 1949.

Druce, R. G., and S. B. Thomas: The microbiological examination of butter, *J. Appl. Bact.*, 22:52, 1959.

Elliker, P. R.: Effect of various bacteria on diacetyl content and flavor of butter, *J. Dairy Sci.*, 28:93, 1945.

————: "Practical Dairy Bacteriology," New York, McGraw-Hill Book Company, Inc., 1949.

Fabian, F. W.: Significance of thermoduric and thermophilic bacteria in milk and their control, *Milk Technol.*, 9:273, 1946a; Cheese as the cause of epidemics, *ibid.*, 9:129, 1946b.

————: Cheese and its relation to disease, *Am. J. Pub. Health*, 37:987, 1947.

Foster, E. M., F. E. Nelson, M. L. Speck, R. N. Doetsch, and J. C. Olson, Jr.: "Dairy Microbiology," Englewood Cliffs, N.J., Prentice-Hall, Inc., 1957.

Gainor, C., and D. E. Wegemer: Studies on a psychrophilic bacterium causing ropi-ness in milk. I. Morphological and physiological considerations, *Appl. Microbiol.*, 2:95, 1954; II. Chemical nature of the capsular polysaccharide, *ibid.*, 2:97, 1954.

Galesloot, T. E.: The cause of the early gas defect in cheese and the means to pre-vent it, *Antonie van Leeuwenhoek*, 13:67, 1947a.

————: An early gas defect in cheese caused by yeasts, *Ned. Melk Zuiveltijdschr.*, October, 1947b, p. 238.

————: Invloed van penicilline op de morphologie van yoghurt-en zuursel-bacterien, *Ned. Melk Zuiveltijdschr.*, 10:64, 1956.

————: Kwaliteitsbepaling van rauwe melk met de resazurineproef, *ibid.*, April/June, 1948, p. 70.

————: Onderzoekingen betreffende de methyleenblauwproef, *ibid.*, 3:205, 1949.

————: De invloed van de pasteurisatietemperatuur op de duurzaamheid van gepasteuriseerde melk, *ibid.*, 9:237, 1955.

Gilman, H. L., and J. C. Marquardt: The occurrence and survival of *Brucella abortus* in Italian cheese curd made from raw and pasteurized milk, *J. Milk Food Tech-nol.*, 14:55, 1951.

Hadfield, W. A.: Cold-loving bacteria, *Southern Dairy Products J.*, June, 1956.

Hale, H. H., W. N. Plastridge, and L. F. Williams: The effect of *Streptococcus agalactiae* infection on milk yield, *Cornell Veterinarian*, **46**:201, 1956.

Hammer, B. W., and F. J. Babel: "Dairy Bacteriology," New York, John Wiley & Sons, Inc., 1957.

Hetrick, J. H., and P. H. Tracy: Effect of high-temperature short-time heat treatments on some properties of milk. I. Inactivation of the phosphatase enzyme, *J. Dairy Sci.*, **31**:867, 1948.

Holmes, A. D., and C. P. Jones: Effect of sunshine upon the ascorbic acid and riboflavin content of milk, *J. Nutrition*, **19**:201, 1945.

Hood, E. G., and K. N. Smith: Bacterial spoilage in process cheese, *Sci. Agr.*, **31**:530, 1951.

Hull, T. G., and L. F. Rettger: The influence of milk and carbohydrate feeding on the intestinal flora of white rats, *Zentr. Bakteriol.*, Abt. 1, Orig., **75**:219, 1915.

Jones, D. L.: Ropy milk: the biology of rope production, *Food Res.*, **19**:246, 1954*a*; II. The influence of physicochemical environment on the formation of ropy substance, *ibid.*, **19**:250, 1954*b*; III. Chemical studies of ropy substance, *ibid.*, **19**:254, 1954*c*.

Kaufmann, O. W., and J. Tobias: A device for collecting and rapidly cooling samples from high-temperature short-time heating units, *J. Dairy Sci.*, **38**:645, 1955.

Lawton, W. C., and F. E. Nelson: The effect of storage temperatures on the growth of psychrophilic organisms in sterile and laboratory pasteurized skimmilks, *J. Dairy Sci.*, **37**:1164, 1954.

Lubert, D. J., and W. C. Frazier: Microbiology of the surface ripening of brick cheese, *J. Dairy Sci.*, **38**:981, 1955.

Morgan, M. E., P. MacLeod, and E. O. Anderson: An improved procedure for microscopic grading of milk intended for pasteurization, *J. Milk Food Tech.*, **15**:3, 1952.

Morris, C. S.: Presence in raw cow's milk of a bactericidal substance specific for certain strains of coliform organisms, *Nature*, **155**:22, 1945.

Nelson, F. E., and M. P. Baker: The influence of time and temperature of plate incubation upon bacterial counts of market milk and related products, particularly after holding under refrigeration, *J. Milk Food Tech.*, **17**:95, 1954.

Nilsson, G.: Studies in the bacterial flora of various yoghurt cultures, *Ann. Roy. Agr. Coll. Sweden*, **16**:441, 1949.

————: Reducing properties of normal and abnormal milk and their importance in bacteriological grading of milk, *Bact. Rev.*, **23**:41, 1959.

Nutting, L. A., and F. W. Barber: The problem of antibiotic detection in milk, *J. Milk Food Tech.*, **19**:162, 1956.

Olsen, E.: Studies on the intestinal flora of infants, Einar Munksgaard, Copenhagen, 1949.

Olson, J. C., Jr., R. B. Parker, and W. S. Mueller: The nature, significance and control of psychrophilic bacteria in dairy products, *J. Milk Food Tech.*, **18**, no. 8, 1955.

Overcast, W. W., and J. D. Skean: Growth of certain lipolytic microorganisms at 4°C. and their influence on free fat acidity and flavor of pasteurized milk, *J. Dairy Sci.*, **42**:1479, 1959.

Plastridge, W. N., and Hale, H. H.: Diagnosis and treatment of mastitis, *Conn. Univ. Storrs Agr. Exp. Sta. Prog. Rep.* no. 14, September, 1956.

Read, R. B., Jr., N. L. Norcross, D. J. Hankinson, and W. Litsky: Come-up time method of milk pasteurization. III. Bacteriological studies, *J. Dairy Sci.*, **40**:28, 1957.

Richards, T., and G. M. El-Sadek: The nature and quantity of fatty acids produced in butterfat by the action of micro-organisms, *J. Dairy Research*, **16**:46, 1949.

Sackett, De L., and G. G. Gralak: The value of the coliform count in the routine examination of milk and dairy products, *J. Milk Food Tech.*, **13**:350, 1950.

Sanders, G. P., and O. S. Sager: Heat inactivation of milk phosphatase in dairy products, *J. Dairy Sci.*, **31**:845, 1948.

Sherman, J. M., K. L. Smiley, and C. F. Niven, Jr.: The serological integrity of *Streptococcus lactis*, *J. Dairy Sci.*, **23**:529, 1940.

Simon, J., and R. Hall: An outbreak of bovine mycotic mastitis associated with dry storage of teat cup inflations, *J. Milk Food Tech.*, 18, no. 12, 1955.

Smith, H. W.: The multiplication of *Staphylococcus aureus* in cow's milk, *Monthly Bull. Ministry of Health and Pub. Health Lab. Ser.*, 16:39, 1957.

Thomas, S. B.: Coli-aerogenes bacteria in raw milk, *J. Appl. Bact.*, 18:331, 1955.

U.S. Public Health Service: "Milk Ordinance and Code," pub. no. 229, 1956.

Wegemer, D. E., and C. Gainor: Studies on a psychrophilic bacterium causing ropiness in milk. II. Chemical nature of the capsular polysaccharide, *Appl. Microbiol.*, 2:97, 1959.

Welch, H., W. R. Jester, and J. M. Burton: Antibiotics in fluid market milk, *Antibiotics and Chemotherapy*, 6:369, 1956.

Yates, A. R., O. R. Irvine, and J. D. Cunningham: Chromatographic studies on proteolytic bacteria in their relationship to flavour development in Cheddar cheese, *Can. J. Agr. Sci.*, 35:337, 1955.

Yotis, W., and Teodoro, R.: The influence of temperature on the generation time of bacteria commonly found in milk, *J. Dairy Res.*, 24:27, 1957.

CHAPTER 23

Bacteriology of Food

Spoilage involves changes which render foods unattractive, unsalable, and unwholesome. According to Oser (1946), spoiled food may be non-injurious even though unfit for human consumption. The stock terms used to describe spoiled foods are filthy, putrid, and decomposed. All such foods are not necessarily inedible. For example, Limburger cheese owes its popularity to the process of putrefaction by which it is made. Soy sauce likewise is manufactured by a process of enzymatic decomposition. Yet these are neither inedible nor uneaten despite these characteristics. In many instances selected microorganisms are inoculated into food products in order to produce certain specific types of decomposition.

The causative factors involved in food spoilage are physical, chemical, and biological. These rarely proceed as single processes but usually go on simultaneously or in sequence so that any case of spoilage may be of an extremely complex nature.

Spoilage by Radiation. One of the most important physical factors responsible for food spoilage is radiation. This may involve visible, ultraviolet, or infrared rays.

Visible light may cause discoloration or undesirable flavors in foods. Many liquid foods are protected from light by being placed in dark bottles. Ultraviolet light is effective in destroying bacteria, yeasts, and molds but, in so doing, may induce other types of spoilage. For example, fats may be oxidized to rancid-smelling compounds, off colors may be imparted to foods, and milk loses much of its riboflavin content.

Infrared rays produce an increase in temperature. Excessive heat may result in dehydration of foods; loss of volatile constituents; alteration of proteins; and changes in weight, volume, texture, and general appearance.

Spoilage by Pressure. Pressure is often responsible for food spoilage. Fruits and vegetables may become unsalable by crushing, pressing, or bruising. Even though damage is not complete, loss of weight and nutrients may occur due to expression of liquids.

Spoilage by Freezing. Treatment of foods by freezing is a most effective method of preservation. The effect is to retard physical, chemical, and biological changes. Unless the process is carefully controlled, undesirable changes in flavor, texture, and keeping qualities may occur.

In slow freezing, large ice crystals may form which cause a disruption of cell walls. On the other hand, quick freezing produces very small ice crystals which do not cause a disintegration of cell walls. Foods so treated may be satisfactorily preserved without spoilage.

Spoilage by Enzymes. Enzymes continue to function even though fruits and vegetables are picked and animals are slaughtered. Unless the enzymes are destroyed, they continue to act during processing and storage of foods, with the result that considerable spoilage may occur. Oxidizing enzymes catalyze the destruction of ascorbic acid (vitamin C) and may produce a deterioration in flavor. Proteolytic enzymes produce autolysis and putrefaction of meats. Amylolytic enzymes hydrolyze carbohydrates to smaller units. Lipolytic enzymes produce a breakdown of fats to glycerol and fatty acids. The fatty acids may be oxidized to peroxides and aldehydes, which are associated with rancidity.

Proper pH control is of considerable importance in the processing of foods. Some natural fruit and vegetable pigments are indicators, and their color is dependent upon the acidity of the products. Proteins, carbohydrates, and fats may undergo undesirable changes if the reaction is unfavorable. Vitamins are particularly sensitive to changes in pH. Vitamin A is stable in alkaline media; pantothenic acid is stable only in a neutral environment; thiamine and ascorbic acid are stable only in acid media. Because of this fact it is difficult or impossible to preserve all vitamins in a given product.

Biological Spoilage. Of all agents involved in the spoilage of foods, the activities of living organisms are undoubtedly the most important. Spoilage is caused principally by bacteria, yeasts, and molds. The organisms may be pathogenic or nonpathogenic, spore-forming or non-spore-forming, thermophilic or mesophilic, aerobic or anaerobic, each requiring special means of prevention and control.

Different kinds of organisms produce different types of changes in food. The decomposition of foods rich in carbohydrates results usually in various types of fermentations. The action of organisms on high-protein foods results in putrefactions. The products of the former are usually harmless, whereas those of the latter are objectionable and even dangerous.

Bacteria are more exacting in their requirements than either the yeasts or the molds. This means that yeasts and molds can multiply under conditions unfavorable to the growth of bacteria. Bacteria require relatively large amounts of moisture, hydrogen-ion concentrations usually near the neutral point, and relatively low osmotic pressures for growth and multiplication. Yeasts can tolerate less moisture, are less exacting in their pH requirements, and can multiply in solutions having higher osmotic pressures. Molds are the least exacting of the fungi. They can withstand relatively high acidities, require far less moisture, even grow on substances which are almost dry, and can tolerate extremely high osmotic pressures.

METHODS EMPLOYED FOR THE PRESERVATION OF FOOD

The methods for the preservation of food were employed long before their modes of action were clearly understood. As their mechanisms became known, various improvements were made. The methods commonly employed for food preservation involve the use of (1) heat, (2) cold, (3) drying, (4) preservatives, and (5) high osmotic pressures.

Heat. The use of heat is the method employed in home and commercial canning of meats, fruits, and vegetables. Heat is used to effect either a complete sterilization or a reduction in the number of organisms that may be present. In the latter case, the organisms that have not been killed are prevented from multiplying. Excessive heat is efficient in destroying all forms of microscopic life. The destructive action of heat is due probably to the coagulation of the protoplasm of living cells, rendering it incapable of carrying on its vital functions. It is not desirable greatly to exceed the minimum temperature required to effect sterilization; otherwise alterations may occur in the appearance, flavor, and composition of foods. Since all bacteria are not necessarily killed, the term "processing" is generally employed in referring to heat-treated canned foods.

The diverse details of canning procedures necessarily vary with the nature of the product to be preserved. There are certain important operations common to all canning procedures: (1) cleansing operations, (2) blanching, (3) exhausting or preheating, (4) sealing the tinned container, (5) heat-processing the sealed container, and (6) cooling the tinned container after thermal processing.

Cleansing Operation. The first and one of the most important steps in commercial canning is the thorough cleansing of the food materials to be preserved. Cleansing serves two purposes: (1) it makes a better-looking product, and (2) it serves to reduce substantially the load of spoilage bacteria that may place a heavy burden on the heat process.

Cleansing may be effected by various types of washers. The raw materials are subjected to high-pressure sprays or strong-flowing streams of water while passing along a moving belt or while being dropped in agitating or revolving screens. With certain food materials, dirt and other large adhering particles are mechanically removed by means of revolving or agitating screens or by strong blasts of air.

Blanching. The blanch involves the immersion of raw food materials (fruits and vegetables) into warm or hot water, or exposure to live steam. This is practiced for several reasons. Blanching may serve only as a hot-water wash where adhering materials cannot be removed with cold water. It may soften fibrous plant tissue so that it will either contract (lose water) or expand (take up water). This ensures proper filling of the container. During the blanching operation, respiratory gases are expelled. This prevents strain on the can during processing and favors the development of a higher vacuum in the finished product. Blanching inhibits the action of respiratory enzymes, especially those of oxidation, to give a product of superior quality and nutritive value. Lastly, blanching fixes the natural color of certain products and makes them more attractive in appearance.

Exhausting or Preheating. All canning procedures provide for the exclusion of as much oxygen (air) as possible. The presence of oxygen is undesirable for two reasons: (1) it may react with the food material and the interior of the container to affect the quality and nutritive value of the food, and (2) it may cause undue strain on the container during the processing period.

The procedure followed in removing gases consists of passing the open can, containing the raw food, through an exhaust box in which hot water or steam is used to expand the food and expel air and other gases from the contents and the head-space area of the can. After the gases are expelled, the can is immediately sealed, heat-processed, and cooled. During the cooling, the contents of the can contract, creating a vacuum. This is accepted as evidence of soundness of the canned product.

With some products, the same effect is produced by preheating the food in kettles, filling into cans while still hot, and immediately sealing the containers. With other products, an exhausting effect is produced by adding boiling water, sirup, or brine to the food in the tin. With still other products, exhausting is accomplished by mechanical means rather than by the use of heat. Special machines are used for withdrawing the air from the cans and sealing at the same time. This process is known as vacuum packing.

Sealing the Tinned Container. Each can must be properly sealed before being subjected to the heat process. The heat destroys any organisms present in the raw food material, and the seal on the can prevents recontamination of the contents. The sealing operation is, therefore, one of the most important steps in the canning procedure.

Heat-processing the Sealed Container. The processing operation usually involves the application of steam under pressure (autoclave). This destroys pathogenic and other organisms capable of causing spoilage of the contents. The seal on the can prevents the contents from becoming recontaminated by the same or other kinds of organisms.

The time required for processing canned foods depends upon various factors, such as character and composition of the food, types and numbers of organisms likely to be present, and hydrogen-ion concentration of the food. Heat penetrates to the center of cans by conduction and convection. Penetration of solid foods by heat takes place by conduction and is relatively slow. Penetration of liquid foods takes place by conduction and convection, with the result that the action is more rapid. The size of the food particles also influences the speed of penetration by heat. The larger the particles, the slower the penetration.

Bacteria are usually more easily killed in an acid or an alkaline environment than in a neutral one. Fruits and vegetables are, therefore, more easily processed than fish and meats. Also, fruits and vegetables are more easily penetrated by heat than are meats and fish. The temperature and time of processing must be determined for each kind of food. In general, non-spore-forming organisms in a liquid medium are destroyed at a temperature of 60°C. in 1 hr., or at 70 to 80°C. in a few minutes. Spores are not destroyed when subjected to the above temperatures. Temperatures of 115°C. for 30 min. or 120°C. for 15 min. will usually destroy all forms of life.

Spiegelberg (1940a, b), in his studies on the spoilage of canned pineapple, concluded that at a pH of 4.5 or below, a temperature of 87.8°C. in the fruit following the cooker was adequate to ensure sterility; at a pH above 4.5, a temperature of 93.3°C. was required to eliminate non-spore-forming types of swells (*Lactobacillus plantarum, Leuconostoc mesenteroides,* and three unnamed types), whereas butyric swells (*Clostridium butyricum*) persisted at even much higher temperatures.

In the processing of foods, an excessive period of heating is avoided to prevent injury to the product. A long exposure at a relatively low temperature is usually preferable to a short exposure at a higher temperature. This applies especially to canned fruits.

For more information see Ball (1947), Sognefest et al. (1948).

Cooling the Tinned Container after Thermal Processing. The last operation in the commercial process involves rapid cooling of the sealed cans. This is necessary in order to check the action of the heat and prevent undue softening or change in color of the contents. The cans may be cooled by means of air or of water.

Air cooling is accomplished in well-ventilated, specially designed storage rooms, where the cans are stacked in rows with ample space for efficient circulation of air. Water cooling is accomplished by allowing water to run into the autoclave in which the cans are processed, or the cans may be removed from the sterilizer and conveyed through tanks of cold water or through cold-water showers.

Cold. Two methods are employed in the preservation of foods by cold temperatures: (1) chilling and (2) freezing.

In the chilling method the temperature is kept just above the freezing point. This is the condition encountered in the usual ice or electric refrigerator in the home. The physical state of the food is unaltered. Chilling retards but does not prevent bacterial action. Since many bacteria slowly multiply just above the freezing point, chilled foods cannot be kept for many weeks.

Ripening or aging refers to the practice of holding meat at a temperature of 1 to 3°C., primarily to increase the tenderness and improve the flavor. Good grades of beef may be ripened for 14 days; lamb may be aged for 7 or 8 days but not longer. Ripening is accomplished chiefly by the action of proteolytic enzymes present in the tissues.

The freezing method is considered the simplest, safest, and sanest method for the preservation of food, provided the following five points are considered: (1) careful selection, (2) proper packaging, (3) freezing at −18°C. or lower, (4) storage at −18°C. with a minimum fluctuation, and (5) avoidance of too long storage.

Careful selection is the first step to successful preservation. Blemishes and decayed spots are preserved with the good unless eliminated before freezing. Any mold or slime must be trimmed carefully from meat before processing.

A number of high-class packaging containers and wrappers have been developed and should be used for proper food preservation. The characteristics of a good packaging material are the following: (1) clean and sanitary; (2) odorless, flavorless, and impervious to odors; (3) mechanically practical; (4) attractive in appearance; (5) protective against desiccation; (6) resistant to oxidation; (7) tough and not brittle at low temperatures; (8) greaseproof and stainproof; and (9) resistant to moisture, vapor, and oxygen (air).

Rapid freezing gives the best results in food preservation. Slow freezing refers to temperatures above −18°C. Sharp freezing applies to temperatures between −18 and −29°C. Quick freezing refers to still lower temperatures. Foods should be frozen rapidly and at temperatures below −18°C. Packages should be completely frozen before packing tightly in a storage cabinet.

The vitamin content of foods is rapidly lost at temperatures above −18°C. Also, rancidity in foods develops more rapidly at higher temperatures. After foods are frozen, the storage temperature should be −18°C. with a minimum fluctuation. Fluctuation promotes dehydration. Snow and ice on the inside of a package usually indicate a fluctuation in the temperature in the storage room.

Contrary to popular belief, frozen foods cannot be kept indefinitely. Foods slowly deteriorate in the frozen state. It is best to plan on a normal turnover with the season. Beef and lamb may be safely preserved for 1 year; fresh pork should not be stored over 9 months; ground meats may be safely kept for 6 months.

Longevity of Pathogens in Frozen Foods. Hartsell (1951) treated beef and peas with *Staphylococcus aureus, Salmonella typhosa, S. oranienburg,* and *Shigella dysenteriae* prior to freezing and reported that the organisms survived many months at −9 and −17.8°C. However, greater destruction of bacteria occurred at −9 than at −17.8°C.

Larkin, Litsky, and Fuller (1955*a, b*) reported the presence of coliform bacteria and fecal streptococci in many frozen fruits, fruit-juice concentrates, and frozen vegetables. Stock cultures of *Escherichia coli, Streptococcus faecalis,* and *S. faecalis* var. *liquefaciens* survived in orange concentrate stored at −10°F. (−23.3°C.) for 147 days.

For more information see Brady, Hoover, and Tucker (1949); Mackintosh, Vail, and Filinger (1949).

Drying. The preservation of foods by drying or dehydration is of ancient origin. Although the process was not employed to any extent at first, it is now of great industrial importance. Practically every type of food is now prepared in dehydrated form, including nuts, vegetables, fruits, eggs, milk, fish, meats, and soups.

Dehydrated foods are probably never sterile. In this respect they differ from most canned foods. Therefore, it is of the utmost importance to prevent entrance into such foods of organisms which are capable of producing food poisoning. This applies especially to the toxigenic forms of *Clostridium botulinum* and certain strains of *Staphylococcus aureus.* Dehydrated foods should also be free from certain intestinal forms likely to be pathogenic to man when taken by mouth, e.g., members of the genera *Salmonella* and *Shigella.* The bacterial count of dried foods should be reasonably low to avoid decomposition or development of undesirable flavors during the period of reconstitution.

To prevent the formation of bacterial toxins in food or the development of organisms pathogenic to man, Haines and Elliot (1944) reported that the product should be dried at a temperature at which significant bacterial growth is unlikely to occur. They concluded that 50°C. was the minimum temperature below which dehydration should not be carried out. Where some heating below this temperature was unavoidable, owing to loss of quality in the product, the period of such heating should not exceed 4 hr. They found that bacterial growth did not occur in foods when the water content was below 15 per cent.

Dehydration of foods is a valuable procedure for several important reasons. Dried foods may be easily preserved for future use. This means that certain foods may be utilized over longer periods of time rather than for only a short season of the year. Dehydration greatly reduces the bulk of a product, conserves space, and facilitates handling. This is a decided advantage from the standpoint of transportation costs. Most of the dehydrated products, if properly prepared, are very good substitutes for fresh foods, being detected from the normal product with difficulty.

Dried foods do not require sterilization or the maintenance of sterile conditions during preparation. They are more economical to use since no waste is involved. Only that amount necessary for use at one time need be prepared.

The use of dehydrated foods also presents several decided disadvantages. Dried products require a long soaking period to restore the water lost by evaporation. The period required for rehydration varies with different foods. If this is not carefully done, the results are likely to be unsatisfactory. Sometimes dehydrated foods become infested with insects owing to improper packaging or handling. Sometimes dried foods become moistened, with the result that conditions become favorable for the growth of bacteria, yeasts, and molds. This applies more especially to the hygroscopic foods, i.e., those which readily absorb moisture from the air.

For more information see Vaughn (1951).

Preservatives. Sometimes chemicals are added to foods to preserve them. These act either by killing the organisms or by merely preventing them from multiplying.

An ideal antiseptic would be one that killed microorganisms or prevented them from multiplying without producing any harmful physiological effect. Apparently such a compound is not yet known. All the commonly used preservatives exert some physiological action on the human body and, unless employed in minute amounts, may produce harmful effects.

The inorganic chemicals commonly employed include boric acid and borates, nitric acid and nitrates, nitrous acid and nitrites, sulfurous acid and sulfites.

Boric acid is a weak antiseptic, saturated solutions being unable to destroy bacteria. However, it does prevent the growth of most bacteria and is used sometimes to preserve butter.

The color of fresh, unheated muscle tissue is due to the presence of a red pigment known as myohemoglobin or myoglobin. This pigment is an integral part of the tissue that does not circulate in the blood stream.

Sodium nitrate and small amounts of sodium nitrite are usually added to salt solutions used for the pickling of meats. The nitrate was believed to react with the hemoglobin of the meat to produce nitric oxide hemoglobin. It is now known that the nitrite reacts with the myohemoglobin of muscle to produce nitric oxide myohemoglobin according to the reaction.

$$\text{NO} + \text{myohemoglobin} \rightarrow \text{nitric oxide myohemoglobin}$$

Some bacteria present on meat are able to reduce nitrate to nitrite. The same or other species produce small amounts of organic acids from the meat which convert the nitrate and nitrite to nitric and nitrous acids, respectively. The nitrous acid then reacts with the myohemoglobin to give nitric oxide myohemoglobin. An acid solution is necessary for the reaction to take place. This compound imparts a bright red color to un-heated cured meat, making it more attractive in appearance. The nitrite plays no part in producing cured flavor. Nitric oxide myohemoglobin, when heated to temperatures which coagulate proteins, becomes con-verted to nitric oxide myochromogen. This compound also is red and is one of the objects gained in curing meats. The nitrate and nitrite also produce an inhibitory effect on the growth of bacteria likely to be pres-ent on meat. Nitrite has been shown to be more effective than nitrate.

Hall (1935) recommended a new method for pickling meats. He used a pickling solution containing salt, nitrate, nitrite, and a small amount of citric acid or some other appropriate acid. The purpose of the acid is to convert the nitrate and nitrite to nitric and nitrous acids. The nitrous acid is then capable of reacting with myohemoglobin to produce the at-tractive red color.

For more information see Castellani and Niven (1955).

Sulfurous acid and sulfites are added to alcoholic liquids, especially wines. The addition of sulfite to greenish, discolored meat restores the original red color to the product. It enjoyed great popularity as an addi-tion to hamburger prepared from old scrap meat. Its use for this purpose is prohibited by law.

The organic chemicals added to foods include benzoic acid and benzo-ates, salicylic acid and salicylates, formaldehyde, creosote, and sorbic acid.

Benzoic acid and benzoates are used for the preservation of vegetables. A small amount of sodium benzoate is sometimes added to tomato catchup. Salicylic acid and salicylates are used as preservatives of fruits and vegetables. Formaldehyde was formerly used as a preservative of milk, but its use for this purpose is forbidden by law. The value of wood smoke in the curing of meats is due to the presence of a small amount of creosote furnished by the burning wood. Sorbic acid is an effective inhibitor of gaseous fermentation by yeasts, which are responsible for large economic losses in brine-cured cucumbers due to bloater (hollow cucumber) formation. Costilow (1957) and Costilow et al. (1957) re-ported that sorbic acid inhibits the growth of yeasts, molds, and many bacteria but does not interfere with the growth of the desirable lactic acid bacteria.

For more information see Robinson and Hills (1959).

High Osmotic Pressures. Some foods are protected from attack by or-ganisms in the presence of appreciable amounts of moisture. This applies to those foods which contain high concentrations of sugar or salt. It is generally stated that these compounds act entirely by osmosis or the withdrawal of water from the cell. This causes a shrinkage of the proto-plasm followed by death of the cell.

The preserving action of salt may involve more than its dehydrating action. Magnesium sulfate has a greater dehydrating effect on proteins than common salt, yet it is less efficient in preventing growth of *Staphylococcus aureus*.

Bacteria capable of resisting high osmotic pressures are called halophilic (salt-loving) organisms. Practically no multiplication occurs in salt concentrations of 25 per cent or higher. A strength of 10 per cent markedly inhibits the growth of the great majority of bacterial species. The pathogenic or disease-producing bacteria are less resistant to strong saline solutions than the saprophytic forms. Cane sugar in the concentration of 60 to 70 per cent usually prevents growth of all types of microorganisms. Occasionally molds may be seen growing on the surface of a closed jar of jelly or bottle of sirup. This is caused by the evaporation of water, which, not being able to escape, condenses back on the surface of the jelly or sirup to produce a layer of less concentrated sugar solution. Some molds are capable of multiplying in this weak sugar solution.

Bacteria are not so sensitive to osmotic changes as are cells of higher plants and animals. For this reason solutions having extremely high osmotic pressure must be used either to kill bacteria or to prevent their multiplication.

BACTERIOLOGY OF MEAT

The presence of living organisms in the tissues and blood of healthy animals is still a controversial issue. Some investigators have reported the presence of organisms in living tissues; others have not been able to verify such findings. Burn (1934) and Jensen and Hess (1941) believed that the invasion of tissues by bacteria was agonal and post mortem rather than ante mortem.

Autolysis of Tissues. Frozen or cold-storage meats can be kept for long periods without showing any signs of spoilage. On the other hand, meats kept at higher temperatures (chilled) show spoilage in much shorter periods. The changes result from the action of autolytic enzymes normally present in meat and those elaborated by the contaminating organisms. Proteins are first hydrolyzed to amino acids, then putrefied with the liberation of bad odors. A short action of the proteolytic enzymes is beneficial in tenderizing meats; a prolonged action will result in decomposition and putrefaction.

Halleck, Ball, and Stier (1958) reported that the predominating organisms found on fresh meat stored at 1.1 to 3.3°C. consisted of nonpigmented *Achromobacter-Pseudomonas* types and lactobacilli during the first two weeks, and *P. fluorescens* type during the latter part of the storage period.

Under ordinary conditions, beef is held at 2.2 to 3.3°C. for 5 days after slaughter before it is released. If the meat is to be ripened to increase tenderness and flavor, it is stored at low temperatures for longer periods. According to Jensen (1954), beef held at the following temperatures and times shows the same degree of tenderness:

21 days at 1.1°C.
8 days at 4.4°C.
5 days at 8.3°C.
3 days at 15.6°C.

Meats are also tenderized by the use of enzyme preparations. Many proteolytic enzymes are employed, including ficin from figs, bromelin from fresh pineapple juice, papain from papaya, etc. The enzymes are allowed to act until the meat shows the proper degree of tenderness. The meat is then heated to destroy the enzyme; otherwise it tends to become mushy and butyrous in texture during culinary heating. Meat in this condition is organoleptically undesirable.

Enzymes are not employed in tenderizing hams or ready-to-eat hams. Ready-to-eat hams are cooked in the smokehouse, and tenderized hams are heated in the smokehouse to an inside temperature of 58.3°C. or higher.

Bacterial Counts of Meats. The sanitary quality of meats cannot be judged by the bacterial counts. There appears to be no correlation between bacterial population and sanitary quality of meat. It is not so much the numbers as it is the kinds of organisms that determine the sanitary quality. Samples showing high counts of saprophytic organisms may produce no harmful effects when ingested; others showing low counts may produce harmful effects. Apparently the best criteria for judging the quality of meat are appearance, feel, and smell. This is sometimes referred to as the organoleptic test.

Bacterial Flora of Meats. Both aerobic and anaerobic organisms are concerned in the spoilage of meats. The aerobic organisms act first and create an environment favorable to the growth of the anaerobes. Then the anaerobes attack the proteins and liberate foul-smelling compounds. The process of putrefaction in nature involves the action of both aerobes and anaerobes, but the changes that occur are chiefly anaerobic in character.

The organisms concerned in meat spoilage may be grouped as follows: (1) Gram-positive, aerobic, spore-bearing rods; (2) Gram-negative, aerobic, non-spore-forming rods; (3) cocci; (4) anaerobes; and (5) molds and yeasts.

The Gram-positive, aerobic, spore-bearing group includes *Bacillus subtilis, B. cereus, B. megaterium, B. pumilus,* etc. These organisms are saprophytes and are capable of liquefying gelatin rapidly.

The Gram-negative, aerobic, non-spore-forming group includes *Escherichia coli, Proteus vulgaris, P. mirabilis, Aerobacter cloacae, Pseudomonas aeruginosa, P. fluorescens, P. putrefaciens,* etc. The members of the genus *Proteus* are very proteolytic in their activities and are capable of initiating some of the changes produced by anaerobes.

Some of the cocci which have been isolated from meats include *Micrococcus candidus, M. caseolyticus, M. conglomeratus, M. flavus, M. freudenreichii, M. varians, Sarcina aurantiaca,* and *Staphylococcus aureus.* All are Gram-positive.

The most pronounced changes on meats are produced by the anaerobic spore-bearing rods. Some of the anaerobes isolated from fresh and spoiled meats are *Clostridium aerofoetidum, Cl. bifermentans, Cl. histolyticum, Cl. lentoputrescens,* and *Cl. sporogenes.* These organisms are responsible for putrefactive changes on proteins, resulting in the liberation of foul-smelling compounds.

The molds that have been found growing on meat belong to the genera *Alternaria, Aspergillus, Cladosporium, Monilia, Mucor, Penicillium,* and *Sporotrichium.* Those belonging to the genera *Mucor* and *Penicillium* have been isolated with greater frequency than any of the others. Spores of such molds are commonly present in air. Several species of yeasts have been isolated from meat kept under refrigeration.

Molds are generally aerobic, growing on or near the surface of meat. Most molds produce pigments which impart discolorations to meat. Molds may be removed by wiping or trimming the surface layer with a knife. If molds are permitted to grow without being checked, they may impart unpleasant odors and flavors to meat.

Dried Beef. Meat is dried in order that it may be preserved for long periods of time. Dried beef is prepared in the following manner: Beef sets are obtained from the carcasses of freshly slaughtered animals and kept under refrigeration until ready to be used. The meat is usually cured in barrels or in tierces. In barrel curing, about 4½ gal. of pickle is used for each 100 lb. of meat. In tierce curing, about 300 lb. of meat and 8 to 12 gal. of pickle are added to each container. The length of the pickling period varies, depending upon the temperature. Sets are usually cured in 75 to 120 days.

Beef ham sets must be well cured; otherwise decomposition may occur during the drying and smoking operation. Beef hams increase in weight about 8 per cent in the curing process. The pickle used is often plain brine and saltpeter, but frequently sugar and a small amount of sodium nitrite are added. A typical pickling solution has the following composition:

	Parts
Sodium chloride (NaCl)	25
Sodium nitrate (NaNO₃)	0.05
Sodium nitrite (NaNO₂)	0.10
Sugar (sucrose)	4
Water, to make	100

After the meat is cured, it is soaked well to remove an excessive amount of salt. The soaking water is usually maintained at a temperature of 60 to 80°F. (16 to 27°C.). Two changes of water are usually employed. The length of the soaking period depends upon the kind of meat, nature of the pickle, length of time in the pickle, etc. Overcured, very salty, and hard-cured meats are soaked longer than mild-cured meats. The soaking period is usually 12 to 24 hr. Meats are soaked for shorter periods in summer than in winter.

The meat is now ready to be dried or dried and smoked. The meat is handled in a dry room heated by means of steam coils or by a hot-air furnace and provided with good air circulation to remove moist air. By this method, the drying may be completed in 5 to 9 days. The room is kept at a temperature of 135°F. for the first two days, then dropped to 115°F. for the remainder of the drying period. Sometimes both drying and smoking are practiced. Wood smoke is produced and distributed in smokehouses in conjunction with heat and air circulation to preserve, color, and flavor cured meats. Smoke is produced by burning wood or sawdust. Hardwoods, such as hickory and maple, are used extensively and impart very desirable flavors to cured meats. Preservation is due not only to desiccation but to absorption of gases and fumes of creosote, pyroligneous acid (a mixture of acetic acid, acetone, methyl alcohol, etc.), and other antiseptic substances found in wood smoke. Thorough drying of the product is essential.

In the final operation, dried beef is chilled at a temperature of 34°F. (1°C.) to facilitate slicing. The outside slices show less moisture than the center pieces. The sliced product is now ready for packaging and distribution.

For more information on meats see Eddy and Kitchell (1959), Jensen (1949, 1954).

Greening of Cured Meat Products. Cured meats and meat products are subject to a type of bacterial spoilage in which the cured meat pigment is oxidized to a greenish color. According to Niven, Buettner, and Evans (1954), the organisms involved are a group of catalase-negative, salt-tolerant heterofermentative lactobacilli which grow at low temperatures and oxidize certain substrates in the meat with the formation of hydrogen peroxide. The green color results from the interaction of hydrogen peroxide with the cured meat pigment.

For more information see Niven and Evans (1957).

BACTERIOLOGY OF FISH

Spoilage of fish is caused largely by bacteria. The kinds of bacteria found on fish and their characteristics are of importance in improving methods of handling and preserving fish products.

It has been reaffirmed repeatedly that the flesh and internal organs of healthy fish are free from bacteria. However, the external slime and the digestive tracts show the presence of many bacteria both in kinds and numbers.

The organisms encountered most frequently on the external surfaces are members of the genera *Achromobacter*, *Corynebacterium*, *Flavobacterium*, *Micrococcus*, *Mycoplana*, and *Pseudomonas*. To a lesser extent, other genera included *Bacillus*, *Clostridium*, *Proteus*, and *Sarcina*.

Nearly all marine bacteria associated with fish are facultative psychrophilic forms having a temperature growth range from −7.5 to 30°C. Of 71 organisms isolated by one investigator, 10 grew at −7.5°C., 22 at −50°C., and 65 at 0°C. Fish spoilage proceeds about twice as fast at 2.8°C. as at −0.3°C. One of the best methods of retarding fish spoilage is to store it at a temperature as close as possible to the freezing point of the muscle (−1.1°C.). Undoubtedly one of the reasons why fish usually spoils more rapidly than meat under storage conditions is that the former is richly contaminated with psychrophiles, whereas the latter is more likely to be contaminated with a higher proportion of mesophiles.

As is true for meat, bacterial counts are valueless as a measure of the degree of spoilage in fresh cod fillets (Castell, Anderson, and Pivnick, 1948). They found a close correlation between the number of psychrophilic Gram-negative bacteria on fillets and their keeping time in cold storage. This correlation degenerated into a "general tendency" which could not always be applied in individual samples if the counts included all organisms growing on plates incubated at 25°C.

For more information see Tarr (1954).

Reddening of Salted Fish. Members of the genus *Halobacterium* are obligate halophilic (salt-loving) rod-shaped bacteria which are highly pleomorphic. They require at least 12 per cent salt for growth and will live even in saturated brine solutions. Motile species have polar flagella; some species are nonmotile. They are Gram-negative. Organisms are generally chromogenic, producing non-water-soluble carotenoid pigments which vary in shade from colorless to orange or even brilliant red. Most species produce a reddening of salted fish where untreated solar salt is used. They are abundant in tidal pools along shores of tropical seas. They redden the water in the pools where solar salt is produced as soon as the brine is concentrated to 18 per cent salt. The organisms are commonly found in untreated solar salt.

For more information see Anderson (1954).

BACTERIOLOGY OF SWEETENED CONDENSED MILK

Sweetened condensed milk is prepared in the following manner: Clean, sweet milk is pasteurized at a temperature of 80 to 90°C. for about 1 min.

to inactivate the enzymes and kill most of the bacteria in the milk which may cause undesirable physical and chemical changes. Cane sugar is added as dry crystals or in the form of a boiled, concentrated solution. The preparation is heated under reduced pressure so that it will boil at a temperature of 50 to 60°C. The milk is reduced to almost one-third of its original volume. The final product contains about 25 per cent water, 40 per cent cane sugar, at least 8 per cent milk fat, and 28 per cent total milk solids including fat. The evaporated and cooled milk is transferred to sterile containers and capped.

Sweetened condensed milk is not sterilized before being placed in cans. The increased osmotic pressure of the preparation, due to the added sugar, is sufficient to prevent multiplication of most organisms. For this reason, only a small percentage of cans of sweetened milk are ever sterile. Occasionally some cans show evidence of attack by organisms. The ends of the cans become blown, owing to the fact that the organisms produce gas from the added sucrose and from the lactose normally present in the milk.

Organisms in Milk. The organisms which have been isolated include micrococci, streptococci, aerobic gas producers (*Escherichia coli*), aerobic spore formers (*Bacillus subtilis*), thermophilic bacteria, anaerobic forms, and yeasts.

The cocci have been encountered in practically every sample of sweetened condensed milk. These organisms are able to survive the temperatures employed in its preparation. Anaerobic organisms cause little trouble, being rarely found in sweetened condensed milk. Coliform organisms are occasionally encountered but offer little trouble. The medium is unfavorable and the cells ultimately die. Bacilli of the aerobic, spore-bearing types are almost always found in both normal and decomposed cans of milk. Some of these organisms are actively proteolytic and may initiate changes on the milk proteins. It is questionable whether they ever produce swells in cans of sweetened condensed milk. The cans contain an insufficient amount of oxygen and too much sugar for active growth to occur. Thermophilic bacteria are often present. They are neither actively proteolytic nor gas producers and, therefore, play no part in the peptonization and fermentation of canned milk.

Yeasts are believed to be the most common organisms causing spoilage of sweetened condensed milk. Many of these organisms are active fermenters, attacking the sucrose with the liberation of gas. This results in the cans having a blown appearance. Not all species found in milk are capable of attacking sucrose. Unless the sugar is fermented, the presence of yeasts does not mean that abnormal changes have taken place. Even the fermentative types grow with difficulty, owing to the fact that the environmental conditions are not favorable. The sources of yeasts in canned milk are (1) contamination of the original fresh milk, (2) contamination of the air of the cannery, and (3) contamination of the added sugar. It is not believed that any of the yeasts found in milk are harmful to man. Decomposed milk is objectionable but practically free from any toxic substances.

BACTERIOLOGY OF EGGS

An egg shell is about $\frac{1}{60}$ in. in thickness and composed largely of calcium carbonate. It is a porous structure, the pores being sufficiently large to permit passage of gases and microscopic solid particles. When fertile eggs are incubated, these pores are the means by which air passes through the shell to furnish oxygen to the developing chick embryo.

Microbial Contamination of Eggs. Normally the oviduct of the hen is sterile, and therefore the shell and internal contents of the egg are also free from organisms. As the egg leaves the oviduct at a temperature of 107°F. (41.7°C.), the shell is completely filled with yolk, white, and shell membranes. During cooling, the contents shrink and air is drawn through the 6000 to 8000 shell pores to form the air cell. Further transpiration of gas occurs as the egg ages.

Eggs are not always laid in clean surroundings. The shell may be soiled with blood, manure, feathers, nest material, or broken eggs. These substances are most likely contaminated with bacteria, which may be drawn through the shell as the egg cools. Studies have shown that from 5 to 12 per cent of all eggs are internally contaminated within a few hours after they are laid. Whether they eventually rot from bacterial causes depends on the kinds and concentrations of organisms, the natural bactericidal properties of the egg, environment, and time.

Function of Shell Membrane. The shell membrane covers the inside surface of the egg shell. It acts as a physical barrier to entrance of bacteria through the shell. This is probably the sole protective function of the membrane, since Kraft, Elliott, and Brant (1958) found that it exerts no bactericidal activity against several types of bacteria known to be capable of causing spoilage in eggs.

Washing Eggs. From 10 to 25 per cent of eggs produced under average farm conditions are soiled at the time of gathering. Under poor management the per cent may be much higher. Even under good conditions the numbers may run from 5 to 10 per cent. Soiled eggs have a lower market value than clean eggs. Therefore the washing of soiled eggs has become a well-established practice.

During washing, bacteria are carried through the shells and eventually penetrate into the egg white and yolk. Thus, the problem of producing and marketing clean, uncontaminated eggs is primarily one of sanitation.

Wet-cleaning operations are more desirable than dry methods. They result in laborsaving, less breakage, more thorough cleaning, and less spoilage if sanitizers are used.

Liquids which have been used for washing eggs include water, $N/10$ sulfuric acid, $N/10$ sodium hydroxide, water glass (1:12), soap, sodium hypochlorite solution (1:100), formalin, alcohol (70 per cent), and detergents or sanitizers.

It is obvious that the washing method cannot affect the incidence of eggs contaminated before they reach that stage, but the use of a good cleaning method should reduce the proportion of eggs which become contaminated during the washing process.

It is generally believed that considerable numbers of eggs are contaminated during improper washing operations. Bacteria and molds contained in the filth removed from the dirty eggs are dispersed in the washing liquid. If the solution is cooler than the internal temperature of the egg, negative pressure is obtained and organisms enter the egg through the pores. Contamination may also occur at a later time if the eggs are removed from a cold room to a warm or humid atmosphere. Condensation forms on the shell and motile cells may enter through the pores.

For more information see Bean and MacLaury (1959), Botwright (1953), Clements and Winter (1956), Winter et al. (1955).

Bactericidal Property of Egg White. The egg seems to have the ability in an appreciable number of cases to destroy completely the invading microorganisms. This is particularly true of the shell membrane and the albumin.

The existence in the whites of eggs of the bactericidal substance *lysozyme* is well established, and it may be assumed with safety that the decrease in the number of contaminated whites on storage is due to the action of this bactericidal agent.

The shell membrane has been shown to contain a substance that exhibited a bactericidal effect on *Pseudomonas aeruginosa*. It appeared that the shell membrane might be a much more important agent in preventing contamination of the interior of the egg than the so-called mucoid layer covering the shell.

For more information see Forsythe, Ayres, and Radlo (1953); Miller and Crawford (1953).

Preservation of Eggs. A number of methods are employed for the preservation of eggs: (1) cold storage, (2) freezing, (3) drying, (4) immersion in sodium silicate solution (water glass), (5) packing in brine or sawdust, (6) coating with petroleum jelly, (7) wrapping in oiled paper, (8) coating with paraffin, (9) immersion in lime water (solution of calcium hydroxide), and (10) dipping in light paraffin oil.

In the cold-storage process the eggs are kept at a temperature of about $-6°C$. If the temperature goes below this point, a nonreversible change takes place in the albumin, preventing the egg from being restored to its normal transparent condition.

Frozen eggs are kept at a temperature of about $-18°C$. or lower until needed. They are used in large quantities by candymakers, bakers, and egg-noodle and macaroni manufacturers, and in other industries. The eggs are removed from the shell, placed in large metal containers, and frozen. Often the whites and yolks are separated because they may be used for different purposes. They are usually cheaper than fresh eggs because they may be prepared during the months of high production.

Bacterial destruction in frozen egg products was greater at or above $0°F$. ($-17.7°C$.) than at lower temperatures.

Eggs may be dried unseparated or first separated into whites and yolks and then dried. Dried yolks, whites, and unseparated eggs are used to a considerable extent in prepared cake and doughnut flours, in ice creams, in macaroni and noodles, and in bakery products, such as meringue and marshmallows. Dried eggs have good keeping qualities if kept dry and cool. However, the presence of a small amount of moisture and a warm atmosphere may be sufficient to permit the growth of organisms and cause spoilage in a short time. It is desirable, therefore, to store dried eggs in a cool place, protected from an excessive amount of moisture.

The other methods used for preserving eggs are designed to prevent the passage of air (oxygen) through the pores of the shell and into the eggs. Regardless of which one of these procedures is followed, the eggs must be kept under cold conditions to prevent decomposition by the enzymes normally present in the egg.

For more information see Funk (1955).

Disease Organisms in Eggs. As stated above, the oviduct of the hen is normally sterile, which means that the shell and internal contents of the egg are also free from organisms. In some instances the ovaries and oviduct may become infected with members of the genus *Salmonella*, and the bacteria may be deposited inside of the egg. More frequently, however, the egg becomes contaminated after it is laid. The salmonellae are deposited on the shell from the intestinal tract of the hen and from other sources in the environment.

Organisms in the pores of the shell are isolated from the egg contents by the shell membranes, which act as mechanical rather than as bactericidal barriers. However, the membranes can be breached by the organisms, leading to extensive bacterial multiplication in the egg contents.

Members of the *Salmonella* which have been isolated from eggs include *S. gallinarum, S. schottmuelleri, S. thompson,* and *S. typhimurium.*

For more information see Frank and Wright (1956); Hobbs and Smith (1955); Jordan (1954, 1956a, b); Newell, Hobbs, and Wallace (1955); Stokes, Osborne, and Bayne (1956); Wright and Frank (1956).

ANTIBIOTICS IN FOODS

Food preservation in canning is generally achieved by killing the microbial flora with heat. The extent of the heating depends largely upon the pH of the product. Acid foods having a pH below 4.5 are conventionally processed in boiling water under atmospheric pressure. The heat-resistant spores likely to be present are, in general, readily destroyed during the heat-treatment or will not germinate under such strongly acid conditions.

However, with meats, vegetables, and other low-acid foods, the problem is different. Medium and nonacid foods having a pH above 4.5 are conventionally processed under high pressures and temperatures. Even then the procedure is not always successful. Spores associated with some food products are among the most heat-resistant bodies known and make absolute sterility almost impossible to achieve without impairing the quality of the canned product or rendering it unfit for human consumption.

Because of the limitations of the thermal processing procedure for both nonacid and low-acid foods, a number of antibiotics have been tested in the hope that some might be found capable of destroying or reducing the thermal resistance of spores and thereby eliminate the need for excessive heat-treatment. These include aureomycin, bacitracin, ciliomycin, circulin, gramicidin, neomycin, nisin, penicillin, streptin, streptomycin, terramycin, subtilin, etc.

Silvestrini, Anderson, and Snyder (1958) reported that the keeping quality of poultry meat was greatly prolonged by (1) the use of 10 p.p.m. aureomycin in a dip solution during processing; or (2) the feeding of a mixture containing 1000 gm. aureomycin per ton of feed to broilers for 1, 2, or 3 days prior to slaughter; or (3) the addition of 500 gm. aureomycin per ton of drinking water for 1 day prior to slaughter. Bacterial spoilage appeared to start in the visceral cavity tissue, followed by spread through the muscle tissue of the skin.

Jay et al. (1957a, b) employed aureomycin in relatively low concentration to prolong the keeping time of beef in carcass or cut form.

Southcott et al. (1958) found aureomycin of value in the preservation of fish fillets.

For more information see Anderson et al. (1958); Barnes and Shrimpton (1959); Boyd et al. (1956); Carey (1956); Castell and Greenough (1957); Castell, Greenough, and Jenkin (1957); Durbin (1956, 1957); Hirsch (1953); Kaufmann, Ordal, and El-Bisi (1954); Wrenshall and McMahan (1956).

FOOD POISONING

Food poisoning refers to the ingestion of food contaminated either with harmful bacteria or with certain soluble excretory products known as toxins. It does not include the toxications which follow the consumption of noxious plants (mushrooms), poisonous fish (mussels), or decomposed foods containing chemical poisons (arsenic, lead, fluorides), or idiosyncrasies associated with certain plant and animal poisons.

At one time food poisoning was believed to be caused by the consumption of decomposed food containing certain chemical compounds known as ptomaines. The term is taken from the Greek and means a dead body. Ptomaines are produced in putrefied meat and other proteinaceous foods. They are basic substances and belong to the group of compounds known as amines. They result chiefly from the decarboxylation of amino acids. A typical reaction is the following:

$$CH_3 \cdot CHNH_2 \cdot COOH \rightarrow CH_3 \cdot CH_2NH_2 + CO_2$$
Alanine   Ethylamine

The amino acid alanine loses carbon dioxide and is converted into ethylamine, a ptomaine. This reaction occurs only at a pH below 7.0 and when putrefaction is in an advanced stage. Ptomaines are poisonous when injected into the tissues, but there appears to be very little evidence that they produce any toxicity when taken by mouth. The ptomaine theory of intoxication is a misconception.

Presence of Bacteria in Foods. The fact that bacteria are present in foods does not mean necessarily that they are harmful. Many saprophytic forms can attack proteins and release ptomaines during the later stages of decomposition. However, most bacteria which are capable of putrefying proteins are harmless when taken by mouth. Facultative and anaerobic species normally present in the intestinal tract of man, and capable of producing putrefactions, are harmless when ingested with food.

Food-poisoning Organisms. There are four genera of bacteria chiefly responsible for true food poisoning. These are (1) *Staphylococcus* (*S. aureus*); (2) *Salmonella* (*S. enteritidis, S. typhimurium*, etc.); (3) *Clostridium* (*Cl. botulinum*, several types, all nonovolytic, *Cl. parabotulinum*, several types, all ovolytic); (4) *Streptococcus*, α type (*S. faecalis, S. faecalis* var. *liquefaciens, S. faecalis* var. *zymogenes*). In addition, *Escherichia coli* and *Proteus vulgaris* have been reported as being responsible for occasional outbreaks of food poisoning.

Staphylococcus aureus. Certain strains of *S. aureus*, under favorable conditions, produce not only exotoxins (hematoxin, dermatoxin, lethal toxin, etc.) but also a potent enterotoxin. The ingestion of foods containing the enterotoxin gives rise to an intoxication, but the symptoms are generally mild. Death rarely occurs.

The organism is widely distributed in nature (Fig. 217). It is found on the nasal mucous membrane and skin (hair follicle); in carbuncles, boils, pyemia, osteomyelitis, and infected cuts or breaks in the skin; and in foods.

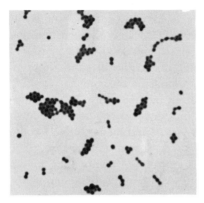

FIG. 217. *Staphylococcus aureus,* an enterotoxin-producing strain.

The majority of people are susceptible to the enterotoxin, being made ill with characteristic symptoms. After ingestion of contaminated foods, symptoms appear in about 3 hr., but the range is from 1 to 6 hr., depending upon dosage and susceptibilty. The symptoms are nausea, vomiting, abdominal cramps, and diarrhea. In more severe cases, disability is great. The patient is weak and prostrate and may go into shock. Blood may be passed in either the vomitus or stools. Symptoms usually begin to disappear in a few hours; most victims recover completely in a few days. Body temperature may be subnormal.

In pure culture, toxin production occurs in 4 to 6 hr. Toxin is produced in the temperature range of 15.5 to 49°C. If foods are held at temperatures below 15°C., toxin is not formed.

Some strains of S. *aureus* can liquefy gelatin; others cannot. Stone (1935, 1943) believed that there was a correlation between gelatin liquefaction and enterotoxin production. He developed a simple method for

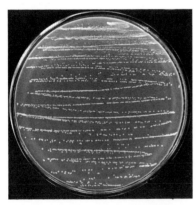
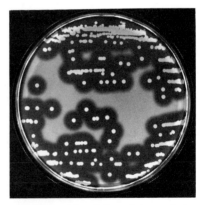

FIG. 218. Left, strain of *Staphylococcus aureus* not capable of liquefying gelatin; right, strain capable of liquefying gelatin. The gelatin agar plates were flooded with a solution of ammonium sulfate to precipitate the gelatin. Clear zones around the colonies indicate digestion of the gelatin by a gelatinase.

separating the gelatin-liquefying strains from the nonliquefiers. A nutrient gelatin agar plate was streaked with a loopful of a broth culture of the organism under examination and incubated at 37°C. for 24 hr. Then a strong solution of ammonium sulfate was poured over the surface of the plate. The ammonium sulfate precipitates protein (gelatin), giving the agar an opaque appearance. The gelatin in the area immediately surrounding each colony is digested, giving a clear agar (Fig. 218). A typical reaction shows clear zones around each colony, with the remainder of the agar appearing opaque. The test does not always show perfect correlation between toxigenicity and ability of a strain to liquefy gelatin.

Chapman (1948) improved and simplified the test by employing a gelatin agar medium containing mannitol, peptone, yeast extract, potassium phosphate, sodium chloride, and ammonium sulfate. Sodium chloride provides selective isolation of staphylococci, improves chromogenesis, and is essential for coagulation of blood. Yeast extract is more favorable for chromogenesis than beef extract. Ammonium sulfate is added directly to the medium for the Stone reaction.

For more information see Dack (1956), Evans and Niven (1950), Hussemann and Tanner (1949), and Jensen (1954).

Salmonella. Members of the *Salmonella* produce chiefly endotoxins. The organisms are ingested with contaminated food and reach the intestinal tract without being destroyed. They multiply in the intestines and liberate endotoxins after death and digestion of the cells (Fig. 219).

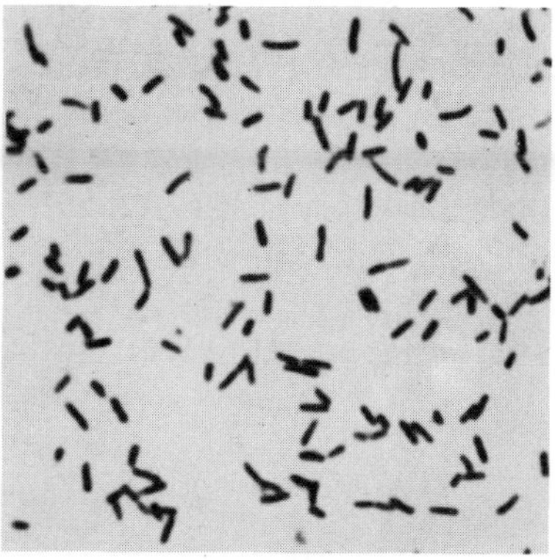

FIG. 219. *Salmonella enteritidis,* an organism that multiplies in the intestinal tract and produces food poisoning by the elaboration of an endotoxin.

Sufficient endotoxin to cause symptoms may be produced in from 6 to 12 hr. Infection is characterized by continued fever, involvement of the lymphoid tissue of the intestines, enlargement of the spleen, and sometimes rose spots on the trunk; it is usually accompanied by a diarrheal condition. Organisms may be present in the feces, urine, and blood. Recovery usually is complete within 2 to 4 days.

Some important species are S. *choleraesuis,* S. *enteritidis,* S. *hirschfeldii,* S. *paratyphi,* S. *schottmuelleri,* and S. *typhimurium.* The last organism probably occurs more frequently than any other species or type not confined to a specific host.

Salmonella species are disseminated in various ways. Rats and mice have been generally considered the main culprits in the spread of salmonellae. The organisms have been recovered from a number of foods. They are found on the shell and in the contents of clean fresh eggs. After processing to egg powder, a high percentage of the samples show the presence of the bacteria. Also, under faulty operating conditions, the organisms may multiply on the processing equipment.

Poultry as it is processed is generally heavily exposed to *Salmonella* contamination. Infections may result from consumption of insufficiently or improperly cooked fowl.

Pork products purchased in the open market showed the presence of *Salmonella*. Evidence indicates that this is not the result of infected hogs on the farm but rather of dissemination of the organisms in the abattoirs. This appears to apply equally well to cattle. It has been shown that the tools used in the preparation of meat and meat products may become contaminated, from which source the organisms may be easily disseminated into other products.

Of the many possible modes of dissemination of the salmonellae, the distribution of these potential pathogens by the egg, poultry, and meat-processing industries appears to be of high importance.

For more information see Clarenburg (1953); Dack (1955); Floyd and Blakemore (1954); Galton, Harless, and Hardy (1955); Galton et al. (1955); Hardy and Galton (1955); McCullough (1958); Olitzky et al. (1956).

Clostridium. Members of the *Cl. botulinum* and *Cl. parabotulinum* species produce their toxic effects by the secretion of powerful soluble exotoxins. The organisms never infect man under natural conditions.

The spores of *Cl. botulinum* and *Cl. parabotulinum* are found in the soil and are likely to be present on many kinds of foods. Since the organisms are anaerobic, the spores will not germinate unless the free oxygen in the environment is almost completely removed. If the spores are not destroyed during heat processing, conditions are generally created which favor their germination (Fig. 220). The vegetative cells then secrete a powerful exotoxin in the food.

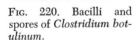

FIG. 220. Bacilli and spores of *Clostridium botulinum.*

The mere tasting of such food may be sufficient to cause death. The toxin can pass through the stomach wall and intestines unchanged, differing in this respect from most bacterial toxins.

Symptoms usually develop suddenly and consist of gastrointestinal pain, headache, diarrhea or constipation, prostration, and several types of paralyses of the central nervous system. Death occurs by cardiac or respiratory paralysis, usually in 3 to 7 days. Severity of symptoms depends on the amount of toxin ingested.

Since the toxins are destroyed by heat, freshly cooked foods are safe.

Nonsterile canned foods and certain meat products which are consumed cold may contain toxin. Commercial processing of foods in this country is generally adequate. Practically all cases of botulism result from the consumption of home-canned, insufficiently heated foods.

Spoiled canned foods or those which are suspicious of being spoiled should never be tasted. If the container is contaminated with *Clostridium*, sufficient toxin may be present in a minute portion of the food to cause death. The suspected food should not be fed to animals or chickens, as they may be highly susceptible. Such foods are best disposed of by thorough cooking to destroy the toxin.

For more information see Ball and Olson (1957), Dack (1956), Dewberry (1950), Dolman (1943), Frazier (1958), Hobbs (1953), Jensen (1954), Tanner and Tanner (1953).

REFERENCES

Anderson, G. W., N. A. Epps, E. S. Snyder, and S. J. Slinger: Comparative effectiveness of feeding aureomycin and dipping in an aureomycin solution as a means of preserving poultry meat, *Poultry Sci.*, 37:174, 1958.

Anderson, H.: The reddening of salted hides and fish, *Appl. Microbiol.*, 2:64, 1954.

Ball, C. O.: Processing food for sterilization, *Food Industries*, 19:44, 174, 338, 1947.

———— and F. C. W. Olson: "Sterilization in Food Technology: Theory, Practice, and Calculations," New York, McGraw-Hill Book Company, Inc., 1957.

Barnes, E. M., and D. H. Shrimpton: The effect of the tetracycline compounds on the storage life and microbiology of chilled eviscerated poultry, *J. Appl. Bact.*, 21:313, 1959.

Bean, K. C., and D. W. MacLaury: The bacterial contamination of hatching eggs and methods for its control, *Poultry Sci.*, 38:693, 1959.

Botwright, W. E.: Detergent-sanitizers for cleaning eggs, *Am. Egg Poultry Rev.*, February, 1953.

Boyd, J. W., H. M. Bluhm, C. R. Muirhead, and H. L. A. Tarr: Use of antibiotics for the preservation of fish and sea foods, *Am. J. Pub. Health*, 46:1531, 1956.

Brady, D. E., G. V. Hoover, and L. N. Tucker: Storage of frozen meats, poultry, eggs, fruits, and vegetables, *Missouri Univ. Agr. Exp. Sta. Research Bull.* 440, 1949.

Burn, C. G.: Experimental studies of postmortem bacterial invasion in animals, *J. Inf. Dis.*, 54:388, 395, 1934.

Carey, B. W.: The biochemistry of antibiotics on the bacteria associated with food spoilage, *Giornale di Microbiol.*, 2:233, 1956.

Castell, C. H., G. S. Anderson, and H. Pivnick: Relation of bacterial counts to quality of cod fillets, *J. Fish. Res. Bd. Can.*, 7:378, 1948.

———— and M. F. Greenough: I. Organisms responsible for odours produced during incipient spoilage of chilled fish muscle, *ibid.*, 14:617, 1957.

————, ————, and N. L. Jenkin: The action of *Pseudomonas* on fish muscle: 2. Musty and potato-like odours, *ibid.*, 14:775, 1957.

Castellani, A. G., and C. F. Niven, Jr.: Factors affecting the bacteriostatic action of sodium nitrite, *Appl. Microbiol.*, 3:154, 1955.

Chapman, G. H.: An improved Stone medium for the isolation and testing of food-poisoning staphylococci, *Food Res.*, 13:100, 1948.

Clarenburg, A.: Sources of contamination in outbreaks of food poisoning caused by *Salmonella* bacteria from meat in the Netherlands, *Proc. Soc. Appl. Bact.*, 16:10, 1953.

Clements, P., and A. R. Winter: The control of molds on shell treated eggs, *Poultry Sci.*, 35:1116, 1956.

Costilow, R. N.: Sorbic acid as a selective agent for cucumber fermentations. III. *Food Tech.*, 11:591, 1957.

———, F. M. Coughlin, E. K. Robbins, and W.-T. Hsu: II. Effect of sorbic acid on the yeast and lactic acid fermentations in brined cucumbers, *Appl. Microbiol.*, 5:373, 1957.

Dack, G. M.: Significance of enteric bacilli in foods, *Am. J. Pub. Health*, 45:1151, 1955.

———: "Food Poisoning," Chicago, University of Chicago Press, 1956.

Dewberry, E. B.: "Food Poisoning. Its Nature, History, and Causation. Measures for Its Prevention and Control," London, Leonard Hill, Ltd., 1950.

Dolman, C. E.: Bacterial food poisoning, *Can. J. Pub. Health*, 34:97, 205, 1943.

Durbin, C. G.: Antibiotics in food preservation, *Am. J. Pub. Health*, 46:1306, 1956.

———: Public health significance of antibiotics in foods, *J. Am. Vet. Med. Assoc.*, 130:280, 1957.

Eddy, B. P., and A. G. Kitchell: Cold-tolerant fermentative Gram-negative organisms from meat and other sources, *J. Appl. Bact.*, 22:57, 1959.

Evans, J. B., and C. F. Niven, Jr.: A comparative study of known food-poisoning staphylococci and related varieties, *J. Bact.*, 59:545, 1950.

Floyd, T. M., and C. F. Blakemore: Isolation of human enteric pathogens from ready-to-eat meats from butcher shops in Cairo, Egypt, *J. Infectious Diseases*, 94:30, 1954.

Forsythe, R. H., J. C. Ayres, and J. L. Radlo: Factors affecting the microbiological populations of shell eggs, *Food Technol.*, 7:49, 1953.

Frank, J. F., and G. W. Wright: The disinfection of eggs contaminated with *Salmonella typhi-murium*, *Can. J. Comp. Med.*, 20:406, 1956.

Frazier, W. C.: "Food Microbiology," New York, McGraw-Hill Book Company, Inc., 1958.

Funk, E. M.: Treating shell eggs to maintain quality, *Missouri Univ. Agr. Exp. Sta. Bull.* 659, 1955.

Galton, M. M., M. Harless, and A. V. Hardy: *Salmonella* isolations from dehydrated dog meals, *J. Am. Vet. Med. Assoc.*, 126:57, 1955.

———, D. C. Mackel, A. L. Lewis, W. C. Haire, and A. V. Hardy: Salmonellosis in poultry and poultry processing plants in Florida, *Am. J. Vet. Res.*, 16:132, 1955.

Haines, R. B., and E. M. L. Elliot: Some bacteriological aspects of dehydrated foods, *J. Hyg.*, 43:370, 1944.

Hall, L. A.: Acid cure for meat, *Food Industries*, 7:533, 1935.

Halleck, F. E., C. O. Ball, and E. F. Stier: Factors affecting quality of prepackaged meat. IV. *Food Tech.*, 12:197, 1958.

Hardy, A. V., and M. M. Galton: Salmonellosis. The role of food processing plants in the dissemination of *Salmonella*, *Am. J. Trop. Med. Hyg.*, 4:725, 1955.

Hartsell, S. E.: The longevity and behavior of pathogenic bacteria in frozen foods: the influence of plating media, *Am. J. Pub. Health*, 41:1072, 1951.

Hirsch, A.: Antibiotics in food preservation, *Proc. Soc. Appl. Bact.*, 16:100, 1953.

Hobbs, B. C.: "Food Poisoning and Food Hygiene," London, Edward Arnold & Co., 1953.

——— and M. E. Smith: Outbreaks of paratyphoid B fever associated with imported frozen egg. II. Bacteriology, *J. Appl. Bact.*, 18:471, 1955.

Hussemann, D. L., and F. W. Tanner: A comparison of strains of staphylococci isolated from foods, *Food Res.*, 14:91, 1949.

Jay, J. M., H. H. Weiser, and F. E. Deatherage: Further studies on the preservation of beef with chlortetracycline, *Food Tech.*, 11:563, 1957a.

———, ———, and ———: Studies on the mode of action of chlortetracycline in the preservation of beef, *Appl. Microbiol.*, 5:400, 1957b.

Jensen, L. B.: "Meat and Meat Foods," New York, The Ronald Press Company, 1949.

———: "Microbiology of Meats," Champaign, Ill., Garrard Press, 1954.

——— and W. R. Hess: A study of ham souring, *Food Res.*, 6:273, 1941.

Jordan, F. T. W.: The survival of *Salmonella gallinarum* in poultry carcasses, *British Vet. J.*, 110:387, 1954.

————: The transmission of *Salmonella gallinarum* through the egg, *Poultry Sci.*, **35**:1019, 1956*a;* The occurrence of *Salmonella gallinarum* in the feces of fowl typhoid, *ibid.*, **35**:1026, 1956*b.*

Kaufmann, O. W., Z. J. Ordal, and H. M. El-Bisi: The effect of several antibiotics on certain spore-forming organisms involved in food spoilage, *Food Res.*, **19**:483, 1954.

Kraft, A. A., L. E. Elliott, and A. W. Brant: The shell membrane as a barrier to bacterial penetration of eggs, *Poultry Sci.*, **37**:238, 1958.

Larkin, E. P., W. Litsky, and J. E. Fuller: Fecal streptococci in frozen foods. I. A bacteriological survey of some commercially frozen foods, *Appl. Microbiol.*, **3**:98, 1955*a;* III. Effect of freezing storage on *Escherichia coli, Streptococcus faecalis,* and *Streptococcus liquefaciens* inoculated orange concentrate, *ibid.*, **3**:104, 1955*b.*

Mackintosh, D. L., G. E. Vail, and G. A. Filinger: Preserving foods by freezing, *Kansas Agr. Exp. Sta. Circ.* 249, 1949.

McCullough, N. B.: Food in the epidemiology of salmonellosis, *Am. Dietetic Assoc.*, **34**:254, 1958.

Miller, W. A., and L. B. Crawford: Some factors influencing bacterial penetration of eggs, *Poultry Sci.*, **32**:303, 1953.

Newell, K. W., B. C. Hobbs, and E. J. G. Wallace: Paratyphoid fever associated with Chinese frozen whole egg, *Brit. Med. J.*, **2**:1296, 1955.

Niven, C. F., Jr., L. G. Buettner, and J. B. Evans: Thermal tolerance studies on the heterofermentative lactobacilli that cause greening of cured meat products, *Appl. Microbiol.*, **2**:26, 1954.

———— and J. B. Evans: *Lactobacillus viridescens* nov. species, a heterofermentative species that produces a green discoloration of cured meat pigments, *J. Bact.*, **73**:758, 1957.

Olitzky, I., A. M. Perri, M. A. Shiffman, and M. Werrin: Smoked fish as a vehicle of Salmonellosis, *Pub. Health Rep.*, **71**:773, 1956.

Oser, B. L.: How foods spoil, *Food Ind.*, **18**:1683, 1946.

Robinson, J. F., and C. H. Hills: Preservation of fruit products by sodium sorbate and mild heat, *Food Technol.*, **13**:251, 1959.

Silvestrini, D. A., G. W. Anderson, and E. S. Snyder: Chlortetracycline as related to the microbiology and preservation of poultry meat, *Poultry Sci.*, **37**:179, 1958.

Sognefest, P., G. L. Hays, E. Wheaton, and H. A. Benjamin: Effect of pH on thermal process requirements of canned foods, *Food Res.*, **13**:400, 1948.

Southcott, B. A., E. G. Baker, J. W. Boyd, and H. L. A. Tarr: Comparative effectiveness of tetracycline antibiotics for fish preservation, *Food Tech.*, **12**:108, 1958.

Spiegelberg, C. H.: *Clostridium pasteurianum* associated with spoilage of an acid canned fruit, *Food Res.*, **5**:115, 1940*a;* Some factors in the spoilage of an acid canned fruit, *ibid.*, **5**:439, 1940*b.*

Stokes, J. L., W. W. Osborne, and H. G. Bayne: Penetration and growth of *Salmonella* in shell eggs, *Food Res.*, **21**:510, 1956.

Stone, R. V.: A cultural method for classifying staphylococci as of the "food poisoning" type, *Proc. Soc. Exp. Biol. Med.*, **33**:185, 1935.

————: Staphylococcic food-poisoning and dairy products, *J. Milk Technol.*, **6**:7, 1943.

Tanner, F. W., and L. P. Tanner: "Food-borne Infections and Intoxications," Champaign, Ill., Garrard Press, 1953.

Tarr, H. L. A.: Microbiological deterioration of fish post mortem, its detection and control, *Bact. Rev.*, **18**:1, 1954.

Vaughn, R. H.: The microbiology of dehydrated vegetables, *Food Res.*, **16**:429, 1951.

Winter, A. R., B. Burkart, P. Clements, and L. MacDonald: Cleaning eggs with detergents and detergent-sanitizers, *Ohio Agr. Exp. Sta. Res. Bull.* 762, 1955.

Wrenshall, C. L., and J. R. McMahan: Recent developments in food uses for antibiotics, *J. Milk and Food Tech.*, **19**: April, 1956.

Wright, G. W., and J. F. Frank: Penetration of eggs by *Salmonella typhimurium,* *Can. J. Comp. Med.*, **20**:453, 1956.

CHAPTER 24

Bacteriology of Soil

It is generally known that soils are derived from weathered rock. However, a mass of weathered rock does not make a soil without the intervention of living processes. Soil has been subjected to the action of air and water, which have altered and removed some of the original components so that the proportions of the various substances in the soil are not the same as in the parent rock. The mineral particles constitute the basis or foundation of the soil but not the whole of it (Fig. 221).

Each kind of soil has its own individuality. The distinctive feature of this individuality is the soil profile, which consists of a series of layers different from one another in color, texture, structure, and other ways. Each layer is called a horizon, and the succession of layers down to the weathered rock forms the complete soil profile. The profile is best studied in soil that has not been disturbed by cultivation, because horizons near the surface become destroyed by mixing, which occurs during cultivation.

KINDS OF ORGANISMS IN SOIL

Generally speaking, soils are excellent culture media for the growth of many kinds of organisms. This is especially true of the cultivated and improved soils. The microscopic life of soil includes bacteria, yeasts, molds, algae, diatoms, and protozoa. The latter includes amoebae, flagellates, ciliates, and rotifers. In addition, there are present various nematodes, insects, etc.

According to McCalla and Goodding (1951), each spoonful of an arable soil may contain billions of living microscopic organisms. Multiply this by the number of spoonfuls of soil in an acre, and you have figures that are astronomical. The bacteria in an acre of soil of average fertility would weigh as much as a medium-sized dairy cow. This seething mass of microorganisms constitutes a crop of 3 to 5 tons per acre-foot of soil that the farmer grows beneath the surface in addition to the crop that he grows above the ground. If this crop of microorganisms beneath the surface is not fed adequately, the crop above ground may suffer from competition, disease, or other adverse effects of the microorganisms. Without the

632

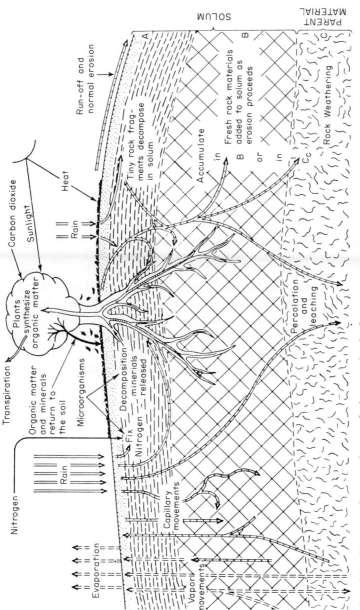

FIG. 221. Diagram showing the interlocking cycles leading to the conversion of rock into soil, making for the maintenance of a cover of vegetation on the ground and the maintenance of the soil. (*From Williamson.*)

microorganic life, the soil would not be the dynamic, perpetual system that sustains all plants and indirectly all animal life.

Since most of the soil inhabitants are aerobic, the organisms are found in greater numbers in the surface layers. The numbers decrease as the depth of the soil increases. A well-aerated soil contains more organisms than one lacking an abundance of oxygen. The numbers and kinds of organisms found in soil depend upon the nature of the soil, depth, season of the year, state of cultivation, reaction, amount of organic matter, temperature, moisture, etc.

Methods are available for counting the organisms in soil as well as for isolating the various species in pure culture. Since the organisms may vary considerably in their growth requirements, many types of culture media must be employed. The organisms may be aerobic, anaerobic, or facultative types.

Many of the species of organisms present in soil grow in associations with others. The phenomena of symbiosis, synergism, commensalism, and antagonism are believed to be of common occurrence. Two species growing together frequently elaborate metabolic waste products not produced by either organism when grown in pure culture. A product of metabolism of one organism may serve as a nutrient for another species. Antagonistic organisms are usually present and serve to combat other species, especially certain important plant pathogens. This explains why it is exceedingly difficult to determine from laboratory studies on pure cultures what actually takes place in the soil (see Chap. 17 for a discussion of the various types of associations).

In general, the same media and methods employed for the cultivation and isolation of heterotrophic bacteria are used for the propagation and separation of the majority of organisms found in the soil. However, the soil contains some species that are specific and do not grow on the usual culture media. Special media and methods must be employed for their cultivation. These include symbiotic nitrogen-fixing bacteria, nonsymbiotic nitrogen-fixing bacteria, sulfur-oxidizing forms, sulfate-reducing species, urea-decomposing bacteria, cellulose-decomposing organisms, and ammonia-oxidizing species.

FUNCTIONS OF ORGANISMS IN SOIL

One of the important functions of soil organisms is to decompose various kinds of organic matter of plant and animal origin. This includes stable manures, green manures, plant stubble, plant roots, organic fertilizers, and other products. The decomposition of such compounds is the result of the activities of bacteria, molds, protozoa, worms, and other organisms present in the soil. Each group selects certain constituents of the organic matter suitable for synthesizing its own characteristic protoplasm.

The organic compounds added to soil as a result of biological action include various sugars, amino acids, pentosans, celluloses, lignins, proteins, fats, waxes, tannins, and pigments. These compounds are further decomposed, resulting in the liberation of soluble organic and inorganic constituents. Some of the inorganic compounds, notably ammonia, may be utilized by plant life as a source of nitrogen.

Organic materials, especially stable and green manures, are said to produce four distinct effects upon soil processes and upon plant growth:

1. They supply inorganic nutrients to plants, especially nitrogen and phosphorus.
2. They affect the physical conditions of the soil, especially the moisture-holding and buffering capacities.
3. They supply certain specific elements that may be limiting factors for the growth of some plants.
4. They favor the development of organisms that secrete substances antagonistic to the growth of certain specific forms responsible for plant diseases.

Higher plants are indispensable to human welfare, and the activities of microbes in the soil are intimately related to plant growth. If it were not for the growth of organisms in soil, all animals, including man, and plants would soon perish. Therefore, life could not exist in the complete absence of soil microorganisms.

BIOLOGY OF SOIL

Soil structure has a significant influence on erosion, water intake, and crop growth. A stable granulated soil will permit rapid water uptake, drainage, aeration, and beneficial microbic activity, whereas a dispersed or compact soil has a low infiltration rate. Crops grow more luxuriantly in fertilized, well-aerated, drained, and granulated soils. The most important factors in maintaining or improving the granulation of soils are the presence of microorganisms and their decomposition products.

According to McCalla (1946):

Growing plants and microorganisms constitute the living phase of the soil. In it are living and nonliving bacteria, viruses, bacteriophages, fungi, algae, protozoa, earthworms, nematodes, and insects. These organisms have numerous enzymatic systems which are capable of producing available nutrients for the growing plants by breaking down some of the many organic compounds in the soil.

Physically, a good soil is made up of about 5 per cent organic and 95 per cent inorganic materials by weight. The influence that the small amount of organic matter in most soils exerts is out of proportion to its weight and is more directly related to the volume it occupies. This organic fraction of the soil is made up of plant and animal remains in all stages of decomposition.

Organisms and their metabolic products are active in the formation and stabilization of soil structure, although they play a greater role in stabilization than in formation. A good soil structure is essential for the smooth integration and performance of the multi-groups of organisms in the soil. The beneficial organisms decay plant and animal residues, liberate plant nutrients, and produce soil-structure-stabilizing substances (Fig. 222). A deterioration of soil structure results in suppressing the activities of the beneficial groups and promoting the growth of microbial groups that render nutrients unavailable. An unfavorable plant root medium soon develops under anaerobic conditions.

Soil structure affects plant growth in numerous ways. For example, it increases water intake and drainage. It has direct effect on plant growth, such as root penetration, aeration, or anchorage. It influences biological activity such as nitrogen fixation,

FIG. 222. Soil structure developed by fungi. Left, untreated Peorian loess; right, Peorian loess in which the growth of fungi has been greatly stimulated. (*After Mc-Calla. Courtesy of Soil Conservation Service.*)

nitrification, or organic matter decay. A good structure holds to a minimum the processes of anaerobic microorganisms, such as the reduction of sulfates or nitrates to forms unavailable or toxic to the plants.

A desirable soil structure can be maintained by following a rotation including a sod crop, and frequent liberal use of manures and crop residues.

NITROGEN CYCLE

Nitrogen is the cornerstone of the structural requirements of all living cells. It is, therefore, absolutely necessary for the growth of bacteria and other organisms. Without an available supply of this element, life could not endure.

A continuous transformation of nitrogen takes place in the soil by various groups of organisms. In the breakdown of protein, the first step is a hydrolysis of the molecules to their constituent building stones, or amino acids. The amino acids are then deaminized with the liberation of ammonia:

1. Proteins + H_2O → amino acids.
2. Amino acids + H_2O → ammonia + carbon residue.

After ammonia has been liberated from various nitrogenous compounds, it may be (1) assimilated by soil organisms and again synthesized into proteins, (2) used by higher plant life as a source of nitrogen, (3) absorbed by the colloidal substances in soil and bound as ammonia, (4) acted upon by other soil forms and oxidized first to nitrites and then to nitrates. The organisms responsible for this last set of reactions belong to the autotrophic group of bacteria and are incapable of utilizing organic compounds for structural or energy purposes.

The nitrates may be utilized by various microorganisms and by higher

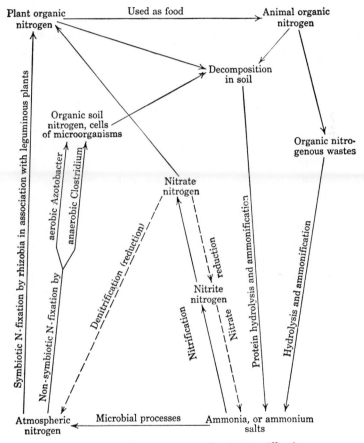

Fig. 223. The nitrogen cycle. (*After Allen.*)

plants and synthesized into proteins, or they may be reduced first to nitrites and finally to free nitrogen. The free nitrogen is lost as far as being available to plant and most microscopic soil life. However, certain bacteria found in the soil have the ability to utilize free nitrogen and make it available to plant life.

Two groups of organisms are responsible for nitrogen fixation. The organisms in one group are nonsymbiotic nitrogen fixers; those in the other group fix nitrogen only when growing in symbiosis on the roots of certain plants. The free nitrogen is transformed into organic compounds which are made available to plants and soil organisms. The nitrogen compounds are then synthesized into proteins. The nitrogen cycle is diagramed in Fig. 223.

QUANTITATIVE EXAMINATION OF SOIL

Soil is the natural habitat of a considerable number of bacterial species, varying from strict autotrophic to heterotrophic forms. Because of this fact, many types of culture media are required to obtain an accurate appraisal of the numbers of organisms present. Such a procedure is out of the question where a rapid determination of the approximate numbers present in a sample of soil is desired.

Soil Colloids. Bacterial organisms are found chiefly in the layer of colloidal material surrounding the inorganic particles of soil. Conn and Conn (1940), McCalla (1940), and others noted that bacteria grew better in the presence of colloidal clay than in its absence. McCalla attributed the stimulation of bacterial growth to the catalytic effect of the clay in speeding up biochemical reactions, either by providing a more efficient utilization of nutritive material or by decreasing the toxic effects of waste products by adsorbing them.

Bacteria in contact with soil colloids adsorb cations. Under normal conditions, the solid material in the soil constitutes about 80 per cent and the water content about 20 per cent. The water is present around and between the particles of soil. Normally, the bacteria probably live in the water films that adhere to the surface of the colloid particles containing adsorbed ions. To quote from McCalla:

The bacterial cell is undoubtedly in close proximity to the soil particles and, assuming that the bacteria may adsorb ions and hold some of them in the outer surface of the cell, this would permit contact exchange of adsorbed ions. Ions with large oscillating volumes would overlap, and exchange between systems could readily take place. Other ions which are strongly adsorbed would not be expected to wander far from the surface of the colloid. On the basis of the displacement of adsorbed methylene blue, the ions would be expected to be adsorbed by the bacteria from the soil colloids in the following series: $H > Al > Fe > Mn > Ba > Ca > Mg > K > NH_4 > Na$.

From the foregoing facts and theoretical considerations it is suggested that in the adsorption of nutrients from the soil by the bacteria, and possibly by living cells in general, an exchange of adsorbed bases takes place between the bacteria and soil colloid as depicted in Fig. 224. In bacterial metabolism large amounts of carbon dioxide and water are formed. In the presence of H_2O, H-ions are produced from the carbon dioxide which may be adsorbed at the cell's surface. When a colloidal clay particle, saturated with adsorbed bases, contacts a bacterium saturated with H-ions, an exchange of ions takes place until an equilibrium is reached. As this equilibrium is upset by the more complete utilization of the adsorbed basic ions in bacterial metabolism, a further exchange may take place, the colloidal clay functioning as a constant reservoir for basic ions utilized in the growth of such organisms.

It is difficult to remove or separate the organisms from this colloidal layer. This means that the number of colonies appearing on an agar plate is not an accurate index of the population of a soil sample. Also, no single culture medium is satisfactory for the growth of all species present in soil.

Two methods are generally employed for estimating the numbers of

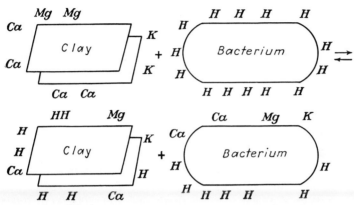

FIG. 224. Mechanism of ion exchange between soil bacteria and colloidal clay. (*After McCalla.*)

microorganisms in soil: (1) the agar plate method and (2) the direct microscopic method.

Agar Plate Method. The procedure is as follows: A weighed sample of soil is mixed with a known volume of sterile water contained in a screwcap bottle. The sample is vigorously shaken to separate as many organisms as possible from the colloidal material surrounding the soil particles. After the coarse particles have separated, a series of dilutions is prepared from the suspension. Aliquot portions from each dilution are transferred to Petri dishes and mixed with melted agar. The plates are incubated at 25°C. for 2 to 14 days. The colonies are counted and the results expressed as the number of organisms per gram of soil (Fig. 225).

Numerous media may be used for isolating soil bacteria. A medium

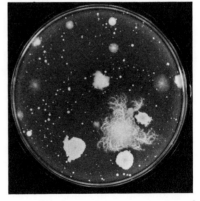

FIG. 225. Quantitative examination of soil by the agar plate method.

containing a small amount of organic matter is more satisfactory than one containing an abundance of this constituent. Peptone in media is particularly unsatisfactory as it permits the overgrowth of spore formers and proteolytic *Pseudomonas,* which prevent the development of the slow-growing bacteria. The same unsatisfactory result occurs if the temperature of incubation is higher than 25°C.

Objections to the Agar Plate Method. The enumeration of the soil population by this method presents several serious errors. Obligate anaerobes do not grow in the presence of oxygen; autotrophic bacteria fail to multiply in organic media; nonsymbiotic nitrogen fixers grow to a limited extent only; many cellulose-decomposing organisms do not grow on the commonly used media; sulfate reducers grow only in a medium containing sulfate; etc. The counts represent only a fraction of the total bacterial population of soil. The method does give an estimate of the number of organisms in soil capable of growing on a nutrient agar medium.

Molds are commonly present in soil, although the numbers appearing on agar plates represent only a small percentage of the total counts. Yeasts are less prevalent than molds, increasing in numbers in acid soils and in soils of orchards and vineyards.

The counts by the agar plate method vary from 200,000 to 100,000,000 per gram of soil. The colonies appearing on plates consist of about 10 to 40 per cent actinomycetes, 50 to 80 per cent non-spore-formers, and 3 to 10 per cent spore bearers.

For more information see Wieringa (1958).

Direct Microscopic Method. The method is as follows: One part of soil is suspended in 10 times its weight of a 0.015 per cent aqueous solution of agar. The purpose of the agar is to fix the organisms to the slide. An area of 4 sq. cm. is ruled off on a microscope slide by means of a china-marking pencil. One-tenth milliliter of the soil suspension is transferred to the ruled area and spread out uniformly. The slide is dried on a flat surface over a water bath, and then covered with a solution consisting of 1 per cent rose bengal dissolved in a 5 per cent aqueous solution of phenol.

In a good preparation, the bacteria take a deep pink or red color, whereas the mineral constituents do not stain. Some of the dead organic matter appears light pink, but most of it stains either yellow or not at all. If the bacteria appear faintly stained or if everything is colored pink, a new preparation should be made. The former condition generally means that the slide has been washed too long; the latter indicates that the staining solution is too old.

The slide is examined under a calibrated oil-immersion objective and the number of organisms per field counted. At least 25 fields are counted and an average taken. Knowing the area and count per field, it is a simple matter to calculate the number of organisms present in a gram of soil.

The direct counts are from 5 to 20 times greater than by the agar plate method. Much of the discrepancy is due to bacteria which fail to grow on the plates rather than to clumps of organisms which do not break up in the plating method.

Objections to the Direct Method. The method records dead organisms which do not develop on agar plates. The organisms must be evenly distributed over the slide. It is advisable to prepare several slides and to take an average of the counts. A disturbing factor is the difficulty of recognizing the bacteria. Many soil forms are too small to be easily distinguished from soil particles. Also many soil particles resemble bacteria. Therefore, considerable experience is necessary in making accurate determinations of the soil population by the direct method.

For more information see Conn (1926); Skinner, Jones, and Mollison (1952).

Variations in Soil Counts. The numbers of organisms in soil are not uniform even over a very small area. In order to increase the accuracy of the determination, several samples from the same plot should be collected and an average taken of all determinations for computing the final count. A single determination may be considered as valueless for calculating the soil population.

It has been reported that if soil is partially sterilized with steam, or with a volatile antiseptic such as toluene, the bacterial count first decreases, followed by a sharp increase in numbers and activity. If a little untreated soil is added, the bacterial count again decreases. The partial sterilization of the soil destroys the protozoa but not the bacteria and is followed by a sharp increase in the latter. The addition of an untreated soil reintroduces protozoa and results again in a decrease in bacterial numbers. The important protozoa responsible for the daily variations in bacterial numbers include ciliates, flagellates, and rhizopods. These organisms are widely distributed in soils.

It has been shown that an inverse relationship exists between the numbers of bacteria and active amoebae in soil. A decrease in numbers of protozoa is followed by an increase in the bacterial population and vice versa. This means that if a soil determination is to be of any value, it is very important that samples be examined from different areas of the same plot as well as at frequent intervals over a long period.

Soil bacteria differ in their edibility by protozoa. Certain groups, such as the root-nodule bacteria, generally are resistant to attack by micro-predators, whereas some strains of *Aerobacter* are attacked by all soil protozoa which have been studied.

For more information see Thornton and Crump (1952).

QUALITATIVE STUDIES OF SOIL ORGANISMS

Lochhead (1940) showed that the qualitative nature of the soil microflora was markedly influenced by the growing plant. In the rhizosphere (the zone influenced by root excretions), the Gram-negative rods were increased in numbers, whereas the Gram-positive rods, cocci, and spore bearers were less abundant.

Most rhizosphere bacteria are saprophytes. Some live on the root surface; others penetrate the roots. Some are restricted to the cortical cells, whereas others go deeper, passing between the cells and invading them. Some are harmless; others are destructive or have a favorable effect on the development of the host.

Bacteria are generally more numerous in the rhizosphere than in soil more distantly removed. They differ from those beyond this zone in being physiologically more active. Also they show (1) a greater proportion of motile forms, (2) a pronounced increase in chromogenic bacteria, and (3) a higher incidence of gelatin liquefiers and glucose fermenters.

This increased growth is unquestionably related to the supply of inorganic and organic nutrients at the root-soil interface. Plant excretion of inorganic substances, growth factors, amino nitrogen, and a variety of other substances have been generally accepted. Also the food materials supplied by sloughed-off root caps, root hairs, and cortical and epidermal cells should not be overlooked, since they are rapidly attacked by soil organisms and supply considerable quantities of organic and inorganic nutrients.

Plant roots affect microbial growth, and the plant in turn is affected by the increased activity of the microbial population of the rhizosphere. The information available is inadequate to indicate whether plant development is increased or impaired by the presence of the rhizosphere organisms.

For more information see Canada Department of Agriculture (1938 to 1957), Katznelson and Stevenson (1956), Lochhead (1957, 1958a, b), Lochhead and Burton (1955, 1956, 1957), Starkey (1958), Zagallo and Katznelson (1957).

CLASSIFICATION OF SOIL BACTERIA

Winogradsky placed soil bacteria into two groups which he named the zymogenous and the autochthonous types (see Conn, 1948).

Zymogenous Bacteria. The zymogenous types consist of actively fermenting organisms requiring for their activity ingredients which are quickly exhausted. They are involved in processes in which organic matter is made available to plants. The added organic matter is rapidly attacked in successive stages, each of which involves a specific group of organisms. The organisms increase rapidly whenever furnished with the special nutrients to which they are adapted, then return again to low numbers until another occasion for active growth occurs. Some of these organisms require special media for laboratory cultivation; others grow on ordinary media.

Organisms of this group include the nitrifiers, nitrogen fixers, cellulose-hydrolyzing bacteria, sulfur-oxidizing forms, acid-fast bacteria, molds, streptomycetes, spore-forming *Bacillus* species, and non-spore-forming *Pseudomonas* or closely related species.

Autochthonous Bacteria. The autochthonous types are more familiarly known as the indigenous or native bacteria. They are found in soil in fairly high and quite constant numbers. They do not change in numbers by the presence or absence of specific nutrients. The exact function of these organisms in soil is not clearly understood. They appear to utilize the same nutrients (salts) as higher plants and display a low level of activity in soil. They utilize the same sources of nitrogen as plants and may be looked upon as rivals. Since bacteria are short-lived and are readily autolyzed after death, their rivalry with plants cannot be considered serious. The autochthonous bacteria produce weak fermentation reactions which make their classification difficult. Because of this fact, they are classified almost entirely on morphology.

The group includes some of the streptomycetes, which are more appropriately classified here rather than under the zymogenous bacteria.

A large number of closely related soil species have characteristics intermediate between the true bacteria and the streptomycetes. The organisms are somewhat pleomorphic. In young cells they appear as rods which may vary in size and shape from straight to bent, curved, swollen, or club-shaped forms. Short filament formation with rudimentary budding may occur. These organisms are placed in the genus *Arthrobacter*. They resemble streptomycetes only in their ability to produce occasional short mycelia.

A number of small, nonpleomorphic, nonsporing, motile rods are found in soil; they differ from the *Arthrobacter* in showing no tendency toward filament formation or the appearance of coccoid forms. These organisms are placed in the genus *Agrobacterium*. Most of these species are plant pathogens.

PRODUCTION OF AMMONIA

Most species of bacteria are capable of decomposing proteins and protein-split products with the liberation of ammonia as one of the compounds. The ammonia is released prior to the utilization of the carbon residue chiefly for energy. The production of ammonia is an essential stage in the formation of nitrate in soil. Most plant crops are largely dependent on soil nitrates for structure and growth.

The decomposition of nitrogenous compounds for energy takes place only in the absence of a rapidly utilizable carbohydrate. In the presence of a rapidly fermentable carbohydrate, bacteria derive their energy from this source, utilizing the nitrogenous compounds for structure only. This results in a greatly lowered production of ammonia and nitrate. Therefore, maximum ammonia production takes place only in the absence of a rapidly fermentable compound.

Urea-hydrolyzing Organisms. Other compounds besides proteins and their degradation products are capable of yielding ammonia by bacterial action. These include nitrogenous compounds of a nonprotein nature.

Stable and barnyard manures are often used as fertilizers because of their nitrogen content. They help to replenish the nitrogen supply of the soil. A high content of urine is often present in such waste material. The most important nitrogen compound present in urine is urea. Many organisms have the power of converting the urea to ammonium carbonate and finally to free ammonia and carbon dioxide, according to the equation

$$O{=}C\diagup_{\diagdown NH_2}^{NH_2} + 2H_2O \rightarrow (NH_4)_2CO_3$$

$$(NH_4)_2CO_3 \rightarrow 2NH_3 + CO_2 + H_2O$$

The presence of urea-hydrolyzing organisms in soil is determined by incorporating urea in a culture medium. The liberation of ammonia from the medium indicates the presence of one or more organisms capable of attacking the compound. The important urea-decomposing organisms include *Bacillus pasteurii*, a Gram-variable spore-forming rod with rounded ends, usually not in chains, producing round, terminal to subterminal spores which cause a bulging of the sporangia, optimum temperature 28 to 35°C.; *Micrococcus ureae*, a Gram-variable, nonmotile, aerobic coccus, appearing singly, in pairs and clumps, optimum temperature 25°C.; *Sarcina ureae*, a Gram-positive coccus, occurring singly, in pairs, and in packets, motile by means of a single flagellum, endospores of an unusual type, located centrally, resist heating to 80°C. for 10 min., optimum temperature 20°C.

The urea bacteria thrive best in media containing urea, especially when made alkaline with ammonium carbonate. The organisms are capable of converting urea rapidly to ammonium carbonate. They are commonly found in air, water, soil, and manure. About 2 per cent of the organisms present in surface soil and about 10 per cent in manure are capable of decomposing urea.

In addition to the above, some members of the genus *Proteus* may utilize urea. This applies also to many coliform and paracolon cultures, especially to the *Aerobacter*.

For more information see Bornside and Kallio (1956a, b) Gibbons and Doetsch (1959).

DIGESTION OF CELLULOSE

The greater part of the organic matter in soil is decomposed by bacteria in the process of acquiring energy. The simpler carbohydrates and some of the polysaccharides are attacked by a large number of soil bacteria. The addition of such compounds to soil causes a rapid increase in the bacterial population.

Cellulose constitutes the chief part of the solid framework (cell walls) of plants. It is one of the most important constituents added to soil. Under normal conditions of temperature and moisture, cellulose disappears almost completely and quite rapidly.

The cellulose molecule is built up of units of β-glucose. Two molecules of β-glucose are combined through a 1,4-linkage to give β-cellobiose. The cellulose molecule consists of a chain of cellobiose units linked end to end through 1,4-β-glucosidic linkages:

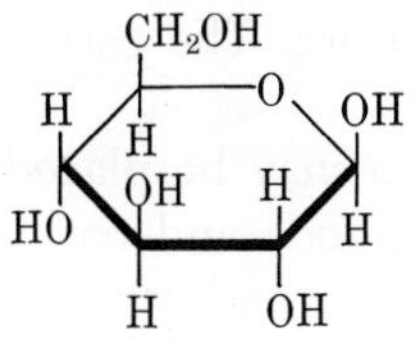

β-Glucose

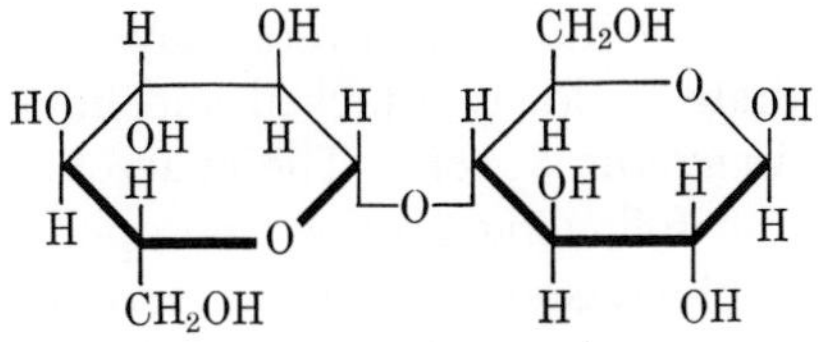

β-Cellobiose

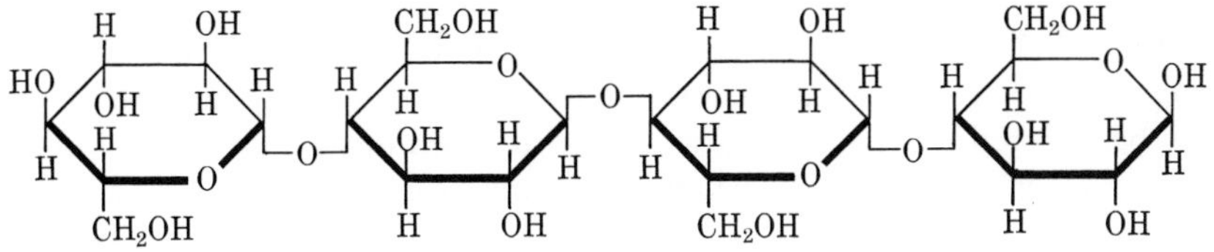

Cellulose chain

The first stage in the utilization of cellulose is a hydrolysis of the molecule to cellobiose, and secondly to glucose. Two enzymes, cellulase and cellobiase, are concerned in the reaction. Cellulase hydrolyzes cellulose to cellobiose, and cellobiase splits cellobiose to two molecules of glucose (see pages 278 and 280).

The two enzymes cellulase and cellobiase accompany each other. They are of tremendous importance in the dissolution of insoluble cellulose in the soil. Since animals do not elaborate a cellulase, the presence of cellulose-decomposing bacteria in the intestines of herbivorous animals is responsible for the hydrolysis of some cellulose.

Organisms Involved. Cellulose is attacked by a wide variety of soil bacteria, including (1) aerobic mesophilic species, (2) aerobic thermophilic forms, (3) anaerobic mesophils, and (4) anaerobic thermophilic types. The organisms utilize cellulose as a source of energy. In addition to the bacteria, a number of molds and protozoa are able to attack cellulose.

Aerobic Species. Almost all of the aerobic mesophilic cellulose bacteria so far isolated have been placed in the genera *Cellfalcicula* (short rods or spindles with pointed ends, Gram-negative); *Cellulomonas* (small, pleomorphic rods, Gram-negative); *Cellvibrio* (long, slightly curved rods with round ends, Gram-negative); *Cytophaga* (flexible, sometimes pointed rods, Gram-negative); *Pseudomonas* (rods, sometimes coccoid, Gram-negative); *Sporocytophaga* (vegetative cells rod-shaped, microcysts spherical); *Vibrio* (short, curved rods, Gram-negative). With the exception of *P. erythra,* all are capable of growing well in the presence of a variety of carbohydrates.

The presence of aerobic organisms can be easily demonstrated by adding soil to a culture medium composed of certain inorganic salts and cellulose or other satisfactory carbohydrate (filter paper, cotton, starch) and incubating for several days at the proper temperature. The carbohydrate is slowly attacked and liquefied.

Anaerobic Species. The anaerobic cellulolytic bacteria may be placed in the following groups: mesophilic non-spore-forming rods and cocci, mesophilic spore formers, thermophilic spore producers, and streptomycetes. Most of the cellulolytic bacteria encountered in nature are anaerobic spore producers of the genus *Clostridium.*

Some anaerobic species are capable of dissolving cellulose at temperatures of 60 to 65°C. These organisms are widely distributed in nature, being found in soil, river mud, and the intestinal contents of animals. They may be isolated by inoculating an inorganic medium containing cellulose with an infusion of rapidly decomposing manure and incubating anaerobically at 65°C. If the organisms are present, the cellulose will be dissolved in 6 to 8 days.

Hungate (1946) isolated a cellulolytic streptomycete from the alimentary tract of termites. The organism produced chiefly propionic acid with smaller quantities of acetic acid and carbon dioxide. The organism proved to be a species of *Micromonospora* (Fig. 226).

The end products of bacterial action on cellulose consist chiefly of acetic, butyric, formic, lactic, propionic, and succinic acids; alcohol; carbon dioxide; and hydrogen. Cellulolytic organisms show considerable variation in the kinds and quantities of end products produced.

Other Organisms. A considerable number of molds and mold-like organisms have been described as being capable of utilizing cellulose. The species that have been most extensively investigated are members of genera *Aspergillus, Penicillium, Monilia, Alternaria, Trichoderma, Mucor, Rhizopus, Merulius, Paxillus, Fusarium, Cladosporium, Chaetomium, Polyporus, Actinomyces,* and others. Molds are commonly found growing on

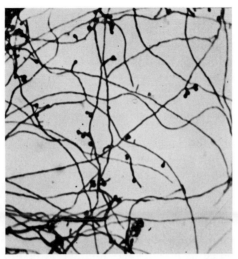

FIG. 226. *Micromonospora propionici,* an anaerobic cellulose-decomposing actinomycete. (*After Hungate.*)

old paper, especially if kept in a damp or humid atmosphere. They have been responsible for the destruction of many valuble manuscripts (Fig. 227).

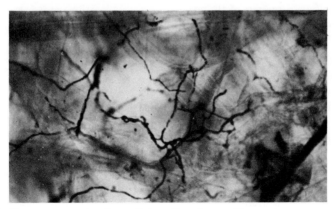

FIG. 227. Photomicrograph of a cellulose-digesting mold growing on paper. (*After Swanson.*)

Specificity of the Reaction. It is generally believed that cellulolytic organisms must have cellulose for energy and cannot substitute any other carbon source. This statement is not strictly correct. Glucose and other carbohydrates have replaced cellulose in the cultivation of a number of species of *Cytophaga*. It is highly probable that glucose can replace cellulose in the metabolism of other cellulose decomposers. The similarity in rates of cellulose, cellobiose, and glucose oxidation by *Cytophaga hutchinsonii* provides good evidence that cellulose is first hydrolyzed to glucose, followed by the utilization of the sugar for energy.

For more information see Bryant and Doetsch (1954), Bryant and Small (1956a, b), Hungate (1947), Kadota (1953, 1954a, b; 1956), McBee (1950), and Sijpesteijn (1949).

SYMBIOTIC NITROGEN FIXATION

It was shown several generations ago that the growth of certain plants in soil resulted in the stimulation of the succeeding plant crop. The fertility of the soil was increased. The plants responsible for this stimulation were almost entirely members of the family Leguminosae.

Hellriegal and Wilfarth (1888) demonstrated that the stimulation was due to an increase in the nitrogen supply of the soil, which resulted from the presence of small tumor-like growths or nodules on the roots of the plants. In the absence of nodules, no stimulation of growth of the succeeding plant crop occurred.

The formation of nodules on roots is the result of the associated growth of plant and bacteria. The bacteria are members of the genus *Rhizobium* and are commonly referred to as the root-nodule bacteria. The organisms live in the cells of the plant roots, where their growth and metabolic activities cause a swelling or nodule to form on the root. The organisms utilize the free nitrogen of the atmosphere and synthesize it into nitrogen compounds. The plant obtains its nitrogen from the synthetic activities of the bacteria, while the organisms derive their food from the plant. The plant and bacteria live together for mutual benefit. Such an association is known as symbiosis.

Formation of the Nodule. The nitrogen-fixing organisms live in the soil in the free state. Recent work indicates that they fix nitrogen only when growing in association with the plant. They gain entrance to the plant through the root hairs or other epidermal cells. The bacteria multiply very rapidly, forming long filaments in the root hairs and into the parenchyma of the root. The organisms cause a rapid proliferation of the surrounding tissue in the innermost cells of the root cortex, which results in the formation of a young nodule (Fig. 228). The young nodule pushes out the overlying parenchyma and epidermis and produces a swelling on the side of the root. A nodule consists of a mass of thin-walled parenchyma cells, which are usually almost filled with the specific organism. A corky layer and branches of a vascular system are also present. This system provides the bacteria with their nutrients, and the plant in turn takes away the nitrogen compounds synthesized by the bacteria.

Nodules vary in shape and size according to the plants on which they occur. Nodules on clover are round or oval; those on pea are commonly round, elongated, and frequently clustered; on the bean and soybean plants nodules are relatively large, round, and firmly attached to the root; those on alfalfa are usually long, finger-like growths.

FIG. 228. Early nodulation of a pea seedling resulting from seed inoculation. (*Courtesy of O. N. Allen.*)

For more information see Allen and Allen (1954), Nutman (1957), Purchase and Nutman (1957).

Nitrogen Fixation in Excised Nodules. Until comparatively recently, nodules removed from roots and placed in culture solutions were reported as being unable to fix nitrogen. Aprison and Burris (1952) placed excised nodules under an atmosphere containing N^{15}. After exposure for 30 min., the nodules were ground in the presence of acid, the pulp centrifuged, and the supernatant liquid analyzed for N^{15}. Fixation was readily and consistently demonstrated.

For more information see Wilson and Burris (1953).

Plants Involved. Nodule formation occurs most successfully on the members of the family Leguminosae. However, there are some species in the family which fail to develop nodules. Moreover, a few nonleguminous plants show the presence of nodules.

According to Allen and Allen (1947), the family Leguminosae contains 429 genera comprising approximately 10,000 species of plants. Of these, 179 genera (41 per cent), containing 946 species (9.4 per cent), have received attention regarding nodulation. Only 77 leguminous species have been consistently listed as lacking nodules.

Organisms. Great masses of organisms are present in the nodule. Their presence may be easily demonstrated by crushing a washed nodule between two glass slides, fixing the smear, and staining by the usual technique. It is a relatively simple matter to isolate a pure culture of the organism from a previously washed and sterilized nodule. The usual culture media are not satisfactory for the cultivation of the organisms. A medium that has yielded very good results is known as Ashby's mannitol phosphate agar, which is an inorganic medium to which is added mannitol as a source of energy. Colonies appear in 5 to 10 days when the plates are incubated at 25°C.

The members of the genus *Rhizobium* are rod-shaped, measuring 0.5 to 0.9 by 1.2 to 3 μ, being motile when young. Cells from nodules are commonly irregular with X-, Y-, star-, pear-, and club-shaped forms. Swollen or vacuolated forms sometimes predominate. These forms are also known as bacteroids (Fig. 229). Round or coccus cells may also be present. Cocci arise from the swollen or vacuolated cells, which later return to the rod form. Some have described the various forms as orderly stages in the life cycle of the organism. It is Gram-negative and aerobic.

The genus includes six species: *Rhizobium leguminosarum, R. phaseoli, R. trifolii, R. lupini, R. japonicum,* and *R. meliloti.* A specific name has not been given to the organism that produces nodules on plants of the so-called "cowpea" group. Walker and Brown (1935) proposed a consolidation of the soybean and cowpea groups as being inoculated by a single species, *R. japonicum.* Reid and Baldwin (1937) would include the lupine group also.

The colonial characteristics of the organisms show some variation, depending upon the plants from which they are isolated. Some species show raised, glistening, semitranslucent, white, slimy, and occasionally viscous colonies with considerable gum formation. In other species the colonies appear small, slightly raised, glistening, opaque, white, and butyrous with little gum formation.

Although the bacteroid form predominates in the nodule, it is usually absent when nodular material is streaked on agar plates (Figs. 230 and 231). After death and dissolution of the nodule, the organisms pass back into the soil as rod-shaped or ovoid cells which can develop flagella. In this stage the organism is able to swim in the soil moisture, and it is probable by such means that it reaches the roots of its host plant.

Cross-inoculation Groups. There are almost as many strains of root-nodule bacteria as susceptible plants. Nitrogen fixers isolated from the nodules of one plant are not necessarily capable of producing nodules

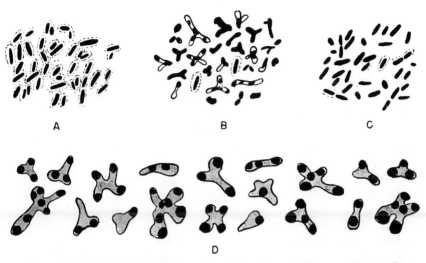

A   B   C

D

FIG. 229. Rods and bacteriods from root nodules. A, rods from a white ineffective nodule; B, bacteroids from a red effective nodule; C, rods from a green ineffective nodule; D, various forms of bacteroids. (*After Virtanen.*)

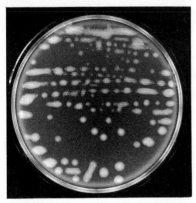

FIG. 230. Agar plate culture of *Rhizobium leguminosarum* incubated 6 days at room temperature. Note the mucoid appearance of the colonies, showing considerable tendency to run together.

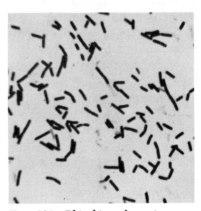

FIG. 231. *Rhizobium leguminosarum* from culture on mannitol agar.

on all legumes. The clover plant grows best when inoculated with nodule bacteria from clover; peas grow best with bacteria from peas; etc. The right pair must be brought together for successful results. The plant and rhizobia must be highly compatible. The fact that legume bacteria are so highly selective was responsible for the recognition of so-called cross-inoculation groups of leguminous plants. Any plant within such a group is inoculable with a culture of the proper organism, usually comprising several strains known to inoculate effectively all the legumes in that particular group.

Cross-inoculation groups, however, have been open to criticism because some strains of bacteria are effective for more than one group. But for all practical purposes these groups offer a convenient and workable plan for the preparation of inoculant cultures. Farmers have been accustomed to ordering legume cultures according to group designations. Seven groups are generally recognized: alfalfa, bean, clover, cowpea, lupine, pea and vetch, and soybean. Wilson (1945) distinguished 22 cross-inoculation groups among the legume bacteria. The causes of this host-plant specificity are unknown.

Organisms in the various cross-inoculation groups show some differences in their fermentation reactions. At best, however, attack on carbohydrates is feeble. With some strains this is probably due to their slow rate of growth on artificial media.

Some of the root-nodule bacteria show a strong tendency to produce large quantities of gum when cultivated on carbohydrate media. Gum formation may be so pronounced as to render the medium strongly viscid. Organisms in different cross-inoculation groups vary considerably in their capacity to produce gum. The gum is nitrogen-free, water-soluble, and precipitated from solution by alcohol or acetone. On heating with a mineral acid, the gum is hydrolyzed to a reducing sugar.

For more information see Allen and Allen (1947); Bisset (1952); Parker, Allen, and Ahlgren (1949); Thornton (1954); and Wilson (1948).

Mechanism of Symbiotic Nitrogen Fixation. Virtanen (1945a, b; 1947) observed two types of nodules on pea plants. One type effectively fixed nitrogen, whereas the other did not. The plants containing the ineffective nodules showed no better growth than the uninoculated controls. Virtanen observed that the ineffective nodules contained only rods surrounded by a slimy layer; the effective nodules contained noticeably swollen bacteroidal forms (Fig. 229). He believed that the slimy layer around the ineffective organisms interfered with their nutrition and oxygen uptake.

The root nodules of leguminous plants that actively fix nitrogen contain a red pigment, whereas the ineffective nodules are devoid of pigment. A positive correlation appears to exist between the concentration of red pigment and the ability of the nodules to fix nitrogen. The pigment changes to green when nitrogen fixation ceases in annual plants at the end of vegetative growth or when the plants are placed in the dark for a few days. The red pigment may be concentrated by treating a suspension of crushed nodules with ammonium sulfate. The pigment is capable of storing and transporting oxygen. Chemically it is a hemoprotein having absorption bands similar to hemoglobin. Virtanen named the pigment leghemoglobin. The green pigment may also be isolated from the green nodules in the same manner as leghemoglobin from the red nodules. It is also a chromoprotein. However, the absorption bands of the green and red pigments are not the same.

A number of theories have been advanced to explain the mechanism of biological nitrogen fixation. The two most important theories appear to be those advanced by Virtanen (1948) and Burris and Wilson (1945).

Theory of Virtanen. Legumes were inoculated with an effective root-nodule organism and grown in a sterile, nitrogen-free medium. Nitrogen compounds appeared immediately after nodule formation. The nitrogen compounds were excreted into the soil from the root nodules rather than from the roots. In some cases considerably over 50 per cent of the total nitrogen fixed was excreted, and it was most powerful in young plants when the nodules were still growing and showed no signs of impairment. The excreted nitrogen was chiefly amino-N as L-aspartic and L-glutamic acids. Some β-alanine was also present which was produced from the L-aspartic acid by decarboxylation. In addition, small amounts of oxime-N and nitrite-N were found in the excretion products. Virtanen proposed the following scheme:

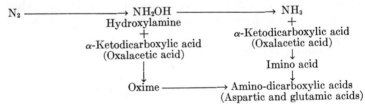

Theory of Burris and Wilson. Hydroxylamine is taken as the central nitrogen compound from which ammonia is formed through reduction, and which can also react directly with keto acid. Their scheme is as follows:

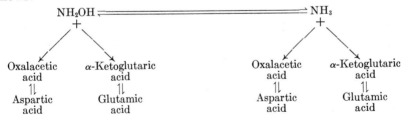

Both theories favor the formation of amino dicarboxylic acids as the primary compounds in biological nitrogen fixation.

For more information see Burris and Wilson (1952), Jensen (1951), Turner (1955), Wieringa and Bakhuis (1957), Wilson (1955), Wilson and Burris (1947, 1953).

Artificial Inoculation of Plants. The efficiency of symbiotic nitrogen fixation has been greatly increased by (1) choice of the proper legumes, (2) development of new varieties of leguminous plants, (3) artificial inoculation of seeds with pure cultures of root-nodule bacteria, and (4) adjustment of the environment to optimum conditions.

Cultures of the rhizobia are frequently added to soil to increase the nitrogen supply. This is generally practiced by soaking the seeds of a legume in a culture of the appropriate species. This procedure has become a well-established practice, especially when a legume plant is seeded for the first time.

For successful results it is extremely important that the strain of organism selected be one that is known to produce effective nodules on the legume. There appears to be no rule to follow in the selection except the actual testing of various strains on the plant to be affected. Greenhouse tests should be supplemented with actual field tests to make sure of the proper selection for the mass production of commercial cultures.

The addition of an abundant supply of nitrate to soil results in a luxuriant plant growth. Under such conditions nodules are probably not formed even though the seeds have been soaked in a culture of the organisms. The suppression of nodule formation is due to a change in the metabolism of the plants. On the other hand, the addition of calcium and phosphorus to soil results in a stimulation of nodule production. Other factors influencing nodule formation include reaction, temperature, moisture, and oxygen content of soil.

For more information see Allen and Allen (1950).

NONSYMBIOTIC NITROGEN FIXATION

In addition to the organisms discussed in the preceding section, the soil harbors certain free-living bacteria that are also capable of fixing free nitrogen.

The first nonsymbiotic nitrogen fixer isolated was *Clostridium pasteurianum*, a motile, Gram-positive, spore-forming, anaerobic rod. It is capable of fixing small amounts of nitrogen. At least 15 other species of clostridia are capable of producing the same reaction. In addition, a number of photosynthetic bacteria of the genera *Rhodospirillum, Chromatium, Rhodomicrobium, Rhodopseudomonas,* and *Chlorobium* have been shown to fix nitrogen gas. However, the most important nonsymbiotic nitrogen-fixing organisms are members of the genus *Azotobacter*.

The genus is characterized by relatively large rods or even cocci, sometimes almost yeast-like in appearance. The cells are without endospores. Flagellation is typically peritrichous. The organisms are Gram-negative, obligate aerobes, usually growing in a film on the surface of the medium. They are capable of fixing atmospheric nitrogen when provided with carbohydrate or other energy source. They grow best on media deficient in nitrogen. Soil and water bacteria are included in the genus.

Three species are recognized: *Azotobacter chroococcum*, *A. agilis*, and *A. indicus* (Fig. 232).

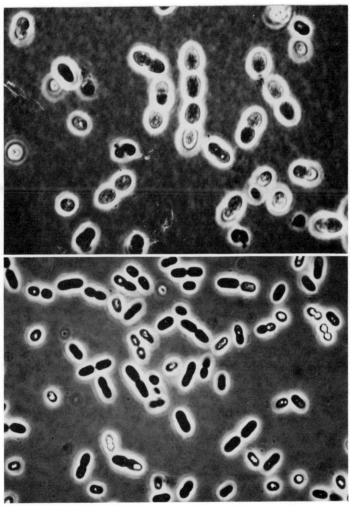

Fig. 232. *Azotobacter*, phase-contrast micrographs. Upper, *A. agilis;* lower, *A. chroococcum.* ×1200. (*Courtesy of H. L. Jensen.*)

In the presence of nitrogen compounds such as ammonium salts, nitrate, urea, aspartic acid, and asparagine, the organisms fail to fix nitrogen. However, the relative availability and probable occurrence of fixed nitrogen compounds in soils are such that they would be unlikely markedly to retard nitrogen fixation by *Azotobacter* under most conditions.

The presence of nitrogen-fixing organisms may be demonstrated by adding a small amount of fertile soil to a mineral medium containing mannitol. The medium is incubated at a temperature of about 25°C. After several days at this temperature, a pellicle begins to form on the surface of the medium. A stained smear of the pellicle material reveals the presence of many typical cells of *Azotobacter*. Depending upon the species, the cells may or may not be surrounded by slime. New cultures are prepared by transferring some of the pellicle to a flask of fresh medium. After several transfers, the culture becomes heavily enriched in *Azotobacter*. A loopful of the pellicle is now streaked over the surface of the same medium solidified with agar. The plate is incubated at 25°C. until colonies appear. A pure culture is obtained by transferring a typical colony to fresh medium.

The organisms are widely distributed in soil. Their absence from certain soils is probably due to an unfavorable pH. Cells of *Azotobacter* cannot develop if the reaction of soil is more acid than pH 6.

The size and shape of cells are subject to great variation, being dependent upon a number of environmental factors, such as composition of the medium, presence of essential minerals, presence of oxygen, temperature of incubation, and reaction of the medium. Esposito and Wilson (1956) reported that molybdenum, iron, and calcium were specifically required by one species for the fixation of nitrogen. Ammonium ion eliminated the need for molybdenum and calcium and had a sparing action on the iron requirement.

Mechanism of Nonsymbiotic Nitrogen Fixation. Virtanen believes that the reaction scheme for nitrogen fixation in *Azotobacter* is the same as in *Rhizobium* (see page 652).

Rhizobium and *Azotobacter* show marked differences in the amounts of their excretion products. Where *Rhizobium* excretes 50 to 80 per cent of the total fixed nitrogen from their nodules, *Azotobacter* excrete only 10 to 25 per cent. Most of the nitrogen fixed by *Azotobacter* is present as cell substance. However, it makes little difference in the end, since the organisms soon die and the total nitrogen content is returned to the soil.

For more information see Allison and Burris (1957), Jensen (1954), Newton, Wilson, and Burris (1953), Wilson (1955).

Azotobacter Inoculation of Soil. Many attempts have been made to increase the nitrogen content of soil by inoculation with pure cultures of *Azotobacter*. In most cases no effect on the yield of nonleguminous plants was obtained, even though unusually high numbers of *Azotobacter* were established in soil. In general, the population steadily decreased in the two or three months following establishment of growth. In a few experiments a detrimental influence was noted. Failures have been attributed to (1) absence of suitable environment, such as proper temperature, moisture, oxygen concentration, food, and reaction of soil; (2) absence of a carbon source; and (3) injurious effects of end products liberated in the decomposition of added carbohydrate.

For more information see Jensen (1954), Wilson and Burris (1960).

AUTOTROPHIC BACTERIA

Chlorophyllous plants are capable of effecting a synthesis of their own organic compounds. They take carbon dioxide and combine it with water in the presence of sunlight to form carbohydrate. Nitrogen is absorbed from the soil in the form of nitrate or other inorganic nitrogen compound and synthesized into protein. The other necessary elements are also taken from the soil in the form of inorganic compounds.

Some bacteria cannot synthesize their complex protoplasm from simple inorganic materials but must have organic compounds such as proteins, peptones, amino acids, and vitamins for growth. These are classified as strictly heterotrophic organisms.

Most bacteria are able to utilize both inorganic and organic compounds for growth. These are facultatively heterotrophic forms and constitute the majority of bacteria found in nature.

In addition to the above, some organisms are able to manufacture all new organic cell material from carbon dioxide, as the main source of carbon, and simple inorganic salts. These are the strictly autotrophic bacteria.

The number of strictly autotrophic species is small. A greater number of species are facultatively autotrophic, being capable of existing both autotrophically and heterotrophically. The strict forms include the nitrifying bacteria and some of the sulfur and iron organisms. The facultative forms can obtain their energy from (1) the oxidation of inorganic substances and carbon from carbon dioxide or (2) purely organic compounds. The hydrogen bacteria, and some of the sulfur and iron forms, are facultatively autotrophic.

For more information see Woods and Lascelles (1954), Bisset and Grace (1954).

NITRIFYING BACTERIA

The nitrifying organisms derive their energy from the oxidation of ammonia to nitrite and nitrite to nitrate. They depend on this oxidation for growth. The nitrifiers fail to grow unless the specific nitrogen compounds are available for energy. Also, they must have carbon dioxide as the only source of carbon.

Nitrosification. The oxidation of ammonia to nitrite is called nitrosification. The organisms involved are members of the genera *Nitrosomonas*, *Nitrosococcus*, *Nitrosospira*, *Nitrosocystis*, and *Nitrosogloea*. The cells are rod-shaped, ellipsoidal, spherical, or spirillar; aerobic; nonsporulating. They grow best at about 25°C. Organisms secure their energy from the oxidation of ammonia to nitrite:

$$2NH_3 + 3O_2 \rightarrow 2HNO_2 + 2H_2O + 79 \text{ Cal.}$$

The organisms fail to grow on media containing organic matter unless compounds of ammonia are present.

Isolation of Organisms. Nitrite formation takes place best in neutral or slightly alkaline media. Since the organisms are strongly aerobic, cultures should be exposed in shallow layers, preferably in Erlenmeyer flasks. The ammonia is oxidized to nitrous acid. This continues until all the ammonia has been oxidized to nitrite. The addition of more ammonium salt results in the continuation of the process, provided there is an excess of insoluble magnesium carbonate to neutralize the nitrous acid as it is formed. When all carbonate has been decomposed, the organisms should be transferred to fresh medium. Colonies may be obtained by streaking the organisms over the surface of the same medium solidified with silicic acid. Inorganic silicic acid is superior to agar as a solidifying agent for the cultivation of nitrifying bacteria.

The newer methods for the preparation of silica gel plates make use of initially nearly pure silica preparations purified by passage through ion exchange resins followed by sterilization. Since the methods of preparation are lengthy, the reader is referred to the reports of Kingsbury and Barghoorn (1954), Pramer (1957), and Smith (1951).

Nitrification. The oxidation of nitrite to nitrate is known as nitrification. Some autotrophic organisms cannot oxidize ammonia to nitrite but can oxidize the latter to nitrate.

$$HNO_2 + \frac{1}{2}O_2 \rightarrow HNO_3 + 21.6 \text{ Cal.}$$

These organisms are placed in the genera *Nitrobacter* and *Nitrocystis.* Since nitrite is seldom found in soils, it may be assumed that the two groups of nitrifying organisms nearly always occur together.

The nitrifiers are widely distributed in nature, being found in practically all neutral and alkaline soils. They are the agents primarily responsible for the appearance in soil of nitrate, which is in turn utilized by higher plants in the synthesis of cell material.

Isolation of Organisms. The medium used is similar to that employed in the preceding section except that sodium nitrite is substituted for the ammonium salt. Since the organisms are also strongly aerobic, the medium is best dispensed in shallow layers in Erlenmeyer flasks. The medium is inoculated with the soil sample and incubated at about 25°C. Several transfers to fresh medium are necessary to obtain a culture rich in nitrifying organisms.

The nitrifying bacteria are peculiarly sensitive to alkalinity, oxidizing little, if any, nitrite to nitrate at values just above pH 7.7. Just below this value, the oxidation of nitrite to nitrate proceeds so rapidly that the purely biological nature of the transformation is open to question.

For more information see Aleem and Alexander (1958), Engel and Alexander (1958, 1960), Lees (1951, 1954), Lewis and Pramer (1958), Meiklejohn (1953, 1954), Quastel and Scholefield (1951).

SULFUR BACTERIA

Sulfur is widely and abundantly distributed in nature, being present in the free and combined form. In the combined form it exists in both inorganic and organic compounds.

Gases emitted from volcanoes contain sulfur dioxide and hydrogen sulfide. Sulfur is present in large quantities in sulfur springs. Volcanic sulfur usually occurs as a sublimate on the walls of vents, probably as the result of action between hydrogen sulfide and sulfur dioxide. The commercial source of sulfur is chiefly as crude brimstone obtained from the sides of volcanoes or mined in certain parts of the world. Extensive deposits are found on the island of Sicily and in Louisiana. Commercially it occurs as brimstone, or as flowers of sulfur, which is prepared from the crude brimstone. Sulfur finds its way into the soil from the decomposition of native rock, from organic manures, and from rain water.

Sulfur is one of the elements absolutely essential to living organisms. It enters into the compositions of all plants and animal cells. The addition of sulfur to a soil low in the element results in a marked stimulation of growth. As the plants and animals die and decompose, the sulfur finds its way into the atmosphere. The gases are dissolved by rain water and again returned to the soil. Some soil organisms are able to convert the sulfur-containing gases to sulfates. Some of the sulfates are utilized by growing plants, and some are leached out by waters and carried off to the ocean. The sulfates in the ocean may be reduced to sulfides and then precipitated by iron as iron sulfide, or they may be converted into insoluble calcium sulfate (gypsum). Deposits of gypsum are believed to have been formed in this manner. Deposits of sulfur probably resulted from the reduction of sulfate to sulfite and then to free sulfur, or from the oxidation of hydrogen sulfide. The sulfur cycle may be diagramed as shown in Fig. 233.

Strictly Autotrophic Sulfur Bacteria. The strictly autotrophic forms are found in the genus *Thiobacillus*.

The cells are small, Gram-negative rods, nonmotile or motile. Energy is derived from the oxidation of incompletely oxidized sulfur compounds, principally from elemental sulfur and thiosulfate but in some cases also from sulfide, sulfite, and polythionates. The principal product of oxidation is sulfate, but sulfur is sometimes formed. The organisms grow under acid or alkaline conditions and derive carbon from carbon dioxide or from bicarbonate in solution.

The strictly autotrophic species include *T. thioparus, T. neapolitanus, T. ferrooxidans, T. concretivorus,* and *T. thiooxidans.* The first two can grow under alkaline conditions; the latter three, under strongly acid conditions. All species are aerobic, some being strictly so.

Organisms may be cultivated in a mineral medium containing thiosulfate as the source of energy. In addition to thiosulfate, one species, *T. ferrooxidans,* can oxidize ferrous iron compounds to ferric hydroxide for energy. The organisms become heavily encrusted with the reddish-colored compound.

Thiobacillus thiooxidans. This organism may be cultivated in an acid

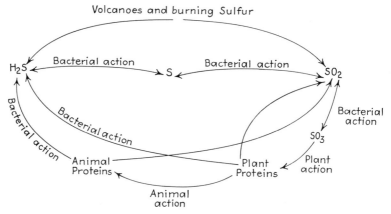

Fig. 233. The sulfur cycle.

mineral medium containing free sulfur. Since it is a strict aerobe, growth is hastened if the medium is exposed in shallow layers. This species is of special interest in that it produces more acid from the oxidation of sulfur and continues to live in a more acid medium than any other living organism yet reported. The hydrogen-ion concentration of the medium increases to pH 0.6 and less. The cells actually grow in 5 to 7 per cent sulfuric acid.

$$2S + 3O_2 + 2H_2O \rightarrow 2H_2SO_4$$

Corrosion of Concrete and Sealing Mixtures. The thiobacilli have been shown to cause serious corrosion of concrete. Sufficient sulfuric acid is produced from the oxidation of sulfur or hydrogen sulfide to dissolve concrete. The species principally involved are *T. thioparus, T. concretivorus,* and *T. thiooxidans.*

Materials containing sulfur are used to seal the joints of cast-iron pipes. The molten mixture is poured into the joints, where it forms an impervious cement. Ordinarily this sealing material remains intact for years, but occasionally the sulfur cement breaks down under biological action. The principal organism producing this breakdown is *T. thiooxidans*, although other species are doubtless involved. The sulfur is first oxidized to sulfate, followed by the reduction of the sulfate to sulfide by sulfate-reducing bacteria (see page 337).

For more information see Baalsrud (1954); Frederick and Starkey (1948); Leathen (1953); Starkey, Jones, and Frederick (1956); Temple and Delchamps (1953); and Umbreit (1954).

Facultatively Autotrophic Sulfur Bacteria. A large number of sulfur organisms do not appear to be strict autotrophs. Because of their questionable nature, they are classified as facultatively autotrophic for convenience.

The organisms are commonly present in water containing dissolved hydrogen sulfide. The gas results from the decomposition of organic matter by saprophytic organisms. The bacteria may be present in such organic materials as decomposing seaweed, rock pools containing dead algae and other lower forms of plant life, stagnant woodland pools, and sewage. Sulfur bacteria have been found in sulfur hot springs and in sulfur mines. Some species are able to grow in water pipes and cause serious obstructions. Foul odors and tastes are produced after death and decomposition of the organisms.

The important facultative sulfur bacteria are found in the families Achromatiaceae, Beggiatoaceae, Chlorobacteriaceae, Thiobacteriaceae, and Thiorhodaceae.

Achromatiaceae. Large cells, spherical to ovoid or shortly cylindrical with hemispherical extremities. Division of cells by constriction in the middle. Do not possess photosynthetic pigments. In natural habitat, cells contain sulfur droplets and sometimes additional inclusions, such as spherules of calcium carbonate. Found in fresh water and marine environments.

Beggiatoaceae. Individual cells generally not visible without staining, occur in trichomes; within trichomes cells arranged in chains. Trichomes show a gliding motion when in contact with substrate; also show flexing movements. When grown in presence of hydrogen sulfide, trichomes contain sulfur globules. Do not possess chlorophyll and phycocyanin. Found in both fresh water and marine environments containing hydrogen sulfide.

Chlorobacteriaceae. Green bacteria, usually small in size, occurring singly or in masses of various shapes and sizes, growing in environments containing high concentrations of hydrogen sulfide and exposed to light. As a rule, do not contain sulfur globules but frequently deposit elemental sulfur outside the cells. Contain chlorophyll-like pigments. Capable of photosynthesis in presence of hydrogen sulfide; do not liberate oxygen.

Thiobacteriaceae. Coccoid, straight, or curved rods. Oxidize sulfur compounds and deposit free sulfur granules within or without the cells. Never filamentous. Colorless bacteria which are sometimes embedded in gelatinous pellicles or in gelatinous bladder-like colonies. Found where hydrogen sulfide occurs, or may oxidize free sulfur, thiosulfate, or related compounds.

Thiorhodaceae. Unicellular organisms, often developing as cell aggregates or families of variable size and shape. Single cells are spheres, ovoids, short rods, vibrios, spirals, long rods, or occasionally chains. Occur in nature in environments containing sulfides and require light for development. Produce a pigment system composed of green bacteriochlorophyll and yellow and red carotenoids. They appear as bluish violet, pale purple, brownish to deep red cell masses. Single cells usually appear to be unpigmented. Anaerobic or microaerophilic organisms with a photosynthetic metabolism in which carbon dioxide is reduced with the aid of special hydrogen donors without the liberation of molecular oxygen. Where these organisms are found in nature, hydrogen sulfide acts as a hydrogen donor, and sulfur accumulates as sulfur droplets in the cells. Probably all can utilize a number of organic substances in place of hydrogen sulfide as hydrogen donors for photosynthesis.

IRON BACTERIA

Iron is found in all living cells. In some species only minute amounts are present, but regardless of the quantitative aspects, the element is absolutely necessary for growth and well-being of all plant and animal cells.

Magnesium rather than iron is present in chlorophyll, the green coloring matter of plants. However, in the absence of iron, leaves do not become green. Also, if iron is withheld from a plant in which the chlorophyll is well developed, the color gradually fades to yellow.

Certain organisms found in water and soil are capable of taking up iron and accumulating it on the surfaces of their cells, where it is quickly oxidized to ferric hydroxide. The important iron bacteria are found in the orders Pseudomonadales and Chlamydobacteriales.

Strictly Autotrophic Iron Bacteria. *Ferrobacillus ferrooxidans* is a strictly autotrophic iron bacillus. It utilizes CO_2 of the atmosphere as a source of carbon and derives its energy from the oxidation of ferrous iron to basic ferric sulfate or insoluble ferric hydroxide. The optimum

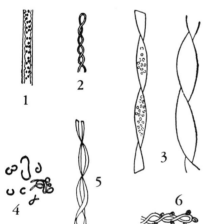

reaction for growth is pH 3.5, and the optimum temperature is 20 to 25°C. The organism is indigenous to bituminous coal regions.

For more information see Leathen, Kinsel, and Braley (1956).

Nonautotrophic Iron Bacteria. A number of nonautotrophic species are found in iron-bearing waters. Such organisms are capable of utilizing both inorganic and organic matter.

Gallionella. Stalked bacteria, the long axis of the rod-shaped cells set at right angles to the axis of the stalks. Stalks are slender, twisted bands, dichotomously branched, composed of ferric hydroxide, completely dissolving in dilute hydrochloric acid (Fig. 234). Multiplication by transverse binary fission. Young cells colorless, later becoming brown to rust red through the accumulation of iron. Twisted filaments easily identified since no other organism of a similar character has even been observed to take such a form. When the loops

Fig. 234. Iron bacteria. 1, *Leptothrix ochracea;* 2, 3, 4, 5, 6, *Gallionella ferruginea.* (*After Ellis.*)

of the coils become encrusted with iron, the filament resembles a row of beads. Presence of a sheath not observed. Organisms attach themselves to pipes and cause extensive deposits of iron which interfere with the flow of water. For this reason, they are sometimes known as the water-pest bacteria. Organisms widely distributed in nature.

For more information see Kucera and Wolfe (1957), Vatter and Wolfe (1956).

Sphaerotilus. Attached or free-floating, colorless trichomes showing false branching, though this may be rare in some species. Sheath shows a homogeneous structure. Sheath may become yellowish or brown with deposition of iron oxide. Deposition of

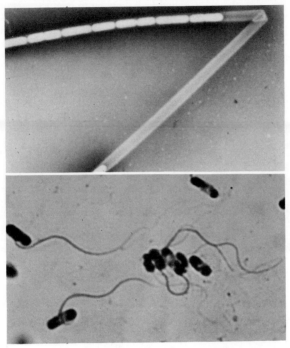

Fig. 235. Photomicrographs of *Sphaerotilus natans.* Upper, cells surrounded by a sheath; lower, individual cells with tufts or subpolar flagella. (*Courtesy of Stokes.*)

iron dependent on environmental factors, not on physiological ability to store iron. Trichomes consist of rod-shaped or ellipsoidal cells surrounded by a firm sheath (Fig. 235). Multiplication occurs both by nonmotile conidia and by motile swarm cells, the latter with a subpolar tuft of flagella. Found in fresh water.

For more information see Stokes (1954).

Leptothrix. Trichomes of cylindrical, colorless cells with a sheath at first thin and colorless, later thicker, yellow or brown, encrusted with iron or manganese oxide. Oxides may be dissolved by dilute acid, exposing the inner cells. If sheath contains manganese oxide, it does not dissolve completely in weak acids. Sheath shows an alveolar structure. Multiplication by cell division with individual cells occasionally slipping out of the sheath as reproductive cells. These are sometimes motile with a tuft of flagella. False branching may occur. Usually found in fresh water. Best known species, *L. ochracea,* is world-wide in distribution (Fig. 234).

Toxothrix. Trichomes composed of cylindrical, colorless cells with a thin primary sheath; latter soon becomes impregnated with iron oxide. Trichomes lie loosely, longitudinally together, in slightly spirally twisted rolls. Continued repetition of this process leads to the development of a thick, secondary sheath from which parallel bundles may separate. False branching may occur. Sheaths do not completely dissolve in weak acids. Cells may slip out of sheath and become motile swarm spores. Found in fresh, iron-bearing waters.

Crenothrix. Trichomes attached to a firm substrate and swollen at the free end. Unbranched or show false branching. Sheaths surrounding trichomes are plainly visible, thin and colorless at the tip and encrusted with iron or manganese oxides at the base. Cells disk-shaped to cylindrical, dividing to produce spherical, nonmotile conidia of two types: micro- and macroconidia. Individual cells may slip out of sheath and form new trichomes. Found in stagnant and running waters which contain organic matter and iron salts. *C. polyspora* only species recognized (Fig. 236).

Clonothrix. Attached trichomes showing false branching. Sheaths organic, encrusted with iron or manganese, broader at the base and tapering toward the tip. Cells colorless, cylindrical. Reproduction by spherical conidia formed in chains by transverse fission of cells; conidia formation acropetal, limited to short branches of the younger portions of the trichomes. Only species, *C. putealis*, widely distributed in rivers and streams with gravelly, manganese-bearing bottoms; also found in water works and pipe lines, where it may cause technical difficulties.

FIG. 236. Filaments of *Crenothrix polyspora*, showing differentiation of base and tip. (*After Zopf.*)

Ferruginous waters usually show the presence of a yellowish- or reddish-colored slime on the stream bottom. The color is due to the deposition of iron in the outer sheaths of the filaments. The accumulation of iron and its oxidation to ferric hydroxide result in the formation of a hard and inelastic membrane, which eventually leads to the death of the organisms. Old filaments show a higher iron content than do young filaments. In some cases, young cells are completely lacking in a deposition of iron in their sheaths. The iron hydroxide may be removed by the application of dilute hydrochloric acid, after which the outer membrane becomes visible.

For more information see Breed, Murray, and Smith (1957); Cholodny (1926); Pringsheim (1949).

BACTERIAL PHOTOSYNTHESIS

Plant photosynthesis may be defined as the synthesis of carbohydrate from carbon dioxide gas and water in chlorophyll-containing tissues with the aid of radiant energy from the sun. The first and last steps of the process may be summarized by the equation

$$6CO_2 + 6H_2O \xrightarrow{\text{Light}} \underset{\text{Glucose}}{C_6H_{12}O_6} + 6O_2$$

The carbon dioxide is reduced to carbohydrate, and the water is decomposed with the liberation of oxygen. The reaction is strictly aerobic.

Certain bacteria classified in the families Thiorhodaceae, Chlorobacteriaceae, and Athiorhodaceae of the suborder Rhodobacteriineae are also capable of producing a photosynthetic reaction. The characteristics of the former two families have already been given. Only the latter family is included here.

Athiorhodaceae. Single-celled organisms, of relatively small size, occurring as spheres, short rods, vibrios, long rods, and spirals. Produce a pigment system composed of bacteriochlorophyll and one or more carotenoids, coloring the cells yellowish brown, olive brown, dark brown, or various shades of red. Color usually not observable with single cells but only with cell masses. Generally microaerophilic. Capable of growth under strictly anaerobic conditions, but only in illuminated cultures by virtue of a photosynthetic metabolism. Latter dependent upon presence of extraneous hydrogen donors, such as alcohols and fatty acids, and does not proceed with evolution of molecular oxygen. Members which can grow in air can also be cultivated in darkness, but only under aerobic conditions.

The green and purple sulfur bacteria of the families Thiorhodaceae and Chlorobacteriaceae can develop in inorganic media containing hydrogen sulfide in the presence of light, and under completely anaerobic conditions. Organisms fail to develop in the absence of hydrogen sulfide and carbon dioxide. Oxygen is not released in the reaction as occurs in green plants.

During growth of the green sulfur bacteria, hydrogen sulfide is oxidized to free sulfur which is deposited outside of the cells:

$$CO_2 + 2H_2S \xrightarrow{\text{Light}} CH_2O + H_2O + 2S$$

During growth of the purple sulfur bacteria, hydrogen sulfide is oxidized to sulfuric acid:

$$2CO_2 + H_2S + 2H_2O \xrightarrow{\text{Light}} 2CH_2O + H_2SO_4$$

The carbon of the carbon dioxide that disappears can be recovered from the bacterial cells as organic carbon. Growth does not occur in the dark even though the environment is anaerobic.

The brown and red nonsulfur bacteria of the family Athiorhodaceae also contain a photosynthetic pigment and are light-sensitive under anaerobic conditions, but they show the following dissimilarities to the green and purple sulfur bacteria:

1. They do not contain sulfur granules within their cells.
2. They reduce carbon dioxide in the presence of extraneous hydrogen donors, including alcohols, fatty acids, hydroxy and keto acids, without the evolution of molecular oxygen. In the presence of butyric acid the reaction becomes

$$CO_2 + C_3H_7 \cdot COOH + H_2O \xrightarrow{\text{Light}} 5CH_2O$$

3. They may produce molecular hydrogen and carbon dioxide in the presence of (*a*) dicarboxylic acid, (*b*) glutamic or aspartic acid as a source of nitrogen, and (*c*) biotin as a growth factor. The net formation of both CO_2 and H_2 is unusual in view of the fact that these organisms can utilize both H_2 and CO_2 by the reaction

$$2H_2 + CO_2 \xrightarrow{\text{Light}} \text{"cell material"}$$

The green and purple sulfur bacteria can be trained to grow in media containing simple organic compounds in place of hydrogen sulfide. Likewise, the brown and red nonsulfur bacteria can be made to grow in media containing hydrogen sulfide in place of certain simple organic compounds. Therefore, the following general equation may be used to express the metabolism of the photosynthetic bacteria:

$$CO_2 + 2H_2A \xrightarrow{\text{Light}} CH_2O + H_2O + 2A$$

For more information see Arnon, Whatley, and Allen (1958); Breed, Murray, and Smith (1957); Gest (1951); Morita (1955, 1958); Newton and Wilson (1953); Ormerod (1956); Vatter and Wolfe (1958).

PHOSPHORUS CYCLE

Phosphorus is never found in the free state in nature, because contact with air causes combination with oxygen. It is found abundantly as calcium phosphate in many minerals. The framework of man and animals

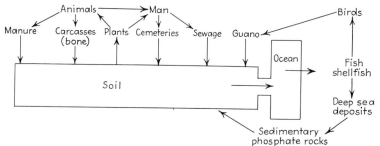

FIG. 237. The phosphorus cycle. (*After Lotka.*)

consists largely of calcium phosphate (bone). Phosphorus is also found in many organic compounds. The phosphorus cycle is diagramed in Fig. 237.

Nucleoproteins. Nucleoproteins are widely distributed in nature, being found in the nuclei and cytoplasm of living cells. They are compounds of nucleic acid combined with protein. Different proteins and nucleic acids have been isolated, indicating that many kinds of nucleoproteins occur in nature. The proteins present are basic in character, being members of the protamines and the histones.

Nucleoproteins give an acid reaction and are insoluble in water. They are soluble in weak alkali but are precipitated from solution on the addition of acid. Nucleoproteins are very complex in composition and unstable chemically. The nucleic acid may be separated from the protein moiety by salts or by cautious addition of acids or alkalies. Some enzymes or weak acids split off some protein, transforming the compound into a mixture of protein and nuclein. The nuclein still contains some protein. More prolonged enzymatic action or treatment with acid removes the remainder of the protein, setting free nucleic acid (Fig. 238).

Nucleic Acids. Nucleic acids are polymers of mononucleotide residues (consisting of phosphoric acid–sugar–base) joined together by sugar phosphate esterifications. Because of the high phosphoric acid content, they are acid in reaction. There are two types: (1) ribonucleic acid

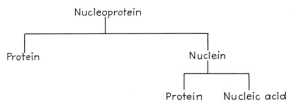

Fig. 238. The hydrolysis of a nucleoprotein to nucleic acid and protein.

(RNA) and (2) desoxyribonucleic acid (DNA). RNA occurs largely in the cytoplasm of living cells with smaller amounts in the nucleus; DNA appears to exist entirely within the nucleus.

On hydrolysis, a unit of either type of nucleic acid yields 4 molecules of phosphoric acid, 4 molecules of sugar, 2 molecules of purines, and 2 of pyrimidines. RNA contains the pentose sugar D-ribose; DNA contains the desoxypentose D-2-ribodesose. The purines adenine and guanine are present in both types of nucleic acids. However, they differ in the kinds of pyrimidines present, RNA containing cytosine and uracil, and DNA containing thymine and cytosine.

A mononucleotide is believed to have the following structure:

$$CH_2O \cdot PO_3H_2$$

$$N=C-NH_2$$
$$HC \quad C-N$$
$$\qquad \qquad CH$$
$$N-C-N$$

Adenylic acid
(9-adenine-5-phosphoribofuranoside)

A nucleotide takes its name from the purine or pyrimidine base present. For example, a nucleotide containing guanine is called guanylic acid; one containing cytosine is called cytidylic acid; etc. In both RNA and DNA carbon 5 of the sugar is joined to the phosphoric acid, and carbon 1 to position 9 of the purines, or to position 3 of the pyrimidines.

It is generally believed that a nucleic acid molecule in its simplest form is a tetranucleotide, each unit of which differs from the others in the nature of the base (purines or pyrimidines), and having a molecular weight of about 1300. In the native state nucleic acid is believed to exist in larger units formed by the polymerization of an unknown number of tetranucleotide units:

$$
\left[
\begin{array}{l}
\overset{\displaystyle \text{HO}}{\underset{\displaystyle \text{HO}}{\text{O}=\text{P}}}\!-\!\text{O}\!-\!\underset{|}{\overset{}{\text{C}_5\text{H}_7\text{O}_2}}\cdot\text{C}_4\text{H}_3\text{N}_2\text{O}_2 \quad (\text{uracil})
\end{array}
\right]_X
$$

O=P—O—$C_5H_7O_2$·$C_4H_3N_2O_2$ (uracil)

O=P—O—$C_5H_7O_2$·$C_5H_4N_5O$ (guanine)

O=P—O—$C_5H_7O_2$·$C_4H_4N_3O$ (cytosine)

O=P—O—$C_5H_8O_3$·$C_5H_4N_5$ (adenine)

Ribonucleic acid

The mononucleotides of both RNA and DNA are joined together by an ester linkage involving the phosphoric acid of one and the sugar of another through carbon 3.

The hydrolysis of RNA and DNA to their constituent units by enzymatic action is shown in Fig. 239.

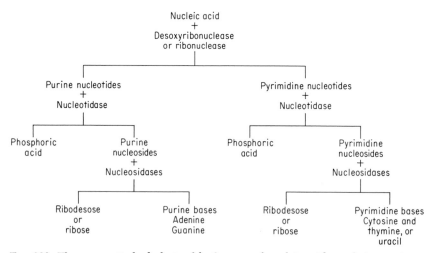

FIG. 239. The enzymatic hydrolysis of both types of nucleic acids to their constituent units.

An electron micrograph of a molecule of DNA shadowed with platinum and magnified 98,000 times is shown in Fig. 240. The importance of DNA in biological research lies in the fact that it is one of the chief constituents of chromosomes and believed to be the primary carrier of genetic information from cell to cell. The thinnest filaments measure about 20 A.

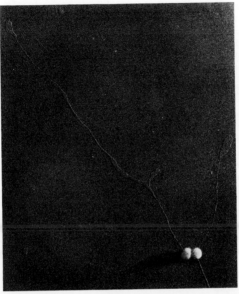

Fig. 240. Electron micrograph of a molecule of desoxyribonucleic acid, shadowed with platinum. ×98,000. Spheres of polystyrene latex added as an aid in focusing. (*Courtesy of Radio Corporation of America.*)

For more information see Bolton (1954), Bolton and Reynard (1954), Gros and Gros (1958), Lombard and Chargaff (1957), Siminovitch and Graham (1955), Stuy (1958), and Todd (1958).

REFERENCES

Aleem, M. I. H., and M. Alexander: Cell-free nitrification by *Nitrobacter*, *J. Bact.*, **76**:510, 1958.

Allen, E. K., and O. N. Allen: Biochemical and symbiotic properties of rhizobia, *Bact. Rev.*, **14**:273, 1950.

Allen, O. N., and E. K. Allen: A survey of nodulation among leguminous plants, *Soil Sci. Soc. Am.*, **12**:203, 1947.

———— and ————: Morphogenesis of the leguminous root nodule, Abnormal and Pathological Plant Growth, *Brookhaven Symposia in Biology*, no. 6, 1954.

Allison, R. M., and R. H. Burris: Kinetics of fixation of nitrogen by *Azotobacter vinelandii*, *J. Biol. Chem.*, **224**:351, 1957.

Aprison, M. H., and R. H. Burris: Time course of fixation of N_2 by excised soybean nodules, *Science*, **115**:264, 1952.

Arnon, D. I., F. R. Whatley, and M. B. Allen: Assimilatory power in photosynthesis, *Science*, **127**:1026, 1958.

Baalsrud, K.: Some aspects of the physiology of thiobacilli. From "Autotrophic Microorganisms," edited by B. A. Fry and J. L. Peel, New York, Cambridge University Press, 1954.

Bisset, K. A.: Complete and reduced life cycles in *Rhizobium, J. Gen. Microbiol.,* 7:233, 1952.

—— and J. B. Grace: The nature and relationships of autotrophic bacteria. From "Autotrophic Micro-organisms," edited by B. A. Fry and J. L. Peel, Cambridge University Press, 1954.

Bolton, E.: Biosynthesis of nucleic acid in *Escherichia coli, Proc. Nat. Acad. Sci.,* 40:764, 1954.

—— and A. M. Reynard: Utilization of purine and pyrimidine compounds in nucleic acid synthesis by *Escherichia coli, Biochim. Biophys. Acta,* 13:381, 1954.

Bornside, G. H., and R. E. Kallio: Urea-hydrolyzing bacilli. I. A physiological approach to identification, *J. Bact.,* 71:627, 1956*a;* II. Nutritional profiles, *ibid.,* 71:655, 1956*b.*

Breed, R. S., E. G. D. Murray, and N. R. Smith: "Bergey's Manual of Determinative Bacteriology," Baltimore, The Williams & Wilkins Company, 1957.

Bryant, M. P., and R. N. Doetsch: A study of actively cellulolytic rod-shaped bacteria of the bovine rumen, *J. Dairy Sci.,* 37:1176, 1954.

—— and N. Small: The anaerobic monotrichous butyric acid–producing curved rod-shaped bacteria of the rumen, *J. Bact.,* 72:16, 1956*a;* Characteristics of two new genera of anaerobic curved rods isolated from the rumen of cattle, *ibid.,* 72:22, 1956*b.*

Burris, R. H., and P. W. Wilson: Biological nitrogen fixation, *Ann. Rev. Biochem.,* 14:685, 1945.

—— and ——: Effect of haemoglobin and other nitrogenous compounds on the respiration of the rhizobia, *Biochem. J.,* 51:90, 1952.

Canada Department of Agriculture: Qualitative studies of soil microorganisms, Ottawa, I–XV (1938–1957).

Cholodny, N.: "Die Eisenbakterien," Jena, Germany, Gustav Fischer Verlagsbuchhandlung, 1926.

Conn, H. J.: An improved stain for bacteria in soil, *Stain Technol.,* 1:125, 1926.

——: The most abundant groups of bacteria in soil, *Bact. Rev.,* 12:257, 1948.

—— and J. E. Conn: The stimulating effect of colloids upon the growth of certain bacteria, *J. Bact.,* 39:99, 1940.

Engel, M. S., and M. Alexander: Growth and autotrophic metabolism of *Nitrosomonas europaea, J. Bact.,* 76:217, 1958.

—— and ——: Autotrophic oxidation of ammonium and hydroxylamine, *Soil Sci. Soc. Am. Proc.,* 24:48, 1960.

Esposito, R. G., and P. W. Wilson: Trace metal requirements of *Azotobacter, Proc. Soc. Exp. Biol. Med.,* 93:564, 1956.

Frederick, L. R., and R. L. Starkey: Bacterial oxidation of sulfur in pipe sealing mixtures, *J. Am. Water Works Assoc.,* 40:729, 1948.

Gest, H.: Metabolic patterns in photosynthetic bacteria, *Bact. Rev.,* 15:183, 1951.

Gibbons, R. J., and R. N. Doetsch: Physiological study of an obligately anaerobic ureolytic bacterium, *J. Bact.,* 77:417, 1959.

Gros, F., and F. Gros: Rôle des acides amines dans la synthèse des acides nucléiques chez *Escherichia coli, Exp. Cell Res.,* 14:104, 1958.

Hungate, R. E.: An anaerobic cellulose-decomposing actinomycete, *Micromonospora propionici,* n. sp., *J. Bact.,* 51:51, 1946; The culture and isolation of cellulose-decomposing bacteria from the rumen of cattle, *ibid.,* 53:631, 1947.

Jensen, H. L.: Nitrification of oxime compounds by heterotrophic bacteria, *J. Gen. Microbiol.,* 5:360, 1951.

——: The *Azotobacteriaceae, Bact. Rev.,* 18:195, 1954.

Kadota, H.: Microbiological studies on the weakening of fishing nets. III. The microbiological deterioration of fishing nets during storage, *Bull. Jap. Soc. Scient. Fish.,* 19:476, 1953; V. A taxonomical study on marine cytophagas, *ibid.,* 20:125, 1954*a;* VI. The microbiological deterioration of fishing nets during storage, *ibid.,* 20:130, 1954*b.*

——: A study on the marine aerobic cellulose-decomposing bacteria, *Memoirs College Agric., Kyoto University,* no. 74, 1956.

Katznelson, H., and I. L. Stevenson: Observations on the metabolic activity of the soil microflora, *Can. J. Microbiol.*, **2**:611, 1956.

Kingsbury, J. M., and E. S. Barghoorn: Silica gel as a microbiological medium: Potentialities and a new method of preparation, *Appl. Microbiol.*, **2**:5, 1954.

Kluyver, A. J., and J. H. Becking: Some observations on the nitrogen fixing bacteria of the genus *Beijerinckia* Derx. From "Biochemistry of Nitrogen," Ann. Acad. Scient. Fennicae, 1955.

Kucera, S., and R. S. Wolfe: A selective enrichment method for *Gallionella ferruginea*, *J. Bact.*, **74**:344, 1957.

Leathen, W. W.: Bacteriologic aspects of bituminous coal mine effluents, *Proc. Penn. Acad. Sci.*, **27**:37, 1953.

————, N. A. Kinsel, and S. A. Braley, Sr.: *Ferrobacillus ferrooxidans*: a chemosynthetic autotrophic bacterium, *J. Bact.*, **72**:700, 1956.

Lees, H.: Isolation of the nitrifying organisms from soil, *Nature*, **167**:355, 1951.

————: The biochemistry of the nitrifying bacteria. From "Autotrophic Micro-organisms," edited by B. A. Fry and J. L. Peel, New York, Cambridge University Press, 1954.

Lewis, R. F., and D. Pramer: Isolation of *Nitrosomonas* in pure culture, *J. Bact.*, **76**:524, 1958.

Lochhead, A. G.: Qualitative studies of soil microorganisms. III. Influence of plant growth on the character of the bacterial flora, *Can. J. Research*, **18**:42, 1940.

————: XV. Capability of the predominant bacterial flora for synthesis of various growth factors, *Soil Sci.*, **84**:395, 1957.

————: The soil microflora, the plant, and the root pathogen, *Trans. Roy. Soc. Can.*, **52**:17, 1958*a*; Soil bacteria and growth-promoting substances, *Bact. Rev.*, **22**:145, 1958*b*.

———— and M. O. Burton: XII. Characteristics of vitamin-B$_{12}$-requiring bacteria, *Can. J. Microbiol.*, **1**:319, 1955.

———— and ————: Importance of soil extract for the enumeration and study of soil bacteria, *Sixième Congrès International de la Science du Sol*, Paris, 1956.

———— and ————: XIV. Specific vitamin requirements of the predominant bacterial flora, *Can. J. Microbiol.*, **3**:35, 1957.

Lombard, A., and E. Chargaff: Aspects of the invariability of a bacterial ribonucleic acid, *Biochim. Biophys. Acta*, **25**:549, 1957.

McBee, R. H.: The anaerobic thermophilic cellulolytic bacteria, *Bact. Rev.*, **14**:51, 1950.

McCalla, T. M.: Physico-chemical behavior of soil bacteria in relation to the soil colloid, *J. Bact.*, **40**:33, 1940.

————: The biology of soil structure, *J. Soil Water Conservation*, **1**:71, 1946.

———— and T. H. Goodding: Microorganisms and their effects on crops and soils, *Nebraska Agr. Exp. Sta.*, Circ. 90, 1951.

Meiklejohn, J.: The nitrifying bacteria: A review, *J. Soil Sci.*, **4**:59, 1953.

————: Some aspects of the physiology of the nitrifying bacteria. From "Autotrophic Micro-organisms," edited by B. A. Fry and J. L. Peel, New York, Cambridge University Press, 1954.

Morita, S.: The effect of light on the metabolism of lactic acid by *Rhodopseudomonas palustris*, *J. Biochem.*, **42**:533, 1955.

————: Aerobic metabolism of acetic acid in *Rhodopseudomonas palustris*, *ibid.*, **45**:651, 1958.

Newton, J. W., and P. W. Wilson: Nitrogen fixation and photoproduction of molecular hydrogen by *Thiorhodaceae*, *Antonie van Leeuwenhoek*, **19**:71, 1953.

————, P. W. Wilson, and R. H. Burris: Direct demonstration of ammonia as an intermediate in nitrogen fixation by *Azotobacter*, *J. Biol. Chem.*, **204**:445, 1953.

Nutman, P. S.: Studies on the physiology of nodule formation. V. Further experiments on the stimulating and inhibitory effects of root secretions, *Ann. Bot.*, N.S., **21**:321, 1957.

Ormerod, J. G.: The use of radioactive carbon dioxide in the measurement of carbon dioxide fixation in *Rhodospirillum rubrum*, *Biochem. J.*, **64**:373, 1956.

672 FUNDAMENTAL PRINCIPLES OF BACTERIOLOGY

Parker, D. T., O. N. Allen, and H. L. Ahlgren: Legume bacteria—only the right kind do the job, *Crops and Soils*, April-May, 1949.
Pramer, D.: The influence of physical and chemical factors on the preparation of silica gel media, *Applied Microbiol.*, **5:**392, 1957.
Pringsheim, E. G.: Iron bacteria, *Biol. Rev.*, **24:**200, 1949.
Purchase, H. F., and P. S. Nutman: Studies on the physiology of nodule formation. VI. The influence of bacterial numbers in the rhizosphere on nodule initiation, *Ann. Bot.*, N.S., **21:**439, 1957.
Quastel, J. H., and P. G. Scholefield: Biochemistry of nitrification in soils, *Bact. Rev.*, **15:**1, 1951.
Sijpesteijn, A. K.: Cellulose-decomposing bacteria from the rumen of cattle, *J. Microbiol. Serol.*, **15:**49, 1949.
Siminovitch, L., and A. F. Graham: Synthesis of nucleic acids in *Escherichia coli*, *Can. J. Microbiol.*, **1:**721, 1955.
Skinner, F. A., P. C. T. Jones, and J. E. Mollison: A comparison of a direct- and a plate-counting technique for the quantitative estimation of soil micro-organisms, *J. Gen. Microbiol.*, **6:**261, 1952.
Smith, W. K.: Improvements in the ion-exchange method of preparing silica sols, *Proc. Soc. Appl. Bact.*, **14:**139, 1951.
Starkey, R. L.: Interrelations between microorganisms and plant roots in the rhizosphere, *Bact. Rev.*, **22:**154, 1958.
———, G. E. Jones, and L. R. Frederick: Effects of medium agitation and wetting agents on oxidation of sulfur by *Thiobacillus thiooxidans*, *J. Gen. Microbiol.*, **15:**329, 1956.
Stokes, J. L.: Studies on the filamentous sheathed iron bacterium *Sphaerotilus natans*, *J. Bact.*, **67:**278, 1954.
Stuy, J. H.: The nucleic acids of *Bacillus cereus*, *J. Bact.*, **76:**179, 1958.
Temple, K. L., and E. W. Delchamps: Autotrophic bacteria and the formation of acid in bituminous coal mines, *Appl. Microbiol.*, **1:**255, 1953.
Thornton, H. G.: The nodule bacteria and their host legumes: Some problems that they still present, *Science Progress*, **166:**185, 1954.
——— and L. M. Crump: Micropredators in soil, *Rep. Rothamst. Exp. Sta.*, 1952, p. 164.
Todd, A.: Synthesis in the study of nucleotides, *Science*, **127:**787, 1958.
Turner, E. R.: The effect of certain adsorbents on the nodulation of clover plants, *Ann. Bot.*, N.S., **19:**149, 1955.
Umbreit, W. W.: Phosphorylation and carbon dioxide fixation in the autotrophic bacterium, *Thiobacillus thiooxidans*, *J. Bact.*, **67:**387, 1954.
Vatter, A. E., and R. S. Wolfe: Electron microscopy of *Gallionella ferruginea*, *J. Bact.*, **72:**248, 1956.
——— and ———: The structure of photosynthetic bacteria, *ibid.*, **75:**480, 1958.
Virtanen, A. I.: Symbiotic nitrogen fixation, *Nature*, **155:**747, 1945a.
———: Roter Farbstoff in den Wurzelknöllchen von Hülsenpflanzen, *S. B. Finn. Akad. Wiss. Comm.*, Jan. 12, 1945b.
———: The biology and chemistry of nitrogen fixation by legume bacteria, *Biol. Rev.*, **22:**239, 1947.
———: Biological nitrogen fixation, *Ann. Rev. Microbiol.*, **2:**485, 1948.
Walker, R. H., and P. E. Brown: The nomenclature of the cowpea group of root-nodule bacteria, *Soil Sci.*, **39:**221, 1935.
Wieringa, K. T.: The problems of standardization of methods in use in microbiological soil research, *Netherlands J. Agric. Sci.*, **6:**61, 1958.
——— and J. A. Bakhuis: Chromatography as a means of selecting effective strains of rhizobia, *Plant and Soil*, **8:**254, 1957.
Williamson, W. T. H.: The living soil, *Discovery*, **12:**15, 1951.
Wilson, J. K.: The symbiotic performance of isolates from soybean with species of *Crotalaria* and certain other plants, *Cornell Univ., Agri. Exp. Sta., Mem.* 267, 1945.
———: Symbiotic segregation of strains of the root nodule bacteria by leguminous plants, *ibid.*, 279, 1948.

Wilson, P. W.: Pathways of biological nitrogen fixation. From "Perspectives and Horizons in Microbiology," edited by S. A. Waksman, New Brunswick, N.J., Rutgers University Press, 1955.

—— and R. H. Burris: The mechanism of biological nitrogen fixation, *Bact. Rev.*, 11:41, 1947.

—— and ——: Biological nitrogen fixation—a reappraisal, *Ann. Rev. Microbiol.*, 7:415, 1953.

—— and ——: Fixation of nitrogen by cell-free extracts from microorganisms, *Science*, 131:1321, 1960.

Woods, D. D., and J. Lascelles: The no man's land between the autotrophic and heterotrophic ways of life. From "Autotrophic Micro-organisms," edited by B. A. Fry and J. L. Peel, New York, Cambridge University Press, 1954.

Zagallo, A. C., and H. Katznelson: Metabolic activity of bacterial isolates from wheat rhizosphere and control soil, *J. Bact.*, 73:760, 1957.

CHAPTER 25

Infection and Immunity

Infection. The term infection may be defined as the invasion of the tissues of the body by pathogenic organisms resulting in the development of a disease process.

Contamination. The terms infection and contamination are not synonymous and should be distinguished from each other. A contaminated object is one that contains bacteria, especially disease producers. A drinking cup may be contaminated with disease bacteria but it is not infected. Likewise, the hands may be contaminated with bacteria without being infected. An infection occurs only after a pathogenic organism reaches the proper site and is able to invade the tissues.

Incubation Period. The incubation period may be defined as the interval of time that elapses from inception to first visible manifestation of an infection. This period may be a few hours, several days, often weeks, and even months. For typhoid fever, it is usually about 10 days. Even though the length of the incubation period may vary, depending upon the virulence of the organisms, it can never be entirely eliminated. What happens during the incubation period is not clearly understood in every case. In rabies, the length of the incubation period is a measure of the time required for the virus to reach the central nervous system. The farther away from the central nervous system the bite of a rabid animal occurs, the longer will be the incubation period.

Communicable Disease. A communicable disease may be defined as one that is transferred naturally from one individual to another. All communicable diseases are infections produced by microscopic organisms, the causative agents of which are transferred from one person to another by contact, by coughing and sneezing, and in other ways. An infectious disease is not necessarily a communicable disease. For example, lockjaw, or tetanus, is an infectious disease but is not communicable in the true sense of the term. The organism produces an infection of wounds and has no natural means of reaching a similar wound in another individual. However, the great majority of infectious diseases are communicable. This includes such diseases as whooping cough (pertussis), mumps (parotitis), measles (rubeola), smallpox, influenza, etc. The most infectious communicable diseases are those which attack the respiratory tract, being usually transferred during coughing, sneezing, and talking.

Endemic, Epidemic, Pandemic. An endemic disease is one that has a low incidence but which is constantly present in a given community.

An epidemic disease is one that attacks many people in a region at the same time. It is widely diffused and rapidly spreading.

A pandemic is a widespread epidemic disease.

Pathogenicity. A pathogenic organism is one capable of producing a disease. Some organisms are pathogenic for man but not for animals; others attack animals but not man; still others invade both man and animals. Therefore, it is necessary to name the host in order to use the term pathogenic correctly.

Saprophyte, Parasite. A saprophyte is an organism that lives on dead or decaying organic matter. It reduces complex dead organic matter to simple soluble compounds which may become available to plants and bacteria.

A parasite is an organism that lives upon or within another living organism. Disease-producing organisms are parasites. However, not all parasites produce disease. *Escherichia coli* lives normally as a harmless parasite in the intestines but only rarely invades the tissues to produce an infection.

Occasionally a saprophyte may develop the ability to invade living tissue to produce disease.

Virulence. Virulence may be defined as the degree of invasiveness of a pathogenic organism. Different strains of the same species may show great variability in their invasive powers. Also, the same strain kept under different conditions may show differences in disease-producing ability.

As a rule, a pathogenic organism decreases in virulence when transferred from its natural environment to artificial culture media. Other unfavorable environmental conditions also reduce the virulence of a pathogenic species. A strain that has been greatly reduced in virulence is said to be attenuated. Some organisms, like the pneumococcus, may lose their virulence entirely when transferred to culture media. Such a culture is said to be nonvirulent or avirulent. Other organisms retain their virulence even though cultivated on culture media for many generations.

Various methods are employed for decreasing the virulence of an organism. In addition to the use of culture media for this purpose, animal passage may be employed. For example, cowpox virus is smallpox virus that has been reduced in virulence for human beings by cultivation in the tissues of the cow.

An organism that is attenuated by passage through one animal species may be increased in virulence by passage through another species. For example, the virulence of the pneumococcus may be increased by passage through white mice. In this manner, an avirulent strain may become so stepped up in virulence that one-millionth milliliter of a broth culture of the organisms will kill a mouse in 48 hr.

For more information see Murray (1955).

Number of Organisms. The number of organisms plays an important part in determining whether or not an infection will occur. A small number of virulent pathogenic organisms may be easily attacked and destroyed, whereas a larger number may not be completely eliminated by the defense mechanisms of the host. This may explain why some individuals are attacked by an organism even though they have been previously immunized against the same species. The immunization will take care of a few invaders but breaks down when a mass attack occurs. In general, the number of organisms required to produce disease is inversely proportional to their virulence.

Path of Infection. Bacteria gain entrance to the body by various routes. Some enter through the broken skin (occasionally through the unbroken skin), some by way of the respiratory passages, others by way of the alimentary tract. The portal of entry determines whether or not pathogenic bacteria are capable of producing an infection. The organism of typhoid fever would probably not produce an infection if rubbed into the broken skin but if swallowed may reach the intestinal tract and produce the disease. The organism of gas gangrene will have no effect if swallowed but may produce a fatal infection if rubbed into the broken skin. Therefore, bacteria must enter the body by the route to which they are adapted. However, this is not the only factor that determines whether or not an infection will result. Man and animals possess several defense mechanisms for destroying invading bacteria. If these mechanisms are vigorous and very active, they will usually defend the host against the disease organisms. On the other hand, if they are below normal and the invaders are very virulent, an infection may occur.

After bacteria invade the tissues, they may attack the host in a variety of ways. The organisms may produce a local inflammation or may localize in the liver, bone marrow, spleen, lymph glands, or other places, giving rise to secondary abscesses or secondary focuses of infection, also known as metastatic infections. Sometimes, organisms invade the blood stream, producing a bacteremia or septicemia (blood poisoning).

Bacterial Waste Products. Bacteria produce a large number of waste products in the culture medium in which they are growing. The formation of some of these compounds is dependent upon the presence of certain specific precursors in the culture medium. The formation of others is not dependent upon the composition of the medium but is a characteristic of the organisms themselves. The composition of the medium merely determines whether the compounds shall be produced in larger or smaller amounts.

To the former group belong such compounds as the ptomaines (amines), indole, skatole, phenol, and hydrogen sulfide. Specific amino acids must be present in the peptone of the medium; otherwise these compounds will not be formed. The latter group includes the true bacterial toxins. These are of two kinds: the exotoxins and the endotoxins.

The exotoxins are elaborated by the bacterial cells and excreted into the surrounding culture medium. These may be recovered by passing the culture through an appropriate filter to remove the bacterial bodies from the medium. Only a few pathogenic bacteria are capable of excreting true soluble toxins of great potency. The symptoms produced are due largely to the toxins excreted by these organisms. In other words, the injection of the cell-free filtrate produces symptoms characteristic of the disease. The best-known members of this group are *Corynebacterium diphtheriae, Clostridium tetani, Cl. botulinum,* some of the sporulating anaerobes isolated from gas gangrene, *Streptococcus pyogenes,* and *Staphylococcus aureus.*

The endotoxins, on the other hand, are not excreted into the surrounding culture medium but remain confined within the bacterial cells. They are released only after the death and dissolution of the organisms. Most bacterial organisms fall in this group. An example is *Salmonella typhosa,* the causative agent of typhoid fever. If a young culture of this organism is filtered, the filtrate will produce only a slight toxicity, whereas the organisms themselves may produce a very toxic effect. Filtrates of old cultures may be very toxic, owing to death and autolysis of many of the organisms, resulting in the liberation of the endotoxins.

Some organisms are capable of elaborating both exotoxins and endotoxins. The organisms of cholera (*Vibrio comma*) and dysentery (*Shigella dysenteriae*) appear to belong to this group, although they elaborate considerably more endotoxin than exotoxin.

Resistance. The power of the body to prevent growth and development of organisms after they have gained entrance is spoken of as resistance. The various defense mechanisms come into play and in most cases quickly remove the invading bacteria. Sometimes the resistance to a disease is characteristic of a species. It is then spoken of as immunity.

Various degrees of immunity have been shown to exist. One race may be immune to a certain disease; another may be susceptible. This does not mean that the former race cannot be given the disease. Small doses of the organisms may be easily disposed of, but massive doses are usually able to overcome the natural defenses of the host, with the result that disease develops. Chickens are immune to anthrax because their body temperature is too high for the growth of the organism. If the body temperature is lowered to 37°C., chickens become susceptible to the disease.

NATURAL IMMUNITY

A race or species may inherit a resistance to a certain infectious disease. This resistance is spoken of as natural immunity.

Species Immunity. Many of the organisms that attack humans do not attack animals. Typhoid fever infections do not occur in animals except after massive experimental inoculations with the specific organisms. Human leprosy has never been transmitted to animals successfully. Meningitis does not occur spontaneously in animals but may be produced experimentally. Many of the animal diseases do not occur spontaneously in man.

It is not known why differences in species susceptibility exist. It may be because of differences in temperature, metabolism, diet, etc. Diseases of warm-blooded animals cannot ordinarily be transmitted to cold-blooded animals, and vice versa.

Racial Immunity. The various races probably exhibit differences in their resistance to disease, although in many cases this may be due to differences in living conditions, to immunity acquired from mild infections in childhood, or to other causes. Negroes and American Indians are said to be more susceptible to tuberculosis than the white race. On the other hand, Negroes exhibit more immunity to yellow fever and malaria than the white race.

Individual Immunity. Laboratory animals of the same species, kept under identical environmental conditions, exhibit only slight differences in their resistance or susceptibility to experimental disease. On the other hand, humans show wide differences in susceptibility to disease. For example, during an epidemic of influenza there are always some individuals who do not contract the disease even though in close contact with the virus. These individuals exhibit a higher degree of resistance than do the majority of people.

ACQUIRED IMMUNITY

An individual of a susceptible species may acquire a resistance to an infectious disease either accidentally or artificially. This resistance is spoken of as an acquired immunity.

Accidental. Many of the infectious diseases, such as typhoid fever, scarlet fever, and measles, usually occur only once in the same individual. The resistance of the host to the disease is increased so that another exposure to the same specific organism usually produces no effect. This resistance or immunity may last for a limited time or for life.

Artificial. Immunity may be acquired artificially by means of vaccines or by the use of immune serums. If the immunity is acquired by means of vaccines, it is spoken of as active immunity; if it is acquired by the use of immune serums, it is spoken of as passive immunity.

Active Immunity. Active artificial immunity may be produced in a variety of ways: (1) by a sublethal dose of a virulent organism, (2) by a sublethal dose of dead bacteria, (3) by an injection of an attenuated culture, or (4) by immunization with bacterial products.

1. Sublethal Dose of Virulent Organisms. This method has been employed experimentally with the organism of cholera. It is not applicable to very virulent organisms, such as *Bacillus anthracis,* the causative agent of anthrax.

2. Sublethal Dose of Dead Bacteria. Active immunization by this method is practiced to a considerable extent against those organisms which produce only small amounts of soluble toxins (exotoxins). The method has been used successfully against typhoid fever, the paratyphoid fevers, and cholera, and to a lesser degree against *Staphylococcus* and *Streptococcus* infections.

The organisms to be used for immunization are grown on a solid medium or in broth. If grown on a solid medium, they are washed off with saline solution. The saline suspension or the broth culture is sterilized by a combination of germicide and heat. The suspension is tested for sterility to make sure all organisms have been killed. If sterile, it is standardized to contain a definite number of bacteria per milliliter.

A vaccine prepared from organisms grown on a solid medium contains only the bacterial antigen in suspension. A vaccine prepared from a broth culture contains not only bacterial bodies but also various excretory products of the organisms. If the organism elaborates an extracellular toxin, the broth-culture vaccine will be more valuable as an immunizing agent than one prepared from the growth on a solid medium. Immune bodies will be developed against both extracellular toxin and bacterial protein.

Vaccines prepared from laboratory stock cultures are known as stock vaccines. Various kinds of stock vaccines are prepared and may be purchased.

Vaccines prepared from two or more species are referred to as mixed vaccines.

Vaccines prepared from a number of types or strains of the same species are called polyvalent vaccines. An example of a commercial preparation of this type is *Streptococcus* vaccine.

Vaccines prepared from organisms freshly isolated from the patient to be treated are called autogenous vaccines. Such vaccines have been shown to be superior to those prepared from stock cultures because various strains of the same species may show some variation in antigenicity.

The vaccines already discussed consist of dead bacteria in suspension. They are sometimes, and more correctly, referred to as bacterins. In a more restricted sense, the term vaccine is applied only to those preparations containing living organisms; but it has now taken on a broader meaning to include biologicals containing both dead and living organisms. The two most important vaccines containing living organisms (viruses) are smallpox and rabies vaccines.

3. Injection of an Attenuated Culture. Pathogenic organisms rapidly lose their virulence by transfer to artificial culture media. Repeated passage through some animals increases virulence, whereas passage through other animals produces the reverse effect.

The virulence of the anthrax organism may be reduced by cultivation at a temperature of 42°C. instead of 37°C. Although the attenuated organism is not capable of producing anthrax, it is satisfactory for immunization against the disease.

Smallpox virus produces smallpox in man and a mild localized disease in cows (cowpox). Smallpox virus becomes modified or attenuated by contact with the cow and produces only a mild infection in man.

Smallpox vaccine is produced by scratching smallpox virus into the shaved skin of the abdomen of the calf. When vesicles appear, the lymph is collected, filtered, and mixed with an equal volume of glycerin as a preservative. This constitutes the smallpox vaccine of commerce.

4. Immunization with Bacterial Products. Some organisms excrete soluble compounds into the surrounding culture medium known as extracellular toxins or exotoxins. They may be recovered in an impure state by centrifugation of the culture, pouring off the supernate, and passing it through an appropriate filter to make sure all living cells are removed.

The symptoms produced by such organisms are largely the result of the action of the soluble products elaborated by the bacterial cells. Immunization occurs following injection of gradually increasing doses of the filtrate or toxin. This method is followed in producing antitoxins against the toxins of *Corynebacterium diphtheriae*, *Clostridium tetani*, *Cl. botulinum*, *Streptococcus pyogenes*, and certain organisms responsible for gas gangrene. Unfortunately, only a few disease organisms are capable of excreting a potent extracellular toxin.

Passive Immunity. In active immunization a certain period of time is necessary before the cells of the host elaborate sufficient antibodies to offer protection to the disease. The method is of value before symptoms of the disease appear. It is essentially a prophylactic treatment. Under some conditions it may be used to incite antibody formation in certain chronic diseases.

In passive immunity, on the other hand, a temporary immunity may be acquired by injecting into the body an immune serum obtained from an immune animal or man. The protection enjoyed is due to the substances present in the immune serum which are transferred to the patient. This type of immunization is practically limited to those diseases caused by organisms which elaborate powerful exotoxins. The active immunization of an animal following the injection of several doses of an exotoxin gives rise to an immune substance known as an antitoxin. The best representatives of this group are diphtheria and tetanus antitoxins, which have been of tremendous importance therapeutically. However, immune serums prepared against organisms that do not produce exotoxins are of value in some diseases. The antisubstances present in the serum of an animal injected with a suspension of bacteria (vaccine) are directed against the proteins of the bacterial bodies. The immune substances possess the power to attack the specific bacteria used in their production. These are known as antibacterial serums as distinguished from antitoxic serums.

Antitoxins are of great value prophylactically, especially after symptoms of disease have appeared. However, passive immunity lasts for only a relatively short period of time. It has been shown that antitoxin injected into humans becomes less and less from day to day and may be expected to disappear from the blood within a period of about 2 weeks. Antibacterial serums are employed before, at the same time that, or soon after infection takes place. Most of them are ineffectual and of minor importance therapeutically.

For more information see Kahn (1954, 1955), Skarnes and Watson (1957).

ANTIGENS

An antigen may be defined as any substance which, when introduced parenterally into an animal, will cause the formation of antibodies. The antibodies are usually found in the circulating blood, and their presence may be recognized by appropriate tests.

As a rule, a substance is not antigenic unless it is foreign to the species receiving the injection. This statement applies only to antigens in circulation. For example, the injection of guinea pig serum into a guinea pig will not produce antisubstances, but the injection of it into a rabbit will result in a vigorous antibody response. Certain proteins of the body that normally do not enter the circulation may also act as antigens in the same species. Protein of the lens of the eye from a guinea pig was found to be antigenic when injected into another guinea pig. Casein from the milk of lactating goats was reported to be antigenic when injected into the same goats.

Oral Immunization. The method generally employed for the administration of antigenic substances is by hypodermic injection. Only rarely have antigens been administered by the oral route.

Available evidence has shown that oral administration is inferior to hypodermic injection. Antigens are incompletely absorbed, and the action is uncertain. According to Dolman (1948):

Once swallowed, antigens become subject to successive hazards to their integrity, and handicaps to their absorption. Before any intimate contact with the intestinal mucosa is achieved, the antigen faces exposure to hydrochloric acid and pepsin; to bile, trypsin, and other proteolytic enzymes of intestinal or even bacterial origin— all liable to be encountered in concentrations and at intervals governed by such variables as the subject's diet, bowel motility, and emotional and physical health, as well as perhaps the state of the weather. Covering the tract is a layer of mucus which presents simultaneously a mechanical barrier, and a menstruum in which leukocytes can better pursue and engulf entangled microorganisms.

Nature of Antigens. Antigens are generally protein in character. It was formerly believed that all antigens were protein, but it has since been shown that there are exceptions. A number of complex carbohydrates of bacterial origin and some lipide-carbohydrate compounds free from protein have been shown to be antigenic.

On the other hand, not all proteins are antigenic. In order that a protein be capable of inciting the production of antibodies, it must be soluble in blood plasma. Unless this occurs, it cannot reach the site of antibody formation. Proteins that have been irreversibly coagulated by heat usually fail to exhibit antigenic activity. There does not appear to be any relationship between protein toxicity and antigenic activity. Many proteins are nontoxic, yet elicit strong antibody responses.

It is not known why some proteins are antigenic and others are not. Gelatin is an example of a protein that is not antigenic. It is lacking in aromatic amino acids, i.e., acids having benzene rings. It contains no tryptophan nor tyrosine and only traces of phenylalanine. Some have concluded from this observation that the presence of aromatic acids is necessary for a protein to be antigenic, although there seems to be some evidence that this statement is not strictly correct.

For more information see Maurer (1958).

Molecular Size of Antigens. Antigenic substances are usually colloidal in solution. This means that they are composed of large molecules. They are held back by collodion membranes or ultrafilters which permit passage of smaller noncolloidal molecules. Diffusible compounds having relatively small molecular weights do not incite antibody formation because they readily pass into cells and are easily attacked and destroyed. Evidence seems to point to the fact that the larger the molecule, the better the antigenic response. An antigenic protein, when hydrolyzed to smaller units, such as peptones, peptides, and amino acids, becomes nonantigenic.

Haptens. Carbohydrates and other nonprotein compounds are generally not antigenic but, when combined with protein, may determine the specific character of the antibody that the whole compound produces, and be capable of reacting only with that antibody. A substance of this type is known as a partial antigen or hapten. Haptens have been recognized in a number of organisms, including *Diplococcus pneumoniae, Shigella dysenteriae, Klebsiella pneumoniae, Bacillus anthracis,* and *Mycobacterium tuberculosis.*

The pneumococcus (*D. pneumoniae*) has been classified into 32 serotypes on the basis of serological reactions, chiefly the Neufeld *Quellung* phenomenon as induced by type-specific immune rabbit serums. So far as known, all types contain the same proteins but differ solely in the composition of the capsular polysaccharides. The polysaccharides are not antigenic but when combined with protein, govern the specific character of the antibodies produced against each type.

For more information see Allen and Kabat (1957), Blattberg (1956, 1957), Kabat and Berg (1953), Kahn (1953), Landy (1956), Landy and Pillemer (1956a, b), and Sasaki (1957).

Antigenic Structure. Members of the genus *Salmonella* are mostly flagellated. Antigens of the flagella (flagellar or *H antigens*) are different from those of the bodies (somatic or *O* antigens). The *H* antigens are present not only in the flagella but also in a thin layer covering the entire cell. The addition to flagellated organisms of an immune serum containing both *O* and *H* antibodies results in agglutination only by the latter antibodies, since *O* antibodies are unable to sensitize the protected *O* antigens. The flagellar antigens may be destroyed by exposing the organisms to alcohol or weak acid, after which the *O* antibodies are able to react with the exposed somatic antigens to give agglutination.

The flagellar antigens are of two types: those which are peculiar to the species or type or possibly to a few species or types (specific, or phase 1) and those which are common to a group of species or types (less specific, or phase 2). At one stage of the culture, specific flagellar antigens may be present; at another stage the group antigens may be present. Therefore, a culture of an organism may consist of one phase or the other, or a mixture of both. The somatic or *O* antigens are represented by Arabic numerals; the specific flagellar antigens by small letters; and the less specific or group flagellar antigens by Arabic numerals. The somatic and flagellar antigens of a few species of *Salmonella* are given in Table 27.

TABLE 27. FLAGELLAR (*H*) AND SOMATIC (*O*) ANTIGENS OF SOME *Salmonella* SPECIES

Group	Species	Somatic (*O*) antigens	Flagellar (*H*) antigens	
			Phase 1 (specific)	Phase 2 (less specific)
A	*Salmonella paratyphi*	1, 2, 12	*a*	
B	*Salmonella abortus ovis*	4, 12	*c*	1, 6
	Salmonella schottmuelleri	1, 4, 5, 12	*b*	1, 2
	Salmonella typhimurium	1, 4, 5, 12	*i*	1, 2
C	*Salmonella choleraesuis*	6, 7	*c*	1, 5
D	*Salmonella typhosa*	9, 12, *Vi*	*d*	

Vi Antigen. It was noted by Felix and Pitt (1934) that smooth strains of S. *typhosa* differed in their agglutinability by O antiserum. They found that the more virulent strains were generally the less agglutinable. This was later shown to be caused by the presence in the virulent strains of a very labile antigenic substance known as the Vi or virulence antigen. Strains possessing maximal amounts of O and Vi antigens showed the highest degree of pathogenicity. The O or somatic antigen and the Vi antigen are believed to be composed of carbohydrate-lipide complexes but different from each other.

The Vi antigen is a surface antigen. It may be visualized as a discontinuous eruption from the deeper parts of the organism which extends out through the O fraction. This covering of the organism by the Vi antigen may be so complete that the O fraction is obscured. Under these conditions, the organism is unable to exhibit the O antigen fraction and thus fails to agglutinate in the presence of the O antiserum or antibody.

The Vi antigen gradually disappears as the organism is carried on laboratory media, until it is completely lost. The strain passes through a number of phases before this occurs. On fresh isolation, the strain is inagglutinable by O antiserum. After a few transfers, the strain acquires O agglutinability. Then the strain is unable to stimulate the formation of Vi antibody, and finally ability to absorb Vi agglutinins from the immune serum is lost.

For more information see Chu, Hoyt, and Pickett (1956); Landy (1953, 1954); Landy et al. (1955); Landy and Webster (1952); Landy, Webster, and Sagin (1954); and Spaun (1956).

Exotoxins. Exotoxins may be defined as high-molecular-weight compounds, generally protein in character, capable of damaging animal cells, and possessing antigenicity, i.e., capable of causing the elaboration of immune substances known as antitoxins. They are formed within bacterial cells and excreted outside into the surrounding medium. They may be recovered by filtering the medium free of bacteria and recovering the toxin in the filtrate. Exotoxins are relatively unstable, being destroyed by moderate heating, ultraviolet light, and storage at room temperature. They are detoxified by formaldehyde to give antigenic substances known as toxoids.

With few exceptions, exotoxins are digested by proteolytic enzymes. Therefore, they are not active when taken orally. Botulinum toxin is an exception in that it is not affected by proteolytic enzymes. This is surprising in view of the fact that the toxin is a protein of the globulin type.

Tetanal, staphylococcal, diphtherial, and other exotoxins also give the usual protein reactions and are considered to be protein in composition.

Mode of Action of Exotoxins. Bacterial toxins exhibit their characteristic action by producing a specific effect on some organ or tissue. The toxins of *Clostridium botulinum* and *Cl. tetani* exhibit a selective affinity for the nervous system. Toxins from hemolytic streptococci designated oxygen-labile streptolysin *O* and oxygen-stable streptolysin *S* attack and dissolve red blood cells. Certain staphylococci produce considerable quantities of the following exotoxins: (1) hemolysin (dissolves red blood cells), (2) leucocidin (dissolves leucocytes), (3) dermonecrotic toxin (necrosis of the skin), and (4) gastroenteric toxin (food poisoning).

It is believed the toxin produces a physical or chemical union or both with the specific tissue or organ involved. Bacterial toxins rapidly disappear from the blood stream, indicating that a union with the specific tissue has occurred.

For more information see Bonventre and Kempe (1959, 1960); Brooks, Curtis, and Eccles (1955); Cardella et al. (1958); Duff, Wright, and Yarinsky (1956); Kurosu (1953); Roth and Pillemer (1955); Spero (1958); Stone (1954); Woiwood and Linggood (1949).

Toxoids. The toxic qualities of exotoxins may be destroyed by treatment with formaldehyde without damaging their antigenic or antitoxin-binding properties. Toxin so modified is known as anatoxin or toxoid.

A number of methods have been used for the purification of diphtheria toxin or toxoid. They include fractional precipitation with ammonium sulfate, precipitation by acid, adsorption on aluminum hydroxide with subsequent elution, precipitation by alcohol or acetone or metallic salts, and the use of ultrafiltration. The addition of about 2 per cent alum to a culture filtrate produces a flocculent precipitate of the toxin or toxoid. The precipitate contains the active antigenic component of the culture.

Pure diphtherial toxoid is a heat-labile protein having an isoelectric point of pH 4.7 ± 0.1. It does not contain sulfur, phosphorus, carbohydrate, or iron. The addition of glycine permits sterilization by filtration and allows storage of these preparations for long periods of time under extreme temperature conditions without deterioration.

For more information see Holt (1948), Levine and Stone (1951), Pillemer et al. (1948), and Ross (1949).

Endotoxins. Unlike the exotoxins, the endotoxins are not excreted but remain closely bound to the bacterial cell. They are liberated in the animal body after the destruction of the cell by autolysis or mechanical disruption. Most endotoxins are composed of protein; a few appear to be carbohydrate-lipide complexes. They are thermostable at 60°C., remain unchanged upon storage or exposure to ultraviolet light, are generally resistant to proteolytic enzymes, and are not detoxified by formaldehyde. Endotoxins are only weakly antigenic, antibodies not being formed to any extent in immunized animals.

For more information see Tauber and Garson (1957).

ANTIBODIES AND THE ANTIGEN-ANTIBODY REACTION

Antibodies are specific substances produced by an animal in response to the introduction of a foreign antigen. The antibodies are produced by certain cells of an animal, then thrown off into the blood stream. The serum containing the antibodies is known as an immune serum or as an antiserum. An immune serum is capable of reacting with the homologous antigen either in vivo or in vitro.

Sites of Antibody Formation. It has been generally accepted that antibody formation is confined mainly to the reticuloendothelial system.

Jaffé (1931) reviewed the vast literature on the reticuloendothelial system and concluded that almost all evidence in favor of its participation in antibody production was of doubtful validity.

A substantial literature has accumulated during the past several years indicating that antibody production occurred in the lymph glands draining the injected area. Very little evidence was obtained for antibody production elsewhere, though the possibility could not be excluded.

For more information see Ehrich and Harris (1942); Oakley, Warrack, and Batty (1949).

The presence of antibodies in an immune serum may be demonstrated in a number of ways, depending upon the nature of the antigen. By such tests, five apparently different kinds of antibodies may be recognized: antitoxins, agglutinins, precipitins, lysins, and opsonins.

Antitoxins. Antitoxins may be defined as immune bodies elaborated by living cells following the injection of bacterial filtrates containing soluble toxins or exotoxins. The bacterial bodies play no part in the reaction except to elaborate the soluble antigenic substances.

An antitoxin is generally prepared by injecting an animal with gradually increasing doses of toxin until a high concentration of antibodies is present in the serum. Then either the animal is bled to death or a safe amount of its blood is removed. If the latter method is followed, the animal may be reimmunized a number of times. After the blood has clotted, it is allowed to stand until a clear straw-colored fluid (serum) separates from the clot. The serum contains the antibodies and is called an *antitoxin*.

The injection of specific antitoxin into a patient suffering from a disease caused by a toxin-producing organism results in neutralization of the toxin without the destruction of either component.

For more information see Bolyn and Moskowitz (1955), Pappenheimer and Yoneda (1957), and Pope (1957).

Agglutinins and Precipitins. When bacteria (antigen) are mixed with specific antiserum, a gathering together or clumping of the organisms occurs. The clumping is due to the presence in the immune serum of antibodies known as agglutinins (Fig. 241).

It was later observed that bacterial filtrates produced precipitates when mixed with specific immune serums. The precipitating antibodies in immune serum are spoken of as precipitins (Fig. 242).

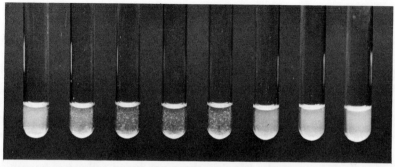

Fig. 241. Agglutination. Various dilutions of typhoid antiserum were mixed with a suspension of *Salmonella typhosa.* The immune serum dilutions increase from left to right. Tube No. 1 does not show agglutination (prozone phenomenon); tubes 2 to 6 inclusive show agglutination; tube 7 does not contain a sufficient number of antibodies to cause agglutination of the antigen. The last tube is the control.

It is believed that agglutination and precipitation are produced by the same antibodies. In agglutination, the antigen consists of particulate matter (bacteria and other cells); in precipitation, the antigen is in solution. The two immune substances may be demonstrated in the same antiserum.

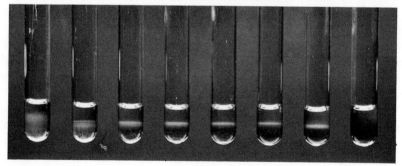

Fig. 242. Precipitation. Various dilutions of horse antiserum were mixed with horse serum. The tube to the left contained the most concentrated antiserum. Note the precipitation at the point of contact of the two solutions. The last tube to the right is the control.

Agglutination and precipitation are similar to the neutralization of toxin by antitoxin in that only two components, namely, antigen and antibody, are concerned in the reaction.

Zone Phenomenon. If an immune serum is diluted sufficiently, it no longer agglutinates the cell suspension. This may also occur even though the dilution of antiserum contains a sufficient number of immune bodies to agglutinate the antigen.

In the series of test tubes shown in Fig. 241, the immune serum dilutions increase from left to right. Agglutination does not occur in the first tube to the left where the serum concentration is strongest. This is called the *prozone*. It has been shown that an inhibitory substance, probably a globulin, is present in serum and interferes with agglutination. This inhibitory substance fails to function on further dilution of the antiserum. Agglutination is strongest in tube 3 and is absent in tube 7, where the antiserum concentration is too low to cause the cells to agglutinate.

Normal Agglutinins and Precipitins. Normal serums of man and animals often possess the power to precipitate or agglutinate the specific homologous antigen, provided the serums are not too highly diluted. It is not known if these normal agglutinins and precipitins are the same as the corresponding immune bodies, i.e., those produced following immunization.

Formalin (solution of formaldehyde), heat, ultraviolet rays, chemicals, etc., in concentrations just strong enough to kill bacteria, do not destroy the agglutinating or precipitating antibodies. However, most immune serums lose their agglutinating or precipitating ability at temperatures of 60 to 65°C.

Presence of Electrolytes. Agglutination does not occur in the complete absence of an electrolyte, such as sodium chloride. However, the addition of only a minute amount of salt to a nonagglutinating mixture of antigen and antibody causes agglutination to occur at once. This applies not only to bacteria but to other cells. Agglutination proceeds in two steps: (1) the antibody becomes fixed to the antigen, and (2) the cells clump together in the presence of electrolyte. The reaction is analogous to the precipitation of colloids by electrolytes. The union of antigen and antibody leads to the formation of an amphoteric colloidal suspension that is easily precipitable by electrolytes.

The precipitation of colloidal particles is determined by the ion of the electrolyte having an electrical charge opposite in sign to that of the colloidal particles. Since bacteria carry negative electrical charges, the positively charged ions of the electrolyte will condition the agglutination of the organisms. The greater the positive charge, the smaller will be the amount of electrolyte required to cause agglutination.

For more information see Califano, Pontieri, and Cavallo (1957).

Lysins. Fresh normal blood serum exerts a bactericidal action. This property is destroyed by heating the serum to a temperature of 56°C. for 30 min. A thermolabile substance known as alexin or complement is destroyed in the heating process.

If cholera organisms are injected into the peritoneal cavity of a guinea pig, previously immunized against the same organism, they lose their motility, break up into fragments, and finally dissolve completely. The same result is achieved by injecting a mixture of cholera bacteria and immune serum into a normal guinea pig. The reaction takes place not only in the presence of unheated immune serum but also in the presence of heated immune serum to which is added a small amount of normal serum. These observations show that two factors are concerned in the phenomenon of bacteriolysis: (1) a thermolabile substance present in normal and immune serum and (2) the immune bodies that are produced during the process of immunization. The immune bodies are specific; the thermolabile substance is not.

Heating an immune serum to 56°C. for 30 min. destroys the complement and the ability of the serum to dissolve the antigen. However, the addition of a small amount of normal serum restores the lytic power of the immune serum. Complement is present in all animal serums and is not increased in amount during immunization. The antibodies are not destroyed when serum is heated to 56°C. for 30 min., and are increased in number during immunization.

Specific lytic immune serums may be prepared not only against bacteria (bacteriolysins) but also against other cellular bodies such as red blood corpuscles (hemolysins) and tissue cells (cytolysins).

This group of antibodies requires three components for action: antigen, antibody, and complement. The antibody first reacts with the antigen. In the absence of complement, no dissolution of the antigen takes place; in the presence of this component, the cells are dissolved. On the other hand, agglutination, precipitation, and antitoxic immune reactions require only two components: antigen and antibody.

For more information see Cavallo et al. (1957); Neter (1956); Ekstedt (1956); Muschel, Chamberlin, and Osawa (1958).

Chemical Nature and Function of Complement. As has already been stated, antibodies are specific for the antigen used in immunization. On the other hand, complement is nonspecific and is not increased on immunization. Antigens (red blood cells, bacteria, etc.) undergo dissolution when acted upon by two factors in serum: (1) the relatively thermostable specific antibody and (2) the thermolabile nonspecific complement. The antibody first unites with the homologous antigen in the presence or absence of complement. Complement does not combine with the antigen or antibody until antigen and antibody unite. When this occurs, the complement becomes bound and, under appropriate conditions, lysis of the antigen takes place.

Guinea-pig complement has been shown to consist of four functionally distinct components, designated by the symbols $C'1$ (mid-piece), $C'2$ (end piece), $C'3$ (third component), and $C'4$ (fourth component). The

$C'1$ component is thermolabile, is precipitated from serum by carbon dioxide or dilute acid, and is characterized as a euglobulin. The $C'2$ fraction remains in solution after the $C'1$ component is precipitated, is also thermolabile, and is characterized as a mucoeuglobulin. The $C'3$ component is inactivated by yeast or zymin and is thermostable. The $C'4$ fraction is inactivated by dilute ammonia or hydrazine, is thermostable, and is also a mucoeuglobulin.

The $C'1$, $C'2$, and $C'4$ components of complement first react with the antigen-antibody combination, after which the antigen is rendered susceptible to the action of $C'3$. This last component behaves as if it were a catalyst, causing a dissolution of the antigen.

Ecker and Seifter (1945) showed that, under the proper conditions of concentration, all the corresponding complement components of man and guinea pig were mutually substitutive. The same was found to hold true for human and rabbit complements.

For more information see Arday, Pillemer, and Lepow (1959); Heidelberger (1951); Pillemer (1943); Pillemer et al. (1953).

Complement-fixation Reaction. This is the name given to an important immunological reaction first demonstrated by Bordet and Gengou (1901). They noted that, when the serum of a patient who had recovered from bubonic plague was mixed with the specific antigen (plague bacilli), a binding or fixing of the complement of the serum occurred, resulting in the dissolution of the organisms. Since no free complement remained in the serum, they applied the name *complement fixation* to the reaction.

Briefly the test is as follows:

1. Antigen and antibody must first unite before dissolution of the cells by complement can occur.
2. The antigen is bound only by the specific antibody.
3. When the antigen and antibody are bound (sensitized antigen), the complement of the serum becomes fixed.
4. The absence of free complement in the serum indicates that it has been fixed by the antigen-antibody union.
5. The presence or absence of free complement in the serum may be detected by adding a mixture of sheep red corpuscles and rabbit serum containing anti-sheep erythrocytic immune substances (previously heated to 56°C. for 30 min. to destroy complement) to the antigen-antibody complex. In the presence of free complement, the sheep cells will undergo dissolution; in its absence, no hemolysis will occur, indicating that the complement has been bound by the antigen-antibody complex.

The test is of value in diagnosing the presence of certain organisms in patients suffering from disease or for the identification of certain antigens by means of specific serums. The test, as performed by Bordet and Gengou, is outlined on the following page.

Opsonins. The immunological phenomena already discussed dealt with reactions between bacteria, bacterial excretory products (toxins), and other antigens with body fluids. These were the first immunological reactions recognized. It was subsequently shown by Metschnikoff (1901) and

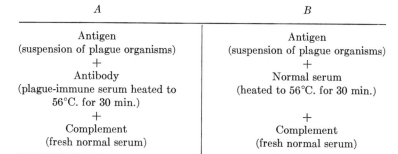

A	B
Antigen (suspension of plague organisms) + Antibody (plague-immune serum heated to 56°C. for 30 min.) + Complement (fresh normal serum)	Antigen (suspension of plague organisms) + Normal serum (heated to 56°C. for 30 min.) + Complement (fresh normal serum)

To both A and B after 5 hr. was added:
Sheep red-cell–immune serum
(heated to 56°C. for 30 min.)
+
Sheep red blood cells

Results:

A. Hemolysis did not occur.

B. Hemolysis occurred.

others that certain body cells also played a part in the defense mechanisms of the host.

The cells that are chiefly concerned in the reaction are the white blood corpuscles known as polymorphonuclear leucocytes, or phagocytes. These cells are capable of wandering to the site of infection; engulfing bacteria, tissue fragments, etc.; and removing them from the infected area (Fig. 243). Since the cells chiefly concerned in the reaction are known as phagocytes, the process is generally referred to as phagocytosis. The leucocytes are sometimes called "scavenger cells" because they clear away bacteria and debris. Many of the leucocytes are destroyed in their attempt to remove the invading bacteria.

The power of phagocytosis is not limited to the polymorphonuclear leucocytes but is possessed by a number of other cells, some of which are fixed tissue cells and some of which are

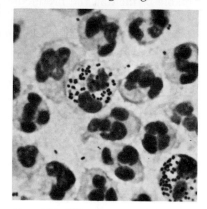

Fig. 243. The phagocytosis of *Neisseria gonorrhoeae* by the polymorphonuclear leucocytes.

wandering cells. The former include the endothelial cells that line the capillaries and sinuses in the liver, spleen, and lymph nodes and other cells of the reticuloendothelial system; the latter include the large mononuclear elements known as the macrophages.

It has been shown that, when leucocytes are washed free of serum and then mixed with bacteria, no phagocytosis occurs. If, however, a small amount of normal serum is added to a mixture of leucocytes and bacteria, active phagocytosis is restored. Antibodies known as bacteriotropins or opsonins are present in serums that prepare the bacteria for phagocytosis. Opsonins are present in normal serum and are increased during the process of immunization.

For more information see Berry and Spies (1949), Hirsch (1956a, b, 1959), Skarnes and Watson (1956), and Suter (1956).

SEROLOGY OF SYPHILIS

A number of tests are employed for the serodiagnosis of syphilis. Some of these are based on the complement-fixation technique; others are flocculation tests. The most important ones are known as (1) the Wassermann test and its many modifications, (2) the Kahn test, and (3) the Kline test.

Wassermann Test. A complement-fixation test was proposed by Wassermann in which the antigen consisted of an aqueous extract of syphilitic fetus. It was found later that the aqueous extract of syphilitic fetus could be replaced by an antigen prepared by extracting with alcohol beef-heart powder, previously extracted with ether, and adding cholesterol or a mixture of cholesterol and lecithin to the alcoholic extract.

The lipoidal suspension is not an antigen in the true sense. It is not capable of inciting the production of immune bodies when injected into an animal. However, since it is capable of binding syphilitic antibodies in the serum of the patient, it is generally spoken of as an antigen.

A type of antibody activity is developed as a result of infection with *Treponema pallidum,* the causative agent of syphilis. Since it is not known if this is a true antibody, it is generally referred to as a reagin. It has the power to react with the lipoidal antigen prepared from beef heart and reinforced by the addition of cholesterol and lecithin. It has been suggested that *T. pallidum* damages tissue cells of the host and causes a lipoidal fraction to split off which acts as a hapten, and this combines with the protein of the bacteria to stimulate the production of antibodies (reagin).

Cardiolipin. Cardiolipin is the name given to a complex phospholipide first isolated by Pangborn (1941) from beef heart in essentially chemically pure form. It is a single substance and on alkaline hydrolysis yields oleic and linoleic acids, a polyester of glycerophosphoric acid, and glycerol.

Cardiolipin, purified lecithin, and purified cholesterol used singly are not antigenic, but certain mixtures of the three act well as antigens in the complement-fixation test for syphilis. Mixtures reproducible to a high degree of accuracy may be prepared from different lots of the components.

Cardiolipin reinforced with lecithin and cholesterol appears to be generally superior in both sensitivity and specificity to the lipoidal suspension prepared by extracting, with alcohol, powdered beef heart previously extracted with ether, and adding lecithin or a mixture of lecithin and cholesterol to the alcoholic extract.

For more information see Giordano, Culbertson, and Higginbotham (1948); Kline (1947); Kolmer and Lynch (1948a, b, c); and Price (1953).

Kahn Test. Precipitation tests for the diagnosis of syphilis have gained in popularity during the past several years. The first practical procedure of this type is the Kahn test. It is now the most commonly employed precipitation test for the diagnosis of syphilis.

The Kahn antigen is prepared by extracting dried beef-heart powder with ether and then alcohol. Cholesterol is added to the alcoholic extract. The cholesterolized extract must be mixed with salt solution to produce an unstable antigen suspension. The antigen suspension contains lipide aggregates. These aggregates disperse when in contact with serum. Then, in syphilitic serum, new aggregates appear in the form of a precipitate, whereas in nonsyphilitic serum no new aggregates appear.

Agitation markedly influences the formation of precipitates in syphilitic serum with antigen suspension. While strongly positive serum will show flocculation immediately on mixing with an appropriate amount of antigen suspension, weakly positive serum requires agitation for several minutes for the formation of a precipitate.

For more information see Kahn (1947), Kahn and McDermott (1948a, b), McDermott and Kahn (1949).

Kline Test. The Kline test is demonstrated as a microscopic slide reaction. It is performed as follows:

Pipette 0.05 ml. of heated serum in a ringed area on a slide.
Add 1 drop (0.008 ml.) of antigen emulsion to the serum.
Rotate the slide for 4 min.
Examine under the microscope at a magnification of 100× for the presence of clumps (Fig. 244).
Results are recorded as negative, weakly positive (± and +), positive (++ and +++), and strongly positive (++++), depending upon the degree of clumping and the size of the clumps.

The antigen originally employed by Kline was made from the alcohol-soluble acetone-insoluble fraction of beef heart, concentrated by evaporation at 50°C.

Kline now recommends a cardiolipin antigen reinforced with lecithin in place of alcohol-soluble acetone-insoluble fraction of beef heart. This antigen shows greater specificity and much greater sensitivity than the original preparation and is now recommended as the standard antigen for the Kline test.

Other flocculation tests and modifications of the Kahn and Kline tests include (1) the Hinton test, (2) the Mazzini test, (3) the Rein-Bossak test, and (4) the V.D.R.L. test.

For more information see Kline (1948) and Mazzini (1951).

The *Treponema pallidum* immobilization (TPI) test, discovered by Nelson and Mayer (1949), is based on the principle that the serum of patients with syphilis contains a specific humoral antibody capable of sensitizing the Nichols strain of *T. pallidum* so that the spirochetes become nonmotile in the presence of active guinea-pig complement. The test itself, while simple in theory, has presented many difficulties in its practical application.

 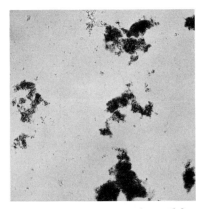

FIG. 244. Kline text for syphilis. Left, negative test. The antigen is not clumped but appears as a homogeneous suspension. Right, positive test. The antigen is clumped and the particles are floating in a clear liquid.

For more information see Harris (1956), Kahn (1954), Miller et al. (1954), Portnoy and Magnuson (1955), Wilkinson and Sequeira (1955).

HYPERSENSITIVITY

The term *allergy* includes all types of reactions of hypersensitiveness except anaphylaxis. The antigen may be protein or nonprotein. In man, there is little tendency to generalized shock. Typical anaphylactic shock has been occasionally observed, but the tendency is for localization of manifestations, especially in the respiratory and gastrointestinal tracts and in the skin. Typical allergic conditions include hay fever, asthma, atopic dermatitis, urticaria (hives), angioneurotic edema, drug allergy, contact dermatitis, migraine, and bacterial allergy.

The term *anaphylaxis* is generally used loosely, but strictly speaking, it is defined as a hypersensitiveness to substances that are antigenic, i.e., capable of stimulating the production of antibodies, when injected into the body.

A guinea pig may be inoculated with a large dose of foreign antigen without any ill effect being noted. The animal is then said to be sensitized. If, after a period of 10 days or more, the animal is given a minute injection of the same antigen (intoxicating dose), violent symptoms may occur and lead to the death of the animal. If the animal recovers, it is usually refractory to another injection of the same antigen. If a guinea pig is given repeated injections of a foreign antigen, at brief intervals of 7 days or less, it does not become hypersensitive and usually shows only a mild reaction. The animal is then said to be desensitized to further injections of the same antigen.

All animal species are not equally susceptible to anaphylaxis. Guinea pigs are more sensitive than any other laboratory animal. Death is due to a bronchial spasm followed by acute asphyxia. Man, on the other hand, usually shows only skin lesions (rash).

The immune bodies responsible for anaphylaxis are probably identical with precipitin and complement-fixing antibodies. Anaphylaxis is believed to be a cellular reaction, taking place within the cells in which the antibody is fixed. Some of the antibodies are released from the cells and may be demonstrated in the blood stream. There is considerable evidence to support the statement that the intoxicating dose is followed by the release of histamine, heparin, and possibly choline, which are responsible for the symptoms of anaphylactic shock.

The symptoms are due to a contraction of the smooth, or nonstriated, muscle tissue. This may be shown by removing a piece of smooth muscle from a sensitized guinea pig and placing it in a solution of the specific antigen. Contraction immediately takes place.

Anaphylaxis is essentially a laboratory phenomenon. Guinea pigs are extremely easy to kill under conditions of anaphylaxis, but it is not very likely that many of them under natural conditions ever die of anaphylactic shock. Artificial conditions are set up in the laboratory that probably seldom or never occur in nature.

Antihistamines. A close similarity exists between the physiological action of histamine and the manifestations of anaphylaxis. It seems likely that the fundamental mechanism involved is the reaction that occurs when an antigen comes in contact with an antibody in a living organism. In this antigen-antibody reaction histamine, or a substance closely related to it, is released. This substance is assumed to be the agent responsible for many of the symptoms of allergy. A number of investigators have shown that the appearance of allergic symptoms coincides with the increase in the histamine content of the blood and sensitive tissues.

Antihistamines are agents that antagonize the action of histamine. These drugs possess physiological activities that are directly opposite to those of histamine.

Histamine causes bronchial constriction, depresses the blood pressure, and stimulates the intestine. On the other hand, antihistamines relax the bronchial musculature, increase the blood pressure, and inhibit the motility of the intestine.

A large number of antihistamines have been synthesized and made available for therapeutic use. Some of these are antazoline hydrochloride (Antistine Hydrochloride), chlorcyclizine hydrochloride (Perazil), chlorothen citrate (Tagathen), doxylamine succinate (Decapryn Succinate), thonzylamine hydrochloride (Anahist), and tripelennamine hydrochloride (Pyribenzamine Hydrochloride).

Skin Test for Allergy. Skin tests may be used to determine if an individual is sensitive to certain foods, pollens, or other proteins. The test is performed by introducing extracts of the various protein substances into the skin of the arm and noting the results. A positive test is indicated by the appearance of a large, localized, inflamed area, or urticarial wheal, surrounding the site of injection. Many different extracts may be tested at the same time; the reaction appears after a few minutes.

For more information see Dragstedt (1941, 1945); Kierland (1953); Logan (1960); Mayer (1949); Rosenberg, Chandler, and Fischel (1958); Tokuda and Weiser (1958).

BLOOD GROUPS

Landsteiner (1900) discovered that, when the red blood cells of certain individuals were mixed with the serum of others, a clumping or agglutination of the red cells occurred. This is an example of isoagglutination. He found that there were present two antigenic components, A and B, in red blood cells and two components in serum that agglutinated them. It was subsequently shown that all human blood could be placed into four groups on the basis of the presence or absence in the erythrocytes of the two antigenic components A and B.

According to Landsteiner, the four blood groups may be represented as shown in Table 28. It may be seen that the red blood cells of the first group do not contain either the A or the B component; the cells of the second group contain only A; the cells of the third group contain only B; and those of the fourth group contain both A and B. Persons in group A do not have serum antibodies capable of agglutinating A cells but do have antibodies that agglutinate B cells; those in group B do not have antibodies capable of agglutinating B cells but do have antibodies that agglutinate A cells; those in group AB do not have either type of antibody; and those in group O have both types of antibodies.

In blood transfusions it is desirable to give blood of the same type. If this is not possible, type O is usually compatible and satisfactory. Therefore type O individuals are designated universal donors. The serum of an O donor contains both A and B antibodies, but they become diluted out by slow administration without producing lysis of the red blood cells of a recipient of type A, B, or AB. On the other hand, group O individuals can receive blood only from type O donors because such blood contains antibodies A and B, which react immediately with red blood cells of donors of types A, B, or AB. Similarly, individuals of type AB are universal recipients because they do not contain antibodies in their serum.

TABLE 28. THE FOUR BLOOD GROUPS OF LANDSTEINER

Group	Antigen in cells	Agglutinin in serum	Reaction* with serum of type				Percentage of occurrence in adults, U.S.
			O	A	B	AB	
O	—	Anti-A + anti-B	—	—	—	—	45
A	A	Anti-B	+	—	+	—	39
B	B	Anti-A	+	+	—	—	12
AB	AB	—	+	+	+	—	4

* + = agglutination.

Blood Typing. For blood typing only antisera for groups A and B are required. Three microscope slides are cleaned and labeled A, B, and C (control). One drop of A (anti-B) serum is placed in the center of the slide labeled A; one drop of B (anti-A) serum is placed in the center of the slide labeled B; and one drop of normal salt solution is placed in the center of the slide labeled C. To each slide is added an equal volume of the unknown blood cell suspension (5 per cent suspension of blood in salt solution). The slides are rocked for about 5 min., then examined under a low-power objective.

If no agglutination occurs on slides A and B, the blood is of group O; if agglutination occurs on both slides A and B, the blood is of group AB; if agglutination occurs on slide A but not B, the blood is of group B; and if agglutination occurs on slide B but not A, the blood is of group A (Fig. 245).

These four groups are of tremendous importance in blood transfusions, in cases of disputed parentage, and in the identification of persons.

For more information see Kabat (1949).

RH FACTOR

Landsteiner and Wiener (1940) discovered another antigen in blood which they named the *Rh* factor. This factor was first demonstrated in the blood cells of rhesus monkeys. Individuals having this antigen are designated *Rh* positive; those lacking this antigen are *Rh* negative. About 85 per cent of American whites are *Rh* positive. Since the factor is antigenic, it is important because of its immunizing ability. Antibodies produced against the *Rh* antigen cause reactions in *Rh* negative individuals who have previously received transfusions with *Rh* positive blood. A second transfusion may produce agglutination and hemolysis of the red blood cells.

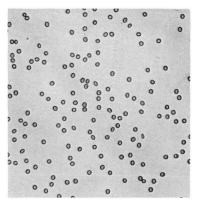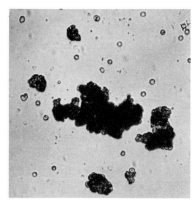

Fig. 245. Blood grouping. Left, group *A* blood cells mixed with group *A* typing serum. Negative agglutination, indicating compatibility. Right, group *A* blood cells mixed with group *B* typing serum. Positive agglutination, indicating incompatibility.

During pregnancy an *Rh* negative mother and an *Rh* positive father may give rise to a fatal disease in the infant known as erythroblastosis, and it may die in utero. The fetus inherits the factor from the father. The mother then becomes immunized to the *Rh* antigen contained in her *Rh* positive fetus, with subsequent passage of the immune anti-*Rh* agglutinins back across the placenta, to produce the disease in the great majority of cases.

REFERENCES

Allen, P. Z., and E. A. Kabat: Studies on the capacity of some polysaccharides to elicit antibody formation in man, *J. Exp. Med.*, **105**:383, 1957.

Arday, F. R., L. Pillemer, and I. H. Lepow: The properdin system and immunity. VIII. Studies on the purification and properties of the third component of human complement, *J. Immunol.*, **82**:458, 1959.

Berry, L. J., and T. D. Spies: Phagocytosis, *Medicine*, **28**:239, 1949.

Blattberg, B.: Increase in bactericidal activity as a result of injection of zymosan, *Proc. Soc. Exp. Biol. Med.*, **92**:745, 1956.

————: Antigenicity of zymosan, *ibid.*, **96**:81, 1957.

Bolyn, A. E., and M. Moskowitz: The recovery of tetanus antitoxin from toxin-antitoxin precipitates, *J. Immunol.*, **75**:441, 1955.

Bonventre, P. F., and L. L. Kempe: Physiology of toxin production by *Clostridium botulinum* types A and B. II. Effect of carbohydrate source on growth, autolysis, and toxin production, *Appl. Microbiol.*, **7**:372, 1959; III. Effect of pH and temperature during incubation on growth, autolysis, and toxin production, *ibid.*, **7**:374, 1959; I. Growth, autolysis, and toxin production, *J. Bact.*, **79**:18, 1960; IV. Activation of the toxin, *ibid.*, **79**:24, 1960.

Bordet, J., and O. Gengou: Sur l'existence de substances sensibilisatrices dans la plupart des sérums antimicrobiens, *Ann. Inst. Pasteur*, **20**:289, 1901.

Brooks, V. B., D. R. Curtis, and J. C. Eccles: Mode of action of tetanus toxin, *Nature*, **175**:120, 1955.

Califano, L., G. Pontieri, and G. Cavallo: Sugli aspetti morfologici della agglutinazione bacterica, *Giornale di Microbiol.*, **4**:1, 1957.

Cardella, M. A., J. T. Duff, C. Gottfried, and J. S. Begel: IV. Production and purification of type C toxin for conversion to toxoid, *J. Bact.*, **75**:360, 1958.

Cavallo, G., O. J. Plescia, K. Amiraian, and M. Heidelberger: III. Dependence of the extent of immune hemolysis upon temperature, *Giornale di Microbiol.*, **3**:1, 1957.

Chu, D. C. Y., R. E. Hoyt, and M. J. Pickett: Immunization to Vi and O antigens of *Salmonella typhi* using a stable antigen in oil, *J. Hyg.*, **54**:592, 1956.

Dolman, C. E.: Oral immunization, *Am. J. Med. Sci.*, **215**:327, 1948.

Dragstedt, C. A.: Anaphylaxis, *Physiol. Rev.*, **21**:563, 1941.

————: The significance of histamine in anaphylaxis, *J. Allergy*, **16**:69, 1945.

Duff, J. T., G. G. Wright, and A. Yarinsky: Activation of *Clostridium botulinum* type E toxin by trypsin, *J. Bact.*, **72**:455, 1956.

Ecker, E. E., and S. Seifter: The interrelation of corresponding complement components of man and guinea pig, *Proc. Soc. Exp. Biol. Med.*, **58**:359, 1945.

Ehrich, W. E., and T. N. Harris: Formation of antibodies in popliteal lymph node in rabbits, *J. Exp. Med.*, **76**:335, 1942.

Ekstedt, R. D.: Further studies on the antibacterial activity of human serum on *Micrococcus pyogenes* and its inhibition by coagulase, *J. Bact.*, **72**:157, 1956.

Felix, A., and R. M. Pitt: New antigen of B. typhosus; its relation to virulence and to active and passive immunisation, *Lancet*, **2**:186, 1934.

Giordano, A. S., C. S. Culbertson, and M. W. Higginbotham: Cardiolipin antigens in serologic tests for syphilis, *Am. J. Clin. Path.*, **18**:193, 1948.

Harris, A.: TPI test as a daily routine laboratory procedure, *Am. J. Pub. Health*, **46**:723, 1956.

Heidelberger, M.: National Academy of Sciences conference on complement, *Proc. Nat. Acad. Sci.*, **37**:185, 1951.

Hirsch, J. G.: Phagocytin: a bactericidal substance from polymorphonuclear leucocytes, *J. Exp. Med.*, **103**:589, 1956a; Studies of the bactericidal action of phagocytin, *ibid.*, **103**:613, 1956b.

————: Immunity to infectious diseases: review of some concepts of Metchnikoff, *Bact. Rev.*, **23**:48, 1959.

Holt, L. B.: The preparation of purified and concentrated diphtheria toxoid from a semi-synthetic medium, *Brit. J. Exp. Path.*, **29**:335, 1948.

Kabat, E. A.: Immunochemical studies on blood group substances, *Bact. Rev.*, **13**:189, 1949.

———— and D. Berg: Dextran—an antigen in man, *J. Immunol.*, **70**:514, 1953.

Kahn, R. L.: Universal serologic reactivity with lipid antigens, *Am. J. Pub. Health*, **37**:283, 1947.

————: Lipid antigen-antibody reactions given by different ethnic groups, *Atti del VI Congresso Internazionale di Microbiologia*, **2**:319, 1953.

————: Serology of syphilis based on recent observations, *Brit. J. Ven. Dis.*, **30**:124, 1954.

————: Tissue-cell defense strategy, *Mich. Alum. Quart. Rev.*, **61**:22, 1954.

————: Tissue response in immunity, *Ann. N.Y. Acad. Sci.*, **59**:281, 1955.

———— and E. B. McDermott: Kahn reactions with cardiolipin antigen compared with Kahn antigen. II. *Am. J. Clin. Path.*, **18**:364, 1948a.

———— and ————: The specificity of the Kahn reaction, *J. Mich. State Med. Soc.*, **47**:1095, 1948b.

Kierland, R. R.: Physical allergies, *Arch. Dermatol. Syphilol.*, **68**:61, 1953.

Kline, B. S.: Cardiolipin lecithin antigen, *Am. J. Clin. Path.*, **17**:874, 1947.

————: Development of a single standard slide test for syphilis, *ibid.*, **18**:185, 1948.

Kolmer, J. A., and E. R. Lynch: Cardiolipin antigens in the Kolmer complement fixation test for syphilis, *J. Venereal Disease Inform.*, **29**:166, 1948a.

Kolmer, J. A., and E. R. Lynch: Cardiolipin and Kolmer antigens in the complement fixation test for syphilis, *Texas State J. Med.*, **44**:312, 1948*b*.

———— and ————: An improved antigen for the Kolmer complement-fixation test for syphilis, *Am. J. Clin. Path.*, **18**:731, 1948*c*.

Kurosu, M.: Studies on the decomposition of diphtheria toxin by soil bacteria, *Jap. J. Exp. Med.*, **23**:347, 1953.

Landsteiner, K.: Zur Kenntnis der antifermentativen, lytischen und agglutinierenden Wirkungen des Blutserums und der Lymphe, *Centr. Bakt.*, **27**:357, 1900.

———— and A. S. Wiener: An agglutinable factor in human blood recognized by immune sera for rhesus blood, *Proc. Soc. Exp. Biol. Med.*, **43**:223, 1940.

Landy, M.: Enhancement of the immunogenicity of typhoid vaccine by retention of the Vi antigen, *Am. J. Hyg.*, **58**:148, 1953.

————: VI. Immunization of human beings with purified Vi antigen, *ibid.*, **60**:52, 1954.

————: Increase in resistance following administration of bacterial lipopolysaccharides, *Ann. N.Y. Acad. Sci.*, **66**:292, 1956.

————, A. G. Johnson, M. E. Webster, and J. F. Sagin: Studies on the O antigen of *Salmonella typhosa*. II. Immunological properties of the purified antigen, *J. Immunol.*, **74**:466, 1955.

———— and L. Pillemer: Elevation of properdin levels in mice following administration of bacterial lipopolysaccharides, *J. Exp. Med.*, **103**:823, 1956*a*.

———— and ————: Increased resistance to infection and accompanying alteration in properdin levels following administration of bacterial lipopolysaccharides, *ibid.*, **104**:383, 1956*b*.

———— and M. E. Webster: III. Immunological properties of purified Vi antigen derived from *Escherichia coli* 5396/38, *J. Immunol.*, **69**:143, 1952.

————, ————, and J. F. Sagin: V. Comparison of the immunological properties of Vi antigens derived from V form *Enterobacteriaceae*, *ibid.*, **73**:23, 1954.

Levine, L., and J. L. Stone: The purification of tetanus toxoid by ammonium sulfate fractionation, *J. Immunol.*, **67**:235, 1951.

Logan, G. B.: Steps toward a better understanding of the acute allergic reaction, *Ann. Allergy*, **18**:17, 1960.

Maurer, P. H.: III. The effect of physical and enzymatic treatments of gelatin on the subsequent precipitin reaction, *J. Exp. Med.*, **107**:125, 1958.

Mayer, R. L.: The experimental basis of antihistaminic therapy, *Intern. Rev. Otolaryngol.*, **11**:17, 1949.

Mazzini, L. Y.: Mazzini cardiolipin microflocculation test for syphilis, *J. Immunol.*, **66**:261, 1951.

McDermott, E. B., and R. L. Kahn: Differences in specificity of cardiolipin and Kahn antigens in 1949 National Serologic Evaluation Survey, *Univ. Hosp. Bull., Univ. Mich.*, **15**:93, 1949.

Metschnikoff, E.: "L'Immunité dans les maladies infectieuses," Paris, Masson et Cie, 1901.

Miller, J. L., M. H. Slatkin, M. Brodey, H. L. Wechsler, and J. H. Hill: Studies with the treponemal immobilizing test, *J. Am. Med. Assoc.*, **154**:1241, 1954.

Murray, E. G. D.: The balance of bacterial virulence, *Trans. Roy. Soc. Can.*, **49**:1, 1955.

Muschel, L. H., R. H. Chamberlin, and E. Osawa: Bactericidal activity of normal serum against bacterial cultures. I. Activity against *Salmonella typhi* strains, *Proc. Soc. Exp. Biol. Med.*, **97**:376, 1958.

Nelson, R. A., and M. M. Mayer: Immobilization of *Treponema pallidum*, in vitro, by antibody produced in syphilitic infection, *J. Exp. Med.*, **89**:369, 1949.

Neter, E.: Bacterial hemagglutination and hemolysis, *Bact. Rev.*, **20**:166, 1956.

Oakley, C. L., G. H. Warrack, and I. Batty: Sites of antibody production, *J. Path. Bact.*, **61**:179, 1949.

Pangborn, M. C.: A new serologically active phospholipid from beef heart, *Proc. Soc. Exp. Biol. Med.*, **48**:484, 1941.

Pappenheimer, A. M., Jr., and M. Yoneda: A reinvestigation of the diphtheria toxin-antitoxin flocculation reaction using ^{35}S-methionine-labelled toxin, *Brit. J. Exp. Path.*, **38**:194, 1957.

Pillemer, L.: Recent advances in the chemistry of complement, *Chem. Rev.*, **33**:1, 1943.

———, O. D. Ratnoff, L. Blum, and I. H. Lepow: The inactivation of complement and its components by plasmin, *J. Exp. Med.*, **97**:573, 1953.

———, R. G. Wittler, F. L. Clapp, and J. N. Adam, Jr.: IV. The preparation of purified diphtherial toxoid for clinical use, *J. Immunol.*, **78**:223, 1948.

Pope, C. G.: Observations on the diphtheria toxin-antitoxin reaction, *Brit. J. Exp. Path.* **38**:207, 1957.

Portnoy, J., and H. J. Magnuson: Immunologic studies with fractions of virulent *Treponema pallidum.* I. Preparation of an antigen by desoxycholate extraction and its use in complement fixation, *J. Immunol.*, **75**:348, 1955.

Price, I. N. O.: III. Choice of a formula for cardiolipin Wassermann antigen for use in the Whitechapel Wassermann technique, *Brit. J. Ven. Dis.*, **29**:175, 1953.

Rosenberg, L. T., M. H. Chandler, and E. E. Fischel: Passive cutaneous anaphylaxis with antigen-antibody complexes and additional antigens, *Proc. Soc. Exp. Biol. Med.*, **98**:451, 1958.

Ross, V.: A method for purifying diphtheria toxoid and combining it with protamine, *J. Immunol.*, **63**:183, 1949.

Roth, F. B., and L. Pillemer: Purification and some properties of *Clostridium welchii* type A theta toxin, *J. Immunol.*, **75**:50, 1955.

Sasaki, T.: Monosaccharide composition of the antigenic polysaccharide of *Pasteurella pseudo-tuberculosis rodentium, Nature,* **179**:920, 1957.

Skarnes, R. C., and D. W. Watson: Characterization of leukin: an antibacterial factor from leucocytes active against Gram-positive pathogens, *J. Exp. Med.*, **104**:829, 1956.

——— and ———: Antimicrobial factors of normal tissue and fluids, *Bact. Rev.*, **21**:273, 1957.

Spaun, J.: Biological standardization of typhoid vaccines by antibody measurements, *Acta Path. Microbiol. Scand.*, **39**:469, 1956.

Spero, L.: The alkaline inactivation of botulinum toxin, *Arch. Biochem. Biophys.*, **73**:484, 1958.

Stone, J. L.: On the mode of release of tetanus toxin from the bacterial cell, *J. Bact.*, **67**:110, 1954.

Suter, E.: Interaction between phagocytes and pathogenic microorganisms, *Bact. Rev.*, **20**:94, 1956.

Tauber, H., and W. Garson: Preparation and some properties of *Neisseria gonorrhoeae* endotoxin, *Proc. Soc. Exp. Biol. Med.*, **95**:669, 1957.

Tokuda, S., and R. S. Weiser: Anaphylaxis in the mouse produced with soluble complexes of antigen and antibody, *Proc. Soc. Exp. Biol. Med.*, **98**:557, 1958.

Wilkinson, A. E., and P. J. L. Sequeira: III. Use of the TPI as a verification test in suspected latent syphilis, *Brit. J. Ven. Dis.*, **31**:143, 1955.

Woiwood, A. J., and F. V. Linggood: Amino-acid constitution of diphtheria toxin and toxoid, *Nature*, **163**:218, 1949.

CHAPTER 26

Bacterial Diseases of Man

Diseases of man and animals are caused not only by bacteria but also by other classes of organisms such as protozoa, yeasts, molds, viruses, and rickettsiae.

Bacteria. Thousands of bacterial species have been studied, but only a very small number of these are capable of producing infection in man and animals. Some organisms are quite specific in that they attack only one host; others are less specific, being capable of naturally infecting more than one host. Scarlet fever occurs naturally only in man. The organism that produces glanders in horses attacks also goats, sheep, dogs, cats, rabbits, guinea pigs, and man. The anthrax bacillus attacks not only cattle, sheep, and horses but also man.

Protozoa. A large number of important diseases of man and animals are produced by protozoa. Among these may be mentioned malaria, which is produced by *Plasmodium vivax, P. malariae,* and *P. falciparum;* African sleeping sickness, caused by *Trypanosoma gambiense* and *T. rhodesiense;* amoebic dysentery, produced by *Endamoeba histolytica;* kala azar, produced by *Leishmania donovani;* and schistosomiasis, caused by at least three species of *Schistosoma.*

Yeasts. A few species of yeasts or yeast-like organisms are known to be parasitic on man and animals. *Candida albicans* produces generally an ulcerative condition of the mouth and throat, which may later become localized in some internal organ, such as the lungs, or produce a generalized infection. When the disease becomes confined to the mucous membranes of the mouth and throat, it is referred to as *thrush.*

North American blastomycosis is an ulcerative infection of the skin and subcutaneous tissues caused by *Blastomyces dermatitidis.* The organism sometimes invades the internal organs, such as lungs, spleen, and kidneys, and the bones.

Coccidioidal granuloma is produced by the yeast-like organism *Coccidioides immitis.* The disease manifests itself in so many forms that no general description can be given. Bronchial or pulmonary lesions are almost always present. The skin and subcutaneous tissues are usually involved. The lesions consist of firm or soft nodules, abscesses, ulcers, sinus infections, etc. The bones and joints may also be involved. The organisms appear in the tissues as large, round or spherical cells with thick cell walls. They are sometimes spoken of as double-contoured bodies. Spores appear in the larger cells. On maturity, the spore-filled cells rupture, releasing the spores. Each spore increases to full size and then repeats the cycle.

Molds. The molds and mold-like organisms produce several very important infections in man.

Probably the best known parasitic molds are those producing dermatophytosis in man. Several genera and species are involved. These organisms produce superficial infections of the keratinized epidermis, the hair, hair sheaths, nails, and skin. Infections by this group of molds are generally referred to as ringworm. When the infection is confined to the feet, it is called *athlete's foot*. Genera of organisms usually producing ringworm and athlete's foot include *Microsporum, Trichophyton,* and *Epidermophyton.*

BACTERIAL DISEASES OF MAN

The number of pathogenic bacteria is so large that it is beyond the scope of a textbook on fundamentals to give a detailed discussion of each disease and its specific etiological agent. For this reason, only a brief outline of the more important diseases of man and animals is included for convenient reference. Several excellent textbooks on the disease organisms are listed at the end of this section and may be consulted by those desiring additional information.

ACTINOMYCES

The *Actinomyces* are members of the order Actinomycetales, which have characteristics intermediate between the true bacteria and the molds. They produce a true mycelium. The vegetative mycelium fragments into elements of irregular size and may exhibit angular branching. Conidia are not produced. Not acid-fast. Anaerobic to microaerophilic.

Actinomyces israeli. Erect aerial hyphae produced under reduced oxygen tension. Hyphae occasionally septate but no spores formed. Measure 1 μ or more in diameter. Large club-shaped forms greater than 5 μ in diameter seen in morbid tissues. Substrate mycelium initially unicellular, and branches may extend into the medium in long filaments or may exhibit fragmentation and characteristic angular branching. Nonmotile. Not acid-fast. Gram-positive.

Disease Produced. Organism produces a granulomatous process, generally localized in the jaw, lungs, or abdomen, and characterized by swellings, at first firm but later breaking down to form multiple draining sinuses. Course of disease long and recovery seldom occurs.

Source of Infection. Oral cavity of man where organism lives around normal carious teeth and in tonsillar crypts without producing an apparent infection.

Mode of Transmission. From the mouth, organism may be swallowed, inhaled, or introduced into jaw tissues by injury. Not known to be transmissible from man to man or from animal to animal.

Incubation Period. Unknown.

Susceptibility and Immunity. Natural susceptibility is low. No immunity following an attack.

Prevalence. Occurs infrequently in man. All races may be affected. More common in males than in females. Disease primarily of domestic animals.

Prevention and Control. Hygiene of oral cavity. Inspection of meat and condemnation of infected carcasses. Destruction of sources of infection.

Disinfection of Discharges from Lesions. Care should be taken to prevent contact with lesions.

Treatment. Prolonged administration of sulfonamide drugs, penicillin, Aureomycin, or chloramphenicol.

BACILLUS

The anthrax organism belongs to the genus *Bacillus,* the members of which are capable of forming heat-resistant spores. Almost all the species are Gram-positive. With the exception of the anthrax bacillus, all members are saprophytic and usually not pathogenic. *B. subtilis* has been known to become pathogenic at times, but this is the exception rather than the rule. The members are typically aerobic, but some can grow in the almost complete absence of oxygen.

Spores are not produced under anaerobic conditions. On the other hand, the anaerobic spore-producing species do form spores under anaerobic conditions. This fact offers a means for the separation of the aerobic from the anaerobic spore formers. By the application of heat to a mixed culture, the vegetative cells are destroyed and leave only the anaerobic spores, which are capable of germinating into vegetative cells under favorable conditions.

Members of the genus *Bacillus* are universally distributed in soil and water. Spores and vegetative cells of such species are easily carried into the air by gentle air currents. This explains why viable spores of such organisms are universally present in air and are responsible for many laboratory contaminations of culture media and cultures.

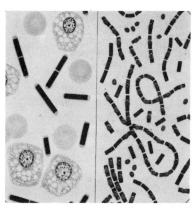

Fig. 246. *Bacillus anthracis.* Left, smear from the liver of an experimentally inoculated guinea pig; right, smear from a 72-hr. agar slant culture. (*From Muir, "Bacteriological Atlas," E. and S. Livingstone, Edinburgh, Scotland.*)

Bacillus anthracis. Cells rod-shaped, measuring 1 to 1.3 by 3 to 10 μ, with square or concave ends, and occurring in long chains. Spores ellipsoidal, measuring 0.8 to 1 by 1.3 to 1.5 μ, central or paracentral, often in chains, do not cause a bulging of the cell, and are produced only under aerobic conditions. They are not formed in the animal body. Germination polar. Nonmotile, Gram-positive.

Disease Produced. The cause of anthrax, an acute specific disease of cattle, sheep, and swine, sometimes occurring in workers handling wool and hides of animals affected with the disease (Fig. 246). Usually occurs as a febrile disease of animals that runs a rapid course and terminates in a septicemia. Mortality rate may run as high as 80 per cent. The infection causes a marked enlargement of the spleen, in which may be found enormous numbers of bacilli.

Two forms occur in man: cutaneous (malignant pustule) and internal anthrax. Cutaneous anthrax is produced by direct inoculation through a cut or abrasion in the skin. This type occurs most frequently in persons working with livestock. It is characterized by the appearance of a small furuncle within 12 to 24 hr. after entrance of the organisms. The furuncle ulcerates and discharges a seropurulent exudate, which may heal and disappear, or gangrene may set in followed by a septicemia. This usually terminates fatally in about 5 days.

The internal or pulmonary type is contracted by inhalation or by swallowing spores of *B. anthracis*. The disease is characterized by a pneumonia that generally terminates fatally. Before death, it is possible to isolate the organism from the sputum. The organism may also be recovered from the blood and spinal fluid.

Diagnosis. In the skin type, smears may be prepared from the seropurulent exudate and stained by Gram's method. The presence of large, Gram-positive, encapsulated organisms without spores is strong evidence for the presence of *B. anthracis*. The organism may be confirmed by guinea-pig inoculation. The animals usually die in 12 hr. to 3 days with a septicemia.

In the pneumonic type, sputum and blood are examined by the Gram technique. Cultures may be prepared by inoculating blood into broth and examining for characteristic organisms after an incubation period of 24 hr. A confirmation test may be made by guinea-pig inoculation as given above.

Source of Infection. Hair, hides, wool, flesh, and feces of infected animals and their manufactured products.

Mode of Transmission. Inhalation of spores, ingestion of insufficiently cooked food, mechanically by flies, accidental inoculation by wounds or scratch.

Incubation Period. Not over 7 days, usually less than 4. In pulmonary cases may be within 24 hr.

Susceptibility and Immunity. Man is less susceptible to the disease than the herbivora but more so than the carnivora. Immunity may develop after recovery from the disease. Active artificial immunity produced in animals by the use of a vaccine. This is not practiced in human beings.

Prevalence. Rarely in humans, and associated with occurrence of disease in animals or from handling hides, hair, and other products from infected animals. Epizootics occur in cattle and sheep.

Prevention and Control. Destruction of animals known to have the disease. Exposed animals should be immunized with vaccine. Milk from infected animal should not be used. Disinfection of discharges from lesions and of articles soiled by such discharges. All hair, wool, and bristles from sources not known to be free of anthrax should be disinfected. Human beings handling hides, wool, and hair should report immediately any skin abrasion. Infection has occurred from the use of shaving brushes and tooth brushes made from unsterilized bristles. Spores very resistant, being destroyed in the autoclave at temperatures above 120°C.

Isolation of infected human beings until lesions have healed. Disinfection of discharges from lesions and articles soiled by such discharges.

Treatment. Penicillin, tetracycline antibiotics, sulfadiazine, or anthrax antiserum.

For more information see Burdon (1956), Smith et al. (1956), Strange and Thorne (1958).

BORDETELLA

Genus includes three species of very small coccobacilli. Motile and nonmotile. On primary isolation, some species dependent upon complex media; all are hemolytic. Carbohydrates not fermented. A dermonecrotic toxin is produced. All are parasitic.

Bordetella pertussis. Minute coccobacilli, measuring 0.2 to 0.3 by 1 μ, occurring singly, in pairs, and occasionally in short chains. Capsules may be demonstrated. Show tendency to bipolar staining. Nonmotile. Gram-negative.

Blood medium excellent for isolation and maintenance. Charcoal may be used instead of blood in certain agar media.

Various forms of the organism have been isolated, including smooth, rough, and intermediate types. The smooth forms are pathogenic, whereas the rough and intermediate forms are not. The organisms may exist in four phases on the basis of serological reactions. Freshly isolated or phase I strains are encapsulated, virulent for laboratory animals, hemolytic, and require the presence of the X and V factors (see page 182). The phase I properties are lost on artificial cultivation, the organisms changing to phases II, III, or IV. Only virulent organisms in phase I are suitable for the production of vaccines.

Disease Produced. Believed to be the cause of whooping cough. The organism is sometimes referred to as the Bordet-Gengou bacillus after the names of its discoverers. Whooping cough is an acute, specific, infectious disease of the trachea and bronchi. It is characterized by a cough typical of the disease and lasts 1 to 2 months. The disease starts as a catarrhal condition followed by an irritating cough. The cough becomes paroxysmal after a period of 1 to 2 weeks. The paroxysms consist of a repeated series of violent coughs often followed by a characteristic long-drawn whoop during inhalation. Paroxysms are sometimes followed by vomiting. The period of communicability probably does not last longer than 3 weeks after the cough appears.

Whooping cough shows its greatest incidence in children under five years of age, and the death rate is highest in those under one year of age. Children suffering from the disease show a predisposition to infections by micrococci, streptococci, pneumococci, and tubercle bacilli.

Diagnosis. The organism may be recovered by the cough-plate method. This consists of exposing a Petri dish, containing an appropriate medium, before a patient's mouth during a cough in the early paroxysmal stage of the infection. The plate is then incubated, and characteristic colonies are isolated.

Source of Infection. Discharges from mucous membranes of larynx and bronchi of infected persons.

Mode of Transmission. Direct contact with an infected person or with the discharges from an infected person. Disease easily spread among children by personal contact. There is no evidence of a carrier state.

Incubation Period. Usually 7 days, almost always within 10 days, and not exceeding 21 days.

Susceptibility and Immunity. Susceptibility to disease general; no natural immunity. Children under seven most susceptible to infection. Children under two most susceptible to fatal attack. One attack confers a definite immunity but not for life; second attacks are known to occur. Passive immunity may be conferred by the use of immune or convalescent serum.

Prevalence. Common among children everywhere regardless of race or climate. About 15 per cent of cases occur in children under two years of age.

Prevention and Control. Vaccination of all children under five years of age. Especially advisable in infants two months old.

Isolation of infected individuals, especially from children. Disinfection of discharges from nose and throat of patient and articles soiled with such discharges. Brief passive immunity may be conveyed to young children by injection of appropriate amounts of hyperimmune or convalescent serum. The tetracycline antibiotics and chloramphenicol tend to abort the infection, but not the symptoms, although minor improvement may follow.

For more information see Cashman (1955), Kind (1958), Winter (1956).

BORRELIA

Members of this genus are classified under the order Spirochaetales, which have characteristics intermediate between the true bacteria and the protozoa. Cells measure 8 to 16 μ in length, with coarse, shallow, irregular spirals, a few of which may be obtuse-angled. Generally taper terminally into fine filaments. Parasitic upon many forms of animal life. Some are pathogenic for man, other mammals, or birds. Generally hematophytic or are found on mucous membranes. Some are transmitted by the bites of arthropods.

Borrelia duttonii. Cells spiral-shaped, measuring 0.35 to 0.5 by 8 to 16 μ, with pointed ends. Spiral amplitude 1.5 μ. Spirals large, wavy, inconstant, about five in number. Terminal finely spiral filaments present. Motility by active corkscrew motion without polarity. Gram-negative.

Disease Produced. The cause of Central and South African relapsing fever (Fig. 247). Pathogenic for mice and rats.

Disease characterized by short febrile paroxysms lasting 2 or 3 days, alternating with afebrile periods of 3 or 4 days. General eruption on the body. Relapses average 6 or 7.

Diagnosis. Diagnosis made by demonstrating the organisms in blood smears at time of second febrile attack, or from blood of mice or rats previously inoculated with the patient's blood.

Source of Infection. An infection of wild rodents transmitted by ticks of the genus *Ornithodorus.* In Texas and Kansas vector is *O. turicata;* in California, Colorado, and Idaho vector is *O. hermsi;* in Montana it is *O. parkeri;* in Panama and Central and South America it is *O. talaje;* and in tropical Africa it is *O. moubata.*

Mode of Transmission. Disease transmitted by bite of a tick.

Incubation Period. From 3 to 6 days, sometimes as short as 2 or as long as 12 days.

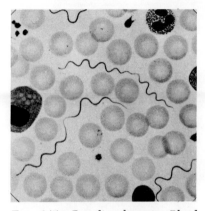

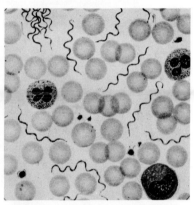

Fig. 247. *Borrelia duttonii.* Blood smear from a case of Central African relapsing fever. It is sometimes referred to as African tick fever. (*From Muir, "Bacteriological Atlas," E. and S. Livingstone, Edinburgh, Scotland.*)

Fig. 248. *Borrelia recurrentis.* Blood smear from a case of European relapsing fever. (*From Muir, "Bacteriological Atlas," E. and S. Livingstone, Edinburgh, Scotland.*)

Susceptibility and Immunity. Susceptibility is general. Active immunity produced during course of disease which overcomes the blood infection, resulting in disappearance of spirochetes from the circulation. Duration of immunity after recovery probably not more than 2 years.

Prevalence. Widespread throughout tropical Africa. Also observed in Spain, North Africa, Arabia, Iran, India, and other parts of central Asia, North and South America. In the United States cases have been reported from 13 widely distributed states.

Prevention and Control. Avoidance of tick-infested areas. Ticks are able to live and remain infective for years without feeding. Use of a tick repellent on trousers and hose.

Treatment. Penicillin, the tetracyclines, and chloramphenicol are effective.

For more information see Kawata, Matsuo, and Aoi (1956).

Borrelia recurrentis. Organisms cylindrical or slightly flattened, measuring 0.35 to 0.5 by 8 to 16 μ with pointed ends. Spiral amplitude 1.5 μ. Spirals large, wavy, inconstant, about five in number. Terminal finely spiral filaments present. Motility by active corkscrew motion without polarity. Gram-negative.

Disease Produced. The cause of European relapsing fever. Transmissible to monkeys, mice, and rats (Fig. 248).

Disease characterized by short febrile paroxysms lasting 2 or 3 days, alternating with afebrile periods of 3 or 4 days. General eruption on the body. Relapses vary from 1 to 10, usually not more than 2. Duration of disease 13 to 16 days.

Diagnosis. Diagnosis made by demonstrating the organisms in dark-field preparations of fresh blood or by inoculating rats with 15 to 25 ml. of patient's blood.

Source of Infection. Natural reservoir of infection not known. Lice become infective in about 16 days after biting an infected person and remain so for life.

Mode of Transmission. Probably by the bite of a louse and the rubbing of its feces into the abrasion in the skin.

Incubation Period. Usually 7 and as long as 12 days.

Susceptibility and Immunity. Susceptibility is general. Active immunity produced during course of disease. Duration of immunity after recovery probably not more than 2 years.

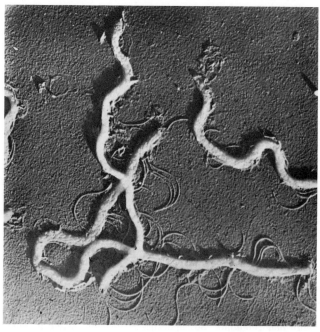

Fig. 249. Electron micrograph of *Borrelia vincentii.* ×11,000. (*After Hampp, Scott, and Wyckoff.*)

Prevalence. Disease prevalent among louse-infested primitive people. Found in parts of Europe, Asia, North and South Africa, and Central America. Has not been observed in the United States.

Prevention and Control. Application of insecticide at appropriate intervals to people living under poor, unhygienic conditions. Improvement of living conditions, including frequent bathing and washing of clothing.

Delousing of patient's clothing and bedroom. Application of insecticide to patient's clothing and body. Application of insecticide to all persons in contact with infected individuals.

Borrelia vincentii. Organisms measure 0.3 by 8 to 12 μ, with 3 to 8 irregular shallow spirals. Motile with a rapid, progressive, vibratory motion. Gram-negative.

Cells cultivated under anaerobic conditions. Cultures may show long forms with only a writhing motion (Fig. 249).

Disease Produced. B. vincentii occurs in association with *Fusobacterium fusiforme* in Vincent's angina, and in acute infection of the tonsils or neighboring parts, and is characterized by the appearance of a pseudomembranous inflamation followed by ulceration. Disease sometimes called *trench mouth* (Fig. 250). The lungs may also become involved. When this occurs, the patient may present the clinical and anatomical picture of pulmonary gangrene, pulmonary abscess, or bronchiectasis.

Cells of *F. fusiforme* are straight or slightly curved rods, 0.5 to 1 by 8 to 16 μ, occurring in pairs with blunt ends together and outer ends pointed, sometimes in short, curved chains or long spirillum-like threads. Granules present. Nonmotile. Anaerobic. Gram-negative.

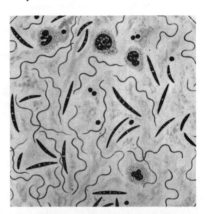

Diagnosis. Disease diagnosed by preparing smears direct from the deeper ulcerated areas, staining by Gram technique, and examining under oil-immersion objective. Characteristic smear shows presence of spirochetes and bacilli in large numbers.

Source of Infection. From deposit on teeth; the oral cavity.

Mode of Transmission. Disease not ordinarily communicable. Under unusual conditions of crowding, such as may prevail among soldiers, the infection may become transmissible. Disease appears to be associated with a state of lowered resistance. The tonsillar ulceration occurs often in individuals whose resistance has been lowered by such diseases as measles, tuberculosis, diabetes, and scarlet fever.

FIG. 250. *Borrelia vincentii* and *Fusobacterium fusiforme* growing in association. Smear prepared from a throat swab, taken from a case of Vincent's angina. (*From Muir, "Bacteriological Atlas,"* E. and S. Livingstone, Edinburgh, Scotland.)

Susceptibility and Immunity. Susceptibility to infection general. Acquired immunity does not follow recovery from the disease.

Prevention and Control. Local lesions usually controlled by treatment with arsenicals or penicillin. Neoarsphenamine, sulfarsphenamine, or bismarsen is effective in curing the pulmonary infection if administered during the first few days of the disease before the beginning of necrosis. Primary tropical ulcers which are caused by these symbiotic organisms also respond to treatment with penicillin.

For more information see Dean and Singleton (1945) and Omata (1959).

BRUCELLA

This genus includes a number of small pathogenic species that produce abortion in animals, Malta fever or undulant fever in man, and a wasting disease of chickens. They invade animal tissue, producing infections of the genital tract, the mammary gland or lymphatic tissues, and the intestinal tract. The genus *Brucella* is named after Bruce, who was the first to isolate the organism of undulant fever from the spleens of persons who had died of the disease on the island of Malta in the Mediterranean.

Brucella abortus. Cells short ellipsoidal rods, occurring singly, in pairs, and occasionally in chains, measuring 0.3 to 0.4 μ in length. Organism requires 10 per cent carbon dioxide for isolation; becomes aerobic after several transfers. Nonmotile. Gram-negative.

Disease Produced. The cause of contagious abortion in cattle. The same effects are produced in mares, sheep, rabbits, and guinea pigs. Causes undulant fever or brucellosis in man.

Brucellosis is a general infection with gradual or insidious onset and is characterized by irregular fever usually of prolonged duration, headache, sweating, chills, pain in the joints and muscles. The usual case follows a long febrile period, returning to normal by lysis. In this country febrile lapses are not common. Recovery is usual but disability may be pronounced.

Diagnosis. Since brucellosis is generally accompanied by a septicemia, a diagnosis can usually be made on the basis of a blood culture.

Agglutinins and complement-fixing antibodies are present in the serum of patients suffering from the disease. In the event the blood culture is negative, it is generally desirable to test the patient's serum for the presence of agglutinins. An agglutination titer of 1:100 or above is positive evidence of undulant fever.

Source of Infection. Tissues, blood, milk, and urine of infected animals, especially goats, swine, and cattle. Laboratory infections are quite common.

Mode of Transmission. Drinking milk from infected animals and by direct contact with infected animals or animal products.

Incubation Period. From 6 to 30 days or more, usually 14 days.

Susceptibility and Immunity. Most persons have some natural immunity or have acquired partial immunity by ingestion of small doses of the organism. Duration of immunity not known. One attack of undulant fever usually protects against a second attack.

Prevalence. More prevalent in males than in females, particularly in persons handling milk, cows, hogs, goats, and in those consuming raw milk of cows or goats. Occurs throughout the United States and Canada, affecting persons of all races. *Brucella suis* infections of greater occurrence in Middle West. Disease more prevalent from May to October.

Prevention and Control. Source of infection should be ascertained. Pasteurization of all milk supplies from cows and goats. Boiling of milk may be more practicable. Animals should be tested by agglutination technique and positive reactors segregated or slaughtered. Education of public and meat handlers on nature of disease and mode of transmission. Vaccination of calves. Care in handling and disposal of discharges and fetus from an aborting animal. Inspection of all meats, especially pork and pork products.

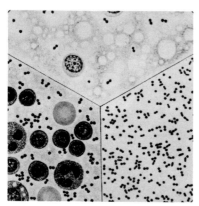

Fig. 251. *Brucella melitensis.* Upper, smear of milk from an infected goat; lower left, spleen smear from a case of Malta fever; lower right, smear prepared from a young culture. (*From Muir, "Bacteriological Atlas," E. and S. Livingstone, Edinburgh, Scotland.*)

Early recognition of disease. Disinfection of body discharges. The tetracycline antibiotics generally produce rapid subsidence of fever and symptoms within several days. Relapse may occur. More satisfactory results obtained from a combination of Aureomycin and dihydrostreptomycin over a period of at least 3 weeks. Blood transfusion may be necessary where acute anemia exists. Disease seldom fatal.

Brucella melitensis. Rods ellipsoidal, measuring 0.3 to 0.4 μ in length, occurring singly and in pairs, rarely in short chains (Fig. 251). Nonmotile. Gram-negative. Non-acid-fast.

Disease Produced. The cause of undulant fever (brucellosis) in man and abortion in goats. May infect cows and hogs and be excreted in their milk. Infectious for all domestic animals.

Undulant fever is a general infection with gradual or insidious onset and characterized by irregular fever usually of prolonged duration, sweating, chills, pain in the joints and muscles.

Diagnosis. Since brucellosis is generally accompanied by a septicemia, a diagnosis can usually be made on the basis of a blood culture. Blood cultures are positive in about 80 per cent of the cases after the second day and the infection may continue in the septicemic form for a number of months.

Agglutinins and complement-fixing antibodies are present in the serum of patients suffering from the disease. In the event the blood culture is negative, it is generally desirable to test the patient's serum for the presence of agglutinins. Agglutinins generally occur in the serum about the tenth day of the fever. An agglutination titer of 1:100, or above, is positive evidence of undulant fever. Since antiserum for *B. melitensis* will cross-agglutinate with *B. abortus* and *B. suis*, agglutinin-absorption tests are necessary for diagnosis.

Source of Infection. Tissues, blood, milk, and urine of infected goats. Disease spread to man through the milk of such animals. The disease in both goats and man is a septicemia. Laboratory infections are quite common.

Mode of Transmission. Drinking milk from infected animals and by direct contact with infected animals or animal products.

Incubation Period. From 6 to 30 days or more, usually 14 days.

Susceptibility and Immunity. Most persons have some natural immunity or have acquired partial immunity by ingestion of small doses of the organism. Duration of immunity not known. One attack of undulant fever protects against a second attack.

Prevalence. More prevalent in males than in females, particularly in persons handling milk, cows, hogs, goats, and in those consuming raw milk of cows or goats. Occurs throughout the United States and Canada, affecting persons of all races. Disease more prevalent from May to October.

Prevention and Control. Source of infection should be ascertained. Pasteurization of all milk supplies from cows and goats. Boiling of milk may be more practicable. Animals should be tested by agglutination technique and positive reactors segregated or slaughtered. Education of public and meat handlers on nature of disease and mode of transmission. Vaccination of animals. Care in handling and disposal of discharges and fetus from an aborting animal. Inspection of all meats, especially pork and pork products.

Early recognition of disease. Disinfection of body discharges. The tetracycline antibiotics generally produce rapid subsidence of fever and symptoms within several days. Relapse may occur. More satisfactory results obtained from a combination of Aureomycin and dihydrostreptomycin over a period of at least 3 weeks. Blood transfusion may be necessary where acute anemia exists. Disease seldom fatal.

Brucella suis. Rods ellipsoidal, measuring 0.3 to 0.4 μ in length, occurring singly and in pairs, rarely in short chains. Nonmotile, non-acid-fast. Gram-negative.

Disease Produced. The cause of undulant fever (brucellosis) in man and abortion in hogs. May infect cows and goats and be excreted in their milk. Infectious for all domestic animals.

Undulant fever is a general infection with gradual or insidious onset and characterized by irregular fever usually of prolonged duration, sweating, chills, pain in the joints and muscles.

Diagnosis. Since brucellosis is generally accompanied by a septicemia, a diagnosis can usually be made on the basis of a blood culture. Blood cultures are positive in about 80 per cent of the cases after the second day and the infection may continue in the septicemic form for a number of months.

Agglutinins and complement-fixing antibodies are present in the serum of patients suffering from the disease. In the event the blood culture is negative, it is generally desirable to test the patient's serum for the presence of agglutinins. Agglutinins generally occur in the serum about the tenth day of the fever. An agglutination titer of 1:100, or above, is positive evidence of undulant fever. Since antiserum for *B. suis* will cross-agglutinate with *B. melitensis* and *B. abortus*, agglutinin-absorption tests are necessary for diagnosis.

Source of Infection. Tissues, blood, milk, and urine of infected animals. Disease spread to man through the milk of such animals. The disease in both hogs and man is a septicemia. Laboratory infections are quite common.

Mode of Transmission. Drinking milk from infected animals and by direct contact with infected animals or animal products.

Incubation Period. From 6 to 30 days or more, usually 14 days.

Susceptibility and Immunity. Most persons have some natural immunity or have acquired partial immunity by ingestion of small doses of the organism. Duration of immunity not known. One attack of undulant fever usually protects against a second attack.

Prevalence. More prevalent in males than in females, particularly in persons handling milk, cows, hogs, goats, and in those consuming raw milk of cows or goats. Occurs throughout the United States and Canada, affecting persons of all races. Disease more prevalent from May to October.

Prevention and Control. Source of infection should be ascertained. Pasteurization of all milk supplies. Boiling of milk may be more practicable. Animals should be tested by agglutination technique and positive reactors segregated or slaughtered. Education of public and meat handlers on nature of disease and mode of transmission. Vaccination of animals. Care in handling and disposal of discharges and fetus from an aborting animal. Inspection of all meats, especially pork and pork products.

Early recognition of disease. Disinfection of body discharges. The tetracycline antibiotics generally produce rapid subsidence of fever and symptoms within several days. Relapse may occur. More satisfactory results obtained from a combination of Aureomycin and dihydrostreptomycin over a period of at least 3 weeks. Blood transfusion may be necessary where acute anemia exists. Disease seldom fatal.

For more information on the *Brucella* see Braun and Kelsh (1954), Gerhardt (1958), Holland and Pickett (1958), Newton and Wilson (1954), Ralston and Payne (1950).

CLOSTRIDIUM

Rod-shaped cells, often swollen at sporulation, producing clostridial, plectridial, clavate, or navicular forms. Motile by means of peritrichous flagella; occasionally nonmotile. Generally Gram-positive. Many species saccharolytic and fermentative, producing various acids, gases (CO_2, H_2, CH_4), and variable amounts of neutral products, i.e., alcohols and acetone. Other species proteolytic, some attacking proteins with putrefaction or more complete proteolysis. Strictly anaerobic or anaerobic, aerotolerant. Catalase lacking except in small amounts in certain aerotolerant forms. Few species obligately thermophilic. Exotoxins sometimes produced. Commonly found in soil and in the intestinal tracts of man and other animals.

Clostridium botulinum, Types B, C, D, E. *Cl. botulinum* comprises a large number of toxic species conveniently divided into a nonovolytic (*Cl. botulinum*) and an ovolytic (*Cl. parabotulinum*) group. Authorities are not yet in agreement on fermentation and on variant subtypes, and the present groups are only tentative and are subject to revision.

Cells rod-shaped with rounded ends, occurring singly, in pairs, and in short to occasionally long chains, measuring 0.5 to 0.8 by 3 to 8 μ. Motile with peritrichous flagella. Spores oval-shaped and located centrally, terminally, or subterminally. Gram-positive.

Disease Produced. The cause of botulism in man and limberneck in chickens. Pathogenic for monkeys, rabbits, guinea pigs, cats, and other animals. Produces a powerful exotoxin that is neurotoxic both on injection and on feeding.

Symptoms develop suddenly with gastrointestinal pain, headache, diarrhea or constipation, prostration, and several types of paralysis of the central nervous system, which are produced by the extracellular neurotropic toxin. Death occurs by cardiac or respiratory paralysis, usually in 3 to 7 days. Severity of symptoms depends upon the amount of toxin ingested in relation to body weight.

Diagnosis. Biological or toxicological tests may confirm presence of the organism or its toxin in suspected food.

Source of Infection. Contaminated smoked, pickled, or canned foods improperly processed (see page 628). Toxin produced only under anaerobic conditions. Toxin easily destroyed by boiling, but spores inactivated only at temperature of autoclave.

Mode of Transmission. Consumption of smoked, pickled, or canned foods containing the exotoxin from containers improperly processed. Most intoxications caused by consuming home-canned foods.

Incubation Period. Usually within 18 hr. after partaking of contaminated food, possibly longer, depending upon amount of food consumed and its toxin content.

Susceptibility and Immunity. Susceptibility to toxin is general. Passive immunity with specific antitoxin of value before symptoms have appeared.

Prevalence. Sporadic cases occur in all countries, usually from home-canned food.

Prevention and Control. Inspection of commercial processing of canned and preserved foods. Education of housewives in methods for the safe processing of home-canned foods. Since the toxin is destroyed on boiling, all home-canned foods should be boiled before serving.

Specific polyvalent antitoxin will neutralize the toxin and is of value before symptoms of disease have developed.

Clostridium histolyticum. Cells rod-shaped, occurring singly and in pairs, measuring 0.5 to 0.7 by 3 to 5 μ. Spores ovoid, subterminal, and cause a bulging of the rods. Motile with peritrichous flagella. Anaerobic, aerotolerant. Gram-positive.

Disease Produced. Originally isolated from war wounds. Apparently widely but sparsely dispersed in soil. Produces at least three antigenic components in toxic culture filtrates: (1) alpha, lethal and necrotizing toxin; (2) beta, collagenase; and (3) cysteine-activated proteinase which attacks altered collagen but not native collagen. Intramuscular injection of small amount of culture into guinea pig produces rapid digestion of muscle tissue. Not toxic on feeding. Pathogenic for small laboratory animals.

Source of Infection. Organism found in soil.

Mode of Transmission. Disease produced by entrance of organism into the broken skin, where it multiplies and produces an extracellular cytolytic toxin.

Susceptibility and Immunity. Susceptibility to toxin is general. Exotoxin may be neutralized by injection of homologous antitoxin.

Clostridium perfringens. Cells rod-shaped, short and plump, occurring singly, in pairs, less frequently in short chains. Measuring 1 to 1.5 by 4 to 8 μ. Spores ovoid, central to excentric, and do not cause a bulging of the rods. Capsules produced. Anaerobic. Nonmotile. Gram-positive.

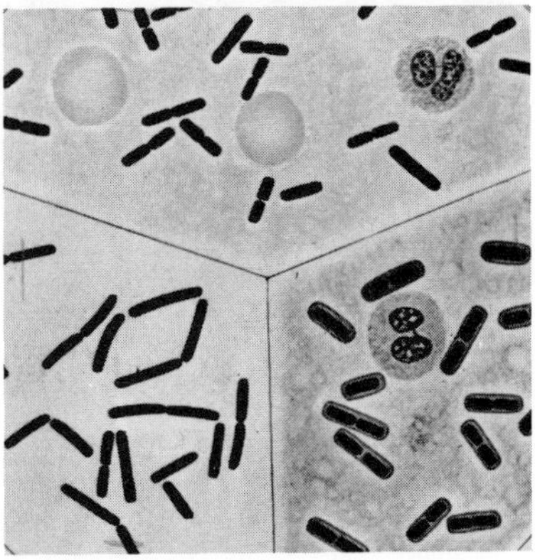

At least 6 types have been established on the basis of variety and nature of toxins present in culture filtrates. Type A is classic human gas gangrene organism; Type F, hemolytic enteritis and enteritis necroticans of humans. Antitoxin from any one type will neutralize the toxin from the other types.

Disease Produced. Isolated from wounds. This anaerobe is the most frequent cause of

FIG. 252. *Clostridium perfringens.* Upper, smear of the exudate from a case of human gas gangrene; lower left, smear from a young agar culture; lower right, another smear from a case of gas gangrene. (*From Muir, "Bacteriological Atlas," E. and S. Livingstone, Edinburgh, Scotland.*)

gas gangrene in man (Fig. 252). The organism produces extensive necrosis and considerable gas in tissues. The gas bubbles cause an expansion in the tissues accompanied by pressure, which results in cutting off the blood supply. This causes the tissues to die. Organisms may be recovered from liver and heart blood.

Cl. perfringens produces a powerful exotoxin which may be obtained in crude form by filtering a culture of the organisms. The exotoxin aids in weakening the patient. The injection of animals with culture filtrates results in the development of a potent antitoxin.

Source of Infection. Soil, street dust, milk, human and animal feces.

Mode of Transmission. Disease due to entrance of organism into the broken skin or wound, where it multiplies and secretes a potent exotoxin.

Susceptibility and Immunity. Susceptibility to infection general. Passive immunity by means of antitoxin may be used for prophylaxis.

Prevention and Control. Antitoxic serums have been used both for prophylaxis and therapeutic administration, and beneficial results have been reported.

For more information see Meyer and Moskowitz (1955) and Smith (1949).

Clostridium tetani. Cells rod-shaped with rounded ends, occurring singly, in pairs, often in long chains and filaments, measuring 0.4 to 0.6 by 4 to 8 μ. Motile with peritrichous flagella. Spores spherical, terminal, and cause a bulging of the rod. Anaerobic. Gram-positive.

Disease Produced. The cause of tetanus in man (Fig. 253). Disease characterized by headache, difficulty in swallowing and opening of the mouth, owing to spasms of the masseter muscles. This is accompanied by a slight stiffness of the neck and spasm of the cheek muscles. Spasms may spread to trunk and back. Swallowing becomes increasingly difficult. Organisms only rarely invade tissues but remain localized in the wound, where they secrete a powerful toxin. The inoculation of horses and other animals with culture filtrates results in development of a powerful antitoxin.

Diagnosis. Disease diagnosed by preparing smears from infected materials, staining by Gram's method, and examining under the microscope for typical cells with spores.

Source of Infection. Soil, street dust, human and animal feces, especially the latter.

Mode of Transmission. Disease produced by entrance of organism into the broken skin or wound, where it multiplies and secretes a powerful exotoxin. Toxin intensely toxic on injection but not on feeding.

FIG. 253. *Clostridium tetani.* Smear from a 72-hr. glucose agar stab culture. The spores are round and situated at one end of the rod. (*From Muir, "Bacteriological Atlas," E. and S. Livingstone, Edinburgh, Scotland.*)

Incubation Period. Symptoms develop after the toxin reaches the central nervous system. This may vary from 4 days to 5 weeks, depending upon the character, extent, and location of wound.

Susceptibility and Immunity. Susceptibility is general. Active artificial immunity may be produced by use of tetanus toxoid (page 685). Three doses of 1 ml. each at intervals of 3 weeks are generally given and are considered capable of producing a high concentration of antitoxic antibodies. Immunity said to last for about 5 years. Toxoid precipitated by alum and given in two injections of 1 ml. each at intervals of 2 to 4 weeks has been reported to produce a greater and more rapid immunity than toxoid.

Prevalence. World-wide in distribution. Most frequent in North America among young males, and in summer months. Prevalent especially in wounds contaminated with fertile or manured soil.

Prevention and Control. Active immunization with tetanus toxoid desirable for those likely to be exposed to infection. Active immunization with toxoid advisable in infancy or early childhood.

The use of tetanus antitoxin is an effective protection against the disease. The injection of about 1500 U.S.A. units of antitoxin in slight injuries and about 2000 to 3000 U.S.A. units in more severe injuries will prevent tetanus. Since antitoxin tends to disappear, an additional injection should be given within 10 days.

After disease has developed, large doses of antitoxin are injected by spinal puncture. At the same time, an intravenous injection of about 10,000 units should be administered. The intraspinal injection should be repeated every 24 hr. until three doses have been given. If intraspinal doses cannot be given, larger intravenous injections should be administered.

For more information see Moss, Waters, and Brown (1955).

CORYNEBACTERIUM

The members of the genus are slender, straight to slightly curved rods, with irregularly stained segments or granules. Frequently show pointed or club-shaped swellings at the ends. Snapping division produces angular and palisade (picket-fence) arrangements of cells. Gram-positive to variable, sometimes young cells and sometimes old cells being Gram-negative. Granules invariably Gram-positive. Generally quite aerobic, but microaerophilic or even anaerobic species occur. Some pathogenic

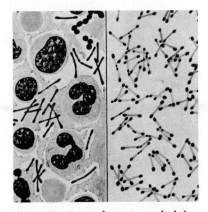

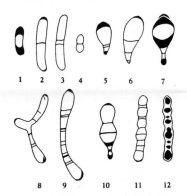

FIG. 254. *Corynebacterium diphtheriae.* Left, smear prepared from a throat swab taken from a case of diphtheria; right, smear from a 12-hr. culture on Loeffler's blood serum medium. (*From Muir, "Bacteriological Atlas," E. and S. Livingstone, Edinburgh, Scotland.*)

FIG. 255. Typical cell forms of *Corynebacterium diphtheriae.* 1, 2, 3, 4, short and long rod-shaped forms; 5, 6, 7, forms club-shaped at one end; 8, branched form; 9, cell club-shaped at both ends; 11, form with cell walls; 12, same cell with nuclear material in the cell compartments. (*After Hewitt.*)

species produce a powerful exotoxin. The group is widely distributed in nature. The best-known species are parasites and pathogens on man and domestic animals. Several species are well-known plant pathogens; still other common species are found in dairy products, water, and soil.

Corynebacterium diphtheriae. Cells rod-shaped, varying greatly in size from 0.3 to 0.8 by 1 to 8 μ, occurring singly. Rods straight or slightly curved, frequently club-shaped at one or both ends. As a rule, rods do not stain uniformly with methylene blue but show alternate bands of stained and unstained material, and one or more metachromatic granules which are best shown by special stains. Nonmotile. Gram-positive (Figs. 254 and 255).

Disease Produced. The cause of diphtheria in man. Pathogenic for guinea pigs, kittens, and rabbits. The organism localizes in the throat, where it produces a powerful extracellular toxin which is absorbed into the blood stream and may cause death unless neutralized by antibodies known as antitoxin.

Diphtheria is an acute, febrile infection, generally of the nose, throat, and tonsils. The throat becomes considerably inflamed, especially the fauces, where a grayish false membrane is formed. The membrane may eventually spread to the entire respiratory tract. The toxic action of the organism results in the destruction of the superficial layer of cells. This is followed by the exudation of a plasma-like fluid which clots and covers the surface of the injured mucous membrane with a tough elastic network of fibrin in which are embedded dead cells and bacteria. The toxin elaborated by the organisms produces an injurious action on the kidneys and muscles of the heart. Injury to the heart is probably the most important action of the toxin.

Carriers. Convalescents usually harbor the organisms for 3 to 4 weeks, after which the bacteria gradually disappear. Three negative throat examinations are generally required before a convalescent is released from quarantine. However, studies on the bacterial flora of normal throats have revealed the presence of a surprisingly high percentage of persons who habitually have the diphtheria organisms in their throats. These are chronic carriers and of no importance unless the organisms are of the virulent type. Whether they are or not can be determined in the laboratory by performing virulence tests on animals.

Diagnosis. A sterile swab is rubbed over the tonsillar region of the throat or the pharynx and then streaked over the surface of coagulated serum known as Loeffler's medium. The swab is also rubbed over the surface of a glass slide and stained with methylene blue. The culture is incubated at 37°C. for 24 hr., and the slide is examined under the microscope for the presence of characteristic barred and granular rods. The slide examination gives a preliminary idea of what to expect from the culture.

Since the culture on blood serum will show the presence of many kinds of organisms, it is necessary to streak some of the mixed growth over the surface of a solid medium contained in a Petri dish to obtain *C. diphtheriae* in pure form. An excellent preparation for this purpose is known as cystine-tellurite medium. Typical colonies of *C. diphtheriae* on this medium are opaque and dark gray or black in color. The organisms are capable of absorbing the potassium tellurite and reducing it to the colored metal. Characteristic colonies are transferred to tubes of Loeffler's coagulated serum medium, incubated at 37°C. for 24 hr., then tested for virulence.

Virulence Test. The method generally employed is the intracutaneous test, performed as follows: Two guinea pigs are used, one being the control. The abdomens of the animals are shaved. The control pig is given 250 units of diphtheria antitoxin intraperitoneally. The growth from a 24-hr. culture of the organism to be tested is emulsified in about 20 ml. of salt solution and 0.15 ml. injected intracutaneously into each pig. If the culture contains virulent diphtheria bacilli, it will produce toxin which will have no effect on the immunized pig but will produce in the other pig a definite local inflammatory lesion in 24 hr. which becomes necrotic in 48 to 72 hr.

Schick Test. This test is employed to determine the susceptibility of an individual to diphtheria. The test is performed as follows: Diphtheria toxin is diluted so that 0.1 ml. contains one-fiftieth of the minimum lethal dose (M.L.D.) required to kill a 250-gm. guinea pig in 96 hr. One-tenth milliliter of toxin so diluted is injected intracutaneously in the arm. The same amount of heated toxin is injected in the other arm as a control. The injected areas are examined daily for several days. Usually the fourth day gives the most reliable readings. The reactions may be recorded as follows:

1. A positive test is indicated by the presence of a slightly raised area of redness 1 to 2 cm. in diameter which appears in 24 to 36 hr. and reaches a maximum in 48 to 72 hr. The reaction persists for about 1 week, then gradually fades, and finally disappears. The control arm shows no reaction.

2. A negative test does not show an area of redness in the test or control arm.

Source of Infection. Discharges from diphtheritic lesions of the pharynx, larynx, trachea, nose, conjunctiva, and vagina; secretions from the healthy pharynx and nose of carriers.

Mode of Transmission. Disease spread from person to person by fingers; by articles such as eating utensils, toys, pencils, handkerchiefs containing nasal discharges and saliva; and by inhalation of droplets expelled from the throat during coughing and sneezing.

Incubation Period. Usually 2 to 5 days, sometimes longer.

Susceptibility and Immunity. One attack of diphtheria usually confers immunity for life. Resistance to disease increases with age. This is believed to be caused by continued exposure to the disease. Passive temporary immunity for a few days or weeks can be conferred, and active immunity of prolonged duration can be artificially induced.

Prevalence. Endemic and epidemic. Disease occurs more frequently in temperate zones and during fall and winter months. One-half of deaths occur in children under five years of age before they have had an opportunity to develop immunity to disease.

Prevention and Control. Isolation of suspected cases of diphtheria. Persons showing a positive Schick test may be susceptible to the disease. All children should be vaccinated against the disease. Active immunization of susceptible individuals may be practiced by use of two types of preparations: (1) toxoid and (2) alum-precipitated toxoid (page 685).

Toxoid. Toxoid is prepared by treating toxin with formaldehyde to destroy its toxic properties without affecting its ability to stimulate the production of antitoxin. Usually three doses at intervals of 1 month are necessary to give a negative Schick test.

Alum-precipitated Toxoid. Toxoid precipitated with alum is superior to ordinary toxoid as an immunizing agent. The precipitate is insoluble and remains in the tissue for a longer period of time before it is completely absorbed. This affords a more prolonged antigenic response. Usually two injections are necessary to render Schick-positive individuals negative.

Milk should be pasteurized to render it free of possible contamination.

Disinfection of all articles which have been in contact with patient, and all articles soiled by discharges of patient.

Therapy. Passive immunization with diphtheria antitoxin in clinical cases. The antitoxin is administered as early in the disease as possible. The dosage is about 10,000 units in mild cases and 30,000 to 50,000 units in severe cases. The antitoxin neutralizes the damaging effect of the toxin (see page 686). Passive immunization lasts usually 2 to 4 weeks. If infection still persists, the dose should be repeated. Penicillin may be used in conjunction with antitoxin but is not a substitute for the latter.

For more information see Beattie (1949); Bojlén and Scheibel (1955); Bowen, Wyman, and McComb (1954); Davis and Mudd (1955); Hewitt (1950); and Saint-Martin (1948).

DIPLOCOCCUS

The pneumococcus (*Diplococcus pneumoniae*) is the causative agent of lobar pneumonia. The disease is nearly always caused by this organism, although other bacteria are occasionally involved.

Diplococcus pneumoniae. Cells oval or spherical, measuring 0.5 to 1.25 μ, typically in pairs, occasionally singly or in short chains. The distal ends of each pair of cells tend to be pointed or lancet-shaped. Encapsulated. Nonmotile (Figs. 256 and 257). Young cells Gram-positive. Usually grow poorly or not at all on artificial media.

Whole bile or 10 per cent solutions of sodium taurocholate or sodium glycocholate added to actively growing broth cultures will dissolve the organisms.

The pneumococci are generally classified according to types. The cells contain two types of antigens: (1) the so-called "somatic antigen" and (2) the "polysaccharide hapten" or soluble specific substances (SSS). The somatic antigen is probably a nucleoprotein and is found to react with all pneumococci regardless of types. The carbohydrate hapten is type specific and serves to differentiate the various types. In other words, by means of immunological reactions, the various types of pneumococci can be distinguished from one another by the composition of the polysaccharide comprising the capsular material. These polysaccharides belong to a group of substances called haptens, or partial antigens. They are not antigenic in themselves but may become so when combined with protein (see page 682).

At least 32 types of *D. pneumoniae* are recognized on the basis of serological reactions, chiefly the *Quellung* phenomenon as induced by type-specific immune rabbit serums.

Typing of Pneumococci. A number of methods are employed for the determination of pneumococcal types:

1. Precipitin Test. A sample of sputum (about 1 ml.) from a suspected case of pneumonia is injected into the peritoneal cavity of a mouse. The animal will appear sick in about 8 hr. The mouse is usually killed after this period of time, the peritoneal cavity opened, and the exudate washed into a Petri dish with the aid of about 2 ml. of saline solution. The washings are centrifugated, and the supernatant liquid is used for the precipitin test.

2. Microscopic Agglutination Test. The peritoneal exudate is prepared as given under (1), and small drops of the washings are placed on a slide. The various type serums are added to the drops and spread out in thin films. The films are allowed to dry, then stained and examined under the microscope for the presence of clumps. The

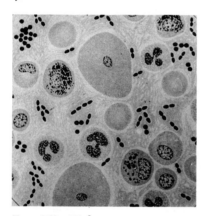

FIG. 256. *Diplococcus pneumoniae.* Smear of sputum from a case of lobar pneumonia. (*From Muir, "Bacteriological Atlas," E. and S. Livingstone, Edinburgh, Scotland.*)

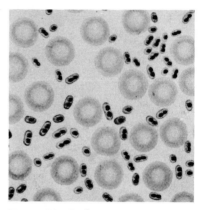

FIG. 257. *Diplococcus pneumoniae.* Smear prepared from the heart blood of an infected mouse. (*From Muir, "Bacteriological Atlas," E. and S. Livingstone, Edinburgh, Scotland.*)

type of serum producing clumps indicates the type of organism present in the peritoneal exudate.

3. Quellung Test. This test is based on the observation that the capsules of pneumococci become swollen when placed in contact with specific immune serum. A loopful of undiluted immune serum is placed on a slide and mixed with a fleck of sputum. A loopful of dilute methylene blue solution is then added and the mixture examined under the microscope. If the mixture is homologous, the capsules will appear swollen with very distinct outlines. The test is made with many types of antiserums and as many flecks of sputum.

Pneumococci, regardless of serological type, manifest three chief culture phases or stages: mucoid, smooth, and rough. The mucoid form represents the typical phase of the species. The most frequently observed dissociative trend is $M \rightarrow S \rightarrow R$. Serological types are recognizable only in the mucoid form, owing to the presence of type-specific polysaccharides in the capsular material. Both smooth and rough forms are devoid of capsular material, but possess species-specific antigens common to all members of the species. Smooth and rough forms are nonpathogenic, possess distinctive growth characteristics, and require special technique for accurate observations.

Disease Produced. The commonest cause of lobar pneumonia, the incidence being as high as 95 per cent. The organism is present in the alveoli and bronchioles of the lung, in the lymph channels, and sometimes in the blood. The organism may also produce pericarditis, arthritis, meningitis, otitis media, mastoiditis, endocarditis, rhinitis, tonsillitis, conjunctivitis, septicemia, osteomyelitis, and peritonitis.

Diagnosis. Organisms may be detected by appropriate laboratory examinations of sputum discharges of the respiratory tract.

Source of Infection. Sputum, blood, and exudates in pneumonia; cerebrospinal fluid in meningitis; saliva from respiratory tract of normal individuals.

Mode of Transmission. Direct contact with infected person or carrier; inhalation of droplets expelled from the throat during coughing and sneezing.

Incubation Period. Generally believed to be 1 to 3 days.

Susceptibility and Immunity. Resistance generally high but may be lowered by exposure to wet and cold, by physical and mental fatigue, and by alcoholism. Acquired immunity may follow an attack of pneumonia. Immunity relatively slight and of short duration.

Prevalence. Affects a large proportion of the population. No race, color, or sex exempt. Occurs in all climates but most often in winter and spring and in colder regions. Epidemics occur under conditions of crowding.

Prevention and Control. Crowding in living and sleeping quarters should be avoided. General resistance should be maintained by adequate nourishing food, sufficient sleep, fresh air, and personal hygiene.

Isolation of suspected cases of pneumonia. Disinfection of discharges from nose and throat, and articles soiled by such discharges.

Treatment consists of intramuscular or oral administration of the appropriate form of penicillin. Tetracycline antibiotics equally effective. Sulfonamides and erythromycin are usually effective.

Mortality rate has been reduced to an insignificant figure since the employment of antibiotics.

For more information see Lund (1957).

ESCHERICHIA

The escherichiae are short rods, motile or nonmotile. Glucose and lactose fermented with production of acid and gas. Acetylmethylcarbinol not produced. Methyl red test positive. Carbon dioxide and hydrogen produced in approximately equal volumes from glucose. Generally not able to utilize uric acid as sole source of nitrogen. Found in feces; occasionally pathogenic to man, producing enteritis, peritonitis, cystitis, etc. Gram-negative. Widely distributed in nature.

Disease Produced. E. coli is a normal inhabitant of the intestinal tract of man and other vertebrate animals. It is generally nonpathogenic; in certain instances it has been found to overcome the defense mechanisms of the body to produce septicemia, peritonitis, inflammation of the liver and gall bladder, cystitis, meningitis, and other infections. Since the organism is found in the intestinal contents, its presence in water and foods generally means contamination with fecal material.

GAFFKYA

The members of this genus occur in the animal body and in special media as tetrads, whereas in ordinary culture media they occur in pairs and irregular masses. Aerobic to anaerobic. The most important species is G. tetragena.

Gaffkya tetragena. Cells spherical, measuring 0.6 to 0.8 μ in diameter, with pseudocapsule (in body fluids) surrounding four of the cells showing typical tetrads. Gram-positive.

Disease Produced. G. tetragena is generally believed to be a normal inhabitant of sputum or saliva. It is found in tuberculous sputum, in the blood in cases of septicemia, in the pus of abscesses, and in the spinal fluid in meningitis. It appears to be a secondary invader of low virulence, invading the tissues only when weakened by some other infectious organism. Pathogenic for Japanese mice (Fig. 258).

HAEMOPHILUS

This genus contains several important disease-producing species. Cells are minute, rod-shaped, sometimes thread-forming, and pleomorphic. Nonmotile. Gram-negative.

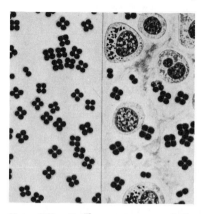

Strict parasites, growing only in presence of certain growth accessory substances. May or may not be pathogenic. Found in various lesions and secretions, as well as in normal respiratory tracts of vertebrates.

Haemophilus influenzae. Cells are minute rods, measuring 0.2 to 0.3 by 0.5 to 2.0 μ, occurring singly, in pairs, occasionally in short chains, at times as long thread forms. Frequently show a marked tendency to bipolar staining. Some strains are encapsulated. Nonmotile. Gram-negative.

H. influenzae is an obligate parasite and grows only in the presence of hemoglobin and other body fluids. It will not grow in the absence of the X and V factors present in blood (see page 182). On the basis of the precipitin reaction, six types (A to F) are recognized. The majority of the strains from the respiratory tract are not type specific.

FIG. 258. *Gaffkya tetragena.* Left, smear from a 24-hr. agar slant culture; right, smear of sputum from a case of chronic tuberculosis. (*From Muir, "Bacteriological Atlas," E. and S. Livingstone, Edinburgh, Scotland.*)

Disease Produced. H. influenzae was at one time believed to be the etiological agent of influenza, but evidence now points to the fact that the disease is caused by a filterable virus (see page 775). The organism is commonly present in the normal nose and throat and has been found to be a secondary invader in a number of bacterial and virus infections, including scarlet fever, measles, chicken pox, and whooping cough. It is also believed to be responsible for cases of endocarditis, sinusitis, meningitis, bronchopneumonia, and acute infectious conjunctivitis, or "pinkeye" (Figs. 259 and 260). Type B organisms have been found to be the cause of severe throat infections in children.

Source of Infection. Discharges from nose and throat or articles soiled by such discharges.

Mode of Transmission. Contact with an infected person; use of towels or other freshly contaminated articles; inhalation of droplets expelled during coughing, sneezing, and talking.

Incubation Period. Usually 24 to 72 hr.

Susceptibility and Immunity. Children under five years most often affected; incidence decreases with age. Immunity after attack low-grade and variable.

Prevalence. May be isolated from pharynges of almost all normal individuals, and virulent encapsulated strains are found in chronic infections of the nasal sinuses and in the pharynges following viral colds.

Prevention and Control. Isolation of infected individuals; avoidance of overcrowding; disinfection of articles soiled by discharges from nose and throat.

The antibiotics Aureomycin, Terramycin, and streptomycin have been found useful in controlling infections.

For more information see Waterworth (1955).

Haemophilus ducreyi. Small rods, measuring 0.5 by 1.5 to 2 μ, with rounded ends, occurring singly and in short chains. Nonmotile. Gram-negative. Requires the X factor for growth.

Disease Produced. The cause of soft chancre or chancroid, an acute inflammatory lesion that occurs upon the genitals or, less frequently, the skin surrounding the

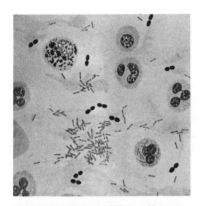

FIG. 259. *Haemophilus influenzae.* Smear of sputum from a case of *influenzal pneumonia.* The oval-shaped cells are *D. pneumoniae.* (*From Muir, "Bacteriological Atlas,"* E. *and* S. *Livingstone, Edinburgh, Scotland.*)

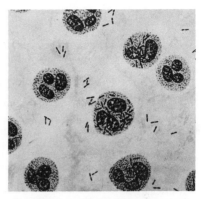

FIG. 260. *Haemophilus influenzae.* Smear of pus from a case of acute conjunctivitis. (*From Muir, "Bacteriological Atlas,"* E. *and* S. *Livingstone, Edinburgh, Scotland.*)

genitals. Lesion starts as a small pustule which eventually ruptures to form an open ulcer. Infection easily spreads to other areas. Genital lesions frequently accompanied by painful inflammatory swelling and suppuration of regional lymph nodes.

Source of Infection. Discharges from ulcerated lesions (Fig. 261).

Mode of Transmission. Chiefly by sexual intercourse or by articles soiled with discharges from ulcerated lesions. Organism quickly loses its viability outside of body and soon dies.

Incubation Period. From 3 to 5 days, or longer.

Susceptibility and Immunity. Susceptibility to disease is general; probably no natural immunity. One attack does not confer protection against subsequent infection.

Prevalence. Widespread in distribution. Particularly common where sexual promiscuity occurs.

Prevention and Control. Disease spread largely by sexual contact. Prophylactic measures before, during, and following exposure to disease.

Avoid sexual contact until lesions are healed. Sulfonamides appear to be specific for disease. Aureomycin and chloramphenicol may be used if organisms have developed resistance to sulfonamides. It is not a serious disease and yields readily to local treatment.

For more information see Deacon et al. (1954, 1956).

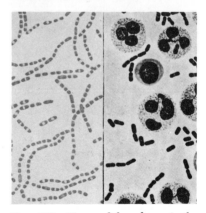

FIG. 261. *Haemophilus ducreyi,* the cause of soft chancre or chancroid. Left, smear from blood culture; right, smear from a soft chancre. (*From Muir, "Bacteriological Atlas,"* E. *and* S. *Livingstone, Edinburgh, Scotland.*)

Haemophilus aegyptius. Small rods, measuring 0.25 to 0.5 by 1 to 2.5 μ, occurring singly, occasionally in short chains, and at times in the form of threads. Show bipolar staining. Nonmotile. Gram-negative. Requires both V and X factors for growth.

Disease Produced. The cause of sore eyes or pinkeye. Lacrimation, irritation, and vascular injection of conjunctivae of one or both eyes, followed by edema of the lids, photophobia, pain, and mucopurulent discharge. A nonfatal disease lasting 2 to 3 weeks. In most cases disease runs a mild course.

Source of Infection. Discharges from conjunctiva or upper respiratory tract of infected persons.

Mode of Transmission. Contact with infected persons through contaminated fingers, or articles soiled with such discharges.

Incubation Period. Generally 24 to 72 hr.

Susceptibility and Immunity. Children under five most often affected; incidence decreases with age. Immunity of low grade and variable.

Prevalence. Disease widespread throughout world, particularly in warmer climates. Largely confined to southern states and California in summer and early autumn.

Prevention and Control. Personal cleanliness, and treatment of affected eyes.

Isolation of affected individuals. Disinfection of discharges and articles soiled by such discharges.

Specific treatment consists of local application of Aureomycin, Terramycin, and streptomycin.

For more information see Huet (1956).

KLEBSIELLA

Klebsiella pneumoniae was first isolated by Friedländer and is usually referred to as Friedländer's bacillus. It is not infrequently found associated with upper respiratory infections in man. In most instances the organism appears to be present as a secondary invader. Less than 1 per cent of pneumonias are caused by this organism.

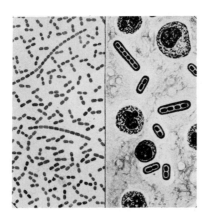

Klebsiella pneumoniae. Rods measuring 0.3 to 0.5 by 5 μ, with rounded ends, occurring singly and in pairs. Encapsulated. Nonmotile. Gram-negative (Fig. 262).

Disease Produced. Associated with infections of the respiratory, intestinal, and genitourinary tracts of man. Isolated from the lungs in lobar pneumonia. Associated with pneumonia and other inflammations of the respiratory tract. May also produce otitis media, empyema, pericarditis, meningitis, and septicemia.

Source of Infection. Buccal and nasal discharges of infected persons or carriers; articles contaminated with such discharges.

Mode of Transmission. By droplet spread; direct contact with infected person or carrier; articles soiled with discharges from nose and throat of such person.

Susceptibility and Immunity. Organism carried in nasopharynx of 1 per cent of normal individuals. Susceptibility of low grade, highest in infants and young children and in the aged. Immunity relatively slight and of short duration.

FIG. 262. *Klebsiella pneumoniae* (Friedländer's bacillus). Left, smear from a culture; right, smear of sputum. (*From Muir, "Bacteriological Atlas," E. and S. Livingstone, Edinburgh, Scotland.*)

Prevention and Control. Isolation of infected persons; concurrent disinfection of discharges from mouth, nose, and contaminated articles. Treatment consists in the use of streptomycin during the acute phase, then of tetracyclines and chloramphenicol.

For more information see Ørskov (1957).

LEPTOSPIRA

The leptospirae are finely coiled organisms 6 to 20 μ in length. Spirals 0.3 μ in depth and 0.4 to 0.5 μ in amplitude. In liquid medium one or both ends are bent into a semicircular hook, each involving one-tenth to one-eighth of the organism. Spinning movements in liquid and vermiform in semisolid agar, forward or backward. Stain with difficulty except with Giemsa stain and silver impregnation. Require oxygen for growth. Chiefly saprophytic organisms, being found in water, and sometimes in normal mouth. Most important member producing disease is *L. icterohaemorrhagiae*, the cause of infectious jaundice or Weil's disease. Most satisfactory method of differentiation based on antigenic structure of leptospires, which can be determined by agglutination-lysis and cross-absorption tests.

Leptospira icterohaemorrhagiae. Cells measure 0.25 to 0.3 by 6 to 9 μ; occasionally 20 to 25μ in length. Spiral amplitude 0.4 to 0.5 μ, regular, rigid; spiral depth 0.3 μ regular. One or more gentle waves occur throughout the entire length. In liquid media, one or both ends may be semicircularly hooked; in semisolid media, organism appears serpentine, waved or bent. Very active flexibility. Axial filament does not extend beyond cell body. Flagella absent.

Disease Produced. The cause of infectious jaundice or Weil's disease in man. Found also in the blood of dogs and wild rats (Fig. 263). An acute systemic infection characterized by headache, malaise, muscular pains, gastrointestinal symptoms, vomiting, and fever at the start, followed by jaundice. About half of patients do not develop jaundice. Relapses occurring in about 20 per cent of all cases. About same percentage of cases are fatal. In severe cases hemorrhages may occur at various sites, and kidney damage may be marked. Organisms found in blood and urine of patients.

Diagnosis. Disease diagnosed by inoculating guinea pigs or hamsters with blood taken early in course of disease.

Source of Infection. Urine and feces of rats, dogs, cats, mice, and other animals. Water and soil become contaminated with discharges of infected animals.

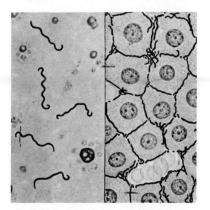

Fig. 263. *Leptospira icterohaemorrhagiae,* the cause of Weil's disease or infectious jaundice in man. Left, smear of urine; right, section of liver from an infected rat. (*From Muir, "Bacteriological Atlas," E. and S. Livingstone, Edinburgh, Scotland.*)

Mode of Transmission. Infection in man probably occurs through rubbing contaminated soil into the skin, eyes, and nose, or from swallowing contaminated water. Disease shows selection for such trades as fish dealers, abattoir workers, sewer workers, miners, veterinarians, and agriculturists. Occasionally infections result from handling dogs and other animals. Organism can penetrate uninjured skin.

Incubation Period. From 4 to 19 days, usually 9 to 10 days.

Susceptibility and Immunity. Susceptibility is general. A refractory state develops following recovery. Immune bodies may be demonstrated for a considerable period after recovery. Urine may show the presence of the organism for months after convalescence.

Prevalence. Disease of world-wide distribution in rats. Sporadic cases in humans reported throughout the United States.

Prevention and Control. Avoidance of swimming in potentially contaminated waters. Rodent control in human habitations.

Disinfection of urine and feces of patients.

Penicillin, streptomycin, and the tetracyclines are leptospirocidal in vitro but of undemonstrated value in vivo.

Vaccine has been employed with promising results. Horse antiserum has been used to advantage.

For more information see Alexander et al. (1956); Burgdorfer (1956); Cox, Stover, and Treick (1958); Hamdy and Ferguson (1957).

MORAXELLA

These organisms are small, short rods which occur as diplobacilli and which are sometimes described as diplococci; occasionally occur singly. Nonmotile. Gram-negative. Do not require V or X factors for growth. Aerobic. Found as parasites and pathogens in warm-blooded animals, being especially found in association with diseases of the eye.

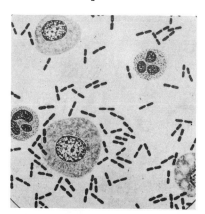

Moraxella lacunata. Short rods, 0.4 to 0.5 by 2 μ, occurring singly, in pairs, and in short chains. Ends rounded or square in the chains.

Disease Produced. The cause of subacute infectious conjunctivitis, or angular conjunctivitis which usually attacks both eyes (Fig. 264). There is rarely much swelling or ulceration of the conjunctiva. Condition runs a subacute or chronic course.

Diagnosis. Made by smear preparations of the pus, which is especially abundant during the night.

Source of Infection. Discharges from conjunctivas.

Fig. 264. *Moraxella lacunata.* Smear of lachrymal secretion from a case of chronic conjunctivitis. (*From Muir, "Bacteriological Atlas," E. and S. Livingstone, Edinburgh, Scotland.*)

Mode of Transmission. Contact with an infected person or with articles freshly soiled with discharges from such a person.

Susceptibility and Immunity. Disease may be produced in human beings by inoculation. No acquired immunity.

Prevention and Control. Isolation of patient; disinfection of conjunctival discharges and articles soiled by such discharges.

For more information see Murray and Truant (1954).

MYCOBACTERIUM

The genus includes a number of species which differ from the great majority of bacteria in containing a higher content of waxy or fatty substances. This material is stained with difficulty but when once stained, resists decolorization with acid. Because of this fact, they are called acid-fast organisms. The members produce diseases characterized by the presence of nodules or tubercles in various organs.

Organisms grow as slender, straight, or slightly curved rods; occasionally slender filaments, but branched forms rarely seen. Nonmotile. Aerobic. Non-spore-forming. Gram-positive.

Mycobacterium tuberculosis. Rods, 0.3 to 0.6 by 0.5 to 4 μ, straight or slightly curved, occurring singly and in occasional threads. Sometimes swollen, clavate, or even branched. Stain uniformly or irregularly, showing banded or beaded forms. Acid-fast. Gram-positive. Growth in all media slow, requiring several weeks for development. Contains mycolic acid, to which it owes its acid-fastness.

Disease Produced. The cause of tuberculosis in man, monkey, dog, and parrot.

Experimentally very pathogenic for guinea pigs but not for rabbits, cats, goats, oxen, or domestic fowls (Fig. 265).

Disease characterized by insidious onset with parenchymal pulmonary infiltration, recognizable by X-ray examination before constitutional symptoms or physical signs appear. Pleurisy almost always first symptom. Advanced disease accompanied by cough, fever, fatigue, and loss in weight.

Diagnosis. Suspected material such as sputum, urine, feces, cerebrospinal fluid, or stomach contents is examined for the presence of tubercle bacilli.

Sputum may be smeared on a slide and stained by the Ziehl-Nelsen acid-fast technique. The presence of typical organisms is usually indicative of infection with the tubercle bacilli.

It is usually advisable to concentrate the tubercle bacilli before making laboratory tests. This may be performed as follows: The infected material is treated with 3 per cent sodium hydroxide to digest the sputum, pus, or other material with which the organisms are mixed. The digested material is then neutralized with acid and centrifugated. Only the sediment is retained. The sediment may be used for (1) preparation of smears for staining and direct microscopic examination, (2) injection into animals, or (3) inoculation of culture media.

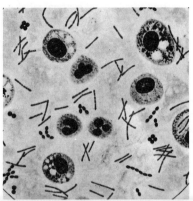

Fig. 265. *Mycobacterium tuberculosis.* Smear of sputum from a case of pulmonary tuberculosis. (*From Muir, "Bacteriological Atlas," E. and S. Livingstone, Edinburgh, Scotland.*)

Animal Inoculation. A guinea pig is inoculated in the groin or the muscle of the thigh with some of the sediment. Enlargement of the regional lymphatic glands occurs in 2 or 3 weeks, and the animal usually dies in about 6 to 8 weeks. On autopsy, the animal shows necrotic areas in the liver and spleen and enlarged lymph nodes filled with caseous material. The lungs and kidneys are rarely attacked.

Inoculation of Culture Media. Some of the sediment may be used for the inoculation of appropriate culture media. A variety of media may be used, consisting largely of egg, glycerin, and some dye to kill or inhibit the growth of contaminating organisms. The media are tubed, slanted, then sterilized by heat. During the heating process, the egg albumin is coagulated, producing a solid medium.

Use of Tuberculins. A large number of tuberculins are available. They are prepared in different ways but consist of filtrates of liquid cultures of the tubercle bacillus. They contain certain products liberated after the death and disintegration of the organisms.

The first tuberculin preparation, known as "Koch's old tuberculin," is prepared as follows: The organisms are cultivated in a slightly alkaline 5 per cent glycerin peptone broth for 6 to 8 weeks. The culture is concentrated in a water bath, heated to 80°C., until reduced to one-tenth of its original volume. The culture is then filtered to remove bacterial debris. The clear filtrate contains the tuberculin.

Tuberculins are used to test the sensitiveness of persons or animals to proteins of the tubercle bacillus. By injecting tuberculin intradermally, a positive test appears in 6 to 8 hr., reaches a maximum in 24 to 48 hr., and generally subsides in 6 to 10 days. It is characterized by a reddening of the skin about 1 cm. in diameter. The reaction is positive in those having active or healed lesions. Since most individuals have healed tuberculous lesions, the test is of limited value.

Source of Infection. Discharges from lesions or articles freshly soiled with discharges, the most important being sputum. Of less importance are discharges from the intestinal and genitourinary tracts, or from lesions of the lymph nodes, bone, and skin. Milk from tuberculous cattle.

Prevalence. One of the most common communicable diseases of man; endemic in practically all populations and races. Incidence and mortality rates declining. Mortality highest among infants and adults beyond middle age.

Mode of Transmission. Through discharges of the respiratory tract, less frequently through discharges of the digestive tract; by inhaling droplets expelled during coughing, sneezing, talking, or singing; by kissing; by use of contaminated eating and drinking utensils; by contaminated dust, flies, etc. Infection results usually from continued contact with an infected individual.

Incubation Period. Variable, depending upon type of disease, age, etc. Probably not less than 1 month, usually much longer.

Susceptibility and Immunity. Susceptibility to infection is general; higher in children under three years of age, lowest from three to twelve years, then relatively high for the remainder of life. Greater in undernourished, fatigued, and neglected persons than in well-fed and well-cared-for persons.

Natural immunity to disease generally negative.

Prevention and Control. Education of public to danger of tuberculosis, mode of spread, and methods of control. Avoid overcrowding. Improve working and living conditions. Isolation and treatment of infected individuals. Pasteurization of milk and milk products. Separation of babies from tuberculous mothers at birth. Slaughtering of tuberculous cattle. Tuberculous patients should be prohibited from handling foods for public consumption.

Disinfection of sputum and articles soiled with it, such as handkerchiefs, towels, paper, and eating and drinking utensils. Disinfection of rooms previously occupied by tuberculous patients. Vaccination of uninfected individuals with BCG (Bacillus Calmette-Guérin) may be useful. Cure based largely on rest, good wholesome food, fresh air, sunshine, and freedom from worry. Surgical, chemotherapeutic, and antibiotic therapy are all supplementary and cannot be substituted for the basic rest treatment.

Combination of streptomycin and para-aminosalicylic acid (PAS) is commonly employed in adults for 6 months to a year or more. Isoniazid either alone or in combination with PAS or streptomycin, or both, is also useful.

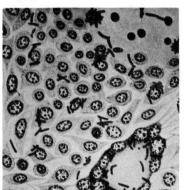

For more information see Bloch and Segal (1955); Crowle (1958); Dubos (1949); Frappier and Guy (1949, 1950); Hardy et al. (1958); Long (1953); Noll (1956); Penso (1954); Pottenger (1948); Riggins and Hinshaw (1949); Rosenthal, Leslie, and Loewinsohn (1948); U.S. Public Health Service (1957).

Mycobacterium bovis. Rods shorter and more plump than the human variety, measuring 1 to 1.5 μ. Short rods often mixed with longer forms. Cells may stain solidly or show a banded or beaded appearance. Less easily cultivated than human species. Acid-fast. Gram-positive.

Fig. 266. *Mycobacterium bovis.* Section of udder of cow suffering from chronic tuberculosis. (*From Muir, "Bacteriological Atlas," E. and S. Livingstone, Edinburgh, Scotland.*)

Disease Produced. The cause of tuberculosis in cattle. May be transmitted to man and domestic animals. Pathogenic for ox, man, monkey, goat, sheep, pig, cat, parrot, cockatoo, and other birds. Experimentally highly pathogenic for rabbit and guinea pig. More highly pathogenic for animals than human type (Fig. 266).

Source of Infection. Tuberculous cows may eliminate organisms in feces, urine, and milk. Milk from infected udders may contain enormous numbers of the organisms.

Mode of Transmission. Infection spread to healthy cows through milk, urine, and feces of diseased cows. Children, particularly those under five years of age, may become infected by drinking contaminated milk from diseased cows.

Susceptibility and Immunity. Susceptibility to infection is general; higher in children under three years of age, lowest from three to twelve years.

Natural immunity to disease generally negative.

Prevention and Control. Education of public to danger of tuberculosis, mode of spread, and methods of control. Isolation and treatment of infected individuals. Pasteurization of milk and milk products. Slaughtering of tuberculous cattle. Tuberculous patients should be prohibited from handling foods for public consumption.

Disinfection of discharges and articles soiled with such discharges. Disinfection of rooms previously occupied by tuberculous patients. Vaccination of uninfected individuals with BCG may be useful. This is a bovine strain rendered avirulent by cultivating for many generations on a bile-glycerol-potato medium. This change appears to be permanent, the loss of virulence not being restored when the organisms are again transferred to the usual culture media. Cure based largely on rest, good wholesome food, fresh air, sunshine, and freedom from worry. Surgical, chemotherapeutic, and antibiotic therapy are all supplementary and cannot be substituted for the basic rest treatment.

Combination of streptomycin and para-aminosalicylic acid (PAS) is commonly employed in adults for 6 months to a year or more. Isoniazid either alone or in combination with PAS or streptomycin, or both, is also useful.

Mycobacterium leprae. Cells rod-shaped, measuring 0.3 to 0.5 by 1 to 8 μ, with parallel sides and rounded ends, staining evenly or at times beaded. When numerous, as from nodules, they are generally arranged in clumps, rounded masses, or in groups of bacilli side by side. Strongly acid-fast. Gram-positive.

Disease Produced. The cause of Hansen's disease, or leprosy in man. Leprosy is a chronic disease which occurs in three forms: (1) anesthetic (nerve) type, (2) nodular (muscle) type, and (3) mixed (combination of 1 and 2) type. Death is rarely due to leprosy but to some secondary invader. Disease shows a low rate of infectivity.

Diagnosis. The bacilli occur in enormous numbers in nodular (lepromatous) cases of the disease and sparsely in the neural form. The disease may be recognized by lesions of the skin and mucous membranes and by neurological manifestations. The present bacteriological means of identification depend on (1) acid-fast staining and (2) failure of the organism to grow on bacteriological media or in laboratory animals. Heated suspensions of the bacilli recovered from nodules produce a positive lepromin reaction in 75 to 97 per cent of normal persons and of neural cases of leprosy, but usually produce no reaction in lepromatous individuals.

Source of Infection. Discharges from lesions.

Mode of Transmission. By intimate and prolonged contact with lepers. Nodules on skin may liquefy, ulcerate, and discharge great masses of the bacilli. Patients showing the presence of acid-fast organisms in smears, even though ulcers are not present, are potentially open cases. It is generally believed that the disease is the result of living under filthy, unsanitary conditions, but there is very little evidence to substantiate this statement. Children contract the disease more easily than adults. Babies of lepers rarely, if ever, become infected if separated at birth. Workers in leper colonies seldom contract the disease.

Incubation Period. Not known, although some claim that it is 1 to 7 years.

Susceptibility and Immunity. Susceptibility uncertain. No racial immunity.

Prevention and Control. Leprosy may be contracted in adult life but is usually acquired in childhood. Infants born of leprous patients should be separated at birth.

Positive cases should be isolated in leprosaria until disease has been arrested. Usually three negative bacteriological tests at intervals of 6 months are required before a patient is released. Paroled individuals should be reexamined every 6 months thereafter. Discharges and articles soiled with discharges should be disinfected. Living premises of patient should be thoroughly cleaned. Treatment based chiefly on rest, good food, fresh air, sunshine, and freedom from worry. Surgical, chemotherapeutic, and antibiotic therapy are all supplementary and cannot be substituted for the basic rest treatment.

Specific treatment consists of administration of sulfones (promin, diasone, diamino-diphenylsulfone (D.D.S.) for long periods. Promin given intravenously, diasone and D.D.S. orally. Streptomycin has value and may be substituted for sulfones.

For more information see Badger (1955); Chatterjee (1955); Erickson (1950); Floch, Fauran, and Mailloux (1957); Hanks (1950); Lavaditi and Chaigneau-Erhard (1951).

NEISSERIA

Genus includes a number of important Gram-negative cocci. Cells occur in pairs with adjacent sides flattened. Growth on nonenriched media may be poor. Aerobic or facultatively anaerobic. Parasites of animals so far as known.

Neisseria gonorrhoeae. Cells spherical, measuring 0.6 to 1 μ, occurring singly and in pairs, the sides flattened where they are in contact and are usually described as coffee-bean-shaped.

Disease Produced. N. gonorrhoeae is the causative agent of gonorrhea in man (Fig. 267). The organism attacks chiefly the human urethra in both sexes, producing an acute catarrhal condition. There is a marked tendency for the infection to spread, producing in the male epididymitis, prostatitis, cystitis, and other inflammatory conditions. In the female, the entire genitourinary tract may be involved, including the cervix. The organism may also invade the blood stream and be carried to various parts of the body. The organism shows a predilection for the synovial membranes of the joints, producing gonorrheal rheumatism, and for the heart valves, causing endocarditis. Organisms may persist for many years and are probably never completely eliminated.

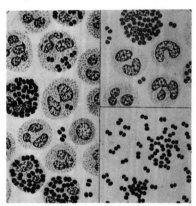

FIG. 267. *Neisseria gonorrhoeae,* the cause of gonorrhea. Left, a smear of pus showing the presence of the organism within the polymorphonuclear leucocytes; upper right, same but stained differently; lower right, smear from a pure culture. (*From Muir, "Bacteriological Atlas," E. and S. Livingstone, Edinburgh, Scotland.*)

Ophthalmia neonatorum. This is an inflammation of the conjunctiva in the newborn which is a consequence of maternal infection. If neglected this is probably the most common cause of blindness. Approximately 10 per cent of all cases of blindness are due to gonorrheal infections. This is easily prevented by instillation of one or two drops of 2 per cent silver nitrate in the eyes of the newborn.

Diagnosis. Direct smears are prepared from the urethral or conjunctival discharges and stained by the Gram method. The smears are examined for the presence of Gram-negative intracellular diplococci slightly flattened at their adjacent surfaces. The organisms may be cultivated by streaking some of the urethral pus over the surface of a blood agar plate and incubating the plate in an atmosphere containing 10 per cent of carbon dioxide. This may be approximated by placing the plate in a screw-cap jar with a lighted candle and replacing the cover.

Oxidase Test. The gonococcus produces an oxidase which causes a 1 per cent solution of dimethyl-paraphenylenediamine to turn first pink, then rose, magenta, and finally black. The test is made by flooding a 24-hr. agar plate culture with the reagent and noting the development of the above series of colors.

Source of Infection. Purulent venereal discharges; blood and pus from infections of the conjunctiva and joints.

Mode of Transmission. Infection in almost every case is transmitted by direct contact from person to person (sexual intercourse); rarely by direct contact with articles freshly soiled with discharges of such persons.

Incubation Period. From 1 to 14 days, usually 3 to 5 days.

Susceptibility and Immunity. Susceptibility is general. An attack of gonorrhea produces very little, if any, immunity.

Prevention and Control. Adequate diagnostic facilities for identification of the gonococcus. Public facilities for prompt and adequate treatment of infected persons. Education of public on mode of transmission and how to avoid infection. Control or elimination of houses of prostitution. Personal hygiene before or immediately after promiscuous sexual intercourse.

Disinfection of discharges from lesions and articles soiled with such discharges.

Specific treatment consists in administration of procaine penicillin in one intramuscular injection.

Neisseria meningitidis. Spherical cells 0.6 to 1 μ in diameter, occasionally larger; occur singly, in pairs with adjacent sides flattened, or occasionally in tetrads. Gram-negative.

Meningococci generally differentiated into four main groups on the basis of agglutination reactions with immune serum. Groups designated as A, B, C, and D. Most strains may be placed into one or another of these four types. As is true with the pneumococci, presence of carbohydrate capsular substances is believed to be responsible for the immunological specificities of the various meningococcal types.

Disease Produced. N. meningitidis is the cause of epidemic meningitis. The disease is characterized by fever, intense headache, nausea, often vomiting, and frequently a skin rash. Delirium and coma may appear early.

The organism attacks the base and cortex of the brain and the surfaces of the spinal cord. The organism is present in the spinal fluid. If growth is heavy, the fluid may be turbid. The organisms may appear both free and within the leucocytes. N. meningitidis is frequently present in the blood stream of patients with meningitis. The organism has also been isolated from persons with arthritis or pericarditis and from the nasopharynx of those with rhinopharyngitis.

Diagnosis. The meningococcus is present in large numbers in the spinal fluid of persons with the disease and may be diagnosed by centrifugating the spinal fluid and examining stained smears of the sediment. The typical picture is the presence of Gram-negative intracellular diplococci. Typical smears of the meningococcus and gonococcus are indistinguishable. They may be distinguished by their cultural reactions.

N. meningitidis may be cultivated by streaking some sediment from spinal fluid over the surface of a blood agar or heated (chocolate) blood agar plate. The plate is then incubated in an atmosphere containing about 10 per cent carbon dioxide.

As in the case of gonococcus, this organism also produces an oxidase that is capable of oxidizing dimethyl-paraphenylenediamine to a black color. The test is made by flooding a 24-hr. plate culture with a 1 per cent

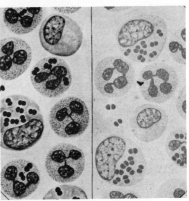

Fig. 268. *Neisseria meningitidis,* the cause of meningococcus meningitis. Left, smear of sediment from a centrifugalized specimen of spinal fluid; right, same but stained differently. (*From Muir, "Bacteriological Atlas," E. and S. Livingstone, Edinburgh, Scotland.*)

solution of the reagent and noting the development of a black color in colonies of the meningococcus.

Source of Infection. Organisms found in the nasopharynx, blood, cerebrospinal fluid, conjunctiva, pus from joints, etc., of persons suffering from the disease (Fig. 268).

Mode of Transmission. The disease is disseminated by direct contact and by droplet infection during coughing and sneezing. The organism is frequently found in the nasopharynx of healthy persons. Such individuals are referred to as carriers because they are able to spread the disease to others. Organisms are very easily killed when outside the body and probably never reach a new individual except by direct contact Epidemics generally develop during periods of overcrowding as occur in army camps.

Incubation Period. From 2 to 10 days, usually 7 days.

Susceptibility and Immunity. Susceptibility to disease slight. Younger age groups more susceptible, but disease may occur at any age. Agglutinins against the organisms are demonstrable in the blood stream after an infection, but the duration of immunity is uncertain.

Prevalence. Endemic and epidemic. Widely distributed throughout the world. Occurs most frequently during winter and spring. An epidemic wave may last 2 to 3 years.

Prevention and Control. Isolation of infected individuals.

Prevention of overcrowding.

Disinfection of discharges from nose and throat, and articles soiled with such discharges.

Specific treatment consists in administration of a large oral dose of sulfadiazine, followed by smaller doses thereafter. In addition, penicillin or one of the tetracyclines may be used.

For more information see Branham (1953, 1956).

PASTEURELLA

The pasteurellae are small, ellipsoidal to elongated rods which show bipolar staining by special methods. Gram-negative. Facultatively anaerobic. May require low oxidation-reduction potential on primary isolation. Parasitic on man, other animals, and birds.

Pasteurella pestis. Rods, 1 by 2 μ, occurring singly. Characteristic bladder, safety-pin, and ring involution forms. Nonmotile. Polar staining. Gram-negative.

Disease Produced. The causative organism of plague in man, rats, ground squirrels, and other rodents. Infectious for mice, guinea pigs, and rabbits.

Human plague may be of three types: (1) bubonic, (2) pneumonic, and (3) septicemic.

Bubonic plague is a severe and highly fatal disease, characterized by high fever, weakness, buboes, sometimes pustules and subcutaneous hemorrhages. The bacteria are carried through the blood and lymph vessels to the lymph glands in the groin, armpits, neck, etc. The bacteria multiply, produce pus, and cause an enlargement of the glands. The glands may ulcerate and discharge their contents. The enlarged glands are referred to as buboes, and the infection is known as bubonic plague.

Pneumonic plague gives the picture of a virulent septic pneumonia. The lungs become engorged, and hemorrhages appear under the pleura. Bacteria are found in large numbers in the peribronchial lymph spaces and in the adjoining alveoli.

The disease may be mild, or it may take an acute septicemic form which generally produces rapid death.

Diagnosis. Blood cultures prove positive in about 30 per cent of cases. Direct smears can be prepared from open buboes, or such material can be inoculated into culture media. If the material is contaminated, it can be purified by inoculating a guinea pig and isolating the plague bacillus from the heart's blood. In the pneumonic type, the organisms are usually present in large numbers in sputum and may be recognized by direct smear.

Source of Infection. Organisms found in buboes, blood, pleural effusion, spleen, and liver of infected persons and rodents. In addition, organisms present in the sputum in cases of pneumonic plague (Fig. 269). The infection usually reaches man through contact with diseased rats.

Mode of Transmission. Transmitted from rat to rat and from rat to man by infected rat fleas, the most important of which are *Xenopsylla cheopis* and *Ceratophyllus fasciatus.* The flea becomes infected by feeding on a diseased rat. The flea next feeds on a person and at the same time deposits feces and possibly some regurgitated blood. The bacilli are then rubbed into the skin by scratching.

Incubation Period. Usually 3 to 6 days.

Susceptibility and Immunity. Susceptibility to disease is general. Immunity after recovery is temporary and relative. Active immunization with a plague bacterin may confer protection for some months. Repeated stimulating injections are necessary.

Prevalence. Rarely occurs in North America. Sporadic cases occur where persons are exposed to infected wild rodents. Disease distributed in various parts of the world.

Prevention and Control. Rat extermination, ratproofing, and other necessary measures. Ratproofing of ships.

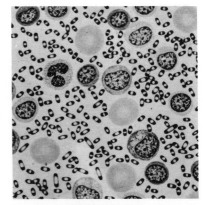

FIG. 269. *Pasteurella pestis,* the cause of bubonic, pneumonic, and septicemic plague in man. Smear prepared from a bubo. (*From Muir, "Bacteriological Atlas,"* E. and S. Livingstone, Edinburgh, Scotland.)

Isolation of infected individuals. Disinfection of sputum and articles soiled with sputum in pneumonic type. Terminal disinfection of walls, floors, and furniture of rooms occupied by patients with plague.

Streptomycin and the tetracyclines are highly effective for all forms of plague when used early. Recurrence of fever during streptomycin therapy may indicate pneumonia caused by Gram-positive cocci. Under such conditions penicillin should be used with streptomycin. Sometimes sulfadiazine used if antibiotics not available.

For more information see Ajl et al. (1955); Eisler, Kubik, and Preston (1958); Fukui et al. (1957); Ogg et al. (1958); Warren et al. (1955).

Pasteurella tularensis. Equal numbers of cocci and rods, 0.2 by 0.2 to 0.7 μ, occurring singly. Extremely pleomorphic (Fig. 270). Nonmotile. May show bipolar staining. Gram-negative. Aerobic. Filterable through Berkefeld filters.

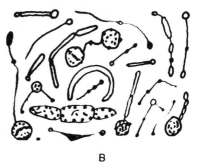

A   B

FIG. 270. Selected morphological units of two strains of *Pasteurella tularensis.* A, strain Ri, 48-hr. culture. Note multiple filamentation at upper left. B, strain Russ, 48-hr. culture. (*After Hesselbrock and Foshay.*)

Disease Produced. Cause of tularemia in man. Onset of disease sudden with chills and fever. Patient usually prostrated and confined to bed. Fever may last for 3 to 4 weeks, followed by slow convalescence. Lymph glands may become swollen and tender, and suppurate in 50 per cent of infections. Organism infectious for rabbits, guinea pigs, rats, muskrats, water rats, gray mice, ground squirrels, beavers, and lemmings.

Diagnosis. Disease diagnosed by (1) animal inoculation, (2) isolation of organism from lesions or discharges, and (3) agglutination test with serum from patient.

Source of Infection. Originally isolated from California ground squirrels and later from more than 30 other forms of wild life in the United States and elsewhere. Also from rabbits, hares, deerfly (*Chrysops discalis*), wood tick (*Dermacentor andersoni* and *D. variabilis*), and possibly other biting insects. Hunters, cooks, and butchers may contract the disease during rabbit-hunting season.

Mode of Transmission. Transmitted by bites of infected flies and ticks and by inoculation through handling of diseased animals, especially in skinning rabbits during the hunting season. Ingestion of insufficiently cooked meat from a diseased animal. Also from drinking contaminated water.

Incubation Period. From 1 to 10 days, usually about 3 days.

Susceptibility and Immunity. All ages susceptible. Recovery from an attack followed by permanent immunity. An immune person exposed to the disease may develop a local infection through a break in the skin, but this does not cause any constitutional disturbance. Disease most prevalent during the hunting season.

Prevention and Control. Avoidance of bites from, or handling of, flies and ticks when working in infected areas during bloodsucking season. Use of rubber gloves in the handling and dressing of rabbits or in performing autopsies on animals likely to be infected. Meat from wild rabbits and other susceptible animals should be thoroughly cooked before eating. Water from infected areas should not be used unless first boiled or disinfected.

Disinfection of discharges from ulcer, lymph glands, or conjunctiva of infected individuals.

Streptomycin, the tetracyclines, and chloramphenicol effective when continued for 4 to 5 days after temperature becomes normal.

For more information see Downs and Moody (1955); Eigelsbach, Braun, and Herring (1951); Hesselbrock and Foshay (1945); Moody (1955); Moody and Downs (1955); Philip, Bell, and Larson (1956); Philip, Gill, and Geary (1954); Shepard, Ribi, and Larson (1955).

SALMONELLA

Rods either motile by means of peritrichous flagella or nonmotile. Gram-negative. Found in bodies of warm-blooded animals, including man, and occasionally in reptiles; frequently found in food eaten by these animals.

Within the limits of the genus *Salmonella,* serological relationships are the chief means of identifying new strains. Over 343 serotypes have been recognized. There is general dissatisfaction with granting of species rank to each of the rapidly mounting number of types.

As the morphology, staining properties, and physiology of the bacteria belonging to the various types are practically identical, only the antigenic structure, source, and habitat have been recorded for the majority of the types listed.

The nomenclature adopted is in accordance with the view that the recognition of similar antigenic structures really identifies serotypes rather than species. In a way, serotypes are varieties in a taxonomic sense, though like horticultural varieties in higher plants, they do not exactly correspond with varieties as usually defined by taxonomists. Where cultural differences rather than antigenic structure have been used to subdivide species, those subdivisions are designated as varieties. However, species rank has been accorded to those organisms (10 in number) which are easily identified because they are commonly encountered and/or cause rather well-established syndromes.

For more information see Breed, Murray, and Smith (1957); Edwards (1956);

Kauffmann and Edwards (1957); Edwards and Fife (1957); Edwards, Fife, and Ewing (1956); Edwards, Kauffmann, and McWhorter (1954); and Felsenfeld (1949).

Salmonella typhosa. Rods, 0.6 to 0.7 by 2 μ, occurring singly, in pairs, and occasionally in short chains. Motile by means of peritrichous flagella; sometimes nonmotile. Gram-negative (Fig. 271).

Disease Produced. The cause of typhoid fever in man. An acute infectious disease characterized by continued fever, involvement of lymphoid tissues, enlargement of spleen, rose spots on the trunk, irritation of walls of gastrointestinal tract with formation of ulcers and production of diarrhea. During first two weeks organism may be recovered from blood; from urine and feces after second week. Widal reaction becomes positive during second week. Disease may be transferred to laboratory animals by inoculation.

Carriers. Typhoid fever may be transferred from person to person by individuals known as carriers. A carrier is one who has recovered from the disease but still continues to discharge the bacilli in the intestinal contents. These organisms are no longer pathogenic to the carrier but are capable of producing typhoid fever when they reach the intestinal tracts of other persons. Carriers generally harbor the organisms in their gall bladder, which is believed to be the reservoir of the bacilli. Removal of the gall bladder appears to be the best method for the treatment of some carriers.

FIG. 271. *Salmonella typhosa.* Smear from a 24-hr. agar slant culture. (*From Muir, "Bacteriological Atlas," E. and S. Livingstone, Edinburgh, Scotland.*)

Diagnosis. Antigenic structure: 9, 12, (Vi), d (see Breed, Murray, and Smith). Motile species contain two antigenic components: (1) flagellar or H antigen and (2) somatic or O antigen (see page 683). Agglutinins may be produced against both components. During infection, both kinds of agglutinins present in blood serum. Typhoid fever may be diagnosed by testing for presence of agglutinins in blood stream.

Widal Reaction. A specific agglutination test for diagnosis of typhoid fever. Test performed by mixing gradually increasing dilutions of patient's serum with a suspension of typhoid bacilli and observing for presence of agglutination of the organisms. Since reaction of patient's serum does not become positive until during second week of infection, test of no value in early days of disease.

During first few days of disease, it is better to make a diagnosis by isolating the organism from feces, preparing a suspension, and testing for agglutination against a specific immune serum.

Source of Infection. Feces and urine of infected persons or carriers.

Mode of Transmission. Transmitted through direct contact with patients or carriers. Foods contaminated by fingers of typhoid patients or carriers. The most common source of typhoid outbreaks is through milk contaminated by a dairy worker. Oysters and shellfish, grown in sewage-polluted waters, may harbor the organism. Water-borne epidemics, due to sewage contamination, sometimes occur.

Incubation Period. From 3 to 35 days, usually 7 to 14 days.

Susceptibility and Immunity. Susceptibility to disease is general. Natural immunity exists to some extent in adults. Permanent acquired immunity usually follows recovery from disease. Active artificial immunity of about 2 years' duration developed by inoculation with typhoid bacterin.

Bacterin prepared by growing a freshly isolated smooth strain on a solid medium, suspending growth in saline, standardizing suspension to contain about 1 billion cells per milliliter, killing organisms at 53°C. for 1 hr., then preserving with 0.25 per cent tricresol.

Three injections of bacterin in doses of 500 million, 1 billion, and 1 billion at intervals of 7 to 10 days are generally sufficient for establishing a satisfactory active immunity.

Prevalence. Widely distributed throughout world. Endemic in some rural areas in United States but occurring now commonly as sporadic cases and small carrier epidemics. Incidence steadily falling owing to protection of water, food, and milk supplies.

Prevention and Control. Protection and purification of water supplies. Sanitary disposal of human sewage. Pasteurization of milk and milk products. Sanitary control of foods and shellfish. Fly control and protection of foods against fly contamination. Periodic examination of individuals who handle foods for public consumption. Immunization of population by use of a bacterin. Education of public on sources of infection and modes of transmission.

Isolation of infected individuals. Disinfection of all bowel and urinary discharges and articles contaminated with such discharges. Vaccination of susceptible members in family or household of patient.

Administration of chloramphenicol in large oral dose followed by oral doses every 6 hr. until temperature normal, then smaller doses for total of 2 weeks.

For more information see Knight et al. (1950); Levaditi, Vaisman, and Henry-Eveno (1950).

Salmonella schottmuelleri. Rods 0.6 to 0.7 by 2 to 3 μ, occurring singly and in pairs. Usually motile by means of peritrichous flagella. Gram-negative.

Disease Produced. The cause of paratyphoid fever in man. Also responsible for cases of food poisoning (see page 627). The disease is not naturally found in animals. Infection characterized by continued fever, involvement of the lymphoid tissues of the intestines, enlargement of the spleen, and sometimes rose spots on the trunk; usually accompanied by a diarrheal condition. Organism may be present in feces, urine, and blood and may be identified by fermentation and serological reactions.

Source of Infection. Feces and urine of infected persons or carriers; water or foods contaminated with discharges of infected persons or healthy carriers.

Mode of Transmission. By direct contact with infected persons or by articles soiled with discharges of infected persons; through water, food, and milk contaminated with discharges of infected persons or carriers; and by insects.

Incubation Period. From 1 to 10 days.

Susceptibility and Immunity. Susceptibility is general. Natural immunity believed to exist in some persons. Acquired immunity is usually permanent after recovery from disease. Active artificial immunity of about 2 years' duration developed after inoculation with a bacterin.

Prevalence. Occurs sporadically or in limited outbreaks from contact with infected persons or from contaminated water, milk, and other foods.

Prevention and Control. Protection and purification of water supplies. Sanitary disposal of human sewage. Pasteurization of milk and milk products. Sanitary control of foods and shellfish. Fly control and protection of foods against fly contamination. Periodic examination of individuals who handle foods for public consumption. Immunization of population by use of a bacterin. Education of public on sources of infection and modes of transmission.

Isolation of infected individuals. Disinfection of all bowel and urinary discharges and articles contaminated with such discharges. Vaccination of susceptible members in family or household of patient.

Administration of chloramphenicol in large oral dose every 6 hr. until temperature normal, then smaller oral doses for total of 2 weeks.

Salmonella paratyphi. Rods, 0.6 by 3 to 4 μ, occurring singly. Usually motile by means of peritrichous flagella. Gram-negative.

Disease Produced. The cause of paratyphoid fever in man. Also responsible for cases of food poisoning (see page 627). Disease is not naturally found in animals. Infection characterized by continued fever, involvement of the lymphoid tissues of the intestines, enlargement of the spleen, and sometimes rose spots on the trunk; usually accompanied by a diarrheal condition. Organism may be present in feces, urine, and blood and may be identified by fermentation and serological reactions.

Source of Infection. Feces and urine of infected persons or carriers; water or foods contaminated with discharges of infected persons or healthy carriers.

Mode of Transmission. By direct contact with infected persons or by articles soiled with discharges of infected persons; through water, food, and milk contaminated with discharges of infected persons or carriers; and by insects.

Incubation Period. From 1 to 10 days.

Susceptibility and Immunity. Susceptibility is general. Natural immunity believed to exist in some persons. Acquired immunity is usually permanent after recovery from disease. Active artificial immunity of about 2 years' duration developed after inoculation with a bacterin.

Prevalence. Occurs sporadically or in limited outbreaks from contact with infected persons or from contaminated water, milk, and other foods.

Prevention and Control. Protection and purification of water supplies. Sanitary disposal of human sewage. Pasteurization of milk and milk products. Sanitary control of foods and shellfish. Fly control and protection of foods against fly contamination. Periodic examination of individuals who handle foods for public consumption. Immunization of population by use of a bacterin. Education of public on sources of infection and modes of transmission.

Isolation of infected individuals. Disinfection of all bowel and urinary discharges and articles contaminated with such discharges. Vaccination of susceptible members in the family or household of patient.

Administration of chloramphenicol in large oral dose every 6 hr. until temperature normal, then smaller oral doses for total of 2 weeks.

Salmonella typhimurium. Rods, 0.5 by 1 to 1.5 μ, occurring singly. Motile by means of peritrichous flagella. Gram-negative.

Disease Produced. Causes food poisoning in man. A natural pathogen for all warm-blooded animals.

Source of Infection. Feces and urine of infected persons or carriers; water or foods contaminated with discharges of infected persons or healthy carriers.

Mode of Transmission. By direct contact with infected persons, or by articles soiled with discharges of infected persons or carriers; through water, food, and milk contaminated with discharges of infected persons or carriers; and by flies.

Incubation Period. From 1 to 10 days.

Susceptibility and Immunity. Susceptibility is general. Natural immunity believed to exist in some persons. Acquired immunity usually permanent after recovery from disease. Active artificial immunity of about 2 years' duration developed after inoculation with a bacterin.

Prevention and Control. Protection and purification of water supplies. Sanitary disposal of human sewage. Pasteurization of milk and milk products. Sanitary control of foods and shellfish. Fly control and protection of foods against fly contamination. Periodic examination of individuals who handle foods for public consumption. Immunization of population by use of a bacterin. Education of public on sources of infection and modes of transmission.

Isolation of infected individuals. Disinfection of all bowel and urinary discharges and articles contaminated with such discharges. Vaccination of susceptible members in the family or household of patient.

Chloramphenicol and tetracyclines have limited and irregular effect.

Salmonella enteritidis. Rods, 0.6 to 0.7 by 2 to 3 μ, occurring singly, in pairs, and occasionally in short chains. Motile by means of peritrichous flagella. Gram-negative.

Disease Produced. A cause of food poisoning in man (see page 627). Organism produces natural infections in domestic and wild animals.

Disease usually characterized by acute diarrhea with abdominal cramps, fever, nausea, and vomiting. Organism may be recovered from feces or from site of localized infection during acute illness.

Source of Infection. Feces and urine of infected persons or carriers; water or foods contaminated with discharges of infected persons or healthy carriers.

Mode of Transmission. By direct contact with infected persons, or by articles soiled with discharges of infected persons; through water, food, and milk contaminated with discharges of infected persons or carriers; and by insects.

Incubation Period. From 1 to 10 days.

Susceptibility and Immunity. Susceptibility is general. Natural immunity believed to exist in some persons. Acquired immunity usually permanent after recovery from disease. Active artificial immunity of about 2 years' duration developed after inoculation with a bacterin.

Prevalence. Occurs sporadically or in limited outbreaks from contact with infected persons or from contaminated water, milk, and other foods.

Prevention and Control. Protection and purification of water supplies. Sanitary disposal of human sewage. Pasteurization of milk and milk products. Sanitary control of foods and shellfish. Fly control and protection of foods against fly contamination. Periodic examination of individuals who handle foods for public consumption. Immunization of population by use of a bacterin. Education of public on sources of infection and modes of transmission.

Isolation of infected individuals. Disinfection of all bowel and urinary discharges and articles contaminated with such discharges. Vaccination of susceptible members in the family or household of patient.

Chloramphenicol and tetracyclines have limited and irregular effect.

SHIGELLA

The shigellae are rods, nonmotile and Gram-negative. Possess distinctive antigenic structures. Pathogenic, causing dysenteries, or nonpathogenic species, all living in bodies of warm-blooded animals. Found in polluted water supplies and flies.

Shigella dysenteriae. Rods, 0.4 to 0.6 by 1 to 3 μ, occurring singly. Nonmotile. Gram-negative.

Disease Produced. The cause of bacillary dysentery in man and monkeys (Fig. 272). Disease characterized by acute onset accompanied by diarrhea, sometimes fever in severe cases, tenesmus, and frequent stools containing blood and mucus. Severe infections most frequent in infants and in elderly debilitated persons. Synonym: shigellosis.

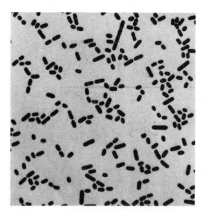

S. dysenteriae produces an active exotoxin which can be changed to toxoid by formalin and heat. It is believed the lesions produced in the gastrointestinal tract of persons suffering from the disease are caused by the toxin rather than the direct action of the organisms.

Carriers. Dysentery may be transferred from person to person by carriers. A carrier is one who has recovered from the disease but still continues to discharge the bacilli in the intestinal contents. These organisms are no longer pathogenic to the carrier but are capable of producing dysentery when they reach the intestinal tracts of other persons.

FIG. 272. *Shigella dysenteriae.* Smear from a 24-hr. culture. (*From Muir, "Bacteriological Atlas," E. and S. Livingstone, Edinburgh, Scotland.*)

Source of Infection. Bowel discharges of infected persons and carriers. Healthy carriers are common.

Mode of Transmission. By direct contact; by eating contaminated foods; by articles soiled with discharges from infected persons or carriers; by drinking contaminated water; and by flies. Disease most prevalent in the summer months.

Incubation Period. From 1 to 7 days, usually less than 4 days.

Susceptibility and Immunity. Susceptibility to disease is general. Disease is more common and symptoms are more severe in children than in adults. Slight acquired immunity of relatively short duration after recovery from the disease.

Prevalence. May be endemic, epidemic, or sporadic. Reduction occurs wherever water supplies are rendered safe, milk is pasteurized, and sewage is disposed of in a hygienic manner. More common in summer months.

Prevention and Control. Purification of public water supplies; pasteurization of public milk supplies; sanitary disposal of sewage; hygienic preparation and handling of public food supplies; periodic examination of individuals who handle foods for public consumption; extermination of flies.

Isolation of infected persons during period of communicability.

Aureomycin, Terramycin, streptomycin, and chloramphenicol given parenterally very effective in relieving symptoms and greatly reducing numbers of organisms in from 24 to 48 hr. Sulfadiazine may be used alone where antibiotics are not available.

Shigella flexneri. Rods, 0.5 by 1 to 1.5 μ, occurring singly, often filamentous and irregularly shaped in old cultures. Nonmotile. Gram-negative.

Disease Produced. The most common cause of dysentery epidemics and sometimes of infantile gastroenteritis. Found in feces of sick and convalescents and of carriers of dysentery bacilli.

Disease characterized by acute onset accompanied by diarrhea, sometimes fever, tenesmus, and frequent stools containing blood and mucus. Symptoms generally milder than in *S. dysenteriae* infections.

Carriers. Disease may be transferred from person to person by carriers. A carrier is one who has recovered from the disease but still continues to discharge the bacilli in the intestinal contents. Organisms are no longer pathogenic to the carrier but may produce dysentery when they reach the intestinal tracts of other persons.

Source of Infection. Bowel discharges of infected persons and carriers. Healthy carriers are common.

Mode of Transmission. By direct contact; by eating contaminated foods; by articles soiled with discharges from infected persons or carriers; by drinking contaminated water; and by flies.

Incubation Period. From 1 to 7 days, usually less than 4 days.

Susceptibility and Immunity. Susceptibility to disease is general. Disease is more common and symptoms are more severe in children than in adults. Slight acquired immunity of relatively short duration after recovery from the disease.

Prevalence. May be endemic, epidemic, or sporadic. Reduction occurs wherever water supplies are rendered safe, milk is pasteurized, and sewage is disposed of in a hygienic manner. More common in summer months.

Prevention and Control. Purification of public water supplies; pasteurization of public milk supplies; sanitary disposal of sewage; hygienic preparation and handling of public food supplies; periodic examination of individuals who handle foods for public consumption; extermination of flies.

Isolation of infected persons during period of communicability.

Aureomycin, Terramycin, streptomycin, and chloramphenicol given parenterally very effective in relieving symptoms and greatly reducing numbers of organisms in from 24 to 48 hr. Sulfadiazine may be used alone where antibiotics are not available.

Shigella sonnei. Rods. Nonmotile. Gram-negative.

Disease Produced. A cause of mild dysentery in man and of infantile gastroenteritis. Found in feces of sick and convalescents and of carriers of dysentery bacilli.

Disease characterized by acute onset accompanied by diarrhea, sometimes fever, tenesmus, and frequent stools containing blood and mucus. Symptoms generally milder than in *S. dysenteriae* infections.

Carriers. Disease may be transferred from person to person by carriers (see page 736).

Source of Infection. Bowel discharges of infected persons and carriers. Healthy carriers are common.

Mode of Transmission. By direct contact; by eating contaminated foods; by articles soiled with discharges from infected persons or carriers; by drinking contaminated water; and by flies.

Incubation Period. From 1 to 7 days, usually less than 4 days.

Susceptibility and Immunity. Susceptibility to disease is general. Disease is more common and symptoms are more severe in children than in adults. Slight acquired immunity of relatively short duration after recovery from the disease.

Prevalence. May be endemic, epidemic, or sporadic. Reduction occurs wherever water supplies are rendered safe, milk is pasteurized, and sewage is disposed of in a hygienic manner. More common in summer months.

Prevention and Control. Purification of public water supplies; pasteurization of public milk supplies; sanitary disposal of sewage; hygienic preparation and handling of public food supplies; periodic examination of individuals who handle foods for public consumption; extermination of flies.

Isolation of infected persons during period of communicability.

Aureomycin, Terramycin, streptomycin, and chloramphenicol given parenterally very effective in relieving symptoms and greatly reducing numbers of organisms in from 24 to 48 hr. Sulfadiazine may be used alone where antibiotics are not available.

STAPHYLOCOCCUS

Spherical cells occurring singly, in pairs, in tetrads, and in irregular clusters. Nonmotile. Gram-positive. Many strains produce an orange or yellow pigment, particularly on media containing high levels of sodium chloride. Most commonly found in boils, furuncles, abscesses, and other suppurative processes. Normally present on skin, and their entrance into a cut or scratch may lead to infection. Under some conditions,

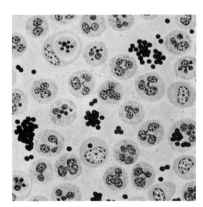

Fig. 273. *Staphylococcus aureus.* Smear of pus showing bacteria and white blood cells. (*From Muir, "Bacteriological Atlas," E. and S. Livingstone, Edinburgh, Scotland.*)

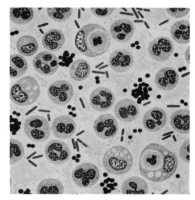

Fig. 274. *Staphylococcus* and *Pseudomonas aeruginosa.* Smear of pus showing bacteria and white blood cells. The two organisms are frequently found together in pyogenic infections. (*From Muir, "Bacteriological Atlas," E. and S. Livingstone, Edinburgh, Scotland.*)

especially during periods of weakened tissue resistance, organisms may invade unbroken skin. Coagulase-positive strains produce a variety of toxins and are thus potentially pathogenic and may cause food poisoning. Facultative parasites and saprophytes.

Staphylococcus aureus. Spheres, 0.8 to 1 μ in diameter, occurring singly, in pairs, in short chains, and in irregular clumps. Nonmotile. Gram-positive.

Some strains develop a golden-yellow, water-insoluble pigment; others show a lemon-colored, water-insoluble pigment; still others are nonpigmented.

Disease Produced. Found on skin and mucous membranes. The causative organism of boils, furuncles, abscesses, and suppuration in wounds (Figs. 273 and 274). Pus consists of an accumulation of bacteria and polymorphonuclear leucocytes in the infected area. The organism rarely produces septicemia but may be a secondary invader in peritonitis, pyemia, cystitis, and meningitis.

Certain strains under favorable conditions produce not only exotoxins (hemotoxin, dermatoxin, lethal toxin, etc.) but also a potent enterotoxin which is a significant cause of food poisoning. Normally also capable of coagulating citrated human or rabbit plasma (Fig. 275). Many strains produce an enzyme capable of dissolving such clots 8 to 12 hr. after incubation.

Source of Infection. Pus, skin, air, contaminated clothing, food, water, etc.

Mode of Transmission. Transmitted by entrance of organisms into a cut or break in the skin or even the unbroken skin.

Susceptibility and Immunity. Susceptibility to infections is general. Stock polyvalent bacterins, autogenous bacterins, and other heat-killed preparations have been used with some success. However, very little immunity is produced.

Prevention and Control. Aseptic surgery; destruction of soiled dressings by burning; oral and skin cleanliness.

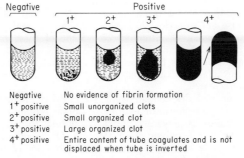

Fig. 275. Types of coagulase test reactions. Negative, no evidence of fibrin formation; 1+ positive, small unorganized clots; 2+ positive, small organized clot; 3+ positive, large organized clot; 4+ positive, entire content of tube coagulates and is not displaced when tube is inverted. (*Courtesy of Warner-Chilcott Laboratories.*)

The introduction of penicillin and other antibiotics has revolutionized the treatment of staphylococcal infections. Sometimes a combination of penicillin and one of the sulfa drugs may be more effective against some resistant strains.

For more information see Amsterdam and Schneierson (1957), Ekstedt and Nungester (1955), Finkelstein and Sulkin (1958), Oeding (1953), Szeto and Halick (1958), Turner and Schwartz (1958).

STREPTOCOCCUS

The streptococci are spherical or ovoid cells, rarely elongated into rods, occurring in pairs or short or long chains. Nonmotile. Gram-positive. Capsules not regularly formed but may become conspicuous with some species under certain conditions. Growth on artificial media slight. Agar colonies very small. Bile-insoluble. Latter property used to differentiate streptococci from pneumococci, which are bile-soluble. Found wherever organic matter containing sugars accumulates. Regularly found in mouth and intestine of man and other animals, dairy products, fermenting plant juices.

Found associated with a variety of pathological conditions including erysipelas, septicemia, puerperal fever, focal infections, sore throat, rheumatic fever, scarlet fever, tonsillitis, arthritis, and vegetative endocarditis.

Classification of Streptococci. The streptococci are among the most difficult groups of bacteria to classify. One of the earliest classifications is that proposed by Brown (1919), who divided the organisms into three groups according to their effect on blood agar:

1. Alpha streptococci, producing a greenish coloration (methemoglobin formation) of the medium and partial hemolysis in the immediate vicinity of the colonies.

2. Beta streptococci, producing completely hemolyzed clear, colorless zones around the colonies.

3. Gamma streptococci, having no effect on blood agar.

The most important contribution to methods for the classification of the streptococci is the serological technique (precipitin test) proposed by Lancefield (1933). On the basis of this method, the streptococci may be placed into the following groups:

Group A. *S. pyogenes.* Under this species are placed those organisms causing scarlet fever, erysipelas, tonsillitis, puerperal fever, septicemia, and sore throat. They are hemolytic, liquefy fibrin, do not curdle milk or hydrolyze sodium hippurate.

Group B. *S. agalactiae.* This species has been isolated from mastitis in cows and occasionally from human sources. It curdles milk, hydrolyzes sodium hippurate, and does not liquefy fibrin. Most strains are hemolytic.

Group C. This group includes three rather clearly defined biochemical groups: (1) *S. equi,* the cause of "strangles" in horses, (2) the "animal pyogenes" *Streptococcus,* and (3) the "human C" *Streptococcus.* Some of these have been isolated from animals; others are of human origin.

Group D. This group includes both hemolytic and nonhemolytic types. The most important member is *S. faecalis* var. *zymogenes.* Other members are *S. faecalis* and *S. faecalis* var. *liquefaciens.*

Group E. This group includes nonpathogenic streptococci isolated from milk. They are hemolytic, do not liquefy fibrin or hydrolyze sodium hippurate.

Group F. This organism is generally present in normal throats and is sometimes referred to as the "minute hemolytic streptococcus." On blood agar plates, the organism produces extremely small pin-point colonies, frequently barely visible, but surrounded by a zone of true hemolysis.

Group G. This is a heterogeneous group of hemolytic streptococci which have been isolated from the normal human throat and nose, vagina, skin, and feces. They are not believed to be of any importance in producing disease in humans.

Streptococcus pyogenes. Spherical or ovoid cells, 0.6 to 1 μ in diameter in cultures, usually spherical in blood and inflammatory exudates, occurring in chains or pairs; in broth culture, usually long chains. Gram-positive.

S. pyogenes placed in Lancefield's group A. This group may be subdivided into serological types by precipitin technique on basis of capsular protein M antigen. Antigen associated with virulence, and antibodies to which it gives rise are primarily concerned with the specific protective action of immune sera. At least 40 types have been identified.

Culture filtrates of typical strains capable of hemolyzing red blood cells. Soluble toxin called a hemolysin. Two types of hemolysin elaborated: one being oxygen-sensitive (streptolysin O), and the other oxygen-stable (streptolysin S). On blood agar, organism produces a type of hemolysis referred to as β-hemolysis that possesses considerable diagnostic importance.

Disease Produced. Found in human mouth, throat, respiratory tract, inflammatory exudates. Produces septic sore throat, septicemia, erysipelas, scarlet fever, puerperal fever, cellulitis, mastoiditis, osteomyelitis, otitis media, peritonitis, and various skin and wound infections (Fig. 276).

Source of Infection. Contaminated milk, pus, sputum, nasal discharges, droplets from mouth and nose, etc.

Mode of Transmission. By direct contact; by inhaling droplets expelled during coughing, sneezing, or talking; by consumption of contaminated milk, etc.

Incubation Period. Usually 2 to 5 days.

Susceptibility and Immunity. Immunity against types of one group does not protect against infection with types from other groups. Immunity slight and of temporary duration. The exception is immunity to scarlet fever. This organism secretes an extracellular toxin against which an antitoxin is produced.

Prevalence. Most prevalent in temperate zones, less common in semitropical and tropical climates. Highest incidence of scarlet fever and streptococcal sore throat occurs during late winter and spring.

Prevention and Control. Pasteurization of milk supplies. Exclusion of infected individuals or carriers from handling foods. Care in treating cuts and abrasions.

Isolation of infected individuals. Disinfection of dressings, discharges, clothing from infected persons. Disinfection of floors, table tops, and contaminated objects.

Various forms of penicillin all effective when administered parenterally. Therapy should be started early and continued for about 10 days. The tetracyclines may be employed for those sensitive to penicillin.

Scarlet Fever. Scarlet fever is an acute febrile disease of the throat accompanied by a scarlet rash. Invasion of other parts of the body may occur, resulting in infections of the middle ear, kidneys, etc.

The scarlet rash is due to the elaboration by the organisms of an extracellular erythrogenic toxin. Immunity to the disease is an immunity to the toxin rather than to the organisms.

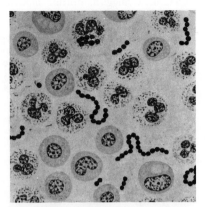

FIG. 276. *Streptococcus pyogenes.* Smear from human pus showing the typical appearance of hemolytic streptococci together with polymorphonuclear and mononuclear leucocytes. (*From Muir, "Bacteriological Atlas,"* E. *and* S. *Livingstone, Edinburgh, Scotland.*)

Scarlet fever is diagnosed by its clinical symptoms and by the isolation of the specific organisms from the throat. For susceptibility to the disease, the Dick test may be used. This test consists of the intradermal injection of 0.1 ml. of a known strength of toxin; the reaction is read after 24 hr. A positive test manifests itself as a bright red area 1.5 to 3 cm. or more in diameter, with swelling and tenderness of the skin.

An antitoxin may be prepared by immunizing animals against culture filtrates of the scarlet fever strain of *S. pyogenes.* Administration of the antitoxin in cases of scarlet fever produces a favorable result on the outcome of the infection. The antitoxin neutralizes the damaging effect of the toxin and, in so doing, decreases the duration of the rash, changes the character and extent of desquamation, and reduces the number of complications.

Various forms of penicillin all effective when given parenterally. Therapy should be started early and continued for about 10 days. The tetracyclines may be employed for those sensitive to penicillin.

For more information see Emmart and Cole (1955), Li (1955), Pentz and Shigemura (1955), Pierce and White (1954), and Schwab (1956).

TREPONEMA

Organisms in this genus measure 3 to 18 μ in length, with acute, regular or irregular spirals; longer forms are due to incomplete division. Terminal filament may be present. Weakly refractive by dark-field illumination in living preparations. Cultivated under strictly anaerobic conditions. Some are pathogenic and parasitic for man and other animals. Generally produce local lesions in tissues.

Treponema pallidum. Cells occur as very fine protoplasmic spirals, 0.25 to 0.3 by 6 to 14 μ. Spiral amplitude 1 μ, regular, fixed; spiral depth, 0.5 to 1 μ. Terminal spiral filament present. Weakly refractive in living state by dark field. Motile by means of a sluggish, drifting motion; stiffly flexible, rarely rotating. Appear black with silver impregnation methods. Cultivated with difficulty under strict anaerobiosis in ascitic fluid with addition of fresh rabbit kidney.

Disease Produced. The cause of syphilis in man. Syphilis is acquired almost entirely by sexual contact. In an acquired infection, disease first manifests itself as a primary lesion. This starts as a papule at the site of infection, increases in size, and finally ulcerates. The ulcer is generally referred to as a chancre. This is followed by constitutional symptoms and lesions of the skin and mucous membranes. Secondary lesions eventually heal and may reappear during the first 5 years after infection. Later manifestations may include disturbances of the cardiovascular and central nervous systems. In congenital syphilis, only secondary and late manifestations are observed.

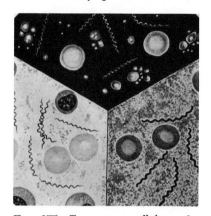

FIG. 277. *Treponema pallidum,* the cause of human syphilis. Upper, exudate from a primary sore, viewed by dark-ground illumination; lower left, smear of material from a chancre; lower right, same but stained by a different method. (*From Muir, "Bacteriological Atlas," E. and S. Livingstone, Edinburgh, Scotland.*)

Diagnosis. Disease in primary stage may be diagnosed by examining the serous exudate from a chancre under dark-ground illumination (Fig. 277). Presence of spirochetes indicates a syphilitic infection. Disease in later stages may be diagnosed by serological reactions (see page 692).

Source of Infection. Discharges from lesions of the skin and mucous membranes; from blood of infected individuals; only rarely from articles freshly soiled with discharges.

Mode of Transmission. By direct personal contact with syphilitic individual, chiefly by sexual intercourse; occasionally by kissing; by dental instruments; only rarely through articles freshly soiled with discharges. Transmitted by syphilitic mother to offspring through placenta (congenital syphilis).

Incubation Period. From 10 to 90 days, average about 21 days.

Susceptibility and Immunity. Susceptibility to disease is universal. Recovery is said to confer some immunity, although reinfections do occur.

Prevalence. Disease world-wide in distribution, varying with age, sex, and race. Occurs most frequently between ages of eighteen and thirty.

Prevention and Control. Adequate treatment facilities, including free distribution of antibiotic agents to physicians for treatment of all cases. Legislation making examinations before marriage compulsory. Control or elimination of houses of prostitution. Education of public to nature, characteristics, prevalence, mode of transmission, how to avoid infection, and how to secure prompt treatment in case of infection. Personal hygiene before or immediately after sexual intercourse with those who may be exposed to infection.

Isolation of infected individuals in the communicable stage. Disinfection of discharges from open lesions and of articles soiled with such discharges.

Treatment consists in the use of large doses of penicillin over a period of time.

For more information see Kawata (1957) and Thomas (1948).

VIBRIO

Members of genus characterized as short, curved rods, single or united into spirals. Motile by means of a single polar flagellum usually relatively short; rarely two or three flagella in one tuft. Grow well and rapidly on the surface of standard media. Some aerobic; others anaerobic. Mostly water forms; also occur as parasites and pathogens.

Vibrio comma. Slightly curved rods, 0.3 to 0.6 by 1 to 5 μ, occurring singly and in spiral chains. Cells may be long, thin, and delicate, or short and thick. May lose their curved form on artificial cultivation. Motile, possessing a single polar flagellum. Gram-negative.

Organism tolerates high alkalinity. Optimum pH 7.6 to 8.0; for primary isolation, pH 9.0 to 9.6.

Vibrios have been classified into 6 groups on the basis of their protein and polysaccharide structures.

Disease Produced. The cause of Asiatic cholera in man. In mild cases, the disease may produce only a diarrhea. In more severe or typical cases, the symptoms may include, in addition to diarrhea, vomiting, "rice-water" stools, and general symptoms of dehydration accompanied by thirst, abdominal pain, and coma. The organisms penetrate the mucosa of the intestines and accumulate in layers next to the submucosa. The organisms may be present in large numbers in the stools. The disease runs a short course, terminating in death sometimes within 12 hr. after the appearance of symptoms.

Diagnosis. V. comma may be isolated from feces of both infected individuals and carriers. The intraperitoneal inoculation of guinea pigs with pure cultures results in the death of the animals within 24 hr.

Carriers. Patients convalescing from the disease usually continue to eliminate the organisms in the feces for about 7 to 14 days after recovery. Healthy carriers may also be found who excrete the cholera vibrio without exhibiting any signs of the disease. Both convalescent and healthy carriers play an important role in the dissemination of the disease.

Source of Infection. Intestinal contents and vomitus of infected persons and feces of convalescent or healthy carriers. Also from food and water.

Mode of Transmission. By water and foods; by contact with infected persons or carriers, or articles soiled with discharges from such persons; by flies.

Incubation Period. From a few hours to 5 days, usually 3 days.

Susceptibility and Immunity. Susceptibility to disease is general. Natural resistance to infection varies. Clinical attack confers a temporary immunity which may last for several years. Active artificial immunity for about 6 to 12 months may be produced by the use of vaccines.

Prevalence. Disease endemic in India and adjacent areas in southeastern Asia. Does not occur in Western Hemisphere.

Prevention and Control. Sanitary disposal of human excreta. Protection of water by boiling. Pasteurization of milk and dairy products. Sanitary preparation and handling of foods in public places. Control or destruction of house flies. Education of public in personal cleanliness.

Isolation of persons suffering from the disease. Disinfection of stools and vomitus and articles soiled by such discharges. Food left by patient should be destroyed by burning. Room occupied by patient should be thoroughly cleaned and disinfected. Carriers should be isolated. Use of cholera vaccine in exposed population groups.

For more information on the pathogenic bacteria see American Public Health Association (1955), Burrows (1959), Dubos (1958), Smith and Conant (1960), Wilson and Miles (1955).

REFERENCES

Ajl, S. J., J. S. Reedal, E. L. Durrum, and J. Warren: I. Purification and properties of the toxin of *Pasteurella pestis, J. Bact.,* **70**:158, 1955.

Alexander, A. D., O. H. Smith, C. W. Hiatt, and C. A. Gleiser: Presence of hemolysin in cultures of pathogenic leptospires, *Proc. Soc. Exp. Biol. Med.,* **91**:205, 1956.

American Public Health Association: "Control of Communicable Diseases in Man," New York, 1955.

Amsterdam, D., and S. S. Schneierson: Relationship between penicillin susceptibility and virulence of *Staphylococcus aureus*, Proc. Soc. Exp. Biol. Med., **96**:750, 1957.

Badger, L. F.: Leprosy in the United States, Pub. Health Rep., **70**:525, 1955.

Beattie, M. I.: Occurrence and distribution of types of C. *diphtheriae*, Am. J. Pub. Health, **39**:1458, 1949.

Bloch, H., and W. Segal: Viability and multiplication of vaccines in immunization against tuberculosis, Am. Rev. Tuberc., **71**:228, 1955.

Bojlén, K., and I. Scheibel. The duration of immunity following diphtheria vaccination, *Danish Med. Bull.*, **2**:70, 1955.

Bowen, H. E., L. Wyman, and J. A. McComb: Cellular vaccines and toxoid in the immunization of animals against diphtheria, Am. J. Hyg., **59**:306, 1954.

Branham, S. E.: Milestones in the history of the meningococcus, Can. J. Microbiol., **2**:175, 1956.

————: Serological relationships among meningococci, Bact. Rev., **17**:175, 1953.

Braun, W., and J. Kelsh: Improved method for cultivation of *Brucella* from the blood, Proc. Soc. Exp. Biol. Med., **85**:154, 1954.

Breed, R. S., E. G. D. Murray, and N. R. Smith: "Bergey's Manual of Determinative Bacteriology," Baltimore, The Williams & Wilkins Company, 1957.

Brown, J. H.: The use of blood agar for the study of streptococci, Rockefeller Institute for Medical Research, New York, Monograph 9, 1919.

Burdon, K. L.: Useful criteria for the identification of *Bacillus anthracis* and related species, J. Bact., **71**:25, 1956.

Burgdorfer, W.: I. Transmission of *Leptospira pomona* by the argasid tick, *Ornithodoros turicata*, and the persistence of this organism in its tissues, Exp. Parasit., **5**:571, 1956.

Burrows, W.: "Textbook of Microbiology," Philadelphia, W. B. Saunders Company, 1959.

Cashman, A. J.: Early immunization against whooping-cough, Brit. Med. J., Sept. 3, 1955, p. 598.

Chatterjee, S. N.: The mechanism of the neural signs and symptoms of leprosy, Int. J. Leprosy, **23**:1, 1955.

Cox, C. D., R. C. Stover, and R. W. Treick: Serological studies on hemolytic antigen from leptospira, Proc. Soc. Exp. Biol. Med., **98**:265, 1958.

Crowle, A. J.: Immunizing constituents of the tubercle bacillus, Bact. Rev., **22**:183, 1958.

Davis, J. C., and S. Mudd: The cytology of a strain of *Corynebacterium diphtheriae*, J. Bact., **69**:413, 1955.

Deacon, W. E., D. C. Albritton, W. F. Edmundson, and S. Olansky: Study of Ducrey's bacillus and recognition of a Gram-positive smooth phase, Proc. Soc. Exp. Biol. Med., **86**:261, 1954.

————, ————, S. Olansky, and W. Kaplan: I. A simple procedure for the isolation and identification of *Hemophilus ducreyi*, J. Invest. Dermatol., **26**:399, 1956.

Dean, H. T., and D. E. Singleton: Vincents infection—A wartime disease, Am. J. Pub. Health, **35**:433, 1945.

Downs, C. M., and M. D. Moody: II. The antigenic properties of variants of *Pasteurella tularensis* in various hosts, J. Bact., **70**:305, 1955.

Dubos, R. J.: Immunological aspects of BCG vaccination, Am. Rev. Tuberc., **60**:670, 1949.

————: "Bacterial and Mycotic Infections of Man," Philadelphia, J. B. Lippincott Company, 1958.

Edwards, P. R.: *Salmonella* and salmonellosis, Ann. N.Y. Acad. Sci., **66**:44, 1956.

———— and M. A. Fire: Occurrence of "induced" antigens in salmonellae isolated from man, J. Bact., **74**:108, 1957.

————, ————, and W. H. Ewing: Newer biochemical methods in the recognition of shigellae and salmonellae, Am. J. Med. Tech., December, 1956, p. 28.

———, F. Kauffmann, and A. C. McWhorter: Studies on *Salmonella* subgroup E₂, *Acta Path. Microbiol. Scand.*, 35:67, 1954.

Eigelsbach, H. T., W. Braun, and R. D. Herring: Studies on the variation of *Bacterium tularense*, *J. Bact.*, 61:557, 1951.

Eisler, D. M., G. Kubik, and H. Preston: Colonial morphology and virulence of *Pasteurella pestis*, *J. Bact.*, 76:41, 1958.

———, ———, and ———: Dissociation in *Pasteurella pestis*: immunological comparisons of smooth and nonsmooth variants, *ibid.*, 76:589, 1958.

———, ———, and ———: Dissociation in *Pasteurella pestis*: interrelations of smooth and nonsmooth variants, *ibid.*, 76:597, 1958.

Ekstedt, R. D., and W. J. Nungester: Coagulase in reversing antibacterial activity of normal human serum on *Micrococcus pyogenes*, *Proc. Soc. Exp. Biol. Med.*, 89:90, 1955.

Emmart, E. W., and R. M. Cole: I. The development in vitro of streptococcal (group C) hyaluronidase, its isolation and use as an antigen in rabbits, *J. Bact.*, 70:596, 1955.

Erickson, P. T.: Relapse following apparent arrest of leprosy by sulfone therapy, *Pub. Health Reports*, 65:1147, 1950.

Felsenfeld, O.: An outline for the identification of salmonellas, *Am. J. Clin. Path.*, 19:106, 1949.

Finkelstein, R. A., and S. E. Sulkin: Characteristics of coagulase positive and coagulase negative staphylococci in serum-soft agar, *J. Bact.*, 75:339, 1958.

Floch, H., P. Fauran, and M. Mailloux: Mode d'action des sulfones dans la lèpre (XI), *Arch. de l'Institut Pasteur de la Guyane Française et de l'Inini*, no. 424, May, 1957.

Frappier, A., and R. Guy: The use of BCG, *Can. Med. Assoc. J.*, 61:18, 1949.

——— and ———: A new and practical B. C. G. skin test (The B. C. G. scarification test) for the detection of the total tuberculous allergy, *Can. J. Pub. Health*, 41:72, 1950.

Fukui, G. M., J. E. Ogg, G. E. Wessman, and M. J. Surgalla: Studies on the relation of cultural conditions and virulence of *Pasteurella pestis*, *J. Bact.*, 74:714, 1957.

Gerhardt, P.: The nutrition of brucellae, *Bact. Rev.*, 22:81, 1958.

Hamdy, A. H., and L. C. Ferguson: Virulence of *Leptospira pomona* in hamsters and cattle, *Am. J. Vet. Res.*, 18:35, 1957.

Hanks, J. H.: Three factors which may influence the experimental transmission of leprosy, *Intern. J. Leprosy*, 18:33, 1950.

Hardy, A. V., F. P. Dunbar, M. B. Jefferies, J. O. Bond, and A. G. Lewis: Bacteriological and epidemiological studies of pulmonary diseases associated with atypical acid-fast bacilli, *Am. J. Pub. Health*, 48:754, 1958.

Hesselbrock, W., and L. Foshay: The morphology of *Bacterium tularense*, *J. Bact.*, 49:209, 1945.

Hewitt, L. F.: Use of antibiotics in the treatment of experimental diphtheria infections, *Brit. J. Exp. Path.*, 31:597, 1950.

Holland, J. J., and M. J. Pickett: A cellular basis of immunity in experimental *Brucella* infection, *J. Exp. Med.*, 108:343, 1958.

Huet, M.: Sur la présence de *Haemophilus influenzae* dans les conjonctivités saisonnières en Tunisie, *Ann. Inst. Pasteur*, 90:106, 1956.

Kauffmann, F., and P. R. Edwards: A revised, simplified Kauffmann-White schema, *Acta Path. Microbiol. Scand.*, 41:242, 1957.

Kawata, T.: Electron microscopy of ultrathin sections of *Borrelia duttonii* and Reiter spirochete, *Yonago Acta Medica*, 2:142, 1957.

———, J. Matsuo, and H. Aoi: Electron microscopic studies on the cellular structure of *Borrelia duttonii*, *Jap. J. Bact.*, 11:911, 1956.

Kind, L. S.: The altered reactivity of mice after inoculation with *Bordetella pertussis* vaccine, *Bact. Rev.*, 22:173, 1958.

Knight, V., F. R. Sanchez, A. R. Sanchez, S. Shultz, and W. McDermott: Antimicrobial therapy in typhoid, *Arch. Internal Med.*, 85:44, 1950.

Lancefield, R. C.: A serological differentiation of human and other groups of hemolytic streptococci, *J. Exp. Med.*, **57**:571, 1933.

Levaditi, C., and H. Chaigneau-Erhard: Activité anti-microbienne de la streptomycine, de l'acide *p*-aminosalicylique et de la diamino-diphényl-sulfone chez les souris contaminées par la bacille de Stefanski, *Compt. rend. soc. biol.*, **145**:328, 1951.

————, A. Vaisman, and J. Henry-Eveno: Action du chloramphénicol synthétique sur le bacille typhique (*Eberthella typhosa*), *La Presse médicale*, **38**:665, 1950.

Li, K.: In vitro variation in group A streptococci with special reference to streptolysin formation, *J. Bact.*, **69**:326, 1955.

Long, E. R.: Tuberculosis in modern society, *Bull. Hist. Med.*, **27**:301, 1953.

Lund, E.: The present status of the pneumococci, including three new pneumococcus types, *Acta Path. Microbiol. Scand.*, **40**:425, 1957.

Meyer, E. A., and M. Moskowitz: The effect of calcium binding agents on the virulence of *Clostridium perfringens* for the white mouse, *J. Bact.*, **69**:111, 1955.

Moody, M. D.: III. The variation of *Pasteurella tularensis* grown in the presence of normal and immune serum from various hosts, *J. Bact.*, **70**:314, 1955.

———— and C. M. Downs: I. The relation between certain pathogenic and immunogenic properties of variants of *Pasteurella tularensis*, *J. Bact.*, **70**:297, 1955.

Moss, G. W. O., G. G. Waters, and M. H. Brown: The efficacy of tetanus toxoid, *Can. J. Pub. Health*, **46**:142, 1955.

Murray, R. G. E., and J. P. Truant: The morphology, cell structure, and taxonomic affinities of the *Moraxella*, *J. Bact.*, **67**:13, 1954.

Newton, J. W., and J. B. Wilson: CO_2 requirements and nucleic acid synthesis by *Brucella abortus*, *J. Bact.*, **68**:74, 1954.

Noll, H.: The chemistry of cord factor, a toxic glycolipid of *M. tuberculosis*, *Adv. in Tuberc. Res.*, **7**:149, 1956.

Oeding, P.: Serological typing of staphylococci. III. Further investigations and comparison to phage typing, *Acta Path. Microbiol. Scand.*, **33**:324, 1953.

Ogg, J. E., S. B. Friedman, A. W. Andrews, and M. J. Surgalla: Factors influencing the loss of virulence in *Pasteurella pestis*, *J. Bact.*, **76**:185, 1958.

Omata, R. R.: Studies on the nutritional requirements of the fusobacteria, *J. Bact.*, **77**:35, 1959.

Ørskov, I.: Biochemical types in the *Klebsiella* group, *Acta Path. Microbiol. Scand.*, **40**:155, 1957.

Penso, G.: XIII. Sull' esistenza di un micelio vero e ramificato in tutte le specie del genere *Mycobacterium*, *Istituto Superiore di Sanita*, vol. 17, 1954.

Pentz, E. I., and Y. Shigemura: The production, concentration, and partial characterization of streptolysin O, *J. Bact.*, **69**:210, 1955.

Philip, C. B., J. F. Bell, and C. L. Larson: Evidence of infectious diseases and parasites in peak population of black-tailed jack rabbits in Nevada, USA, 1951–52, *Proc. Int. Cong. Zoo.*, Copenhagen, 1956.

————, G. D. Gill, and J. M. Geary: Notes on the rabbit tick, *Haemaphysalis leporispalustris* (Packard), and tularemia in central Alaska, *J. Parasit.*, **40**:1, 1954.

Pierce, W. A., Jr., and A. G. C. White: Hyaluronic acid formation by *Streptococcus pyogenes*, *Proc. Soc. Exp. Biol. Med.*, **87**:50, 1954.

Pottenger, F. M.: "Tuberculosis: A Discussion of Phthisiogenesis, Immunology, Pathologic Physiology, Diagnosis, and Treatment," St. Louis, The C. V. Mosby Company, 1948.

Ralston, R. J., and E. H. Payne: Treatment of chronic brucellosis with chloramphenicol and aureomycin, *J. Am. Med. Assoc.*, **142**:159, 1950.

Riggins, H. M., and H. C. Hinshaw: Streptomycin-tuberculosis research project of the American Trudeau Society, *Am. Rev. Tuberc.*, **59**:140, 1949.

Rosenthal, S. R., E. I. Leslie, and E. Loewinsohn: BCG vaccination in all age groups, *J. Am. Med. Assoc.*, **136**:73, 1948.

Saint-Martin, M.: Use of Mueller's potassium tellurite medium in the detection of *Corynebacterium diphtheriae*, *Can. J. Pub. Health*, **39**:148, 1948.

Schwab, J. H.: II. Comparative properties of intracellular hemolysin, streptolysin S', and streptolysin O, *J. Bact.,* **71:**100, 1956.

Shepard, C. C., E. Ribi, and C. Larson: Electron microscopically revealed structural elements of *Bacterium tularense* and their in vitro and in vivo role in immunologic reactions, *J. Immunol.,* **75:**7, 1955.

Smith, D. T., and N. F. Conant: "Zinsser Bacteriology," New York, Appleton-Century-Crofts, Inc., 1957.

Smith, H., D. W. Tempest, J. L. Stanley, P. W. Harris-Smith, and R. C. Gallop: VII. Two components of the anthrax toxin: their relationship to known immunising aggressins, *Brit. J. Exp. Path.,* **37:**263, 1956.

Smith, L. De S.: Clostridia in gas gangrene, *Bact. Rev.,* **13:**233, 1949.

Strange, R. E., and C. B. Thorne: Further purification studies on the protective antigen of *Bacillus anthracis* produced in vitro, *J. Bact.,* **76:**192, 1958.

Szeto, I. L., and P. Halick: Production of staphylo-coagulase in a special medium, *J. Bact.,* **75:**316, 1958.

Thomas, E. W.: Recent developments in the treatment of syphilis, *Am. J. Pub. Health,* **38:**1361, 1948.

Turner, F. J., and B. S. Schwartz: The use of a lyophilized human plasma standardized for blood coagulation factors in the coagulase and fibrinolytic tests, *J. Lab. and Clin. Med.,* **52:**888, 1958.

U.S. Public Health Service: Experimental studies of vaccination, allergy and immunity in tuberculosis, *Am. J. Hyg.,* **65:**248, 1957.

Warren, J., U. Walz, J. S. Reedal, and S. J. Ajl: II. Immunological properties of purified *Pasteurella pestis* toxin, *J. Bact.,* **70:**170, 1955.

Waterworth, P. M.: The stimulation and inhibition of the growth of *Haemophilus influenzae* on media containing blood, *Brit. J. Exp. Path.,* **36:**186, 1955.

Wilson, G. S., and A. A. Miles: "Topley and Wilson's Principles of Bacteriology and Immunity," Baltimore, The Williams & Wilkins Company, 1955.

Winter, J. L.: Studies in pertussis immunity. III. Immunization of children with live and killed vaccine, *Proc. Soc. Exp. Biol. Med.,* **92:**832, 1956.

CHAPTER 27

Bacterial Viruses

A virus may be defined as a submicroscopic unit capable of multiplication only within specific cells. The bacterial viruses are agents which invade or parasitize living bacterial cells.

Twort (1915) noticed certain transparent areas in a culture of a *Staphylococcus* that were free from bacterial growth. He found that if he touched one of these areas with an inoculating loop, then streaked it over the surface of an agar culture of the same species of *Staphylococcus*, clear transparent areas developed along the line of streaking. He also found that if the material from transparent areas was filtered through a Berkefeld filter, the filtrate contained a substance that was capable of dissolving a broth culture of the organisms. This lytic action was shown to be transmissible in series.

d'Herelle (1917), independently of Twort, observed the same phenomenon; he named the lytic principle bacteriophage. The term is usually abbreviated to phage and means literally bacteria-eating agent. At the present time phages are generally referred to as bacterial viruses because they have characteristics similar to plant and animal viruses.

The Growth Cycle. Extracellular bacteriophages are called mature or resting particles. They are obligate parasites and are dependent upon living bacteria for growth. They occur in nature wherever their hosts are found. Phages show signs of life when they encounter a receptive bacterium. The sperm-shaped phage attaches itself to the bacterial wall by the tip of its tail (Fig. 278); then after digesting a portion of the wall, the phage injects its desoxyribonucleic acid (DNA) core into the bacterial cell. The protein shell remains outside of the parasitized cell. It serves entirely as a protective device and delivery mechanism for the DNA. The phage DNA now duplicates itself many fold, while at the same time the protein that makes up the coat of the virus is produced in sufficient quantity to take care of the phage DNA. From the moment of invasion by phage, the bacterium manufactures viral DNA and protein instead of bacterial protein, DNA, and ribonucleic acid (RNA).

As a first step, the phage nucleic acid strands and the protein coats are reassembled into infectious particles. The completed phage particles escape only when the bacterial cell lyses, which it does shortly after

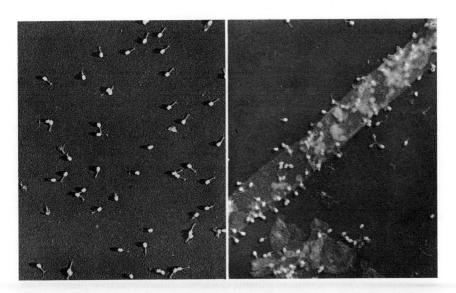

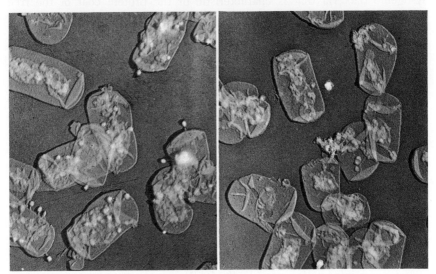

FIG. 278. Typhoid bacteriophage. Upper left, purified typhoid phage; upper right, phage particles adsorbed to *Salmonella typhosa;* lower left, interaction of phage and bacilli in the presence of tryptophan; lower right, same in the absence of tryptophan. Note that the phage particles do not attach themselves to the bacilli. (*Courtesy of Kay and Sampson.*)

invasion. This is known as the lytic cycle of phage growth and is necessary for phage perpetuation.

For more information see Hercik (1955); Herriott and Barlow (1957); Hershey (1953, 1955, 1956, 1957a, b); Hershey, Dixon, and Chase (1953); Jesaitis (1957); Murphy (1957); Puck and Lee (1954, 1955); Sinsheimer (1956); Visconti (1953); Volkin and Astrachan (1956).

Sometimes infection can proceed without lysis of the cell. The infected cell survives and continues to multiply, yielding infected daughter cells. It does so by virtue of the prophage it contains. Only occasionally do infected cells lyse. A pure culture of intact infected cells is called a lysogenic culture. Therefore, a lysogenic culture is one in which the bacterial cells multiply in a normal manner but possess and transmit to their descendants the ability to produce bacteriophage.

A culture may yield phage in only 1 cell in 1000. The rate is generally quite low because the production of phage is lethal to the bacterial cell. Phage particles cannot be demonstrated in lysogenic bacteria. Artificial disruption of a lysogenic organism does not liberate active phage. Also, serological tests have failed to reveal the presence of an antigen in the lysogenic bacteria that is characteristic of the protein coat of the free phage particle. Prophage lacks this protein covering and probably exists in the form of free DNA.

For more information see G. Bertani (1953, 1958), L. E. Bertani (1957), Jacob and Wollman (1953, 1957), Lederberg and Lederberg (1953), Miller and Goebel (1954).

Induction. By exposure to ultraviolet light, and in other ways, prophage may be induced to acquire the characters of virulence. Active development of phage follows, and as many as 90 per cent of the cells in the culture may burst and liberate free particles.

Prophage is composed of DNA. It is a specific structure attached to a chromosomal locus. Normally the prophage divides with the bacterial nucleus so that lysogenesis is hereditary. In this situation it is innocuous. It becomes virulent and multiplies only if it is detached from the chromosome. Inducing agents initiate some slow change in the nucleic acid metabolism of the bacterial cell, resulting in the rupture of the nuclear material with the separation of prophage.

For more information see Lwoff (1953).

Enumeration of Phage Particles. Phage particles may be enumerated by the number of clearings or plaques produced when introduced into an agar layer heavily seeded with the specific bacterium (Fig. 279). The particles may also be enumerated by quantitative electron microscopy. Under favorable conditions, from 50 to 100 per cent of the visible particles form plaques.

Morphology. Probably all phages are composed of a head and tail structure (Fig. 281). The phage particle consists of a shell of protein surrounding a nucleic acid core. The particles can be emptied of their nucleic acid by osmotic shock, leaving a protein shell resembling the intact particle in form.

All phages appear to function in the same manner: (1) attachment to the cell to be parasitized; (2) puncturing of the cell with the tail of the phage particle and injection of the nucleic acid inside the bacterial cell. The tail contains terminal fibrils which act as a cementing substance to hold the tail firmly in place. Then the tail pin punctures the cell wall, apparently aided by an enzyme.

Much of the work on phages has been carried out on a nonmotile strain of *Escherichia coli* susceptible to seven strains of virus numbered T1 to T7 (Fig. 280). The T3 and T7 phages have an almost spherical head and a very short tail. The other T phages are tadpole-shaped with hexagonal heads and long tails. These viruses have been purified and found to consist entirely of desoxyribonucleic acid (DNA) and protein. The head and tail sizes of the T phages are given in Table 29.

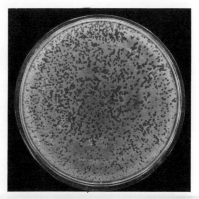

Fig. 279. Melted agar was inoculated with a mixture of *Staphylococcus aureus* and specific bacteriophage, then incubated. The clear areas or plaques represent places where growth has been eaten away by the bacteriophage.

TABLE 29. DIMENSIONS OF T PHAGES SUBJECTED TO FREEZE- AND AIR-DRYING*
(In millimicrons)

	T1	T2	T3	T4	T5	T6	T7
Head	65	95 × 65	47	85 × 70	80	95 × 65	47
Tail	150 × 10	100 × 25	15 × 10	110 × 15	180 × 10	100 × 25	15 × 10

* T2, T3, T6, and T7, frozen-dried; T1, T4, and T5, air-dried.

Electron micrographs of other virus particles are shown in Figs. 281, 282, and 283.

Composition. Phage particles appear to be composed almost entirely of protein and DNA. Other constituents include a small amount of a typical protein, a simple polypeptide, one or two free amino acids, and two purine derivatives. None of these minor constituents appears to be associated with the DNA.

Antigenic Composition. Phages are good antigens, being capable of stimulating antibody production when introduced into an animal body.

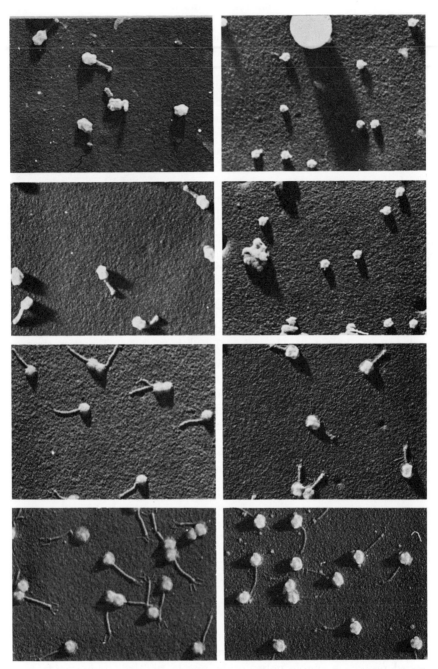

FIG. 280. The seven T phages. From left to right, top row, phages T2 and T3, frozen-dried; second row, phages T6 and T7, frozen-dried; third row, phages T1 and T4, air-dried; bottom row, phage T5, air-dried, deposited in gelatin, and same, air-dried, fixed in formalin. (*Courtesy of Williams and Fraser, Virus Laboratory, University of California, Berkeley.*)

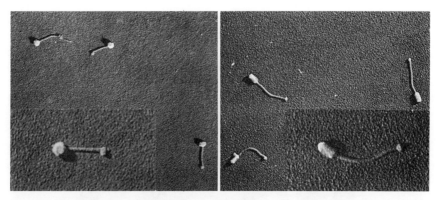

FIG. 281. *Staphylococcus* bacteriophages. Left, phage S5; right, phage S6, both prepared by freeze-drying. ×20,000. Inserts ×40,000. (*Courtesy of Seto, Kaesberg, and Wilson.*)

They are serologically distinct from their host cells. As far as is known, antiserum against a bacterium does not react with the virus that is active on that bacterium. Phages are serologically heterogeneous but may be placed into a number of distinct groups.

Phage T2 contains at least two surface antigens corresponding to head and tail proteins. Only the antibody produced against the tail parts is effective in neutralizing the infectivity of viral particles.

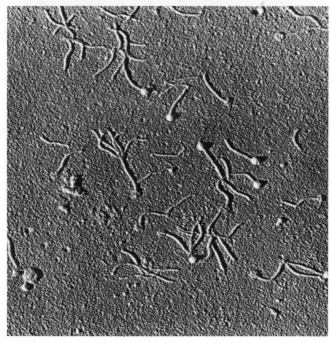

FIG. 282. Electron micrograph of bacteriophage active against *Corynebacterium diphtheriae*. ×30,000. (*After Freeman.*)

Identification of Bacteria by Bacteriophage. Craigie and Yen developed a successful method for the typing of *Salmonella typhosa* strains by means of *Vi* bacteriophage. Different types can be identified by means of certain specific *Vi* preparations which cannot be demonstrated by any serological method. The technique has been adopted as a routine procedure in many laboratories. It has proven of great value in medical and epidemiological work, especially with enteric organisms, streptococci, staphylococci, etc.

For more information see Atkinson (1957); Boyd and Bidwell (1957); Craigie and Felix (1947); Della Vida (1957); Edwards, Fife, and Moore (1955); Edwards and Wilson (1957); Felix and Callow (1951); Fusillo

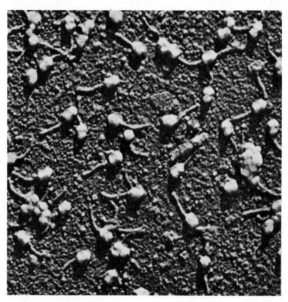

Fig. 283. Electron micrograph of *Streptomyces griseus* bacteriophage. ×45,000. (*Courtesy of Eli Lilly and Company.*)

et al. (1954); Smith and Cherry (1957); Wassermann and Saphra (1955); Welsch, Corbaz, and Ettlinger (1957).

Therapeutic Value of Bacteriophage. When phages were first discovered high hopes were entertained for their use as therapeutic agents. Since phage particles lyse bacteria readily in vitro, it was believed that they would prove equally effective in vivo. A few years ago it was a common practice for physicians to prescribe phages for many kinds of infections. Unfortunately, clinical observations have not borne out this claim, and it is probable that phages exert no appreciable effect upon the outcome of infections. Their use for this purpose has been largely discontinued.

For general information see Adams (1959), Boyd (1956), Burnet (1955), Burnet and Stanley (1959), Delbrück et al. (1950), Hershey

(1959), Luria (1953, 1959), Rhodes and van Rooyen (1958), and Williams (1956).

REFERENCES

Adams, M. H.: "Bacteriophages," New York, Interscience Publishers, Inc., 1959.

Atkinson, N.: The bacteriophage grouping scheme compared with other schemes using bacteriophage for exact strain identification in the salmonellas, *Australian J. Exp. Biol. Med. Sci.*, 35:1, 1957.

Bertani, G.: Infections bactériophagiques secondaires des bactéries lysogènes, *Ann. institut Pasteur*, 84:1, 1953.

————: Lysogeny. From "Advances in Virus Research," New York, Academic Press, Inc., 5:151, 1958.

Bertani, L. E.: The effect of inhibition of protein synthesis on the establishment of lysogeny, *Virology*, 4:53, 1957.

Boyd, J. S. K.: Bacteriophage, *Biol. Rev.*, 31:71, 1956.

———— and D. E. Bidwell: The type A phages of *Salmonella typhimurium*: Identification by a standardized cross-immunity test, *J. Gen. Microbiol.*, 16:217, 1957.

Burnet, F. M.: "Principles of Animal Virology," New York, Academic Press, Inc., 1955.

———— and W. M. Stanley: "The Viruses," *ibid.*, 1959, vol. 2.

Craigie, J., and A. Felix: Typing of typhoid bacilli with Vi bacteriophage, *Lancet*, 1:823, 1947.

d'Herelle, F.: "The Bacteriophage and Its Clinical Application," Springfield, Ill., Charles C Thomas, Publisher, 1930.

Delbrück, M., et al.: "Viruses," Pasadena, California Institute of Technology, 1950.

Della Vida, B. L.: Studi sulla tipizzazione batteriofagica di *Micrococcus pyogenes*, *Giornale di Microbiol.*, 4:138, 1957.

Edwards, P. R., M. A. Fife, and G. M. Moore: The differentiation of *Klebsiella* types 1 and 2 by bacteriophage, *Pub. Health Lab.*, 13:57, 1955.

———— and V. R. Wilson: Effect of symbiotic phages in the typing of *Salmonella paratyphi* B, *J. Bact.*, 73:292, 1957.

Felix, A., and B. R. Callow: Paratyphoid-B Vi-phage typing, *Lancet,* July 7, 1951, p. 10.

Fusillo, M. H., R. N. Roerig, J. F. Metzger, and K. F. Ernst: Phage typing antibiotic-resistant staphylococci, *Am. J. Pub. Health*, 44:317, 1954.

Hercik, F.: Electron microscopy of phage *E. coli* development inside the host cell, *Biochem. Biophys. Acta*, 18:1, 1955.

Herriott, R. M., and J. L. Barlow: The protein coats or "ghosts" of coli phage T2. II. The biological functions, *J. Gen. Physiol.*, 41:307, 1957.

Hershey, A. D.: Nucleic acid economy in bacteria infected with bacteriophage T2. II. Phage precursor nucleic acid, *J. Gen. Physiol.*, 37:1, 1953.

————: An upper limit to the protein content of the germinal substance of bacteriophage T2, *Virology*, 1:108, 1955.

————: Genetic structure and function in bacteriophage T2. From "Enzymes: Units of Biological Structure and Function," New York, Academic Press, Inc., 1956.

————: Bacteriophages as genetic and biochemical systems. From "Advances in Virus Research," New York, Academic Press, Inc., 4:25, 1957*a*.

————: Some minor components of bacteriophage T2 particles, *Virology*, 4:237, 1957*b*.

————: Bacteriophages. From "Viral and Rickettsial Infections of Man," edited by T. M. Rivers and F. L. Horsfall, Philadelphia, J. B. Lippincott Company, 1959.

————, J. Dixon, and M. Chase: Nucleic acid economy in bacteria infected with bacteriophage T2. I. Purine and pyrimidine composition, *J. Gen. Physiol.*, 36:777, 1953.

Jacob, F., and E. L. Wollman: Induction of phage development in lysogenic bacteria, *Cold Spring Harbor Symp. Quant. Biol.*, 18:101, 1953.

Jacob, F., and E. L. Wollman: Genetic aspects of lysogeny. From "Symposium on the Chemical Basis of Heredity," edited by W. D. McElroy and B. Glass, Baltimore, Johns Hopkins Press, 1957.

Jesaitis, M. A.: The nucleic acids of T2, T4, and T6 bacteriophages, *J. Exp. Med.*, **106**:223, 1957.

Lederberg, E. M., and J. Lederberg: Genetic studies of lysogenicity in *Escherichia coli*, *Genetics*, **38**:51, 1953.

Luria, S. E.: "General Virology," New York, John Wiley & Sons, Inc., 1953.

———: Viruses as determinants of cellular functions. From "Proceedings of the Third Canadian Cancer Conference," New York, Academic Press, Inc., 1959.

Lwoff, A.: Lysogeny, *Bact. Rev.*, **17**:269, 1953.

Miller, E. M., and W. F. Goebel: Nature of prophage in lysogenic bacteria, *J. Exp. Med.*, **100**:525, 1954.

Murphy, J. S.: A phage-associated enzyme of *Bacillus megaterium* which destroys the bacterial cell wall, *Virology*, **4**:563, 1957.

Puck, T. T., and H. H. Lee: Mechanism of cell wall penetration by viruses. I. An increase in host cell permeability induced by bacteriophage infection, *J. Exp. Med.*, **99**:481, 1954; II. Demonstration of cyclic permeability change accompanying virus infection of *Escherichia coli* B cells, *ibid.*, **101**:151, 1955.

Rhodes, A. J., and C. E. van Rooyen: "Textbook of Virology," Baltimore, The Williams & Wilkins Company, 1958.

Sinsheimer, R. L.: The glucose content of the desoxyribonucleic acids of certain bacteriophages, *Proc. Nat. Acad. Sci.*, **42**:502, 1956.

Smith, P. B., and W. B. Cherry: Identification of *Malleomyces* by specific bacteriophages, *J. Bact.*, **74**:668, 1957.

Visconti, N.: Resistance to lysis from without in bacteria infected with T2 bacteriophage, *ibid.*, **66**:247, 1953.

Volkin, E., and L. Astrachan: Phosphorus incorporation in *Escherichia coli* ribonucleic acid after infection with bacteriophage T2, *Virology*, **2**:149, 1956.

Wassermann, M. M., and I. Saphra: The use of bacteriophages in typing *Salmonella* cultures, *J. Bact.*, **69**:97, 1955.

Welsch, M., R. Corbaz, and L. Ettlinger: Phage typing of streptomycetes, *Schweizerische Zeit. Allgemeine Path. Bakt.*, **20**:454, 1957.

Williams, R. C.: Relations between structure and biological activity of certain viruses, *Proc. Nat. Acad. Sci.*, **42**:811, 1956.

——— and D. Fraser: Morphology of the seven T-bacteriophages, *J. Bact.*, **66**:458, 1953.

CHAPTER 28

Bacterial and Viral Diseases of Plants

BACTERIA

The first recorded observation on a bacterial disease of plants dates back to the work of Burrill (1881), who discovered the causative organism of pear blight. This work was confirmed by Waite (1891), who isolated the etiological agent and proved its pathogenicity. Since then a large number of bacterial plant pathogens have been isolated and described. It is safe to assume that there are as many bacterial diseases of plants as of man and animals.

Before an organism can be stated definitely to be the causative agent of a plant disease, it must be isolated from the plant tissue and its pathogenicity proved beyond doubt. Koch (1883) postulated certain requirements that should be met before an organism could be said to be the cause of a specific disease. These requirements have been generally accepted by both plant and animal pathologists. Koch's postulates are as follows:

1. An organism must be consistently associated with the disease in question.
2. The organism must be isolated in pure culture and accurately described.
3. The organism in pure culture, when inoculated into healthy plants, must be capable of reproducing the disease.
4. The organism must be reisolated from the diseased plant tissue and shown to be identical with the original species.

The bacterial diseases of plants may be placed into five groups on the basis of the location and character of the lesions produced: (1) soft rots, (2) vascular diseases or wilts, (3) blights, (4) intumescence diseases, and (5) local lesions or spots.

Soft Rots. Organisms responsible for soft rots reduce the plant tissue to a soft, very moist, pulpy mass. The condition may be better recognized as a state of rottenness. The attack may or may not be due to a specific organism.

The organisms producing soft rots differ from other forms found in soil in that they attack healthy plant tissue by the secretion of an extra-cellular protopectinase. The enzyme dissolves the pectin or cement-like material that binds the plant cells. The action is probably hydrolytic, resulting in the liberation of soluble sugars which are utilized by the bacteria for food. The plant becomes reduced to a mass of separate cells, which become converted later into a slimy, pulpy material.

In most cases, the specific organism is accompanied or closely followed by many saprophytic soil bacteria and fungi. These organisms find a favorable environment in the exposed cells and produce relatively large quantities of ammonia by the deaminization of the amino acids present in the proteins of dead plant tissue. The ammonia produces a destruction of the neighboring plant cells and rapidly reduces the plant to a slimy, pulpy, foul-smelling mass. The unpleasant odor is due to the secondary invaders. Plants decayed by pure cultures of the specific disease organisms do not give off an objectionable odor.

The organisms causing soft rots are members of the genus *Erwinia* (see page 416). The important species include the following: *E. ananas*, the cause of brown rot of the fruitlets of pineapple; *E. aroideae*, the cause of soft rot of calla, potato, eggplant, cauliflower, radish, cucumber, cabbage, parsnip, turnip, and tomato; *E. atroseptica*, responsible for black rot of stem and tuber of potato and other vegetables; *E. carotovora*, the cause of black rot in carrot, cabbage, celery, cucumber, eggplant, iris, muskmelon, hyacinth, onion, parsnip, pepper, potato, radish, tomato, turnip, and other plants; *E. chrysanthemi*, responsible for a soft rot on many fleshy vegetables; *E. dissolvens*, isolated from rotting corn stalks; and *E. rhapontici*, the cause of crown rot of rhubarb.

For more information see Garber and Shaeffer (1957); Katznelson (1955); Starr, De Ley, and Kilgore (1957); Starr and Mandel (1950); and Taylor (1951).

Vascular Diseases or Wilts. The bacterial wilts constitute a group of very important and destructive diseases of plants. The infecting organisms multiply and accumulate in large numbers in the vascular system, causing an interruption in the flow of sap in the plant. A complete interruption in the flow of sap results in a rapid wilting of the plant. A partial interruption results in the growth of a sickly plant which makes poor headway and finally dies. In some cases death is due to the action of secondary invaders.

Some important organisms causing wilt diseases are *Xanthomonas stewartii*, the cause of wilt disease of corn; *Corynebacterium insidiosum*, the agent of vascular disease of alfalfa; *C. michiganense*, the cause of canker of tomato; *Erwinia tracheiphila*, the etiological agent of wilt of cucumber, cantaloupe, muskmelon, pumpkin, and squash; *Pseudomonas solanacearum*, the cause of brown rot of potato, tobacco, and tomato; *Xanthomonas vasculorum*, the causative organism of gummosis of sugar cane.

For more information see Hildebrandt (1950).

Blights. Organisms producing blight diseases are capable of penetrating considerable distances between cells, leaving the neighboring tissue intact. The bacteria grow in the plant juices without producing any digestion of the tissues. The rods produce usually a discoloration of the leaves and branches. Death is due probably to an interference with the flow of plant sap.

Some of the organisms producing blights are *Erwinia amylovora*, the agent of fire blight or pear blight, isolated from the blossoms, leaves, and twigs of pear and apple trees; *Pseudomonas medicaginis*, the etiological agent of stem blight of alfalfa, isolated from brown lesions on the leaves and stems; *P. mori*, the cause of mulberry blight, isolated from blighted shoots; *P. pisi*, the agent of stem blight of field and garden peas, isolated from water-soaked lesions on stems and petioles; *Xanthomonas juglandis*, the cause of walnut blight, isolated from black spots on the leaves and nuts of English walnuts; and *X. phaseoli*, the cause of blight of bean, hyacinth bean, lupine, and other plants.

For more information see Corey and Starr (1957).

Intumescence Diseases. Some bacteria produce galls or tumors on plants. These excrescences or abnormal growths are produced by the action of certain organisms on the meristematic tissue of the plants. Tissues infected in this manner are grouped under the intumescence diseases.

In some infections the galls remain small; in others they may assume large proportions. Sugar beets have been known to carry tumors larger than the original plants. The bacteria are believed to elaborate some irritating metabolic product that causes rapid division of the neighboring plant cells. Some believe that tumor infections in plants are similar to cancerous growths in man and animals. Intracellular organisms are not necessary for the development of the characteristic lesions.

The important organisms producing intumescence diseases include *Agrobacterium gypsophilae*, the cause of galls on *Gypsophila paniculata* and related plants; *A. rhizogenes*, the agent producing hairy root of apple and other plants; *A. rubi*, the cause of cane gall on raspberries and blackberries; *A. tumefaciens*, the etiological organism of galls on Paris daisy; *A. pseudotsugae*, the cause of galls on Douglas fir in California; *Corynebacterium fascians*, the agent of fasciation on sweet pea, chrysanthemum, geranium, petunia, tobacco, etc.; *Pseudomonas savastanoi*, the etiological organism of olive galls; *P. tonelliana*, the cause of oleander galls; and *Xanthomonas beticola*, the cause of galls on sugar beets and garden beets.

For more information see Braun and Elrod (1946); Felt (1940); Hildebrandt (1950); Klein and Klein (1956); Riker, Spoerl, and Gutsche (1946); and Stonier (1956).

Local Lesions or Spots. In many plant diseases the attack is restricted to a small area around the point of entry. These diseases are grouped under local lesions or spots.

The organisms responsible for leaf-spot diseases produce a vigorous attack on the plant, with the result that the cells become heavily infected and strongly discolored. The discolored areas dry up and frequently fall out, leaving holes in the leaves.

Some of the organisms causing leaf-spot diseases are *Pseudomonas angulata,* the agent of angular leaf spot of tobacco; *P. maculicola,* the cause of cauliflower spot; *P. mellea,* the etiological agent of leaf spot of tobacco; *Xanthomonas cucurbitae,* the cause of leaf spot of squash and related plants; *X. malvacearum,* the agent of angular leaf spot of cotton; and *X. ricinicola,* the cause of leaf spot of castor bean.

Mode of Infection. The mode of entry of bacteria into the plant is usually through wounds. Roots, leaves, and stems are easily injured mechanically by means of agricultural implements, by animals, etc. Plants become easily infected following injury to the roots, whereas sound plants remain free from bacterial attack. Hailstones are known to produce injury to plants and make them vulnerable to infection. However, the usual cause of plant injury is through the bite of various insects. Sometimes the insects carry the etiological agent on their mouth parts, making it possible to injure and infect the plant in one operation.

In many of the leaf and fruit infections, the organisms gain entry through natural openings known as stomata. The organisms pass from the stomata into the intercellular spaces. The bacteria greatly reduce the resistance of the cells by suffocation or poisoning and make it possible for the etiological agent to enter the affected plant cells.

Bacteria may enter plants by way of the hydathodes or organs for the excretion of water. An excessive elimination of water results in the collection of considerable moisture on the plant surface. Bacteria readily collect in the water droplets, making it possible for some to gain entrance to the plant.

Lenticels are also unprotected openings, which may offer bacteria a path for invasion of the plant. These organs are cortical pores in the stems of woody plants through which air penetrates to the interior.

Many insects are responsible for plant infections. Their proboscises or legs act as carriers of bacteria that are capable of attacking the plant. This is especially true of those plants which produce nectars designed to attract bees and other insects for the fertilization of flowers.

For more information see Brian (1954), Dickson (1956), Elliott (1951), and Green (1946).

PLANT VIRUSES

A virus may be defined as a disease-producing agent, often referring to one too small to be seen with the usual light microscope. Viruses show the following characteristics:

1. They are very small, being generally below microscopic visibility. However, they may be seen by the electron microscope.

2. They maintain themselves only within certain specific living cells.

3. They produce typical and similar disease in suitable hosts in unbroken series.

4. They are antigenic, being capable of stimulating antibody production when introduced into an animal body.

5. They show great capacity for variation.

Iwanowski (1892) was probably the first to report the existence of ultramicroscopic particles capable of producing disease. He showed that the agent causing tobacco mosaic disease passed through a filter that retained all of the bacteria then known. Since that time many filter-passing agents causing diseases of plants, animals, and bacteria have been discovered.

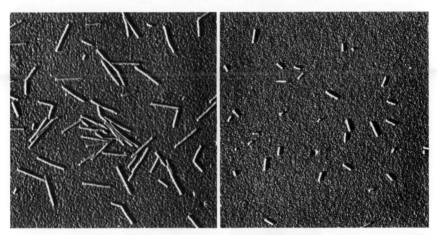

Fig. 284. Electron micrographs of tobacco mosaic virus crystals (left) and sonically treated virus (right). (*Courtesy of Harris and Knight.*)

Viruses vary considerably both in size and shape. Tobacco mosaic virus is rod-shaped (Fig. 284); the viruses of tomato bushy stunt (Fig. 285), southern bean mosaic, tobacco ringspot, brome grass mosaic (Fig. 286), turnip yellow mosaic (Fig. 287), and squash mosaic are spherical in shape. They are nonmotile and are not known to multiply by fission as do the bacteria.

There are probably more plant diseases caused by viruses than by bacteria. They are the causes of some of the most destructive diseases of agricultural crops. It is safe to say that almost all cultivated plants are affected by at least one virus. It is not uncommon to encounter plants affected by two or more viruses. For example, the potato is susceptible to at least 25 viruses, and the tobacco plant to at least 12 virus infections. Because of these multiple infections it is often very difficult, if not impossible, to identify a virus by the symptoms produced.

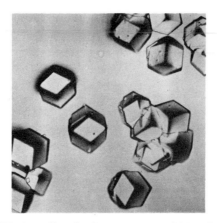

Fig. 285. Crystalline bushy stunt virus. (*After Stanley.*)

For more information see Cosentino, Paigen, and Steere (1956); Harris and Knight (1955); Kaesberg (1956); Ross (1957).

Nature of Plant Viruses. The exact nature of plant viruses is not clearly understood. Some believe they are living particles of submicroscopic size which develop by multiplication of preexisting forms (see page 769). Others are of the opinion that plant viruses are not living organisms but autocatalytic bodies capable of producing an injurious action in a sus-

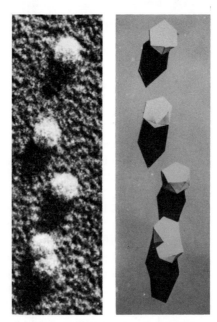

Fig. 286. Left, electron micrograph of lightly shadowed brome grass mosaic virus. Right, icosahedral models of the particles shown on the left. (*Courtesy of Kaesberg.*)

ceptible plant cell with the result that the cell is stimulated to produce more virus of the same kind. The cell is eventually destroyed, after which the autocatalytic agent spreads to other cells of the host. Supporting this belief is the work of Stanley (1935), who isolated the virus of tobacco mosaic (TMV) disease from infected tobacco and cucumber plants in

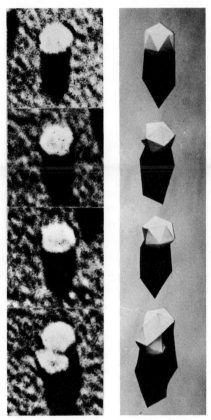

Fig. 287. Left, electron micrographs of heavily shadowed turnip yellow mosaic virus. Right, icosahedral models of particles shown on left. (*Courtesy of Kaesberg.*)

the form of fine, needle-shaped rods or crystals in a high state of purity which were capable of reproducing the disease in healthy plants.

Chemical Structure of Plant Viruses. Stanley (1935) isolated from Turkish tobacco plants, diseased with tobacco mosaic, a high-molecular-weight crystalline ribonucleoprotein that possessed the properties of TMV. Repeated recrystallization failed to change the infectivity of the crystals (Fig. 284). The virus crystals have been shown to be composed of pure ribonucleoprotein molecules.

Similar crystals have also been obtained from unrelated plants diseased with TMV. The reports of Stanley on TMV have stimulated work on other agents causing plant diseases, with the result that a number of different viruses have been obtained in crystalline form.

Tobacco Mosaic Virus. Many strains of TMV have been recognized in nature. The virus nucleoproteins isolated from various sources are similar in physical and chemical properties, yet different from each other and from ordinary TMV. A virus may become modified after cultivation in an unnatural host. Such a modified virus is probably accompanied by a change in the physical and chemical properties of the specific nucleo-protein. Therefore, typical symptoms of a plant virus disease are produced only by a nonmutated strain inoculated into a natural host plant.

For more information see Ginoza and Atkinson (1955), Reddi (1957), Rowen and Ginoza (1956).

Molecular Weight of TMV. By means of chemical and X-ray determinations, Franklin and Holmes (1956) reported that the molecular weight of TMV was about 40×10^6, or approximately 40 million. Ginoza and Norman (1957) by means of X-ray inactivation studies concluded that the molecular weight of the infectious nucleic acid portion of the nucleo-protein was between 2 and 3 million. The two components were present in the proportion of about 1 part nucleic acid to 10 parts protein.

Reconstitution of Tobacco Mosaic Virus. Fraenkel-Conrat and Williams (1955) isolated native protein and ribonucleic acid from TMV by treatment with pH 10.5 buffer and the detergent sodium dodecyl sulfate. Free ribonucleic acid was shown to be infectious, whereas the protein component was devoid of this characteristic. At pH 6.0 a mixture of these components was shown to reconstitute active virus. Typical lesions of tobacco mosaic were produced in susceptible plants, indicative of re-generation of up to 5 per cent of the original infectivity. Electron micro-graphs revealed rod-shaped particles indistinguishable from the original TMV particles (Fig. 288). The rods contained about 5 per cent of ribo-nucleic acid as a central core surrounded by a helix of protein.

In later communications, Fraenkel-Conrat (1956) and Fraenkel-Conrat and Singer (1957) reported on mixed reconstitution experiments per-formed with protein and nucleic acid fractions isolated from different strains of TMV. The reconstitution of virus particles from protein and nucleic acid of different strains yielded very active preparations, one of which showed higher infectivity than one of its parent strains. The nature of the disease provoked by mixed virus preparations resembled in each case that characteristic of the virus supplying the nucleic acid. In contrast to these properties, the serological characteristics of mixed virus prepara-tions were those of the virus supplying the protein. In other words, im-munological specificity is primarily an attribute of the protein, and in-fectivity of the nucleic acid.

For more information see Bawden and Pirie (1957); Commoner (1958);

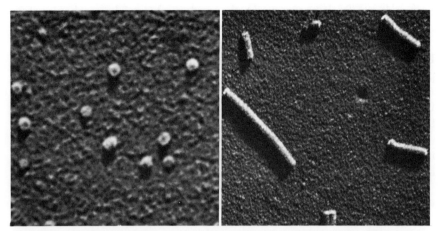

Fig. 288. Fragmented and reconstituted virus. Left, tobacco mosaic virus protein. Right, particles of reconstituted virus. Morphology identical with undegraded TMV. (*Courtesy of Fraenkel-Conrat.*)

Commoner, Lippincott, and Symington (1959); Engler and Schramm (1959); Hart (1955); Jeener, Lemoine, and Lavand'homme (1954); Kassanis (1959); Pirie (1956); Schramm, Schumacher, and Zillig (1955); Schramm and Zillig (1955); Wang and Commoner (1955).

AGENTS RESPONSIBLE FOR THE DISSEMINATION OF VIRUSES

Probably all viruses causing plant diseases are disseminated by insects. Other methods, of less importance, include (1) wind, (2) water, (3) soil, (4) seed, and (5) pollen.

Wind. Wind plays a minor role in the dissemination of plant viruses. However, there may be exceptions. For example, TMV is very resistant to desiccation and may be wind-borne in the form of dried, crumbled plant tissue. The virus is capable of readily infecting healthy plants through slight wounds.

Water. Water appears to be of little importance in the spread of plant viruses. Here again there may be exceptions. It is possible to infect healthy plants with tobacco necrosis by bathing the roots in water containing the virus. The virus can infect healthy plants without artificial wounding.

Soil. The soil itself is not an agent for the transmission of plant viruses. Infection may occur through roots and other underground parts of plants by soil water or by insects working in the soil. Since it is very difficult to observe underground parts of plants, the mechanism of infection by this route remains obscure. However, it has been definitely shown that wheat mosaic virus may be transmitted underground through roots or the crown, or both. The virus is capable of surviving in the soil for some time and is difficult to remove by thorough washing. The mechanism for the entrance of the virus into plants is not known.

Seed. Seed transmission of plant diseases does occur for some viruses. Bean mosaic virus is transmitted in this manner in about 50 per cent of plants under experimental conditions. The results are usually inconsistent. A plant may show both healthy and infected seeds. Plants of the family Leguminosae appear to be more susceptible to infection by this route than plants of other families.

Pollen. Virus infections may be transmitted to seeds by pollen from infected plants. In the plant Jimson weed, up to 79 per cent of the seeds may become infected. Bean seeds may also be infected in this manner.

Insect Transmission. The most important agents for transmitting plant viruses are insects. Some insects transmit the virus mechanically, others biologically. The former method occurs usually in those insects which have chewing mouth parts. The latter method occurs only in the sucking insects, but transmission by these insects is not always biological.

According to Leach (1940), biological transmission of plant viruses by insects has usually one or more of the following attributes:

1. An apparent multiplication or increase of the virus in the insect's body.
2. An incubation period in the body of the insect, i.e., a necessary period after feeding on infected plants before the insect becomes infective or viruliferous.
3. A degree of specificity between the insect and the virus that it transmits.
4. An obligatory relationship.
5. A relation between the age or life stage of the insect and its ability to transmit the virus.
6. Congenital transmission of the virus from one generation to the next.

For more information see Bawden (1950), Jones (1950), Smith (1957), Stanley (1938, 1943), Storey (1939).

REFERENCES

Bawden, F. C.: "Plant Viruses and Virus Diseases," Waltham, Mass., The Chronica Botanica Co., 1950.

——— and N. W. Pirie: The activity of fragmented and reassembled tobacco mosaic virus, *J. Gen. Microbiol.*, **17**:80, 1957.

Braun, A. C., and R. P. Elrod: Stages in the life history of *Phytomonas tumefaciens*, *J. Bact.*, **52**:695, 1946.

Brian, P. W.: The use of antibiotics for control of plant diseases caused by bacteria and fungi, *J. Appl. Bact.*, **17**:142, 1954.

Burrill, T. J.: Anthrax of fruit trees; or the so-called fire-blight of pear, and twig blight of apple trees, *Proc. Am. Assoc. Advance Sci.*, **29**:583, 1881.

Commoner, B.: The biochemical basis of tobacco mosaic virus infectivity. From "Fourth International Congress of Biochemistry," **7**:17, 1958.

———, J. A. Lippincott, and J. Symington: Replication of tobacco mosaic virus, *Nature*, **184**:1992, 1959.

Corey, R. R., and M. P. Starr: Colony types of *Xanthomonas phaseoli*, *J. Bact.*, **74**:137, 1957.

Cosentino, V., K. Paigen, and R. L. Steere: Electron microscopy of turnip yellow mosaic virus and the associated abnormal protein, *Virology*, **2**:139, 1956.

Dickson, J. G.: "Diseases of Field Crops," New York, McGraw-Hill Book Company, Inc., 1956.

Elliott, C.: "Manual of Bacterial Plant Pathogens," Waltham, Mass., The Chronica Botanica Co., 1951.

Engler, R., and G. Schramm: Infectious ribonucleic acid as precursor of tobacco mosaic virus, Nature, 183:1277, 1959.

Felt, E. P.: "Plant Galls and Gall Makers," Ithaca, N.Y., Comstock Publishing Associates, Inc., 1940.

Fraenkel-Conrat, H.: The role of the nucleic acid in the reconstitution of active tobacco mosaic virus, J. Am. Chem. Soc., 78:882, 1956.

────── and B. Singer: Virus constitution. II. Combination of protein and nucleic acid from different strains, Biochim. Biophys. Acta, 24:540, 1957.

────── and R. C. Williams: Reconstitution of active tobacco mosaic virus from its inactive protein and nucleic acid components, Proc. Nat. Acad. Sci., 41:690, 1955.

Franklin, R. E., and K. C. Holmes: The helical arrangement of the protein sub-units in tobacco mosaic virus, Biochim. Biophys. Acta, 21:405, 1956.

Garber, E. D., and S. G. Shaeffer: Free histidine content of turnip varieties and their resistance to histidine requiring mutants of Erwinia aroideae, J. Bact., 74:392, 1957.

Ginoza, W., and D. E. Atkinson: Comparison of some physical and chemical properties of eight strains of tobacco mosaic virus, Virology, 1:253, 1955.

────── and A. Norman: Radiosensitive molecular weight of tobacco mosaic virus nucleic acid, Nature, 179:520, 1957.

Green, D. E.: "Diseases of Vegetables," New York, St. Martin's Press, Inc., 1946.

Harris, J. I., and C. A. Knight: Studies on the action of carboxypeptidase on tobacco mosaic virus, J. Biol. Chem., 214:215, 1955.

Hart, R. G.: Infectivity measurements of partially degraded tobacco mosaic virus, Virology, 1:402, 1955.

Hildebrandt, A. C.: Some important galls and wilts of plants and the inciting bacteria, Bact. Rev., 14:259, 1950.

Iwanowski, D.: Ueber die Mosaikkrankheit der Tabakspflanze, Cent. Bakt. Abt. II, 5:250, 1892.

Jeener, R., P. Lemoine, and C. Lavand'homme; Détection et propriétés de formes du virus de la mosaique du tabac dépourvues d'acide ribonucléique et non infectieuses, Biochim. Biophys. Acta, 14:321, 1954.

Jones, D. R.: On the nomenclature and identity of the coliform soft-rot bacteria, Trans. Brit. Mycological Soc., 33:73, 1950.

Kaesberg, P.: Structure of small "spherical" viruses, Science, 124:626, 1956.

Kassanis, B.: Comparison of the early stages of infection by tobacco mosaic virus and its nucleic acid, J. Gen. Microbiol., 20:704, 1959.

Katznelson, H.: The metabolism of phytopathogenic bacteria. I. Comparative studies on the metabolism of representative species, J. Bact., 70:469, 1955.

Klein, D. T., and R. M. Klein: Quantitative aspects of transformation of virulence in Agrobacterium tumefaciens, J. Bact., 72:308, 1956.

Leach, J. G.: "Insect Transmission of Plant Diseases," New York, McGraw-Hill Book Company, Inc., 1940.

Pirie, N. W.: Some components of tobacco mosaic virus preparations made in different ways, Biochem. J., 63:316, 1956.

Reddi, K. K.: Structural differences in the nucleic acids of some tobacco mosaic virus strains. I. Monopyrimidine nucleotides in ribonuclease digests, Biochim. Biophys. Acta, 25:528, 1957.

Riker, A. J., E. Spoerl, and A. E. Gutsche: Some comparisons of bacterial plant galls and of their causal agents, Botan. Rev., 12:57, 1946.

Ross, A. F.: Responses of plants to concurrent infection by two or more viruses, Trans. N.Y. Acad. Sci., 19:236, 1957.

Rowen, J. W., and W. Ginoza: Unit particle lengths of strains of tobacco mosaic virus, Biochim. Biophys. Acta, 21:416, 1956.

Schramm, Von G., G. Schumacher, and W. Zillig: Über die Struktur des Tabakmosaikvirus, III. Der Zerfall in alkalischer Lösung, *Zeit. Naturforsch.*, 10b:481, 1955.

Schramm, Von G., and W. Zillig: IV. Die Reaggregation des nucleinsäurefreien Proteins, *ibid.*, 10b:493, 1955.

Smith, K. M.: "Recent Advances in the Study of Plant Viruses," London, J. & A. Churchill, 1957.

Stanley, W. M.: Isolation of a crystalline protein possessing the properties of tobacco mosaic virus, *Science*, 81:644, 1935.

———: Virus proteins—a new group of macromolecules, *J. Phys. Chem.*, 42:55, 1938.

———: Chemical structure and the mutation of viruses. From "Virus Diseases," edited by T. M. Rivers, Ithaca, N.Y., Cornell University Press, 1943.

Starr, M. P., J. De Ley, and W. W. Kilgore: Catabolism of hexuronic acids by *Erwinia* and *Aerobacter, Science*, 125:929, 1957.

——— and M. Mandel: The nutrition of phytopathogenic bacteria. IV. Minimal nutritive requirements of the genus *Erwinia, J. Bact.*, 60:669, 1950.

Stonier, T.: Radioautographic evidence for the intercellular location of crown gall bacteria, *Am. J. Bot.*, 43:647, 1956.

Storey, H. H.: Transmission of plant viruses by insects, *Botan. Rev.*, 5:240, 1939.

Taylor, C. B.: The soft-rot bacteria of the coliaerogenes group, *Proc. Soc. Appl. Bact.*, 14:95, 1951.

Wang, T-Y., and B. Commoner: The formation of infectious nucleoprotein from tobacco mosaic virus protein and tobacco leaf DNA, *Proc. Nat. Acad. Sci.*, 42:831, 1956.

CHAPTER 29

Viral Diseases of Man

The etiological agents of disease discussed in Chap. 26 can be seen with the aid of a light microscope. A few of the animal viruses are barely visible under the highest power of a light microscope. However, their presence may be demonstrated by examination under an electron microscope or by the inoculation of the virus-containing material into a susceptible animal.

Nature of Viruses. Viruses show no evidence of respiration or biochemical activity. Studied in vitro, they do not exhibit any of the characteristics of living material. Yet, when inoculated into a susceptible host, they are able to invade the cells and multiply intracellularly. All evidence points to the fact that they are obligate intracellular parasites and do not multiply outside living cells.

The rickettsiae are more complex than the viruses. They show the fine morphological structures of bacteria and multiply by binary fission. Their growth is inhibited by the same drugs which antagonize bacteria.

Viruses show considerable variation in size. The larger viruses, e.g., the members of the psittacosis-granuloma group, are visible under a light microscope, stain with basic dyes, are inhibited in growth by antibiotics and other drugs, and are presumed to divide by binary fission. They appear to be more closely related to the rickettsiae than to other viruses. The larger viruses are also more complex structurally, biochemically, and antigenically than the smaller members. They all contain desoxyribonucleoprotein together with other constituents. Poliomyelitis virus, on the other hand, is much smaller, simpler in structure, and composed of ribonucleoprotein.

Inclusion Bodies. Individual virus particles are sometimes referred to as elementary bodies. Masses of viruses or "colonies" are sometimes called intracellular inclusions.

The infectious property of viruses resides in the elementary bodies. These bodies bear the same relationship to virus infections as the pneumococcus does to pneumonia.

The larger elementary bodies, i.e., those over 200 mμ, can be seen with a light microscope in stained preparations. The smaller viruses can only be seen with an electron microscope.

Intracellular inclusions may be present in the nucleus or the cytoplasm of parasitized cells. Nuclear inclusions are eosinophilic. Inclusions of this type are found in chickenpox, yellow fever, herpes simplex, and poliomyelitis. Cytoplasmic inclusions may be eosinophilic or basophilic. Inclusions of the former type are found in fowlpox, rabies, and vaccinia; the latter type are present in trachoma, psittacosis, and pneumonitis.

Size and Shape of Virus Particles. The size of a virus may be determined by filtration, by rate of centrifugation, by diffusion, and by measurement under a light microscope if the virus particles are large, or by electron microscopy if the particles are beyond the range of visibility of a light microscope. The most accurate results are obtained by means of an electron microscope.

Viruses show great variation in size and shape, ranging from about 10 to 300 mμ (Table 30). Some viruses are smaller than the largest protein molecule; others are larger than the smallest bacteria. In between

TABLE 30. SIZE OF SOME VIRUSES AND REFERENCE MATERIALS DETERMINED BY ELECTRON MICROSCOPY

Particle	Diameter or width $\times$ length, mμ
Red blood corpuscle	7500
Serratia marcescens	750
Rickettsia prowazekii (epidemic typhus)	500 $\times$ 1100
Rickettsia typhi (endemic typhus)	450 $\times$ 1000
Miyagawanella psittaci (psittacosis)	455
Lymphogranuloma venereum	330
Canary pox	265 $\times$ 311
Smallpox	275
Fowlpox	264 $\times$ 322
Mumps	230
Chickenpox	175
Tobacco mosaic	15 $\times$ 280
Herpes simplex	150
Rabies	125
Influenza B (Lee)	123
Newcastle disease	115
Influenza A (PR8)	100
Staphylococcus bacteriophage	100
Adenovirus	90
E. coli bacteriophage T1	Head 50, tail 12 $\times$ 120
Equine encephalitis (Eastern)	42
Equine encephalitis (Western)	40
Tomato bushy stunt	26
Poliomyelitis (Lansing)	25
Coxsackie	24
Yellow fever	22
Hemocyanin molecule	22
Foot-and-mouth disease	10
Hemoglobin molecule (horse)	3 $\times$ 15
Egg albumin	2.5 $\times$ 10

these two extremes, other viruses form an almost continuous spectrum. Some viruses are spherical, some are ovoid, others are cubes or minute parallelepipeds, still others are rod-shaped.

Cultivation of Viruses. Living cells of plant or animal tissue are required for the successful propagation of plant or animal viruses. They grow in the intracellular position and are liberated only on rupture of the cell. Although viruses multiply only in living cells, it does not follow that all viruses can be cultivated in this manner. Many viruses have not been successfully cultivated. Some animal viruses may be cultivated in minced embryo medium, on the chorioallantoic membrane of the developing chick, in living tissue fragments embedded in plasma, and in trypsinized tissue suspensions (single cells) placed in test tubes and rotated in the horizontal position to encourage growth in monolayers on the glass walls. Plant viruses cannot be propagated in animal tissues. They require plant tissues for successful multiplication. Root-tip cultures are usually used for this purpose.

Most viruses growing in living tissue produce little or no change in cells that can be detected by microscopic examination. With certain other viruses, such as herpes and cowpox, inclusions may be formed, or cytopathogenic degeneration may occur.

For more information see Melnick et al. (1957).

Chemical Structure. Reasonably pure preparations of many viruses have been prepared and investigated. The crystalline plant viruses are composed of pure nucleoprotein molecules (see page 763). The animal viruses appear to be more complex in composition.

Influenza virus has been shown to be composed of a lipoprotein complex containing ribonucleic acid (RNA). Equine encephalomyelitis virus is a high-molecular-weight complex containing carbohydrate, cholesterol, phospholipide, fatty acid, and also RNA. Vaccinia virus, on the other hand, contains desoxyribonucleic acid (DNA) together with carbohydrate, lipide, cholesterol, biotin, and copper.

For more information see Hoyer et al. (1958).

Mutation of Viruses. Viruses show great capacity for variation or mutation. Once a virus becomes modified, it generally persists indefinitely. The ability of a particle to mutate is a property not ordinarily ascribed to molecules but to living organisms.

For example, influenza virus loses its virulence for mice on passage through embryonated eggs. The virulence may be restored by several passages of this avirulent strain through mice. Virulence is increased for mice, but there is no increase in virulence for the chick embryo.

Another example would be the decrease in virulence of smallpox virus for man. Vaccine virus is derived from smallpox by repeated passage through calves. Antigenically, smallpox is indistinguishable from vaccinia, differing only in its ability to produce the disease smallpox.

Resistance of Viruses. Viruses are heat-labile and sensitive to the same agents that affect bacteria, but they are, in general, more resistant. They are readily destroyed at 60°C. for 30 min. They survive long periods when kept in the frozen state in dry ice at −60°C. Infectivity is rapidly lost when stored in the usual home refrigerator (about 4°C.).

Some viruses are resistant to desiccation; most are not. Infectious small-pox virus has been recovered from dry pox crusts stored at room temperature for at least one year.

The addition of 0.5 per cent phenol to vaccine virus does not destroy its infectivity. Glycerin in a concentration of 50 per cent gradually destroys bacteria but has no appreciable effect on viruses. On the other hand, viruses are susceptible to oxidative destruction. This may be largely prevented by adding a suitable reducing agent, such as cysteine, to the virus suspension.

Virus infections do not respond to treatment with sulfa drugs, penicillin, and other antibiotics. This is generally believed to be associated with the method of multiplication of viruses, which are dependent upon the parasitized cell and have no metabolic process that can be blocked by drugs. Exceptions are the basophilic group of viruses, such as psittacosis, trachoma, and pneumonitis, which are sensitive to a number of antibiotics. The antibiotics are not virucidal but are effective by virtue of their ability to interfere with the process of multiplication.

Immunity in Virus Diseases. Recovery from a virus disease usually confers strong, almost lasting immunity. Second attacks of such virus diseases as smallpox, mumps, measles, poliomyelitis, and chickenpox rarely occur. On the other hand, with some virus infections—influenza, common cold, herpes simplex (cold sores, fever blisters)—the immunity developed is of short duration. Various immune substances have been identified in the circulating blood, including agglutinins, precipitins, and complement-fixing and neutralizing antibodies.

Recovery from a virus disease does not mean necessarily that the etiological agent is entirely eliminated from the host. The virus may persist in the recovered individual for life. The agent is believed to be stored in certain living cells where it cannot be spread to others, or come in contact with circulating antibodies. Consequently, if the host cells are not destroyed by the virus, the two can live together without the infecting agent ever coming in contact with the humoral antibodies.

Some important viral infections and their characteristics are as follows:

Chickenpox (Varicella). An acute, extremely contagious virus disease characterized by fever, mild constitutional symptoms, a cutaneous eruption involving the superficial layers of the skin, lasting 3 to 4 days, and leaving a granular scab. Vesicles tend to be more abundant on the covered parts of the body. Sometimes vesicles may be so few as to escape observation. Lesions also appear on scalp and on mucous membranes of upper respiratory tract.

Source of Infection. Secretions from respiratory tract of infected persons (Fig. 289). Disease may be communicable before eruption is in evidence.

Mode of Transmission. From person to person by direct contact; by articles freshly soiled with discharges from infected persons.

Incubation Period. From 2 to 3 weeks; usually 14 to 16 days.

Disease communicable probably not more than 1 day before nor more than 6 days after appearance of vesicles. Especially communicable in early stages of eruption.

Susceptibility and Immunity. Susceptibility to disease universal among those who have not had an attack. About 70 per cent of persons have had the disease by the

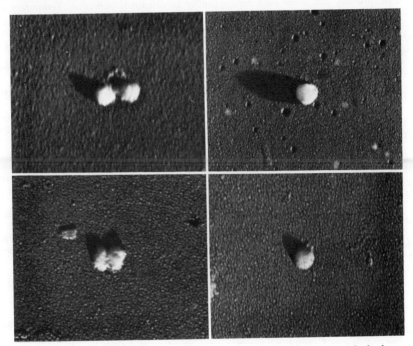

Fig. 289. Electron micrographs of varicella virus from human cases of chickenpox, gold-shadowed. ×24,800. (*After Nagler and Rake.*)

time they are fifteen years of age. Recovery from the disease usually confers permanent active immunity.

Prevention and Control. Isolation of infected persons for period of communicability. Disinfection of discharges from nose and throat and articles soiled by such discharges.

For more information see Nagler and Rake (1948), Reagan et al. (1953), Stokes (1959).

Common Cold. The etiological agent is one or more viruses, although at one time numerous bacteria were believed to be the cause of the infection.

Disease Produced. An acute, highly communicable, catarrhal infection of the nose, throat, larynx, sinuses, trachea, and larger bronchi, lasting usually 2 to 7 days. Infection usually accompanied by a rise in temperature on the first day and by chilly sensations with coryza and lassitude.

Other minor respiratory infections of a similar character include acute respiratory diseases (ARD) and respiratory illness—adenoidal pharyngeal conjunctival (RI—APC).

Infection has been transmitted experimentally to chimpanzees and man by a filterable agent. Reagan et al. (1954a) reported the cultivation of the filter-passing agent in the chorioallantoic cavity of embryonating eggs.

Source of Infection. Discharges from nose and throat of infected persons or from articles freshly soiled with discharges from such persons.

Mode of Transmission. Usually directly by droplets of infected saliva sprayed into the air during coughing, sneezing, and talking, or indirectly from articles freshly soiled with such discharges.

Incubation Period. Probably 12 to 72 hr. Communicability limited to early stages of disease, although the virus remains in discharges for an undetermined period.

Susceptibility and Immunity. Susceptibility to disease is universal. Temporary active immunity of approximately 1 month follows recovery from the disease.

Prevalence. Most individuals contract one or more colds each year. Both sexes about equally susceptible to disease. Incidence higher in children under five years of age and becomes less after twenty years.

Prevention and Control. Infected persons should avoid contact with others. Rest in bed during the acute stage is advisable. Nasal and mouth discharges should be kept away from others and disposed of, preferably by burning. Disinfection of eating and drinking utensils.

For more information see Ginsberg (1957); Hilleman et al. (1956); Hilleman, Werner, and Stewart (1955); Horsfall (1959); Jordan and Denny (1957); Morgan et al. (1956); Reagan et al. (1954a, b); Rowe and Huebner (1956).

Dengue. A disease caused by at least two immunologically distinct virus types.

Disease Produced. An acute infection of sharp onset, usually with two paroxysms of short duration, accompanied by fever, intense headache, pains in muscles and joints, and irregular eruption. Eruption appears usually 3 to 4 days after onset of fever.

Source of Infection. From blood of infected persons 1 day before and up to 5 days after onset.

Mode of Transmission. By the bite of several species of mosquitoes, including *Aëdes aegypti, A. albopictus,* and *A. scutellaris.* The mosquito becomes infectious 8 to 11 days after feeding on an infected person.

Incubation Period. From 3 to 15 days, usually 5 to 6 days.

Susceptibility and Immunity. Susceptibility to disease universal. Two immunologically distinct strains known. Homologous immunity of long duration; heterologous immunity of short duration.

Prevalence. May occur wherever specific mosquitoes exist. Disease found mainly in the tropics and subtropics.

Prevention and Control. Elimination of mosquitoes and their breeding places. Use of repellents.

Isolation of patients in screened rooms previously treated with insecticide.

For more information see Sabin (1950, 1959) and Schlesinger (1949).

Encephalitis (Arthropod-borne). In the United States and Canada, includes Eastern and Western equine and St. Louis types of human disease; in some South American countries, includes Venezuelan equine type; in Japan, Korea, China, includes Japanese B type; in European and Siberian Russia, includes Russian spring-summer type.

Disease Produced. Mild cases of all types characterized by headache, fever, stiff neck and back, tight muscles, possibly drowsiness with changes in spinal fluid. Moderately severe cases characterized by acute onset, high fever, stupor, meningeal signs, coma, spasticity, tremors, rarely flaccid paralysis. Each form of disease caused by a specific virus.

Source of Infection. Wild and domestic birds serve as principal source of mosquito infection for U.S. types. Mites of chickens and wild birds may be infected. Man probably not a source of infection for U.S. types.

Mode of Transmission. Russian spring-summer type tick-borne; all others transmitted by mosquitoes.

Incubation Period. Usually 5 to 15 days.

Susceptibility and Immunity. Susceptibility to disease usually highest in childhood and old age. Permanent active immunity against specific virus believed to follow recovery from disease.

Prevalence. Disease occurs usually in summer or early fall. Endemic in the United States in hot valley areas, and epidemic in some dry farm areas of Middle West, South, and East.

Prevention and Control. Destroying larvae and feeding places of vector mosquitoes. Screening of sleeping quarters. Avoiding exposure during hours when mosquitoes are biting. Education of public to mode of spread and control.

For more information see Olitsky and Casals (1959), Olitsky and Clarke (1959).

Influenza. Disease formerly believed to be caused by the organism *Haemophilus influenzae* but it is now known to be produced by a virus. In typical severe cases *H. influenzae* is also present but is probably of secondary importance (see page 720).

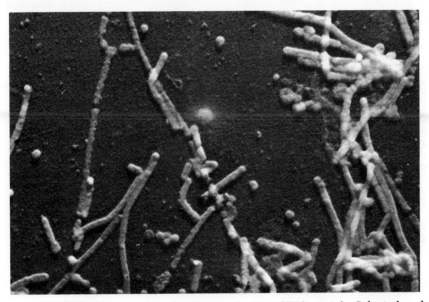

Fig. 290. Electron micrograph of influenza A virus (PR8 strain). Spherical and filamentous forms are seen in close association. ×25,300. (*After Murphy, Karzon, and Bang.*)

Two distinct types of influenza virus, designated as types A and B, have been long identified. Type A is the older and more widely distributed (Fig. 290); type B has usually been found in smaller and more localized outbreaks. Some outbreaks are not caused by either A or B but by a third type designated C.

Virus capable of passing through most filters, resists freezing for about 2 weeks, and retains its potency in 50 per cent glycerol for the same length of time. When dried from the frozen state (lyophilized), virus retains its potency for at least 6 weeks in the refrigerator. Virus inactivated by mercurials, which would indicate the presence of –SH groups (cysteine), and reactivated by sodium thioglycollate. Lee strain (type B) virus inactivated at 50 to 54°C. in 15 min. and by as little as 0.05 per cent formalin in 18 hr. Virus inactivated by intense ultraviolet irradiation.

Virus sensitive to strong oxidizing agents such as iodine, salts of heavy metals, Mercurochrome, and the wetters Phemerol, Roccal, and sodium dodecyl sulfate. It is only slightly affected by reducing agents, sulfathiazole, dilute phenol solutions, glucose, ammonium sulfate, calcium chloride, and sodium thiosulfate.

Disease Produced. Influenza is an acute virus infection characterized by sudden onset, fever of 1 to 7 days' duration, catarrh of the respiratory tract (sometimes alimentary tract), pains in the head and muscles, coryza, sore throat, bronchitis, and a tendency to pneumonic complications. The disease produces marked prostration. Virus capable of infecting mice, ferrets, and possibly swine intranasally.

Source of Infection. Discharges from nose and throat of infected persons or from articles freshly soiled with discharges from such individuals.

Mode of Transmission. By direct contact with infected persons, by droplet infection, or by articles freshly soiled with discharges from nose and throat of infected individuals.

Incubation Period. Usually 24 to 72 hr.

Susceptibility and Immunity. Susceptibility to disease is general, although some have natural immunity. Acquired immunity of short duration, possibly as long as 1 year, follows recovery from the disease and is effective only against the particular type which caused the infection.

Prevalence. Epidemics may affect up to 50 per cent of population within 4 to 6 weeks. Pandemics occur at irregular intervals.

Prevention and Control. Education of public to the dangers of droplet infection from spitting, sneezing, and coughing in the presence of others. Use of common eating and drinking utensils, towels, etc., should be avoided. Use of disposable tissue and napkins should be encouraged.

Isolation of infected persons during acute stage. Disinfection of discharges from nose and throat or articles freshly soiled by such discharges. Patients should be put to bed at the beginning of an attack. During epidemics, overcrowding should be avoided.

Some success achieved by administration of currently available vaccines, provided the infecting strain matches closely the antigenic component of the vaccine. Vaccine should be administered in advance of infection.

Antibiotics or sulfa drugs not effective but may be used to combat complications due to secondary invaders.

For more information see Ackermann and Maassab (1955); Ada and Perry (1955, 1956); Burnet and Lind (1956); Francis (1959); Frommhagen, Freeman, and Knight (1958); Frommhagen and Knight (1956); Gotlieb and Hirst (1954); Jensen and Francis (1953); Morgan, Howe, Rose, and Moore (1956); Murphy, Karzon, and Bang (1950); Rhodes and van Rooyen (1958).

Measles (Rubeola, Morbilli). A filterable virus capable of passing through Berkefeld N and Seitz filters. Can be preserved at −35 or −72°C. for as long as 4 weeks and for several days at 0°C. At room temperature virus remains infective for 36 hr. Virus may be dried from frozen state and remain active for at least 15 weeks. Can withstand 10 per cent ether for 40 min.

Claims that the virus of measles has been cultivated appear questionable.

Disease Produced. A specific, highly contagious disease, characterized by fever; catarrhal symptoms of the eyes, nose, and throat; an early eruption of the mouth; Koplik spots; a cutaneous rash followed by desquamation during convalescence.

Source of Infection. Secretions of nose and throat of infected persons.

Mode of Transmission. Directly from person to person; by droplets of infected saliva sprayed into the air during coughing, sneezing, and talking; by articles freshly soiled with discharges from an infected individual.

Measles is one of the most easily transmitted of the communicable diseases.

Incubation Period. After exposure, fever appears in about 10 days; rash in 13 to 15 days, occasionally shorter or longer.

Susceptibility and Immunity. Susceptibility to disease is general. Disease occurs most commonly in children between five and fourteen years of age.

Permanent acquired immunity usually follows recovery from disease.

Prevalence. Universal, almost all persons (up to 90 per cent) have had an attack at some time during life. Disease common in childhood.

Prevention and Control. Immune globulin may be used for passive immunization of children under three years of age in families where cases of measles occur.

Isolation of infected persons during periods of communicability to protect them from possibility of reinfection and as protection to others. Isolation period usually 7 days from first appearance of rash. Disinfection of articles soiled with fresh discharges from nose and throat of infected persons.

Passive immunity may be transferred to healthy individuals before symptoms of measles appear by the injection of convalescent serum or serum from a person who has recovered from the disease. Such passive immunity may persist for about 4 weeks. During an epidemic, convalescent serum may either prevent the disease or modify the severity of the attack. In the latter instance a mild case of measles is usually sufficient to produce a lasting immunity.

Antibiotics or sulfa drugs not effective but may be used to combat complications due to secondary invaders.

For more information see Katz, Milovanovic, and Enders (1958), and Rake (1959a).

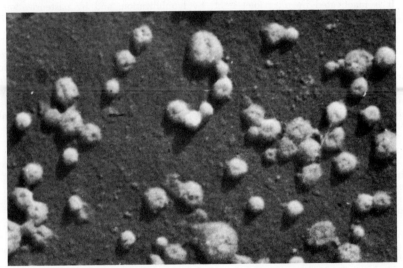

Fig. 291. Electron micrograph of mumps virus shadowed with chromium. ×28,800. (*After Weil, Beard, Sharp, and Beard.*)

Mumps (Infectious Parotitis). Virus has been cultivated in the yolk sac, amniotic sac, and allantoic sac of the developing chick embryo. Measurements of particle size range from 90 to 340 mμ. Weil et al. (1948), by means of electron micrographs, found the virus particles to be circular and ranging in size from 106 to 282 mμ, with an average of 190 mμ (Fig. 291).

Disease Produced. Mumps is an acute, specific, contagious disease characterized by fever and inflammation of the salivary glands. The parotid, submaxillary, and sublingual glands may be infected, although the parotid is most frequently involved. Sometimes the ovaries and testes may be attacked.

Source of Infection. Secretions of the mouth and possibly the nose.

Mode of Transmission. By direct contact with infected persons or by articles freshly soiled with discharges from mouth and nose of such individuals.

Incubation Period. From 12 to 26 days, usually 18 days.

Susceptibility and Immunity. Susceptibility to disease is general. Recovery from infection usually confers permanent active immunity. Complement-fixing antibodies regularly appear or increase in concentration in the sera of persons during an attack of mumps or during convalescence.

Prevalence. Mumps less prevalent than other diseases of childhood. Occurs more frequently during winter and spring. Occurrence of disease sporadic and epidemic. In large cities, it is endemic. Outbreaks frequently occur during periods of over-crowding.

Prevention and Control. Infected persons should be isolated until 7 days after swelling of salivary glands has subsided. Disinfection of eating and drinking utensils.

For more information see Enders (1959), Henle and Deinhardt (1955), and Lundbäck (1955).

Poliomyelitis (Infantile Paralysis). This virus is one of the smallest known, measuring 25 mμ in diameter.

It is a ribonucleoprotein and has been prepared in crystalline form. The ribonucleic acid may be separated from the protein and is capable of producing infections.

The virus is one of the most stable known. It resists inactivation by alcohol, phenol, formalin, chlorine, antibiotics, and by repeated freezing and thawing.

It is inactivated by ultraviolet light, by lyophilization, and by pasteurization at 62°C. for 30 min.

Disease Produced. Poliomyelitis is widely prevalent. In only a small proportion of infected persons is the disease clinically recognizable. In its recognizable form poliomyelitis is an acute, systemic infectious disease that involves the central nervous system. Disease characterized usually by fever, headache, vomiting, constipation, drowsiness alternating with irritability, almost always stiffness of neck and spine, tremor, and exaggeration of muscular reflexes. In about half of such cases paralysis may develop in the first few days, which shows a marked tendency for improvement after it has reached its height. Diagnosis depends upon detection of a flaccid paralysis characteristically irregular in its involvement of muscular tissue.

All strains fall into three immunologically distinct types designated types 1, 2, and 3 (Fig. 292).

Source of Infection. Nose and throat discharges of infected persons; also from those not suffering from clinically recognized attack of disease. Virus also present in feces.

Virus recovered from throat swabs and throat washings of poliomyelitis patients collected 3 to 13 days after onset of disease.

A study of four households attacked by poliomyelitis provided evidence of widespread distribution of virus in the members of these units. Of 20 members in these households, 16 had polio virus in their intestinal discharges, 7 had virus in the oropharynx.

Mode of Transmission. It is believed that the virus enters by way of nose and mouth, either from a carrier or from a person with a subclinical infection. There is some evidence that disease may be spread by milk, water supplies, swimming pools, food, sewage, and insects. Flies have been shown to be contaminated with the virus.

Rhodes et al. (1950) showed that a strain of human polio virus in stool survived after addition to river water for at least 188 days and retained its property of inducing paralysis in monkeys. Storage of the contaminated water was at −4°C., and the dilution of the human stool was about 1:200. The fact that the virus could survive for such a prolonged period would seem to have some epidemiological implications.

Lensen et al. (1949) found that in samples of natural waters having a pH range of 7.9 to 8.3, virus was consistently inactivated within 10 min. in presence of 0.05 p.p.m. residual free chlorine. In experiments at a higher pH range (10 to 11.25), 0.1 to 0.15 p.p.m. residual chlorine was necessary to achieve the same results.

Incubation Period. Usually 7 to 14 days; may be as early as 3 and as late as 35 days. Period of greatest communicability may be from latter part of incubation period to first week of the acute illness.

Susceptibility and Immunity. Susceptibility to infection is general. Children are believed to be more susceptible than adults, although definite proof is still lacking. Active immunity produced after recovery from the disease. Duration of immunity unknown, but second attacks are rare.

Prevalence. Infection widespread throughout the world. Paralytic cases more prevalent in temperate climates. Cases more numerous in summer and early fall. Children one to sixteen years of age appear to be more susceptible than adults.

Prevention and Control. Infected individuals should be isolated for 2 weeks after symptoms appear. Disinfection of nose, throat, and bowel discharges, and articles soiled with such discharges.

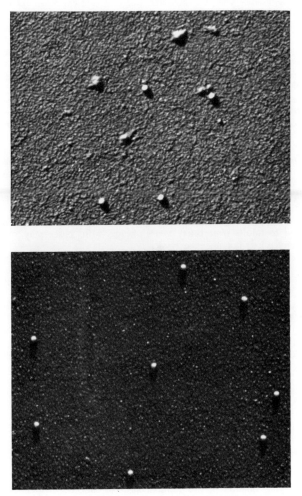

FIG. 292. Poliomyelitis virus particles. Upper, Leon strain, type 3; lower, Mahoney strain, type 1. (*Courtesy of Sabin Hennessen, and Warren.*)

All children with fever should be isolated and kept in bed pending outcome of diagnosis. Protection of children from contact with others during an epidemic. Avoidance of nose and throat operations on children during an epidemic. During period when disease is prevalent, crowds should be avoided as far as possible.

For more information see Bazeley and Thayer (1954); Bodian (1959); Boyd (1953); Gifford and Syverton (1957); Howe and Wilson (1959); Hsiung and Melnick (1955); Koprowski (1955); Lahelle (1955); Maassab, Loh, and Ackermann (1957); Oddo (1957); Sabin, Hennessen, and Warren (1954); Salk (1955a, b, 1959); Schwerdt et al. (1954).

Psittacosis (Ornithosis). Virus particles relatively large, measuring 455 mμ in diameter, and approaching the size of small bacteria. Particles visible under a light microscope. Virus filterable through membranes which retain bacteria. Virus stains Gram-negatively, is susceptible to sulfonamides, penicillin, tetracyclines, and other chemotherapeutic agents which antagonize bacteria. However, in its mode of multiplication intracellularly, and its relationship to the metabolism of animal cells, it behaves more like the true viruses than to other classes of microorganisms.

Virus easily cultivated on the chorioallantoic membrane of the developing chick.

Disease Produced. Psittacosis is a contagious disease of parrots, parakeets, love birds, canaries, and other birds. It resembles influenza and is transmissible to man. In man disease characterized by high fever, headache, backache, thirst, changes in tongue and pharynx, stupor or depression, rapid pulse, diarrhea or constipation, enlargement of spleen; symptoms of atypical pneumonia or of a typhoidal state, with rales and cardiac dullness. Sputum light yellow in color and of extreme viscosity. White blood count is normal or slightly increased early, with leucopenia later.

Source of Infection. Canaries, pigeons, parrots, parakeets, love birds, and other birds. Birds that appear to be well occasionally transmit the infection.

Mode of Transmission. Virus present in blood, saliva, and feces of infected birds. Disease transmitted by contact with such birds or their recent surroundings.

Incubation Period. From 6 to 15 days in human cases.

Susceptibility and Immunity. All ages susceptible. Disease more severe in higher age groups. Recovery from disease confers immunity.

Prevalence. Outbreaks usually sudden and caused by exposure to sick birds. Deaths usually confined to adults over thirty years of age. Mild cases may result from exposure to infected birds not necessarily sick.

Prevention and Control. Strict regulation of traffic in birds of the parrot family. Education of public in dangers of birds of the parrot family, particularly of those freshly imported. Homes and pet shops harboring infected birds should be quarantined.

Disease may be diagnosed by presence of virus in saliva and blood during the first week of the infection. Serum contains complement-fixing antibodies. Infected persons should be isolated during the febrile and acute clinical stage. Masks should be worn when handling patients with coughs. Disinfection of discharges and articles soiled with such discharges. Infected birds should be disposed of by burning. Buildings in which infected birds were housed should be thoroughly cleaned and disinfected.

Specific treatment consists of administration of the tetracycline antibiotics or chloramphenicol until patient afebrile. Repeat if relapse occurs.

For more information see Christensen (1957) and Meyer (1959).

Rabies (Hydrophobia, Canine Madness). Particles large, measuring 125 to 150 mμ in diameter. Virus capable of passing through Berkefeld and the coarser Chamberland filters, but not through Seitz filter pads. Infected tissues may be stored in undiluted glycerol for several weeks at room temperature, for several months in the refrigerator, and for 1 or 2 years at subzero temperatures. The virus is reduced in virulence (attenuated) by drying infected tissue (spinal cords of rabbits) suspended over pellets of potassium hydroxide as a dehydrating agent, by exposure to 1 per cent phenol, and by heating to 54 to 56°C. for 1 hr. or less. Virus best preserved by drying from the frozen state followed by storage at refrigerator temperature. Repeated freezing and thawing of virus suspensions results in loss of infectivity.

Disease Produced. An acute encephalitis caused by a neurotropic virus acquired from the bite of a rabid animal, usually the dog. Disease characterized by depression, itching at site of primary infection, and fever. Patient becomes uneasy, swallowing becomes difficult, salivation marked, followed by attacks of delirium. Paralysis of the face muscles, eyes, and tongue appears, gradually spreading to the trunk and limbs.

Cause of death may be determined by demonstrating the presence of Negri bodies in the nerve cells of brain or spinal cord, or by emulsifying a small portion of the hippocampus in sterile saline and inoculating subdurally into guinea pigs or rabbits. Death occurs in about 16 days, and Negri bodies can be demonstrated in the brain tissue.

Source of Infection. Infected animals, chiefly dogs; vampire bats also involved.

Mode of Transmission. Virus present in saliva and is usually transmitted to man by bite of a rabid animal. Infections have occurred by contact of saliva with a scratch or break in the skin.

Incubation Period. Usually 2 to 6 weeks, sometimes as long as 6 months, depending upon site of wound in relation to richness of nerve supply and distance of nerve path to brain.

Susceptibility and Immunity. Susceptibility to disease is general. Natural immunity in man and animals not known to exist. Active artificial immunity may be developed by use of vaccine.

Prevalence. Occurs throughout the world except in Australia, New Zealand, Hawaii, and other Pacific and Atlantic islands. More prevalent in dogs than in other animals. Incidence in man is low.

Prevention and Control. A dog or other animal that has bitten a person should be isolated and observed for a proper period of time. If rabies is suspected, animal should be killed and brain examined for presence of Negri bodies. If examination is positive, person bitten should be given antirabic vaccination immediately before symptoms appear.

Wound caused by bite or scratch of a suspected animal should be thoroughly cleaned and irrigated with a solution of tincture of green soap or other satisfactory antiseptic. Dogs over six months of age should be vaccinated annually.

Vaccine consists of an emulsion of infected rabbit brain in saline containing 0.25 per cent phenol, and incubated at 37°C. to kill the virus. Recommended treatment consists of daily subcutaneous injections for 14 days. Treatment is generally sufficient to produce an active artificial immunity. Vaccine useless after symptoms appear.

Use of vaccine has been instrumental in greatly reducing the mortality rate. In persons so treated, death rate has dropped to 1 per cent.

For more information see Hodes (1955), Johnson (1959), Koprowski and Burkhart (1954).

Rubella (German Measles). A specific, mild virus infection, characterized by fever, a cutaneous eruption sometimes resembling that of measles, sometimes that of scarlet fever, or both. Rubella usually appears without other symptoms, but is almost always accompanied by enlargement of the postauricular, suboccipital, and cervical lymph nodes.

Source of Infection. Secretions of mouth and nose.

Mode of Transmission. Directly from person to person; by droplets of infected saliva sprayed into the air during coughing, sneezing, and talking; by articles freshly soiled with discharges of an infected individual.

Incubation Period. From 10 to 20 days; usually 18 days.

Susceptibility and Immunity. Susceptibility to disease is general in children. Permanent acquired immunity usually follows recovery from disease. Disease more prevalent in adults than measles.

Prevalence. Occurs most commonly in children. More prevalent in winter and spring.

For more information see Rake (1959b).

Smallpox (Variola). Virus capable of passing through most filters, resistant to low temperatures, to 50 per cent glycerol, and to 0.5 per cent phenol; sensitive to heat, being destroyed at 55°C. or over. Cytoplasmic inclusions are characteristic of the infection. These are believed to be masses of virus particles and may be demonstrated in various tissues but are most characteristic in epithelial cells (Fig. 293).

Disease Produced. An acute, specific infectious disease characterized by sudden onset, usually with severe chill, with rapidly rising temperature, followed by an eruption passing through papular, vesicular, and pustular stages. Permanent scars frequently remain. Eruption most abundant and earliest on face, next on forearms, wrists, and hands, favoring the limbs more than trunk. Lesions more abundant on shoulders and chest than on loins or abdomen.

Vaccinia and alastrim are milder forms of the disease, presumably caused by the same virus which has become altered in virulence.

Source of Infection. Lesions of mucous membranes and skin of infected persons.

Mode of Transmission. Contact with diseased persons; by articles soiled with discharges from such persons.

Incubation Period. From 7 to 16 days, usually 12 days. Milder types tend to have longer incubation periods.

Susceptibility and Immunity. Susceptibility to infection is universal, but not every individual exposed to virus contracts the disease. Permanent active immunity usually follows recovery from disease. Artificial active immunity may be effective for as long as 20 years or for less than 2 years.

Vaccine-immune serum has been shown to contain agglutinating, precipitating, complement-fixing, and neutralizing antibodies.

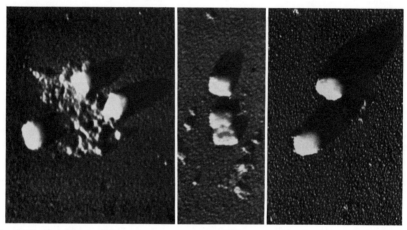

Fig. 293. Variola virus from human case of smallpox, shadowed with gold. ×24,800. (*After Nagler and Rake.*)

Prevalence. Distribution sporadic or endemic and occurs almost everywhere. Frequency greatest in winter; least in summer.

Prevention and Control. Isolation of infected individuals in screened wards. Disinfection of articles soiled with discharges from infected individuals. Thorough cleaning and disinfection of premises.

General vaccination in early childhood. This affords protection for about 5 years. Children on entering school should be revaccinated, and the entire population should be so treated when disease appears in severe form.

Vaccine most generally employed is prepared from calf lymph, obtained by rubbing the virus into the scarified abdomen of calves six months old. After 5 days, the scarified areas are scraped under aseptic conditions. The harvested pulp is mixed with twice its weight of water and passed through a sieve. The emulsion is preserved by the addition of glycerin and phenol to give a final concentration of 50 per cent of the former and 0.5 per cent of the latter. The preserved pulp is stored at 10°C.

Another vaccine that has been extensively employed is prepared by growing the virus in a medium composed of minced chick embryo tissue suspended in Tyrode's solution. This is a living-tissue medium.

For more information see Cabasso et al. (1954), Cutchins and Warren (1958), Downie (1959), Overman and Tamm (1957).

Yellow Fever. Particles smaller than most known viruses, measuring only 22 mμ in diameter. Virus readily passes through Seitz, Berkefeld, and Chamberland filters;

is readily inactivated by heat and germicides; may be preserved in 50 per cent glycerol for several months; retains its activity in the frozen state for a long time; resists desiccation from frozen state and may remain viable for many months; is inactivated by dilution in physiologic salt solution; and multiplies in tissue culture.

Disease Produced. An acute, specific virus disease characterized by sudden onset, fever, chills, prostration, headache, muscular pain, some destruction of red blood cells, congestion of mucous membranes, black vomit, mild albuminuria, and jaundice. Leucopenia is the rule. Disease of short duration. Fatality among indigenous populations of endemic regions less than 5 per cent; for others may be as high as 40 per cent.

Source of Infection. Blood of infected persons, monkeys, and probably other wild animals.

Mode of Transmission. By the bite of *Aëdes aegypti* and other species of mosquitoes, of which *Hemagogus* appears to be the most important in South America.

Incubation Period. Usually 3 to 6 days, occasionally longer.

Susceptibility and Immunity. Susceptibility to disease is general. Permanent acquired immunity follows recovery from disease. Active immunity of about 6 years' duration may be developed by inoculation of a vaccine.

Vaccine prepared by inoculating chick embryos with virus and incubating at 37°C. for 4 days. Embryos harvested and reduced to a pulp in a blender. Juice measured into ampules and desiccated from the frozen state. Ampules filled with nitrogen gas before sealing. Vaccine stored in refrigerator. For use, vaccine reconstituted with saline and injected subcutaneously.

Prevalence. Endemic among human beings and some animals, chiefly in Western and Central Africa. Epidemic among primates in South America except Uruguay and Chile. Still endemic in jungle form in Panama.

Prevention and Control. Control of breeding places of *Aëdes aegypti* and its elimination. Active immunization of persons exposed to infection.

Isolation of infected persons during first 4 days of fever, and protection from mosquitoes. Immunization of exposed population by the use of attenuated virus only feasible method for control of yellow fever. Effective duration about 6 years.

For more information see Theiler (1959).

For general information on viruses and viral diseases see Ackermann (1958), American Public Health Association (1955), Burnet (1960), Burnet and Stanley (1959), Colter (1957), Luria (1953), Pollard et al. (1960), Rhodes and van Rooyen (1958), Rivers and Horsfall (1959).

REFERENCES

Ackermann, W. W.: Cellular aspects of the cell-virus relationship, *Bact. Rev.,* **22:**223, 1958.

———— and H. F. Maassab: Growth characteristics of influenza virus. Biochemical differentiation of stages of development. II. *J. Exp. Med.,* **102:**393, 1955.

Ada, G. L., and B. T. Perry: Infectivity and nucleic acid content of influenza virus, *Nature,* **175:**209, 1955.

———— and ————: Influenza virus nucleic acid: Relationship between biological characteristics of the virus particle and properties of the nucleic acid, *J. Gen. Microbiol.,* **14:**623, 1956.

American Public Health Association: "Control of Communicable Diseases in Man," New York, 1955.

Bazeley, P. L., and J. R. Thayer: The growth of poliomyelitis virus in tissue culture. I. The use of a stationary bottle technique, *Austral. J. Exp. Biol. Med. Sci.,* **32:**23, 1954.

Bodian, D.: Poliomyelitis: Pathogenesis and histopathology. From "Viral and Rickettsial Infections of Man," edited by T. M. Rivers and F. L. Horsfall, Jr., Philadelphia, J. B. Lippincott Company, 1959.

Boyd, T. E.: Immunization against poliomyelitis, *Bact. Rev.*, **17**:339, 1953.

Burnet, F. M.: "Principles of Animal Virology," New York, Academic Press, Inc., 1960.

―――― and P. E. Lind: Comparative study of recombinants of different types of influenza A virus with the strain WSE, *Austral. J. Exp. Biol. Med. Sci.*, **34**:1, 1956.

―――― and W. M. Stanley: "The Viruses," New York, Academic Press, Inc., 1959, vol. 3.

Cabasso, V. J., R. F. Korns, I. F. Moore, and H. R. Cox: Primary response of children to glycerinated or dried smallpox vaccines of calf lymph or chick embryo origin, *Am. J. Pub. Health*, **44**:194, 1954.

Christensen, P. M.: "Ornithosis. A Study of Virus and Antigen," Copenhagen, S. L. Møllers Bogtrykkeri, 1957.

Colter, J. S., H. H. Bird, A. W. Moyer, and R. A. Brown: Infectivity of ribonucleic acid isolated from virus-infected tissues, *Virology*, **4**:522, 1957.

Cutchins, E., and J. Warren: Comparative susceptibility of cell cultures to vaccinia virus: Application to the standardization of smallpox vaccine, *Proc. Soc. Exp. Biol. Med.*, **97**:456, 1958.

Downie, A. W.: Smallpox, cowpox and vaccinia. From "Viral and Rickettsial Infections of Man," edited by T. M. Rivers and F. L. Horsfall, Jr., Philadelphia, J. B. Lippincott Company, 1959.

Enders, J. F.: Tissue-culture technics employed in the propagation of viruses and rickettsiae, *ibid.*, 1959.

Francis, T., Jr.: Influenza, *ibid.*, 1959.

Frommhagen, L. H., N. K. Freeman, and C. A. Knight: The lipid constituents of influenza virus, chick allantoic membrane, and sedimentable allantoic protein, *Virology*, **5**:173, 1958.

―――― and C. A. Knight: The polysaccharide and ribonucleic acid content of purified influenza virus, *ibid.*, **2**:430, 1956.

Gifford, G. E., and J. T. Syverton: Replication of polio-virus in primate cell cultures maintained under anaerobic conditions, *ibid.*, **4**:216, 1957.

Ginsberg, H. S.: Biological and physical properties of the adenoviruses, *Ann. N.Y. Acad. Sci.*, **67**:383, 1957.

Gotlieb, T., and G. K. Hirst: The formation of doubly antigenic particles from influenza A and B virus and a study of the ability of individual particles of X virus to yield two separate strains, *J. Exp. Med.*, **99**:307, 1954.

Henle, G., and F. Deinhardt: Propagation and primary isolation of mumps virus in tissue culture, *Proc. Soc. Exp. Biol. Med.*, **89**:556, 1955.

Hilleman, M. R., R. A. Stallones, R. L. Gauld, M. S. Warfield, and S. A. Anderson: Prevention of acute respiratory illness in recruits by adenovirus (RI-APC-ARD) vaccine, *ibid.*, **92**:377, 1956.

―――――, J. H. Werner, and M. T. Stewart: Grouping and occurrence of RI (prototype RI-67) viruses, *ibid.*, **90**:555, 1955.

Hodes, H. L.: Present day problems in rabies, *Bull. N.Y. Acad. Med.*, **31**:569, 1955.

Horsfall, F. L., Jr.: Common cold. From "Viral and Rickettsial Infections of Man," edited by T. M. Rivers and F. L. Horsfall, Jr., Philadelphia, J. B. Lippincott Company, 1959.

Howe, H. A., and J. L. Wilson: Poliomyelitis, *ibid.*, 1959.

Hoyer, B. H., E. T. Bolton, R. A. Ormsbee, G. Le Bouvier, D. S. Ritter, and C. L. Larson: Mammalian viruses and rickettsiae, *Science*, **127**:859, 1958.

Hsiung, G. D., A. Mannini, and J. L. Melnick: Plaque assay of measles virus on *Erythrocebus patas* monkey kidney monolayers, *Proc. Soc. Exp. Biol. Med.*, **98**:68, 1958.

―――― and J. L. Melnick: Plaque formation with poliomyelitis, Coxsackie, and orphan (Echo) viruses in bottle cultures of monkey epithelial cells, *Virology*, **1**:533, 1955.

Jensen, K. E., and T. Francis, Jr.: The antigenic composition of influenza virus measured by antibody-absorption, *J. Exp. Med.*, **98**:619, 1953.

Johnson, H. N.: Rabies. From "Viral and Rickettsial Infections of Man," edited by T. M. Rivers and F. L. Horsfall, Jr., Philadelphia, J. B. Lippincott Company, 1959.

Jordan, W. S., Jr., and F. W. Denny, Jr.: Failure to transmit common cold to suckling hamsters, *Proc. Soc. Exp. Biol. Med.*, **95**:651, 1957.

Katz, S. L., M. V. Milovanovic, and J. F. Enders: Propagation of measles virus in cultures of chick embryo cells, *ibid.*, **97**:23, 1958.

Koprowski, H.: Immunization of man against poliomyelitis with attenuated preparations of living virus, *Ann. N.Y. Acad. Sci.*, **61**:1039, 1955.

————— and R. L. Burkhart: Newer knowledge concerning rabies, *Proc. Book, Am. Vet. Med. Assoc.*, 1954, p. 461.

Lahelle, O.: Development of human fibroblastic subculture, and isolation of poliomyelitis viruses in subcultures, *Acta Path. Microbiol. Scand.*, **36**:47, 1955.

Lensen, S. G., M. Rhian, M. R. Stebbins, R. C. Backus, and C. E. Peterson: Inactivation of partially purified poliomyelitis virus in water by chlorination, *Am. J. Pub. Health*, **39**:1120, 1949.

Lundbäck, H.: Cultivation of mumps virus in embryonated eggs, *Acta Path. Microbiol. Scand.*, **37**:103, 1955.

Luria, S. E.: "General Virology," New York, John Wiley & Sons, Inc., 1953.

Maassab, H. F., P. C. Loh, and W. W. Ackermann: Growth characteristics of poliovirus in HeLa cells: Nucleic acid metabolism, *J. Exp. Med.*, **106**:641, 1957.

Melnick, J. L., G. D. Hsiung, C. Rappaport, D. Howes, and M. Reissig, *Tex. Rep. Biol. Med.*, **15**:496, 1957.

Meyer, K. F.: Psittacosis—lymphogranuloma venereum group. From "Viral and Rickettsial Infections of Man," edited by T. M. Rivers and F. L. Horsfall, Jr., Philadelphia, J. B. Lippincott Company, 1959.

Morgan, C., C. Howe, H. M. Rose, and D. H. Moore: Structure and development of viruses observed in the electron microscope. IV. Viruses of the RI-APC group, *J. Biophys. Biochem. Cytol.*, **2**:351, 1956; III. Influenza virus, *J. Exp. Med.*, **104**:171, 1956.

Murphy, J. S., D. T. Karzon, and F. B. Bang: Studies of influenza A (PR8) infected tissue cultures by electron microscopy, *Proc. Soc. Exp. Biol. Med.*, **73**:596, 1950.

Nagler, F. P. O., and G. Rake: The use of the electron microscope in diagnosis of variola, vaccinia, and varicella, *J. Bact.*, **55**:45, 1948.

Oddo, F. G.: L'evoluzione dell infezione di cellule HeLa con virus poliomielitico studiata attraverso le alterazioni morfologiche e la dimostrazione di antigene virale a mezzo di anticorpi fluorescenti, *Giornale Microbiol.*, **4**:153, 1957.

Olitsky, P. K., and J. Casals: Arthropod-borne group A virus infections of man. From "Viral and Rickettsial Infections of Man," edited by T. M. Rivers and F. L. Horsfall, Jr., Philadelphia, J. B. Lippincott Company, 1959.

————— and D. H. Clarke: Arthropod-borne group B virus infections of man, *ibid.*, 1959.

Overman, J. R., and I. Tamm: Multiplication of vaccinia virus in the chorioallantoic membrane in vitro, *Virology*, **3**:173, 1957.

Pollard, E. C., et al.: "Inactivation of Viruses," New York Academy of Sciences, **83**:513, 1960.

Rake, G.: Measles. From "Viral and Rickettsial Infections of Man," edited by T. M. Rivers and F. L. Horsfall, Jr., Philadelphia, J. B. Lippincott Company, 1959*a*.

—————:Rubella, *ibid.*, 1959*b*.

Reagan, R. L., W. C. Day, S. Moore, and A. L. Brueckner: Electron microscopic studies of the virus of varicella (chickenpox) from monkey serum, *Tex. Rep. Biol. Med.*, **11**:74, 1953.

—————, E. D. Palmer, M. T. Stewart, and A. L. Brueckner, *ibid.*, **12**:174, 1954*a*.

—————, —————, E. C. Delaha, S. R. Cook, A. L. Brueckner, and H. E. Nelson: Electron microscopic studies of an egg-adapted virus isolated from a patient with a common cold, *ibid.*, **12**:1067, 1954*b*.

Rhodes, A. J., E. M. Clark, D. S. Knowles, A. M. Goodfellow, and W. L. Donohue:

Prolonged survival of human poliomyelitis virus in experimentally infected river water, *Can. J. Pub. Health*, **41**:146, 1950.

―――― and C. E. van Rooyen: "Textbook of Virology," Baltimore, The Williams & Wilkins Company, 1958.

Rivers, T. M., and F. L. Horsfall, Jr.: "Viral and Rickettsial Infections of Man," Philadelphia, J. B. Lippincott Company, 1959.

Rowe, W. P., and R. J. Huebner: Present knowledge of the clinical significance of the adenoidal-pharyngeal-conjunctival group of viruses, *Am. J. Trop. Med. Hyg.*, **5**:453, 1956.

Sabin, A. B.: The dengue group of viruses and its family relationships, *Bact. Rev.*, **14**:225, 1950.

――――: Dengue. From "Viral and Rickettsial Infections of Man," edited by T. M. Rivers and F. L. Horsfall, Jr., Philadelphia, J. B. Lippincott Company, 1959.

――――, W. A. Hennessen, and J. Warren: Ultrafiltration and electron microscopy of three types of poliomyelitis virus propagated in tissue culture, *Proc. Soc. Exp. Biol. Med.*, **85**:359, 1954.

Salk, J. E.: Present status of the problem of vaccination against poliomyelitis, *Am. J. Pub. Health*, **45**:285, 1955a.

――――: Vaccination against paralytic poliomyelitis. Performance and prospects, *ibid.*, **45**:575, 1955b.

――――: Poliomyelitis: control. From "Viral and Rickettsial Infections of Man," edited by T. M. Rivers and F. L. Horsfall, Jr., Philadelphia, J. B. Lippincott Company, 1959.

Schlesinger, R. W.: The diagnosis of dengue. From "Diagnosis of Viral and Rickettsial Infections," edited by F. L. Horsfall, Jr., New York, Columbia University Press, 1949.

Schwerdt, C. E., R. C. Williams, W. M. Stanley, F. L. Schaffer, and M. E. McClain: Morphology of Type II poliomyelitis virus (MEF$_1$) as determined by electron microscopy, *Proc. Soc. Exp. Biol. Med.*, **86**:310, 1954.

Stokes, J., Jr.: Varicella—herpes zoster group. From "Viral and Rickettsial Infections of Man," edited by T. M. Rivers and F. L. Horsfall, Jr., Philadelphia, J. B. Lippincott Company, 1959.

Theiler, M.: Yellow fever, *ibid.*, 1959.

Weil, M. L., D. Beard, D. G. Sharp, and J. W. Beard: Purification and sedimentation and electron micrographic characters of the mumps virus, *Proc. Soc. Exp. Biol. Med.*, **68**:309, 1948.

CHAPTER 30

Rickettsial Diseases of Man

The rickettsial diseases or rickettsioses of man may be defined as specific infections induced by small, often pleomorphic, rod-shaped to coccoid organisms which usually occur intracytoplasmically in lice, fleas, ticks, and mites. Occasionally occur extracellularly in gut lumen. They bear a morphologic resemblance to bacteria but are biologically related to viruses. The rickettsiae are readily visible in microscopic preparations. The pathologic lesions occur chiefly in the blood vessels, being caused by the presence of organisms and not by their toxins.

Organisms. The rickettsiae are so named in honor of Howard Taylor Ricketts, who was the first to give a description of the organisms in connection with his studies on Rocky Mountain spotted fever and later on typhus fever. He succeeded in isolating from the blood of typhus fever patients very short bacillus-like rods measuring about 0.3 μ in diameter and 2 μ or less in length. The organisms were stained readily by Giemsa stain and possessed a faintly stained bar through the middle, giving each organism the appearance of a diplobacillus. Nonmotile. Gram-negative. Ricketts's observations were later confirmed by da Rocha-Lima (1916).

Following Ricketts's discovery, Hegler and Prowazek (1913) reported the presence of similar organisms in the blood of patients with typhus fever and in lice that had fed on infected persons.

The rickettsiae are found typically in arthropods. The species pathogenic for man occur intracytoplasmically only, or both intracytoplasmically and intranuclearly. The organisms have not been cultivated on the usual laboratory media. However, they can be cultivated in the various tissue culture media. From the standpoint of size, the rickettsiae occupy a position intermediate between the bacteria and the viruses. With the exception of one pathogenic species, they do not pass through filters that retain bacteria.

Classification. Depending upon the specific arthropod vector, the important rickettsial diseases may be divided as follows:

1. Louse-borne typhus (epidemic or classical typhus).
2. Flea-borne typhus (murine or endemic typhus).
3. Tick-borne typhus (Rocky Mountain spotted fever, Q fever).
4. Mite-borne typhus (tsutsugamushi fever, rickettsialpox).

For more information see Philip (1956).

Typhus Fever. This disease is generally differentiated into (A) epidemic or classical typhus (louse-borne), and (B) endemic or murine typhus (flea-borne).

A. *Epidemic or Classical Typhus.* Etiological agent is *Rickettsia prowazekii.* Organisms are minute, cocco-bacillary, sometimes ellipsoidal or long, rod-shaped cells which are occasionally filamentous. Often occur in pairs and occasionally in chains. In infected lice the minute coccoid and paired coccoid forms predominate over the short and long rods and over the filamentous forms, which are up to 40 μ in length. Single cells from yolk sacs measure 0.3 to 0.7 by 0.5 to 2 μ (Fig. 294). Occur intracytoplasmically in vascular endothelial cells and in serosal cells. Nonmotile.

Organisms cultivated in plasma tissue cultures of mammalian cells, in the louse intestine, and in chorioallantoic membrane and yolk sac of developing chick embryo.

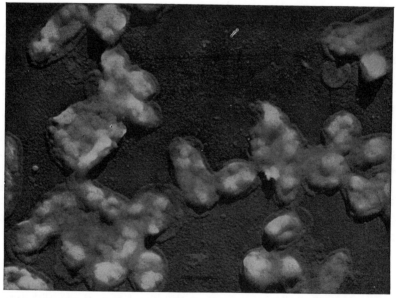

Fig. 294. Electron micrograph of *Rickettsia prowazekii,* the etiological agent of epidemic or classical typhus (louse-borne). ×20,000. (*After van Rooyen and Scott.*)

Cells readily inactivated at 50°C. in 15 to 30 min., by 0.5 per cent phenol and 0.1 per cent formalin.

Disease Produced. Onset of disease often sudden and characterized by headache, chills, fever, and general pains, a macular eruption on the fifth or sixth day, and toxemia. The fever falls usually by rapid lysis after about 14 days. Organisms may be found in the blood vessels of the skin, kidneys, muscles, brain, and testes. Mortality varies from 10 to 40 per cent, depending upon epidemics and age. Pathogenic for man, apes, monkeys, guinea pigs, cotton rats, gerbils, and the louse.

Serum from patients with epidemic typhus agglutinates *Proteus OX*$_{19}$ and *OX*$_2$. This test is referred to as the Weil-Felix reaction. Former strain more commonly agglutinated and is strain customarily employed. Reaction usually becomes positive during second week of disease, reaches its height about time of convalescence, then disappears rather rapidly.

Source of Infection. Lice infected by feeding on blood of man with the febrile disease. Man is the reservoir.

Mode of Transmission. Organism transmitted from man to man by the louse *Pediculus humanus* that has fed on an infected person. Organisms present in feces of louse. Cells inoculated by scratching louse feces into the wound produced by the bite or into other superficial breaks in the skin. Dirty clothing contaminated with louse feces may disseminate organisms into air, from where they may reach the respiratory tract.

Incubation Period. From 6 to 15 days, most often 12 days.

Susceptibility and Immunity. Susceptibility to disease is general. Acquired immunity follows recovery from disease, but it is not always permanent.

Prevalence. Disease prevalent among people living under crowded and unhygienic conditions. Cases more prevalent during colder months.

Prevention and Control. Delousing of infected persons and isolation from others. Use of insecticides on clothing and bedding of patient and special treatment of hair for louse eggs. Use of vaccine for immunization. Vaccine prepared by growing rickettsiae in yolk sac of developing chick embryo. Suspension after purification is in-

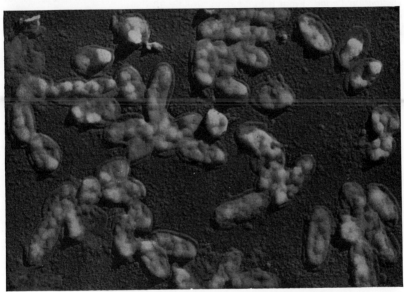

Fig. 295. Electron micrograph of *Rickettsia typhi*, the etiological agent of endemic or murine typhus (flea-borne). ×20,000. (*After van Rooyen and Scott.*)

activated by formalin. Vaccine generally given in two injections and confers considerable protection. Reimmunization should be practiced every few months where danger of disease is present. Vaccination reduces risk of infection, modifies course of disease, and lowers mortality rate.

Incidence may be greatly reduced by improving living conditions, by more frequent bathing, and by reduction in louse infestation.

Use of appropriate antibiotics, such as the tetracyclines or chloramphenicol, will shorten course of disease.

For more information see Weiss and Dressler (1958).

B. Endemic or Murine Typhus (Flea-borne). Etiological agent is *Rickettsia typhi*. Cells resemble *R. prowazekii* in morphology and staining properties (Fig. 295). Nonmotile. Gram-negative.

Organisms cultivated in plasma tissue cultures of mammalian cells; in fleas and lice; in the peritoneal cavities of X-rayed rats; in the lungs of white mice and white rats following intranasal inoculation; in the lungs of rabbits following intratracheal inoculation; in the chorioallantoic membrane and yolk sac of the developing chick embryo.

Disease Produced. Clinical picture identical with that of the epidemic or louse-borne type, except that symptoms are generally much less severe. Rash usually does not appear before fifth day and may comprise only a few macules which tend to disappear in a day or so. Death rate for all ages about 2 per cent.

Distinguishable from rickettsiae of Rocky Mountain spotted fever, Q fever, and tsutsugamushi disease by complement fixation, agglutination and precipitation tests, less readily from *R. prowazekii* by these tests. Serum from patients agglutinates *Proteus* OX_{19}.

Source of Infection. Fleas infected from rats, especially *Rattus norvegicus,* which are the reservoir.

Mode of Transmission. Organism transmitted from rodent to man by the flea *Xenopsylla cheopis.* Organisms present in feces of flea. Cells inoculated by scratching louse feces into wound produced by bite of insect. Dirty clothing contaminated with louse feces may disseminate organisms into air, from where they may be inhaled.

Incubation Period. From 6 to 14 days, usually 12 days.

Susceptibility and Immunity. Susceptibility to disease is general. Acquired immunity follows recovery from disease but is not always permanent.

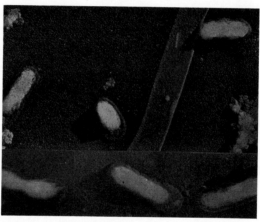

Fig. 296. Electron micrograph of *Rickettsia rickettsii,* the etiological agent of Rocky Mountain spotted fever. $\times 20,000.$ (*After van Rooyen and Scott.*)

Prevalence. Widely distributed in temperate, semitropical, and tropical climates. Transmission occurs throughout the year but more frequently during warmer months.

Prevention and Control. Control of rat population by trapping, poisoning, and ratproofing. Trapping and poisoning must be continuous to be of any practical value. Ratproofing only method that may be considered of permanent value.

Vaccine prepared against endemic typhus in the same manner as for epidemic type is available and presumably equally effective.

Use of appropriate antibiotics, such as the tetracyclines or chloramphenicol, will shorten course of disease.

For more information see Bovarnick and Snyder (1949), Cohn et al. (1958), Karp (1954), Topping et al. (1945), van Rooyen and Scott (1949), Wissig et al. (1956).

Rocky Mountain Spotted Fever (Tick-borne). Etiological agent is *Rickettsia rickettsii.* Minute paired organisms surrounded by a narrow clear zone or halo; often lanceolate, resembling in appearance a minute pair of pneumococci. Average 0.6 by 1.2 $\mu.$ Nonmotile (Fig. 296). In the tick three forms may be recognized by Giemsa stain: (1) pale blue bacillary forms, curved and club-shaped; (2) smaller, bluish rods with deeply staining chromatoid granules; and (3) more deeply staining, purplish, lanceolate forms. Occurs in the cytoplasm and nucleus in all types of cells in the tick; also occurs in mammals in the vascular endothelium, in macrophages, in the serosal cells of the peritoneal cavity and in smooth muscle cells of arteriolar walls.

May be cultivated in plasma tissue cultures of mammalian cells, on the chorio-allantoic membrane, in the yolk sac of the chick embryo, and in ticks.

White blood cell count usually shows a slight increase over the normal. Serum from patients with spotted fever agglutinates *Proteus OX₁₉* and usually *OX₂*. Distinguishable from *R. prowazekii* and *R. typhi* by complement fixation and by agglutination with specific antigens. Agglutination reaction usually becomes positive toward end of second week, reaches its peak during convalescence, then disappears rather rapidly.

Cells inactivated at 50°C. in 10 min., and by 0.5 per cent phenol and 0.1 per cent formalin. Destroyed by desiccation in about 10 hr.

Disease Produced. A specific infectious disease characterized by sudden onset, fever, headache, pains in muscles and joints, chills, a macular eruption, usually first on the extremities and rapidly spreading over most of the body, irritability and hyperesthesia of the skin, an enlarged spleen, and catarrh of the respiratory tract. Patients show a history of either tick bite or exposure to ticks. Death rate varies with age and locality; in this country for all ages, it is about 20 per cent.

Source of Infection. Infected ticks. In the eastern and southern United States, the common vector is the dog tick *Dermacentor variabilis;* in the northwestern States it is the wood tick *D. andersoni;* in the southwestern United States, it may occasionally be the lone-star tick *Amblyomma americanum.* In Brazil, the common vector is A. *cajennense.* Infection passed from generation to generation in ticks. Probably maintained in ticks by larvae feeding on susceptible wild rodents.

Mode of Transmission. Disease transmitted by bite of infected tick or contact with tick material, such as blood or feces on the unbroken skin.

Incubation Period. From 3 to 10 days.

Susceptibility and Immunity. Susceptibility to disease general. Acquired immunity follows recovery from disease, but it is not always permanent.

Prevalence. Occurs throughout North America, western Canada, western and central Mexico, Colombia, and Brazil. Disease more prevalent in spring and early summer, corresponding to time of appearance of adult ticks.

Prevention and Control. All ticks on patients should be removed and destroyed. Avoidance of areas known to be infested with ticks. Removal of ticks from body as promptly as possible without crushing. Destruction of ticks in infested areas by clearing and burning vegetation, by destruction of small animals known to be infested with ticks.

Vaccine available which is prepared from yolk sac of developing chick embryo. Vaccination lessens chances of infection and lowers mortality rate. Protection good for 1 to 2 years. Vaccine of no value after infection once acquired.

Specific treatment consists of daily oral doses of the tetracycline antibiotics or chloramphenicol until patient is afebrile, then for one or two additional days after that.

For more information see Harrell (1949), van Rooyen and Scott (1949).

Q Fever. Etiological agent is *Coxiella burnetii.* Small, bacterium-like, pleomorphic organisms varying in size from coccoid forms to well-marked rods (Fig. 297). Occur as intracellular microcolonies with diffuse or compact distribution of organisms through the cytoplasm. Also seen extracellularly, where they appear as small, lanceolate rods, diplobacilli, and occasionally segmented filamentous forms. Small lanceolate rods, 0.25 by 0.4 to 0.5 μ, bipolar forms 0.25 by 1 μ, diplobacilli 0.25 by 1.5 μ. Nonmotile. Gram-negative.

May be cultivated in plasma tissue cultures, in the yolk sacs of chick embryos, and by injection into meal worms and certain other arthropods.

Agent readily passes through Berkefeld N filters, which are impermeable to ordinary bacteria, and W filters, which are impermeable to typhus and Rocky Mountain spotted fever rickettsiae. Resists a temperature of 60°C. for 1 hr., and 0.5 per cent formalin and 1 per cent phenol when tested in fertile eggs.

Disease Produced. Q fever characterized by sudden onset, chilly sensations, headache, weakness, malaise, and severe sweats. Virus-like or atypical pneumonia occurs

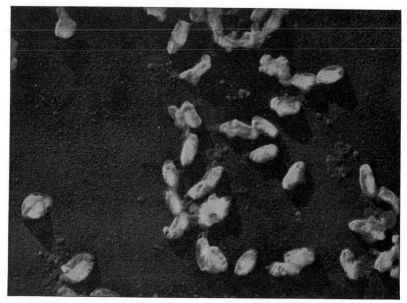

Fig. 297. Electron micrograph of *Coxiella burnetii*, the etiological agent of Q fever. ×20,000. (*After van Rooyen and Scott.*)

in majority of cases. Attended by mild cough, scanty expectoration, and chest pain. Upper respiratory tract essentially normal. Death rate negligible. Disease diagnosed by complement-fixation reaction.

Source of Infection. Patient frequently shows history of contact with cattle, sheep, goat, or tick. Agent pathogenic for man, guinea pig, and white mouse. Mild infections occur in monkey, dog, white rat, rabbit, and cow. Etiologic agent abundant in mammary gland and milk of infected cows; also present in milk of sheep and goats.

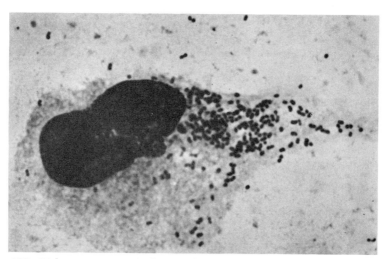

Fig. 298. *Rickettsia tsutsugamushi* in infected animal tissue cell. (*After Philip.*)

Mode of Transmission. Usually by air-borne dissemination of organisms. Contact with infected animals, such as cows, sheep, goats, has accounted for a large proportion of cases reported. Agent may or may not be destroyed in pasteurization. Milk important medium for dissemination of organisms. Infected ticks may also be involved in transmission.

Incubation Period. Usually 2 to 3 weeks.

Susceptibility and Immunity. Susceptibility is general. An attack confers immunity for an indefinite period. Vaccination increases resistance to disease.

Prevalence. Disease widespread. Outbreaks have occurred among slaughterhouse workers in Texas and Illinois. Endemic focuses in northern and southern California. Cases reported from several states in the United States. Largest outbreaks among troops in Italy and Greece during World War II.

Prevention and Control. Pasteurization or boiling of milk from cows, sheep, and goats. Control of importation of domestic animals. Immunization with vaccine found useful.

Oral treatment with the tetracycline antibiotics or chloramphenicol until patient afebrile and for several days after that.

For more information see Bell, Parker, and Stoenner (1949); Dyer (1949); Huebner, Jellison, and Beck (1949); Meiklejohn and Lennette (1950); Stoker (1950); and Wentworth (1955).

Tsutsugamushi Disease, Mite-borne (Scrub Typhus). Etiological agent is *Rickettsia tsutsugamushi* (Fig. 298). Small, pleomorphic bacterium-like organisms, usually wider and less sharply defined than cells of *R. prowazekii, R. typhi, R. rickettsii,* and *Coxiella burnetii.* Ellipsoidal or rod-shaped, often appearing as a diplococcus or as a short bacillus with bipolar staining resembling that of the plague bacillus. Diffusely distributed in the cytoplasm of the cell. Measure 0.3 to 0.5 by 0.8 to 2 μ. Nonmotile. Gram-negative.

Cultivated in plasma tissue cultures of mammalian cells, on the chorioallantoic membrane and in the yolk sac of the chick embryo.

Cells readily inactivated by heat and chemicals. Destroyed at 50°C. in 10 min., and by 0.5 per cent phenol and 0.1 per cent formalin.

Disease Produced. An acute, specific infection of man prevalent in Japan and characterized by sudden onset, fever, malaise, chills, and headache. Primary sores develop at site of insect bite, caused by secretions of the insect and accompanied by adenitis of the regional lymph nodes. A skin eruption appears on the trunk, may spread to the arms and legs, and ordinarily disappears after several days. The spleen and liver are congested, and there may be cloudy swelling in the parenchymatous organs and cellular necrosis. Convalescence usually occurs in 2 to 3 weeks.

Source of Infection. Infected larval mites of *Trombicula akamushi* and related species. The infection is passed from generation to generation in mites and maintained by feeding upon diseased wild rodents, especially mice and rats.

Mode of Transmission. By bite of infected mites. The mites become infected in the larval stage by feeding on infected rodents (Fig. 299).

Incubation Period. Usually 7 to 10 days; may be as long as 21 days.

Susceptibility and Immunity. Susceptibility to disease is general. An attack confers long immunity against homologous strain. Second and even third attacks are not uncommon in endemic areas.

Serum from patient usually agglutinates *Proteus OXK.* Agglutination reaction usually becomes positive toward end of second week, reaches its peak during convalescence, then disappears rather rapidly.

Prevalence. Widely distributed. Southeastern Asia, islands of west and south Pacific, Japan, Formosa, East Indies, and Australia.

Prevention and Control. Wearing of miteproof clothing recommended in areas infested with mites. Grass and scrub on localities for camp sites should be cut level with the ground and burned. Camp area should also be burned, preferably with a flame thrower. Cots should be used to keep bedding from contact with the ground. Sleeping on ground should be avoided. Body should be kept clean by thorough soaping and scrubbing of skin. Impregnation of clothing with anti-mite fluids and powders. Immunization with living attenuated vaccine sometimes successful.

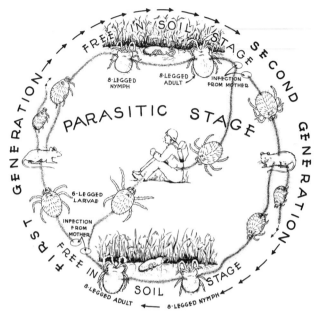

FIG. 299. The "cycle" of *Rickettsia tsutsugamushi* in nature through two generations in mites. (*After Philip.*)

Specific treatment consists of daily doses of one of the tetracycline antibiotics or chloramphenicol until patient is afebrile. A second course of treatments given after one week to prevent relapse.

For more information see Bozeman et al. (1956), Jackson and Smadel (1951), Philip (1948, 1949), Rights and Smadel (1948), Smadel et al. (1951).

Rickettsialpox. Etiological agent is *Rickettsia akari*. Minute diplobacilli and bipolarly stained rods. Resemble typical rickettsiae morphologically, measure 0.6 by 0.9 to 1.4 μ, occur intracytoplasmically. Nonmotile. Gram-negative (Fig. 300).

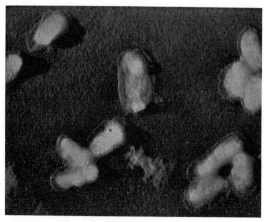

FIG. 300. Electron micrograph of *Rickettsia akari*, the etiological agent of rickettsialpox. $\times 20,000$. (*After van Rooyen and Scott.*)

May be cultivated in yolk sac of chick embryo and in intrarectally injected body lice. No growth on artificial media.

Disease Produced. A recently recognized disease characterized by an initial lesion, chills, fever, rash, and a mild to severe nonfatal course. Initial lesion appears as a firm papule followed by fever. Most commonly found on covered parts of body and progresses from the papular stage to vesiculation, eschar formation, and finally a pigmented scar. Fever accompanied by headache, muscular pain, and general malaise. Complement-fixation test becomes positive between second and third week and may be used for diagnosis.

Source of Infection. Infected house mice (*Mus musculus*).

Mode of Transmission. Organism transmitted from mouse to mouse, probably from mouse to man by a rodent mite (*Allodermanyssus sanguineus*).

Incubation Period. Probably 10 to 24 days.

Susceptibility and Immunity. Susceptibility to disease is general. Immunity follows an attack but duration unknown.

Prevention and Control. Elimination of rodents.

Specific treatment consists of use of one of the tetracycline antibiotics or chloramphenicol.

For more information see Fuller (1954); Huebner, Jellison, and Armstrong (1947).

For general information see American Public Health Association (1955), Bedson et al. (1955), Blank and Rake (1955), Breed, Murray, and Smith (1957), Dalldorf (1955), Hartman, Horsfall, and Kidd (1954), Rivers (1959), Rhodes and van Rooyen (1958).

REFERENCES

American Public Health Association: "Control of Communicable Diseases in Man," New York, 1955.

Bedson, S. P., A. W. Downie, F. O. MacCallum, and C. H. Stuart-Harris: "Virus and Rickettsial Diseases," London, Edward Arnold & Co., 1955.

Bell, E. J., R. R. Parker, and H. G. Stoenner: Q fever, *Am. J. Pub. Health,* **39**:478, 1949.

Blank, H., and G. Rake: "Viral and Rickettsial Diseases of the Skin, Eye, and Mucous Membranes of Man," Boston, Little, Brown & Company, 1955.

Bovarnick, M. R., and J. C. Snyder: Respiration of typhus rickettsiae, *J. Exp. Med.,* **89**:561, 1949.

Bozeman, F. M., H. E. Hopps, J. X. Danauskas, E. B. Jackson, and J. E. Smadel: A tissue culture system for quantitative estimations of *Rickettsia tsutsugamushi,* *J. Immunol.,* **76**:475, 1956.

Breed, R. S., E. G. D. Murray, and N. R. Smith: "Bergey's Manual of Determinative Bacteriology," Baltimore, The Williams & Wilkins Company, 1957.

Burnet, F. M.: "Principles of Animal Virology," New York, Academic Press, Inc., 1955.

Cohn, Z. A., F. E. Hahn, W. Ceglowski, and F. M. Bozeman: Unstable nucleic acids of *Rickettsia mooseri, Science,* **127**:282, 1958.

Dalldorf, G.: "Introduction to Virology," Springfield, Ill., Charles C. Thomas, Publisher, 1955.

da Rocha-Lima, H.: Zur Aetiologie des Fleckfiebers, *Vorläufige Mitt. Berl. Klin. Wochschr.,* **53**:567, 1916.

Dyer, R. E.: Q fever, *Am. J. Pub. Health,* **39**:471, 1949.

Fuller, H. S.: Studies of rickettsialpox. III. Life cycle of the mite vector, *Allodermanyssus sanguineus, Am. J. Hyg.,* **59**:236, 1954.

Harrell, G. T.: Rocky Mountain spotted fever, *Medicine,* **28**:333, 1949.

Hartman, F. W., F. L. Horsfall, Jr., and J. G. Kidd: "The Dynamics of Virus and Rickettsial Infections," New York, McGraw-Hill Book Company, Inc., Blakiston Division, 1954.

Huebner, R. J., W. L. Jellison, and C. Armstrong: Rickettsialpox—a newly recognized rickettsial disease. V. Recovery of *Rickettsia akari* from a house mouse (*Mus musculus*), *Pub. Health Reports*, **62**:777, 1947.

——, ——, and M. D. Beck: Q fever—a review of current knowledge, *Ann. Int. Med.*, **30**:495, 1949.

Jackson, E. B., and J. E. Smadel: Immunization against scrub typhus. II. Preparation of lyophilized living vaccine, *Am. J. Hyg.*, **53**:326, 1951.

Karp, A.: An immunological purification of typhus rickettsiae, *J. Bact.*, **67**:450, 1954.

Meiklejohn, G., and E. H. Lennette: Q fever in California. I. Observations on vaccination of human beings, *Am. J. Hyg.*, **52**:54, 1950.

Philip, C. B.: Tsutsugamushi disease (scrub typhus) in World War II, *J. Parasit.*, **34**:169, 1948.

——: Scrub typhus, or tsutsugamushi disease, *Sci. Monthly*, **69**:281, 1949.

——: Comments on the classification of the order *Rickettsiales*, *Can. J. Microbiol.*, **2**:261, 1956.

Rhodes, A. J., and C. E. van Rooyen: "Textbook of Virology," Baltimore, The Williams & Wilkins Company, 1958.

Rights, F. L., and J. E. Smadel: Studies on scrub typhus (tsutsugamushi disease). III. Heterogenicity of strains of *R. tsutsugamushi* as demonstrated by cross-vaccination studies, *J. Exp. Med.*, **87**:339, 1948.

Rivers, T. M.: "Viral and Rickettsial Infections of Man," Philadelphia, J. B. Lippincott Company, 1959.

Smadel, J. E., H. L. Ley, Jr., F. H. Diercks, R. Traub, V. J. Tipton, and L. P. Frick: Immunization against scrub typhus. I. Combined living vaccine and chemoprophylaxis in volunteers, *Am. J. Hyg.*, **53**:317, 1951.

Stoker, M. G. P.: Q fever in Great Britain, *Lancet*, **259**:616, 1950.

Topping, N. H., I. A. Bengtson, R. G. Henderson, C. C. Shepard, and M. J. Shear: Studies of typhus fever, National Institute of Health, U.S. Public Health Service, *Bull.* 183, 1945.

van Rooyen, C. E., and G. D. Scott: Electron microscopy of typhus rickettsiae, *Can. J. Research*, E, **27**:250, 1949.

Weiss, E., and H. R. Dressler: Growth of *Rickettsia prowazekii* in irradiated monolayer cultures of chick embryo entodermal cells, *J. Bact.*, **75**:544, 1958.

Wentworth, B. B.: Historical review of the literature on Q fever, *Bact. Rev.*, **19**:129, 1955.

Wissig, S. L., L. G. Caro, E. B. Jackson, and J. E. Smadel: Electron microscopic observations on intracellular rickettsiae, *Am. J. Path.*, **32**:1117, 1956.

Index

797